Contents in Brief

Focal Points and Connections
See page T17 for key.

About the Cover

Fractions and decimals and the relationship between fractions and decimals are featured topics in Fourth grade. On the cover, the pitcher is wearing a fraction. It is equivalent to 0.5. Have students find the other fraction on the cover that is equivalent to 0.5.

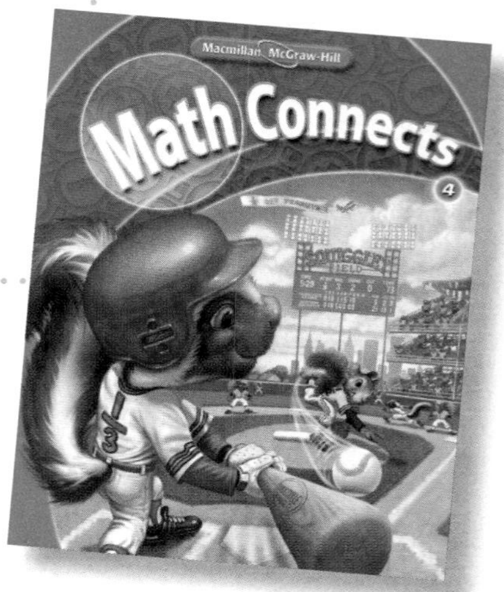

Three Horizontally Aligned Programs

- Common vocabulary
- Common manipulatives
- Common authors
- Common technology
- Common Professional Development

Grade 4

NSF-funded, integrated performance assessment aligned with investigative instruction

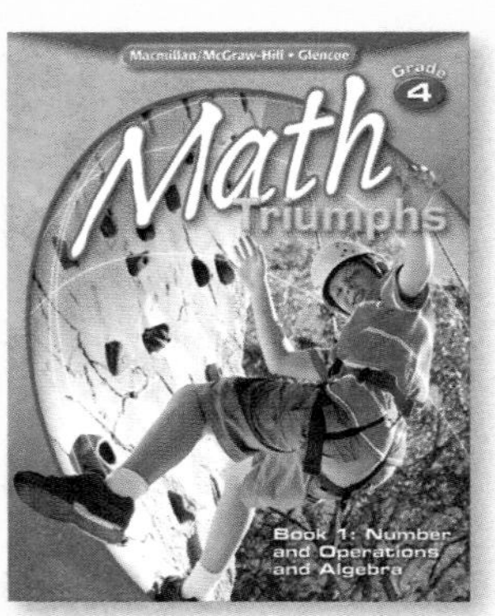

Grade 4

Intensive Intervention for students two or more years below grade level (Tier 3 RTI)

The McGraw·Hill Companies

 **Macmillan/McGraw-Hill**

Send all inquiries to:
Macmillan/McGraw-Hill
8787 Orion Place
Columbus, OH 43240-4027

ISBN: 978-0-02-105744-3 *(Teacher Edition)*
MHID: 0-02-105744-3 *(Teacher Edition)*
ISBN: 978-0-02-105733-7 *(Student Edition)*
MHID: 0-02-105733-8 *(Student Edition)*

Math Connects, Grade 4

Printed in the United States of America.

5 6 7 8 9 10 WEB 16 15 14 13 12 11 10

Benefits of Student Edition Organization

Math Connects, grade 4 Student Edition, has a 4-part organization.

1. **Start Smart** gets students ready for grade 4 with a review of key math standards from grade 4 that are prerequisites for grade 4.
2. **Chapters 1-15** Each chapter has coherent groups of lessons focused on related grade 4 math standards and the NCTM Focal Points.
3. **Preparing for Standardized Tests** provides test success tips, step-by-step solutions for standards-based multiple-choice questions, and an extensive practice section to review before your state test.
4. **Looking Ahead** prepares students for success with lessons on several key math standards.

The organization and pacing of ***Math Connects*** helps ensure in-depth coverage of all grade 4 standards, success on your state test, and a good start for grade 5.

The School Year

about 155 school days

Teach **Start Smart** and **Chapters 1-15**.

Use the **Preparing for Standardized Tests** throughout the year as needed by your students.

Your State Test

about 20 school days

Teach **Looking Ahead**

Pacing Guide Each chapter includes days for review and assessment.	
Start Smart	Optional
Chapter 1	9 days
Chapter 2	10 days
Chapter 3	13 days
Chapter 4	11 days
Chapter 5	10 days
Chapter 6	8 days
Chapter 7	9 days
Chapter 8	12 days
Chapter 9	8 days
Chapter 10	12 days
Chapter 11	12 days
Chapter 12	13 days
Chapter 13	9 days
Chapter 14	10 days
Chapter 15	9 days
Total	155 days
State Test	
Looking Ahead	20 days

Authors

Mary Behr Altieri
Putnam/Northern Westchester BOCES
Yorktown Heights, New York

Don S. Balka
Professor Emeritus
Saint Mary's College
Notre Dame, Indiana

Roger Day, Ph.D.
Mathematics Department Chair
Pontiac Township High School
Pontiac, Illinois

Philip D. Gonsalves
Mathematics Coordinator
Alameda County Office of Education and California State University East Bay
Hayward, California

Ellen C. Grace
Mathematics Consultant
Albuquerque, New Mexico

Stephen Krulik
Professor Emeritus Mathematics Education
Temple University
Cherry Hill, New Jersey

Carol E. Malloy, Ph.D
Associate Professor of Mathematics Education
University of North Carolina at Chapel Hill
Chapel Hill, North Carolina

Rhonda J. Molix-Bailey
Mathematics Consultant
Mathematics by Design
Desoto, Texas

Lois Gordon Moseley
Staff Developer
NUMBERS: Mathematics Professional Development
Houston, Texas

Brian Mowry
Independent Math Educational Consultant/Part-Time Pre-K Instructional Specialist
Austin Independent School District
Austin, Texas

Christina L. Myren
Consultant Teacher
Conejo Valley Unified School District
Thousand Oaks, California

Jack Price
Professor Emeritus
California State Polytechnic University
Pomona, California

Mary Esther Reynosa
Instructional Specialist for Elementary Mathematics
Northside Independent School District
San Antonio, Texas

Rafaela M. Santa Cruz
SDSU/CGU Doctoral Program in Education
San Diego State University
San Diego, California

Robyn Silbey
Math Content Coach
Montgomery County Public Schools
Gaithersburg, Maryland

Kathleen Vielhaber
Mathematics Consultant
St. Louis, Missouri

Contributing Authors

Donna J. Long
Mathematics Consultant
Indianapolis, Indiana

FOLDABLES® **Dinah Zike**
Educational Consultant
Dinah-Might Activities, Inc.
San Antonio, Texas

Consultants

Macmillan/McGraw-Hill wishes to thank the following professionals for their feedback. They were instrumental in providing valuable input toward the development of this program in these specific areas.

Mathematical Content

Viken Hovsepian
Professor of Mathematics
Rio Hondo College
Whittier, California

Grant A. Fraser, Ph.D.
Professor of Mathematics
California State University, Los Angeles
Los Angeles, California

Arthur K. Wayman, Ph.D.
Professor of Mathematics Emeritus
California State University, Long Beach
Long Beach, California

Assessment

Jane D. Gawronski, Ph.D.
Director of Assessment and Outreach
San Diego State University
San Diego, California

Cognitive Guided Instruction

Susan B. Empson, Ph.D.
Associate Professor of Mathematics and Science Education
University of Texas at Austin
Austin, Texas

English Learners

Cheryl Avalos
Mathematics Consultant
Los Angeles County Office of Education, Retired
Hacienda Heights, California

Kathryn Heinze
Graduate School of Education
Hamline University
St. Paul, Minnesota

Family Involvement

Paul Giganti, Jr.
Mathematics Education Consultant
Albany, California

Literature

David M. Schwartz
Children's Author, Speaker, Storyteller
Oakland, California

Vertical Alignment

Berchie Holliday
National Educational Consultant
Silver Spring, Maryland

Deborah A. Hutchens, Ed.D.
Principal
Norfolk Highlands Elementary
Chesapeake, Virginia

Reviewers

Each Reviewer reviewed at least two chapters of the Student Edition, giving feedback and suggestions for improving the effectiveness of the mathematics instruction.

Ernestine D. Austin
Facilitating Teacher/Basic Skills Teacher
LORE School
Ewing, NJ

Susie Bellah
Kindergarten Teacher
Lakeland Elementary
Humble, Texas

Megan Bennett
Elementary Math Coordinator
Hartford Public Schools
Hartford, CT

Susan T. Blankenship
5th Grade Teacher – Math
Stanford Elementary School
Stanford, KY

Wendy Buchanan
3rd Grade Teacher
The Classical Center at Vial
Garland, TX

Sandra Signorelli Coelho
Associate Director for Mathematics
PIMMS at Wesleyan University
Middletown, CT

Joanne DeMizio
Asst. Supt., Math and Science Curriculum
Archdiocese of New York
New York, NY

Anthony Dentino
Supervisor of Mathematics
Brick Township Schools
Brick, NJ

Lorrie L. Drennon
Math Teacher
Collins Middle School
Corsicana, TX

Ethel A. Edwards
Director of Curriculum and Instruction
Topeka Public Schools
Topeka, Kansas

Carolyn Elender
District Elementary Math Instructional Specialist
Pasadena ISD
Pasadena, Texas

Monica Engel
Educator Second Grade
Pioneer Elementary School
Bolingbrook, IL

Anna Dahinden Flynn
Math Teacher
Coulson Tough K–6 Elementary
The Woodlands, TX

Brenda M. Foxx
Principal
University Park Elementary
University Park, MD

Katherine A. Frontier
Elementary Teacher
Laidlaw
Western Springs, IL

Susan J. Furphy
5th Grade Teacher
Nisley Elementary
Grand Jct., CO

Peter Gatz
Student Services Coordinator
Brooks Elementary
Aurora, IL

Amber Gregersen
Teacher – 2nd Grade
Nisley Elementary
Grand Junction, CO

Roberta Grindle
Math and Language Arts Academic Intervention Service Provider
Cumberland Head Elementary School
Plattsburgh, NY

Sr. Helen Lucille Habig, RSM
Assistant Superintendent/ Mathematics
Archdiocese of Cincinnati
Cincinnati, OH

Holly L. Hepp
Math Facilitator
Barringer Academic Center
Charlotte, NC

Martha J. Hickman
2nd Grade Teacher
Dr. James Craik Elementary School
Pomfret, MD

Margie Hill
District Coordinating Teacher for Mathematics, K–12
Blue Valley USD 229
Overland Park, KS

Carol H. Joyce
5th Grade Teacher
Nathanael Greene Elementary
Liberty, NC

Stella K. Kostante
Curriculum Coach
Roosevelt Elementary
Pittsburgh, PA

Pamela Fleming Lowe
Fourth Grade eMINTS Teacher
O'Neal Elementary
Poplar Bluff, MO

Lauren May, NBCT
4th Grade Teacher
May Watts Elementary School
Naperville, IL

Lorraine Moore
Grade 3 Math Teacher
Cowpens Elementary School
Cowpens, SC

Shannon L. Moorhead
4th Grade Teacher
Centerville Elementary
Anderson, SC

Gina M. Musselman, M.Ed
Kindergarten Teacher
Padeo Verde Elementary
Peoria, AZ

Jen Neufeld
3rd Grade Teacher
Kendall
Naperville, IL

Cathie Osiecki
K–5 Mathematics Coordinator
Middletown Public Schools
Middletown, CT

Phyllis L. Pacilli
Elementary Education Teacher
Fullerton Elementary
Addison, IL

Cindy Pearson
4th/5th Grade Teacher
John D. Spicer Elementary
Haltom City, TX

Herminio M. Planas
Mathematics Curriculum Specialist
Administrative Offices-Bridgeport Public Schools
Bridgeport, Connecticut

Jo J. Puree
Educator
Lackamas Elementary
Yelm, WA

Teresa M. Reynolds
Third Grade Teacher
Forrest View Elementary
Everett, WA

Dr. John A. Rhodes
Director of Mathematics
Indian Prairie SD #204
Aurora, IL

Amy Romm
First Grade Teacher
Starline Elementary
Lake Havasu, AZ

Delores M. Rushing
Numeracy Coach
Dept. of Academic Services-Mathematics Department
Washington, DC

Daniel L. Scudder
Mathematics/Technology Specialist
Boone Elementary
Houston, TX

Laura Seymour
Resource Teacher Leader – Elementary Math & Science, Retired
Dearborn Public Schools
Dearborn, MI

Petra Siprian
Teacher
Army Trail Elementary School
Addison, IL

Sandra Stein
K–5 Mathematics Consultant
St. Clair County Regional Educational Service Agency
Marysville, MI

Barb Stoflet
Curriculum Specialist
Roseville Area Schools
Roseville, MN

Kim Summers
Principal
Dynard Elementary
Chaptico, MD

Ann C. Teater
4th Grade Teacher
Lancaster Elementary
Lancaster, KY

Anne E. Tunney
Teacher
City of Erie School District
Erie, PA

Joylien Weathers
1st Grade Teacher
Mesa View Elementary
Grand Junction, CO

Christine F. Weiss
Third Grade Teacher
Robert C. Hill Elementary School
Romeoville, IL

Mathematics Teacher Handbook

Table of Contents

PreK–12 Mathematics: Focus on Grade 4

Welcome to Math Connects

Concepts • Skills • Problem Solving

The only true vertically aligned PreK–12 Mathematics Curriculum

Math Connects offers three dimensions of vertical alignment.

❶ Content Design

Vertical content alignment is a process that ensures you and your students experience an articulated, coherent sequence of content from grade level to grade level. This provides you with the assurance that content is introduced, reinforced, and assessed at appropriate times in the series, eliminating gaps and unnecessary duplication. You are able to target your instruction to student needs because you are not teaching content intended to be covered later or that students have previously mastered.

❷ Instructional Design

Our strong vertical alignment in instructional approach from PreKindergarten through Algebra 2 provides a smooth transition for students from elementary to middle school to high school. Our common vocabulary, technology, manipulatives, lesson planning, and Data-Driven Decision Making reduces the confusion students often encounter when transitioning between grade levels without this built-in articulation.

❸ Visual Design

The student pages of ***Math Connects*** have a consistent visual design from grade to grade. This aids students' transition from elementary school to middle school and from middle school to Algebra 1. Students are more likely to succeed when they are already familiar with how to navigate student pages.

PreK-2 | 3–5

5 Keys to Success

❶ Backmapping

According to College Board research, about 80% of students who successfully complete Algebra 1 and Geometry by 10th grade attend and succeed in college. (Changing the Odds: Factors Increasing Access to College, 1990) ***Math Connects*** was conceived and developed by backmapping with the final result in mind–student success in Algebra 1 and beyond.

❷ Balanced, In-Depth Content

Math Connects was developed to specifically target the skills and topics that give students the most difficulty, such as Problem Solving, in each grade span.

Grades K–2	Grades 3–5
1. Problem Solving 2. Money 3. Time 4. Measurement 5. Fractions 6. Computation	1. Problem Solving 2. Fractions 3. Measurement 4. Decimals 5. Time 6. Algebra

Grades 6–8	Grades 9–12
1. Fractions 2. Problem Solving 3. Measurement 4. Algebra 5. Computation	1. Problem Solving 2. Fractions 3. Algebra 4. Geometry 5. Computation 6. Probability

– *K–12 Math Market Analysis Survey,* Open Book Publishing, 2006

❸ Ongoing Assessment

Math Connects includes diagnostic, formative, and summative assessment; data-driven instruction; intervention options; and performance tracking, as well as remediation, acceleration, and enrichment tools throughout the program.

❹ Intervention and Differentiated Instruction

A three-tiered Response To Intervention (RTI) is provided.

TIER 1 **Daily Intervention** Reteach masters and Alternative Strategy suggestions address concepts from a different modality or learning style.

TIER 2 **Strategic Intervention** Teachers can use the myriad of intervention tips and ancillary materials, such as the Strategic Intervention Guide (1–5) and Study Guide and Intervention (6–8).

TIER 3 **Intensive Intervention** For students who are two or more years below grade level, ***Math Triumphs*** provides step-by-step instruction, vocabulary support, and data-driven decision making to help students succeed.

❺ Professional Development

Math Connects includes many opportunities for teacher professional development. Additional learning opportunities in various formats–video, online, and on-site instruction–are fully aligned and articulated from Kindergarten through Algebra 2.

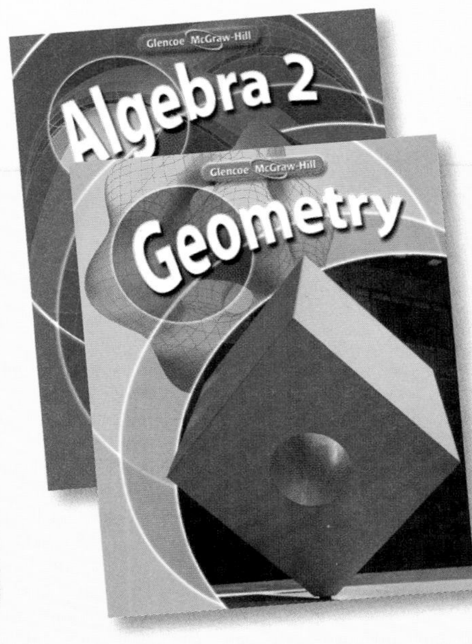

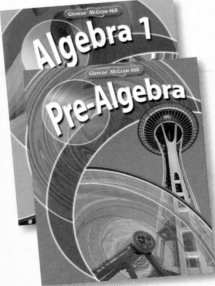

6–8 | **Pre-Algebra and Algebra 1** | **Geometry and Algebra 2**

The Research Base

Continuous research with teachers, students, academician, and leading experts helps to build a solid foundation for ***Math Connects.***

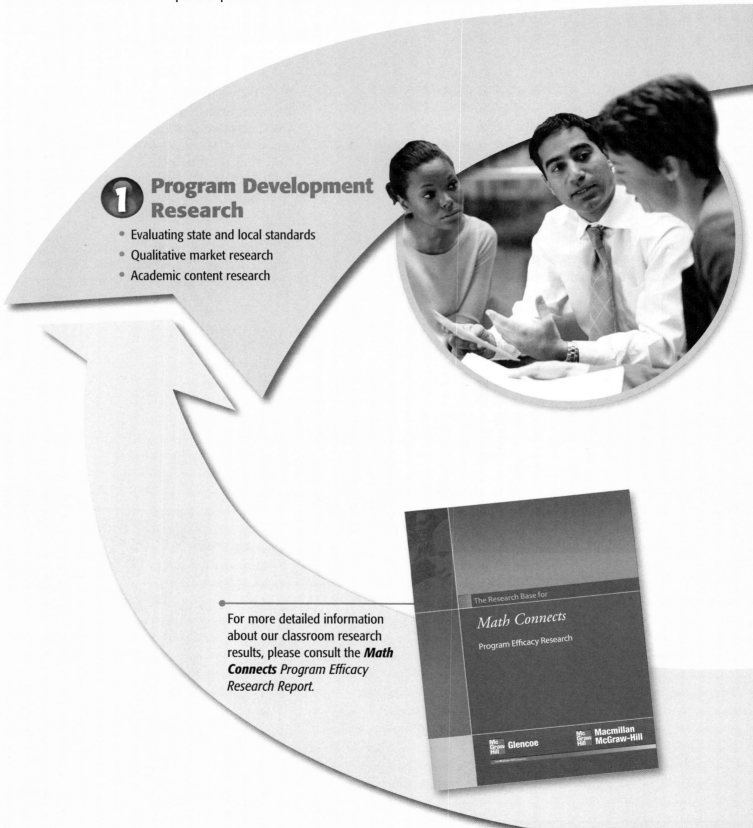

1 Program Development Research

- Evaluating state and local standards
- Qualitative market research
- Academic content research

For more detailed information about our classroom research results, please consult the ***Math Connects*** *Program Efficacy Research Report.*

The Research Base for
Math Connects
Program Efficacy Research
Glencoe
Macmillan McGraw-Hill

for *Math Connects*

2 Formative Research

- Pedagogical research base
- Classroom field tests
- Teacher advisory boards
- Academic consultants and reviewers

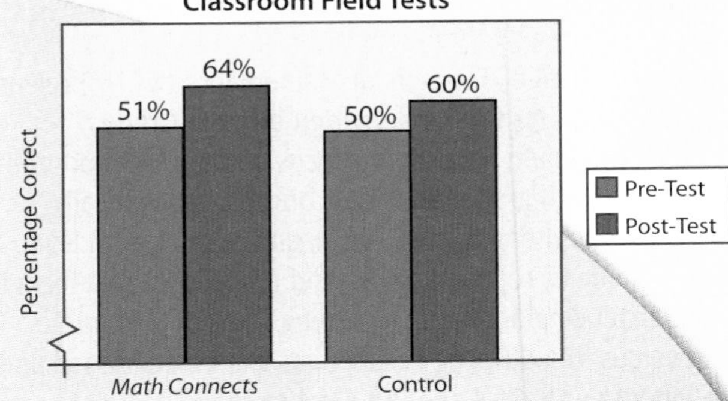

Students using a field test of the ***Math Connects*** program **(experimental group)** had ***higher*** pre-test to post-test gains than students using other textbook programs **(control group).**

3 Summative Research

- Evidence of increased test scores
- Quasi-experimental program efficacy research
- Longitudinal studies
- Qualitative program evaluations

Access all ***Math Connects*** research at macmillanmh.com.

NCTM Focal Points

The NCTM Focal Points

In 2006, the National Council of Teachers of Mathematics (NCTM) released the Curriculum Focal Points for Pre-Kindergarten through Grade 8 Mathematics. These Curriculum Focal Points focus on the most important mathematical topics for each grade level. The concepts are vertically-aligned and expect a level of depth, complexity, and rigor at each level. They comprise related ideas, concepts, skills, and procedures that form the foundation for understanding and lasting learning. The Focal Points emphasize depth versus breadth. The Focal Points will be addressed and highlighted throughout our PreK-8 and Pre-Algebra series.

What is the benefit to you in your classroom?

These Focal Points identify content for each grade level that should be mastered in order for your students to have true mathematical understanding–being able to not only calculate the answer, but to explain the answer and how to apply the calculation. The NCTM Focal Points were used as the basis in the development of ***Math Connects.*** The authors have incorporated the Focal Points into the content to assist you in building depth of understanding.

NCTM Focal Points for Grade 4	Supporting Chapters in ***Math Connects***
Number and Operations and Algebra	Chapters 4, 5, 6, 7
Number and Operations	Chapters 13, 14, 15
Measurement	Chapters 11, 12
Connections to the Focal Points	
Algebra	Chapters 2, 5
Geometry	Chapters 9, 10, 11, 12
Measurement	Chapter 9
Data Analysis	Chapter 3
Number and Operations	Chapters 1, 2, 8, 13, 14, 15

KEY

G4-FP1 Grade 4 Focal Point 1	**G4-FP6C** Grade 4 Focal Point 6 Connection
G4-FP2 Grade 4 Focal Point 2	**G4-FP7C** Grade 4 Focal Point 7 Connection
G4-FP3 Grade 4 Focal Point 3	**G4-FP8C** Grade 4 Focal Point 8 Connection
G4-FP4C Grade 4 Focal Point 4 Connection	
G4-FP5C Grade 4 Focal Point 5 Connection	

The Curriculum Focal Points identify key mathematical ideas for this grade. They are not discrete topics or a checklist to be mastered; rather, they provide a framework for the majority of instruction at a particular grade level and the foundation for future mathematics study. The complete document may be viewed at www.nctm.org/focalpoints.

G4-FP1 *Number and Operations* **and** *Algebra:* **Developing quick recall of multiplication facts and related division facts and fluency with whole number multiplication**

Students use understandings of multiplication to develop quick recall of the basic multiplication facts and related division facts. They apply their understanding of models for multiplication (i.e., equal sized groups, arrays, area models, equal intervals on the number line), place value, and properties of operations (in particular, the distributive property) as they develop, discuss, and use efficient, accurate, and generalizable methods to multiply multidigit whole numbers. They select appropriate methods and apply them accurately to estimate products or calculate them mentally, depending on the context and numbers involved. They develop fluency with efficient procedures, including the standard algorithm, for multiplying whole numbers, understand why the procedures work (on the basis of place value and properties of operations), and use them to solve problems.

G4-FP2 *Number and Operations:* **Developing an understanding of decimals, including the connections between fractions and decimals**

Students understand decimal notation as an extension of the base-ten system of writing whole numbers that is useful for representing more numbers, including numbers between 0 and 1, between 1 and 2, and so on. Students relate their understanding of fractions to reading and writing decimals that are greater than or less than 1, identifying equivalent decimals, comparing and ordering decimals, and estimating decimal or fractional amounts in problem solving. They connect equivalent fractions and decimals by comparing models to symbols and locating equivalent symbols on the number line.

G4-FP3 *Measurement:* **Developing an understanding of area and determining the areas of two-dimensional shapes**

Students recognize area as an attribute of two-dimensional regions. They learn that they can quantify area by finding the total number of same-sized units of area that cover the shape without gaps or overlaps. They understand that a square that is 1 unit on a side is the standard unit for measuring area. They select appropriate units, strategies (e.g., decomposing shapes), and tools for solving problems that involve estimating or measuring area. Students connect area measure to the area model that they have used to represent multiplication, and they use this connection to justify the formula for the area of a rectangle.

Connections to the Focal Points

G4-FP4C *Algebra:* Students continue identifying, describing, and extending numeric patterns involving all operations and nonnumeric growing or repeating patterns. Through these experiences, they develop an understanding of the use of a rule to describe a sequence of numbers or objects.

G4-FP5C *Geometry:* Students extend their understanding of properties of two-dimensional shapes as they find the areas of polygons. They build on their earlier work with symmetry and congruence in grade 3 to encompass transformations, including those that produce line and rotational symmetry. By using transformations to design and analyze simple tilings and tessellations, students deepen their understanding of two-dimensional space.

G4-FP6C *Measurement:* As part of understanding two-dimensional shapes, students measure and classify angles.

G4-FP7C *Data Analysis:* Students continue to use tools from grade 3, solving problems by making frequency tables, bar graphs, picture graphs, and line plots. They apply their understanding of place value to develop and use stem-and-leaf plots.

G4-FP8C *Number and Operations:* Building on their work in grade 3, students extend their understanding of place value and ways of representing numbers to 100,000 in various contexts. They use estimation in determining the relative sizes of amounts or distances. Students develop understandings of strategies for multidigit division by using models that represent division as the inverse of multiplication, as partitioning, or as successive subtraction. By working with decimals, students extend their ability to recognize equivalent fractions. Students' earlier work in grade 3 with models of fractions and multiplication and division facts supports their understanding of techniques for generating equivalent fractions and simplifying fractions.

Program Philosophy

Balanced Instruction, Vertically-Aligned from Grades PreK through Algebra 1

The vertical alignment of ***Math Connects*** PreK-8 and ***Algebra 1*** incorporates a balance of instruction throughout. These programs provide students a balanced approach to mathematics by:

- investigating concepts and building conceptual understanding.
- developing, reinforcing, and mastering computational and procedural skills.
- applying mathematics to problem-solving situations.

This sequence of Student Edition pages illustrates the vertically-aligned development of the conceptual understanding and corresponding computational and procedural skills for an important algebra topic.

Primary Students use two-color counters to model addition sentences. This activity forms a basis for future understanding of and success in solving algebraic equations.

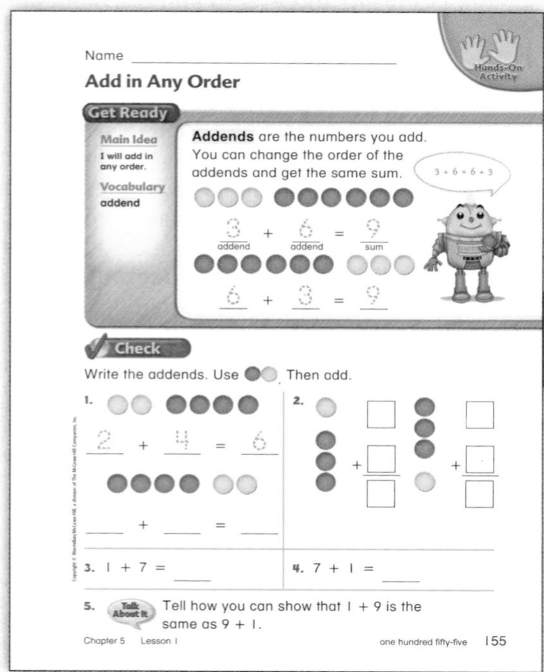

Name ____________

Hands-On Activity

Add in Any Order

Get Ready

Main Idea
I will add in any order.

Vocabulary
addend

Addends are the numbers you add. You can change the order of the addends and get the same sum.

3 + 6 = 6 + 3

3 + 6 = 9
addend addend sum

6 + 3 = 9

Check

Write the addends. Use counters. Then add.

1. 2 + 4 = 6
   ___ + ___ = ___

2.

3. 1 + 7 = ___

4. 7 + 1 = ___

5. Talk About It Tell how you can show that 1 + 9 is the same as 9 + 1.

Chapter 5 Lesson 1 one hundred fifty-five 155

Math Connects, Grade 1,
Student Edition, page 155

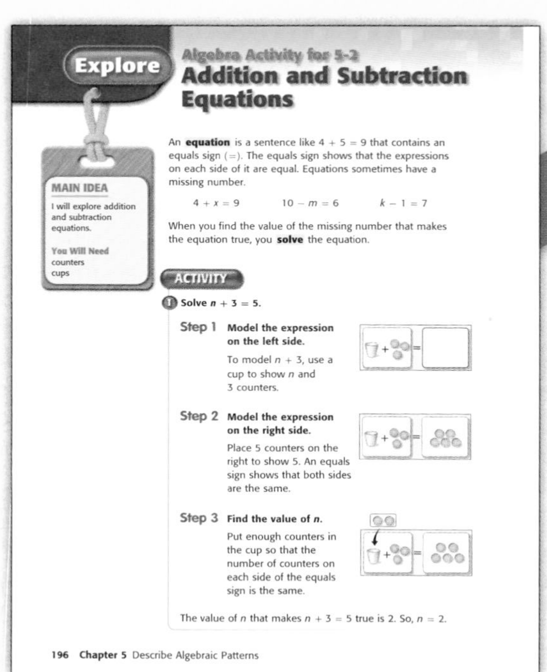

Explore

Algebra Activity for 5-2

Addition and Subtraction Equations

MAIN IDEA
I will explore addition and subtraction equations.

You Will Need
counters
cups

An **equation** is a sentence like $4 + 5 = 9$ that contains an equals sign (=). The equals sign shows that the expressions on each side of it are equal. Equations sometimes have a missing number.

$4 + x = 9$ $10 - m = 6$ $k - 1 = 7$

When you find the value of the missing number that makes the equation true, you **solve** the equation.

ACTIVITY

1 **Solve $n + 3 = 5$.**

Step 1 **Model the expression on the left side.**
To model $n + 3$, use a cup to show n and 3 counters.

Step 2 **Model the expression on the right side.**
Place 5 counters on the right to show 5. An equals sign shows that both sides are the same.

Step 3 **Find the value of n.**
Put enough counters in the cup so that the number of counters on each side of the equals sign is the same.

The value of n that makes $n + 3 = 5$ true is 2. So, $n = 2$.

196 **Chapter 5** Describe Algebraic Patterns

Math Connects, Grade 4,
Student Edition, page 196

Intermediate Students build on their experience with counters to using cups and counters to model and solve addition and subtraction equations. The exercises are designed to help students bridge the gap from using cups and counters to solving equations symbolically.

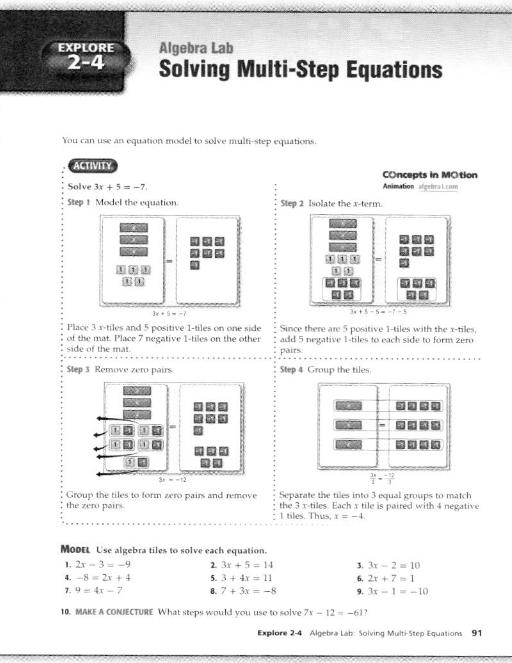

Explore 2-4

Algebra Lab

Solving Multi-Step Equations

You can use an equation model to solve multi-step equations.

ACTIVITY

Concepts in Motion
Animation algebra1.com

Solve $3x + 5 = -7$.

Step 1 Model the equation.

$3x + 5 = -7$

Place 3 x-tiles and 5 positive 1-tiles on one side of the mat. Place 7 negative 1-tiles on the other side of the mat.

Step 2 Isolate the x-term.

$3x + 5 - 5 = -7 - 5$

Since there are 5 positive 1-tiles with the x-tiles, add 5 negative 1-tiles to each side to form zero pairs.

Step 3 Remove zero pairs.

$3x = -12$

Group the tiles to form zero pairs and remove the zero pairs.

Step 4 Group the tiles.

$\frac{3x}{3} = \frac{-12}{3}$

Separate the tiles into 3 equal groups to match the 3 x-tiles. Each x tile is paired with 4 negative 1 tiles. Thus, $x = -4$.

MODEL Use algebra tiles to solve each equation.

1. $2x - 3 = -9$
2. $3x + 5 = 14$
3. $3x - 2 = 10$
4. $-8 = 2x + 4$
5. $3 + 4x = 11$
6. $2x + 7 = 1$
7. $9 = 4x - 7$
8. $7 + 3x = -8$
9. $3x - 1 = -10$
10. MAKE A CONJECTURE What steps would you use to solve $7x - 12 = -61$?

Explore 2-4 Algebra Lab: Solving Multi-Step Equations 91

Glencoe Algebra 1,
Student Edition, page 91

Algebra 1 Students continue the use of algebra tiles to investigate solving multi-step equations. In the next lesson, students apply the procedure developed in the Algebra Lab to a symbolic approach.

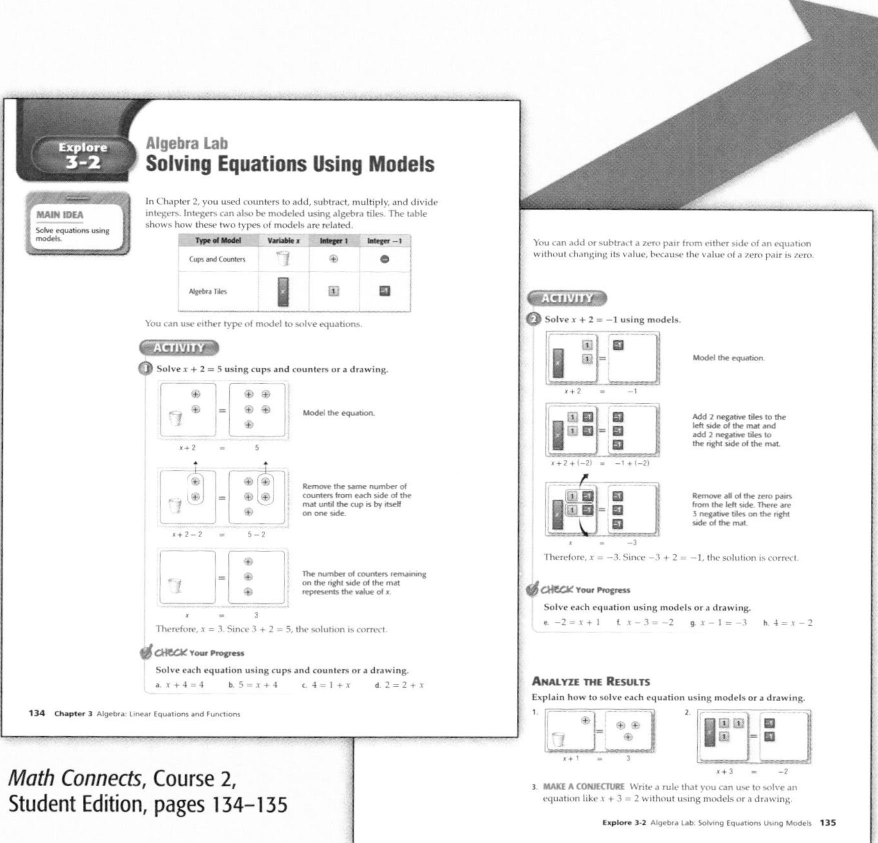

Explore 3-2

Algebra Lab

Solving Equations Using Models

MAIN IDEA
Solve equations using models.

In Chapter 2, you used counters to add, subtract, multiply, and divide integers. Integers can also be modeled using algebra tiles. The table shows how these two types of models are related.

Type of Model	Variable x	Integer 1	Integer −1
Cups and Counters			
Algebra Tiles			

You can use either type of model to solve equations.

ACTIVITY

1 Solve $x + 2 = 5$ using cups and counters or a drawing.

$x + 2 = 5$ — Model the equation.

$x + 2 - 2 = 5 - 2$ — Remove the same number of counters from each side of the mat until the cup is by itself on one side.

$x = 3$ — The number of counters remaining on the right side of the mat represents the value of x.

Therefore, $x = 3$. Since $3 + 2 = 5$, the solution is correct.

CHECK Your Progress

Solve each equation using cups and counters or a drawing.

a. $x + 4 = 4$ b. $5 = x + 4$ c. $4 = 1 + x$ d. $2 = 2 + x$

134 Chapter 3 Algebra: Linear Equations and Functions

You can add or subtract a zero pair from either side of an equation without changing its value, because the value of a zero pair is zero.

ACTIVITY

2 Solve $x + 2 = -1$ using models.

$x + 2 = -1$ — Model the equation.

$x + 2 + (-2) = -1 + (-2)$ — Add 2 negative tiles to the left side of the mat and add 2 negative tiles to the right side of the mat.

$x = -3$ — Remove all of the zero pairs from the left side. There are 3 negative tiles on the right side of the mat.

Therefore, $x = -3$. Since $-3 + 2 = -1$, the solution is correct.

CHECK Your Progress

Solve each equation using models or a drawing.

e. $-2 = x + 1$ f. $x - 3 = -2$ g. $x - 1 = -3$ h. $4 = x - 2$

ANALYZE THE RESULTS

Explain how to solve each equation using models or a drawing.

1. $x + 1 = 3$
2. $x + 3 = -2$
3. MAKE A CONJECTURE Write a rule that you can use to solve an equation like $x + 3 = 2$ without using models or a drawing.

Explore 3-2 Algebra Lab: Solving Equations Using Models 135

Math Connects, Course 2,
Student Edition, pages 134–135

Middle School Students represent the variable x as a cup, as a counter, or as a written x. In this Algebra Lab, students make the transition from cups and counters to the more abstract algebra tiles. In the next lesson, students solve simple equations symbolically.

Continuity of Instruction The instructional sequence described demonstrates the power of backward mapping from the desired result, success in Algebra 1. This process of development avoids gaps and overlaps between grade levels and ensures that at each grade level the concepts and skills are built on the strong foundation developed in previous grades. The same approach was used across all strands throughout the entire PreK-12 series.

Program Philosophy Balance of Instruction

Relevant Problem Solving

Math Connects provides students with the appropriate development of problem-solving strategies, skills, and applications from PreK through grade 5. In grades 6–8, students continue to learn and apply problem-solving skills and strategies. Students are provided with ongoing opportunities to apply their math skills and solve problems using visual thinking, logical reasoning, number sense, and algebra.

Problem-Solving Strategies and Skills

Problem-Solving Strategy or **Skill** lessons introduce students to multiples methods for solving problems all using the *four-step* plan.

- Understand
- Plan
- Solve
- Check

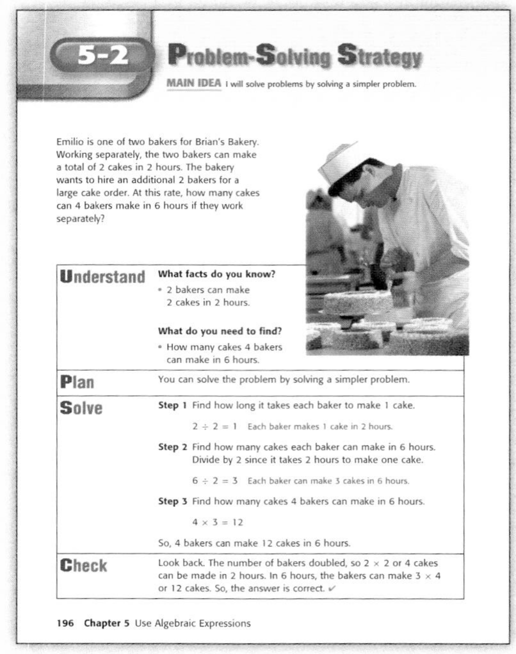

5-2 Problem-Solving Strategy

MAIN IDEA I will solve problems by solving a simpler problem.

Emilio is one of two bakers for Brian's Bakery. Working separately, the two bakers can make a total of 2 cakes in 2 hours. The bakery wants to hire an additional 2 bakers for a large cake order. At this rate, how many cakes can 4 bakers make in 6 hours if they work separately?

Understand What facts do you know?
- 2 bakers can make 2 cakes in 2 hours.

What do you need to find?
- How many cakes 4 bakers can make in 6 hours.

Plan You can solve the problem by solving a simpler problem.

Solve Step 1 Find how long it takes each baker to make 1 cake.

$2 \div 2 = 1$ Each baker makes 1 cake in 2 hours.

Step 2 Find how many cakes each baker can make in 6 hours. Divide by 2 since it takes 2 hours to make one cake.

$6 \div 2 = 3$ Each baker can make 3 cakes in 6 hours.

Step 3 Find how many cakes 4 bakers can make in 6 hours.

$4 \times 3 = 12$

So, 4 bakers can make 12 cakes in 6 hours.

Check Look back. The number of bakers doubled, so 2×2 or 4 cakes can be made in 2 hours. In 6 hours, the bakers can make 3×4 or 12 cakes. So, the answer is correct. ✓

196 Chapter 5 Use Algebraic Expressions

Math Connects, Grade 5
Student Edition, page 196

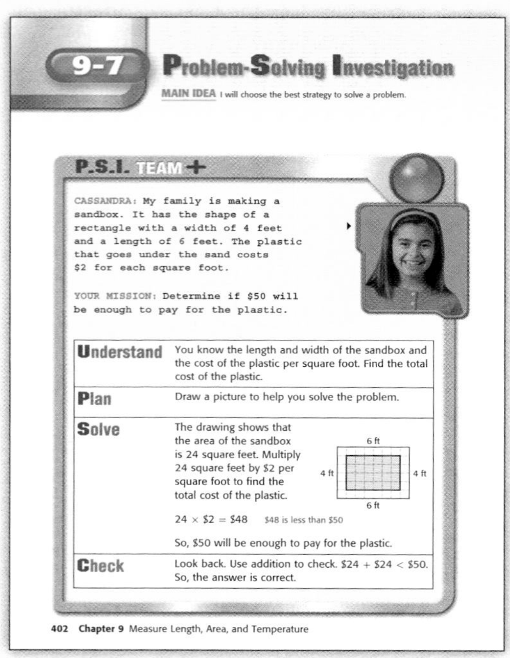

9-7 Problem-Solving Investigation

MAIN IDEA I will choose the best strategy to solve a problem.

P.S.I. TEAM +

CASSANDRA: My family is making a sandbox. It has the shape of a rectangle with a width of 4 feet and a length of 6 feet. The plastic that goes under the sand costs $2 for each square foot.

YOUR MISSION: Determine if $50 will be enough to pay for the plastic.

Understand You know the length and width of the sandbox and the cost of the plastic per square foot. Find the total cost of the plastic.

Plan Draw a picture to help you solve the problem.

Solve The drawing shows that the area of the sandbox is 24 square feet. Multiply 24 square feet by $2 per square foot to find the total cost of the plastic.

6 ft
4 ft
4 ft
6 ft

$24 \times \$2 = \$48$ $48 is less than $50

So, $50 will be enough to pay for the plastic.

Check Look back. Use addition to check. $\$24 + \$24 < \$50$. So, the answer is correct.

402 Chapter 9 Measure Length, Area, and Temperature

Math Connects, Grade 3
Student Edition, page 402

Problem-Solving Investigations

Problem-Solving Investigation lessons help students learn to choose appropriate strategies and apply them in problem-solving situations.

Real-World Problem Solving

Each chapter has a Problem Solving lesson that makes a tie to another discipline. These lessons encourage students to see problem solving in real-world applications.

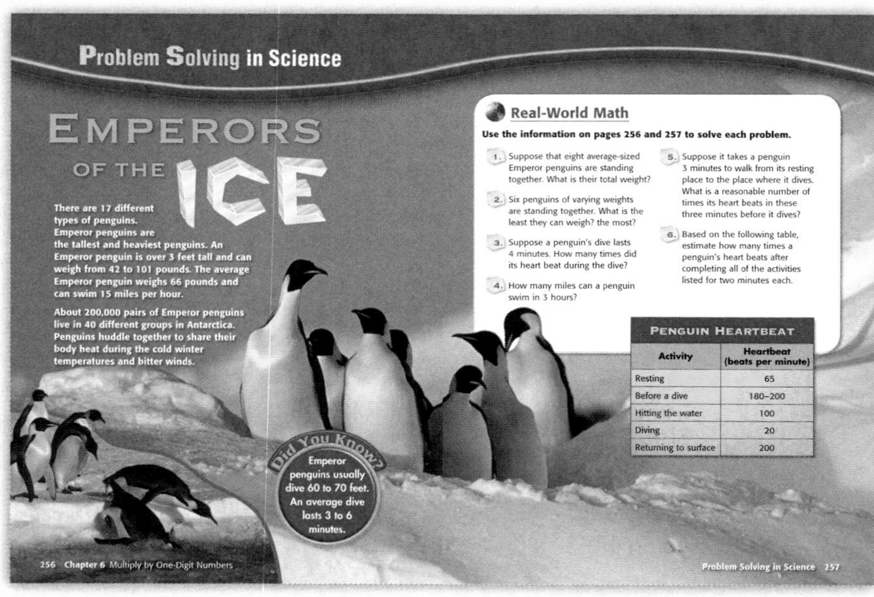

Problem Solving in Science

EMPERORS OF THE ICE

There are 17 different types of penguins. Emperor penguins are the tallest and heaviest penguins. An Emperor penguin is over 3 feet tall and can weigh from 42 to 101 pounds. The average Emperor penguin weighs 66 pounds and can swim 15 miles per hour.

About 200,000 pairs of Emperor penguins live in 40 different groups in Antarctica. Penguins huddle together to share their body heat during the cold winter temperatures and bitter winds.

Did You Know? Emperor penguins usually dive 60 to 70 feet. An average dive lasts 3 to 6 minutes.

Real-World Math

Use the information on pages 256 and 257 to solve each problem.

1. Suppose that eight average-sized Emperor penguins are standing together. What is their total weight?
2. Six penguins of varying weights are standing together. What is the least they can weigh? the most?
3. Suppose a penguin's dive lasts 4 minutes. How many times did its heart beat during the dive?
4. How many miles can a penguin swim in 3 hours?
5. Suppose it takes a penguin 3 minutes to walk from its resting place to the place where it dives. What is a reasonable number of times its heart beats in these three minutes before it dives?
6. Based on the following table, estimate how many times a penguin's heart beats after completing all of the activities listed for two minutes each.

PENGUIN HEARTBEAT

Activity	Heartbeat (beats per minute)
Resting	65
Before a dive	180–200
Hitting the water	100
Diving	20
Returning to surface	200

256 Chapter 6 Multiply by One-Digit Numbers

Problem Solving in Science 257

Math Connects, Grade 4
Student Edition, pages 256–257

Real-World Problem Solving Readers

Fiction and nonfiction leveled readers extend problem-solving skills and strategies and make real-world applications. The books are provided for On Level, Sheltered English, and Spanish readers.

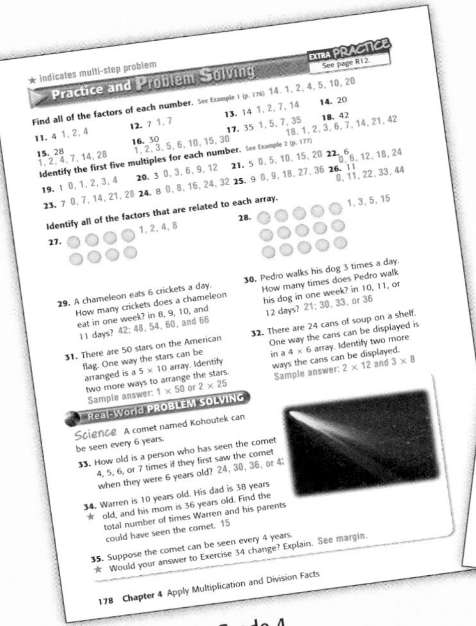

★ indicates multi-step problem

Practice and Problem Solving

EXTRA PRACTICE See page R12.

Find all of the factors of each number. See Example 1 (p. 176)

11. 4 1, 2, 4
12. 7 1, 7
13. 14 1, 2, 7, 14
14. 20 1, 2, 4, 5, 10, 20
15. 28 1, 2, 4, 7, 14, 28
16. 30 1, 2, 3, 5, 6, 10, 15, 30
17. 35 1, 5, 7, 35
18. 42 1, 2, 3, 6, 7, 14, 21, 42

Identify the first five multiples for each number. See Example 2 (p. 177)

19. 1 0, 1, 2, 3, 4
20. 3 0, 3, 6, 9, 12
21. 5 0, 5, 10, 15, 20
22. 6 0, 6, 12, 18, 24
23. 7 0, 7, 14, 21, 28
24. 8 0, 8, 16, 24, 32
25. 9 0, 9, 18, 27, 36
26. 11 0, 11, 22, 33, 44

Identify all of the factors that are related to each array.

27. 1, 2, 4, 8
28. 1, 3, 5, 15

29. A chameleon eats 6 crickets a day. How many crickets does a chameleon eat in one week? in 8, 9, 10, and 11 days? 42; 48, 54, 60, and 66
30. Pedro walks his dog 3 times a day. How many times does Pedro walk his dog in one week? in 10, 11, or 12 days? 21; 30, 33, or 36
31. There are 50 stars on the American flag. One way the stars can be arranged is a 5 × 10 array. Identify two more ways to arrange the stars. Sample answer: 1 × 50 or 2 × 25
32. There are 24 cans of soup on a shelf. One way the cans can be displayed is in a 4 × 6 array. Identify two more ways the cans can be displayed. Sample answer: 2 × 12 and 3 × 8

Real-World PROBLEM SOLVING

Science A comet named Kohoutek can be seen every 6 years.

33. How old is a person who has seen the comet 4, 5, 6, or 7 times if they first saw the comet when they were 6 years old? 24, 30, 36, or 42
34. ★ Warren is 10 years old. His dad is 38 years old, and his mom is 36 years old. Find the total number of times Warren and his parents could have seen the comet. 15
35. ★ Suppose the comet can be seen every 4 years. Would your answer to Exercise 34 change? Explain. See margin.

178 Chapter 4 Apply Multiplication and Division Facts

Math Connects, Grade 4
Student Edition, page 162

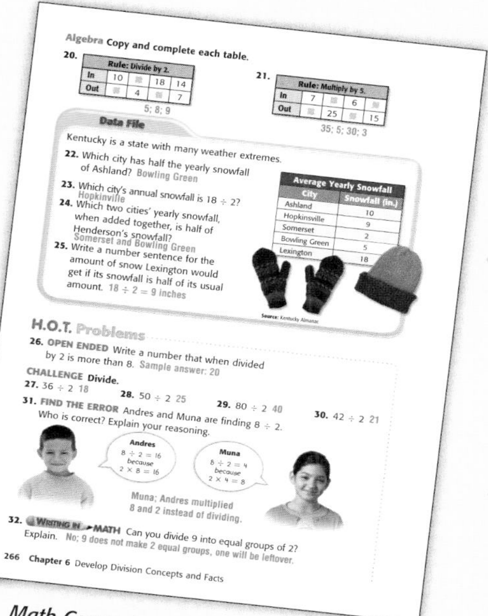

Algebra Copy and complete each table.

20.

Rule: Divide by 2.				
In	10	■	18	14
Out	■	4	■	7

5; 8; 9

21.

Rule: Multiply by 5.				
In	7	■	6	■
Out	■	25	■	15

35; 5; 30; 3

Data File

Kentucky is a state with many weather extremes.

22. Which city has half the yearly snowfall of Ashland? Bowling Green
23. Which city's annual snowfall is 18 ÷ 2? Hopkinville
24. Which two cities' yearly snowfall, when added together, is half of Henderson's snowfall? Somerset and Bowling Green
25. Write a number sentence for the amount of snow Lexington would get if its snowfall is half of its usual amount. 18 ÷ 2 = 9 inches

Average Yearly Snowfall	
City	Snowfall (in.)
Ashland	10
Hopkinsville	9
Somerset	2
Bowling Green	5
Lexington	18

Source: Kentucky Almanac

H.O.T. Problems

26. **OPEN ENDED** Write a number that when divided by 2 is more than 8. Sample answer: 20

CHALLENGE Divide.

27. 36 ÷ 2 18
28. 50 ÷ 2 25
29. 80 ÷ 2 40
30. 42 ÷ 2 21

31. **FIND THE ERROR** Andres and Muna are finding 8 ÷ 2. Who is correct? Explain your reasoning.

Andres: 8 ÷ 2 = 16 because 2 × 8 = 16
Muna: 8 ÷ 2 = 4 because 2 × 4 = 8

Muna; Andres multiplied 8 and 2 instead of dividing.

32. WRITING IN MATH Can you divide 9 into equal groups of 2? Explain. No; 9 does not make 2 equal groups, one will be leftover.

266 Chapter 6 Develop Division Concepts and Facts

Math Connects, Grade 3
Student Edition, page 266

Multi-Step Word Problems

Multi-step word problems are not simple computation problems using the numbers given. Students must analyze exactly what the problem is asking and how to use the information given. These problems are starred in the Teacher Edition.

H.O.T. Problems

H.O.T. Problems require students to use **Higher Order Thinking** skills to solve problems.

Looking Ahead

Looking Ahead lessons introduce important concepts and skills that students can use.

Math Connects, Grade 5
Student Edition, page LA0–LA1

Comprehensive Assessment System

Data-Driven Decision Making

Math Connects offers frequent and meaningful assessment of student progress within the curriculum structure and printed teacher support materials. See pages T22 and T23 for digital assessment solutions.

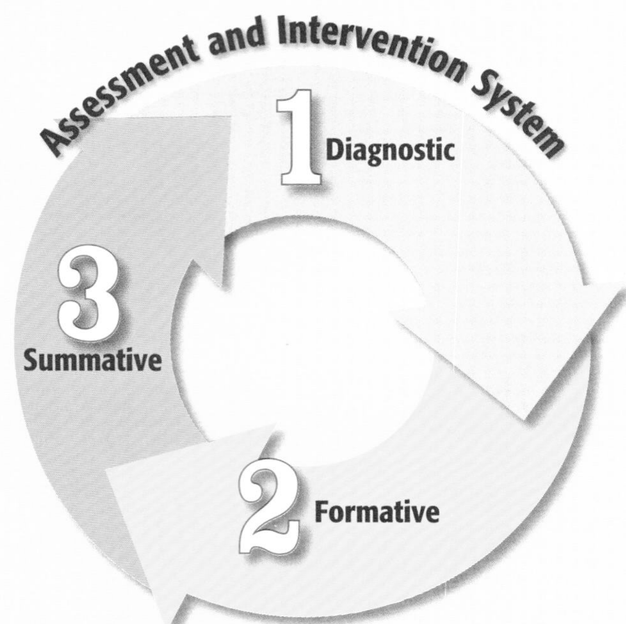

1 Diagnostic

Initial Assessment Assess students' knowledge **at the beginning of the year** with the *Diagnostic and Placement Tests*. This booklet will help you determine whether your students need additional materials and resources to meet grade-level standards.

Entry-Level Assessment Assess students' prior knowledge **at the beginning of a chapter or lesson** with one of the following options.

Student Edition

- Are You Ready?

Teacher Edition

- Intervention Options
- 5-Minute Check

Additional Resources

- Chapter Resource Masters, Chapter Diagnostic Test

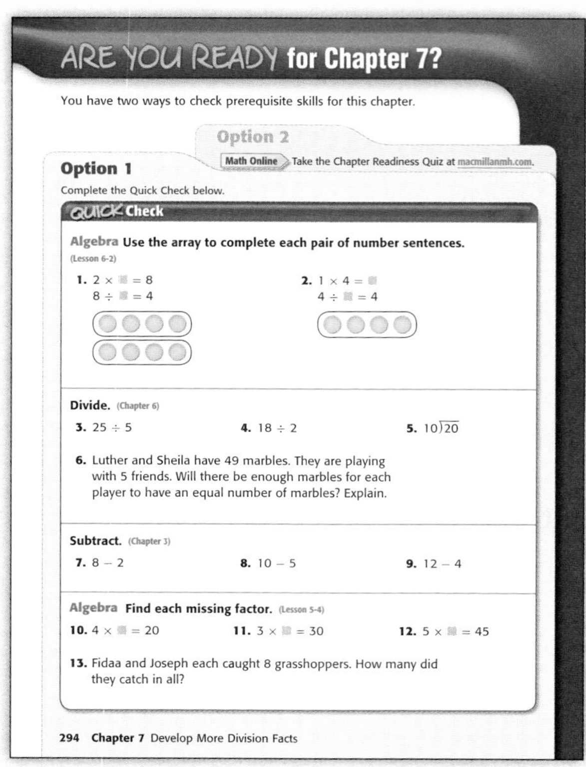

ARE YOU READY for Chapter 7?

You have two ways to check prerequisite skills for this chapter.

Option 2
Math Online Take the Chapter Readiness Quiz at macmillanmh.com.

Option 1
Complete the Quick Check below.

QUICK Check

Algebra Use the array to complete each pair of number sentences. (Lesson 6-2)

1. 2 × ■ = 8
8 ÷ ■ = 4

2. 1 × 4 = ■
4 ÷ ■ = 4

Divide. (Chapter 6)

3. 25 ÷ 5
4. 18 ÷ 2
5. $10\overline{)20}$

6. Luther and Sheila have 49 marbles. They are playing with 5 friends. Will there be enough marbles for each player to have an equal number of marbles? Explain.

Subtract. (Chapter 3)

7. 8 − 2
8. 10 − 5
9. 12 − 4

Algebra Find each missing factor. (Lesson 5-4)

10. 4 × ■ = 20
11. 3 × ■ = 30
12. 5 × ■ = 45

13. Fidaa and Joseph each caught 8 grasshoppers. How many did they catch in all?

294 Chapter 7 Develop More Division Facts

Math Connects, Grade 3
Student Edition, page 294

Formative

Progress Monitoring Determine if students are progressing adequately as you teach each lesson. Use the assessments to differentiate lesson instruction and practice.

Student Edition

- Mid-Chapter Check
- Find the Error
- Check What You Know
- Talk About It
- Writing in Math
- Study Guide and Review
- Foldables™

Teacher Edition

- Alternate Teaching Strategy
- Step 4 (Assess) of the Teaching Plan
- Quick Check
- Data-Driven Decision Making

Additional Resources

Chapter Resource Masters

- Mid-Chapter Test
- 3 Quizzes

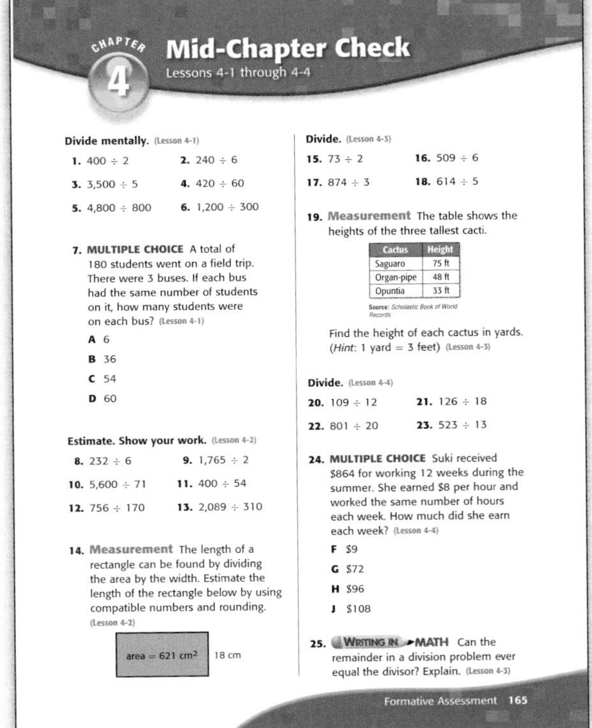

CHAPTER 4 **Mid-Chapter Check**
Lessons 4-1 through 4-4

Divide mentally. (Lesson 4-1)

1. 400 ÷ 2
2. 240 ÷ 6
3. 3,500 ÷ 5
4. 420 ÷ 60
5. 4,800 ÷ 800
6. 1,200 ÷ 300

7. **MULTIPLE CHOICE** A total of 180 students went on a field trip. There were 3 buses. If each bus had the same number of students on it, how many students were on each bus? (Lesson 4-1)
   A 6
   B 36
   C 54
   D 60

Estimate. Show your work. (Lesson 4-2)

8. 232 ÷ 6
9. 1,765 ÷ 2
10. 5,600 ÷ 71
11. 400 ÷ 54
12. 756 ÷ 170
13. 2,089 ÷ 310

14. **Measurement** The length of a rectangle can be found by dividing the area by the width. Estimate the length of the rectangle below by using compatible numbers and rounding. (Lesson 4-2)

area = 621 cm²   18 cm

Divide. (Lesson 4-3)

15. 73 ÷ 2
16. 509 ÷ 6
17. 874 ÷ 3
18. 614 ÷ 5

19. **Measurement** The table shows the heights of the three tallest cacti.

Cactus	Height
Saguaro	75 ft
Organ-pipe	48 ft
Opuntia	33 ft

Source: Scholastic Book of World Records

Find the height of each cactus in yards. (*Hint*: 1 yard = 3 feet) (Lesson 4-3)

Divide. (Lesson 4-4)

20. 109 ÷ 12
21. 126 ÷ 18
22. 801 ÷ 20
23. 523 ÷ 13

24. **MULTIPLE CHOICE** Suki received $864 for working 12 weeks during the summer. She earned $8 per hour and worked the same number of hours each week. How much did she earn each week? (Lesson 4-4)
   F $9
   G $72
   H $96
   J $108

25. WRITING IN MATH Can the remainder in a division problem ever equal the divisor? Explain. (Lesson 4-3)

Formative Assessment 165

Math Connects, Grade 5
Student Edition, page 165

Summative

Summative Evaluation Assess student success in learning the concepts in each chapter.

Student Edition

- Chapter Test
- Test Practice
- Foldables™

Teacher Edition

- Data-Driven Decision Making

Additional Resources

Chapter Resource Masters

- Oral Assessment
- Listening Assessment
- 4 Leveled Chapter Tests
- Cumulative Test

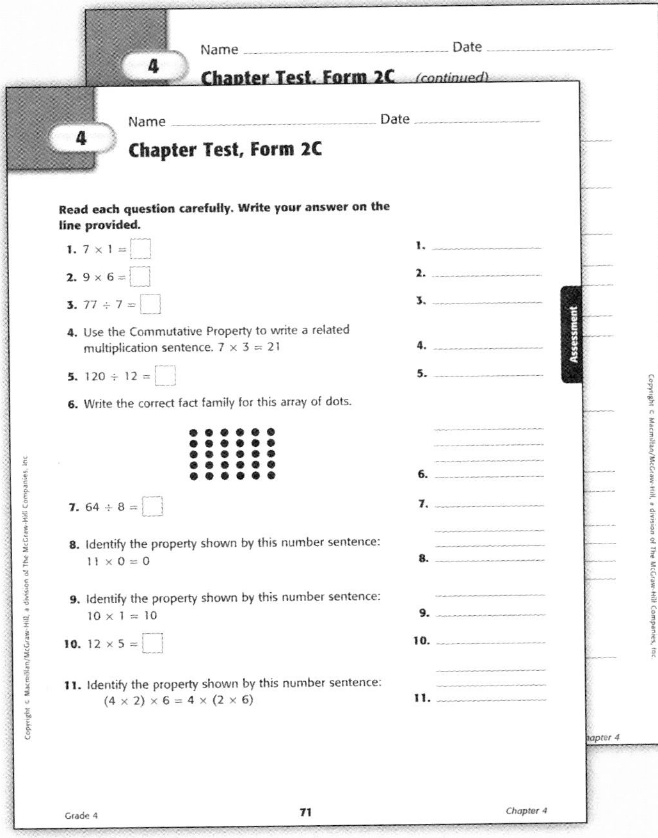

4 Name ______ Date ______
Chapter Test, Form 2C *(continued)*

4 Name ______ Date ______
Chapter Test, Form 2C

Read each question carefully. Write your answer on the line provided.

1. 7 × 1 = ☐   1. ______
2. 9 × 6 = ☐   2. ______
3. 77 ÷ 7 = ☐   3. ______
4. Use the Commutative Property to write a related multiplication sentence. 7 × 3 = 21   4. ______
5. 120 ÷ 12 = ☐   5. ______
6. Write the correct fact family for this array of dots.   6. ______
7. 64 ÷ 8 = ☐   7. ______
8. Identify the property shown by this number sentence: 11 × 0 = 0   8. ______
9. Identify the property shown by this number sentence: 10 × 1 = 10   9. ______
10. 12 × 5 = ☐   10. ______
11. Identify the property shown by this number sentence: (4 × 2) × 6 = 4 × (2 × 6)   11. ______

Assessment

Grade 4   71   Chapter 4

Math Connects, Grade 4
Chapter 8 Resource Masters, pages 71–72

Comprehensive Assessment System

Data-Driven Decision Making

Math Connects provides digital assessment options to create, customize, administer, and instantly score a variety of assessments. These digital solutions offer the same quality assessments and reporting as the print resources in easy-to-use technology tools.

Math Connects, Grade 4

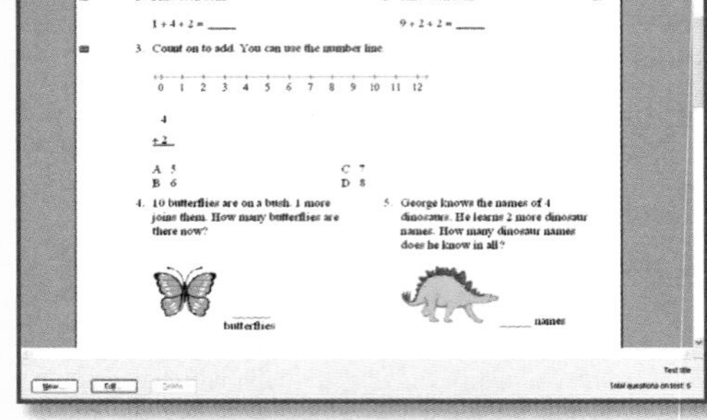

Math Connects, Grade 4

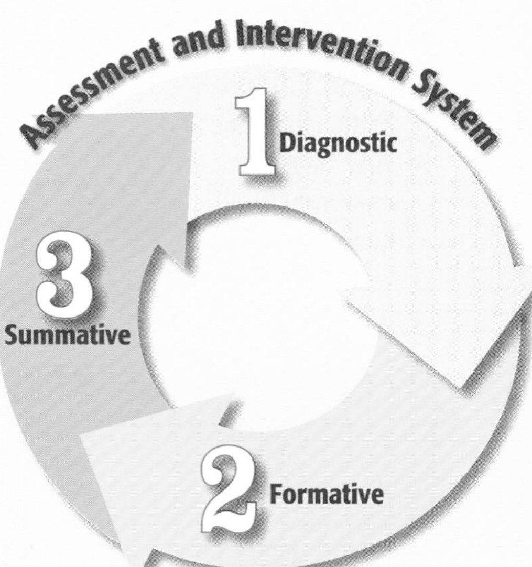

Advance Tracker helps teachers administer online tests, diagnose student achievement, and create prescriptive reports for a student or class.

ExamView Assessment Suite allows teachers to create and customize their own assessment and assignments. Print in one or two columns to match state test.

1 Diagnostic

Initial Assessment Assess students' knowledge **at the beginning of the year** with the *Diagnostic and Placement Tests.* These assessments will help you determine whether your students need additional materials and resources to meet grade-level standards.

- Diagnostic and Placement Tests

- Diagnostic and Placement Tests

Entry–Level Assessment Assess students' prior knowledge **at the beginning of a chapter or lesson.**

Math Online macmillanmh.com Students can complete online tests and the results are emailed to the teacher.

- Chapter Readiness

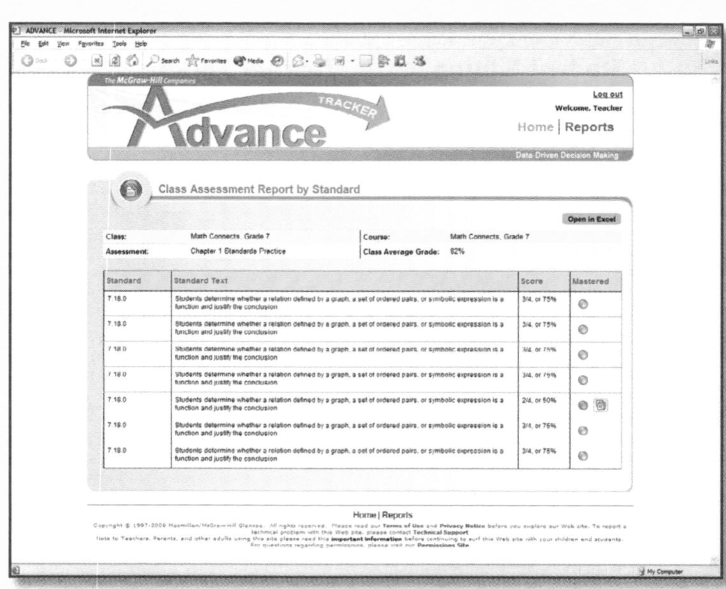

Math Connects, Grade 5 Advance Tracker

Formative

Progress Monitoring Determine if students are progressing adequately as you teach each lesson. Use the assessments to differentiate lesson instruction and practice.

- Mid-Chapter Test
- Study Guide and Review

Math Online macmillanmh.com

- Self-Check Quizzes

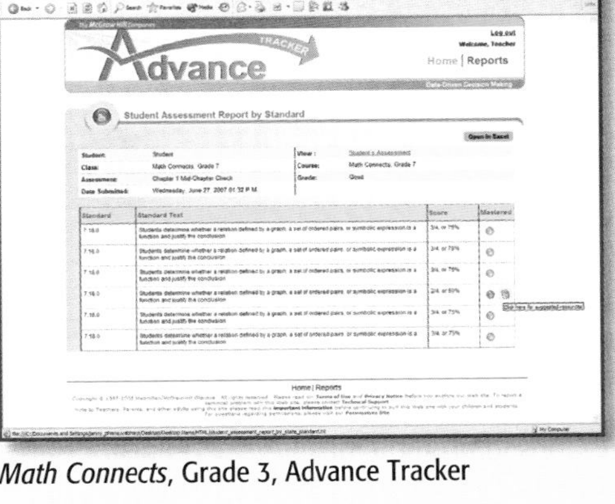

Math Connects, Grade 3, Advance Tracker

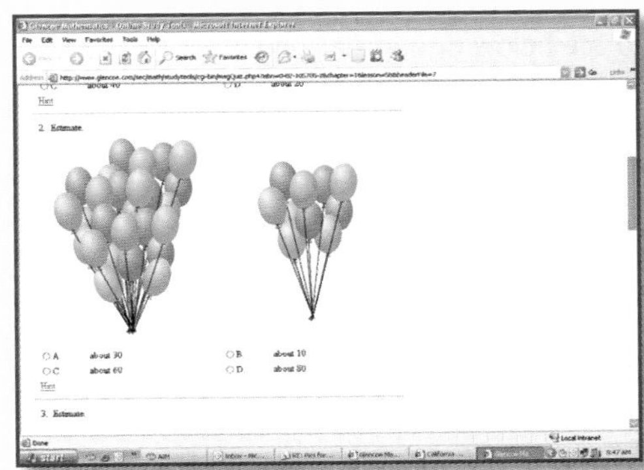

Math Connects, Grade 4, Self-Check Quiz

Summative

Summative Evaluation Assess students' success in learning the concepts in each chapter.

- Chapter Tests
- Cumulative Standardized Test Practice

- Chapter Tests
- Cumulative Standardized Test Practice

macmillanmh.com

- Chapter Tests

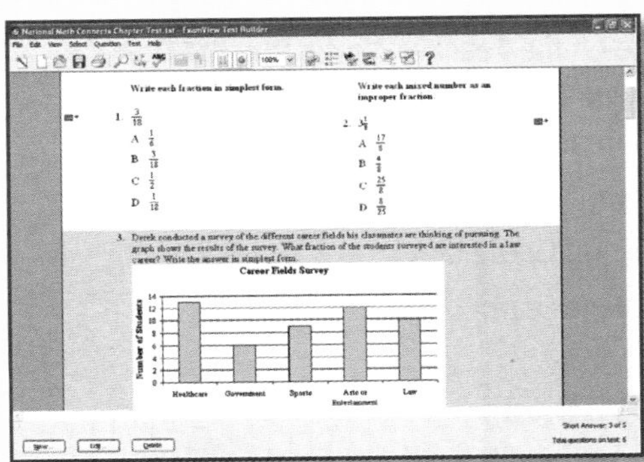

Math Connects, Grade 5, ExamView Assessment Suite

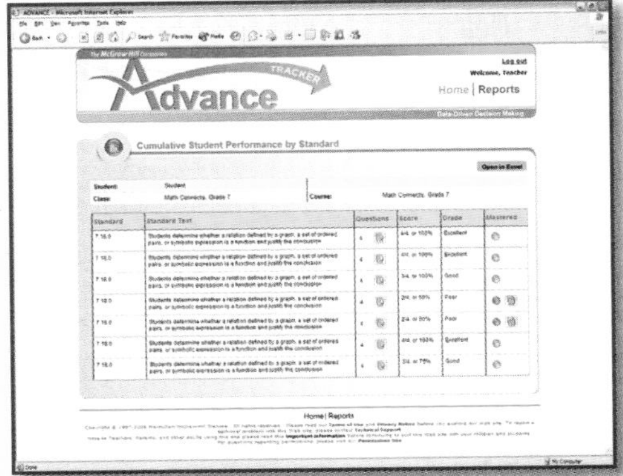

Math Connects, Grade 4, Advance Tracker

Differentiated Instruction

Reaching All Learners

Math Connects, provides extensive support for reaching all learners.

Every chapter and lesson includes suggestions for identifying and meeting your students' needs. Strategies include differentiation in pacing and student grouping, alternate approaches, ways to enhance instruction with manipulatives, questions to promote higher-order thinking, and language hints.

Personalize instruction for:

- BL Students who are below or approaching grade level
- ELL English language learners
- AL Students who are above or beyond grade level

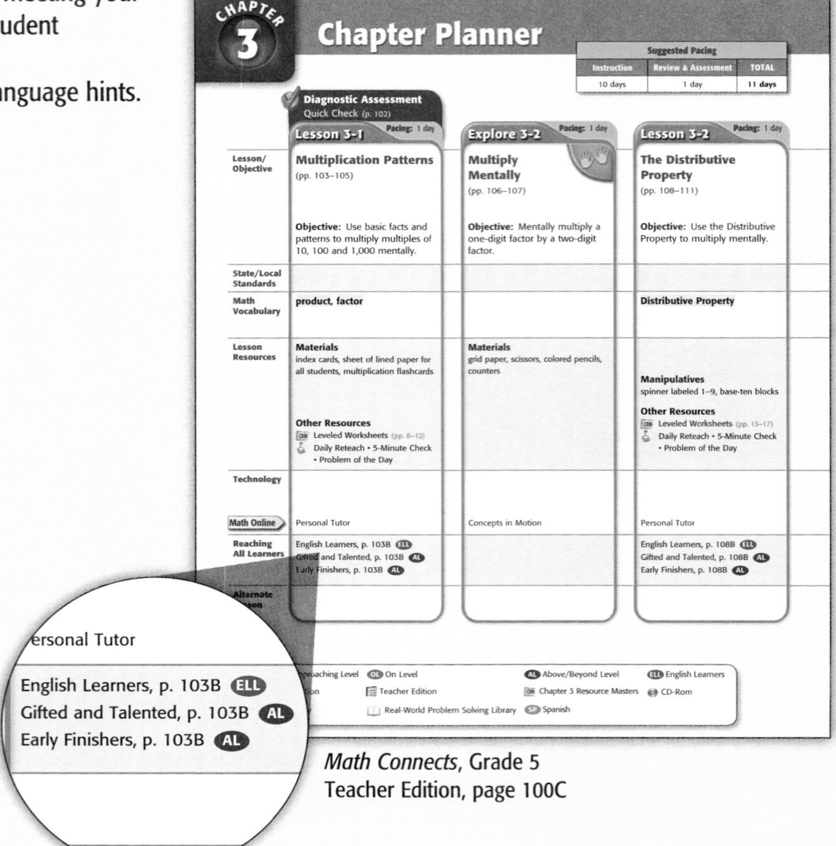

CHAPTER 3 Chapter Planner

Suggested Pacing		
Instruction	Review & Assessment	TOTAL
10 days	1 day	**11 days**

Diagnostic Assessment
Quick Check (p. 102)

	Lesson 3-1 Pacing: 1 day	Explore 3-2 Pacing: 1 day	Lesson 3-2 Pacing: 1 day
Lesson/ Objective	**Multiplication Patterns** (pp. 103–105) **Objective:** Use basic facts and patterns to multiply multiples of 10, 100 and 1,000 mentally.	**Multiply Mentally** (pp. 106–107) **Objective:** Mentally multiply a one-digit factor by a two-digit factor.	**The Distributive Property** (pp. 108–111) **Objective:** Use the Distributive Property to multiply mentally.
State/Local Standards			
Math Vocabulary	**product, factor**		**Distributive Property**
Lesson Resources	**Materials** index cards, sheet of lined paper for all students, multiplication flashcards **Other Resources** Leveled Worksheets (pp. 8–12) Daily Reteach • 5-Minute Check • Problem of the Day	**Materials** grid paper, scissors, colored pencils, counters	**Manipulatives** spinner labeled 1–9, base-ten blocks **Other Resources** Leveled Worksheets (pp. 13–17) Daily Reteach • 5-Minute Check • Problem of the Day
Technology			
Math Online	Personal Tutor	Concepts in Motion	Personal Tutor
Reaching All Learners	English Learners, p. 103B ELL Gifted and Talented, p. 103B AL Early Finishers, p. 103B AL		English Learners, p. 108B ELL Gifted and Talented, p. 108B AL Early Finishers, p. 108B AL
Alternate Lesson			

OL On Level · AL Above/Beyond Level · ELL English Learners · Teacher Edition · Chapter 3 Resource Masters · CD-Rom · Real-World Problem Solving Library · SP Spanish

ersonal Tutor
English Learners, p. 103B ELL
Gifted and Talented, p. 103B AL
Early Finishers, p. 103B AL

Math Connects, Grade 5
Teacher Edition, page 100C

Leveled Exercise Sets

The assignments for each lesson are leveled for students.

- BL Below or Approaching Grade Level
- OL on Grade Level
- AL Above or Beyond Grade Level

Leveled Resources

All of the blackline masters and transparencies that accompany the program, as well as all of the Teacher Edition pages, are available on the **TeacherWorks Plus™ CD-ROM.** Resources and assignments are leveled for students who are:

- BL Below or Approaching Grade Level
- OL On Grade Level
- AL Above or Beyond Grade Level
- ELL English Language Learners

Learning Stations

Cross-curricular learning centers offer students guided opportunities to explore chapter concepts as individuals or in small groups. Content areas include:

- Science
- Social Studies
- Reading
- Art
- Health
- Writing
- Music

Learning Station cards are English on one side and Spanish on the other.

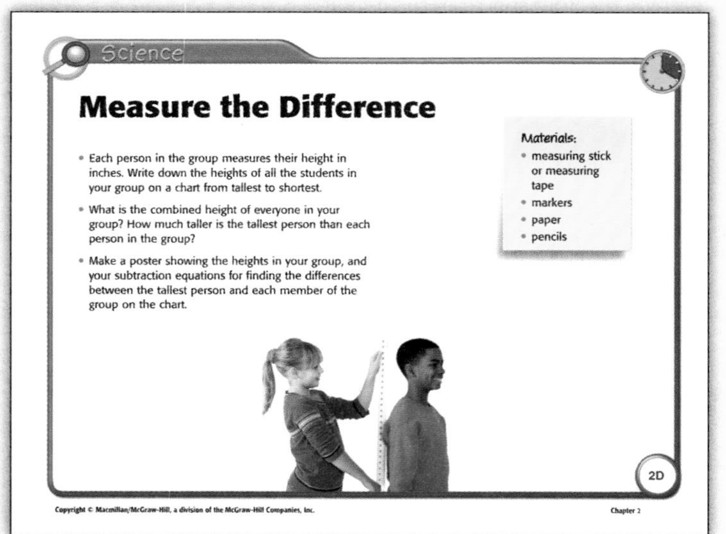

Math Connects, Grade 4
Learning Station Card 2D

Advanced Learners

Acceleration and Enrichment Resources and assignments for students who are above level may be used with advanced learners. In particular, the **Enrich Masters** provide students with valuable opportunities for extending your lessons.

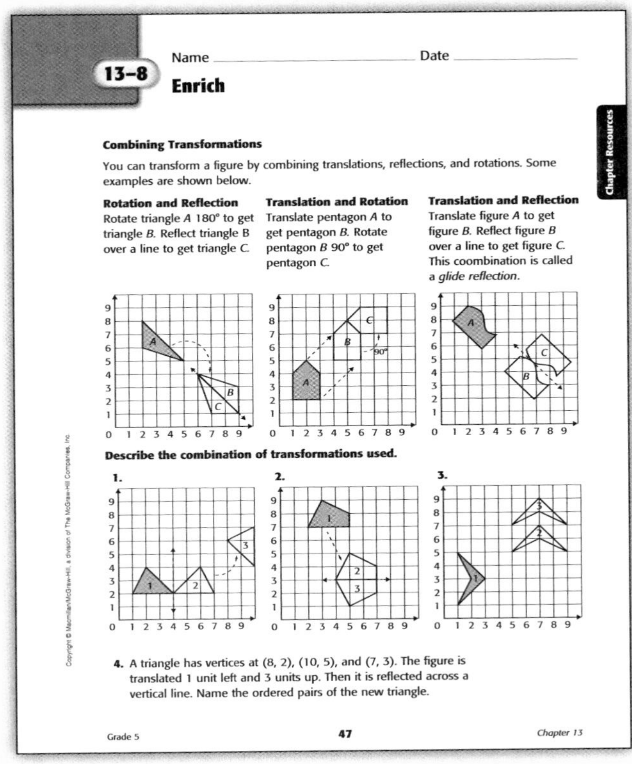

13-8

Name ______________________ Date ______________

Enrich

Combining Transformations

You can transform a figure by combining translations, reflections, and rotations. Some examples are shown below.

Rotation and Reflection
Rotate triangle *A* 180° to get triangle *B*. Reflect triangle B over a line to get triangle *C*.

Translation and Rotation
Translate pentagon *A* to get pentagon *B*. Rotate pentagon *B* 90° to get pentagon *C*.

Translation and Reflection
Translate figure *A* to get figure *B*. Reflect figure *B* over a line to get figure *C*. This coombination is called *a glide reflection*.

Describe the combination of transformations used.

1.

2.

3.

4. A triangle has vertices at (8, 2), (10, 5), and (7, 3). The figure is translated 1 unit left and 3 units up. Then it is reflected across a vertical line. Name the ordered pairs of the new triangle.

Grade 5 47 Chapter 13

Math Connects, Grade 5,
Chapter 13 Resource Masters, page 47

ELL English Language Learners

Our authors have identified seven keys for effective instruction with English language learner students and used them throughout the program.

1. Simplify language, not concepts.
2. Activate background knowledge.
3. Teach in multiple modalities.
4. Use core vocabulary and common use verbs.
5. Express mathematical understanding in different ways.
6. Incorporate higher-level problem-solving skills.
7. Provide a mathematics-rich classroom environment.

The English Language Learners Guide provides additional support for English language learner students that can be used alone or with core instruction in the Student Edition and Teacher Edition.

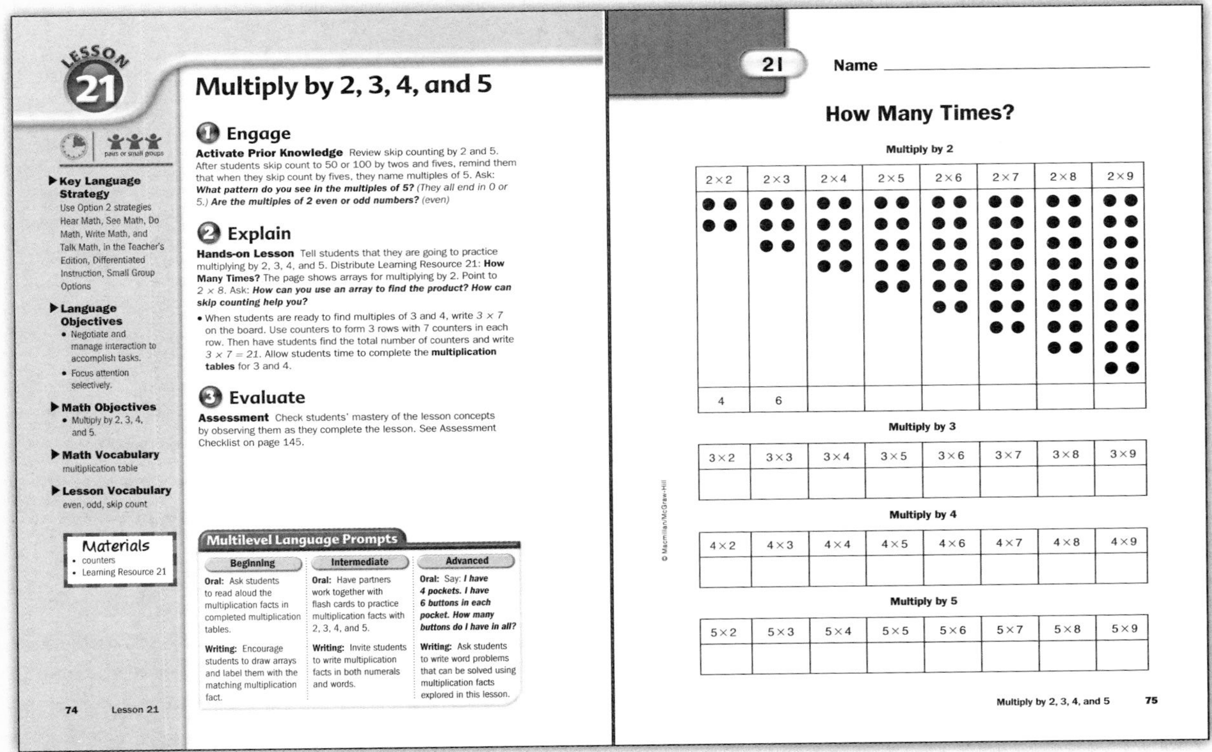

LESSON 21

Multiply by 2, 3, 4, and 5

pairs or small groups

▶ Key Language Strategy
Use Option 2 strategies Hear Math, See Math, Do Math, Write Math, and Talk Math, in the Teacher's Edition, Differentiated Instruction, Small Group Options

▶ Language Objectives
- Negotiate and manage interaction to accomplish tasks.
- Focus attention selectively.

▶ Math Objectives
- Multiply by 2, 3, 4, and 5.

▶ Math Vocabulary
multiplication table

▶ Lesson Vocabulary
even, odd, skip count

Materials
- counters
- Learning Resource 21

1 Engage

Activate Prior Knowledge Review skip counting by 2 and 5. After students skip count to 50 or 100 by twos and fives, remind them that when they skip count by fives, they name multiples of 5. Ask: ***What pattern do you see in the multiples of 5?*** *(They all end in 0 or 5.)* ***Are the multiples of 2 even or odd numbers?*** *(even)*

2 Explain

Hands-on Lesson Tell students that they are going to practice multiplying by 2, 3, 4, and 5. Distribute Learning Resource 21: **How Many Times?** The page shows arrays for multiplying by 2. Point to *2 × 8*. Ask: ***How can you use an array to find the product? How can skip counting help you?***

- When students are ready to find multiples of 3 and 4, write *3 × 7* on the board. Use counters to form 3 rows with 7 counters in each row. Then have students find the total number of counters and write *3 × 7 = 21*. Allow students time to complete the **multiplication tables** for 3 and 4.

3 Evaluate

Assessment Check students' mastery of the lesson concepts by observing them as they complete the lesson. See Assessment Checklist on page 145.

Multilevel Language Prompts

Beginning	Intermediate	Advanced
Oral: Ask students to read aloud the multiplication facts in completed multiplication tables.	**Oral:** Have partners work together with flash cards to practice multiplication facts with 2, 3, 4, and 5.	**Oral:** Say: ***I have 4 pockets. I have 6 buttons in each pocket. How many buttons do I have in all?***
Writing: Encourage students to draw arrays and label them with the matching multiplication fact.	**Writing:** Invite students to write multiplication facts in both numerals and words.	**Writing:** Ask students to write word problems that can be solved using multiplication facts explored in this lesson.

74 Lesson 21

21 Name ______________________

How Many Times?

Multiply by 2

2×2	2×3	2×4	2×5	2×6	2×7	2×8	2×9
4	6						

Multiply by 3

3×2	3×3	3×4	3×5	3×6	3×7	3×8	3×9

Multiply by 4

4×2	4×3	4×4	4×5	4×6	4×7	4×8	4×9

Multiply by 5

5×2	5×3	5×4	5×5	5×6	5×7	5×8	5×9

Multiply by 2, 3, 4, and 5 75

Math Connects, Grade 3
ELL Guide, pages 74–75

Blending Your Instruction

Basal – NSF-Funded – Tier 3 Intervention

Math Connects, IMPACT Mathematics, and ***Math Triumphs*** provide a three-pronged approach to mathematics instruction. This unique combination provides built-in strategies to easily tip the balance of instruction to a more conceptual approach or to a more skills-based approach, depending on the needs of your students.

These programs are horizontally aligned in the following ways.

- Common vocabulary
- Common manipulatives
- Common teacher planning guides
- Common technology
- Common authors
- Common professional development

Basal Program—Focused on Comprehensive Instruction

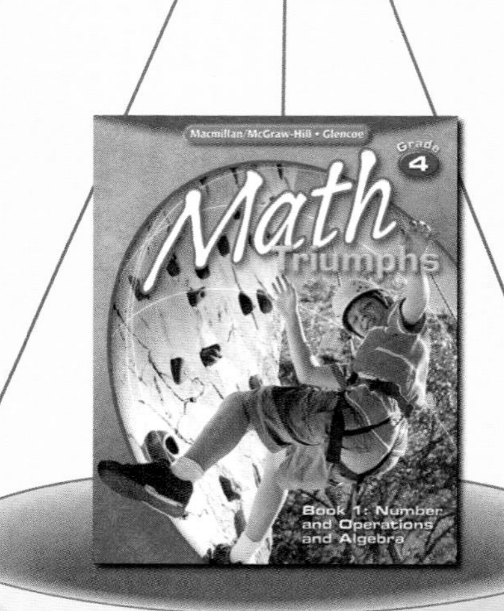

NSF Program—Focused on Investigations

Intensive Intervention (Tier 3 RTI)—Focused on Skills

RTI (Response to Intervention)

In the ***Math Connects*** Teacher Editions, the Data-Driven Decision Making chart provides a comprehensive RTI (Response to Intervention) beginning with diagnostic review and continuing with prescriptions at all three RTI tiers.

- **Tier 1** – Leveled exercise sets and leveled resources
- **Tier 2** – Strategic Intervention Guide (1–5), Study Guide and Intervention (6–8)
- **Tier 3** – Intensive Intervention, ***Math Triumphs***

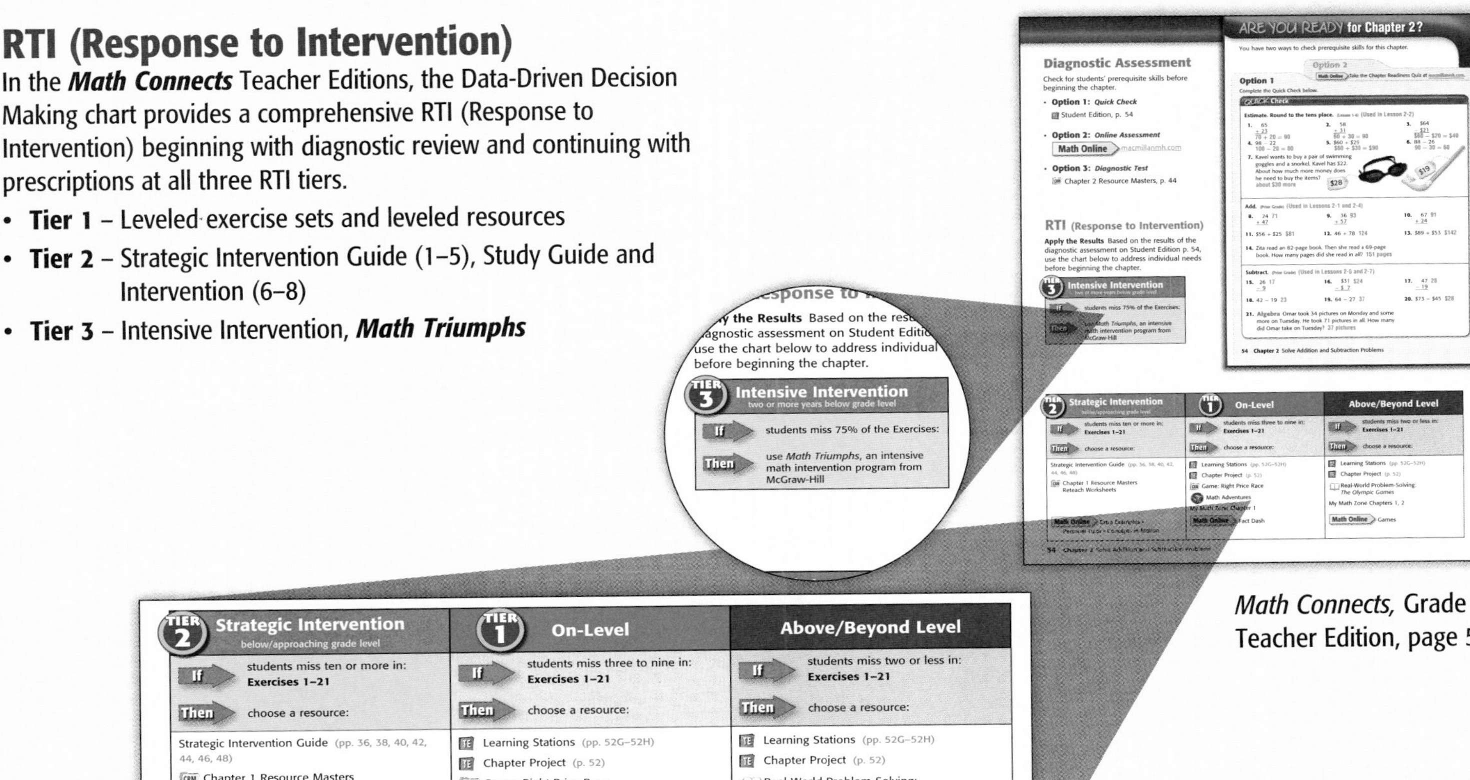

Math Connects, Grade 4
Teacher Edition, page 54

The Chapter Planner, also in the Teacher Edition of ***Math Connects,*** references alternative lessons found in ***IMPACT Mathematics.*** These lessons provide opportunities for investigative instruction with hands-on explorations.

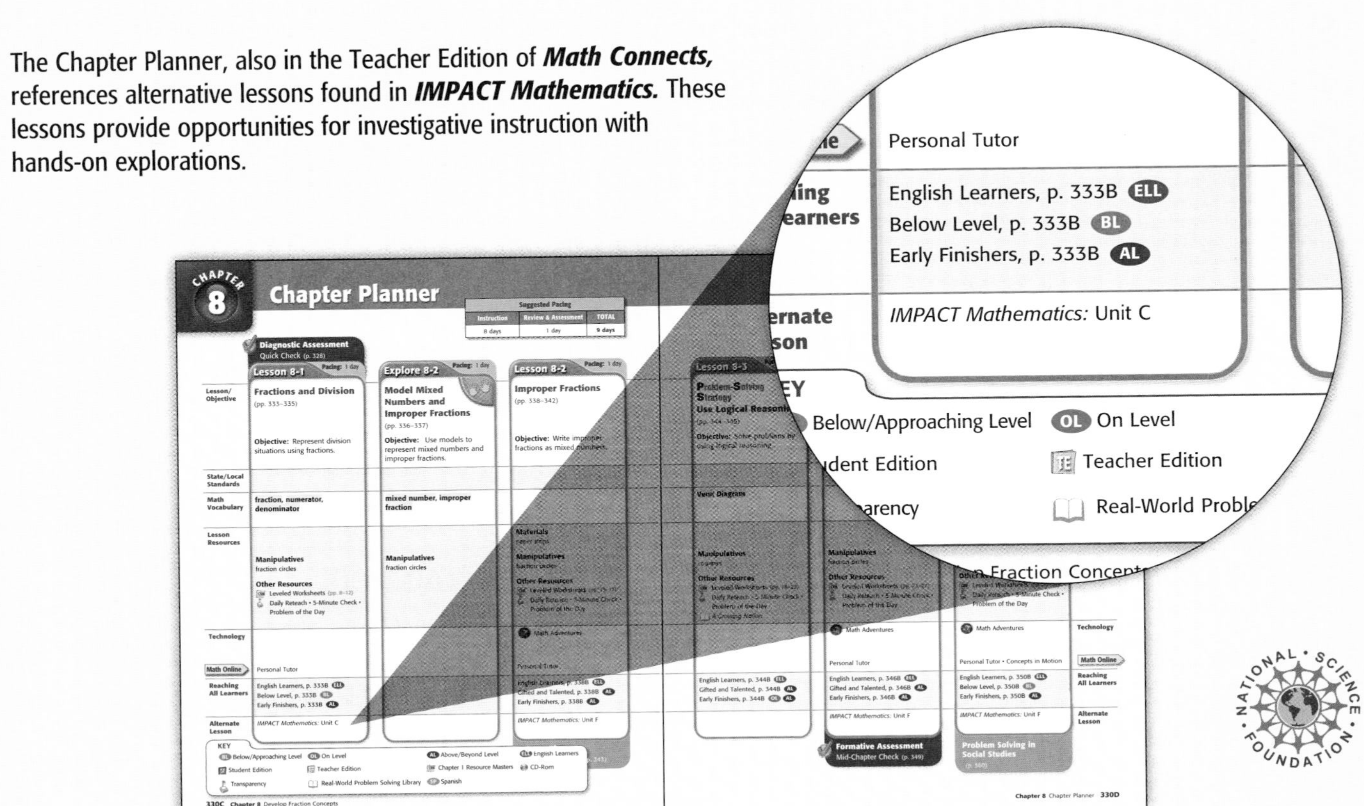

Math Connects, Grade 5
Teacher Edition, pages 330C–330D

Planning for Success

Ease of Use

Math Connects has a strong instructional model that includes differentiated instructional options, reteaching, reinforcement, and extension options, Teacher Tips to help address various learners, Pre-AP/Advanced items, and assessment linked with instruction.

Convenient Lesson Planning at Your Fingertips

The **Chapter Overview** helps you plan your instruction by showing the objectives to be covered, suggested pacing, and coverage of Focal Points.

TeacherWorks™ Plus

This electronic lesson planner contains multi-purpose management software including the Teacher Edition pages, program blackline masters, and daily calendars that make planning a snap.

CHAPTER 4 **Chapter Overview**

Chapter-at-a-Glance

In Chapter 4, the emphasis is on the meaning of multiplication and multiplication facts with 2, 4, 5, and 10.

Lesson	Math Objective	State/Local Standards
EXPLORE 4-1 **Meaning of Multiplication** (pp. 157–158)	Use models to explore multiplication.	
4-1 **Arrays and Multiplication** (pp. 159–161)	Use arrays to multiply.	
4-2 **Multiply by 2** (pp. 162–164)	Multiply by 2.	
EXTEND 4-2 **Model Multiplication** (pp. 165–166)	Use technology to multiply.	
4-3 **Multiply by 4** (pp. 168–170)	Multiply by 4.	
4-4 **Problem-Solving Skill: Extra or Missing Information** (pp. 172–173)	Solve a problem by identifying extra or missing information.	
4-5 **Multiply by 5** (pp. 174–176)	Multiply by 5.	
4-6 **Multiply by 10** (pp. 178–181)	Multiply by 10.	
4-7 **Problem-Solving Investigation: Choose a Strategy** (pp. 184–185)	Choose the best strategy to solve a problem.	
4-8 **Multiply by 0 and 1** (pp. 186–188)	Multiply by 0 and 1.	

Develop Multiplication Concepts and Facts

BIG Idea There are 144 multiplication combinations from 1 × 1 to 12 × 12, most of which are learned without difficulty. Students can use several different strategies to make sense of multiplication facts.

- Multiplication is repeated addition. For example, 4 × 3 is the same as adding the number 4 three times. (4 × 3 = 4 + 4 + 4 = 12)
- Multiplication can be represented visually using arrays. The fact 4 × 3 can be demonstrated by an array of pictures or objects with 4 columns and 3 rows.
- Skip counting by a number is the same as multiplying by 1, 2, 3, and so on. To count by 4s, say 4, 8, 12, 16. . .

Use these and other strategies to emphasize the meaning of multiplication. Continued practice in a variety of contexts will lead students to commit facts to memory.

Algebra Students learn about the properties of multiplication. This concept will help prepare them for algebra concepts, such as solving equations and inequalities. (Lessons 4-1 and 4-8)

G3-FP1 *Number and Operations and Algebra:* **Developing understandings of multiplication an[d] and strategies for basic multiplication facts [...] division facts**

Students understand the meanings of m[...] of whole numbers through the use of [...] equal-sized groups, arrays, area mod[...] number lines for multiplication, an[...] partitioning, and sharing for divisi[...] addition and multiplication (e.g., [...] the distributive property) to mult[...] increasingly sophisticated strate[...] solve multiplication and division [...] By comparing a variety of solutio[...] multiplication and division as inv[...]

G3-FP4C *Algebra:* Understand[...] and the relationship between mult[...] of algebra readiness that develops a[...] analysis of patterns and relationships [...] division should occur at this grade leve[...] foundation for later understanding of func[...] describing relationships in context with such [...] number of legs is 4 times the number of chairs."

154A Chapter 4 Develop Multiplication Concepts and Facts

Math Connects, Grade 3
Teacher Edition, page 154A

Develop Multiplication Concepts and Facts

Skills Trace
Vertical Alignment

Second Grade
In second grade, students learned to:
- Multiply by using repeated addition, arrays, and counting by multiples.

Third Grade
During this chapter, students learn to:
- Multiply by 2, 4, 5, 10, 0 and 1, and use arrays.

After this chapter, students learn to:
- Multiply by 3, 6, 7, 8, 9, 11, and 12.
- Multiply by a two-digit number.

Fourth Grade
In fourth grade, students learn to:
- Multiply by one- and two-digit numbers.
- Find multiples of whole numbers.

Backmapping and Vertical Alignment McGraw-Hill's ***Math Connects*** program was concieved and developed with the final results in mind: student success in Algebra 1 and beyond. The authors, using the **NCTM Focal Points and Focal Connections** as their guide, developed this brand-new series by backmapping from Algebra 1 concepts, and vertically aligning the topic so that build upon prior skills and concepts and serve as a foundation for future topics.

Math Vocabulary

The following math vocabulary words for Chapter 4 are listed in the glossary of the ***Student Edition.*** You can find interactive definitions in 13 languages in the ***eGlossary*** at macmillanmh.com.

array Objects or symbols displayed in rows and columns. (p. 159A)

Commutative Property of Multiplication The property that states that the order in which numbers are multiplied does not change the product. (p. 159A)
Example: 7 × 2 = 2 × 7

factor A number that is multiplied by another number (p. 159A)

Identity Property of Multiplication If you multiply a number by 1, the product is that number. (p. 186A)
Example: 8 × 1 = 8 = 1 × 8

multiplication An operation on two numbers to find their product. It can be thought of as repeated addition. (p. 157A)
Example: 3 × 8 = 24 can also be written as 8 + 8 + 8 = 24

multiply Find the product of two or more numbers. (p. 157A)

product The answer to a multiplication problem. (p. 159A)

Zero Property of Multiplication The property that states any number multiplied by zero is zero. (p. 186A)
Example: 0 × 5 = 0

Visual Vocabulary Cards
Use Visual Vocabulary Cards 3, 9, 29, and 37 to reinforce the vocabulary in this lesson. (The Define/Example/Ask routine is printed on the back of each card.)

array

Chapter 4 Chapter Overview 154B

Math Connects, Grade 3
Teacher Edition, page 154B

Vertical Alignment Skills Trace

Topics are presented to build upon prior grade level skills and concepts and to serve as a foundation for future topics.

What the Research Says

Citations from **research** help to validate ***Math Connects*** program. An additional Research Bibliography can be found in the **Teacher Reference Handbook.**

Professional Development

Targeted professional development has been articulated throughout the program. Actual classroom video clips are especially helpful when planning lessons and differentiating instruction. See page T32 for more information.

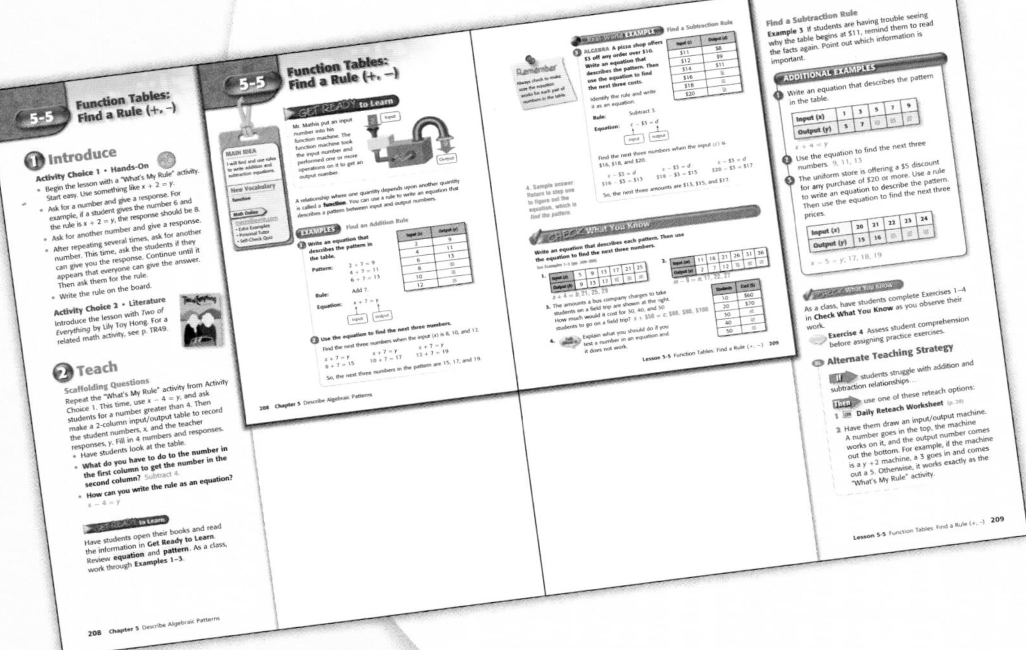

Math Connects, Grade 4
Teacher Edition, pages 208–209

Four-Step Teaching Plan

Organizes your instruction as you **Focus** and **Teach** and help your students **Practice** and **Assess** what they've learned.

Scaffolding Questions

Each lesson contains **Scaffolding Questions** for you to use to help students investigate and understand the main ideas of the lesson.

Additional Examples

Each **Additional Example** mirrors the example in the Student Edition. The Additional Examples are also available as a PowerPoint® presentation on the **Interactive Classroom** CD-ROM.

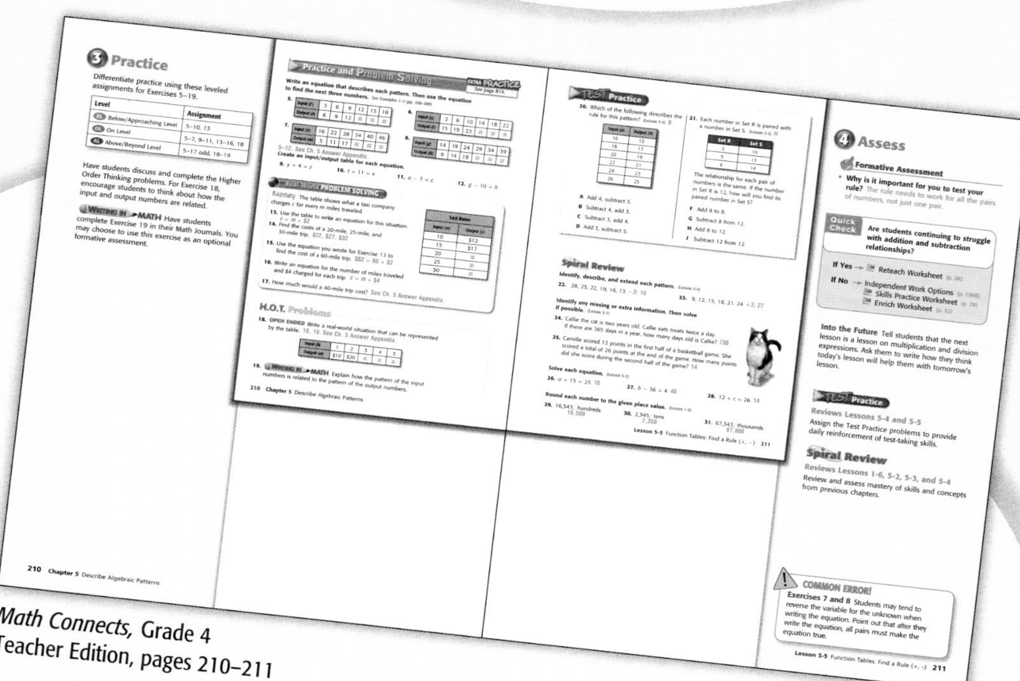

Math Connects, Grade 4
Teacher Edition, pages 210–211

Differentiated Practice

Because most classrooms include students at a wide range of ability levels, **Differentiated Practice** allows you to customize your assignments.

Vertical Alignment

Vertical Alignment at the beginning of each chapter shows the objectives that lead into and follow the current lesson's content for a coherent PreK–12 scope and sequence.

Planning for Success
State-of-the-Art Technology

Math Connects provides fully integrated technology resources for teachers, students, and parents.

For Teachers

TeacherWorks™ Plus is your all-in-one planner and resource center.
- entire Teacher Edition
- all print ancillaries
- electronic lesson planner

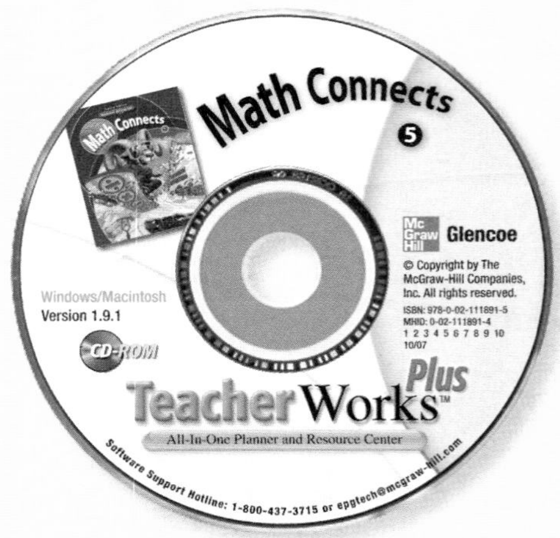

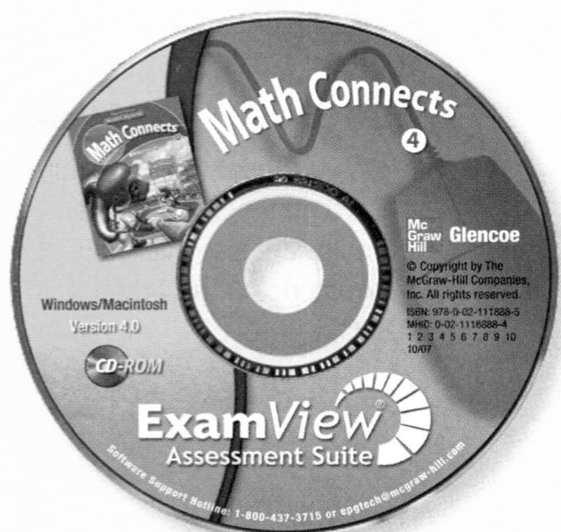

ExamView® Assessment Suite allows teachers to create and customize their own assessment and assignments.

New features:
- correlated to state standards
- online content update
- one- or two-column formatting

Use **Interactive Classroom** to guide instruction using PowerPoint ™
- In-Class Examples
- 5-Minute Check Transparencies
- Concepts in Motion
- links to **Math Online**

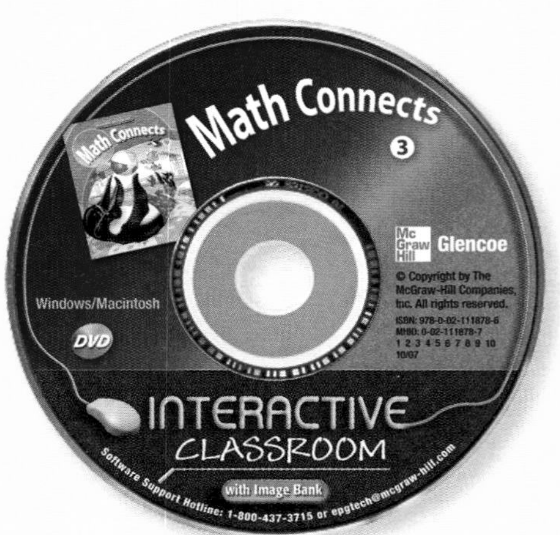

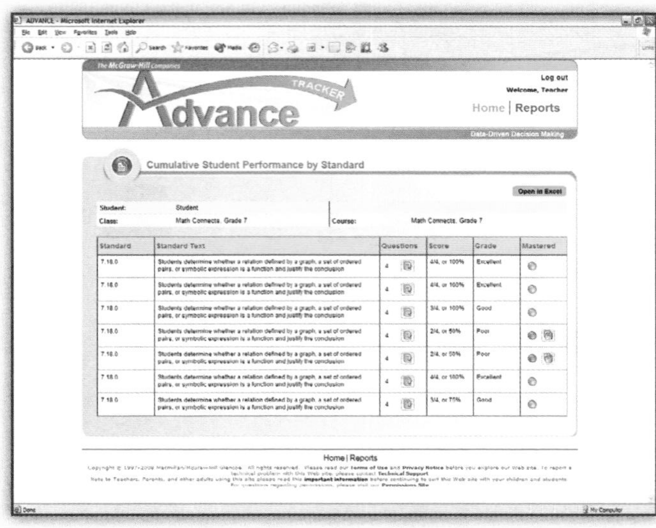

 Learner Management System helps you track progress and differentiate your instruction.
- formative assessments aligned to standards
- links to intervention help

Other Technology: My Math Zone (CD-ROM)
Math Songs (English and Spanish, CD-ROM)

For Students

StudentWorks™ Plus is your students' backpack solution.

- entire Student Edition
- all student worksheets
- links to **Math Online**

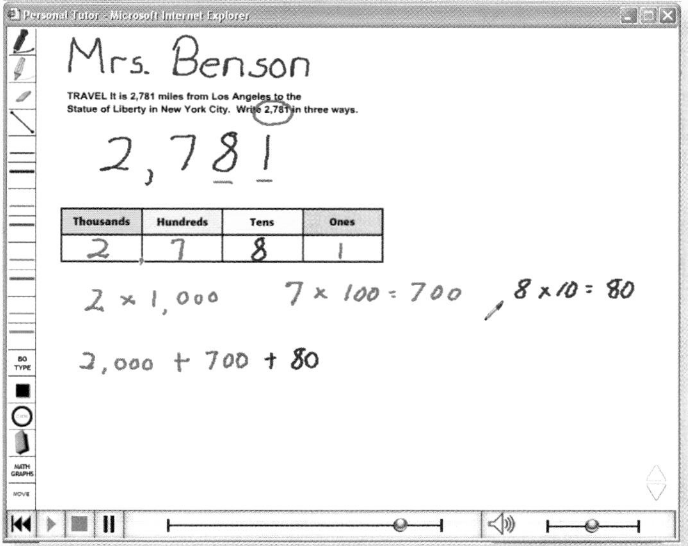

Math Online provides a wealth of resources – convenient for students and parents!

- Self-Check Quizzes
- Personal Tutor
- Concepts in Motion
- eGlossary (14 languages)
- And much, much more!

Math Online *Math Connect's* **eBook** is easy to use, easy to read, and packed with features.

- links to online study tools and resources right from the page
- includes audio

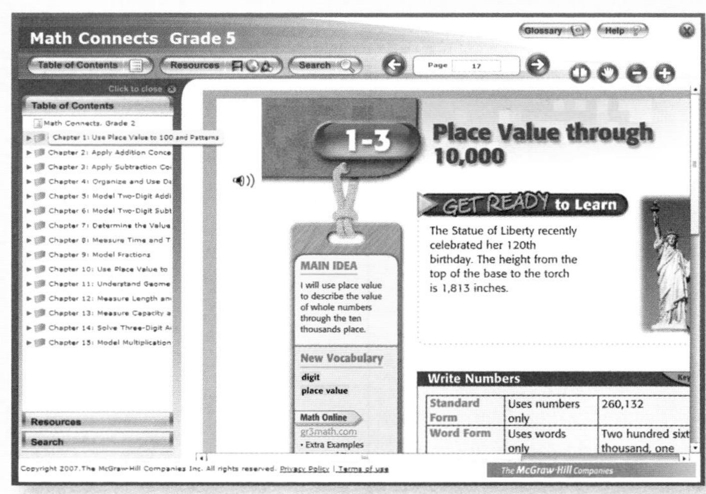

Other Technology: Math Adventures with Dot and Ray (online and CD-ROM)
Math Tool Chest (online and CD-ROM)

PreK-12 Data-Driven Professional Development

McGraw-Hill Professional Development (MHPD) provides a comprehensive plan for mathematics that is fully aligned and articulated with ***Math Connects K–8*** and the ***Glencoe Mathematics*** high school series.

Professional Development Needs	Online Courses	DVD Workshops	Video Library	Teach-Use-Succeed	Ready-Access Math
Has immediate classroom application	✓	✓	✓	✓	✓
Builds content knowledge	✓	✓			✓
Promotes best teaching practices		✓	✓		
Supports new and experienced teachers	✓	✓	✓	✓	✓
Allows customization of courses	✓	✓			✓
Can be self-paced	✓	✓		✓	✓
Adaptable for various timeframes	✓	✓	✓	✓	✓
Is grade-level specific			✓	✓	✓
Promotes a learning community	✓	✓			✓
Provides vertically-aligned content	✓	✓	✓		✓
Helps with RTI (Response to Intervention), Tiers 1–3	✓	✓	✓		✓

Use students' mathematics achievement data to help develop a targeted Professional Development Plan.

Accredited Online Courses

(available for purchase)

- Watch video clips of math classrooms Complete interactive exercises Develop electronic portfolios.
- Complete each 3- to 5-hour online module one segment at a time.
- University credit (additional tuition charge)

DVD Workshops

- Watch video clips of classroom mathematics lessons and commentaries by leading educators.
- Complete lessons and activities.

MHPD Online

- Access this online Professional Development resource for K–12 educators.
- Link to relevant Web sites.
- Download grade-level student resources.

Video Library Math Online

- Access hundreds of K–12 video clips.
- See clips that illustrate mathematics content and instructional strategies.
- Watch demonstrations or commentaries by math specialists

Teach-Use-Succeed Textbook Implementation Modules

- Watch an experienced teacher demonstrate the *Math Connects* K–8 Student Editions, Teacher Editions, and program ancillaries
- Online or DVD

Ready-Access Math, Personalized Professional Development

- Access training materials for nearly 300 mathematics professional development lessons.
- Create a customized sequence of professional development sessions.
- Deliver 45–60 minute after-school professional development sessions.

Teacher Edition

Macmillan McGraw-Hill

Math Connects

4

Table of Contents

Volume 1

Authors

Altieri • Balka • Day • Gonsalves • Grace • Krulik
Malloy • Molix-Bailey • Moseley • Mowry • Myren
Price • Reynosa • Santa Cruz • Silbey • Vielhaber

Mc Graw Hill Macmillan/McGraw-Hill

Contents

Start Smart

H.O.T. Problems

CHAPTER 1 Use Place Value to Represent Whole Numbers

Focal Points and Connections

G4-FP8C Number and Operations

Chapter 2 Solve Addition and Subtraction Problems

Focal Points and Connections

G4-FP4C Algebra
G4-FP8C Number and Operations

Test Practice 61, 67, 69, 83, 89, 90, 91

H.O.T. Problems
Higher Order Thinking 57, 61, 67, 74, 82

WRITING IN MATH 57, 61, 63, 67, 68, 69, 71, 74, 77, 82, 89

CHAPTER 3 Organize, Display, and Interpret Data

G4-FP7C Data Analysis

Test Practice 101, 107, 111, 127, 139, 140, 141

H.O.T. Problems
Higher Order Thinking 97, 101, 107, 110, 114, 126, 130

WRITING IN MATH 97, 101, 103, 107, 110, 111, 114, 117, 119, 123, 126, 130, 139

Apply Multiplication and Division Facts

Focal Points and Connections

G4-FP1 Number and Operations and Algebra

Chapter 5 Describe Algebraic Patterns

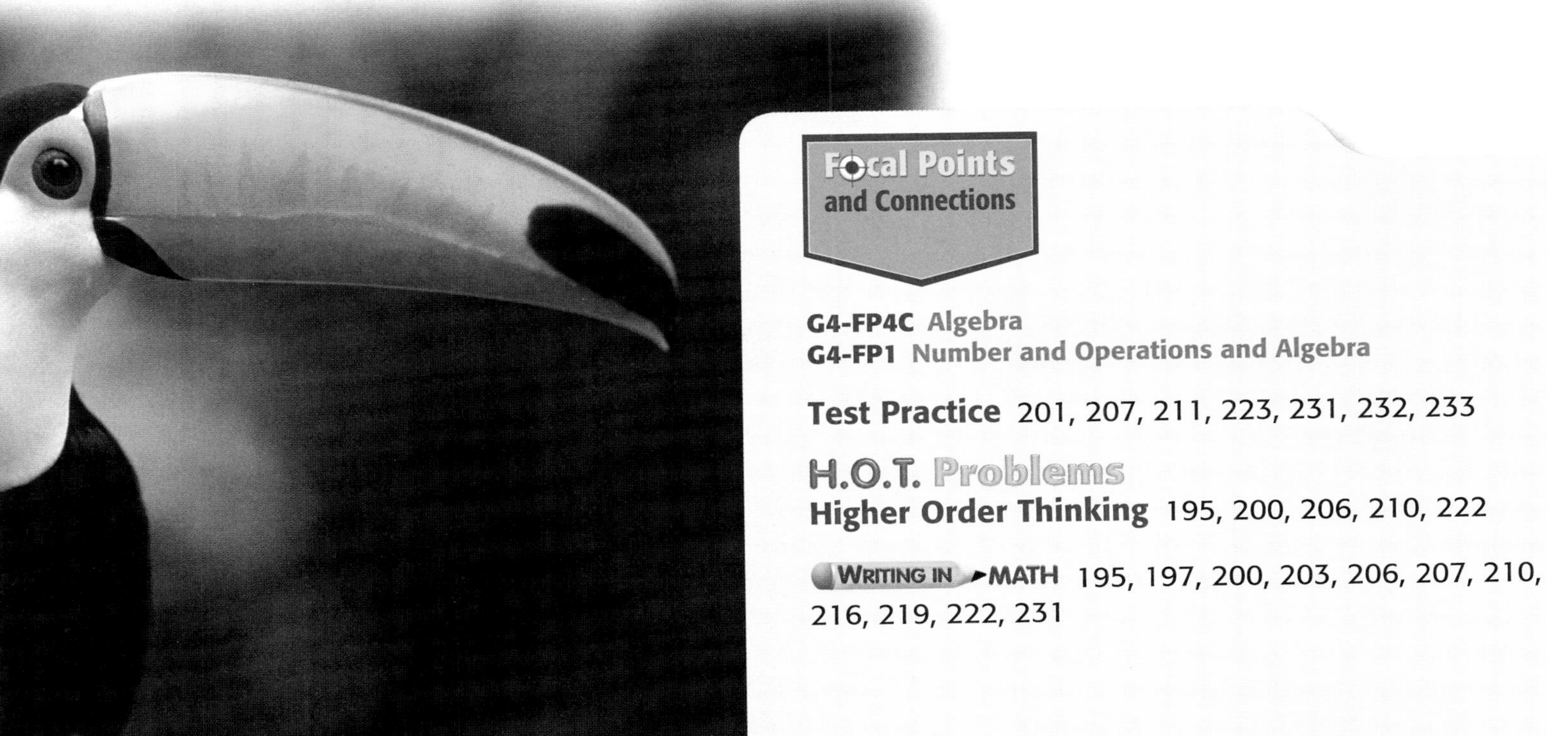

Focal Points and Connections

G4-FP4C Algebra
G4-FP1 Number and Operations and Algebra

Contents

Chapter 6 Multiply by One-Digit Numbers

Focal Points and Connections

G4-FP1 Number and Operations and Algebra

Test Practice 249, 255, 261, 267, 268, 269

H.O.T. Problems
Higher Order Thinking 239, 244, 248, 255, 261

Writing in Math 239, 241, 244, 248, 249, 251, 255, 261, 267

CHAPTER 7 Multiply by Two-Digit Numbers

G4-FP1 Number and Operations and Algebra

Chapter 8 Divide by One-Digit Numbers

Focal Points and Connections

G4-FP8C Number and Operations

CHAPTER 9 Identify and Describe Geometric Figures

G4-FP6C Measurement
G4-FP5C Geometry

Understand and Develop Spatial Reasoning

Focal Points and Connections

G4-FP5C Geometry

Test Practice 403, 409, 415, 433, 434, 435

H.O.T. Problems
Higher Order Thinking 397, 403, 408, 415, 420, 424

WRITING IN MATH 397, 399, 403, 405, 408, 409, 411, 415, 417, 420, 424, 433

Chapter 11 Measure Length, Area, and Temperature

G4-FP3 Measurement
G4-FP5C Geometry

Test Practice 453, 459, 479, 480, 481

H.O.T. Problems
Higher Order Thinking 443, 445, 452, 458, 462, 471

WRITING IN MATH 440, 443, 445, 447, 449, 452, 453, 458, 462, 465, 467, 471, 479

Chapter 12 Measure Capacity, Weight, and Volume

G4-FP3 Measurement
G4-FP5C Geometry

Test Practice 489, 495, 501, 507, 515, 523, 531, 532

H.O.T. Problems
Higher Order Thinking 489, 491, 494, 500, 506, 510, 515, 523

WRITING IN MATH 485, 491, 497, 503, 506, 519, 531

CHAPTER 13 Describe and Compare Fractions

Focal Points and Connections

G4-FP2 Number and Operations
G4-FP8C Number and Operations

Test Practice 543, 553, 557, 571, 572, 573

H.O.T. Problems
Higher Order Thinking 539, 543, 551, 557, 563

WRITING IN MATH 539, 543, 545, 547, 551, 553, 557, 563, 565, 571

Use Place Value to Represent Decimals

Focal Points and Connections

G4-FP2 Number and Operations
G4-FP8C Number and Operations

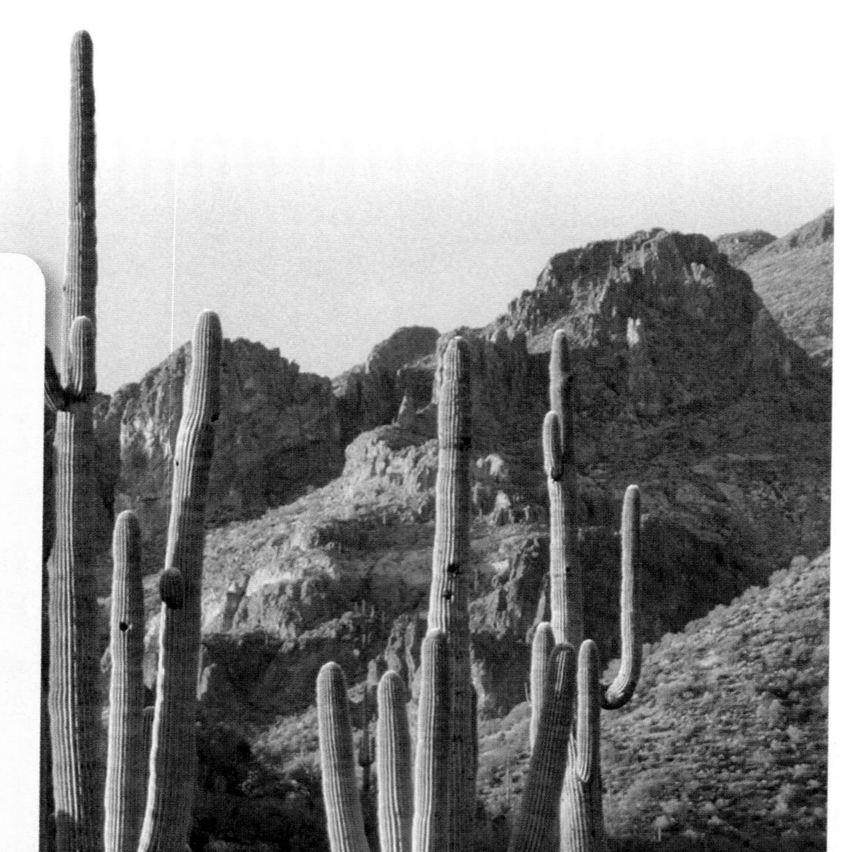

CHAPTER 15 Add and Subtract Decimals

Focal Points and Connections

G4-FP2 Number and Operations
G4-FP8C Number and Operations

Contents

Looking Ahead

Problem-Solving Projects

H.O.T. Problems

Student Handbook

Built-In Workbook

Reference

To the Student

As you gear up to study mathematics, you are probably wondering, "What will I learn this year?"

- **Number and Operations:** Estimate and find products of whole numbers, including multidigit whole numbers.
- **Number and Operations:** Understand decimals and relate fractions and decimals.
- **Measurement:** Understand and find areas of two-dimensional figures.

Along the way, you'll learn more about problem solving, how to use the tools and language of mathematics, and how to THINK mathematically.

How to Use Your Math Book

Have you ever been in class and not understood all of what was being presented? Or, you understood everything in class, but got stuck on how to solve some of the homework problems? Don't worry. You can find answers in your math book!

- **Read** the MAIN IDEA at the beginning of the lesson.
- **Find** the New Vocabulary words, **highlighted in yellow**, and read their definitions.
- **Review** the EXAMPLE problems, solved step-by-step, to remind you of the day's material.
- **Refer** to the EXTRA PRACTICE boxes that show you where you can find extra exercises to practice a concept.
- **Go** to Math Online where you can find extra examples to coach you through difficult problems.
- **Review** the notes you've taken on your FOLDABLES®.
- **Refer** to the Remember boxes for information that may help you with your examples and homework practice.

Start Smart

Begin the year with the lessons found in the **Start Smart** section. These lessons help students get ready for the coming year by reviewing and reinforcing skills and concepts they learned in third grade. The Start Smart lessons also prepare for skills and concepts students will need for success in fourth grade.

Initial Assessment

Inventory/Placement Test At the beginning of the year, administer the Inventory/Placement Test found in the Chapter 1 Resource Masters. This two-page test assesses key concepts from third grade and concepts that students will need during the coming year.

Use the results to help differentiate instruction for each student throughout the year and to identify what concepts to review before beginning Chapter 1.

CRM **Chapter 1 Resource Masters**

Inventory/Placement Test (p. 43–44)

Scavenger Hunt

Introduce students to their student edition textbook with the Scavenger Hunt. Have students work alone, in pairs, or small groups to complete the activity.

CHAPTER 1

Let's Get Started

Use the Treasure Hunt below to learn where things are located in each chapter.

1. What is the title of Chapter 1? Use Place Value to Represent Whole Numbers
2. What is the Main Idea of Lesson 1-1? I will read and write whole numbers to hundred thousands.
3. How do you know which words are vocabulary words? they are bold and highlighted
4. What are the vocabulary words for Lesson 1-1? digit, place value, period, standard form, word form, expanded form
5. What is the key concept shown in Lesson 1-6? Rounding Whole Numbers
6. How many Examples are presented in Lesson 1-4? 2
7. What is the Web address where you could find extra examples? macmillanmh.com
8. On page 29, there is a Remember tip box. How does the Remember tip help you? It helps you know what to do first.
9. How many exercises are there in Lesson 1-5? 21
10. Suppose you need more practice on a concept. Where can you go for Extra Practice? You can go to the back of the book.
11. Suppose you're doing your homework on page 38 and you get stuck on Exercise 16. Where could you find help? Examples 1–3 (pp. 36–37)
12. What is the web address that would allow you to take a self-check quiz to be sure you understand the lesson? macmillanmh.com
13. On what pages will you find the Chapter 1 Study Guide and Review? pp. 44–48
14. Suppose you can't figure out how to do Exercise 36 in the Study Guide and Review on page 48. Where could you find help? Lesson 1-7 (pp. 40–41)

MATH? SYMBOLS

Start Smart

Let's Review!

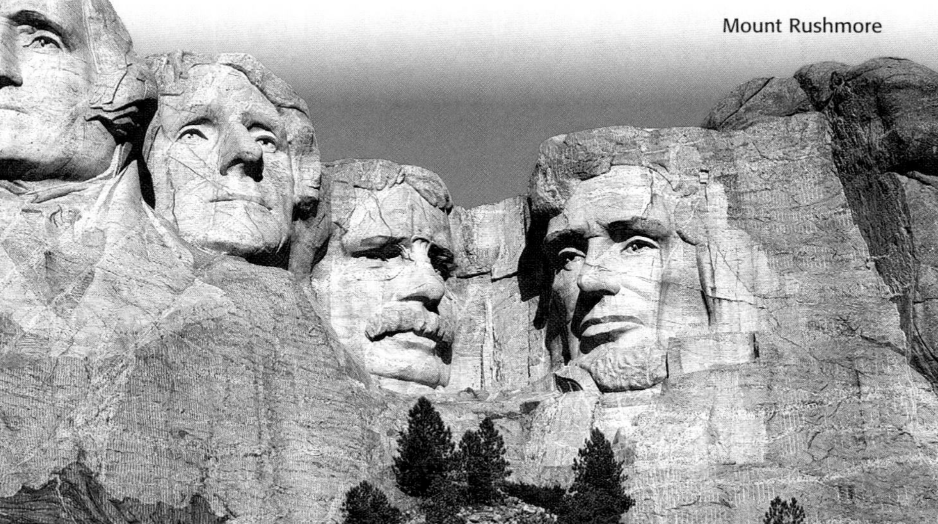

Mount Rushmore

End-of-Year Assessment

At the end of the year, use the End-of-Year Test to assess student comprehension of the skills and concepts presented in Grade 4. Each question in the End-of-Year Test provides the lesson number from Grade 4 where the concept was first presented to help you review any areas where students continue to struggle.

CRM **Chapter 15 Resource Masters**

End-of-Year Test (p. 66)

Lesson Planner

Objectives

Identify and use the steps in a four-step problem-solving process.

Activate Prior Knowledge

Read and discuss the introduction on p. 2 and **Did You Know** on p. 3.

- Lead a discussion about mountains and fill in the "K" column on a KWL chart.
- **Has anyone seen or visited Mount Haystack or other mountains? Where is Mount Haystack or the Adirondack Mountain Range located?** New York
- **What are some other interesting attractions in New York?** Answers will vary.
- Ask students what else they would like to know about mountains or Mount Haystack. Fill in the "W" column with their responses.
- After discussing the information in **Did You Know,** have students suggest ideas to write in the "L" column.

Problem Solving

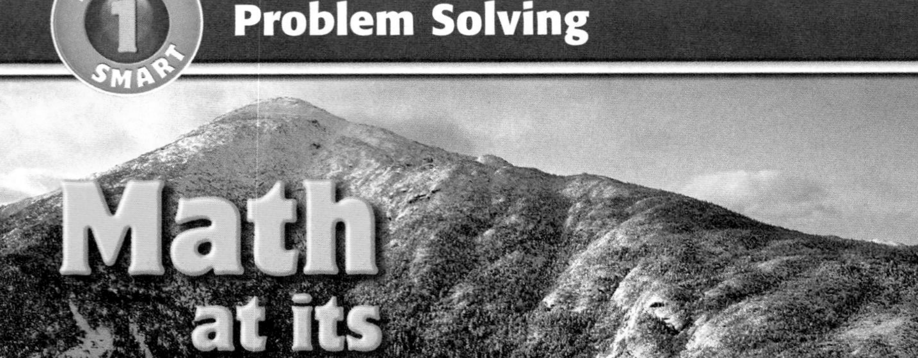

Hiking New York's many mountains is a popular activity. The table shows the heights of four of the tallest mountain peaks in the state.

What is the difference in height between Mount Haystack and Gray Peak?

Mountain Peaks	
Mountain	Height (ft)
Mount Marcy	5,344
Mount Haystack	4,960
Mount Skylight	4,920
Gray Peak	4,840

Source: Adirondack Mountain Club

You can use the four-step problem-solving plan to solve math problems. The four steps are Understand, Plan, Solve, and Check.

Understand

- **Read the problem carefully.**
- **What facts do you know?**
- **What facts do you need to find?**

The table lists the heights of the mountain peaks. You need to find the difference in height between Mount Haystack and Gray Peak.

Plan

- **How do the facts relate to each other?**
- **Plan a strategy to solve the problem.**

To find the difference, subtract the height of Gray Peak from the height of Mount Haystack.

Solve

- **Use your plan to solve the problem.**

4,960	Mount Haystack
− 4,840	Gray Peak
120	

So, Mount Haystack is 120 feet taller than Gray Peak.

Check

- **Look back.**
- **Does your answer make sense?**
- **If not, solve the problem another way.**

Mount Haystack is almost 5,000 feet tall. Gray Peak is almost 4,900 feet tall. So, an answer close to 100 feet makes sense.

Did you Know

The Adirondack Mountain range has more than one hundred summits, ranging from under 1,200 feet to over 5,000 feet in height.

CHECK What You Know

1. List the four steps of the four-step plan. understand, plan, solve, check
2. WRITING IN MATH The table shows the heights above sea level of cities in New York. Write a real-world problem using the table. Sample answer: What is the difference in height between Buffalo and Albany?

Height Above Sea Level

City	Height (ft)
Albany	285
Buffalo	724
Rochester	559
Syracuse	421

Source: Red Oaks Trading, Ltd.

More FUN Facts

- Mount Haystack is the third highest peak in New York.
- It gets its name from its resemblance to a rounded haystack.
- It is not visited by many hikers because it is steep and challenging.
- Orson Phelps was the first person to climb Mount Haystack in 1849.
- Many people try to climb all of the original 46 mountains in the Adirondack Mountain Range. There is a Forty Sixers club for those who have successfully reached each of these peaks.

Four-Step Problem-Solving Plan

Understand Using the questions, review what students know and need to find.

Plan Have them use the facts they know to choose the operation needed to solve the problem.

Solve Guide students to use subtraction to solve the problem.

- Look at the numbers in the subtraction problem. **What digits are the same?** ones and thousands
- **How do you find the difference?** Subtract the ones, tens, and hundreds digits.
- **How much taller is Mount Haystack than Gray Peak?** 120 feet

Check Have students look back at the problem to make sure that the answer makes sense given the facts in the problem.

Using the Exercises

Exercise 1 Remind students that in a process, steps are done in a certain order to complete a task. They should list and describe the four steps in the correct order.

WRITING IN MATH Help students with this exercise by asking them to identify the facts given in the table.

- **What are some different ways to use these facts?** find the difference in heights, order the heights, find the lowest or highest height above sea level

Assess and Close

- Fill in the "L" column of the KWL chart with additional facts about Mount Haystack.

Mountain Peaks

- Have students work with a partner to write a problem using the data about mountain heights on p. 2.
- Ask them to write a problem and then show the solution using the four-step plan.
- Encourage students to clearly show and label each of the four steps in their solution.

Lesson Planner

Objectives

Select the appropriate operation to solve word problems, and use addition, subtraction, multiplication, and division to solve problems.

Activate Prior Knowledge

Read and discuss the introduction on p. 4 and **Did You Know** on p. 5.

- Lead a discussion about the eastern tiger salamander and fill in the "K" column on a KWL chart.
- **Has anyone ever seen an eastern tiger salamander? If so, where did you see it?** Fill in the "K" column with students' responses.
- **What else would you like to know about eastern tiger salamanders?** Fill in the "W" column.
- After discussing the information in **Did You Know,** have students suggest ideas to write in the "L" column.

Number and Operations

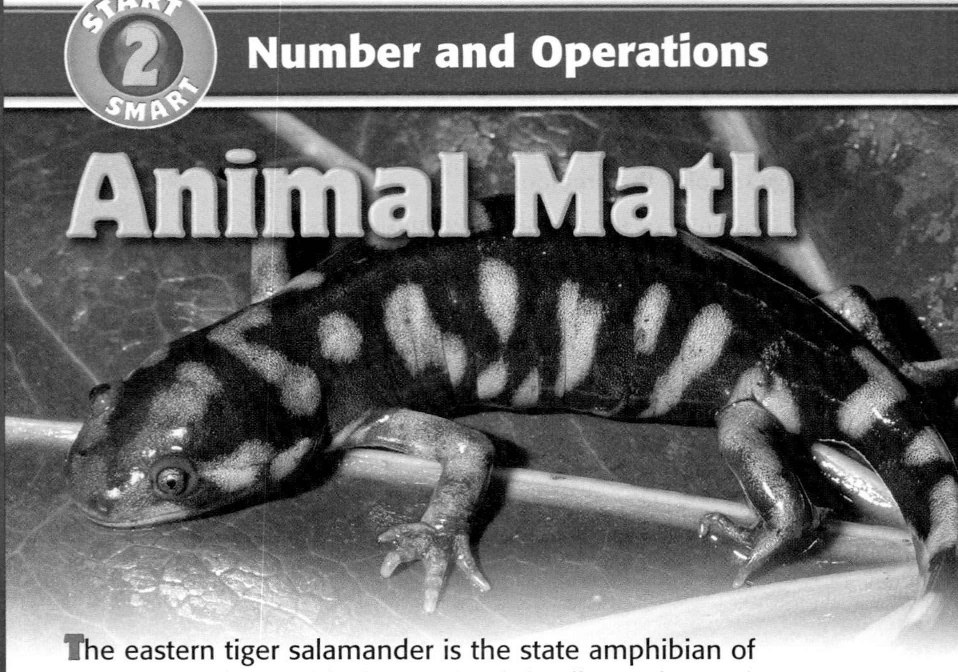

Animal Math

The eastern tiger salamander is the state amphibian of Illinois. It is the world's largest land-dwelling salamander.

Addition and Subtraction

1. Suppose an eastern tiger salamander lays 28 eggs one year and 35 eggs the next year. How many more eggs does it need to lay to total 100 eggs? 37 eggs

For Exercises 2–4, use the table.

Eastern Tiger Salamander Facts
• Length is 7–13 inches.
• Life expectancy is 12–15 years.

Source: Ohio Historical Society

2. What is the greatest total length for three eastern tiger salamanders if they were placed end to end? 39 inches
3. What is the greatest number of years that four generations of eastern tiger salamanders could live? 60 years
4. Suppose an eastern tiger salamander that was born in 2009 lived until 2023. How many years did the salamander live? 14 years

Additional Answer

10. Sample answer: yes; The deer would swim 2×13 or 26 miles each day. At this rate, the deer would swim 7×26 or 182 miles in one week.

CHECK What You Know Multiplication and Division

The state animal of Illinois is the white-tailed deer.

5. White-tailed deer are about 4 feet tall. What is their height in inches? (1 foot = 12 inches) about 48 in.
6. Male deer weigh 130 to 220 pounds. What is the greatest weight of three male deer? 660 lbs
7. White-tailed deer eat 5 to 9 pounds of food daily. Find the greatest amount of food a deer can eat in a week. 63 lb

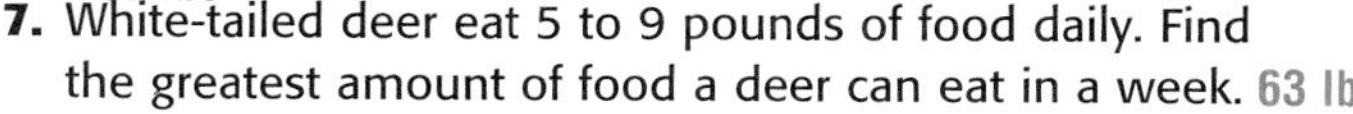

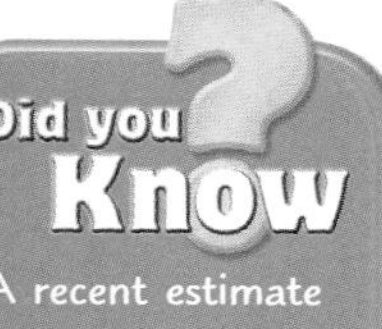

Did you Know

A recent estimate of the white-tailed deer population in the United States was 30 million.

For Exercises 8–10, use the table.

White-tailed Deer Stats
• Maximum running speed is 40 miles per hour.
• Maximum swimming speed is 13 miles per hour.
• Maximum vertical jump is 9 feet.
• Maximum horizontal jump is 30 feet.

Source: National Wildlife Federation

8. Suppose a white-tailed deer ran at its top speed for a total of five hours in a week. What distance would this deer travel? 200 mi
9. If a white-tailed deer jumps its maximum horizontal jump six times, what total distance would it jump? 180 ft
10. WRITING IN ➤MATH Suppose a deer swims at its maximum speed for a total of two hours each day. Would this deer swim more than 175 miles in one week? Explain. See margin.

More FUN Facts

- After hatching, it takes an eastern tiger salamander about three weeks before they lose their gills and become adults.
- Foods in their diet include large insects, earthworms, amphibians, and small mice.
- Eastern tiger salamanders are often kept as pets.
- Its tail is about half of its body length.
- It is rarely seen because it spends most of its time underground.
- Illinois schoolchildren voted to select the white-tailed deer as the state animal in 1980. The vote was made official in 1982.

Addition and Subtraction

- Tell students that the exercises use interesting facts about eastern tiger salamanders. Explain that they will need to decide which operation to use to solve the problems.
- **What are some words or phrases that indicate addition should be used? subtraction?** Words and phrases such as *in all, total, difference, how much more,* or *how much less* should be mentioned.
- Record ideas on the board for students to use as a reference. Have students complete Exercises 1–4.

Multiplication and Division

- Explain that students will now solve problems about white-tailed deer that require multiplication and division. Again, they must decide the appropriate operation needed for each problem.
- Discuss common situations that indicate the use of multiplication and division. An example for multiplication is: given the information for one item, find the total for more than one item. A common division situation involves separating a number of items into equal groups and finding the number in each group.

Using the Exercises

Exercises 6–7 Ask students to first identify which weights should be used to solve the problems.

Exercise 10 Make sure students understand that this is a multi-step problem.

WRITING IN ➤MATH Remind students of the words, phrases, and situations discussed in the introduction to the lesson. Suggest they use these concepts in their explanation.

Assess and Close

- Fill in the "L" column of the KWL chart with more facts about eastern tiger salamanders.

Different Operations

- Use the information about eastern tiger salamanders in **More Fun Facts** to describe situations that involve different operations. Ask students to tell what operation(s) can be used to solve the problem.

Lesson Planner

Objectives

Use patterns to solve problems. Analyze a pattern and explain the rule it follows.

Activate Prior Knowledge

Read and discuss the introduction on p. 6 and **Did You Know** on p. 7.

- Lead a discussion about building sandcastles and fill in the "K" column on a KWL chart.
- **How many students have built a sandcastle? Has anyone competed in or seen a sandcastle building competition?** Fill in the "K" column with students' responses.
- **What else would you like to know about building sandcastles?** Fill in the "W" column.
- After discussing the information in **Did You Know,** have students suggest ideas to write in the "L" column.

Patterns

- Tell students that a pattern is a sequence of numbers, figures, or symbols that follows a rule or design. For example: 1, 3, 5, 7, 9...
- **What patterns do you see in your everyday life?** floor tiles, wallpaper, etc.
- Have students analyze the pattern in the table on p. 6 before they work on Exercises 1–3.

Algebra

A competition to make the world's largest sandcastle is held each year during the Sun Fun Festival in Myrtle Beach, South Carolina.

Patterns

A pattern is a set of numbers or figures that follows a rule. Finding a pattern is a useful problem-solving strategy.

For Exercises 1 and 2, use the table. It shows the cost of sand buckets.

1. How much would 4 sand buckets cost? $8
2. Find the total cost of 8 sand buckets. $16
3. One bag of shells costs 25¢. Two bags cost 50¢. Three bags cost 75¢. How much will 5 bags cost? 125¢

Cost of Sand Buckets

Number of Sand Buckets	Cost ($)
1	2
2	4
3	6

CHECK What You Know — Number Sentences

A sandcastle team has 6 members. In the competition, they built 48 small sandcastles. If each team member built the same number of sandcastles, how many sandcastles did they each build?

Did you Know
The tallest sandcastle ever recorded was 49 feet tall.

Number of sandcastles		Number of people		Number of castles built by each member
48	÷	6	=	■

You know that $48 \div 6 = 8$. So, each member built 8 sandcastles.

Choose the number sentence that can be used to solve each problem. Then solve each problem.

4. There are 9 people on Tomas' sandcastle team. If each member builds 5 castles, how many castles will they build in all? B; 45 castles

5. Holly has 14 tickets to a music concert. She gave some of her tickets away. If she has 5 tickets left, how many tickets did she give away? A; 9 tickets

6. Before lunch, Eric built 5 sandcastles. After lunch, he had built a total of 14 castles. How many sandcastles did Eric build after lunch? C; 9 sandcastles

7. Mrs. Hawkins spent $45 on souvenir T-shirts. If she bought a total of 5 T-shirts at the same price, how much did each T-shirt cost? D; $9

A 14 − ■ = 5

B 9 × 5 = ■

C 5 + ■ = 14

D 45 ÷ 5 = ■

8. WRITING IN ► MATH Write a real-world problem that can be represented by using a number sentence. See students' work.

More *FUN* Facts

- The Sun Fun Festival was first started in 1951 as a way to celebrate the beginning of the tourist season in Myrtle Beach, South Carolina.
- The Sun Fun Festival includes many activities, such as an air force display, a jet ski race, a jet ski stunt show, concerts, and a charity beach run.
- This festival is the longest running event in Myrtle Beach history.
- This festival is consistently named one of the Southeast Tourism Society's Top 20 Events.

Number Sentences

- Share with students that a number sentence is an equation using numbers with the = sign, or the $<$ or $>$ sign. For example: $5 + 4 = 9$ or $8 > 6$.
- Have students read the information in the example. Then complete Exercises 4–7. Discuss their responses as a class.

Using the Exercises

Exercises 1–3 Before students complete Exercise 1, explain that a rule is a sentence (could be a number sentence) that explains how to find the next object or number in a pattern. For example, in the pattern 1, 3, 5, 7, 9, the rule is add 2 to the preceding number to find the next number in the pattern.

Exercise 4 If students are having difficulty, emphasize that they need to find the total number of sandcastles built by Tomas's team.

WRITING IN ► MATH Have students work in pairs to complete Exercise 8. Invite students to share their problems with the class.

Assess and Close

- Fill in the "L" column of the KWL chart with additional facts about sandcastle building.

Pattern Puzzles

- Divide students into small groups and distribute shells or other beach-related objects.
- Ask each group to brainstorm categories of shells they want to use in their patterns.
- Have them create a rule for their pattern.
- Make sure that students understand that their rule must work for all shells in their pattern.

Lesson Planner

Objectives

Choose the appropriate units and the best estimates of weight or mass for common items. Use a scale to identify the weight or mass of an object.

Activate Prior Knowledge

Read and discuss the introduction on p. 8 and **Did You Know** on p. 9.

- Lead a discussion about corn and fill in the "K" column on a KWL chart.
- **How many students enjoy eating corn? Does anyone know what corn can be used to make?**
- **What else would you like to know about corn?** Fill in the "W" column.
- After discussing the information in **Did You Know,** have students suggest ideas to write in the "L" column.

Weight

- Give students ten kernels of corn. Ask them to estimate the weight. Then have students check their estimates using a pan balance or scale that measures in ounces.
- Continue by having students estimate and measure the weights of other items. Suggest that they find items that weigh about an ounce and about a pound.

Measurement

Corn is the number one field crop in the United States. The area of the United States where most corn is produced is called the Corn Belt. One state in the Corn Belt is Kentucky. Kentucky produces 150 million bushels each year.

Weight

Weight tells how heavy an object is. An ounce (oz) and a pound (lb) are customary units of weight.
16 ounces (oz) = 1 pound (lb)

1. Find the total weight of the ears of corn shown. 2 lb
2. Which is a better estimate for the weight of 10 corn kernels: 1 ounce or 1 pound? Explain your answer. Sample answer: 1 oz; 1 pound is too much weight for 10 corn kernels.

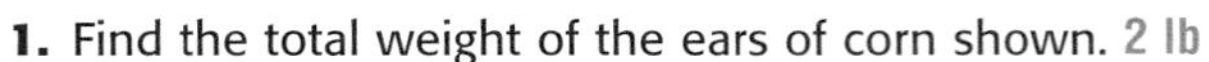

Compare. Use >, <, or =.

3. 12 oz ● 1 lb <
4. 34 oz ● 2 lb >
5. 3 lb ● 48 oz =

CHECK What You Know **Mass**

Mass is the amount of matter an object has. Metric units of mass are gram (g) and kilogram (kg).
1,000 grams (g) = 1 kilogram (kg)

6. What is the total mass of the ears of corn shown? 2 kg or 2,000 g
7. Which is a better estimate for the mass of 16 ears of corn: 10 grams or 4 kilograms? Explain your answer. 4 kg; The 8 ears of corn shown weight 2 kg. So, 16 ears of corn would weight twice as much or $2 \times 2 = 4$ kg.

Did you Know

A pound of corn consists of about 1,300 kernels.

Compare. Use >, <, or =.

8. 100 g ● 1 kg <
9. 3,000 g ● 3 kg =
10. 1,200 g ● 1 kg >

11. Order the masses below from least to greatest:

3 kg, 100 g, 300 g, 100 kg

100 g, 300 g, 3 kg, 100 kg

12. **WRITING IN ►MATH** Find two objects in the classroom that weigh more than one ounce. Find two objects that weigh less than one ounce. Explain each choice.
See students' work.

Start Smart 9

More FUN Facts

- An ear of corn averages 800 kernels in 16 rows.
- In the United States, corn production measures more than two times that of any other crop.
- Corn is a major part of many food items like cereals, peanut butter, snack foods, and soft drinks.
- Corn is produced on every continent of the world except Antarctica.
- Corn was so valuable to settlers that it was used in place of money.
- There are over 3,500 uses for corn. Some include soap, ink, auto fuel, livestock feed, sweetener, oil, and food.

Mass

- Discuss the definition of mass with students. Point out that the word *mass* is used with metric measures while the word *weight* is used with customary measures.
- Students may find it helpful to compare metric units with customary units. Point out that a kilogram is heavier than a pound and that a gram is lighter than an ounce.

Using the Exercises

Exercise 3–5 Suggest that students convert the pound measurements to ounces and then rewrite each comparison.

Exercise 7 Invite students to share their solution strategies. Some may divide 16 ears of corn by 4 to get a mass of 4 kilograms. Others may calculate that 1 ear of corn has a mass of $\frac{1}{4}$ kilogram and multiply $\frac{1}{4}$ by 16.

WRITING IN ►MATH Refer students to the kernel-weighing activity previously mentioned. Suggest that they use the results of that activity to help them identify the objects and explain their reasoning.

Assess and Close

- Fill in the "L" column of the KWL chart with additional facts about corn.

Weight and Mass of Food

- Display some food packages that have measurements labeled in ounces, pounds, grams, and kilograms.
- Allow students to look at the packages and record the measurements. Ask them to convert the measure to an equivalent one or to compare by giving a close estimate. For example, a canned good labeled 642 grams is about a half-kilogram.

Lesson Planner

Objectives

Use appropriate geometric vocabulary to describe two-dimensional and three-dimensional figures.

Activate Prior Knowledge

Read and discuss the introduction on p. 10 and **Did You Know** on p. 11.

- Lead a discussion about castles and older buildings and figures, and fill in the "K" column on a KWL chart.
- **Does anyone recognize the building in the picture at the top of the page? Has anyone visited a cultural arts center?** Fill in the "K" column with students' responses.
- **What else would you like to know about cultural arts centers?** Fill in the "W" column with their responses.
- After discussing the information in **Did You Know,** have students suggest ideas to write in the "L" column.
- Invite students to locate objects in the classroom that look like cubes, pyramids, cylinders, rectangular prisms, spheres, and cones. Discuss the attributes of these figures.

Start Smart 5 **Geometry**

There are many historic buildings in the United States. The Arts Castle in Delaware, Ohio, was originally built as a private home. Its current owner is the Delaware County Cultural Arts Center.

CHECK What You Know **Three-Dimensional Figures**

Three-dimensional figures are commonly found in architecture. Here are some characteristics of three-dimensional figures.

- Three-dimensional figures have length, width, and height.

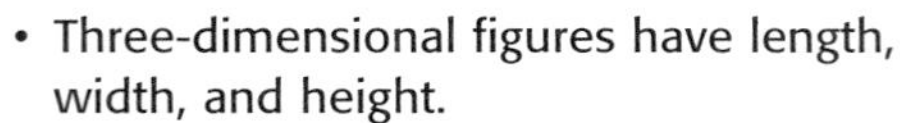

- A flat side of a three-dimensional figure is called a **face**.

- An **edge** is the line segment where two faces meet.

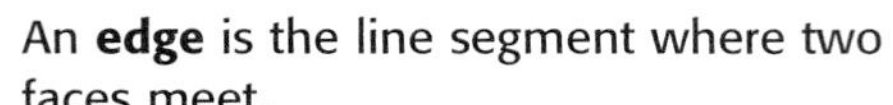

- The point where three or more edges meet is a **vertex**.

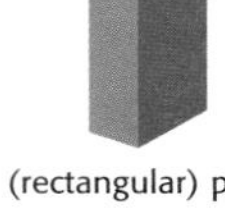

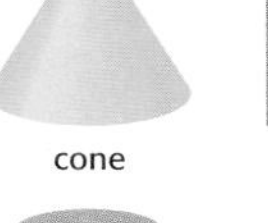

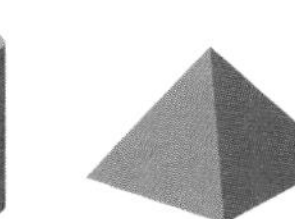

10 Start Smart

Additional Answer

7. Sample answer: A textbook is a rectangular prism; a globe is a sphere; a marker is a cylinder.

1. Which three-dimensional figure has one vertex? cone
2. Which three-dimensional figure has two faces? cylinder
3. Which three-dimensional figure does a book represent? rectangular prism

Two-Dimensional Figures

A two-dimensional figure has length and width. Two-dimensional figures are all around us. Just take a look at the traffic signs below.

stop sign

railroad sign

speed limit

yield sign

4. Which sign is an example of an octagon? stop sign
5. Which sign(s) contains right angles? speed limit sign
6. Explain the difference between an isosceles triangle and an equilateral triangle. Which of these triangles is a yield sign? Sample answer: An isosceles triangle has at least 2 equal sides. An equilateral triangle has 3 equal sides; equilateral or isosceles
7. Look for three-dimensional and two-dimensional figures in your classroom. Draw and label each figure. See margin.
8. **WRITING IN MATH** Describe a real-world three-dimensional figure. Then exchange papers with a classmate to see if he or she can guess the figure. Sample answer: This object is rolled in games. It has 6 faces; number cube.

Did you Know?
The Arts Center hosts many special events each year and has art classes for all ages.

More FUN Facts

- The street where the Arts Castle is located is named Elizabeth Street after the original owners' daughter.
- The building was built from blue limestone that was quarried close by in what is now called Blue Limestone Park.
- The Arts Castle was built as a wedding gift in 1846.
- The Arts Castle was owned by Ohio Wesleyan University for a time and was used for the university's Art Department.

Three-Dimensional Figures

- Tell students to study the pictures of the solid figures near the bottom of p. 10.
- **How is a sphere different than all other figures?** It has no faces, edges, or vertices.
- **Which other figures have curved surfaces?** cylinder and cone

Two-Dimensional Figures

- Discuss with students the attributes of the figures depicted in the signs. Ask questions such as the following:
- **How many sides does the speed limit sign have?** 4
- **How many angles does the yield sign have?** 3
- Ask students to use what they know about the attributes of the two-dimensional and three-dimensional figures to complete Exercises 4–7.

Using the Exercises

Exercise 5 You may want to remind students that all squares and rectangles have right angles, and that sometimes triangles and other polygons have right angles.

Exercise 7 Before students complete this exercise, review the differences between three-dimensional and two-dimensional figures.

WRITING IN MATH To help students with Exercise 8, suggest that they make a chart with heading titled *faces, edges,* and *vertices.* Under each heading they can record information about number and shape (when appropriate). Encourage students to use the information in the chart to write their descriptions.

Assess and Close

- Fill in the "L" column of the KWL chart with additional facts about libraries and figures.

Three-Dimensional Models

- Put students in pairs and provide them with toothpicks and gumdrops or marshmallows.
- Ask each pair of students to use these materials to make models of two different three-dimensional figures.
- Have partners place their models on a piece of paper. Encourage them to record as many attributes as they can for the figures, including the names of the figures.

Lesson Planner

Objectives

Interpret and compare data in pictographs and bar graphs. Generate questions, collect responses, and display data in a bar graph.

Activate Prior Knowledge

Read and discuss the introduction on p. 12 and **Did You Know** on p. 13.

- Lead a discussion about sports teams and fill in the "K" column on a KWL chart.
- **How many students have seen or attended a North Carolina professional sports team's game? What was the team and sport?** Fill in the "K" column with students' responses. Record tallies for the number of students responding for each team.
- **What else would you like to know about these teams?** Fill in the "W" column with their responses.
- After discussing the information in **Did You Know,** have students suggest ideas to write in the "L" column.

Football is a popular sport. There are four professional sports teams in North Carolina, including professional football.

Pictographs

A pictograph shows data by using pictures. The pictograph at the right shows the number of football games a professional football team played each month during a recent regular season.

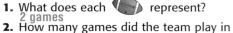

1. What does each 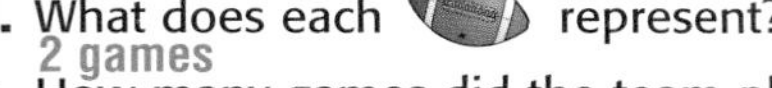 represent? 2 games
2. How many games did the team play in November? in December? 4; 5
3. During which month were less than four games played? October

Source: Carolina Panthers

Additional Answer

5. Sample answer: Basketball and hockey; The height of the bars for these two sports is even with the 1 on the vertical axis.

CHECK What You Know Bar Graphs

A bar graph compares data by using bars of different heights. The graph below shows the number of North Carolina's professional sports teams.

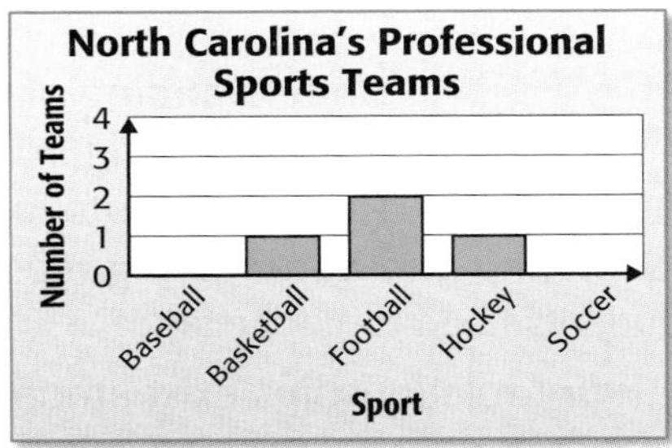

Source: North Carolina Department of Commerce

Arena football was invented in 1981 during an indoor soccer game when its rules were written on an envelope.

4. Which sport(s) has the fewest teams? the greatest? baseball and soccer; football
5. Which two sports have one team? How do you know? See margin.
6. What is the difference between the greatest and least number of teams? 2
7. What is the total number of teams? 4
8. Follow these steps to take a survey. Then make a bar graph to show the results. See students' work.
   - Ask each student to name his or her favorite sport.
   - Make a tally chart to show how many students like each sport.
   - Make a bar graph from the tally chart.
9. WRITING IN ▸MATH Write a sentence that describes what your graph shows. See students' work.

More FUN Facts

- The first professional sports team in North Carolina was the National Basketball Association's Charlotte Hornets, which began play in the 1987–1988 NBA season.
- North Carolina remains without a Major League Baseball team despite many efforts to attract a team to the state.
- On June 19, 2006, the Carolina Hurricanes, a National Hockey League (NHL) team won the Stanley Cup. The Hurricanes are the first professional sports team from North Carolina to win their sport's highest championship.

Pictographs

- Refer to the pictograph on p. 12. Ask students to identify the features of the graph (title, labels, and key) and explain the purpose of each.
- Have students mention different data that could be displayed on a pictograph.

Bar Graphs

- Discuss the bar graph on p. 13. **What information does the graph show?** how many professional sports teams there are in North Carolina for different sports
- Have students locate the title and labels on both axes. Ask what the scale is on the graph. Encourage students to compare and contrast the bar graph with the pictograph.
- Direct students to analyze the bar graph to complete Exercises 4–7.

Using the Exercises

Exercise 2 Invite students to share the strategies used for answering the question (e.g., skip counting, multiplication).

Exercise 4 You may want to point out that students do not have to use actual numbers to answer these questions. They can simply look at the lengths of the bars.

WRITING IN ▸MATH Ask volunteers to share their sentences about what their graphs show. As a class, discuss any similarities and differences between students' descriptions.

Assess and Close

- Fill in the "L" column of the KWL chart with additional facts about sports teams.

Sports Pictograph

- Refer to the information collected about students who have watched or attended games of North Carolina professional sports teams.
- Have pairs of students use this data to make a pictograph. You may want to discuss with the class what to use as a key.
- Tell students to analyze their graph and write about what the graph shows.

Chapter Overview

Chapter-at-a-Glance

In Chapter 1, the emphasis is on whole-number place value through millions.

Lesson	Math Objective	State/Local Standards
1-1 **Place Value Through Hundred Thousands** (pp. 17–19)	Read and write whole numbers to hundred thousands.	
EXPLORE **1-2** **How Big is One Million?** (pp. 20–21)	Explore the concept of a million.	
1-2 **Place Value Through Millions** (pp. 22–25)	Read and write whole numbers through the millions.	
1-3 **Problem-Solving Strategy: The Four-Step Plan** (pp. 26–27)	Solve problems using the four-step plan.	
1-4 **Compare Whole Numbers** (pp. 28–30)	Compare whole numbers.	
1-5 **Order Whole Numbers** (pp. 32–34)	Order whole numbers through the millions.	
1-6 **Round Whole Numbers** (pp. 36–39)	Round whole numbers through the millions.	
1-7 **Problem-Solving Investigation: Choose a Strategy** (pp. 40–41)	Choose the best strategy to solve a problem.	

Use Place Value to Represent Whole Numbers

BIG Idea Understanding place value is essential for developing skills in all areas of mathematics. These concepts form the basis for estimating and determining reasonableness of answers. Students need to understand:

- ***what*** relationships exist among ones, tens, hundreds, and so on.
- ***which*** numbers are greater than or less than others.
- ***why*** digits in numbers represent what they do.
- ***how*** multi-digit numbers are composed and decomposed.

Algebra Students compare and order whole numbers. This concept will help prepare them for algebra concepts, such as writing inequalities. (Lessons 1-4 and 1-5)

G4-FP8C ***Number and Operations:*** Building on their work in grade 3, students extend their understanding of place value and ways of representing numbers to 100,000 in various contexts. They use estimation in determining the relative sizes of amounts or distances. Students develop understandings of strategies for multidigit division by using models that represent division as the inverse of multiplication, as partitioning, or as successive subtraction. By working with decimals, students extend their ability to recognize equivalent fractions. Students' earlier work in grade 3 with models of fractions and multiplication and division facts supports their understanding of techniques for generating equivalent fractions and simplifying fractions.

Use Place Value to Represent Whole Numbers

Skills Trace

Vertical Alignment

Third Grade

In third grade, students learned to:

- Count, read, write, and identify place value of whole numbers through ten thousands.
- Compare, order, and round numbers through ten thousands.

Fourth Grade

During this chapter, students learn to:

- Read and write whole numbers through the millions.
- Compare and order whole numbers through the millions.
- Round whole numbers through the millions.

After this chapter, students learn to:

- Add, subtract, multiply, and divide whole numbers.

Fifth Grade

In fifth grade, students learn to:

- Read, write compare, and order whole numbers.
- Read, write, compare, and order decimals through thousandths.

Backmapping and Vertical Alignment **McGraw-Hill's *Math Connects*** program was conceived and developed with the final results in mind: student success in Algebra 1 and beyond. The authors, using the **NCTM Focal Points and Focal Connections** as their guide, developed this brand-new series by backmapping from Algebra 1 concepts, and vertically aligning the topics so that they build upon prior skills and concepts and serve as a foundation for future topics.

Math Vocabulary

The following math vocabulary words for Chapter 1 are listed in the glossary of the ***Student Edition.*** You can find interactive definitions in 13 languages in the ***eGlossary*** at macmillanmh.com

digit A symbol used to write numbers. The ten digits are 0, 1, 2, 3, 4, 5, 6, 7, 8, 9. (p. 17A)

estimate A number close to an exact value; an estimate indicates about how much. (p. 36A)
Example: 47 + 22 (estimate 50 + 20) is about 70.

expanded form The representation of a number as a sum that shows the value of each digit. (p. 17A)
Example: 536 can be written as 500 + 30 + 6.

is equal to (=) Having the same value. (p. 28A)

is greater than (>) The number on the left of the symbol is greater than the number on the right. (p. 28A)
Example: 5 > 3 (5 is greater than 3.)

is less than (<) The number on the left side of the symbol is less than the number on the right side. (p. 28A)
Example: 4 < 7 (4 is less than 7.)

place value The value given to a digit by its position in a number. (p. 17A)

rounding (or round) To find the nearest value of a number based on a given place value. To change the value of a number to one that is easier to work with. (p. 36A)

standard form The usual way of writing a number that shows only its digits, no words. (p. 17A)

Visual Vocabulary Cards

Use Visual Vocabulary Cards 12, 14, 15, and 42 to reinforce the vocabulary in this lesson. (The Define/Example/Ask routine is printed on the back of each card.)

round

Chapter Planner

Suggested Pacing		
Instruction	Review & Assessment	TOTAL
8 days	1 day	**9 days**

Diagnostic Assessment
Quick Check (p. 16)

	Lesson 1-1 (Pacing: 1 day)	Explore 1-2 (Pacing: 1 day)	Lesson 1-2 (Pacing: 1 day)
Lesson/ Objective	**Place Value Through Hundred Thousands** (pp. 17–19) **Objective:** Read and write whole numbers to hundred thousands.	**How Big is One Million?** (pp. 20–21) **Objective:** Explore the concept of a million.	**Place Value Through Millions** (pp. 22–25) **Objective:** Read and write whole numbers through the millions.
State/Local Standards			
Math Vocabulary	**digit**, **place value**, **period**, **standard form**, **word form**, **expanded form**		
Lesson Resources	**Materials** WorkMat 4: Place-Value Chart **Manipulatives** spinner **Other Resources** CRM Leveled Worksheets (pp. 8–12) Daily Reteach • 5-Minute Check • Problem of the Day	**Materials** thousand cube sheet, scissors, tape	**Materials** transparency, WorkMat 4: Place-Value Chart **Manipulatives** stopwatch, counters **Other Resources** CRM Leveled Worksheets (pp. 13–17) Daily Reteach • 5-Minute Check • Problem of the Day
Technology	Math Song Track #1		Math Song Track #5
Math Online	Personal Tutor	Concepts in Motion	Personal Tutor
Reaching All Learners	English Learners, p. 17B ELL Below Level, p. 17B BL Early Finishers, p. 17B AL		English Learners, p. 22B ELL Gifted and Talented, p. 22B AL Early Finishers, p. 22B AL
Alternate Lesson			

KEY

BL Below/Approaching Level — OL On Level — AL Above/Beyond Level — ELL English Learners
SE Student Edition — TE Teacher Edition — CRM Chapter 1 Resource Masters — CD-Rom
Transparency — Real-World Problem Solving Library

Use Place Value to Represent Whole Numbers

	Lesson 1-3 (Pacing: 1 day)	Lesson 1-4 (Pacing: 1 day)	Lesson 1-5 (Pacing: 1 day)
Lesson/ Objective	**Problem-Solving Strategy The Four-Step Plan** (pp. 26–27) **Objective:** Solve problems using the four-step plan.	**Compare Whole Numbers** (pp. 28–30) **Objective:** Compare whole numbers.	**Order Whole Numbers** (pp. 32–34) **Objective:** Order whole numbers through the millions.
State/Local Standards			
Math Vocabulary		**number line**, **is greater than (>)**, **is less than (<)**, **is equal to (=)**	
Lesson Resources	**Materials** index cards **Other Resources** CRM Leveled Worksheets (pp. 18–22) Daily Reteach • 5-Minute Check • Problem of the Day *Rivers and Mountains of the United States*	**Materials** scissors, tape, ruler, grid paper **Other Resources** CRM Leveled Worksheets (pp. 23–27) Daily Reteach • 5-Minute Check • Problem of the Day	**Materials** index cards **Other Resources** CRM Leveled Worksheets (pp. 28–32) Daily Reteach • 5-Minute Check • Problem of the Day
Technology **Math Online**		Math Tool Chest • Math Adventures Personal Tutor	Math Adventures Personal Tutor
Reaching All Learners	English Learners, p. 26B ELL Gifted and Talented, p. 26B AL Early Finishers, p. 26B OL AL	English Learners, p. 28B ELL Below Level, p. 28B BL Early Finishers, p. 28B OL AL	English Learners, p. 32B ELL Below Level, p. 32B BL Early Finishers, p. 32B AL
Alternate Lesson			
		Formative Assessment Mid-Chapter Check (p. 31)	**Game Time** Greater Number Game (p. 35)

Chapter Planner

	Lesson 1-6 Pacing: 1 day	Lesson 1-7 Pacing: 1 day
Lesson/ Objective	**Round Whole Numbers** (pp. 36–39) **Objective:** Round whole numbers through the millions.	**Problem-Solving Investigation** **Choose a Strategy** (pp. 40–41) **Objective:** Choose the best strategy to solve a problem.
State/Local Standards		
Math Vocabulary	**estimate**, **rounding (or round)**	
Lesson Resources	**Other Resources** CRM Leveled Worksheets (pp. 33–37) Daily Reteach • 5-Minute Check • Problem of the Day	**Materials** index cards, poster board, markers **Manipulatives** money **Other Resources** CRM Leveled Worksheets (pp. 38–42) Daily Reteach • 5-Minute Check • Problem of the Day *Rivers and Mountains of the United States*
Technology	Math Adventures	
Math Online	Personal Tutor	Concepts in Motion
Reaching All Learners	English Learners, p. 36B ELL Below Level, p. 36B BL Early Finishers, p. 36B AL	English Learners, p. 40B ELL Gifted and Talented, p. 40B AL Early Finishers, p. 40B OL AL
Alternate Lesson		

Problem Solving: Science (p. 42)

Summative Assessment
- Study Guide/Review (p. 44)
- Chapter Test (p. 49)
- Test Practice (p. 50)

Assessment Options

Diagnostic Assessment

- SE *Option 1:* Quick Check (p. 16)
- *Option 2:* Online Quiz macmillanmh.com
- CRM *Option 3:* Diagnostic Test (p. 46)
- CRM *Option 4:* Chapter Pretest (p. 47)

Formative Assessment

- TE Alternate Teaching Strategy (every lesson)
- SE Talk About It (every lesson)
- SE Writing in Math (every lesson)
- SE Check What You Know (every lesson)
- TE Ticket Out the Door (p. 30)
- TE Yesterday's News (pp. 25, 34)
- SE Mid-Chapter Check (p. 31)
- CRM Lesson Quizzes (p. 48–50)
- CRM Mid-Chapter Test (p. 51)

Summative Assessment

- SE Chapter Test (p. 49)
- SE Test Practice (p. 50)
- CRM Vocabulary Test (p. 52)
- CRM Leveled Chapter Tests (pp. 57–68)
- CRM Cumulative Test Practice (pp. 70–72)
- CRM Oral Assessment (p. 53)
- ExamView® Assessment Suite
- Advance Tracker

Professional Development

Targeted professional development has been articulated throughout **McGraw-Hill's *Math Connects*** program. The **McGraw-Hill Professional Development Video Library** provides short videos that support the **NCTM Focal Points and Focal Connections.** For more information visit macmillanmh.com.

Model Lessons

Instructional Strategies

Assessment Tip

Knowing how to count, order, and compare numbers to 1,000,000 will help students to better understand whole number operations.

- This assessment can be done as a whole class. You will need a set of digit cards, 0–9.
- On a piece of paper, have the students draw six blank lines in a row.
- Tell the students they will try to build the largest six-digit number they can with the digit cards that you will draw. Each blank will contain one digit. You can either replace the card after it is drawn or keep it out. Draw six times.
- Observe the various six-digit numbers and make note of any students who are having difficulty making the largest number. Repeat with similar types of problems.

Teacher Notes

The one-stop Assessment Options planner organizes the resources available for diagnostic, formative, and summative assessment in this chapter.

Learning Stations

Cross-Curricular Links

Cross-Curricular Learning Stations give students self-guided opportunities to explore chapter concepts.

Writing

pair | LOGICAL

Tell Me How

- Along with a partner, each person writes instructions on how to compare numbers using a number line.
- Exchange your written instructions with each other.
- Each partner gives the other three five-digit numbers to place on a number line in the proper order. Use your written instructions to do this task.
- Were you able to follow each other's instructions? If not, how are they different? How would you change the way they are written?

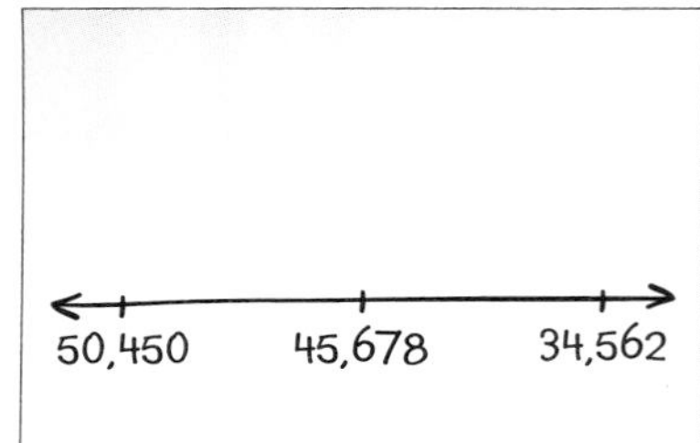

Materials:

- paper
- pencils

Art

individual | VISUAL

Computer Colors

Each color displayed on a computer monitor can be chosen from a palette of 16,777,216 colors. That is over 16 million colors!

- Write the number 16,777,216 horizontally across the top of your paper.
- Underneath each digit write the word form for the place value of that digit vertically.
- Use as many colors as you can for your letters and numbers.

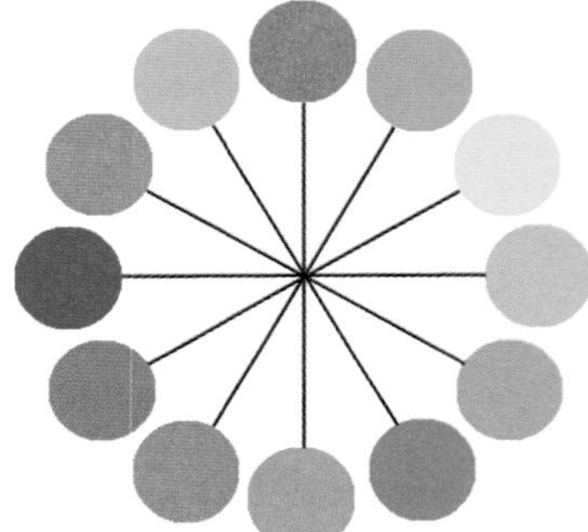

Materials:

- markers
- paper
- pencil

Music

individual | LOGICAL

Music Countdown

In the past few years, some of the most popular CDs sold 3,478,361; 2,527,490; 5,137,468; and 4,968,606 albums.

- Choose one album and write the total number of CDs sold three different ways.
- Create a number line from 2,000,000 to 6,000,000. Then use the number line to order the CDs from least to greatest.
- Create a poster showing the CDs ordered from the best-seller to the least-seller. Write the numbers in standard, word and expanded form.

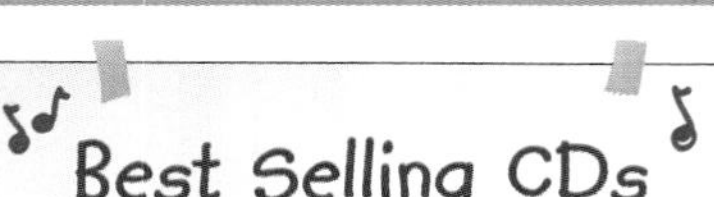

6,535,819

six million, five hundred thirty-five thousand, eight hundred nineteen

6,000,000 + 500,000 + 30,000 + 5,000 + 800 + 10 + 9

Materials:

- posterboard
- markers
- paper
- pencil

Use Place Value to Represent Whole Numbers

Science

group | VISUAL

Elephant Lineup

An adult male elephant can weigh up to 13,200 pounds. An adult female elephant can weigh up to 7,000 pounds. Make an elephant card and line up your elephants!

- Each person in the group makes his or her own elephant index card, gluing a picture of an elephant to the card and writing down any weight between 7,000 pounds and the top elephant weight, 13,200 pounds.
- Now line up your elephants from the least weight to the greatest.

Materials:
- pictures of elephants from magazines
- index cards
- glue
- markers

Health

group | SPATIAL

Calories Count

Make Calorie cards and compare the numbers!

- The average kid needs between 1,600 and 2,500 Calories per day. Make a Calorie card for yourself, drawing a picture and writing down a Calorie count between 1,600 and 2,500. It can be any number you choose between those two amounts.
- Now put all of your cards down on the table. Arrange the numbers from least to greatest.
- Which card is the closest to 2,000 Calories?

Materials:
- index cards
- markers
- paper
- pencils

Social Studies

pair | VISUAL

Pick a Population

- Make one card for each of the following cities and your own city, using the city name and population.

  Memphis, TN: 650,100
  Los Angeles, CA: 3,844,829
  Louisville, KY: 256,231
  Charleston, SC: 106,712
  Phoenix, AZ: 1,461,575
  Dallas, TX: 1,213,825

- Shuffle the cards. Each partner picks one card. Which city has the greatest population? Compare the populations using place value.
- Now, order the cards from least to greatest.

Materials:
- index cards
- markers

Introduce the Chapter

 Real World: Numbers in the News

Materials: newspapers or magazines

Share with students that they are going to learn about place value in this chapter. Explain that the value of a digit depends on its place in the number.

Have students:

- Divide into small groups.
- Look through the pages of newspapers or magazines and find examples of whole numbers. Challenge students to find numbers of different sizes. See which group can find the largest number.
- Have each group write one number on the board.

Work with students to analyze each group's number. Choose one number and tell students the place value of each digit. Then ask for volunteers as you analyze the number on the board as a class.

Direct students to Student Edition p. 14. Have students read the paragraph at the top of the page.

- **Give an example of a whole number that you used yesterday.** Sample answers: the outside temperature, the distance from school to home, the number of people in the family

WRITING IN ▶MATH

Starting the Chapter
Have students write a short paragraph in their Math Journals explaining how numbers are used in other school subjects such as social studies and science. Suggest that they give specific examples.

Key Vocabulary Introduce the key vocabulary in the chapter using the routine below.

Define: Place value is the value given to a digit by its place in the number.
Example: The 4 in 485 is in the hundreds place, the 8 is in the tens place, and the 5 is in the ones place.
Ask: When is it useful to know the place value of a number?

Read-Aloud Anthology For an optional reading activity to introduce this chapter's math concepts, see the Read-Aloud Anthology on p. TR24.

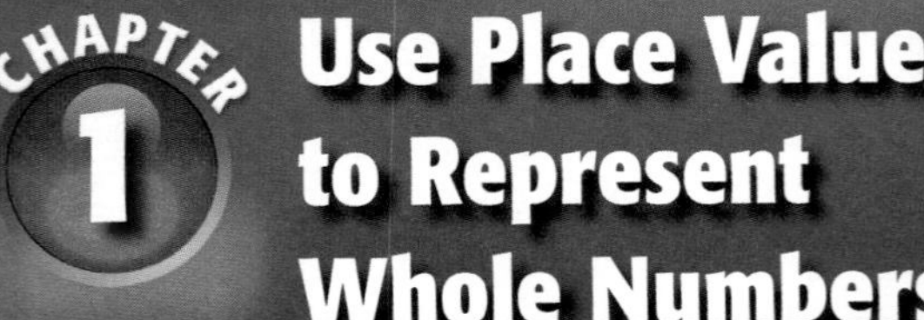

BIG Idea What is place value?

Place value is the value given to a digit by its position in a number.

Example The honeybee is the state insect for 16 states. Among these are North Carolina, Oklahoma, and Utah. The table shows some facts about the honeybee. Notice that each number has a different value.

Honeybee Facts
• Travels 15 miles per hour
• Makes 154 trips to make one tablespoon of honey
• Wing stroke of 11,400 times per minute

Source: National Honey Board

What will I learn in this chapter?

- Read and write whole numbers to millions.
- Compare and order whole numbers.
- Round whole numbers.
- Use the four-step plan to solve problems.

Key Vocabulary

place value
standard form
expanded form
is greater than (>)
is less than (<)

Math Online Student Study Tools at macmillanmh.com

14 Chapter 1 Use Place Value to Represent W

Chapter Projects apply chapter concepts and skills through extended activities and provide additional assessment opportunities

 Chapter 1 Project

What's That Cost?

Students make a poster showing a list of items they normally buy, and compare the prices.

- Students come up with a list of items they buy. Items can range from food to clothing to music CDs or video games. They research the prices and make a poster showing the items with prices, from least expensive to most expensive.
- Students may decorate the poster with magazine pictures of the items and use markers to make their presentation colorful.
- Challenge students to round the prices to the nearest dollar, and then list them again from least expensive to most expensive.

CRM *Refer to Chapter 1 Resource Masters, p. 55, for a rubric to assess students' progress on this project.*

Foldables® are a unique way to enhance students' study skills. Encourage students to add to their Foldable as they work through the chapter and to use it to review for their chapter test.

The Literature List presents all of the literature referenced in the chapter.

FOLDABLES® Study Organizer Make this Foldable to help organize information about place value. Begin with one sheet of notebook paper.

1. **Fold** a sheet of aper lengthwise. eave a two-inch ab at the top.
2. **Fold** the right side and the left side to make three equal sections.
3. **Unfold** the sides. Then cut along the creases as shown.
4. **Label** as shown. Take notes as you move through the chapter.

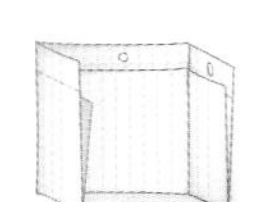

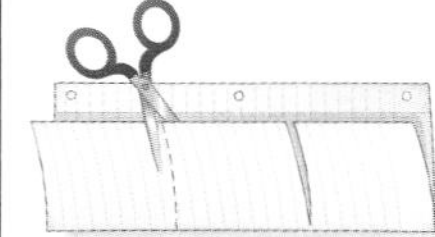

Use Place Value to Represent Whole Numbers
Place Value through Hundred Thousands | Place Value through Millions | Compare, Order, and Round Whole Numbers

ELL National ESL Standards Alignment for Chapter 1

Lesson, Page	ESL Standard	Modality	Level
1-1, p. 17B	Goal 1, Standard 3, h	Linguistic, Visual	Intermediate
1-2, p. 22B	Goal 2, Standard 3, h	Logical	Intermediate
1-3, p. 26B	Goal 2, Standard 2, f	Linguistic, Visual	Advanced
1-4, p. 28B	Goal 2, Standard 1, h	Auditory, Visual	Beginning
1-5, p. 32B	Goal 1, Standard 1, a	Logical, Spatial	Intermediate
1-6, p. 36B	Goal 2, Standard 2, f	Kinesthetic, Intrapersonal	Intermediate
1-7, p. 40B	Goal 2, Standard 2, b	Linguistic, Visual	Advanced

The National ESL Standards can be found in the Teacher Reference Handbook.

FOLDABLES® Dinah Zike's Foldables

Guide students through the directions on p. 15 to create their own Foldable graphic organizers for place value and number sense. Students may also use their Foldables to study and review for chapter assessment.

When to Use It Lessons 1-1, 1-2, 1-3, 1-4, and 1-5. (Additional instructions for using the Foldables with these lessons are found on pp. 31 and 44.)

Chapter 1 Literature List

Lesson	Book Title
1-1	**Earth Day—Hooray!** Stuart J. Murphy
1-2	**How Much is a Million?** David Schwartz
1-3	**Counting Jennie** Helena Clare Pittman
1-4	**Hottest Coldest Highest Deepest** Steve Jenkins
1-5	**Centipede's 100 Shoes** Tony Ross
1-6	**Coyotes All Around** Stuart J. Murphy
Any	**Sea Squares** Joy N. Hulme
Any	**Score One for the Sloths** Helen Lester

- Read the Math at Home letter found in the Chapter 1 Resource Masters, p. 4, with the class and have each student sign it. (A Spanish version is found on p. 5.)
- Send home copies of the Math at Home letter with each student.

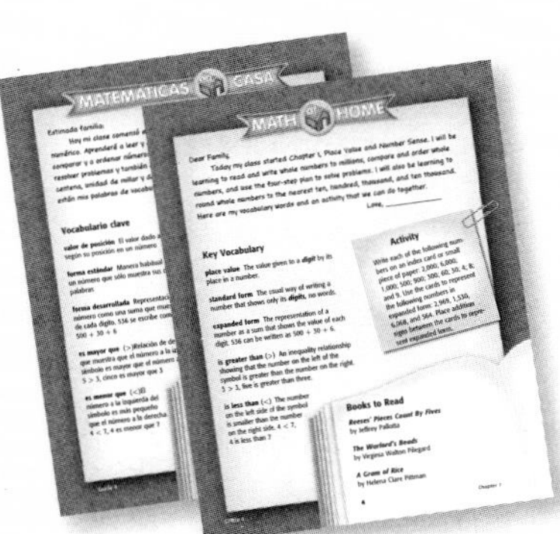

Diagnostic Assessment

Check for students' prerequisite skills before beginning the chapter.

- **Option 1:** ***Quick Check***
  SE Student Edition, p. 16
- **Option 2:** ***Online Assessment***
  Math Online macmillanmh.com
- **Option 3:** ***Diagnostic Tests***
  CRM Chapter 1 Resource Masters, p. 46–47

RTI (Response to Intervention)

Apply the Results Based on the results of the diagnostic assessment on Student Edition p. 16, use the chart below to address individual needs before beginning the chapter.

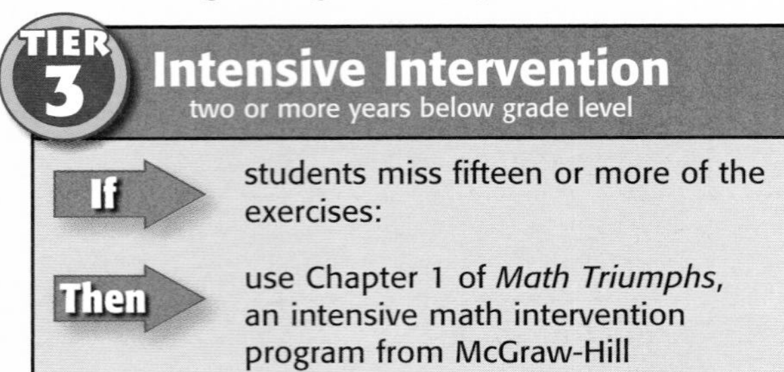

TIER 3 Intensive Intervention two or more years below grade level

If students miss fifteen or more of the exercises:

Then use Chapter 1 of *Math Triumphs*, an intensive math intervention program from McGraw-Hill

ARE YOU READY for Chapter 1?

You have two ways to check prerequisite skills for this chapter.

Option 2

Math Online Take the Chapter Readiness Quiz at macmillanmh.com

Option 1

Complete the Quick Check below.

QUICK Check

Write each number in word form and expanded form. (Prior Grade) (Used in Lessons 1-1 and 1-2)

1.

Ones		
hundreds	tens	ones
	6	4

sixty-four; $60 + 4$

2.

Ones		
hundreds	tens	ones
9	9	5

nine hundred ninety-five; $900 + 90 + 5$

3. 79 **4.** 30 **5.** 90 **6.** 165

3–10. See Ch. 1 Answer Appendix.

7. 347 **8.** 692 **9.** 1,840 **10.** 4,505

11. Write 300 + 20 + 1 in standard form and word form. 321; three hundred twenty-one

Compare. Use >, <, or =. (Prior Grade) (Used in Lessons 1-4 and 1-5)

12. 40 ● 4 > **13.** 59 ● 59 = **14.** 888 ● 898 < **15.** 682 ● 700 <

16. Nora earned $425. She wants to buy a video game system that costs $375. Does she have enough money? Explain. yes; $425 > $375

Round to the nearest ten. (Prior Grade) (Used in Lesson 1-6)

17. 26 30 **18.** 4 0 **19.** 18 20 **20.** 75 80

21. 152 150 **22.** 175 180 **23.** 347 350 **24.** 508 510

25. **Measurement** Ann Arbor, Michigan, is 65 miles from Lansing, Michigan. Would it be reasonable to say that Ann Arbor is about 70 miles from Lansing? Explain. yes; To the nearest 10, 65 rounds to 70.

16 **Chapter 1** Use Place Value to Represent W

Each chapter provides three options for Diagnostic Assessment. Based on the results, Intervention Options include suggestions for intensive and strategic students, as well as on-level and above-level students.

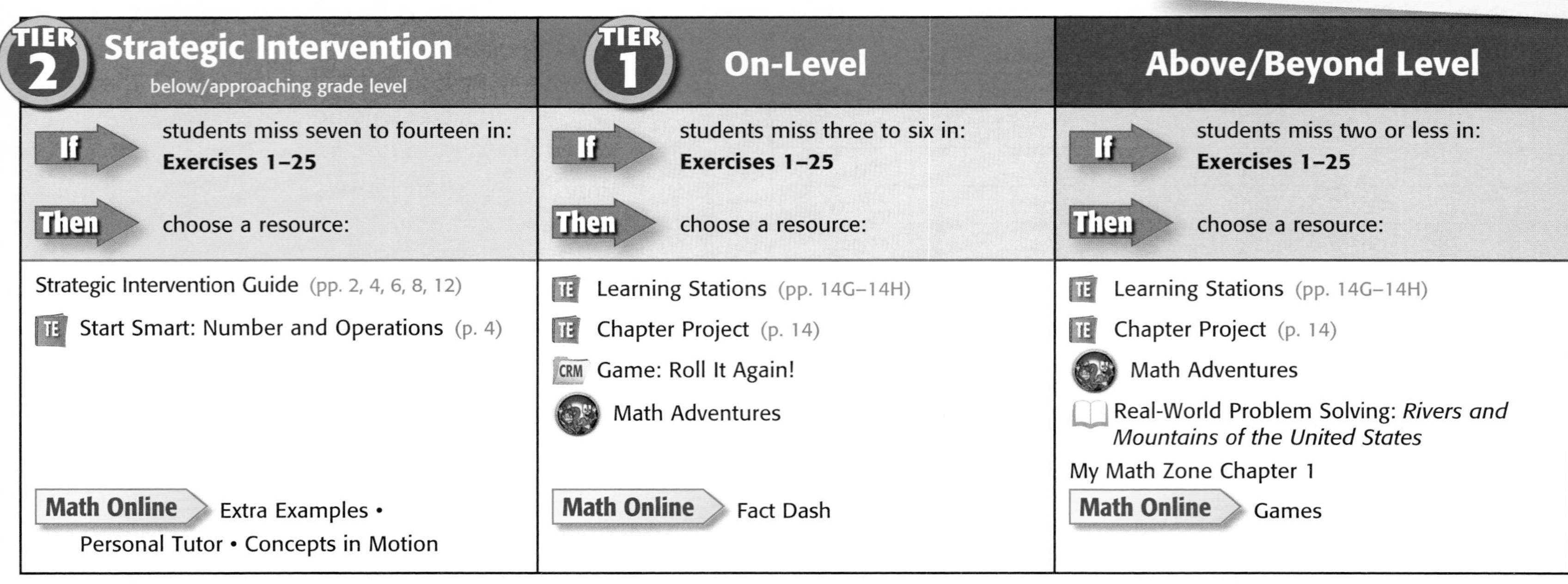

TIER 2 Strategic Intervention (below/approaching grade level)	TIER 1 On-Level	Above/Beyond Level
If students miss seven to fourteen in: **Exercises 1–25**	**If** students miss three to six in: **Exercises 1–25**	**If** students miss two or less in: **Exercises 1–25**
Then choose a resource:	**Then** choose a resource:	**Then** choose a resource:
Strategic Intervention Guide (pp. 2, 4, 6, 8, 12) TE Start Smart: Number and Operations (p. 4) **Math Online** Extra Examples • Personal Tutor • Concepts in Motion	TE Learning Stations (pp. 14G–14H) TE Chapter Project (p. 14) CRM Game: Roll It Again! Math Adventures **Math Online** Fact Dash	TE Learning Stations (pp. 14G–14H) TE Chapter Project (p. 14) Math Adventures Real-World Problem Solving: *Rivers and Mountains of the United States* My Math Zone Chapter 1 **Math Online** Games

LESSON 1-1

Place Value Through Hundred Thousands

Lesson Planner

Objective

Read and write whole numbers to hundred thousands.

Vocabulary

digits, **place value**, **period**, **standard form**, **word form**, **expanded form**

Resources

Materials: WorkMat 4: Place-Value Chart

Manipulatives: spinner

Literature Connection: *Earth Day—Hooray!* by Stuart J. Murphy

Teacher Technology
TeacherWorks • Interactive Classroom • Math Songs Track #1 Lesson Plan

The 5-Minute Check provides a quick review and assessment of a previous lesson. Use the Problem of the Day to challenge students with additional review and higher-order questions.

Focus on Math Background

In the previous grade, students were introduced to and used place value through 10,000. Unfortunately, few students have a deep understanding of the concept of place value. Understanding that the *value* of a digit depends on the *place* of the digit within a number is essential to comprehending the algorithms we teach. Our number system, the base ten system, is based on the number 10, and all of our numbers can be written using the ten digits, 0 through 9. Learning to write numbers in standard, word, and expanded form helps students read, write, and compare numbers.

Standard form: 408,035
Word form: four hundred eight thousand, thirty-five
Expanded form: 400,000 + 8,000 + 30 + 5

Daily Routine

Use these suggestions before beginning the lesson on p. 17.

5-Minute Check

(Reviews Number and Operations Start Smart.)

Find the value.

1. 10 × 3 30 **2.** 100 − 30 70
3. 16 ÷ 4 4 **4.** 15 + 10 25

Problem of the Day

Lucy is learning about numbers. She thinks that 3,528 is greater than 3,533 since 8 is greater than 3. Is Lucy correct? Explain. Sample answer: No; check students' explanations.

Building Math Vocabulary

Write the lesson vocabulary words and their definitions on the board.

Have students record these new vocabulary words and their definitions in their Math Journals. Have them give an example of each.

Visual Vocabulary Cards
Use Visual Vocabulary Card 12 to reinforce the vocabulary introduced in this lesson. (The Define/Example/Ask routine is printed on the back of each card.)

Each lesson includes suggestions for differentiating instruction. These strategies are keyed for English Language Learners, students above grade level, struggling students, and students with special needs.

Differentiated Instruction

Small Group Options

Option 1 Below Level (BL)

VISUAL, SPATIAL

Materials: five 3 × 5 index cards, cut in half per student set; one 3 × 5 index card, cut in fourths, 1 piece per student; written forms of numbers if desired

- Write a single digit, 0–9, on each half-card.
- Put a comma on one smaller card piece. Reserve other pieces for commas on more card sets.
- Say each of these numbers: 175; 4,896; 20,751; 3,468. Students should arrange their cards to form the numbers.
- Observe as students arrange the number cards and place the comma, or hand the students the written form of the number to arrange number cards. Give help as needed. Increase or decrease number size as needed.
- Point to individual digits and ask the value.

Option 2 English Language Learners (ELL)

LINGUISTIC, VISUAL

Materials: sets of numbered self-sticking notes, place-value grids
Core Vocabulary: place, in, number
Common Use Verb: say

Talk Math This strategy activates students' background knowledge by using native language to scaffold reading numbers in English.

- Place self-sticking notes into the grid and say: "Say this number in your native language."
- Allow students to read them, repeating for all the classroom languages.
- Label each place value and say: "7 [any number] is **in** the tens **place**." Repeat for each place value, reading "7 tens" as you go.
- Have students repeat the process in pairs or small groups.

Small Group and Independent Work Options offer classroom flexibility for students who need additional help or self-directed activity suggestions after completing their work.

Independent Work Options

Option 1 Early Finishers (AL)

VISUAL, SPATIAL

Materials: paper and pencil

Have students create a 6-digit number. Ask them to identify the standard form, write the word form, and write the expanded form.

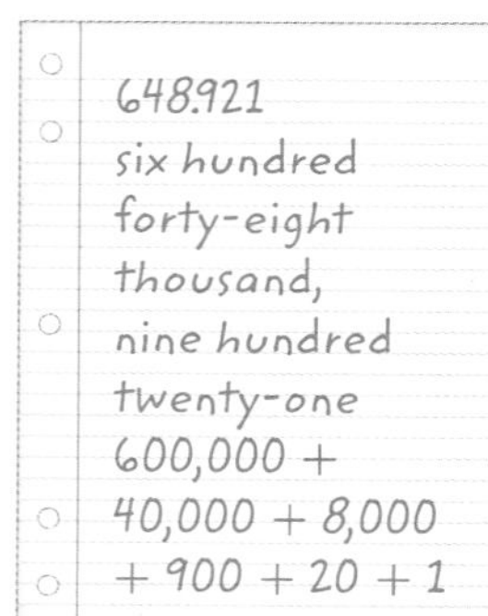

648,921
six hundred
forty-eight
thousand,
nine hundred
twenty-one
600,000 +
40,000 + 8,000
+ 900 + 20 + 1

Option 2 Student Technology

Math Online macmillanmh.com

Personal Tutor • Extra Examples

Option 3 Learning Station: Writing (p. 14G)

Direct students to the Writing Learning Station for opportunities to explore and extend the lesson concept.

Option 4 Problem-Solving Practice

Reinforce problem-solving skills and strategies with the Problem-Solving Practice worksheet.

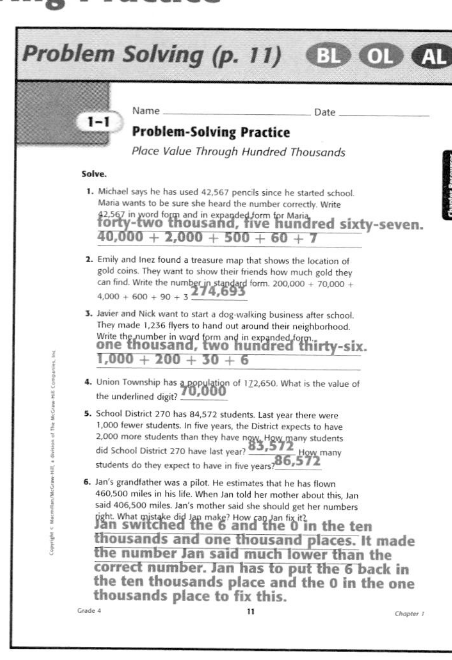

Problem Solving (p. 11) BL OL AL

1-1 Name ______ Date ______

Problem-Solving Practice

Place Value Through Hundred Thousands

Solve.

1. Michael says he has used 42,567 pencils since he started school. Maria wants to be sure she heard the number correctly. Write 42,567 in word form and in expanded form for Maria.
forty-two thousand, five hundred sixty-seven.
40,000 + 2,000 + 500 + 60 + 7
2. Emily and Inez found a treasure map that shows the location of gold coins. They want to show their friends how much gold they can find. Write the number in standard form. 200,000 + 70,000 + 4,000 + 600 + 90 + 3 **274,693**
3. Javier and Nick want to start a dog-walking business after school. They made 1,236 flyers to hand out around their neighborhood. Write the number in word form and in expanded form.
one thousand, two hundred thirty-six.
1,000 + 200 + 30 + 6
4. Union Township has a population of 172,650. What is the value of the underlined digit? **70,000**
5. School District 270 has 84,572 students. Last year there were 1,000 fewer students. In five years, the District expects to have 2,000 more students than they have now. How many students did School District 270 have last year? **83,572** How many students do they expect to have in five years? **86,572**
6. Jan's grandfather was a pilot. He estimates that he has flown 460,500 miles in his life. When Jan told her mother about this, Jan said 406,500 miles. Jan's mother said she should get her numbers right. What mistake did Jan make? How can Jan fix it?
Jan switched the 6 and the 0 in the ten thousands and one thousand places. It made the number Jan said much lower than the correct number. Jan has to put the 6 back in the ten thousands place and the 0 in the one thousands place to fix this.

Chapter Resources

Grade 4 11 Chapter 1

1-1 Place Value Through Hundred Thousands

GET READY to Learn

The average lead pencil can draw a line that is almost 184,800 feet (about 35 miles) long. Do you know the value of each digit in 184,800?

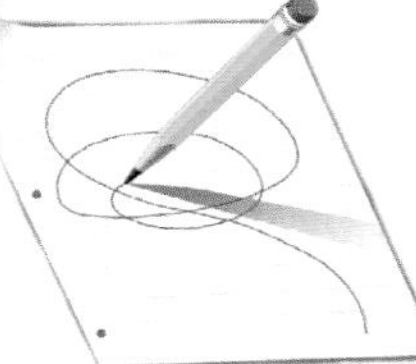

MAIN IDEA

I will read and write whole numbers to hundred thousands.

New Vocabulary

digit
place value
period
standard form
word form
expanded form

Math Online

macmillanmh.com
- Extra Examples
- Personal Tutor
- Self-Check Quiz

A **digit** is any of the symbols used to write numbers 0, 1, 2, 3, 4, 5, 6, 7, 8, 9. A **place-value** chart shows the value of the digits in a number. Each group of three digits is called a **period**. Each period is separated by a comma.

Period			Period		
Thousands			**Ones**		
hundreds	tens	ones	hundreds	tens	ones
1	8	4,	8	0	0

EXAMPLE Identify Value of Digits

1 **Write the value of the underlined digit in 18<u>4</u>,800.**

Step 1 Write the number in a place-value chart.

Thousands			**Ones**		
hundreds	tens	ones	hundreds	tens	ones
1	8	(4),	8	0	0

Step 2 Identify the column where the 4 is located. Circle it.

Step 3 Replace all the digits that are to the right of the 4 with zeros.

The underlined digit has a value of 4,000. This is because the 4 is in the thousands place.

Scaffolding Questions help focus and direct students' thinking and clarify the lesson concept.

1-1 Place Value Through Hundred Thousands

1 Introduce

Activity Choice 1 • Hands-On

- Use a spinner labeled 0–9. Spin to generate four random numbers. As a number is generated, ask students to write the digit in any column on a place-value chart through thousands.
- Ask students to write the number they created in as many ways as they know how. Tell them to use words and numbers.
- Repeat if time allows.

Activity Choice 2 • Literature

Introduce the lesson with *Earth Day—Hooray!* by Stuart J. Murphy. For a related math activity, see p. TR41.

2 Teach

Scaffolding Questions

Write the number 184,800 on a transparency of a place-value chart.

- **How many hundred thousands are there?** 1
- **How many ten thousands are there?** 8
- **How many thousands are there?** 4
- **How many hundreds are there?** 8
- **How many tens are there?** 0
- **How many ones are there?** 0
- **What is the value of each digit in the number 184,800?** 100,000; 80,000; 4,000; 800; 0; 0

GET READY to Learn

Have students open their books and read the paragraph under **Get Ready to Learn**. Introduce **digits**, **place value**, **period**, **standard form**, **word form**, and **expanded form**. As a class, work through **Examples 1–3**.

The Four-Step Teaching Plan shows you how to Introduce, Teach, Practice, and Assess each lesson. Each lesson ends with a creative strategy for closing the lesson.

Read and Write Numbers

Example 2 Remind students that when writing a number in word form, a comma is placed after the word *thousand*.

ADDITIONAL EXAMPLES

1. Write the value of the underlined digit in 26,513. 6,000
2. Write 86,012 in word form and expanded form. eighty-six thousand, twelve; 80,000 + 6,000 + 10 + 2
3. Write five thousand, four hundred six in standard form and expanded form. 5,406; 5,000 + 400 + 6

Additional Examples, which are included for every example in the Student Edition, exactly parallel the examples in the text. Step-by-step solutions for these examples are included in Interactive Classroom.

BL Alternate Teaching Strategy

If students have trouble writing different forms of a number...

Then use one of these reteach options:

1. CRM **Daily Reteach Worksheet** (p. 8)
2. Have them use place-value charts as a model until they are comfortable writing all forms. Show them how the expanded form of 184,800 fits into a place-value chart. Repeat with other numbers.

CHECK What You Know

As a class, have students complete Exercises 1–11 in **Check What You Know** as you observe their work.

Exercise 11 Assess student comprehension before assigning practice exercises.

COMMON ERROR!

Exercises 12–19 Students may write the word associated with the place rather than the value of the underlined digit. For example, in Exercise 12 students may write hundreds rather than the value of the number 800.

Standard form is the usual way to write a number using digits. **Word form** is the way you read or say a number. **Expanded form** shows the value of each digit.

Remember

Standard form, word form, and expanded form are types of place-value notation.

5. five thousand, seven hundred eighty-nine; 5,000 + 700 + 80 + 9
6. eighteen thousand, forty-six; 10,000 + 8,000 + 40 + 6
7. forty-nine thousand, nine hundred nine; 40,000 + 9,000 + 900 + 9
8. two hundred seventy thousand, six; 200,000 + 70,000 + 6

EXAMPLES Read and Write Numbers

2 **Write 628,371 in word form and expanded form.**

Thousands			Ones		
hundreds	tens	ones	hundreds	tens	ones
6	2	8	3	7	1

Word form: six hundred twenty-eight thousand, three hundred seventy-one

Expanded form: 600,000 + 20,000 + 8,000 + 300 + 70 + 1

3 **Write *one hundred five thousand, twenty-six* in standard form and expanded form.**

Standard form: 105,026

Expanded form: 100,000 + 5,000 + 20 + 6

CHECK What You Know

Write the value of the underlined digit. See Example 1 (p. 17)

1. 32,086 80
2. 78,387 300
3. 109,378 0 ten thousands
4. 590,320 500,000

Write each number in word form and expanded form. See Examples 2 and 3 (p. 18)

5. 5,789
6. 18,046
7. 49,909
8. 270,006
9. Write *one hundred thousand, two hundred fifty-six* in standard form and expanded form. See Examples 2 and 3 (p. 18) 100,256; 100,000 + 200 + 50 + 6
10. China has 555,200 fast food restaurants. Write 555,200 in word form. five hundred fifty-five thousand, two hundred
11. Talk About It: Do 800,600 and 860,000 represent the same values? Explain. no; The digits have different values.

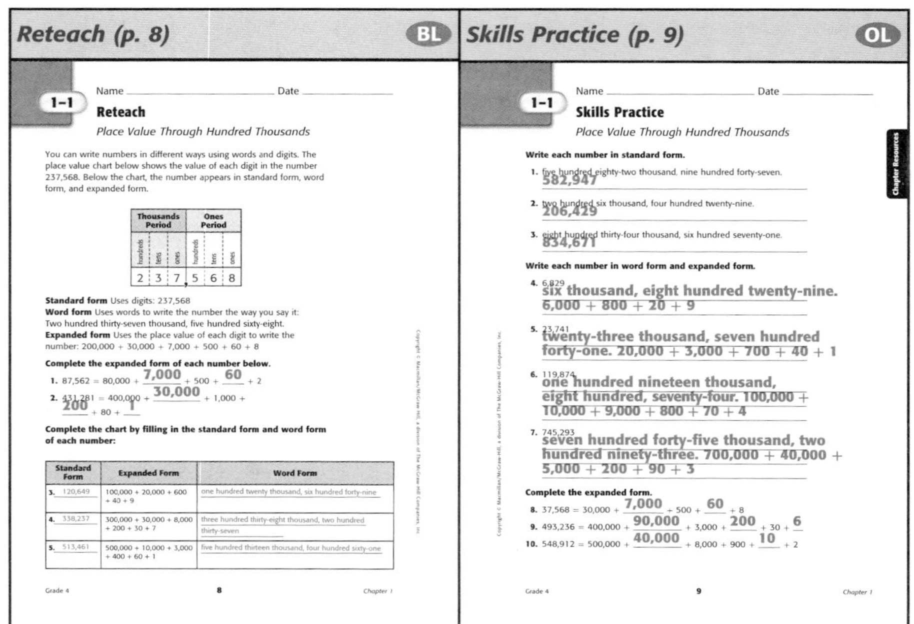

Reteach (p. 8) BL

1-1 Name ______ Date ______

Reteach

Place Value Through Hundred Thousands

You can write numbers in different ways using words and digits. The place value chart below shows the value of each digit in the number 237,568. Below the chart, the number appears in standard form, word form, and expanded form.

Thousands Period			Ones Period		
hundreds	tens	ones	hundreds	tens	ones
2	3	7	5	6	8

Standard form Uses digits: 237,568
Word form Uses words to write the number the way you say it: Two hundred thirty-seven thousand, five hundred sixty-eight.
Expanded form Uses the place value of each digit to write the number: 200,000 + 30,000 + 7,000 + 500 + 60 + 8

Complete the expanded form of each number below.

1. 87,562 = 80,000 + 7,000 + 500 + 60 + 2
2. 431,281 = 400,000 + 30,000 + 1,000 + 200 + 80 + 1

Complete the chart by filling in the standard form and word form of each number:

Standard Form	Expanded Form	Word Form
3. 120,649	100,000 + 20,000 + 600 + 40 + 9	one hundred twenty thousand, six hundred forty-nine
4. 338,237	300,000 + 30,000 + 8,000 + 200 + 30 + 7	three hundred thirty-eight thousand, two hundred thirty-seven
5. 513,461	500,000 + 10,000 + 3,000 + 400 + 60 + 1	five hundred thirteen thousand, four hundred sixty-one

Grade 4 8 Chapter 1

Skills Practice (p. 9) OL

1-1 Name ______ Date ______

Skills Practice

Place Value Through Hundred Thousands

Write each number in standard form.

1. five hundred eighty-two thousand, nine hundred forty-seven. 582,947
2. two hundred six thousand, four hundred twenty-nine. 206,429
3. eight hundred thirty-four thousand, six hundred seventy-one. 834,671

Write each number in word form and expanded form.

4. 6,829 six thousand, eight hundred twenty-nine. 6,000 + 800 + 20 + 9
5. 23,741 twenty-three thousand, seven hundred forty-one. 20,000 + 3,000 + 700 + 40 + 1
6. 119,874 one hundred nineteen thousand, eight hundred, seventy-four. 100,000 + 10,000 + 9,000 + 800 + 70 + 4
7. 745,293 seven hundred forty-five thousand, two hundred ninety-three. 700,000 + 40,000 + 5,000 + 200 + 90 + 3

Complete the expanded form.

8. 37,568 = 30,000 + 7,000 + 500 + 60 + 8
9. 493,236 = 400,000 + 90,000 + 3,000 + 200 + 30 + 6
10. 548,912 = 500,000 + 40,000 + 8,000 + 900 + 10 + 2

Grade 4 9 Chapter 1

Chapter Resources

Practice and Problem Solving

EXTRA PRACTICE See page R2.

Write the value of the underlined digit. See Example 1 (p. 17)

12. 59,833 800 **13.** 72,134 70,000 **14.** 93,743 40 **15.** 174,305 70,000

16. 593,802 0 tens **17.** 826,193 800,000 **18.** 830,259 9 **19.** 926,794 900,000

Write each number in word form and expanded form. See Examples 2 and 3 (p. 18)

20. 5,050 **21.** 3,791 **22.** 57,402 **23.** 89,074

24. 243,895 **25.** 485,830 **26.** 649,320 **27.** 784,132

20–27. See Ch. 1 Answer Appendix.

Write each number in standard form and expanded form. See Examples 2 and 3 (p. 18)

28. twenty-five thousand, four hundred eight 25,408; 20,000 + 5,000 + 400 + 8

29. forty thousand, eight hundred eleven 40,811; 40,000 + 800 + 10 + 1

30. seven hundred sixty-one thousand, three hundred fifty-six
761,356; 700,000 + 60,000 + 1,000 + 300 + 50 + 6

Write each number in word form and standard form. 31–33. Ch. 1 Answer Appendix.

31. 7,000 + 600 + 30 + 5 **32.** 20,000 + 900 + 70 + 6 **33.** 60,000 + 80 + 4

Real-World PROBLEM SOLVING

Science The photo shows an African elephant.

34. African elephants can weigh up to 14,432 pounds. What is the value of the underlined digit? 10,000

35. Write 14,432 in expanded form.

36. A zookeeper weighed a newborn African elephant. He was 232 pounds. After one year, the elephant had gained 1,000 pounds. Write the elephant's new weight in standard form and word form.

35. 10,000 + 4,000 + 400 + 30 + 2
36. 1,232; one thousand, two hundred thirty-two

H.O.T. Problems require students to use Higher Order Thinking skills to solve problems.

H.O.T. Problems

37. OPEN ENDED Write a six-digit number that has a 9 in the hundreds place and a 6 in the hundred thousands place. Sample answer: 654,931

38. WRITING IN ►MATH Explain how the value of the 4 in 694,213 will change if you move it to the tens place. The value will decrease.

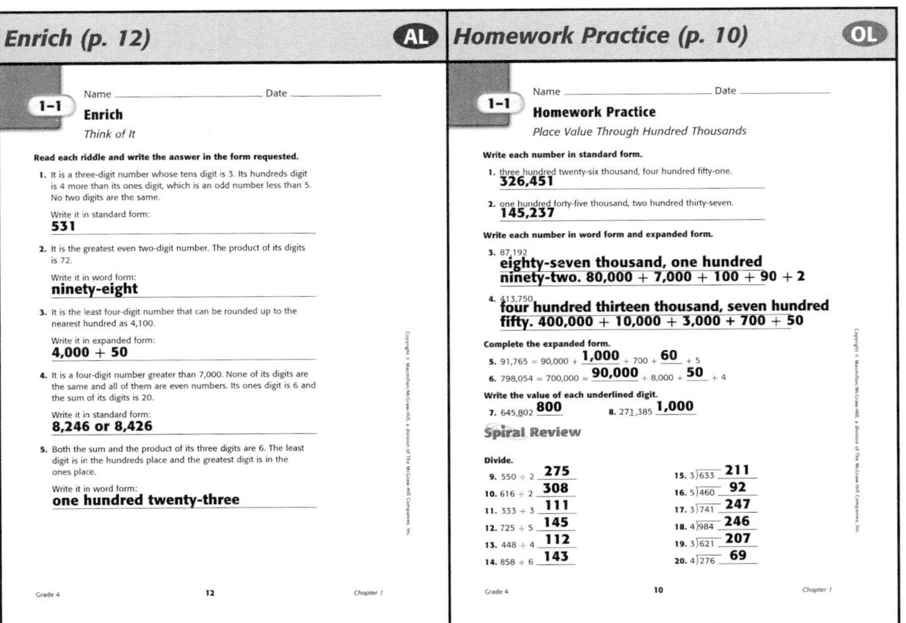

Enrich (p. 12) AL

1-1 Name ______ Date ______

Enrich

Think of It

Read each riddle and write the answer in the form requested.

1. It is a three-digit number whose tens digit is 3. Its hundreds digit is 4 more than its ones digit, which is an odd number less than 5. No two digits are the same.
Write it in standard form: **531**

2. It is the greatest even two-digit number. The product of its digits is 72.
Write it in word form: **ninety-eight**

3. It is the least four-digit number that can be rounded up to the nearest hundred as 4,100.
Write it in expanded form: **4,000 + 50**

4. It is a four-digit number greater than 7,000. None of its digits are the same and all of them are even numbers. Its ones digit is 6 and the sum of its digits is 20.
Write it in standard form: **8,246 or 8,426**

5. Both the sum and the product of its three digits are 6. The least digit is in the hundreds place and the greatest digit is in the ones place.
Write it in word form: **one hundred twenty-three**

Grade 4 12 Chapter 1

Homework Practice (p. 10) OL

1-1 Name ______ Date ______

Homework Practice

Place Value Through Hundred Thousands

Write each number in standard form.

1. three hundred twenty-six thousand, four hundred fifty-one. **326,451**
2. one hundred forty-five thousand, two hundred thirty-seven. **145,237**

Write each number in word form and expanded form.

3. 87,192 **eighty-seven thousand, one hundred ninety-two. 80,000 + 7,000 + 100 + 90 + 2**
4. 413,750 **four hundred thirteen thousand, seven hundred fifty. 400,000 + 10,000 + 3,000 + 700 + 50**

Complete the expanded form.

5. 91,765 = 90,000 + **1,000** + 700 + **60** + 5
6. 798,054 = 700,000 = **90,000** + 8,000 + **50** + 4

Write the value of each underlined digit.

7. 645,802 **800** 8. 271,385 **1,000**

Spiral Review

Divide.

9. 550 ÷ 2 **275**
10. 616 ÷ 2 **308**
11. 333 ÷ 3 **111**
12. 725 ÷ 5 **145**
13. 448 ÷ 4 **112**
14. 858 ÷ 6 **143**
15. 3)633 **211**
16. 5)460 **92**
17. 3)741 **247**
18. 4)984 **246**
19. 3)621 **207**
20. 4)276 **69**

Grade 4 10 Chapter 1

3 Practice

Differentiate practice using these leveled assignments for Exercises 12–38.

Level	Assignment
BL Below/Approaching Level	12–15, 20–23, 28–29, 32–33, 35–36
OL On Level	12–17, 21–26, 29–36, 38
AL Above/Beyond Level	13–35 odd, 37–38

Have students complete the Higher Order Thinking problems. Encourage students to use a place-value chart to answer the exercises.

WRITING IN ►MATH Have students complete Exercise 38 in their Math Journals. You may choose to use this exercise as an optional formative assessment.

4 Assess

Formative Assessment

Write the number 729,000 on the board.

- **What is the value of the 2?** 20,000
- **How will the value of the 2 change if you move it to the tens place?** Its value will change to 20.

Quick Check **Are students continuing to struggle with reading and writing whole numbers to hundred thousands?**

If Yes → Small Group Options (p. 17B)
Strategic Intervention Guide (p. 106)

If No → Independent Work Options (p. 17B)
CRM Skills Practice Worksheet (p. 9)
CRM Enrich Worksheet (p. 12)

Into the Future Write the number 5,256,901 on the board. Ask the students how they would show this number using a place-value chart. Possible answers would describe adding a millions column to the place-value chart.

Lesson Planner

Objective

Explore the concept of a million.

Resources

Materials: thousand cube sheet, scissors, tape

Teacher Technology

 macmillanmh.com

Concepts in Motion

1 Introduce

Introduce the Concept

- Before beginning this lesson, assess students' understanding of the size of 1,000,000 by asking questions such as the following:
- **Are there one million people who live on your street?**
- **Is it one million miles from your house to the White House in Washington, D.C.?**
- **How big do you think a million is? What might you count by millions?**
- Tell students that the activity in this lesson will help them understand the value of 1,000,000.

2 Teach

Activity Before students make their own thousand cube, you may want to cut one out and tape it together to show the students. It is often helpful for the students to see a completed cube so they know what they are making.

Walk through the steps of the activity as a class while the students construct their first cube. This will help things run smoothly.

Explore Math Activity for 1-2

How Big is One Million?

MAIN IDEA

I will explore the concept of a million.

You Will Need

thousand cube sheet
scissors
tape

Math Online
macmillanmh.com
• Concepts in Motion

You can use models to help understand the value of 1,000,000.

ACTIVITY **Model 1,000,000.**

Step 1 **Model 1,000.**

Cut out a thousand cube model. Fold the edges where the sides meet and form a cube. This shows 1,000.

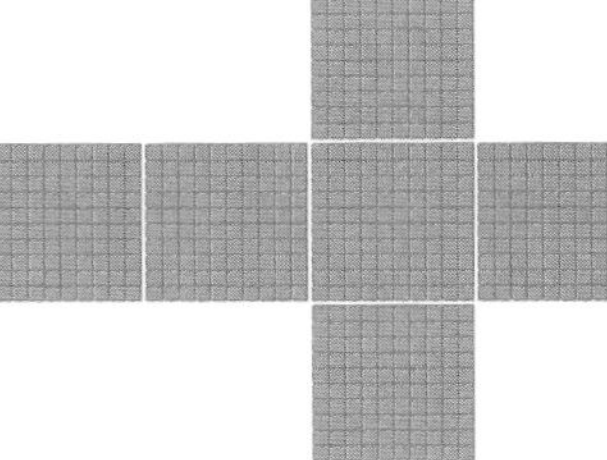

Step 2 **Model 10,000.**

Work with your classmates. Use 10 of the cubes to show 10,000.

Step 3 **Model 100,000.**

Make more cubes to build a model of 100,000.

Step 4 **Create 1,000,000.**

Suppose you were to build a model of 1,000,000. How many more 100,000 models would you need? (*Hint:* There are ten 100,000s in 1,000,000.)

Concepts in Motion are online animations of key concepts. They are also available on StudentWorks Plus and TeacherWorks Plus.

Explore and Extend activities use manipulatives and models to help students learn key concepts.

20 Chapter 1

Think About It

1. How did you build a model of 10,000? Sample answer: Stack ten 1,000s cubes.
2. Describe what your model of 1,000,000 looks like. Sample answer: Ten 100,000s cubes put together.
3. How are the models you built and drew like the models for ones, tens, and hundreds? 3, 4. See margin.
4. What number patterns did you see as you built and drew these models?

CHECK What You Know

Write the number shown by each model.

5. 7,000

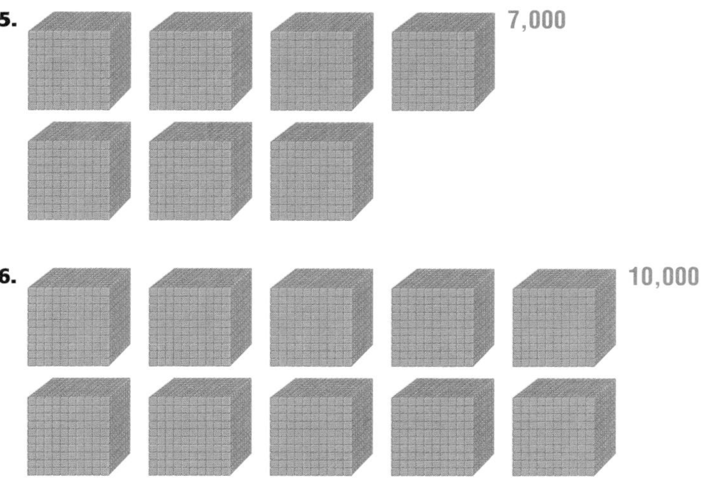

6. 10,000

7. The model at the right shows 1,000. How many tens are in 1,000? 100

8. How many thousands are in 1,000,000? 1,000
9. Explain how to determine how long it would take to count to one million. 9, 10. See margin.
10. WRITING IN MATH How many hundreds are there in 1,000,000? Explain your answer.

Every effort is made to show answers on the reduced Student Edition page, or in the margin of the Teacher Edition. Answers that do not fit in either of these places can be found in Answer Appendix pages at the end of each chapter.

Think About It

Assign Exercises 1–4 to assess student comprehension of the concept presented in the Activity.

3 Assess

Formative Assessment

Use Exercises 5–10 to assess whether students comprehend the concept of a million.

From Concrete to Abstract Use Exercise 8 to bridge the gap between building one million from thousand cubes and the concept of the number of thousands in one million.

Extending the Concept

- **Which is greater, 100,000 or 1,000,000?** 1,000,000

Additional Answers

3. Sample answer: The thousand cube resembles a unit cube, the ten-thousand rod resembles a tens rod, and the hundred thousand flat resembles a hundreds flat.
4. Sample answer: The thousand cube is 1,000 times greater than a unit cube. The ten-thousand rod is 1,000 times greater than a rod. The hundred thousand flat is 1,000 times greater than a hundreds flat.
9. Sample answer: Find out how long it takes to count to 100. Then use the place-value pattern above to estimate that it would take 10,000 times that to count to a million.
10. There are 10 hundreds in 1 thousand, 100 hundreds in 10 thousand, 1,000 hundreds in 100,000, and 10,000 hundreds in 1 million.

LESSON 1-2

Place Value Through Millions

Lesson Planner

Objective

Read and write whole numbers through the millions.

Review Vocabulary

place value, standard form, expanded form

Resources

Materials: transparency, WorkMat 4: Place-Value Chart

Manipulatives: stopwatch, counters

Literature Connection: *How Much is a Million?* by David Schwartz

Teacher Technology
TeacherWorks • Interactive Classroom • Math Songs Track #5 Lesson Plan

Daily Routine

Use these suggestions before beginning the lesson on p. 22.

5-Minute Check

(Reviews Lesson 1-1)

Write the value of the underlined digit.

1. 131,1<u>6</u>6 60
2. <u>7</u>2,015 70,000
3. <u>9</u>99,760 900,000
4. 6<u>2</u>,824 2,000

Problem of the Day

What do the numbers in List A have in common that the numbers in List B do not?
List A: 106; 800; 676; 440; 862; 594
List B: 23; 717; 8; 425; 1; 237; 40; 362
The numbers in List A are all 3-digit even numbers.

Focus on Math Background

The understanding of large numbers has become increasingly important as distances, amounts of money, and numbers of people are frequently expressed in millions. Just how big is a million? The Math Activity that precedes this lesson provides a way of helping students explore the size of 1,000,000. Moving from the thousands period to the millions period shows students how flexible our number system is. 1,000,000 has just 1 more digit than 100,000, but it is 10 times greater!

Focus on Math Background provides background information for each lesson. This information would be especially valuable to new teachers or those new to teaching mathematics.

Review Math Vocabulary

Write the review vocabulary words and their definitions on the board.

Take a few minutes to review each word with the students. It is important that they understand the definitions for this lesson.

Differentiated Instruction

Small Group Options

Option 1 INTRAPERSONAL, LINGUISTIC

Gifted and Talented AL

Materials: encyclopedia or almanac

Challenge students to find examples of millions and billions in an encyclopedia or almanac, and list the results in a chart.

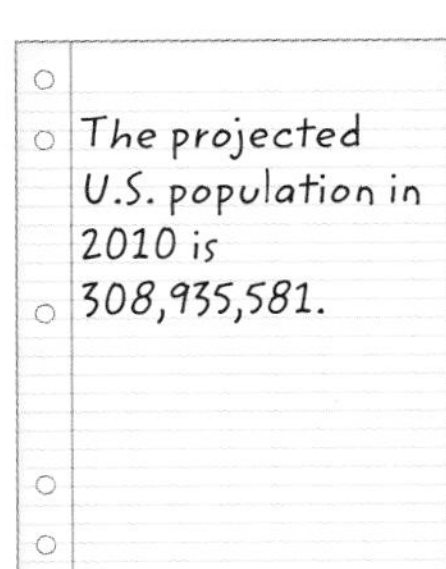

Option 2 LOGICAL

English Language Learners ELL

Materials: chalk, pictures of expensive items (homes, cars, stores, apartment buildings, etc.)

Core Vocabulary: how much, it, it's

Common Use Verb: is

Write Math This strategy uses background knowledge to deepen understanding of value and allows practice writing and reading large numbers.

- Post a picture and label it with a price tag in the thousands or more as appropriate.
- Say, "**How much is a ____ (name of the item)?**"
- Post the price tag. Write and say: **"It's** ____ (dollar amount)."
- Display the other pictures.
- Have students draw an item and write the price they think it is worth underneath.
- Model reading their price in the scaffold and encourage students to repeat.
- Repeat as time permits.

Use this worksheet to provide additional support for English Language Learners.

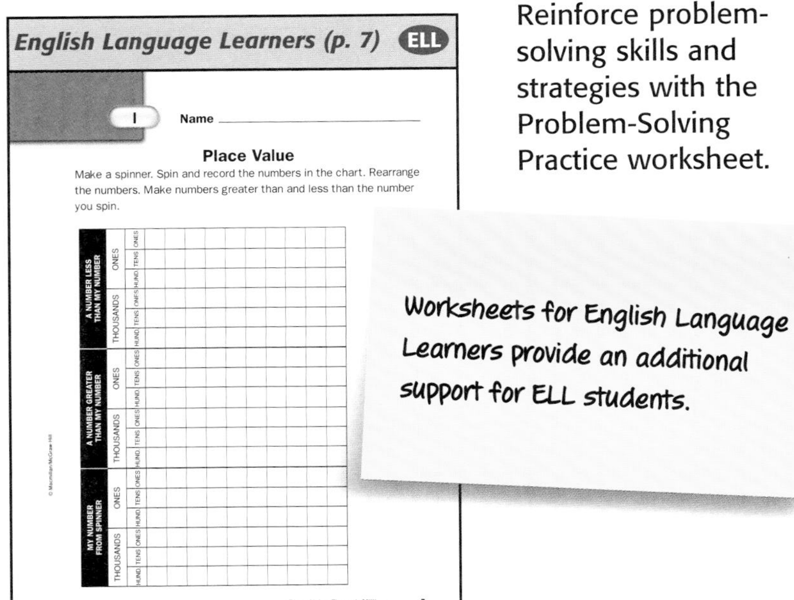

English Language Learners (p. 7) ELL

1 Name ____________

Place Value

Make a spinner. Spin and record the numbers in the chart. Rearrange the numbers. Make numbers greater than and less than the number you spin.

MY NUMBER FROM SPINNER	THOUSANDS	HUND.
		TENS
		ONES
	ONES	HUND.
		TENS
		ONES
A NUMBER GREATER THAN MY NUMBER	THOUSANDS	HUND.
		TENS
		ONES
	ONES	HUND.
		TENS
		ONES
A NUMBER LESS THAN MY NUMBER	THOUSANDS	HUND.
		TENS
		ONES
	ONES	HUND.
		TENS
		ONES

© Macmillan/McGraw-Hill

Place Value Through Millions 7

Worksheets for English Language Learners provide an additional support for ELL students.

Independent Work Options

Option 1 LOGICAL, SOCIAL

Early Finishers AL

Materials: paper and pencil

- Display this riddle for pairs of students to solve:

> I am a 7-digit number. The sum off my digits is 27. The value of my thousands digit is 5,000 and the value of my hundreds digit is 700. My hundred-thousands digit is 2 less than my thousands digit and 3 less than my millions digit. My ones digit is 3 less than my hundreds digit and 2 more than my tens digit. Who am I? 6,305,724

Option 2

Student Technology

Math Online macmillanmh.com

Personal Tutor • Extra Examples

Option 3

Learning Station: Art (p. 14G)

Direct students to the Art Learning Station for opportunities to explore and extend the lesson concept.

Option 4

Problem-Solving Practice

Reinforce problem-solving skills and strategies with the Problem-Solving Practice worksheet.

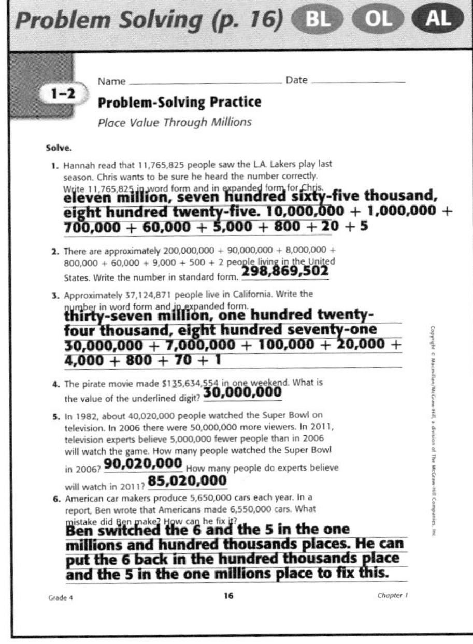

Problem Solving (p. 16) BL OL AL

1–2 Name ____________ Date ____________

Problem-Solving Practice

Place Value Through Millions

Solve.

1. Hannah read that 11,765,825 people saw the L.A. Lakers play last season. Chris wants to be sure he heard the number correctly. Write 11,765,825 in word form and in expanded form for Chris. **eleven million, seven hundred sixty-five thousand, eight hundred twenty-five. 10,000,000 + 1,000,000 + 700,000 + 60,000 + 5,000 + 800 + 20 + 5**
2. There are approximately 200,000,000 + 90,000,000 + 8,000,000 + 800,000 + 60,000 + 9,000 + 500 + 2 people living in the United States. Write the number in standard form. **298,869,502**
3. Approximately 37,124,871 people live in California. Write the number in word form and in expanded form. **thirty-seven million, one hundred twenty-four thousand, eight hundred seventy-one 30,000,000 + 7,000,000 + 100,000 + 20,000 + 4,000 + 800 + 70 + 1**
4. The pirate movie made $135,634,554 in one weekend. What is the value of the underlined digit? **30,000,000**
5. In 1982, about 40,020,000 people watched the Super Bowl on television. In 2006 there were 50,000,000 more viewers. In 2011, television experts believe 5,000,000 fewer people than in 2006 will watch the game. How many people watched the Super Bowl in 2006? **90,020,000** How many people do experts believe will watch in 2011? **85,020,000**
6. American car makers produce 5,650,000 cars each year. In a report, Ben wrote that Americans made 6,550,000 cars. What mistake did Ben make? How can he fix it? **Ben switched the 6 and the 5 in the one millions and hundred thousands places. He can put the 6 back in the hundred thousands place and the 5 in the one millions place to fix this.**

Grade 4 16 Chapter 1

Place Value Through Millions

1 Introduce

Activity Choice 1 • Hands-On 

- Ask students to count to 100. Use a stopwatch to time how long it takes them. Use that information to answer these questions:
- **How long would it take to count to 1,000?** multiply their time by 10
- **How long would it take to count to 100,000?** multiply their time by 1,000
- **How long would it take to count to 1,000,000?** multiply their time by 10,000
- You may have to do the multiplication for the students. This activity is to help students understand the value of a million.

Activity Choice 2 • Literature

Introduce the lesson with *How Much is a Million?* by David Schwartz. For a related math activity, see p. TR41.

2 Teach

Scaffolding Questions

Display the following information:

City Populations	
Chicago, IL	2,842,518
Jacksonville, FL	782,623
New York, NY	12,831,970

Source: U.S. Census Bureau

- **What is the population of Jacksonville, FL?** 782,623
- **What is the population of Chicago, IL?** 2,842,518
- **What is the population of New York, NY?** 12,831,970
- **Which city has the largest population?** New York, NY

GET READY to Learn

Have students open their books and read the information in **Get Ready to Learn**. Review **place value, standard form** and **expanded form**. As a class, work through **Examples 1 and 2**.

Examples illustrate all of the concepts taught in the lesson and closely mirror the exercises in the exercise sets.

1-2 Place Value Through Millions

MAIN IDEA

I will read and write whole numbers through the millions.

Math Online

macmillanmh.com

- Extra Examples
- Personal Tutor
- Self-Check Quiz

GET READY to Learn

Baseball is one of America's favorite sports. The graph shows how many fans attended games for three teams during recent years. The attendance numbers are in the millions.

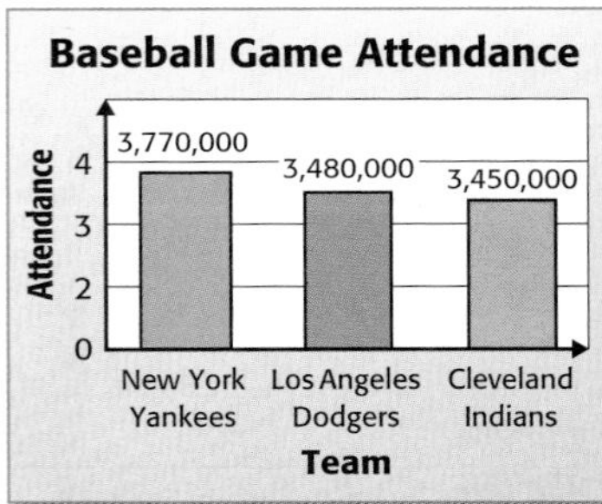

Source: *Scholastic Book of World Records*

A place-value chart can be used to read and write numbers in the millions. The place-value chart below shows the value of each digit in 3,770,000, the attendance at the New York Yankees baseball games.

Period: Millions			Period: Thousands			Period: Ones		
		ones	hundreds	tens	ones	hundreds	tens	ones
		3	7	7	0	0	0	0

Read and Write Numbers

1 **SCIENCE The human eye blinks an average of 5,500,000 times a year. Write 5,500,000 in three ways.**

Standard form: 5,500,000

Word form: five million, five hundred thousand

Expanded form: 5,000,000 + 500,000

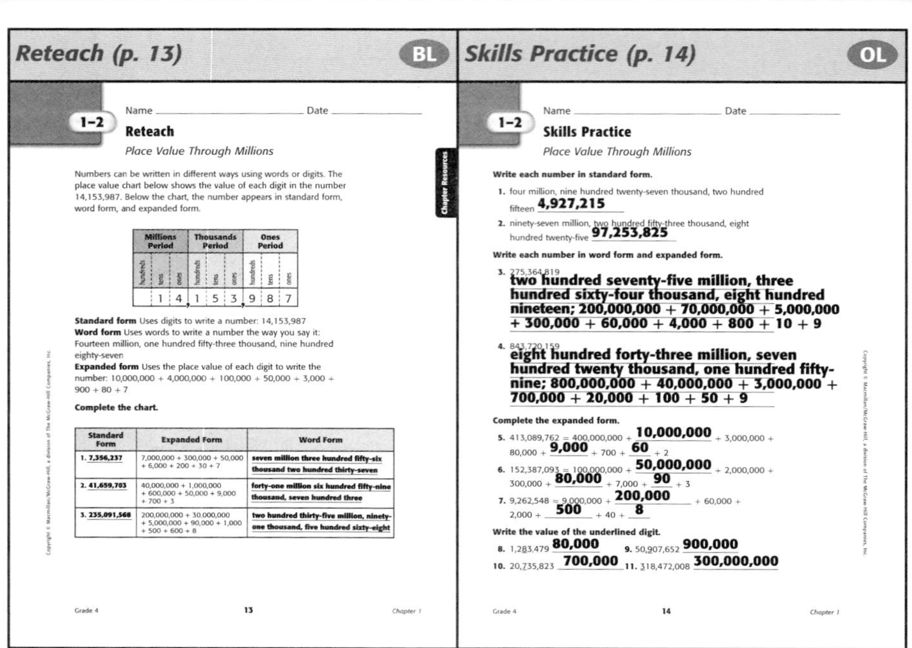

Reteach (p. 13) BL

1-2 Name ______ Date ______

Reteach

Place Value Through Millions

Numbers can be written in different ways using words or digits. The place value chart below shows the value of each digit in the number 14,153,987. Below the chart, the number appears in standard form, word form, and expanded form.

Millions Period			Thousands Period			Ones Period		
hundreds	tens	ones	hundreds	tens	ones	hundreds	tens	ones
	1	4	1	5	3	9	8	7

Standard form Uses digits to write a number: 14,153,987
Word form Uses words to write a number the way you say it: Fourteen million, one hundred fifty-three thousand, nine hundred eighty-seven
Expanded form Uses the place value of each digit to write the number: 10,000,000 + 4,000,000 + 100,000 + 50,000 + 3,000 + 900 + 80 + 7

Complete the chart.

Standard Form	Expanded Form	Word Form
1. **7,356,237**	7,000,000 + 300,000 + 50,000 + 6,000 + 200 + 30 + 7	**seven million three hundred fifty-six thousand two hundred thirty-seven**
2. **41,659,703**	40,000,000 + 1,000,000 + 600,000 + 50,000 + 9,000 + 700 + 3	**forty-one million six hundred fifty-nine thousand, seven hundred three**
3. **235,091,568**	200,000,000 + 30,000,000 + 5,000,000 + 90,000 + 1,000 + 500 + 600 + 8	**two hundred thirty-five million, ninety-one thousand, five hundred sixty-eight**

Grade 4 13 Chapter 1

Skills Practice (p. 14) OL

1-2 Name ______ Date ______

Skills Practice

Place Value Through Millions

Write each number in standard form.

1. four million, nine hundred twenty-seven thousand, two hundred fifteen **4,927,215**
2. ninety-seven million, two hundred fifty-three thousand, eight hundred twenty-five **97,253,825**

Write each number in word form and expanded form.

3. 275,364,819 **two hundred seventy-five million, three hundred sixty-four thousand, eight hundred nineteen; 200,000,000 + 70,000,000 + 5,000,000 + 300,000 + 60,000 + 4,000 + 800 + 10 + 9**
4. 843,720,159 **eight hundred forty-three million, seven hundred twenty thousand, one hundred fifty-nine; 800,000,000 + 40,000,000 + 3,000,000 + 700,000 + 20,000 + 100 + 50 + 9**

Complete the expanded form.

5. 413,089,762 = 400,000,000 + **10,000,000** + 3,000,000 + 80,000 + **9,000** + 700 + **60** + 2
6. 152,387,093 = 100,000,000 + **50,000,000** + 2,000,000 + 300,000 + **80,000** + 7,000 + **90** + 3
7. 9,262,548 = 9,000,000 + **200,000** + 60,000 + 2,000 + **500** + 40 + **8**

Write the value of the underlined digit.

8. 1,283,479 **80,000**
9. 50,907,652 **900,000**
10. 20,735,823 **700,000**
11. 318,472,008 **300,000,000**

Grade 4 14 Chapter 1

Real-World EXAMPLE Read and Write Numbers

2 **CARS** **United States citizens own *one hundred thirty-five million, seven hundred thousand* cars. Write this number in standard form and expanded form.**

5. two thousand seven; 2,000 + 7
6. forty-three thousand, nine hundred eighty; 40,000 + 3,000 + 900 + 80
7. three hundred two thousand, eight hundred six; 300,000 + 2,000 + 800 + 6
8. thirty-eight million, eight hundred seventy-five; 30,000,000 + 8,000,000 + 800 + 70 + 5

One hundred thirty-five million, seven hundred thousand is written in the place-value chart below.

Millions			Thousands			Ones		
hundreds	tens	ones	hundreds	tens	ones	hundreds	tens	ones
1	3	5	7	0	0	0	0	0

Standard form: 135,700,000

Expanded form: 100,000,000 + 30,000,000 + 5,000,000 + 700,000

CHECK What You Know

Write the value of the underlined digit. See Examples 1 and 2 (pp. 22–23)

1. 469,999 90 **2.** 1,040,710 1,000,000 **3.** 35,098,098 90,000 **4.** 83,023,215 80,000,000

Write each number in word form and expanded form. See Example 1 (p. 22)

5. 2,007 **6.** 43,980 **7.** 302,806 **8.** 38,000,875

Write each number in standard form and expanded form. See Example 2 (p. 23)

9. nine hundred thousand, five hundred fifty-two 900,552; 900,000 + 500 + 50 + 2

10. two hundred forty-six million, nine hundred thousand, eighteen 246,900,018; 200,000,000 + 40,000,000 + 6,000,000 + 900,000 + 10 + 8

11. On Sunday, 2,617,000 newspapers were sold. Write the number of newspapers sold in word form and expanded form.

12. Talk About It Explain how to find the value of the underlined digit in the number 26,057,928.

11, 12. See Ch. 1 Answer Appendix.

Web addresses, or URLs, are provided to point students to online assets such as Personal Tutor, Extra Examples, and Self-Check Quizzes.

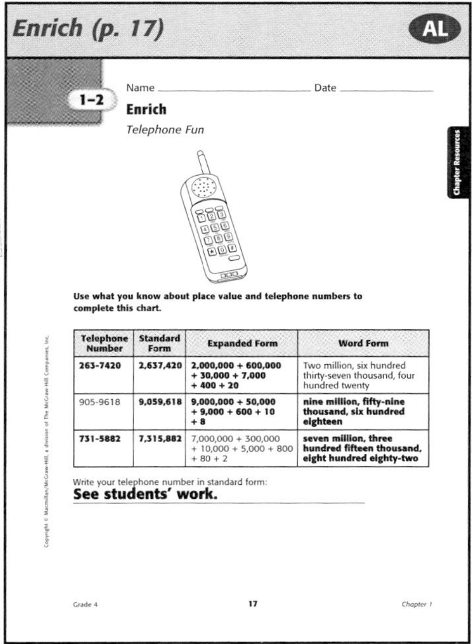

Enrich (p. 17) AL

Name ______ Date ______

1–2 **Enrich**

Telephone Fun

Use what you know about place value and telephone numbers to complete this chart.

Telephone Number	Standard Form	Expanded Form	Word Form
263-7420	2,637,420	2,000,000 + 600,000 + 30,000 + 7,000 + 400 + 20	Two million, six hundred thirty-seven thousand, four hundred twenty
905-9618	9,059,618	9,000,000 + 50,000 + 9,000 + 600 + 10 + 8	nine million, fifty-nine thousand, six hundred eighteen
731-5882	7,315,882	7,000,000 + 300,000 + 10,000 + 5,000 + 800 + 80 + 2	seven million, three hundred fifteen thousand, eight hundred eighty-two

Write your telephone number in standard form:
See students' work.

Grade 4 17 Chapter 1

Read and Write Numbers

Example 1 Point out that a comma appears after the word *million* in the word form of 5,500,000 but not after the word *thousand* since there are no hundreds, tens, or ones in the number.

ADDITIONAL EXAMPLES

1 The students at Harvey Elementary School have saved 3,100,750 pennies. Write 3,100,750 in standard form, word form and expanded form. 3,100,750; three million, one hundred thousand, seven hundred fifty; 3,000,000 + 100,000 + 700 + 50

2 The total area of China is three million, seven hundred five thousand, four hundred seven square miles. Write this number in standard form. 3,705,407

CHECK What You Know

As a class, have students complete Exercises 1–12 in **Check What You Know** as you observe their work.

Exercise 12 Assess student comprehension before assigning practice exercises.

BL Alternate Teaching Strategy

If students have trouble writing the expanded form for numbers with zeros correctly…

Then use one of these reteach options:

1 CRM **Daily Reteach Worksheet** (p. 13)

2 Have students place 0 through 9 counters in each column on the place-value chart. Ask students to read the number and write the number in expanded form, word form, and standard form.

Write two or three 7-digit numbers on the board. Have pairs work together to use the counters to show the numbers on the place-value chart.

When they have represented a number correctly, have students write the number in expanded form, word form, and standard form.

3 Practice

Differentiate practice using these leveled assignments for Exercises 13–42.

Level	Assignment
BL Below/Approaching Level	13–16, 21–24, 29–30, 33–38
OL On Level	13–18, 21–24, 27–32, 34–38, 40–41
AL Above/Beyond Level	14–38 even, 39–42

Have students discuss and complete the Higher Order Thinking problems. Encourage them to use a place-value chart to find their answers.

WRITING IN MATH Have students complete Exercise 42 in their Math Journals. You may choose to use this exercise as an optional formative assessment.

Additional Answers

21. twenty-nine thousand, two hundred five; 20,000 + 9,000 + 200 + 5

22. eighty-two thousand, nine; 80,000 + 2,000 + 9

23. nine hundred one thousand, four hundred fifty-two; 900,000 + 1,000 + 400 + 50 + 2

24. two hundred thousand, thirteen; 200,000 + 10 + 3

25. thirty million, eight hundred forty-two thousand, eighty-five; 30,000,000 + 800,000 + 40,000 + 2,000 + 80 + 5

26. sixty-three million, nine hundred thirty thousand, fifty-three; 60,000,000 + 3,000,000 + 900,000 + 30,000 + 50 + 3

27. three hundred nineteen million, nine hundred ninety-nine thousand, nine hundred ninety; 300,000,000 + 10,000,000 + 9,000,000 + 900,000 + 90,000 + 9,000 + 900 + 90

28. eight hundred million, four hundred ninety-three thousand, three hundred one; 800,000,000 + 400,000 + 90,000 + 3,000 + 300 + 1

COMMON ERROR!

Students often use the word "and" when writing a number in word form. Point out that the word "and" is used only when writing the word form of a number with a decimal point.

Practice and Problem Solving

EXTRA PRACTICE See page R2.

Write the value of the underlined digit. See Examples 1 and 2 (pp. 22–23)

13. 132,685 600
14. 309,573 300,000
15. 309,841 9,000
16. 7,824,015 10
17. 40,245,854 40,000
18. 68,210,397 60,000,000
19. 73,581,209 200
20. 97,530,284 7,000,000

Write each number in word form and expanded form. See Example 1 (p. 22)

21. 29,205
22. 82,009
23. 901,452
24. 200,013
25. 30,842,085
26. 63,930,053
27. 319,999,990
28. 800,493,301

21–28. See margin.

Write each number in standard form and expanded form. See Example 2 (p. 23)

29. two hundred thirty-eight thousand, three hundred seventy 238,370; 200,000 + 30,000 + 8,000 + 300 + 70

30. four million, ninety-four thousand, two hundred fifteen 4,094,215; 4,000,000 + 90,000 + 4,000 + 200 + 10 + 5

31. eighty three million, twenty-three thousand, seven 83,023,007; 80,000,000 + 3,000,000 + 20,000 + 3,000 + 7

32. three hundred four million, eight hundred thousand, four hundred 304,800,400; 300,000,000 + 4,000,000 + 800,000 + 400

Write each number in word form and standard form.

33. 200,000 + 60,000 + 3,000 + 200 + 70 + 3 two hundred sixty-three thousand, two hundred seventy-three; 263,273

34. 1,000,000 + 900,000 + 50,000 + 6,000 + 200 + 20 + 5 one million, nine hundred fifty-six thousand, two hundred twenty-five; 1,956,225

35. As of 2005, the population of Philadelphia was 1,463,281. Write Philadelphia's population in word form. one million, four hundred sixty-three thousand, two hundred eighty-one

36. Measurement The land area for Florida is 100,000 + 30,000 + 9,000 + 800 + 50 + 2 square kilometers. Write the area in word form. See margin.

Real-World PROBLEM SOLVING

Planets The Sun and Earth are shown. 37, 38. See margin.

37. The distance from Earth to the Sun is 92,955,793 miles. Write this number in word form and expanded form.

38. The amount of time that American astronauts have spent in space is about 13,507,804 minutes. Is this number read as *thirteen million, fifty-seven thousand, eight hundred four*? Explain.

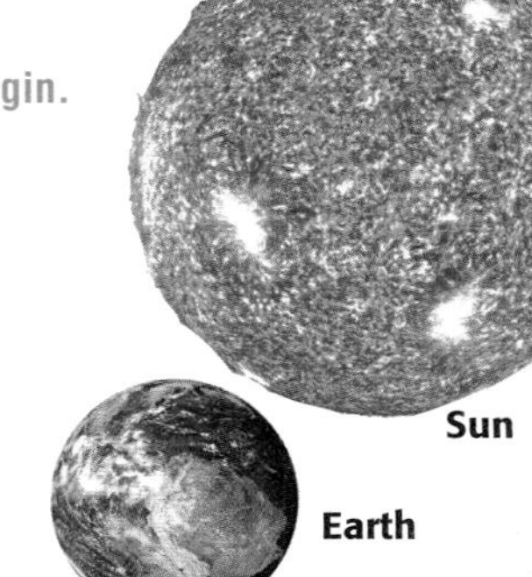

Additional Answers

36. one hundred thirty-nine thousand, eight hundred fifty-two

37. ninety-two million, nine hundred fifty-five thousand, seven hundred ninety-three; 90,000,000 + 2,000,000 + 900,000 + 50,000 + 5,000 + 700 + 90 + 3

38. No. The correct way to read this number is thirteen million, five hundred seven thousand, eight hundred four.

H.O.T. Problems

39. OPEN ENDED Write an eight-digit number that has a 7 in the ten millions place and a number in the thousands place with a value of 2,000. Sample answer: 76,312,000

40. CHALLENGE Write the number with the smallest value using the digits 1 through 9. Use each digit only once. 123,456,789

41. NUMBER SENSE Is the following statement *true* or *false*? Explain your answer. See margin.

1,000 thousands = 1,000,000

42. WRITING IN ▸MATH Explain how you know what number is missing in 3,947 = 3,000 + ■ + 40 + 7. 3,947 has a 9 in the hundreds place; therefore, you know the missing digit has a value of 900.

TEST Practice

43. Which number below is the word form of 57,302? (Lesson 1-1) C

A five thousand, three hundred two

B fifty-seven thousand, three hundred twenty

C fifty-seven thousand, three hundred two

D five hundred thousand, three hundred two

44. Yosemite National Park hosts three million, three hundred seventy thousand visitors each year. What is this number in standard form? (Lesson 1-2) G

F 3,307,000

G 3,370,000

H 30,307,000

J 30,370,000

Test Practice exercises help students solidify their knowledge of multiple-choice format.

Spiral Review

Write each number in standard form and expanded form. (Lesson 1-2)

45. three thousand five 3,000 + 5; 3,005

46. four million, six hundred thirty-seven thousand, five hundred four 4,000,000 + 600,000 + 30,000 + 7,000 + 500 + 4; 4,637,504

47. seventeen million, twenty thousand, four hundred fifty-eight 10,000,000 + 7,000,000 + 20,000 + 400 + 50 + 8; 17,020,458

Write the value of the underlined digit. (Lesson 1-1)

48. 10,4̲98 400 **49.** 12,004̲ 4 **50.** 3̲0,182 30,000

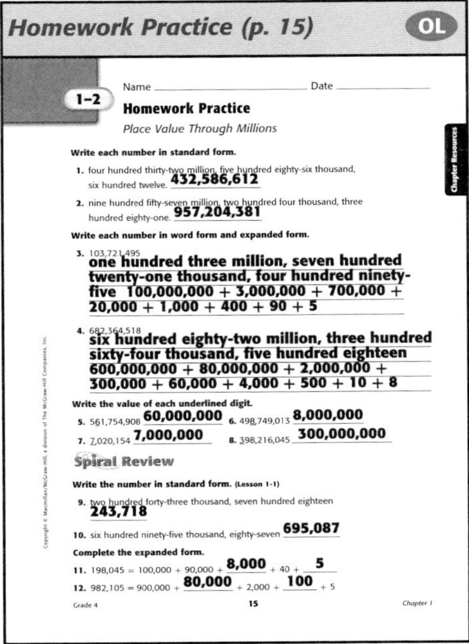

Homework Practice (p. 15) OL

1-2 Name ______ Date ______

Homework Practice

Place Value Through Millions

Write each number in standard form.

1. four hundred thirty-two million, five hundred eighty-six thousand, six hundred twelve. **432,586,612**
2. nine hundred fifty-seven million, two hundred four thousand, three hundred eighty-one. **957,204,381**

Write each number in word form and expanded form.

3. 103,721,495 **one hundred three million, seven hundred twenty-one thousand, four hundred ninety-five 100,000,000 + 3,000,000 + 700,000 + 20,000 + 1,000 + 400 + 90 + 5**
4. 682,364,518 **six hundred eighty-two million, three hundred sixty-four thousand, five hundred eighteen 600,000,000 + 80,000,000 + 2,000,000 + 300,000 + 60,000 + 4,000 + 500 + 10 + 8**

Write the value of each underlined digit.

5. 56̲1,754,908 **60,000,000** 6. 498̲,749,013 **8,000,000**
7. 7̲,020,154 **7,000,000** 8. 3̲98,216,045 **300,000,000**

Spiral Review

Write the number in standard form. (Lesson 1-1)

9. two hundred forty-three thousand, seven hundred eighteen **243,718**
10. six hundred ninety-five thousand, eighty-seven **695,087**

Complete the expanded form.

11. 198,045 = 100,000 + 90,000 + **8,000** + 40 + **5**
12. 982,105 = 900,000 + **80,000** + 2,000 + **100** + 5

Grade 4 15 Chapter 1

Chapter Resources

4 Assess

Formative Assessment

- **How many different ways can you write a number? Explain and give an example of each way.** Sample answer: 3 ways; standard form, use digits to write the number; word form, use words to write the number; and expanded form, write the number showing the value of each digit.

Quick Check **Are students continuing to struggle with reading and writing whole numbers through the millions?**

If Yes → Strategic Intervention Guide (p. 108)

If No → Independent Work Options (p. 22B)
CRM Skills Practice Worksheet (p. 14)
CRM Enrich Worksheet (p. 17)

Yesterday's News Write a few sentences about how yesterday's concepts helped you with today's new material.

TEST Practice

Reviews Lessons 1-1 and 1-2

Assign the Test Practice problems to provide daily reinforcement of test-taking skills.

Spiral Review

Reviews Lesson 1-1 and 1-2

Review and assess mastery of skills and concepts from previous chapters.

Additional Answer

41. Sample answer: true; 10 thousands = 10,000; 100 thousands = 100,000; so 1,000 thousands = 1,000,000

1-3 Problem-Solving Strategy
The Four-Step Plan

Problem-Solving Strategy and Problem-Solving Investigation lessons help students learn different problem-solving skills and strategies for solving word problems.

Lesson Planner

Objective

Solve problems using the four-step plan.

Resources

Materials: index cards

Literature Connection: *Counting Jennie* by Helena Clare Pittman

Teacher Technology
TeacherWorks • Interactive Classroom

Real-World Problem Solving Library
Math and Social Studies: *Rivers and Mountains of the United States*
Use these leveled books to reinforce and extend problem-solving skills and strategies.

Leveled for:
- OL On Level
- ELL Sheltered English
- SP Spanish

For additional support, see the Real-World Problem Solving Teacher Guide.

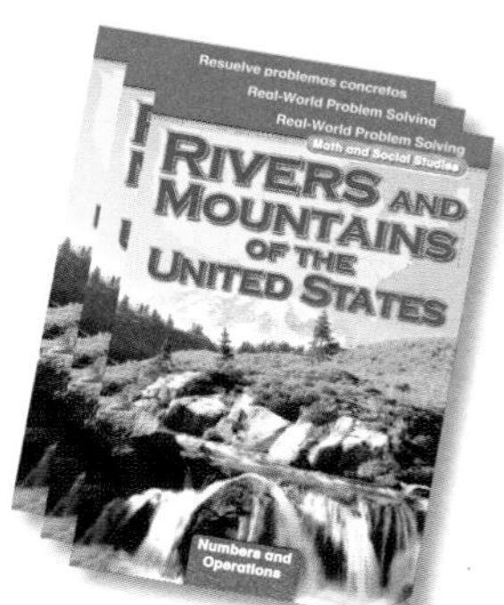

Daily Routine

Use these suggestions before beginning the lesson on p. 26.

5-Minute Check

(Reviews Lesson 1-2)

Write each number two different ways.

1. 5,376 five thousand three hundred seventy-six; 5,000 + 300 + 70 + 6
2. twenty-five thousand, seven hundred eighty-nine 25,789; 20,000 + 5,000 + 700 + 80 + 9
3. 200,000 + 30,000 + 1 230,001; two hundred thirty thousand, one
4. 765,149,372 seven hundred sixty-five million, one hundred forty-nine thousand, three hundred seventy-two; 700,000,000 + 60,000,000 + 5,000,000 + 100,000 + 40,000 + 9,000 + 300 + 70 + 2

Problem of the Day

Calid gets a weekly allowance of $5. He spends $2 on a snack and $1 on baseball cards. How much money does he have left? Calid spent $3; $5 – $3 = $2

The Real-World Problem Solving Readers, which include fiction and non-fiction leveled readers, extend problem-solving skills and strategies and make real-world connections.

Differentiated Instruction

Small Group Options

Option 1 Gifted and Talented AL

LOGICAL

Materials: paper and pencil

- Pose the following problem:

Tim wants to invite 5 boys to go with him to a baseball game. Tickets for the boys are $9 each. Tim's dad and another boy's dad will go with them. Adult tickets will each cost $4 extra. If they budget $100 for the outing, how much will be left for food at the ball park? $20

Tim + 5 boys = 6 × $9 = $54
Tim's dad + dad = 2 × ($9 + $4) = $26
Total = $80
$100 − $80 = $20 for food

Option 2 English Language Learners 

LINGUISTIC, VISUAL

Materials: four pictures of party-planning stages
Core Vocabulary: first, next, last
Common Use Verb: comes

Talk Math This strategy helps students use the vocabulary of ordering to help students understand using the four-step plan.

- Say: "We want to have a party." Show four pictures of the planning steps. Say: "This comes first ... comes next ... then ... comes last."
- Have students chorally repeat.
- Allow groups to order and say their order, explaining why. If necessary, restate student language.
- Continue using this sequence with the math four-step plan, having students draw four pictures illustrating an event. Allow students to share their event sequence with each other or with the group.

Independent Work Options

Option 1 Early Finishers OL AL

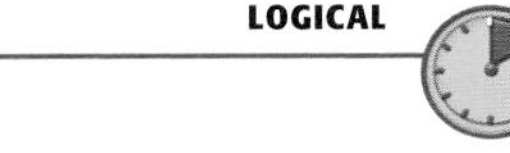

LOGICAL

Materials: paper and pencil

- Have students write a real-world problem that can be solved using the four-step plan learned in this lesson. They can then exchange their problem with a partner and solve their partner's problem.

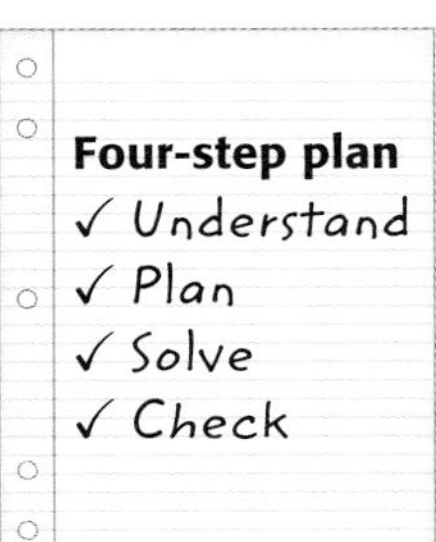

Option 2 Student Technology

Math Online macmillanmh.com

Personal Tutor • Extra Examples

Option 3 Learning Stations: Music (p. 14G)

Direct students to the Music Learning Station for opportunities to explore and extend the lesson concept.

1-3 Problem-Solving Strategy

1 Introduce

Activity Choice 1 • Review

- Write the following problem on the board:

  A roller coaster has 8 cars. Each car has 4 wheels. How many wheels are there in all on 2 roller coasters? 64 wheels

- Ask students to think about the problem-solving strategies they used last year.
- **Which strategy would you use to solve this problem?** *draw a picture*

Activity Choice 2 • Literature

Introduce the lesson with *Counting Jennie* by Helena Clare Pittman. For a related math activity, see p. TR41.

2 Teach

Have students read the problem on amusement parks. Guide them through the problem-solving steps.

Understand Using the questions, review what students know and need to find.

Plan Have students discuss their strategy.

Solve Guide students to use the four-step problem-solving plan to solve the problem.

- **How many scouts are in the troop?** 6 scouts
- **How much is the admission cost for one child?** $12
- **What operation would you use to find the total cost?** multiplication

Check Have students look back at the problem to make sure that the answer fits the facts given.

COMMON ERROR!

Exercise 5 Students may fail to see that this exercise is a multi-step problem. They may just compare 55 to 12 and determine that team 1 answered the most questions correctly. Remind them to read the question carefully.

1-3 Problem-Solving Skill

MAIN IDEA I will solve problems using a four-step plan.

There are six girls in Dina's scout troop. They are planning a trip to the local amusement park. Admission for children is $12. What is the total cost of admission for everyone to go?

Understand	**What facts do you know?** • There are six scouts who want to go. • The price of admission is $12 for each girl. **What do you need to find?** • The total cost of admission for all the girls.
Plan	To find the total cost, you can use addition. There are 6 girls, and it will cost $12 each. So, add 12 six times.
Solve	$12 + $12 + $12 + $12 + $12 + $12 = $72 or 6 × $12 = $72 So, the troop needs $72 to go to the amusement park.
Check	Look back. One way to check the answer is to use a drawing. $12 6 There are 6 × 12 or 72 squares, so the answer is correct.

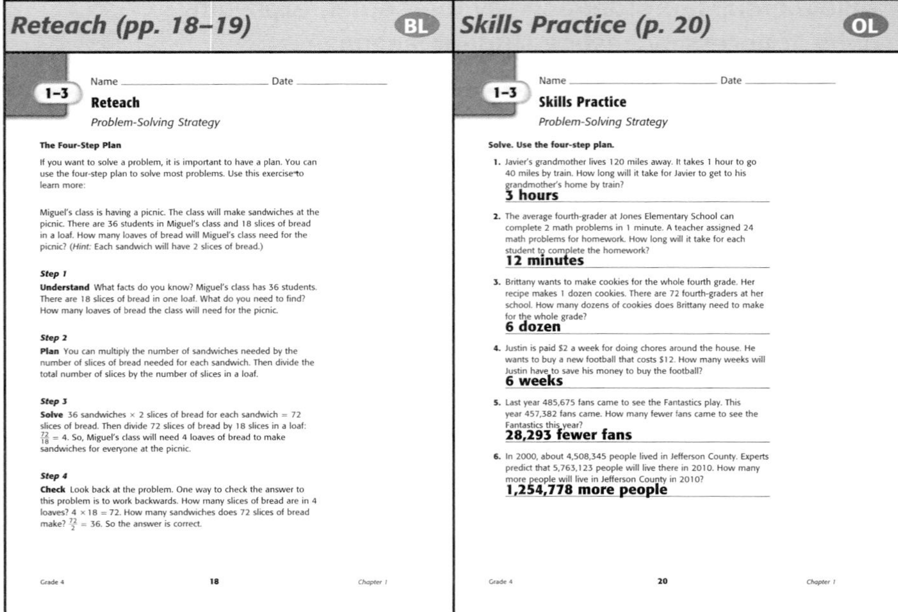

Reteach (pp. 18–19) BL

1-3 Name ______ Date ______

Reteach

Problem-Solving Strategy

The Four-Step Plan

If you want to solve a problem, it is important to have a plan. You can use the four-step plan to solve most problems. Use this exercise to learn more:

Miguel's class is having a picnic. The class will make sandwiches at the picnic. There are 36 students in Miguel's class and 18 slices of bread in a loaf. How many loaves of bread will Miguel's class need for the picnic? (*Hint:* Each sandwich will have 2 slices of bread.)

Step 1

Understand What facts do you know? Miguel's class has 36 students. There are 18 slices of bread in one loaf. What do you need to find? How many loaves of bread the class will need for the picnic.

Step 2

Plan You can multiply the number of sandwiches needed by the number of slices of bread needed for each sandwich. Then divide the total number of slices by the number of slices in a loaf.

Step 3

Solve 36 sandwiches × 2 slices of bread for each sandwich = 72 slices of bread. Then divide 72 slices of bread by 18 slices in a loaf: $\frac{72}{18} = 4$. So, Miguel's class will need 4 loaves of bread to make sandwiches for everyone at the picnic.

Step 4

Check Look back at the problem. One way to check the answer to this problem is to work backwards. How many slices of bread are in 4 loaves? $4 \times 18 = 72$. How many sandwiches does 72 slices of bread make? $\frac{72}{2} = 36$. So the answer is correct.

Grade 4 18 Chapter 1

Skills Practice (p. 20) OL

1-3 Name ______ Date ______

Skills Practice

Problem-Solving Strategy

Solve. Use the four-step plan.

1. Javier's grandmother lives 120 miles away. It takes 1 hour to go 40 miles by train. How long will it take for Javier to get to his grandmother's home by train? **3 hours**
2. The average fourth-grader at Jones Elementary School can complete 2 math problems in 1 minute. A teacher assigned 24 math problems for homework. How long will it take for each student to complete the homework? **12 minutes**
3. Brittany wants to make cookies for the whole fourth grade. Her recipe makes 1 dozen cookies. There are 72 fourth-graders at her school. How many dozens of cookies does Brittany need to make for the whole grade? **6 dozen**
4. Justin is paid $2 a week for doing chores around the house. He wants to buy a new football that costs $12. How many weeks will Justin have to save his money to buy the football? **6 weeks**
5. Last year 485,675 fans came to see the Fantastics play. This year 457,382 fans came. How many fewer fans came to see the Fantastics this year? **28,293 fewer fans**
6. In 2000, about 4,508,345 people lived in Jefferson County. Experts predict that 5,763,123 people will live there in 2010. How many more people will live in Jefferson County in 2010? **1,254,778 more people**

Grade 4 20 Chapter 1

ANALYZE the Skill

Refer to the problem on the previous page. 1–3. See Ch.1 Answer Appendix.

1. Explain why addition was used to solve the problem.

2. In the problem, the price for an adult admission was not included. Suppose the price of an adult ticket is $8 more than a child's ticket. Find the total cost of three adult tickets. Explain.

3. Refer to Exercise 2. Draw a model to check. Explain how the model shows that your answer is correct.

4. If three adults were to go on the trip with the scouts, how much would admission cost for everyone to go? Explain how you found your answer.
$72 + (20 \times 3) = 72 + 60 = 132$

★ indicates multi-step problem

PRACTICE the Skill

EXTRA PRACTICE See page R2.

Solve. Use the four-step plan.

★**5.** A class is playing a game. Each correct answer is worth 5 points. Team 1 has 55 total points. Team 2 has answered 12 questions correctly. Who has answered more questions correctly?
Team 2; $55 \div 5 = 11$ and $11 < 12$

6. **Measurement** Rosa is downloading music. It takes about 3 minutes to download one song. About how long will it take her to download an album with 10 songs? 30 min

7. Casey's mom is the baseball coach for his team. She spent $50 on 10 baseballs. How much would 1 baseball cost? $5

★**8.** William can make 4 bracelets in an hour. With Daisy's help, they can make twice as many in an hour. If they work for 2 hours, how many bracelets can they make? 16 bracelets

★**9.** The opening phrase of the Gettysburg Address is shown. A score is 20 years. How many years would be in four score and seven years? 87 yr

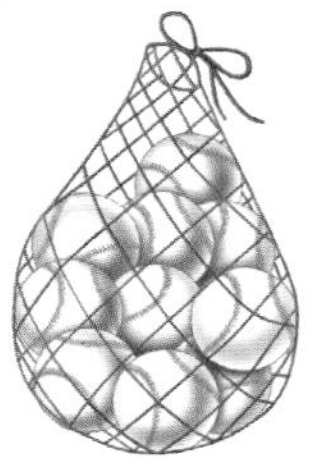

Four score and seven years ago our fathers brought forth on this

10. **Measurement** Scott spends 1 hour a day in math class. How many hours does he spend in math class in four weeks in which there are no days off except weekends? 20 hr

11. Karl Freidrich Benz invented the first gasoline-powered automobile in 1885. Estimate how many years ago this automobile was invented.
about 120 yr

12. **WRITING IN ▶MATH** Select one problem from Exercises 5–11. Explain how you solved the problem.
See students' work.

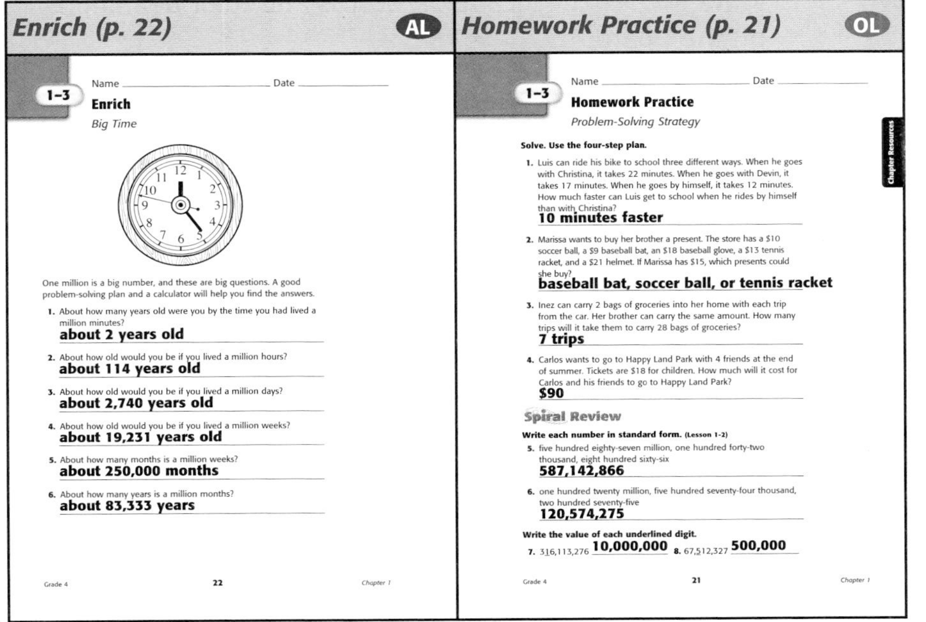

Enrich (p. 22) AL

1-3 Name ________ Date ________

Enrich

Big Time

One million is a big number, and these are big questions. A good problem-solving plan and a calculator will help you find the answers.

1. About how many years old were you by the time you had lived a million minutes?
about 2 years old
2. About how old would you be if you lived a million hours?
about 114 years old
3. About how old would you be if you lived a million days?
about 2,740 years old
4. About how old would you be if you lived a million weeks?
about 19,231 years old
5. About how many months is a million weeks?
about 250,000 months
6. About how many years is a million months?
about 83,333 years

Grade 4 22 Chapter 1

Homework Practice (p. 21) OL

1-3 Name ________ Date ________

Homework Practice

Problem-Solving Strategy

Chapter Resources

Solve. Use the four-step plan.

1. Luis can ride his bike to school three different ways. When he goes with Christina, it takes 22 minutes. When he goes with Devin, it takes 17 minutes. When he goes by himself, it takes 12 minutes. How much faster can Luis get to school when he rides by himself than with Christina?
10 minutes faster
2. Marissa wants to buy her brother a present. The store has a $10 soccer ball, a $9 baseball bat, an $18 baseball glove, a $13 tennis racket, and a $21 helmet. If Marissa has $15, which presents could she buy?
baseball bat, soccer ball, or tennis racket
3. Inez can carry 2 bags of groceries into her home with each trip from the car. Her brother can carry the same amount. How many trips will it take them to carry 28 bags of groceries?
7 trips
4. Carlos wants to go to Happy Land Park with 4 friends at the end of summer. Tickets are $18 for children. How much will it cost for Carlos and his friends to go to Happy Land Park?
$90

Spiral Review

Write each number in standard form. (Lesson 1-2)

5. five hundred eighty-seven million, one hundred forty-two thousand, eight hundred sixty-six
587,142,866
6. one hundred twenty million, five hundred seventy-four thousand, two hundred seventy-five
120,574,275

Write the value of each underlined digit.

7. 3<u>1</u>6,113,276 **10,000,000** 8. 67,<u>5</u>12,327 **500,000**

Grade 4 21 Chapter 1

BL Alternate Teaching Strategy

If students have trouble remembering the steps in the four-step problem-solving plan…

Then use one of these reteach options:

1 CRM **Daily Reteach Worksheet** (pp. 18–19)

2 Have them make index cards detailing the steps of the four-step plan. Students can use these index cards as a reference until they become comfortable with using the four-step plan. They can bring the cards home with them to assist them as they complete their homework assignment.

3 Practice

Using the Exercises

Exercise 8 requires students to know the meaning of the phrase "twice as many."

Exercise 10 assumes that students have math 5 days a week and that there are 4 weeks in a month.

4 Assess

Formative Assessment

- **What are the four steps of the four-step plan? Explain each step in your own words.** Understand, Plan, Solve, Check; See students' work.

Quick Check provides reteaching suggestions for students who continue to struggle.

Quick Check **Are students continuing to struggle with using the four-step plan to solve problems?**

If Yes → CRM Reteach Worksheet (pp. 18–19)

If No → Independent Work Options (p. 26B)
CRM Skills Practice Worksheet (p. 20)
CRM Enrich Worksheet (p. 22)

LESSON 1-4

Compare Whole Numbers

Lesson Planner

Objective

Compare whole numbers.

Vocabulary

number line, **is greater than (>)**, **is less than (<)**, **is equal to (=)**

Resources

Materials: scissors, tape, ruler, grid paper

Literature Connection: *Hottest Coldest Highest Deepest* by Steve Jenkins

Teacher Technology

TeacherWorks • Interactive Classroom

Daily Routine

Use these suggestions before beginning the lesson on p. 28.

5-Minute Check

(Reviews Lesson 1-3)

Solve. Use the four-step plan.

A hamster can travel about 5 times as fast as a roach. A roach can go 1 mile in an hour. How far can a hamster travel in one hour? 5 miles in one hour

Problem of the Day

Rey writes these numbers on a card. What are the next two numbers in the pattern? Identify the pattern.

2,000; 1,200; 800; 600; 500; ____; ____. 450, 425; subtract 800 in the first term, then subtract half the amount each time

Focus on Math Background

At this point, students should be starting to understand that *number* is different from *digit.* For example, the number 100, whose digits are ones and zeros, is greater than 99, whose digits are all nines. For students to comprehend the relative size of numbers, they must understand place value. Number lines are useful in that students can see how two numbers are related. The symbols $<$ (is less than), $>$ (is greater than), and $=$ (is equal to) are used when writing number sentences that compare two numbers, for example, $5 < 8$.

Building Math Vocabulary

Write the lesson vocabulary words and their definitions on the board.

Have students record these words in their Math Journals. In addition to the examples given in the definitions, have them write examples of their own.

Differentiated Instruction

Small Group Options

SPATIAL, INTRAPERSONAL

Option 1 Below Level BL

Materials: two 1-inch circles of colored paper per student

- Have students place a colored circle under the first digit of each of two numbers to be compared.
- If the first digit of each pair is identical, move right to the next digit in each number and repeat the comparison.
- Compare until unlike digits are found. Underline those digits. Remove circles and identify value.
- Place symbol: >, <, =
- Repeat process as necessary.

23,781   23,645

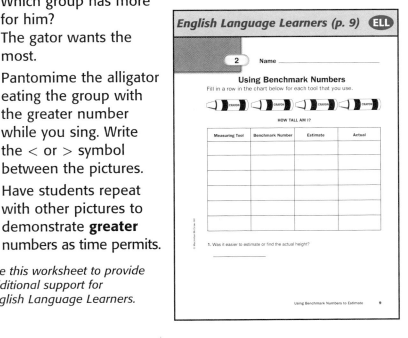

23,781 > 23,645

AUDITORY, VISUAL

Option 2 English Language Learners ELL

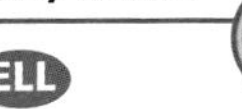

Materials: pipe cleaner, picture of an alligator, and pictures of food with quantity listed

Core Vocabulary: has more, group, the most

Common Use Verb: wants

Hear Math This strategy uses visuals and music to activate background knowledge and connect it with greater than and comparative ideas.

- Sing the following to the tune of "Farmer in the Dell":

  The gator wants the most. (repeat)
  Which group has more for him?
  The gator wants the most.

- Pantomime the alligator eating the group with the greater number while you sing. Write the < or > symbol between the pictures.
- Have students repeat with other pictures to demonstrate **greater** numbers as time permits.

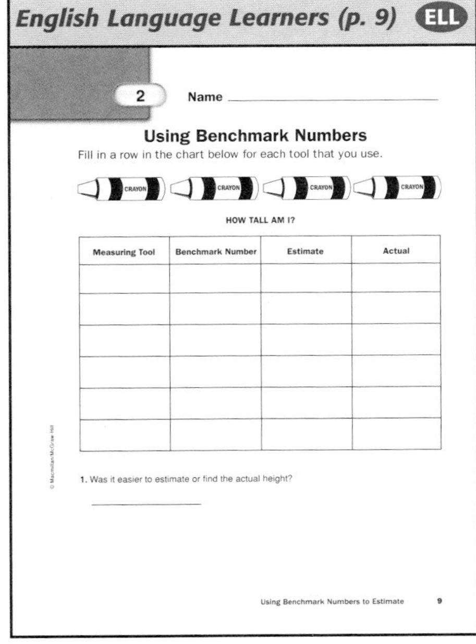

English Language Learners (p. 9) ELL

2 Name ____________

Using Benchmark Numbers

Fill in a row in the chart below for each tool that you use.

HOW TALL AM I?

Measuring Tool	Benchmark Number	Estimate	Actual

1. Was it easier to estimate or find the actual height?

____

Using Benchmark Numbers to Estimate 9

Use this worksheet to provide additional support for English Language Learners.

Independent Work Options

VISUAL, SPATIAL

Option 1 Early Finishers OL AL

Materials: paper, pencil, scissors, glue, newspaper

- Have students look through a newspaper to find real-life examples of comparisons. Have students cut out their examples and glue them onto a piece of paper. These examples may be displayed on a bulletin board.

Option 2 Student Technology

Math Online macmillanmh.com

Math Tool Chest Place Value

Personal Tutor • Extra Examples

Math Adventures

This program is supported by a wealth of technology options on CD-ROM, on DVD, and online.

Option 3 Learning Station: Health (p. 14H)

Direct students to the Health Learning Station for opportunities to explore and extend the lesson concept.

Option 4 Problem-Solving Practice

Reinforce problem-solving skills and strategies with the Problem-Solving Practice worksheet.

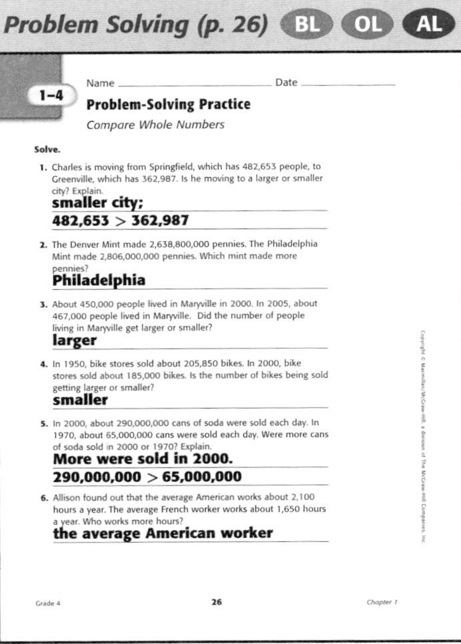

Problem Solving (p. 26) BL OL AL

1–4 Name ____________ Date ____________

Problem-Solving Practice

Compare Whole Numbers

Solve.

1. Charles is moving from Springfield, which has 482,653 people, to Greenville, which has 362,987. Is he moving to a larger or smaller city? Explain.
   smaller city;
   482,653 > 362,987
2. The Denver Mint made 2,638,800,000 pennies. The Philadelphia Mint made 2,806,000,000 pennies. Which mint made more pennies?
   Philadelphia
3. About 450,000 people lived in Maryville in 2000. In 2005, about 467,000 people lived in Maryville. Did the number of people living in Maryville get larger or smaller?
   larger
4. In 1950, bike stores sold about 205,850 bikes. In 2000, bike stores sold about 185,000 bikes. Is the number of bikes being sold getting larger or smaller?
   smaller
5. In 2000, about 290,000,000 cans of soda were sold each day. In 1970, about 65,000,000 cans were sold each day. Were more cans of soda sold in 2000 or 1970? Explain.
   More were sold in 2000.
   290,000,000 > 65,000,000
6. Allison found out that the average American works about 2,100 hours a year. The average French worker works about 1,650 hours a year. Who works more hours?
   the average American worker

Grade 4 26 *Chapter 1*

1-4 Compare Whole Numbers

1 Introduce

Activity Choice 1 • Hands-On

- Have students create a number line that can be taped to their desks or notebooks.
- Have students cut a piece of notebook paper in half lengthwise. Tell them to use a ruler to draw a straight line lengthwise in the center of the paper. They should label the line from 0 to 10.
- **Are the numbers on the right end of the number line greater than or less than the numbers on the left end?** greater than
- **Are the numbers on the left end of the number line greater than or less than the numbers on the right end?** less than

Tell students that an easy way to remember this is the number line has the greater than and less than symbols on it.

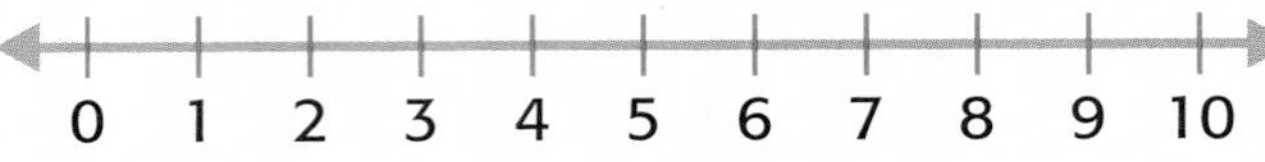

Activity Choice 2 • Literature

Introduce the lesson with *Hottest Coldest Highest Deepest* by Steve Jenkins. For a related math activity, see p. TR41.

2 Teach

Scaffolding Questions

Tell students that an experienced babysitter makes $12 per hour while a sitter with less experience makes $8 per hour. Have students draw a number line from 0 to 15 and graph 12 and 8 on it.

- **Which number is the farthest to the right on the number line?** 12
- **Which babysitter gets paid more?** the experienced babysitter

GET READY to Learn

Have students open their books and read the paragraph under **Get Ready to Learn**. Introduce **number line**, **is greater than (>)**, **is less than (<)**, and **is equal to (=)**. As a class, work through **Examples 1 and 2**.

Each lesson begins with two Activity Choices: a Hands-On Activity and a Literature Connection

1-4 Compare Whole Numbers

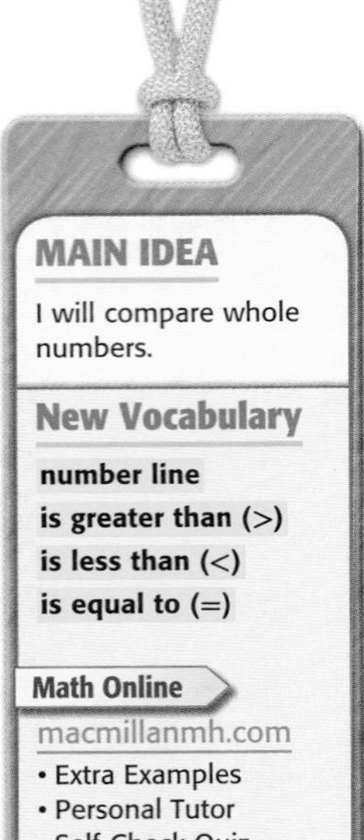

MAIN IDEA
I will compare whole numbers.
New Vocabulary
number line
is greater than (>)
is less than (<)
is equal to (=)
Math Online
macmillanmh.com
• Extra Examples
• Personal Tutor
• Self-Check Quiz

GET READY to Learn

On average, a first-year police officer earns $41,793 in one year. A first-year firefighter earns $41,294 in one year. Which occupation pays more for the first year?

You can use a number line to compare numbers. A **number line** is a line with numbers on it in order at regular intervals. The symbols below are used to show relationships of numbers.

is greater than	is less than	is equal to
>	<	=

Real-World EXAMPLE Use a Number Line

1 **JOBS Which occupation pays more for the first year: police officer or firefighter?**

On a number line, numbers to the right are greater than numbers to the left.

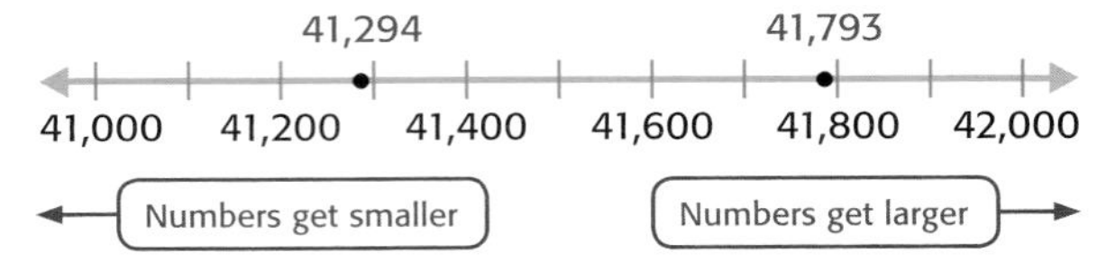

41,793 is to the right of 41,294.

So, 41,793 is greater than 41,294.

Therefore, 41,793 > 41,294.

So, police officers earn more money than firefighters.

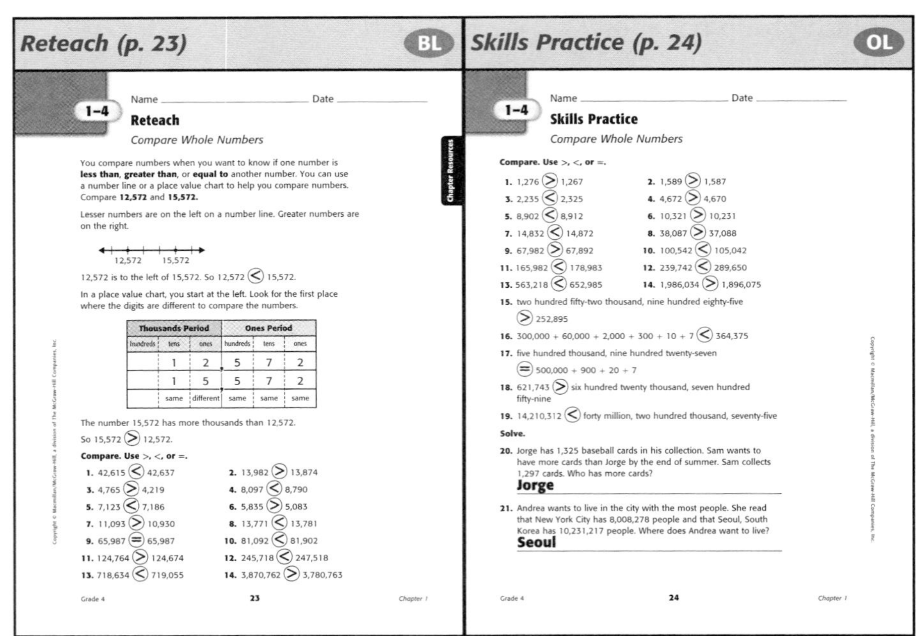

Reteach (p. 23) BL

1–4 Name ________ Date ________

Reteach

Compare Whole Numbers

You compare numbers when you want to know if one number is **less than**, **greater than**, or **equal to** another number. You can use a number line or a place value chart to help you compare numbers. Compare **12,572** and **15,572.**

Lesser numbers are on the left on a number line. Greater numbers are on the right.

12,572 15,572

12,572 is to the left of 15,572. So 12,572 (<) 15,572.

In a place value chart, you start at the left. Look for the first place where the digits are different to compare the numbers.

Thousands Period			Ones Period		
hundreds	tens	ones	hundreds	tens	ones
	1	2	5	7	2
	1	5	5	7	2
	same	different	same	same	same

The number 15,572 has more thousands than 12,572.

So 15,572 (>) 12,572.

Compare. Use >, <, or =.

1. 42,615 (<) 42,637
2. 13,982 (>) 13,874
3. 4,765 (>) 4,219
4. 8,097 (<) 8,790
5. 7,123 (<) 7,186
6. 5,835 (>) 5,083
7. 11,093 (>) 10,930
8. 13,771 (<) 13,781
9. 65,987 (=) 65,987
10. 81,092 (<) 81,902
11. 124,764 (>) 124,674
12. 245,718 (<) 247,518
13. 718,634 (<) 719,055
14. 3,870,762 (>) 3,780,763

Grade 4 23 Chapter 1

Chapter Resources

Skills Practice (p. 24) OL

1–4 Name ________ Date ________

Skills Practice

Compare Whole Numbers

Compare. Use >, <, or =.

1. 1,276 (>) 1,267
2. 1,589 (>) 1,587
3. 2,235 (<) 2,325
4. 4,672 (>) 4,670
5. 8,902 (<) 8,912
6. 10,321 (>) 10,231
7. 14,832 (<) 14,872
8. 38,087 (>) 37,088
9. 67,982 (>) 67,892
10. 100,542 (<) 105,042
11. 165,982 (<) 178,983
12. 239,742 (<) 289,650
13. 563,218 (<) 652,985
14. 1,986,034 (>) 1,896,075
15. two hundred fifty-two thousand, nine hundred eighty-five (>) 252,895
16. 300,000 + 60,000 + 2,000 + 300 + 10 + 7 (<) 364,375
17. five hundred thousand, nine hundred twenty-seven (=) 500,000 + 900 + 20 + 7
18. 621,743 (>) six hundred twenty thousand, seven hundred fifty-nine
19. 14,210,312 (<) forty million, two hundred thousand, seventy-five

Solve.

20. Jorge has 1,325 baseball cards in his collection. Sam wants to have more cards than Jorge by the end of summer. Sam collects 1,297 cards. Who has more cards?
Jorge
21. Andrea wants to live in the city with the most people. She read that New York City has 8,008,278 people and that Seoul, South Korea has 10,231,217 people. Where does Andrea want to live?
Seoul

Grade 4 24 Chapter 1

To compare numbers, you can also use place value.

Real-World EXAMPLE Use Place Value

2 **DATA The table shows the two most popular names in the United States. Which name is more popular?**

Last Name	Number of People
Miller	1,253,913
Jones	1,836,509

Source: *Top 10 of Everything*

Remember
Before comparing numbers, always line up the ones place.

Check What You Know exercises are intended to be completed in class. Example references show students where to look back for review.

Step 1 Line up the numbers so that the digits in the ones place align.
1,253,913
1,836,509

Step 2 Begin at the greatest place. Compare the digits.
1,253,913
1,836,509
Since 1 = 1, go to the next place.

Step 3 Compare the digits in the next place on the right.
1,253,913
1,836,509
8 > 2

So, 1,836,509 is greater. Therefore, the more popular last name is Jones.

CHECK What You Know

Compare. Use >, <, or =. See Examples 1 and 2 (pp. 28–29)

1. 1,798 ● 1,789 >
2. 7,440 ● 7,436 >
3. 25,409 ● 26,409 <
4. 50,402 ● 50,406 <
5. 655,543 ● 556,543 >
6. 10,027,301 ● 10,207,301 <
7. Jun collects stamps and baseball cards. He has 1,834 stamps and 1,286 baseball cards. Does he have more stamps or more baseball cards? stamps
8. **Talk About It** Explain why any five-digit number is less than any six-digit number. See margin.

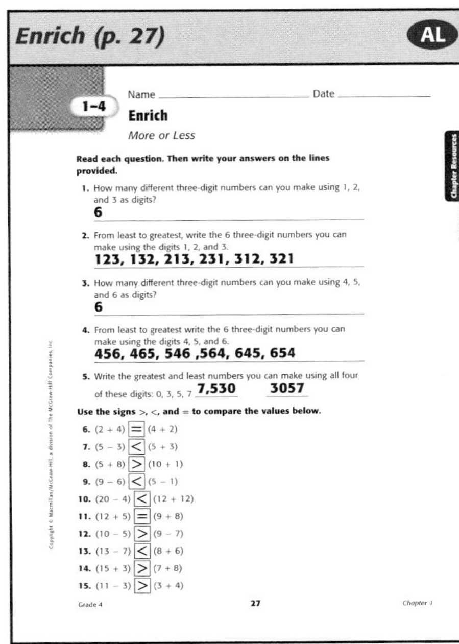

Enrich (p. 27) **AL**

1–4 Name ____________ Date ____________

Enrich

More or Less

Read each question. Then write your answers on the lines provided.

1. How many different three-digit numbers can you make using 1, 2, and 3 as digits?
6
2. From least to greatest, write the 6 three-digit numbers you can make using the digits 1, 2, and 3.
123, 132, 213, 231, 312, 321
3. How many different three-digit numbers can you make using 4, 5, and 6 as digits?
6
4. From least to greatest write the 6 three-digit numbers you can make using the digits 4, 5, and 6.
456, 465, 546 ,564, 645, 654
5. Write the greatest and least numbers you can make using all four of these digits: 0, 3, 5, 7 **7,530** **3057**

Use the signs >, <, and = to compare the values below.

6. (2 + 4) = (4 + 2)
7. (5 − 3) < (5 + 3)
8. (5 + 8) > (10 + 1)
9. (9 − 6) < (5 − 1)
10. (20 − 4) < (12 + 12)
11. (12 + 5) = (9 + 8)
12. (10 − 5) > (9 − 7)
13. (13 − 7) < (8 + 6)
14. (15 + 3) > (7 + 8)
15. (11 − 3) > (3 + 4)

Grade 4 27 Chapter 1

Chapter Resources

The Alternate Teaching Strategy provides two suggestions for remediation for students who did not grasp the concept.

Use Place Value

Example 2 Tell students that you always begin comparing numbers at the greatest place value, which is always the digit that is farthest left. Remind them that only digits in the same place can be compared.

ADDITIONAL EXAMPLES

1. A middle school principal earns $97,032 in one year. An elementary school principal earns $94,485 in one year. Who gets paid more? middle school principal
2. Jorge traveled 1,296 miles during his summer vacation. Kai traveled 1,967 miles during her summer vacation. Who traveled more miles? Kai

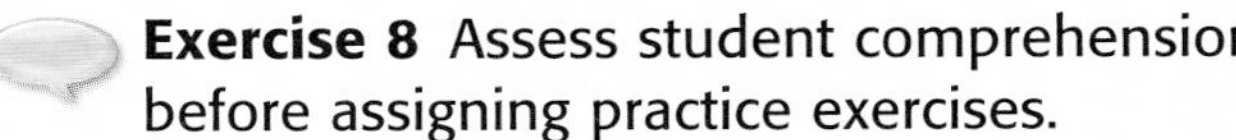

As a class, have students complete Exercises 1–8 in **Check What You Know** as you observe their work.

Exercise 8 Assess student comprehension before assigning practice exercises.

BL Alternate Teaching Strategy

If students have trouble comparing numbers…

Then use one of these reteach options:

1. CRM **Daily Reteach Worksheet** (p. 23)
2. Have students write the numbers on grid paper, one under the other, lining up the digits of the numbers by place value. Tell them to begin at the left and compare until they find the place where the digits are different.
3. Have students use Math Tool Chest to help complete the problem-solving exercises.

Additional Answer

8. Sample answer: A five-digit number is in the ten thousands and a six-digit number is in the hundred thousands. The more digits a number has, the bigger it is. So, a five-digit number would be to the left of a six-digit number on a number line.

3 Practice

Differentiate practice using these leveled assignments for Exercises 9–30.

Level	Assignment
BL Below/Approaching Level	9–16, 21–22, 24
OL On Level	10–19, 22–24, 28
AL Above/Beyond Level	9–27 odd, 26–30

Have students discuss and complete the Higher Order Thinking problems. Encourage them to double check their answers.

WRITING IN MATH Have students complete Exercise 28 in their Math Journals. You may choose to use this exercise as an optional formative assessment.

4 Assess

Formative Assessment

- **Explain why any 4-digit whole number is greater than any 3-digit whole number.** The thousands place has more value than the hundreds place.

Quick Check **Are students continuing to struggle with comparing whole numbers?**

If Yes → Small Group Options (p. 28B)
Strategic Intervention Guide (p. 6)

If No → Independent Work Options (p. 28B)
CRM Skills Practice Worksheet (p. 24)
CRM Enrich Worksheet (p. 27)

Ticket Out the Door Ask students to use place value to compare 9,827,188 and 9,827,198. Tell them to show all their work and explain the steps they used to compare the numbers.

COMMON ERROR!

Exercise 27 Students may have trouble comparing a number written in standard form with a number written using words. For these students, suggest that they change the numbers that are written in word form to standard form before comparing.

Practice and Problem Solving

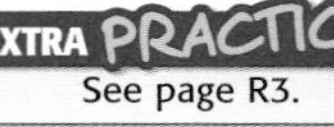

See page R3.

Compare. Use >, <, or =. See Examples 1 and 2 (pp. 28–29)

9. 3,030 ● 3,030 = **10.** 5,980 ● 5,090 > **11.** 6,789 ● 6,798 <

12. 9,623 ● 9,623 = **13.** 23,001 ● 23,010 < **14.** 18,041 ● 18,040 >

15. 76,101 ● 77,000 < **16.** 12,683 ● 12,638 > **17.** 304,999 ● 305,049 <

18. 701,010 ● 701,010 = **19.** 2,999,214 ● 2,999,214 =

Copy and complete to make the number sentence true.

20. 658,431 < ■00,000 7, 8, or 9

21. 1,342,646 > 1,■89,035 0, 1, or 2

22. Delaney received 1,127 E-mails in a year. Patricia received 1,132 E-mails. Who received more E-mails? Patricia

23. Hassan read 2,365 pages during the school year. Anjelita read 2,382 pages during the school year. Who read more pages during the school year? Anjelita

Real-World PROBLEM SOLVING

Technology The table shows the top four online languages.

24. Which language is used most on the Internet? English

25. Which language is used less on the Internet, Japanese or Spanish? Spanish

Top Online Languages

Language	Internet Users
Chinese	105,736,236
English	286,642,757
Japanese	66,763,838
Spanish	55,887,063

Source: *Top 10 of Everything*

H.O.T. Problems

26. OPEN ENDED Write a seven-digit number that is greater than 8,458,942. Sample answer: 8,458,945

27. WHICH ONE DOESN'T BELONG? Which number does not belong? Explain. 10 hundreds does not belong because it equals 1,000 not 10,000.

10,000 | 10 hundreds | ten thousand | 100 hundreds

28. WRITING IN MATH Explain how to compare numbers using place value. See Ch. 1 Answer Appendix.

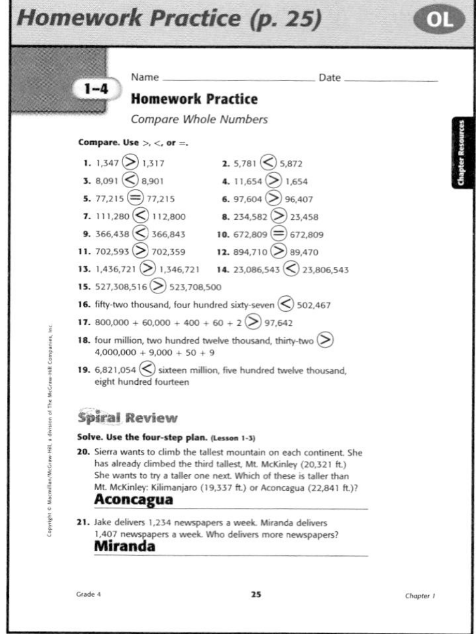

Homework Practice (p. 25) OL

1-4 Name ____________ Date ____________

Homework Practice

Compare Whole Numbers

Compare. Use >, <, or =.

1. 1,347 (>) 1,317
2. 5,781 (<) 5,872
3. 8,091 (<) 8,901
4. 11,654 (>) 1,654
5. 77,215 (=) 77,215
6. 97,604 (>) 96,407
7. 111,280 (<) 112,800
8. 234,582 (>) 23,458
9. 366,438 (<) 366,843
10. 672,809 (=) 672,809
11. 702,593 (>) 702,359
12. 894,710 (>) 89,470
13. 1,436,721 (>) 1,346,721
14. 23,086,543 (<) 23,806,543
15. 527,308,516 (>) 523,708,500
16. fifty-two thousand, four hundred sixty-seven (<) 502,467
17. 800,000 + 60,000 + 400 + 60 + 2 (>) 97,642
18. four million, two hundred twelve thousand, thirty-two (>) 4,000,000 + 9,000 + 50 + 9
19. 6,821,054 (<) sixteen million, five hundred twelve thousand, eight hundred fourteen

Spiral Review

Solve. Use the four-step plan. (Lesson 1-3)

20. Sierra wants to climb the tallest mountain on each continent. She has already climbed the third tallest, Mt. McKinley (20,321 ft.) She wants to try a taller one next. Which of these is taller than Mt. McKinley: Kilimanjaro (19,337 ft.) or Aconcagua (22,841 ft.)? **Aconcagua**

21. Jake delivers 1,234 newspapers a week. Miranda delivers 1,407 newspapers a week. Who delivers more newspapers? **Miranda**

Chapter Resources

Grade 4 25 Chapter 1

Mid-Chapter Check

Lessons 1-1 through 1-4

Write each number in word form and expanded form. (Lesson 1-1)

1. 2,384
2. 917,022

1–4. See Ch. 1 Answer Appendix.

Write each number in standard form and expanded form. (Lesson 1-1)

3. nineteen thousand, two hundred six
4. two hundred seventy-two
5. There are 3 schools. Each school has 297 students. How many students are in all three schools? Write in standard form and word form. (Lesson 1-1) 891; eight hundred ninety-one
6. **MULTIPLE CHOICE** Which number below is the standard form of twelve thousand, five hundred seven? (Lesson 1-1) C

   A 1,257

   B 12,057

   C 12,507

   D 12,570

Write the value of the underlined digit. (Lesson 1-2)

7. 31,687 600
8. 8,320,579 20,000
9. Erika is writing the greatest number possible using the digits shown.

   Write the number in expanded form. (Lesson 1-2) See Ch. 1 Answer Appendix.

10. What is 20,000,000 + 8,000,000 + 300,000 + 6,000 + 30 + 7 in standard form and word form? (Lesson 1-2) See Ch. 1 Answer Appendix.
11. **MULTIPLE CHOICE** Which word form represents 7,402,644? (Lesson 1-2) H

    F seven million, forty-two thousand, six hundred four

    G seven thousand, four hundred two

    H seven million, four hundred two thousand, six hundred forty-four

    J seven million, two hundred four thousand, six hundred four

Compare. Use >, <, or =. (Lesson 1-4)

12. 2,481 ● 2,814 <
13. 200 + 70 + 8 ● 700 + 80 + 2 <

Algebra Find the value of *x*. (Lesson 1-4)

14. $5{,}000 + x + 9 = 5{,}709$ 700
15. $40{,}000 + 6{,}000 + x = 46{,}009$ 9
16. Coty traveled 2,643 miles by air. Ramiro traveled 2,643 miles by car. Who traveled farther? Explain. (Lesson 1-4) See Ch. 1 Answer Appendix.
17. On Monday Dylan used a pedometer to record 15,725 steps. On Tuesday he took 15,806 steps. On which day did he take more steps? (Lesson 1-4) Tuesday
18. **WRITING IN MATH** Explain how to find the number missing in the following expanded form sentence. 8,000,000 + 5,000 + 90 + 3 = 8,■05,093 (Lesson 1-2) See Ch. 1 Answer Appendix.

Formative Assessment 31

The Mid-Chapter Check reviews skills and concepts presented in previous lessons. Students' results can be used for Data-Driven Decision Making

Lessons 1-1 through 1-4

Formative Assessment

Use the Mid-Chapter Check to assess students' progress in the first half of the chapter.

Customize and create multiple versions of your Mid-Chapter Check and the test answer keys.

FOLDABLES Dinah Zike's Foldables

Use these lesson suggestions to incorporate the Foldables during the chapter.

Lesson 1-1 Under the first tab, students demonstrate that they can read and write numbers through hundred thousands using standard form, expanded form, and word form.

Lesson 1-2 Under the second tab, students demonstrate that they can read and write numbers through the millions using standard form, expanded form, and word form.

Lessons 1-3 to 1-5 Under the third tab, students write, compare, order, and round numbers through the millions.

Data-Driven Decision Making

Based on the results of the Mid-Chapter Check, use the following resources to review concepts that continue to give students problems.

Exercises	State/Local Standards	What's the Math?	Error Analysis	Resources for Review
1–6 Lesson 1-1		Read and write whole numbers to hundred thousands.	Does not understand "expanded form." Does not understand "standard form." Does not know correct words for place value.	Strategic Intervention Guide (pp. 2, 6, 8) CRM Chapter 1 Resource Masters (Reteach Worksheets) Math Adventures My Math Zone Chapter 1 Math Online Extra Examples • Concepts in Motion
7–11, 18 Lesson 1-2		Read and write whole numbers to millions.	Does not understand "expanded form." Does not understand "standard form." Does not know correct words for place value.	
12–17 Lesson 1-4		Compare whole numbers.	Reverses "less than" and "greater than" signs. Does not know place value.	

LESSON 1-5 Order Whole Numbers

Lesson Planner

Objective

Order whole numbers through the millions.

Review Vocabulary

is greater than (>), is less than (<)

Resources

Materials: index cards

Literature Connection: *Centipede's 100 Shoes* by Tony Ross

Teacher Technology

TeacherWorks • Interactive Classroom

Daily Routine

Use these suggestions before beginning the lesson on p. 32.

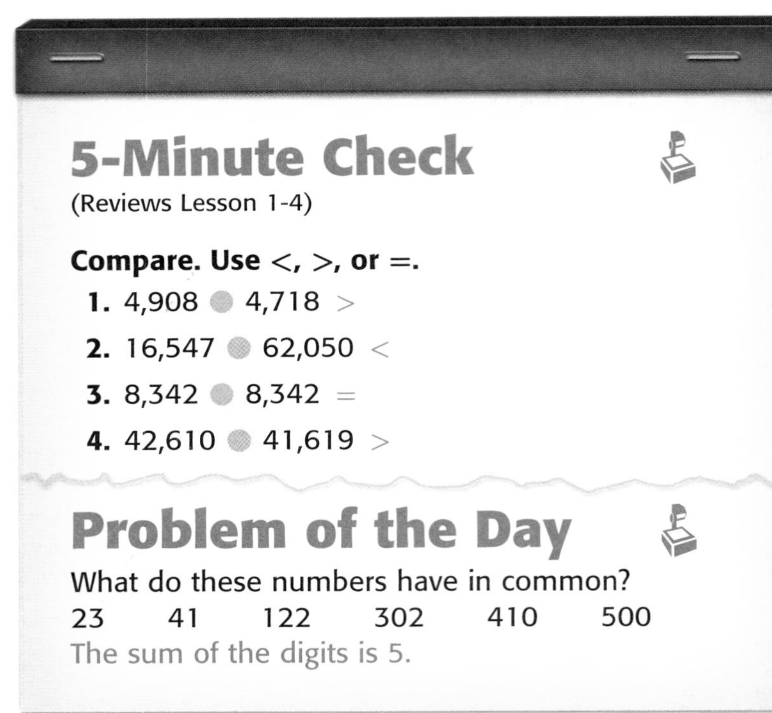

5-Minute Check

(Reviews Lesson 1-4)

Compare. Use <, >, or =.

1. 4,908 ● 4,718 >
2. 16,547 ● 62,050 <
3. 8,342 ● 8,342 =
4. 42,610 ● 41,619 >

Problem of the Day

What do these numbers have in common?

23 41 122 302 410 500

The sum of the digits is 5.

Focus on Math Background

Once students can compare two numbers, they are ready to order three or more numbers. Ordering a set of numbers is a series of comparisons of two numbers. Place value and number lines once again prove to be valuable tools. When students use what they know about place value to order numbers, they must be sure to line up the numbers so that they are comparing digits with the same place value.

Review Math Vocabulary

Write the review vocabulary words and their definitions on the board.

Ask students to write several sentences for each vocabulary word and leave a fill-in-the-blank space where the word would go. Have them trade papers with a partner and complete the sentences.

Differentiated Instruction

Small Group Options

Option 1 Below Level BL

Materials: three index cards for each pair of students, cut in half both vertically and horizontally to create 12 equal pieces, 1 piece of plain paper per student

- Write one of the numbers 0, 2, 3, 5, 8, 9 on each of the card pieces. Do it twice to make two card sets of 6.
- Draw six $1\frac{1}{2}''$ lines across the center of the plain paper to denote the place value of digits.
- Hand pairs of students the prepared papers and have them write the place value under each section. Hand a set of 6 card pieces to each student.
- Have students place their cards on lines on the paper. Students then check to see who arranged the greatest number or least number.
- Have students read their numbers aloud.
- Increase or decrease the number of cards according to ability levels.

LOGICAL, SPATIAL

Option 2 English Language Learners ELL

Materials: note cards, (numbered 1–1000), masking tape
Core Vocabulary: my/your place, between, in order
Common Use Verb: find/found

Do Math This strategy allows students to internalize the target math skill and then to vocalize their understanding.

- Put a masking tape number line on the floor with 0 labeled on the left end.
- Pass out note cards. Say: "Find your place on the line." Allow students to order themselves from 0 on.
- Model writing a number card and move yourself into place on the line. Say: "I found my place between __ and __."
- Students repeat while the audience checks for accuracy as time permits.

Independent Work Options

VISUAL, SPATIAL

Option 1 Early Finishers AL

Materials: place-value charts through hundred thousands, spinners numbered 0–9

- Provide students with place-value charts and spinners.
- Have students generate 4-digit numbers using the spinner. They should record the numbers on their place-value charts. Then they should compare the two numbers and write a number sentence using $<$, $>$, or $=$.
- Repeat using 5- and 6-digit numbers.

Option 2 Student Technology

Math Online macmillanmh.com

Personal Tutor • Extra Examples

 Math Adventures

Option 3 Learning Station: Science (p. 14H)

Direct students to the Science Learning Station for opportunities to explore and extend the lesson concept.

Option 4 Problem-Solving Practice

Reinforce problem-solving skills and strategies with the Problem-Solving Practice worksheet.

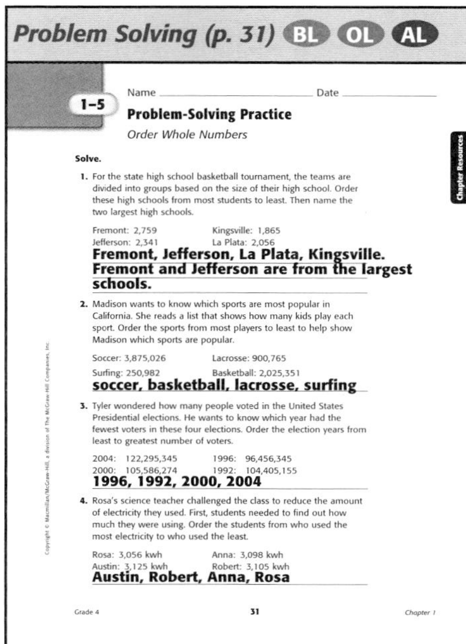

Problem Solving (p. 31) BL OL AL

1-5 Name ________ Date ________

Problem-Solving Practice

Order Whole Numbers

Solve.

1. For the state high school basketball tournament, the teams are divided into groups based on the size of their high school. Order these high schools from most students to least. Then name the two largest high schools.

   Fremont: 2,759 Kingsville: 1,865
   Jefferson: 2,341 La Plata: 2,056

   Fremont, Jefferson, La Plata, Kingsville. Fremont and Jefferson are from the largest schools.

2. Madison wants to know which sports are most popular in California. She reads a list that shows how many kids play each sport. Order the sports from most players to least to help show Madison which sports are popular.

   Soccer: 3,875,026 Lacrosse: 900,765
   Surfing: 250,982 Basketball: 2,025,351

   soccer, basketball, lacrosse, surfing

3. Tyler wondered how many people voted in the United States Presidential elections. He wants to know which year had the fewest voters in these four elections. Order the election years from least to greatest number of voters.

   2004: 122,295,345 1996: 96,456,345
   2000: 105,586,274 1992: 104,405,155

   1996, 1992, 2000, 2004

4. Rosa's science teacher challenged the class to reduce the amount of electricity they used. First, students needed to find out how much they were using. Order the students from who used the most electricity to who used the least.

   Rosa: 3,056 kwh Anna: 3,098 kwh
   Austin: 3,125 kwh Robert: 3,105 kwh

   Austin, Robert, Anna, Rosa

Chapter Resources

Grade 4 31 Chapter 1

1-5 Order Whole Numbers

1 Introduce

Activity Choice 1 • Hands-On 

- Give each student an index card. Ask them to write a 5-digit number on the card.
- Have students walk around the room and compare their numbers with at least four other students one at a time. They should decide whether their number is greater than, less than, or equal to the other number.
- Then have students form groups of three. Ask them to look at the numbers on the cards of the students in the group and order the numbers from least to greatest.

Activity Choice 2 • Literature

Introduce the lesson with *Centipede's 100 Shoes* by Tony Ross. For a related math activity, see p. TR42.

2 Teach

Scaffolding Questions

Conduct a quick survey in your class to determine the types of pets students have.

- **How many students have a cat?** Answers will vary.
- **How many students have a dog?** Answers will vary.
- **How many students have a fish?** Answers will vary.
- **How many students have a pet that is not a cat, dog or fish?** Answers will vary.
- **What type of pet is most popular in the class?** Answers will vary.

Guide students as they order the number of pets owned by students in the class from least to greatest.

GET READY to Learn

Have students open their books and read the paragraph under **Get Ready to Learn**. Review **is greater than (>)** and **is less than (<)**. As a class, work through **Examples 1 and 2**.

1-5 Order Whole Numbers

MAIN IDEA

I will order whole numbers through the millions.

Math Online

macmillanmh.com

- Extra Examples
- Personal Tutor
- Self-Check Quiz

GET READY to Learn

Having a dog is very popular. The table shows the number of Yorkshire Terriers, Beagles, and German Shepherds in the United States. Which dog breed is most popular? least popular?

Dog Breeds in the U.S.

Dog Breed	Number
Yorkshire Terrier	47,238
Beagle	42,592
German Shepherd	45,868

Source: American Kennel Club

To order numbers, you can use a number line or place value.

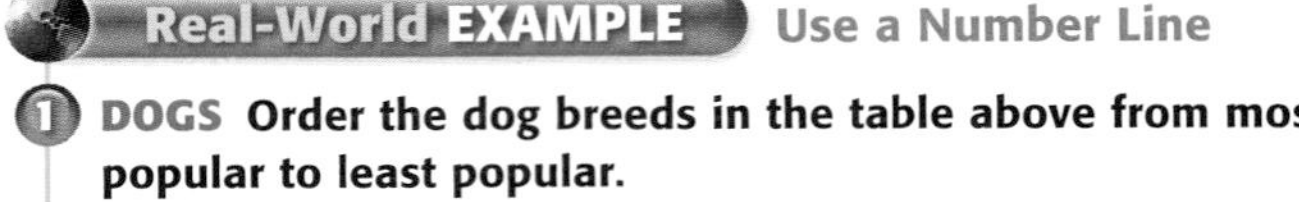

Use a Number Line

1 **DOGS Order the dog breeds in the table above from most popular to least popular.**

Graph each number on a number line.

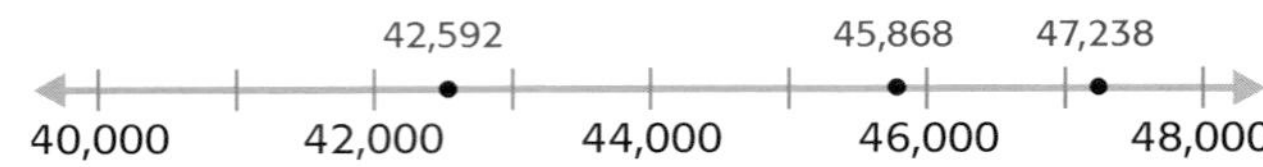

47,238 is the farthest to the right.

45,868 is between 42,592 and 47,238.

42,592 is the farthest to the left.

The order is Yorkshire Terrier, German Shepherd, Beagle.

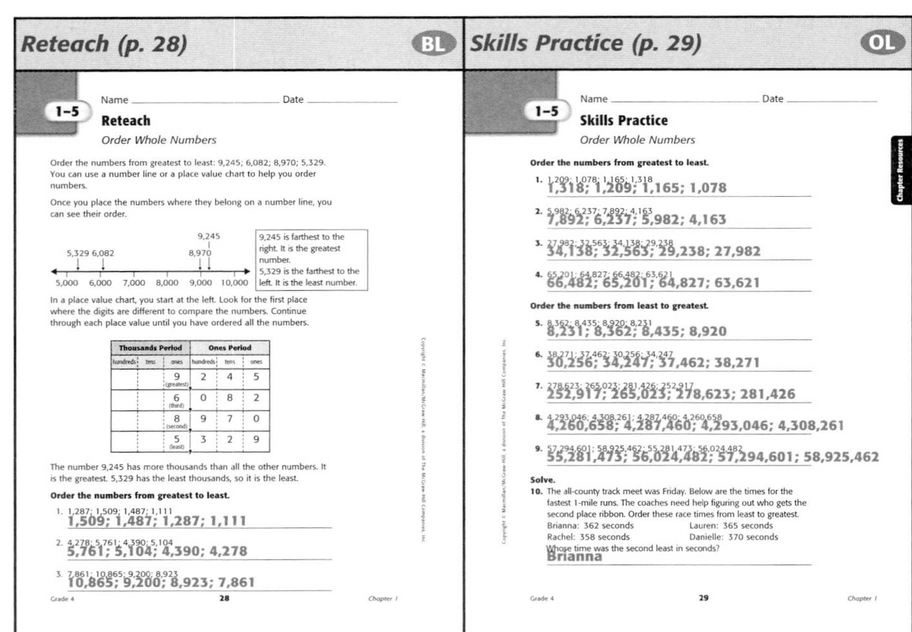

Reteach (p. 28) BL

1-5 Name ________ Date ________

Reteach

Order Whole Numbers

Order the numbers from greatest to least: 9,245; 6,082; 8,970; 5,329. You can use a number line or a place value chart to help you order numbers.

Once you place the numbers where they belong on a number line, you can see their order.

5,329 6,082 8,970 9,245
5,000 6,000 7,000 8,000 9,000 10,000

9,245 is farthest to the right. It is the greatest number.
5,329 is the farthest to the left. It is the least number.

In a place value chart, you start at the left. Look for the first place where the digits are different to compare the numbers. Continue through each place value until you have ordered all the numbers.

Thousands Period			Ones Period		
hundreds	tens	ones	hundreds	tens	ones
		9 (greatest)	2	4	5
		6 (third)	0	8	2
		8 (second)	9	7	0
		5 (least)	3	2	9

The number 9,245 has more thousands than all the other numbers. It is the greatest. 5,329 has the least thousands, so it is the least.

Order the numbers from greatest to least.

1. 1,287; 1,509; 1,487; 1,111
   1,509; 1,487; 1,287; 1,111
2. 4,278; 5,761; 4,390; 5,104
   5,761; 5,104; 4,390; 4,278
3. 7,861; 10,865; 9,200; 8,923
   10,865; 9,200; 8,923; 7,861

Grade 4 28 Chapter 1

Skills Practice (p. 29) OL

1-5 Name ________ Date ________

Skills Practice

Order Whole Numbers

Order the numbers from greatest to least.

1. 1,209; 1,078; 1,165; 1,318
   1,318; 1,209; 1,165; 1,078
2. 5,982; 6,237; 7,892; 4,163
   7,892; 6,237; 5,982; 4,163
3. 27,982; 32,563; 34,138; 29,238
   34,138; 32,563; 29,238; 27,982
4. 65,201; 64,827; 66,482; 63,621
   66,482; 65,201; 64,827; 63,621

Order the numbers from least to greatest.

5. 8,362; 8,435; 8,920; 8,231
   8,231; 8,362; 8,435; 8,920
6. 38,271; 37,462; 30,256; 34,247
   30,256; 34,247; 37,462; 38,271
7. 278,623; 265,023; 281,426; 252,917
   252,917; 265,023; 278,623; 281,426
8. 4,293,046; 4,308,261; 4,287,460; 4,260,658
   4,260,658; 4,287,460; 4,293,046; 4,308,261
9. 57,294,601; 58,925,462; 55,281,473; 56,024,482
   55,281,473; 56,024,482; 57,294,601; 58,925,462

Solve.

10. The all-county track meet was Friday. Below are the times for the fastest 1-mile runs. The coaches need help figuring out who gets the second place ribbon. Order these race times from least to greatest.
    Brianna: 362 seconds — Lauren: 365 seconds
    Rachel: 358 seconds — Danielle: 370 seconds
    Whose time was the second least in seconds?
    Brianna

Grade 4 29 Chapter 1

Chapter Resources

Real-World EXAMPLE Use Place Value

2 **OIL** The table shows the number of barrels of oil used each day in different countries. Use place value to order the data from greatest to least.

Oil Usage	
Country	**Barrels per Day**
Brazil	2,199,000
Canada	2,200,000
India	2,130,000
United States	19,650,000

Source: *CIA World Fact Book*

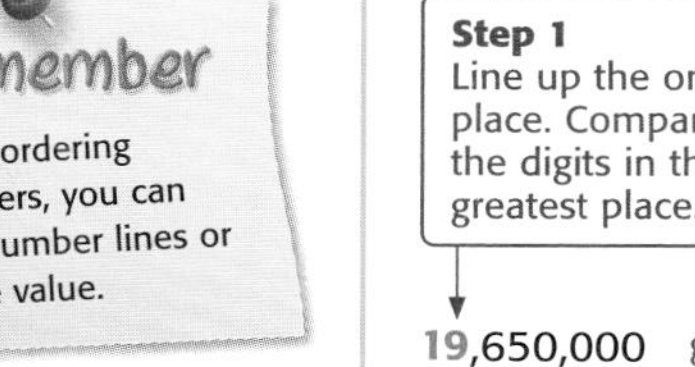

Remember
When ordering numbers, you can use number lines or place value.

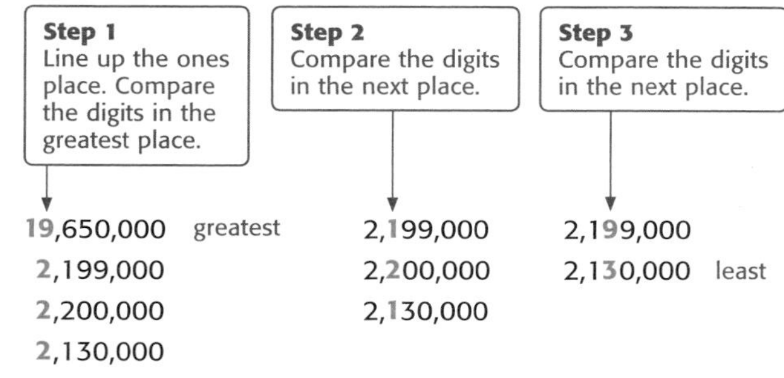

Step 1 Line up the ones place. Compare the digits in the greatest place.

19,650,000 greatest
2,199,000
2,200,000
2,130,000

Step 2 Compare the digits in the next place.

2,199,000
2,200,000
2,130,000

Step 3 Compare the digits in the next place.

2,199,000
2,130,000 least

The numbers ordered from greatest to least are 19,650,000; 2,200,000; 2,199,000; and 2,130,000.

So, the order is the United States, Canada, Brazil, and India.

CHECK What You Know

Order the numbers from greatest to least. See Examples 1 and 2 (pp. 32–33)

1. 3,456; 4,356; 3,465; 6,543
   6,543; 4,356; 3,465; 3,456
2. 52,482; 50,023; 56,028; 63,340
   63,340; 56,028; 52,482; 50,023
3. 87,035; 80,562; 78,035; 79,003
   87,035; 80,562; 79,003; 78,035
4. 145,099; 154,032; 145,004; 159,023
   159,023; 154,032; 145,099; 145,004
5. **Measurement** Order the lakes shown in the table from greatest to least surface area.
   5. Lake Okeechobee, Lake Seminole, Lake Apopka, Lake Tohopekaliga, Lake Harris

Florida Lakes	
Lake	**Surface Area (acres)**
Lake Apopka	30,875
Lake Harris	13,788
Lake Tohopekaliga	18,810
Lake Okeechobee	467,200
Lake Seminole	37,500

Source: World Atlas Travel

6. **Talk About It** When ordering whole numbers, explain what you do when the digits in the same place have the same value.
   Compare the value of the digit to the right.

Use Place Value

Example 2 Tell students that if the numbers they are ordering do not have equal numbers of digits, the ones with the most digits are greater than the numbers with fewer digits.

ADDITIONAL EXAMPLES

1 Refer to the data from Example 1 on p. 32. Order the dog breeds from least popular to most popular. Beagle, German Shepherd, Yorkshire Terrier

2 The populations of three cities are listed below. Use place value to order the population numbers from least to greatest.
San Diego: 1,223,400
Detroit: 951,270
Philadelphia: 1,517,550
951,270; 1,223,400; 1,517,550

CHECK What You Know

As a class, have students complete Exercises 1–6 in **Check What You Know** as you observe their work.

Exercise 6 Assess student comprehension before assigning practice exercises.

BL Alternate Teaching Strategy

If students incorrectly compare the digits when ordering numbers…

Then use one of these reteach options:

1. CRM **Daily Reteach Worksheet** (p. 28)
2. Remind them to make sure they are comparing the same place values.

Explain that it will help them to write the numbers one under the other and take care in aligning digits with the same place value. You may have students use place-value charts or grid paper to aid them in comparing and ordering numbers until they are proficient.

Enrich (p. 32) AL

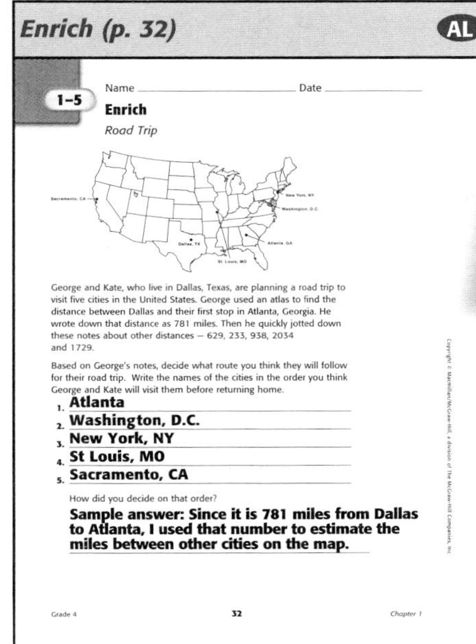

1-5 Name ________ Date ________
Enrich
Road Trip

George and Kate, who live in Dallas, Texas, are planning a road trip to visit five cities in the United States. George used an atlas to find the distance between Dallas and their first stop in Atlanta, Georgia. He wrote down that distance as 781 miles. Then he quickly jotted down these notes about other distances – 629, 233, 938, 2034 and 1729.

Based on George's notes, decide what route you think they will follow for their road trip. Write the names of the cities in the order you think George and Kate will visit them before returning home.

1. Atlanta
2. Washington, D.C.
3. New York, NY
4. St Louis, MO
5. Sacramento, CA

How did you decide on that order?
Sample answer: Since it is 781 miles from Dallas to Atlanta, I used that number to estimate the miles between other cities on the map.

Grade 4 32 Chapter 1

Reteach, Skills Practice, Problem-Solving Practice, Enrich, and Homework Practice masters are shown for each lesson in the Student Edition. These masters can be found in the Chapter Resource Masters.

3 Practice

Differentiate practice using these leveled assignments for Exercises 7–21.

Level	Assignment
BL Below/Approaching Level	7–12, 15, 17
OL On Level	8–13, 16–18, 20
AL Above/Beyond Level	8–18 even, 19–21

Have students discuss and complete the Higher Order Thinking problems. Encourage them to read the problems carefully and check their work.

WRITING IN MATH Have students complete Exercise 21 in their Math Journals. You may choose to use this exercise as an optional formative assessment.

4 Assess

Formative Assessment

Write 35,716; 31,902; and 31,161 on the board.

- **Explain how to use a number line to order the numbers.** Write the numbers on a number line. The number farthest right is the greatest and the number farthest left is the least.
- **Explain how to use place value to order the numbers.** Compare the digits in the ten thousands place, then the thousands place, then the hundreds place.

Quick Check **Are students continuing to struggle with comparing whole numbers?**

If Yes → Strategic Intervention Guide (p. 9)

If No → Independent Work Options (p. 32B)
CRM Skills Practice Worksheet (p. 29)
CRM Enrich Worksheet (p. 32)

Yesterday's News Ask students to explain how Lesson 1-4 helped them with what they learned in today's lesson.

COMMON ERROR!

Exercises 17–18 Students may have trouble understanding what the exercises are asking. It might be helpful to define the word *migration*.

Practice and Problem Solving

See page R3.

Order the numbers from greatest to least. See Examples 1 and 2 (pp. 32–33)

7. 2,004; 1,906; 2,006; 1,507
2,006; 2,004; 1,906; 1,507

8. 3,521; 3,512; 1,243; 3,306
3,521; 3,512; 3,306; 1,243

9. 79,920; 82,234; 97,902; 90,125
97,902; 90,125; 82,234; 79,920

10. 12,378; 12,783; 12,873
12,873; 12,783; 12,378

11. 138,023; 138,032; 139,006; 183,487
183,487; 139,006; 138,032; 138,023

12. 258,103; 248,034; 285,091; 248,934
285,091; 258,103; 248,934; 248,034

13. 6,052,264; 6,025,264; 6,052,462
6,052,462; 6,052,264; 6,025,264

14. 12,345,678; 1,234,567; 123,456,789
123,456,789; 12,345,678; 1,234,567

15. Rank the following cities in the United States from least to greatest population.

City Population

City	Population
Baltimore	635,815
Boston	559,034
Indianapolis	784,118
Seattle	573,911

Source: U.S. Census Bureau

Boston, Seattle, Baltimore, Indianapolis

16. Order the cars from most expensive to least expensive.

Most Expensive Cars

Car	Price
Bugatti Veyron 16.4	$1,192,057
Leblanc Mirabeau	$645,084
Pagani Zonda Roadster	$667,321
Saleen S7	$555,000

Source: *Forbes*

Bugatti Veyron 16.4, Pagani Zonda Roadster, Leblanc Mirabeau, Saleen S7

Data File

Most blue whales migrate south, from the waters off New York State to Panama. The table shows the blue and other whale migration distances and populations.

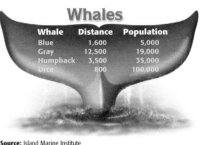

Whales

Whale	Distance	Population
Blue	1,600	5,000
Gray	12,500	19,000
Humpback	3,500	35,000
Orca	800	100,000

Source: Island Marine Institute

17. Order the migration distances of the whales from least to greatest.

18. Order the whale populations from least to greatest.

17. orca, blue, humpback, gray

18. blue, gray, humpback, orca

H.O.T. Problems

19. OPEN ENDED Write three numbers that are greater than 750,000 but less than 760,000. Sample answer: 750,001; 755,000; 759,999

20. NUMBER SENSE Use the digits 2, 3, 4, and 9 to create four numbers. Order them from least to greatest.
Sample answer: 2,349; 2,439; 2,493; 2,934

21. WRITING IN MATH Write a real-word problem in which you would order three numbers from least to greatest. See students' work.

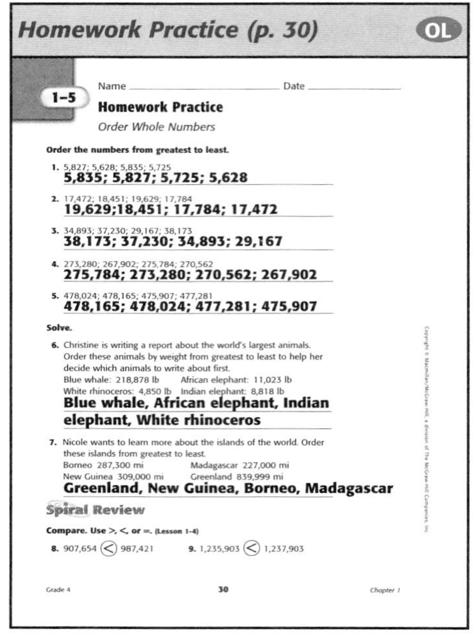

Homework Practice (p. 30) OL

1–5 Name ________ Date ________

Homework Practice

Order Whole Numbers

Order the numbers from greatest to least.

1. 5,827; 5,628; 5,835; 5,725
5,835; 5,827; 5,725; 5,628

2. 17,472; 18,451; 19,629; 17,784
19,629;18,451; 17,784; 17,472

3. 34,893; 37,230; 29,167; 38,173
38,173; 37,230; 34,893; 29,167

4. 273,280; 267,902; 275,784; 270,562
275,784; 273,280; 270,562; 267,902

5. 478,024; 478,165; 475,907; 477,281
478,165; 478,024; 477,281; 475,907

Solve.

6. Christine is writing a report about the world's largest animals. Order these animals by weight from greatest to least to help her decide which animals to write about first.
Blue whale: 218,878 lb African elephant: 11,023 lb
White rhinoceros: 4,850 lb Indian elephant: 8,818 lb
Blue whale, African elephant, Indian elephant, White rhinoceros

7. Nicole wants to learn more about the islands of the world. Order these islands from greatest to least.
Borneo 287,300 mi Madagascar 227,000 mi
New Guinea 309,000 mi Greenland 839,999 mi
Greenland, New Guinea, Borneo, Madagascar

Spiral Review

Compare. Use >, <, or =. (Lesson 1-4)

8. 907,654 (<) 987,421 9. 1,235,903 (<) 1,237,903

Grade 4 30 Chapter 1

Greater Number Game

Compare Whole Numbers

Get Ready!

Players: 2 players

You will need: 40 index cards

Get Set!

Each player gets 20 index cards. Separate the cards into 2 piles of 10. On each card in the first pile, write a number in standard form that has no more than 4 digits.

Next, write the expanded form of each number on one of the cards in the second pile.

Go!

- Combine both sets of cards.
- Shuffle and deal the cards.
- Place your cards facedown. Turn over the top card at the same time as your partner.
- The person who turns over the greatest number takes both cards. If the cards are equal, keep turning over cards until a player can take the cards.
- Play until one person has all the cards.

Game Time Greater Number Game **35**

Differentiated Practice

Use these leveled suggestions to differentiate the game for all learners.

Level	Assignment
BL Below/Approaching Level	Students may use place-value charts to help them compare the numbers.
OL On Level	Have students play the game with the rules as written.
AL Above/Beyond Level	Students create the game using 5-digit numbers.

Greater Number Game

Math Concept:
Compare Whole Numbers

Materials: 40 index cards, pencils

Introduce the game on p. 35 to your students to play as a class, in small groups, or at a learning workstation to review concepts introduced in this chapter.

Instructions

- Each student gets 20 cards. Students split their cards into two piles of 10 cards. They label 10 of the cards with numbers with no more than 4 digits each, in standard form. They label the other 10 cards with the corresponding expanded form of each number, as shown on page 35.
- Students shuffle all the cards together and one student deals them out evenly.
- Each player places his or her cards in front of them in a pile, and flips over the top card on his or her pile at the same time.
- The player whose card has the greatest number wins both cards and sets them aside. If the cards are equal, the players keep turning cards over until one player can win the cards.
- Play continues until one player has all the cards.

Extend the Game

Have students make the game using more cards or different numbers.

LESSON 1-6

Round Whole Numbers

Lesson Planner

Objective

Round whole numbers through the millions.

Vocabulary

estimate, **rounding (or round)**

Resources

Literature Connection: *Coyotes All Around* by Stuart J. Murphy

Teacher Technology

TeacherWorks • Interactive Classroom

Daily Routine

Use these suggestions before beginning the lesson on p. 36.

5-Minute Check

(Reviews Lesson 1-5)

The Nile River is about 4,160 miles long. The Mississippi River is about 2,340 miles long. The Amazon River is about 4,000 miles long. Order the rivers from shortest to longest.
Mississippi, Amazon, Nile

Problem of the Day

Mrs. Jacob writes numbers on the board in a pattern. What are the next three numbers in the pattern? 10, 20, 40, 70, 110, ___, ___, ___. Describe the pattern. 160, 220, 290; The number added to each number in the pattern is 10 greater than the previous number added.

Focus on Math Background

When we find an approximation for a number, we sometimes use a method referred to as *rounding*. There are many different rules for rounding, but the method shown in this lesson is the most common. For example,

- 6<u>2</u>9 rounded to the nearest hundred is 600 since the digit in the tens place is 4 or less.
- 6<u>8</u>1 rounded to the nearest hundred is 700 since the digit in the tens place is 5 or greater.

Rounding to lesser place values results in more exact or better estimates. For example, round 175,250 to thousands and ten thousands.

ten thousands → 180,000 thousands → 175,000

The lesser value is a better estimate.

Learning to round numbers provides the underpinning for estimating sums, differences, products, and quotients.

Building Math Vocabulary

Write the lesson vocabulary words and their definitions on the board.

Discuss each vocabulary word with students. Ask them when they might use each word. Point out that the word *estimate* has different pronunciations depending on whether it is used as a noun or a verb.

Visual Vocabulary Cards

Use Visual Vocabulary Cards 15 and 42 to reinforce the vocabulary introduced in this lesson. (The Define/Example/Ask routine is printed on the back of each card.)

Differentiated Instruction

Small Group Options

Option 1 Below Level BL

LINGUISTIC

Materials: paper and pencil

- Have student(s) write the largest 4-digit number possible using the digits 3, 5, 6, and 8. 8,653
- Then have them say the number, underline the number in the thousands place and circle the number in the hundreds place. 8; 6
- **Which digit would you look at to round to the thousands place?** 6
- Round the number to the nearest thousand. 9,000
- Repeat using the digits 9, 2, 1, 4 to find the smallest 4-digit number. Round to the nearest hundred.

Option 2 English Language Learners ELL

KINESTHETIC, INTRAPERSONAL

Materials: maps, toy car

Core Vocabulary: closer city, finding, where

Common Use Verb: did live/lived

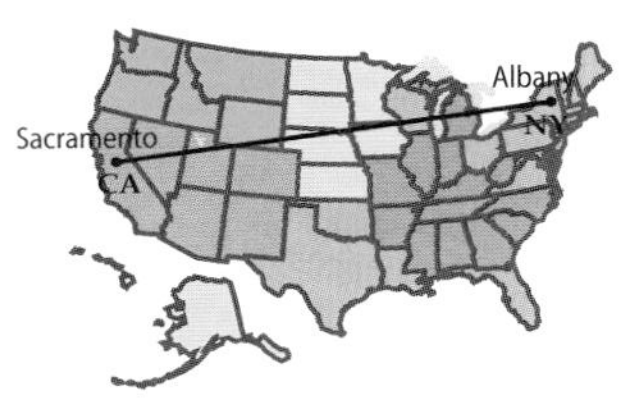

See Math This strategy connects positional vocabulary and the concept of rounding.

- Show a map of a student's home country. Ask: "**Where did** you **live**?" Have a student point out his or her former home.
- Say: "Which **city** is **closer** to **where** you ***lived***?" Discuss using the toy car to move between cities.
- Say: **"Finding** the **closer city** is like 'rounding' in math. Rounding is **finding** the number that is closer." Demonstrate on a number line.
- For a stronger visual/linguistic connection, emphasize the round tires and math use of round.

English Language Learners (p. 11) ELL

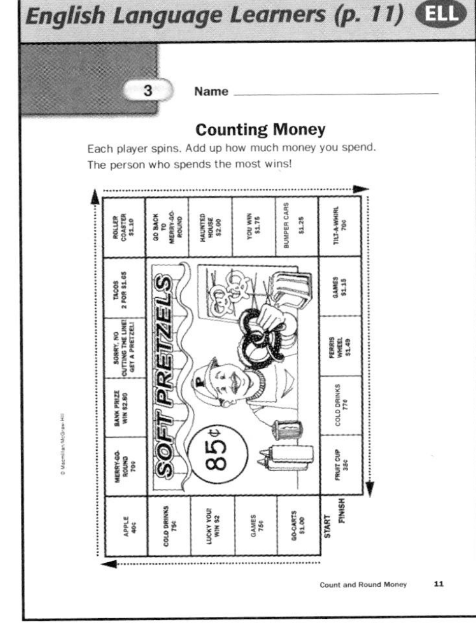

3 Name

Counting Money

Each player spins. Add up how much money you spend. The person who spends the most wins!

Count and Round Money 11

Use this worksheet to provide additional support for English Language Learners.

Independent Work Options

Option 1 Early Finishers AL

LOGICAL

Materials: grocery or department store flyers

- Distribute flyers to students. Tell them to pick 5 items that they would like to buy.
- First have them add the prices of all the items they have chosen and round the total cost. Next, have them round each individual price and then add to get the total.
- Ask them to write a paragraph explaining why the total cost is different (or not, if the total cost has not changed).

Option 2 Student Technology

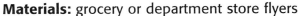

Math Online macmillanmh.com

Personal Tutor • Extra Examples

Math Adventures

Option 3 Learning Station: Art (p. 14G)

Direct students to the Art Learning Station for opportunities to explore and extend the lesson concept.

Option 4 Problem-Solving Practice

Reinforce problem-solving skills and strategies with the Problem-Solving Practice worksheet.

Problem Solving (p. 36) BL OL AL

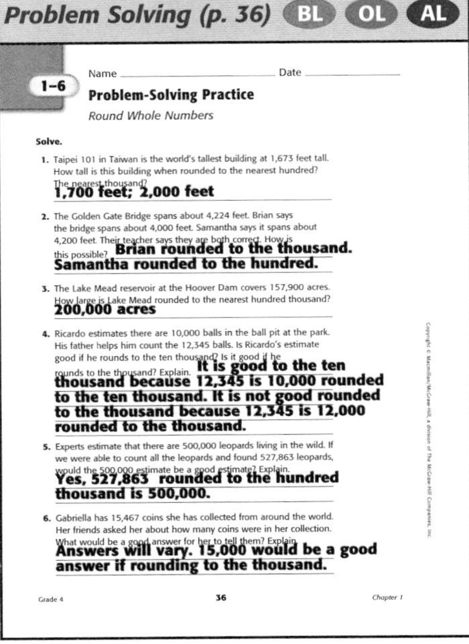

1–6 Name ________ Date ________

Problem-Solving Practice

Round Whole Numbers

Solve.

1. Taipei 101 in Taiwan is the world's tallest building at 1,673 feet tall. How tall is this building when rounded to the nearest hundred? The nearest thousand? **1,700 feet; 2,000 feet**
2. The Golden Gate Bridge spans about 4,224 feet. Brian says the bridge spans about 4,000 feet. Samantha says it spans about 4,200 feet. Their teacher says they are both correct. How is this possible? **Brian rounded to the thousand. Samantha rounded to the hundred.**
3. The Lake Mead reservoir at the Hoover Dam covers 157,900 acres. How large is Lake Mead rounded to the nearest hundred thousand? **200,000 acres**
4. Ricardo estimates there are 10,000 balls in the ball pit at the park. His father helps him count the 12,345 balls. Is Ricardo's estimate good if he rounds to the ten thousand? Is it good if he rounds to the thousand? Explain. **It is good to the ten thousand because 12,345 is 10,000 rounded to the ten thousand. It is not good rounded to the thousand because 12,345 is 12,000 rounded to the thousand.**
5. Experts estimate that there are 500,000 leopards living in the wild. If we were able to count all the leopards and found 527,863 leopards, would the 500,000 estimate be a good estimate? Explain. **Yes, 527,863 rounded to the hundred thousand is 500,000.**
6. Gabriella has 15,467 coins she has collected from around the world. Her friends asked her about how many coins were in her collection. What would be a good answer for her to tell them? Explain. **Answers will vary. 15,000 would be a good answer if rounding to the thousand.**

Grade 4 36 Chapter 1

Round Whole Numbers

1 Introduce

Activity Choice 1 • Hands-On 

- Draw a number line between 700 and 800 on the board. Put a tic mark halfway between 700 and 800.
- Tell students that the distance between Las Vegas, Nevada, and Boise, Idaho, is 758 miles.
- **Where would you find 758 on this number line?** Sample answer: just to the right of the tic mark
- Locate and label 758 on the number line.

Activity Choice 2 • Literature

Introduce the lesson with *Coyotes All Around* by Stuart J. Murphy. For a related math activity, see p. TR42.

2 Teach

Scaffolding Questions

Draw a number line from 6,000 to 7,000 on the board. Locate and label 6,500.

- **Name a number that is between 6,000 and 6,500.** Answers will vary; Sample answer: 6,425
- **Name a number that is between 6,500 and 7,000.** Answers will vary; Sample answer: 6,865
- **Is 6,491 closer to 6,000 or 7,000? How can you tell?** 6,000; The distance between 6,491 and 6,000 is less than the distance between 6,491 and 7,000.

Using the same process work with students to round numbers to the ten thousands, the hundred thousands, and the millions place.

- **What do you notice about the zeros?** each higher place value has a higher number of zeros.

GET READY to Learn

Have students open their books and read the paragraph under **Get Ready to Learn**. Introduce **estimate** and **rounding (or round)**. As a class, work through **Examples 1–3**.

1-6 Round Whole Numbers

MAIN IDEA

I will round whole numbers through the millions.

New Vocabulary

estimate

rounding (or round)

Math Online

macmillanmh.com

- Extra Examples
- Personal Tutor
- Self-Check Quiz

GET READY to Learn

A certain tractor weighs 17,554 pounds. About how much does it weigh?

When you do not need an exact answer, you can **estimate** by **rounding**. You can use a number line to round.

Real-World EXAMPLES Round Whole Numbers

1 MEASUREMENT To the nearest thousand, how much does the tractor weigh?

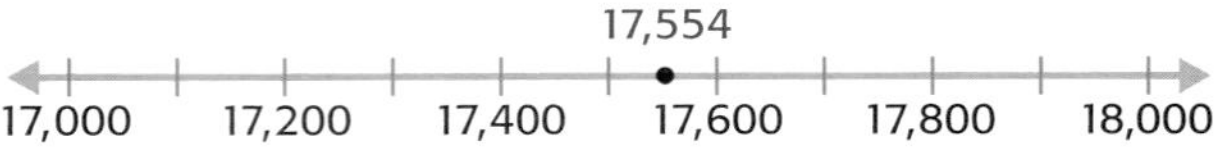

On the number line, 17,554 is closer to 18,000 than 17,000. So, round 17,554 to 18,000.

2 WORLD RECORDS The most dominoes that were set up and toppled by one person is 303,621. How many dominoes is this to the nearest ten thousand?

303,621

300,000 302,000 304,000 306,000 308,000 310,000

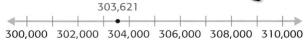

On the number line, 303,621 is closer to 300,000 than 310,000. So, round 303,621 to 300,000.

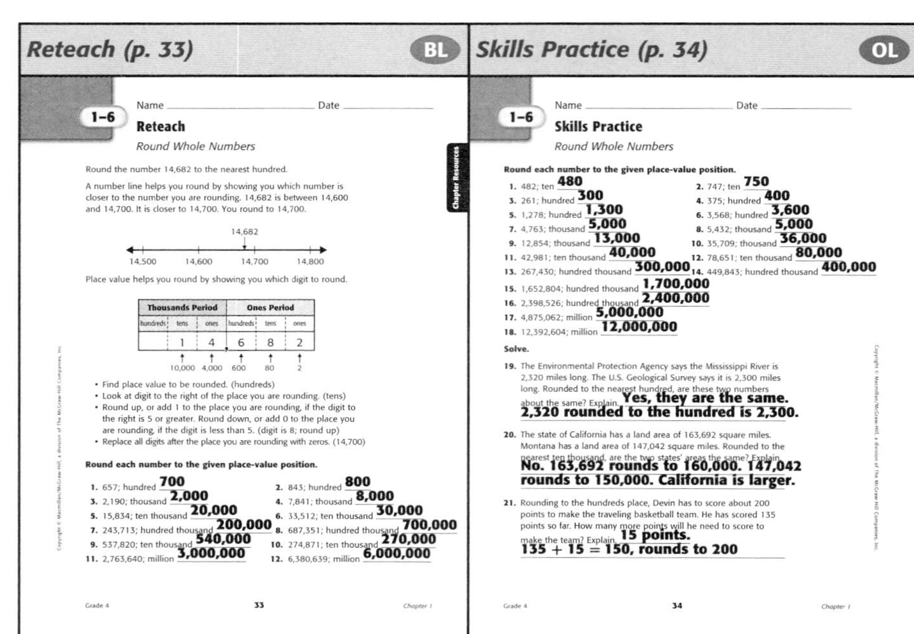

Reteach (p. 33) BL

1-6 Name ________ Date ________

Reteach

Round Whole Numbers

Round the number 14,682 to the nearest hundred.

A number line helps you round by showing you which number is closer to the number you are rounding. 14,682 is between 14,600 and 14,700. It is closer to 14,700. You round to 14,700.

14,682

14,500 14,600 14,700 14,800

Place value helps you round by showing you which digit to round.

Thousands Period			Ones Period		
hundreds	tens	ones	hundreds	tens	ones
	1	4,	6	8	2
	10,000	4,000	600	80	2

- Find place value to be rounded. (hundreds)
- Look at digit to the right of the place you are rounding. (tens)
- Round up, or add 1 to the place you are rounding, if the digit to the right is 5 or greater. Round down, or add 0 to the place you are rounding, if the digit is less than 5. (digit is 8; round up)
- Replace all digits after the place you are rounding with zeros. (14,700)

Round each number to the given place-value position.

1. 657; hundred **700**
2. 843; hundred **800**
3. 2,190; thousand **2,000**
4. 7,841; thousand **8,000**
5. 15,834; ten thousand **20,000**
6. 33,512; ten thousand **30,000**
7. 243,713; hundred thousand **200,000**
8. 687,351; hundred thousand **700,000**
9. 537,820; ten thousand **540,000**
10. 274,871; ten thousand **270,000**
11. 2,763,640; million **3,000,000**
12. 6,380,639; million **6,000,000**

Grade 4 33 Chapter 1

Chapter Resources

Skills Practice (p. 34) OL

1-6 Name ________ Date ________

Skills Practice

Round Whole Numbers

Round each number to the given place-value position.

1. 482; ten **480**
2. 747; ten **750**
3. 261; hundred **300**
4. 375; hundred **400**
5. 1,278; hundred **1,300**
6. 3,568; hundred **3,600**
7. 4,763; thousand **5,000**
8. 5,432; thousand **5,000**
9. 12,854; thousand **13,000**
10. 35,709; thousand **36,000**
11. 42,981; ten thousand **40,000**
12. 78,651; ten thousand **80,000**
13. 267,430; hundred thousand **300,000**
14. 449,843; hundred thousand **400,000**
15. 1,652,804; hundred thousand **1,700,000**
16. 2,398,526; hundred thousand **2,400,000**
17. 4,875,062; million **5,000,000**
18. 12,392,604; million **12,000,000**

Solve.

19. The Environmental Protection Agency says the Mississippi River is 2,320 miles long. The U.S. Geological Survey says it is 2,300 miles long. Rounded to the nearest hundred, are these two numbers about the same? Explain. **Yes, they are the same. 2,320 rounded to the hundred is 2,300.**

20. The state of California has a land area of 163,692 square miles. Montana has a land area of 147,042 square miles. Rounded to the nearest ten thousand, are the two states' areas the same? Explain. **No. 163,692 rounds to 160,000. 147,042 rounds to 150,000. California is larger.**

21. Rounding to the hundreds place, Devin has to score about 200 points to make the traveling basketball team. He has scored 135 points so far. How many more points will he need to score to make the team? Explain. **15 points. 135 + 15 = 150, rounds to 200**

Grade 4 34 Chapter 1

Place value can also be used to round numbers.

Vocabulary Link

Key Concept boxes highlight definitions, formulas, and other important ideas. Multiple representations—words, symbols, examples, formulas, models—help students understand the concepts.

Rounding Whole Numbers

Key Concept

Underline the digit to be rounded.

Look at the digit to the right of the place being rounded.

If the digit is 4 or less, do not change the underlined digit. If the digit is 5 or greater, add 1 to the underlined digit.

Replace all digits after the underlined digit with zeros.

Real-World EXAMPLE Round Whole Numbers

3 MEASUREMENT Saturn is 120,536 kilometers wide. Round this number to the nearest thousand.

You need to round 120,536 to the nearest thousand.

Step 1	Underline the digit in the place to be rounded. In this case, the 0 in the thousands place is to be rounded.	120,536
Step 2	Look at the digit to the right of the underlined digit, which is 5.	120,536
Step 3	Since the digit is 5 or greater, add 1 to the underlined digit.	121,536
Step 4	Replace all digits after the underlined digit with zeros.	121,000

To the nearest thousand, 120,536 is rounded to 121,000.

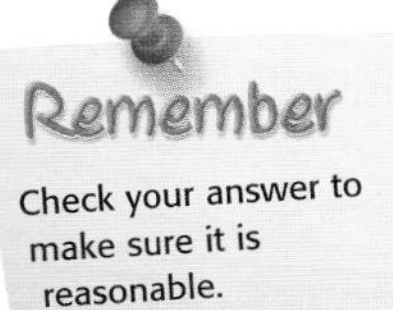

Remember

Check your answer to make sure it is reasonable.

Check

The number line shows that the answer is correct.

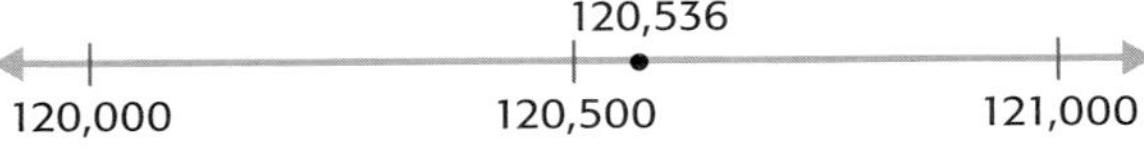

Round Whole Numbers

Example 1 Tell students that if a number is exactly halfway between two possible rounded numbers, the number is always rounded to the greater number. For example, 17,500 is halfway between 17,000 and 18,000, so rounded to the nearest thousand, it rounds to 18,000.

ADDITIONAL EXAMPLES

1. A library has 95,876 books. To the nearest thousand, how many books does the library have? 96,000 books
2. A local radio station claims that it has 571,395 loyal listeners. How many listeners is this rounded to the nearest ten thousand? 570,000 listeners
3. A wildlife refuge is said to be home to 569,400 birds. Round 569,400 to the nearest thousand. 569,000

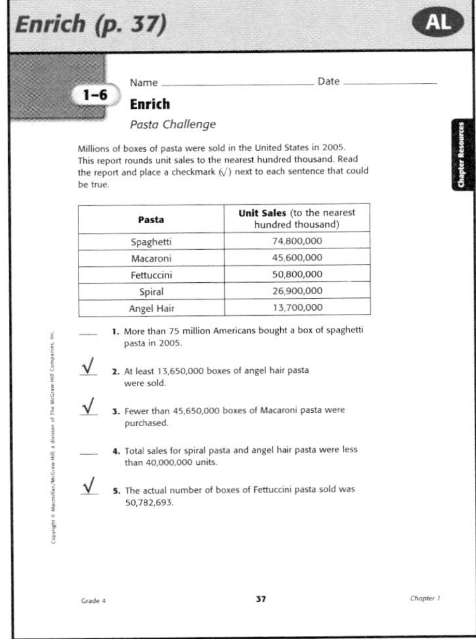

Enrich (p. 37) AL

Name ____________ Date ____________

1-6 **Enrich**

Pasta Challenge

Millions of boxes of pasta were sold in the United States in 2005. This report rounds unit sales to the nearest hundred thousand. Read the report and place a checkmark (√) next to each sentence that could be true.

Pasta	Unit Sales (to the nearest hundred thousand)
Spaghetti	74,800,000
Macaroni	45,600,000
Fettuccini	50,800,000
Spiral	26,900,000
Angel Hair	13,700,000

___ 1. More than 75 million Americans bought a box of spaghetti pasta in 2005.

√ 2. At least 13,650,000 boxes of angel hair pasta were sold.

√ 3. Fewer than 45,650,000 boxes of Macaroni pasta were purchased.

___ 4. Total sales for spiral pasta and angel hair pasta were less than 40,000,000 units.

√ 5. The actual number of boxes of Fettuccini pasta sold was 50,782,693.

Chapter Resources

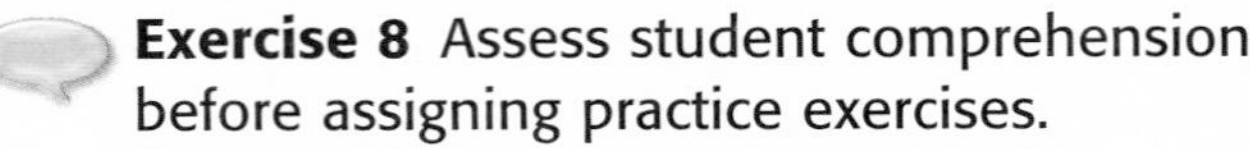

As a class, have students complete Exercises 1–8 in **Check What You Know** as you observe their work.

Exercise 8 Assess student comprehension before assigning practice exercises.

BL Alternate Teaching Strategy

If students have trouble identifying the digits talked about in the rounding rules...

Then use one of these reteach options:

1 CRM **Daily Reteach Worksheet** (p. 33)

2 Have them underline the digit to be rounded and circle the digit to the right of the place being rounded. Show students an example of rounding to the nearest thousand:

53,⑥91

Point out that the circled digit tells them whether to leave the underlined digit as it is or to increase it by 1.

3 Practice

Differentiate practice using these leveled assignments for Exercises 9–27.

Level	Assignment
BL Below/Approaching Level	9–14, 23–24
OL On Level	10–20, 22–24, 26
AL Above/Beyond Level	9–23 odd, 25–27

Have students discuss and complete the Higher Order Thinking problems. Encourage them to check their work.

WRITING IN MATH Have students complete Exercise 27 in their Math Journals. You may choose to use this exercise as an optional formative assessment.

COMMON ERROR!

Exercises 9–20 Students may have trouble identifying the digit in the given place-value position. To help these students, suggest that they keep a place-value chart on their desks.

Exercise 10 Students may incorrectly round this number to 390. Point out that adding 1 to 9 is 10, so the rounded number is 400.

CHECK What You Know

Round each number to the given place-value position. See Examples 1–3 (pp. 36–37)

1. 927; ten 930
2. 934; hundred 900
3. 4,282; thousand 4,000
4. 43,032; ten thousand 40,000
5. 593,205; hundred thousand 600,000
6. 1,709,385; million 2,000,000
7. The largest house made out of playing cards used 91,800 cards. To the nearest thousand, how many cards were used? 92,000
8. Talk About It Write the smallest number that you can round to the thousands place to get 8,000. Explain. Sample answer: 7,500; 5 will round the 7 up and the 4 in 7,499 will not

Practice and Problem Solving

EXTRA PRACTICE See page R3.

Round each number to the given place-value position. See Examples 1–3 (pp. 36–37)

9. 568; ten 570
10. 396; ten 400
11. 297; hundred 300
12. 148,245; hundred 148,200
13. 4,752; thousand 5,000
14. 493,580; thousand 494,000
15. 519,158; hundred thousand 500,000
16. 791,275; hundred thousand 800,000
17. 77,690; hundred 77,700
18. 95,230; thousand 95,000
19. 3,190,236; million 3,000,000
20. 4,303,985; million 4,000,000

21. yes; 29,028 when rounded to the nearest ten thousand would be about 30,000.

21. **Measurement** Earth's highest peak is Mount Everest. It is 29,028 feet high. Is this about 30,000 feet high? Explain.
22. **Measurement** The highest point in New Jersey is High Point. It is 1,803 feet high. Is this about 1,000 feet high? Explain.

22. no; 1,803 rounded to the nearest thousand would be 2,000.

Real-World PROBLEM SOLVING

Literature The graphic shows the number of characters that are in the longest novel in the world.

Source: *Guinness Book of World Records*

23. Round this number to the nearest hundred thousand. 14,200,000
24. To which place would this number be rounded if the rounded number was 14,156,100? hundreds place

Differentiated practice options provide suggestions for the exercises that are appropriate for below-level, on-level, or above-level students.

H.O.T. Problems

25. OPEN ENDED Write five numbers that would round to one million. See margin.

26. FIND THE ERROR Amanda and Martin round 83,275,925 to the hundred thousands place. Who is correct? Explain.

Amanda
80,000,000

Martin
83,300,000

26. Martin; Amanda's error is that she rounded to the ten millions place.

27. WRITING IN ▶MATH Create a real-world problem that involves rounding a number and results in an answer of 670,000. See margin.

TEST Practice

28. Which shows the correct order from least to greatest? (Lesson 1-5) B

A 1,245; 2,451; 5,412; 4,152

B 2,124; 4,215; 4,512; 5,214

C 5,214; 4,512; 4,215; 2,124

D 2,512; 2,215; 4,124; 4,421

29. Yuma, Arizona, is the sunniest place in the world. Round Yuma's average hours of sunlight each year to the nearest thousand. (Lesson 1-6) F

Top Two Sunniest Places	
Location	Hours of Sunlight Each Year
Yuma, Arizona	4,127
Phoenix, Arizona	4,041

F 4,000 **H** 4,200

G 4,100 **J** 5,000

Spiral Review

Order the numbers from greatest to least. (Lesson 1-5)

30. 685; 700; 660
700; 685; 660

31. 1,363; 1,468; 1,333
1,468; 1,363; 1,333

32. 12,009; 12,090; 12,900
12,900; 12,090; 12,009

Compare. Use >, <, or =. (Lesson 1-4)

33. 163 ● 165 <

34. 16,094 ● 16,090 >

35. 1,866 ● 1,866 =

36. The tallest mountain in the United States is 20,320 feet tall. Round this number to the nearest thousand. (Lesson 1-3) 20,000

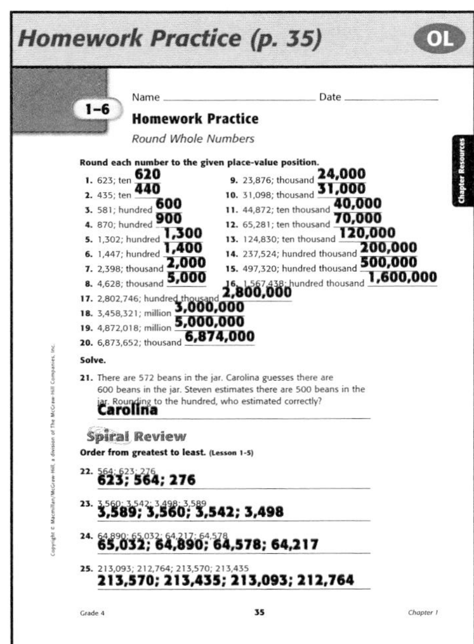

Homework Practice (p. 35) OL

1-6 Name ________ Date ________

Homework Practice

Round Whole Numbers

Round each number to the given place-value position.

1. 623; ten **620**
2. 435; ten **440**
3. 581; hundred **600**
4. 870; hundred **900**
5. 1,302; hundred **1,300**
6. 1,447; hundred **1,400**
7. 2,398; thousand **2,000**
8. 4,628; thousand **5,000**
9. 23,876; thousand **24,000**
10. 31,098; thousand **31,000**
11. 44,872; ten thousand **40,000**
12. 65,281; ten thousand **70,000**
13. 124,830; ten thousand **120,000**
14. 237,524; hundred thousand **200,000**
15. 497,320; hundred thousand **500,000**
16. 1,567,438; hundred thousand **1,600,000**
17. 2,802,746; hundred thousand **2,800,000**
18. 3,458,321; million **3,000,000**
19. 4,872,018; million **5,000,000**
20. 6,873,652; thousand **6,874,000**

Solve.

21. There are 572 beans in the jar. Carolina guesses there are 600 beans in the jar. Steven estimates there are 500 beans in the jar. Rounding to the hundred, who estimated correctly? **Carolina**

Spiral Review

Order from greatest to least. (Lesson 1-5)

22. 564; 623; 276 **623; 564; 276**
23. 3,560; 3,542; 3,498; 3,589 **3,589; 3,560; 3,542; 3,498**
24. 64,890; 65,032; 64,217; 64,578 **65,032; 64,890; 64,578; 64,217**
25. 213,093; 212,764; 213,570; 213,435 **213,570; 213,435; 213,093; 212,764**

Grade 4 35 Chapter 1

Chapter Resources

4 Assess

Formative Assessment

- **Explain how to round to the nearest thousand.** Think about the thousand before and after the number. Find the thousand closer to the number.

Quick Check **Are students continuing to struggle with rounding whole numbers?**

If Yes → Small Group Options (p. 36B)
Strategic Intervention Guide (p. 16)

If No → Independent Work Options (p. 36B)
CRM Skills Practice Worksheet (p. 34)
CRM Enrich Worksheet (p. 37)

Name the Math Have students round 1,561,976 to the nearest million. Ask them to explain each step of the process. 2,000,000; See students' explanations.

TEST Practice

Reviews Lessons 1-5 and 1-6

Assign the Test Practice problems to provide daily reinforcement of test-taking skills.

Spiral Review

Reviews Lessons 1-3, 1-4, and 1-5

Review and assess mastery of skills and concepts from previous chapters.

Additional Answers

25. Sample answer: 500,000; 900,000; 800,000; 700,000; 600,000

27. Sample answer: The baseball game lasted 674,961 seconds. How many seconds would that be rounded to the nearest ten thousand?

1-7 Problem-Solving Investigation
Choose a Strategy

Lesson Planner

Objective

Choose the best strategy to solve a problem.

Resources

Materials: poster board, markers

Manipulatives: money

Teacher Technology

TeacherWorks • Interactive Classroom

Real-World Problem Solving Library
Math and Social Studies: *Rivers and Mountains of the United States*

Use these leveled books to reinforce and extend problem-solving skills and strategies.

Leveled for:

- OL On Level
- ELL Sheltered English
- SP Spanish

For additional support, see the Real-World Problem Solving Teacher Guide.

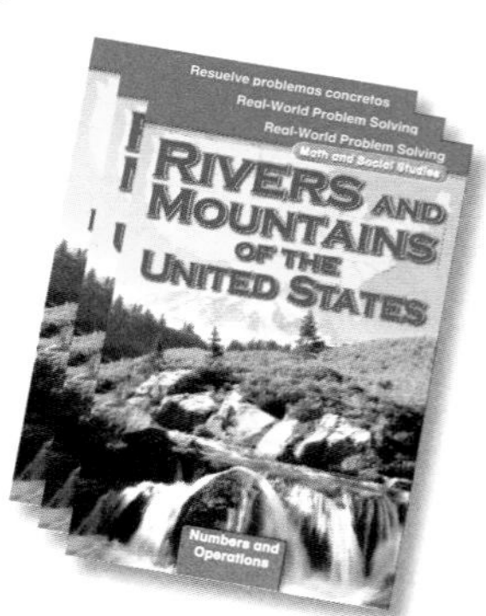

Daily Routine

Use these suggestions before beginning the lesson on p. 40.

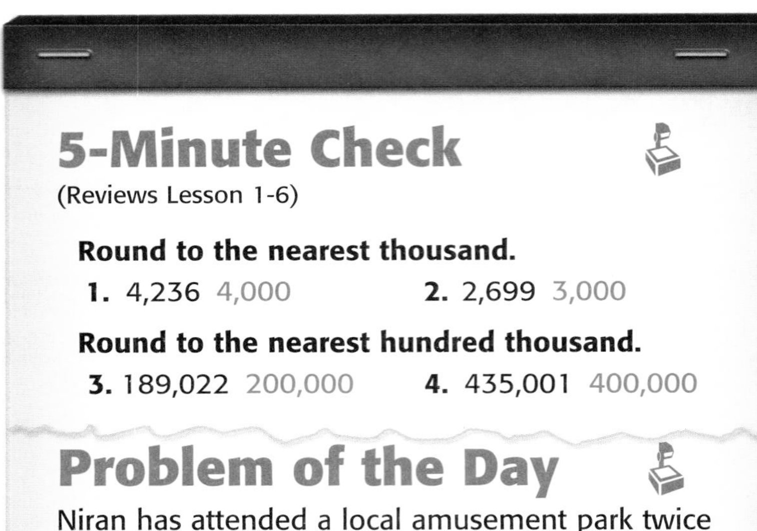

5-Minute Check

(Reviews Lesson 1-6)

Round to the nearest thousand.

1. 4,236 4,000 **2.** 2,699 3,000

Round to the nearest hundred thousand.

3. 189,022 200,000 **4.** 435,001 400,000

Problem of the Day

Niran has attended a local amusement park twice every year since he was 5 years old. How old is Niran if he has been to the amusement park 20 times? 15 years old

Differentiated Instruction

Small Group Options

Option 1 Gifted and Talented AL

LOGICAL

Materials: paper and pencil

- Pose the problem at the right:
- How many new cards will Ryan receive in trades? 22 cards
- Some of the cards Ryan and his friends have are really valuable. He will have to trade 5 of his extra cards to get a special one. **How many special cards could he get if he has 31 cards to trade?** 6 special cards

> Ryan collects and trades baseball cards with his friends. He has 44 extra cards in his collection he wishes to trade. He has agreed to trade 2 of his cards for one special card from his friends.

Option 2 English Language Learners ELL

LINGUISTIC, VISUAL

Materials: paper, pencil
Core Vocabulary: in, this/that, can write
Common Use Verb: have/has

Write Math This strategy introduces preposition use and possessives in simple word problems.

- Write 3 + 4 on the board. Write 3 on a self-sticking note, and 4 on another note. Put the 3 self-sticking note on an open box as you say: "This box has 3 on it."
- Repeat for 4.
- Say: "I **have** 3 pencils in the box" as you place them. Repeat for 4.
- Say: "I can write a word problem for 3 + 4." Write: "I **have** [blank] pencils in this box." Repeat for the second box, changing "***this***" to "***that***."
- Say: "How many do I **have** in all?"
- Have students write a word problem using the scaffold.
- Have students share problems. Repeat as time permits.

Independent Work Options

Option 1 Early Finishers OL AL

LOGICAL

Materials: index cards

- Give students 1–2 index cards and ask them to write a word problem on the front of each card that uses what they have learned in the chapter.
- Collect the cards and shuffle. Distribute the cards and have students solve the problems on the back of the cards. Discuss solutions with a partner.

Option 2 Student Technology

Math Online macmillanmh.com

Personal Tutor • Extra Examples

Option 3 Learning Station: Social Studies (p. 14H)

Direct students to the Social Studies Learning Station for opportunities to explore and extend the lesson concept.

1-7 Problem-Solving Investigation

1 Introduce

Activity Choice • Review

- Divide the class into groups of 2 or 3. Give each group 10 assorted coins. Ask each group to make up a word problem based on the coins they were given. Have them share their problems with the class.
- Choose a problem from one of the groups. Solve the problem using the four-step plan.

2 Teach

Have students read the problem on trading dollars to pesos. Guide them through the problem-solving steps.

Understand Using the questions, review what students know and need to find.

Plan Have them discuss their strategy.

Solve Guide students to use the four-step plan to solve the problem.

- **What is the pattern on the table?** add 11
- **How many pesos will the family get for $8?** 88

Check Have students look back at the problem to make sure that the answer fits the facts given in the problem.

COMMON ERROR!

Exercises 2, 5, 6, 8, 10, 11 If students have difficulty with these problems, give them play money and have them act them out.

1-7 Problem-Solving Investigation

MAIN IDEA I will choose the best strategy to solve a problem.

P.S.I. TEAM +

TORY: My family is going on vacation to Mexico. Before we go, we have to trade our dollars for Mexican pesos. For every dollar we will get about 11 pesos.

YOUR MISSION: Find about how many pesos Tory's family will get for $8.

Understand You know that one dollar is about 11 pesos.

You need to find about how many pesos they will get for $8.

Plan For every 1 dollar, they get 11 pesos. Make a table to solve the problem.

Solve

Dollars	$1	$2	$3	$4	$5	$6	$7	$8
Pesos	11	22	33	44	55	66	77	88

+11 +11 +11 +11 +11 +11 +11

The pattern is to add 11. You can also solve this using multiplication. $8 \times 11 = 88$.
The family can expect to get about 88 pesos for $8.

Check There is a second pattern in the table. When the digit in the dollar row is changed to pesos, the dollar digit is repeated twice. For example, $5 is 55 pesos. The answer, $8 is 88 pesos, follows this pattern.

So, the answer is correct.

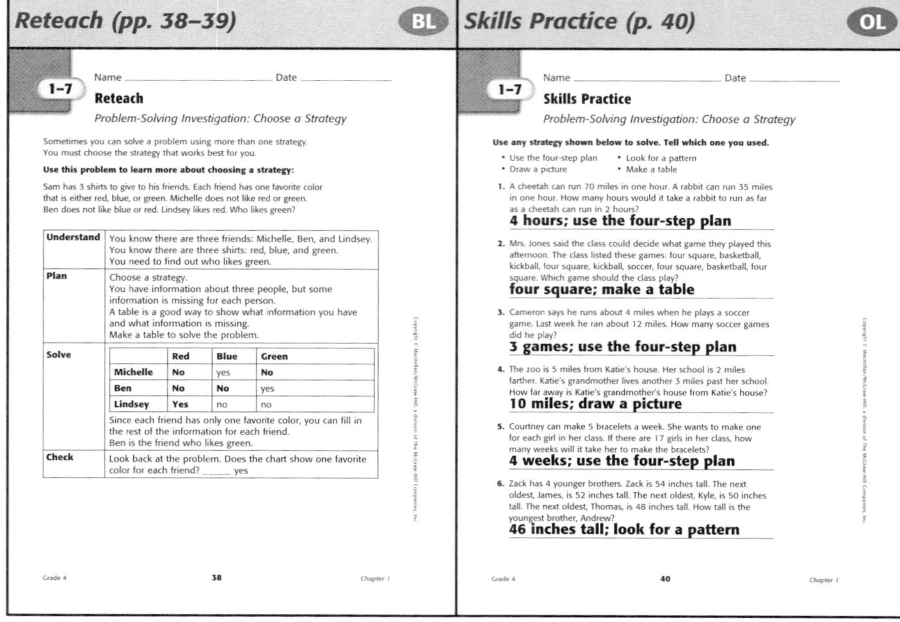

Reteach (pp. 38–39) BL

1-7 Name ______ Date ______

Reteach

Problem-Solving Investigation: Choose a Strategy

Sometimes you can solve a problem using more than one strategy. You must choose the strategy that works best for you.

Use this problem to learn more about choosing a strategy:

Sam has 3 shirts to give to his friends. Each friend has one favorite color that is either red, blue, or green. Michelle does not like red or green. Ben does not like blue or red. Lindsey likes red. Who likes green?

Understand	You know there are three friends: Michelle, Ben, and Lindsey. You know there are three shirts: red, blue, and green. You need to find out who likes green.
Plan	Choose a strategy. You have information about three people, but some information is missing for each person. A table is a good way to show what information you have and what information is missing. Make a table to solve the problem.
Solve	(see table below) Since each friend has only one favorite color, you can fill in the rest of the information for each friend. Ben is the friend who likes green.
Check	Look back at the problem. Does the chart show one favorite color for each friend? ______ yes

	Red	Blue	Green
Michelle	**No**	yes	**No**
Ben	**No**	**No**	yes
Lindsey	**Yes**	no	no

Skills Practice (p. 40) OL

1-7 Name ______ Date ______

Skills Practice

Problem-Solving Investigation: Choose a Strategy

Use any strategy shown below to solve. Tell which one you used.

- Use the four-step plan
- Look for a pattern
- Draw a picture
- Make a table

1. A cheetah can run 70 miles in one hour. A rabbit can run 35 miles in one hour. How many hours would it take a rabbit to run as far as a cheetah can run in 2 hours?
   4 hours; use the four-step plan
2. Mrs. Jones said the class could decide what game they played this afternoon. The class listed these games: four square, basketball, kickball, four square, kickball, soccer, four square, basketball, four square. Which game should the class play?
   four square; make a table
3. Cameron says he runs about 4 miles when he plays a soccer game. Last week he ran about 12 miles. How many soccer games did he play?
   3 games; use the four-step plan
4. The zoo is 5 miles from Katie's house. Her school is 2 miles farther. Katie's grandmother lives another 3 miles past her school. How far away is Katie's grandmother's house from Katie's house?
   10 miles; draw a picture
5. Courtney can make 5 bracelets a week. She wants to make one for each girl in her class. If there are 17 girls in her class, how many weeks will it take her to make the bracelets?
   4 weeks; use the four-step plan
6. Zack has 4 younger brothers. Zack is 54 inches tall. The next oldest, James, is 52 inches tall. The next oldest, Kyle, is 50 inches tall. The next oldest, Thomas, is 48 inches tall. How tall is the youngest brother, Andrew?
   46 inches tall; look for a pattern

★ indicates multi-step problem

Mixed Problem Solving

See page R4.

Use the four-step plan to solve.

1. **Measurement** A black bear weighs 25 pounds more than a gorilla. Use the information in the table to find how much a black bear weighs. 425 lb

Large Animal Weights	
Animal	**Weight (pounds)**
Gorilla	400
Black bear	■
Lion	440

★2. A watch costs $34. A pair of sunglasses costs $6. How much change would you receive if you bought one watch and one pair of sunglasses and paid with a $50 bill? $10

3. Jade has 3 sticker sheets with 6 stickers on each sheet. How many stickers does she have in all? 18 stickers

★4. **Measurement** A robin can fly 20 miles in one hour. An eagle can fly 40 miles in one hour. How many hours will it take a robin to fly as far as an eagle in 3 hours? 6 hr

5. A video game store buys used video games for $10 each. Vivian wants a new video game for $77. How many used games must she sell to buy the new game? 8 games

★6. Lee wants a motorized scooter. He earns $8 a week, and already has $11. How many weeks will he have to save all of his money to buy the scooter? 8 wk

7. Turi burns about 350 calories for every hour he skis. The last time he skied, he burned 1,200 calories. Did he ski over 3 hours? Explain. See Ch. 1 Answer Appendix.

8. **Algebra** Leticia earns $20 each time she babysits. How many times will she need to babysit to earn $120? 6 times

9. Jack's basketball games are 4 quarters that are each 8 minutes long. Is it possible for Jack to play 35 minutes in a game? Explain. no; there are 32 minutes in a game.

10. Xavier saved three $10 bills, six $5 bills, and twelve $1 bills. Does he have enough money to buy this MP3 player? no

11. **WRITING IN MATH** Refer to Exercise 10. Suppose Xavier has 5 bills and the total is $37. Explain the steps you would take to find which bills he has. See Ch. 1 Answer Appendix.

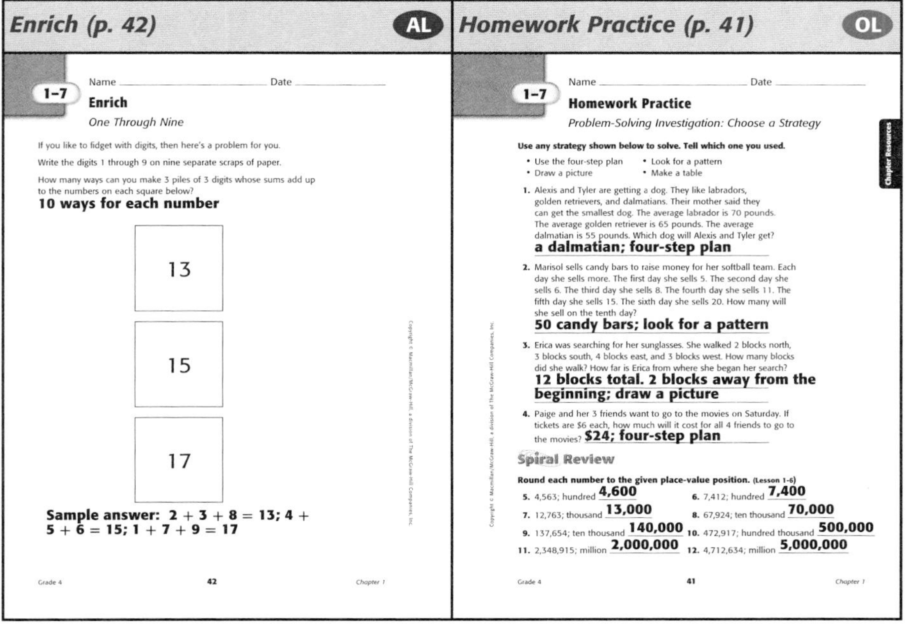

Enrich (p. 42) AL

1-7 Name ____________ Date ________

Enrich

One Through Nine

If you like to fidget with digits, then here's a problem for you.

Write the digits 1 through 9 on nine separate scraps of paper.

How many ways can you make 3 piles of 3 digits whose sums add up to the numbers on each square below?
10 ways for each number

13

15

17

Sample answer: 2 + 3 + 8 = 13; 4 + 5 + 6 = 15; 1 + 7 + 9 = 17

Grade 4 42 Chapter 1

Homework Practice (p. 41) OL

1-7 Name ____________ Date ________

Homework Practice

Problem-Solving Investigation: Choose a Strategy

Chapter Resources

Use any strategy shown below to solve. Tell which one you used.

- Use the four-step plan
- Look for a pattern
- Draw a picture
- Make a table

1. Alexis and Tyler are getting a dog. They like labradors, golden retrievers, and dalmatians. Their mother said they can get the smallest dog. The average labrador is 70 pounds. The average golden retriever is 65 pounds. The average dalmatian is 55 pounds. Which dog will Alexis and Tyler get? **a dalmatian; four-step plan**

2. Marisol sells candy bars to raise money for her softball team. Each day she sells more. The first day she sells 5. The second day she sells 6. The third day she sells 8. The fourth day she sells 11. The fifth day she sells 15. The sixth day she sells 20. How many will she sell on the tenth day? **50 candy bars; look for a pattern**

3. Erica was searching for her sunglasses. She walked 2 blocks north, 3 blocks south, 4 blocks east, and 3 blocks west. How many blocks did she walk? How far is Erica from where she began her search? **12 blocks total. 2 blocks away from the beginning; draw a picture**

4. Paige and her 3 friends want to go to the movies on Saturday. If tickets are $6 each, how much will it cost for all 4 friends to go to the movies? **$24; four-step plan**

Spiral Review

Round each number to the given place-value position. (Lesson 1-6)

5. 4,563; hundred **4,600**
6. 7,412; hundred **7,400**
7. 12,763; thousand **13,000**
8. 67,924; ten thousand **70,000**
9. 137,654; ten thousand **140,000**
10. 472,917; hundred thousand **500,000**
11. 2,348,915; million **2,000,000**
12. 4,712,634; million **5,000,000**

Grade 4 41 Chapter 1

BL Alternate Teaching Strategy

If students have trouble remembering the four steps of the strategy…

Then use one of these reteach options:

1 CRM **Daily Reteach Worksheet** (pp. 38–39)

2 Have them create posters to show the strategies. Hang the posters around the room.

3 Practice

Using the Exercises

Exercises 1–11 involve choosing a strategy to solve the problem. Take time to review three strategies that were introduced in Grade 3: draw a picture, look for a pattern, and make a table. You may want to go through the exercises as a class to make sure everyone knows the best strategy to use before solving the problem.

4 Assess

Formative Assessment

Have students draw a picture to solve the problem:

Ciana's bedroom is 12 feet by 12 feet. She wants to put new tile on the floor. The tile measures 2 feet by 2 feet. How many tiles will she need? 36 tiles

Quick Check **Are students continuing to struggle with the four-step plan?**

If Yes → Small Group Options (p. 40B)

If No → Independent Work Options (p. 40B)
CRM Skills Practice Worksheet (p. 40)
CRM Enrich Worksheet (p. 42)

Lesson Planner

Objective

Interpret information and data from science to solve problems.

National Standard 

Students should develop an understanding of the characteristsics of organisms.

Vocabulary

expanded form, **word form**, **round**

Activate Prior Knowledge

Before you turn students' attention to the pages, ask them to discuss marine mammals.

- **Name some marine mammals you know. Which ones have fur?** whales, seals; Seals have fur.
- **Name some characteristics that all mammals share.** They are warm-blooded; they give birth to live young.

Using the Student Page

Ask students to read the information on p. 42 and answer these questions:

- **Which dolphin has the greatest population?** Spotted dolphin
- **If you round the population of the Northern Fur Seal to the nearest ten thousand, how many are there?** 990,000

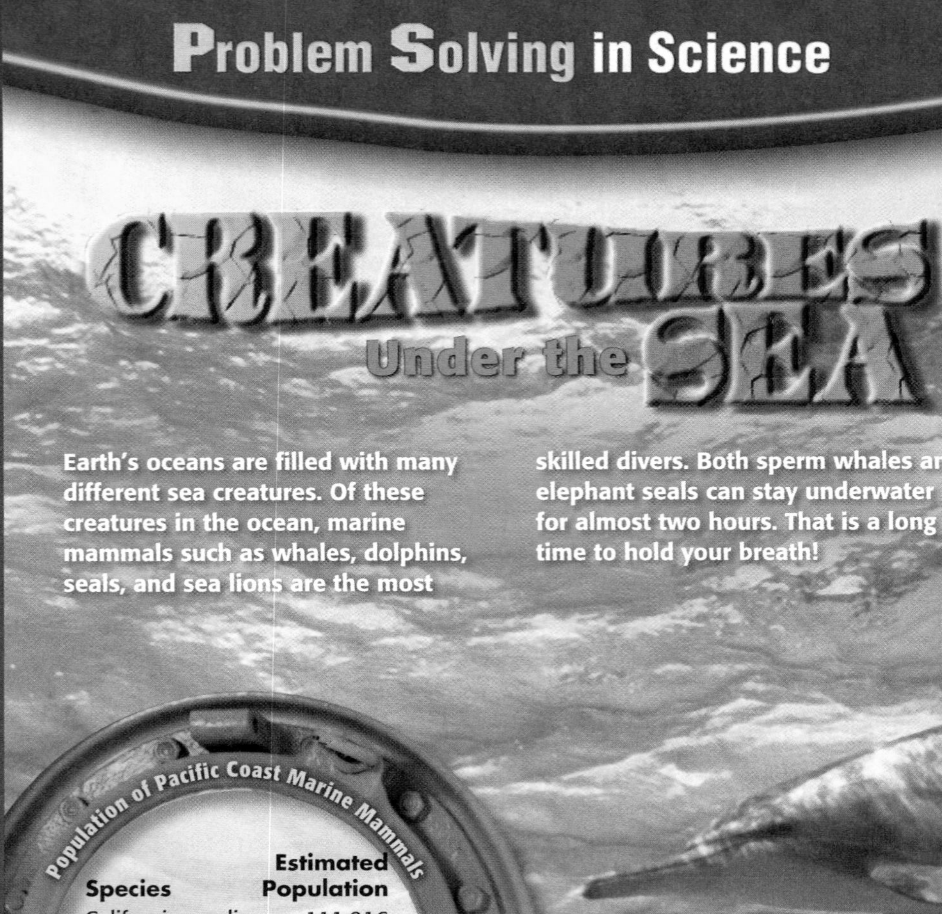

CREATURES Under the SEA

Earth's oceans are filled with many different sea creatures. Of these creatures in the ocean, marine mammals such as whales, dolphins, seals, and sea lions are the most skilled divers. Both sperm whales and elephant seals can stay underwater for almost two hours. That is a long time to hold your breath!

Population of Pacific Coast Marine Mammals

Species	Estimated Population
California sea lion	111,016
Gray whale	20,869
Hawaiian monk seal	1,300
Northern fur seal	988,000
Pacific harbor seal	131,826
Spinner dolphin	631,000
Spotted dolphin	731,000

Source: National Biological Service

The cross-curricular Real-World Problem Solving lessons connect math to real-world applications.

Real-World Math

6. California sea lion; gray whale; Hawaiian monk seal; spinner dolphin; and spotted dolphin

Use the information on pages 42 and 43 to solve each problem.

1. Which marine mammal species has the greatest population? Write in expanded and word forms. See margin.
2. There are about 20,000 blue whales. Your friend tells you that there are more blue whales than gray whales. Is your friend right? Explain. no; There are more gray whales since 20,869 > 20,000.
3. A humpback whale can eat up to 9,000 pounds of food a day. Is this more or less than a blue whale eats? How much more or less? more; 1,500 pounds more
4. A sea lion can dive 400 feet. Some seals can dive 5,314 feet. Dolphins can dive up to 1,000 feet. List these dives from greatest to least. 4, 5. See margin.
5. You are told that there are about 132,000 Pacific harbor seals. Is this true when you round to the nearest thousand? Explain.
6. Which animal populations, when rounded to the nearest thousand, have a one in the thousands place?

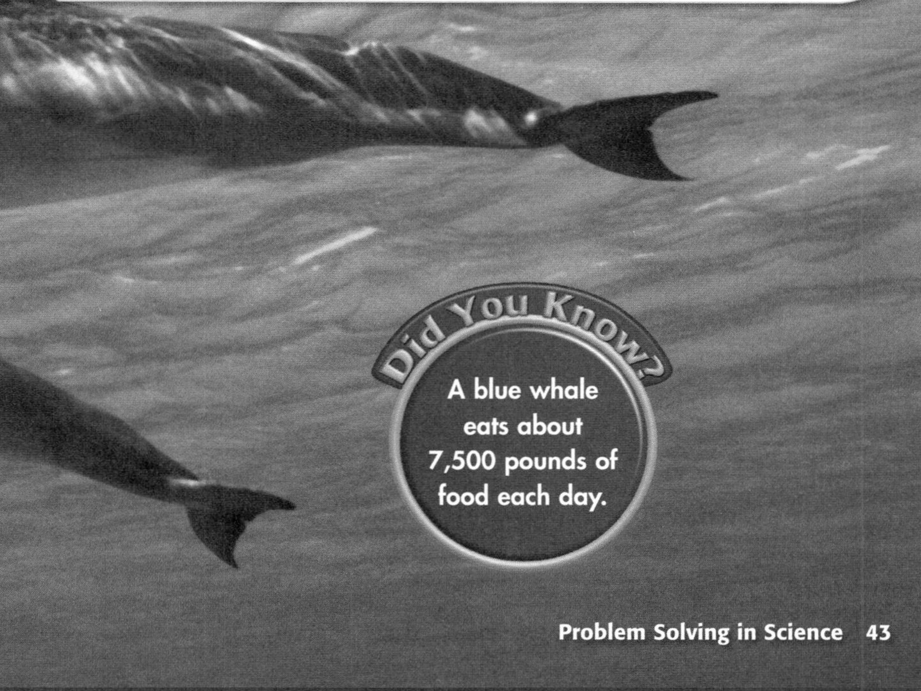

Did You Know?
A blue whale eats about 7,500 pounds of food each day.

Real-World Math

Assign the exercises on p. 43. Encourage students to choose a problem-solving strategy before beginning each exercise. If necessary, review the strategies suggested in Lesson 1-7, p. 40.

Exercise 2 Remind students that they can compare using place-value charts.

Exercise 4 Remind students that *endangered* means that an animal's population is dangerously small.

Exercise 7 Tell students that they need to round first before they can tell what number will be in the thousands place for each population.

WRITING IN MATH Have students create a word problem that uses the information found in the text and in the picture on p. 42.

Extend the Activity

Have students research other endangered marine mammals and compare their populations to the ones on p. 42.

Additional Answers

1. Northern fur seal; 900,000 + 80,000 + 8,000; nine hundred eighty-eight thousand
4. Seal, 5,314; dolphin, 1,000 feet; sea lion, 400 feet
5. Yes; 131,826 rounded to the nearest thousand is 132,000.

Chapter 1 Study Guide and Review

FOLDABLES Dinah Zike's Foldables

Use these lesson suggestions to incorporate the Foldable during the chapter. Students can then use their Foldable to review for the test.

Lesson 1-5 Under the third tab, students form, compare, order, and round numbers through the millions.

Key Vocabulary

The page references after each word denote where that term was first introduced. If students have difficulty answering Exercises 1–6, remind them they can use the page references to review the vocabulary terms.

Vocabulary Review

Review chapter vocabulary using one of the following options.

- **Visual Vocabulary Cards** (12, 15, and 42)
- **eGlossary** at macmillanmh.com

Students can use the Vocabulary Check in the Study Guide and Review to review the vocabulary of the chapter.

Chapter 1 Study Guide and Review

- STUDY TO GO
- Vocabulary Review

FOLDABLES Study Organizer GET READY to Study

Be sure the following Key Vocabulary words and Key Concepts are written in your Foldable.

Place Value and Number Sense
Place Value through Hundred Thousands | Place Value through Millions | Compare, Order, and Round Whole Numbers

Key Concepts

Place Value (pp. 17–19 and 22–25)

- A **place-value** chart shows the value of the digits in a number.

Thousands			Ones		
hundreds	tens	ones	hundreds	tens	ones
	2	1	8	3	3

Read and Write Numbers (pp. 17–19 and 22–25)

- **Standard form:** 21,833
- **Word form:** twenty-one thousand, eight hundred thirty-three
- **Expanded form:** 20,000 + 1,000 + 800 + 30 + 3

Compare Numbers (pp. 28–30)

- To compare numbers, use **is greater than** (>), **is less than** (<), or **is equal to** (=).

123 > 122 478 < 874 925 = 925

Key Vocabulary

estimate (p. 36)
is greater than (>) (p. 28)
is less than (<) (p. 28)
place value (p. 17)
rounding (p. 36)

Vocabulary Check

Choose the vocabulary word that completes each sentence.

1. When you do not need an exact answer, you can ___?___. estimate
2. To help you read and write numbers, you can use ___?___. place value
3. When you do not need an exact answer, you can estimate by ___?___. rounding
4. The ___?___ of the 7 in 7,495 is the thousands. place value
5. The symbol > is used to show that a number is ___?___ another number. greater than
6. The symbol < is used to show that a number is ___?___ another number. less than

Chapter 1 Project

What's That Cost?

Alone, in pairs, or in small groups, have students discuss the results of their completed chapter project with the class. Assess their work using the Chapter Project rubric found in Chapter 1 Resource Masters, p. 55.

Lesson-by-Lesson Review

1-1 Place Value Through Hundred Thousands (pp. 17–19)

Example 1
Write 5,789 in three different ways.

Thousands			Ones		
hundreds	tens	ones	hundreds	tens	ones
		5	7	8	9

Standard form: 5,789

Word form: five thousand, seven hundred eighty-nine

Expanded form: 5,000 + 700 + 80 + 9

Write each number in word form and expanded form. 7–9. See margin.

7. 18,045 **8.** 94,804

9. Write *four hundred thirty thousand, two hundred fifty-six* in standard form and expanded form.

Write the value of the underlined digit.

10. 190,843 90,000 **11.** 84,299 200

12. The Petrified Forest National Park in northeast Arizona is 93,533 acres. Write this number in word form and expanded form. See margin.

1-2 Place Value Through Millions (pp. 22–25)

Example 2
Write *nine million, three hundred seventy-two thousand, five hundred* in standard form and expanded form.

Word form: nine million, three hundred seventy-two thousand, five hundred

Standard form: 9,372,500

Expanded form: 9,000,000 + 300,000 + 70,000 + 2,000 + 500

Write each number in standard form and expanded form.

13. two thousand, six hundred ninety-seven

14. nine million, four hundred six thousand, two hundred seventy-one

13–15. See margin.

15. León has a baseball card collection of 4,826 cards. He sells 215 cards to another collector. How many cards does he have left? Write in word form and expanded form.

Students can complete the exercises in the Lesson-by-Lesson Review as they prepare for the chapter test. If they need extra help, examples are provided.

Lesson-by-Lesson Review

Have students complete the Lesson-by-Lesson Review on pp. 45–48. Then you can use ExamView® Assessment Suite to customize another review worksheet that practices all the objectives of this chapter or only the objectives on which your students need more help.

Intervention If the given examples are not sufficient to review the topics covered by the questions, use the page references next to the exercises to review that topic in the Student Edition.

Additional Answers

7. eighteen thousand, forty-five; 10,000 + 8,000 + 40 + 5

8. ninety-four thousand, eight hundred four; 90,000 + 4,000 + 800 + 4

9. 430,256; 400,000 + 30,000 + 200 + 50 + 6

12. ninety three thousand, five hundred thirty-three; 90,000 + 3,000 + 500 + 30 + 3

13. 2,697; 2,000 + 600 + 90 + 7

14. 9,406,271; 9,000,000 + 400,000 + 6,000 + 200 + 70 + 1

15. four thousand, six hundred eleven; 4,000 + 600 + 10 + 1

CHAPTER 1 Study Guide and Review

Additional Answers

19. Sample answer: yes; Trent has 3 nights to read the book, so, he will read 20 + 20 + 20 or 60 pages in 3 days.

20. Sample answer: no; Repeated addition can be used to find the distance the car can travel on 10 gallons of gas, which is 250 miles.

1-3 Problem-Solving Skill: The Four-Step Plan (pp. 26–27)

Example 3
Dorota saves $2 each week. How much will she save after 2 months?

Understand Dorota saves $2 each week. You need to find how much money will she save after 2 months.

Plan There are 4 weeks in 1 month. Use repeated addition to find how much money she has saved after 2 months.

Solve First, find how much she saved in one month.

$2	1 week
$2	1 week
$2	1 week
+ $2	1 week
$8	

Now, find the amount saved in two months.

$8	1 month
+ $8	1 month
$16	

So, Dorota will save $16 after 2 months.

Check Count by two's 8 times.
2, 4, 6, 8, 10, 12, 14, 16

So, the answer is correct.

Solve. Use the four-step plan.

16. Cynthia earns 5 points at the library for each book she reads. She wants to earn 75 points in order to win the grand prize. How many books does she need to read? 15 books

17. Darius has $72. He wants to buy the bike shown. How much more money does he need? $28

18. Kristina earned $22 dollars babysitting. She owes her mom $17. How much will Kristina have left after she pays her mom? $5

19. Trent has to read a book by Friday. It is Tuesday and he has 60 pages left to read. If he reads 20 pages a night for the next 3 nights, will he finish the book? Explain.

20. **Measurement** Presta's family is going to the mountains 280 miles away. The family's car can go 25 miles on a gallon of gas, and the gas tank holds 10 gallons. Can they travel to the mountains without stopping to fill up the gas tank? Explain.

1-4 Compare Whole Numbers (pp. 28–30)

Example 4
Compare 1,278 ● 1,500.
Use >, <, or =.

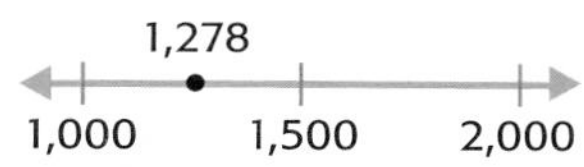

1,500 is to the right of 1,278.
So, 1,500 is greater than 1,278.
1,278 is less than 1,500.
Therefore, 1,278 < 1,500.

Compare. Use >, <, or =.

21. 25,689 ● 25,679 >

22. 54,820 ● 58,240 <

23. 109,050 ● 109,050 =

24. 234,461 ● 234,641 <

25. Jaya ate 2,142 calories on Monday. On the same day her brother ate 2,111 calories. Who had more calories on Monday? Jaya

1-5 Order Whole Numbers (pp. 32–34)

Example 5
Order 54,282; 65,820; and 52,466 from greatest to least.

First, line up the ones place. Compare the digits in the greatest place.

54,282
65,820 ← greatest
52,466

Then, compare the digits in the next place.

54,282
52,466

4 > 2. So, 54,282 is the next greatest number.

The numbers ordered from greatest to least are 65,820; 54,282; and 52,466.

Order the numbers from greatest to least.

26. 12,378; 12,784; 12,837
12,837; 12,784; 12,378

27. 138,023; 138,032; 139,006
139,006; 138,032; 138,023

28. 456,980; 612,701; 611,036
612,701; 611,036; 456,980

29. The table shows the population of three states. Order these states from greatest to least population.

State	Population
Illinois	12,831,970
Kentucky	4,206,074
South Carolina	4,321,249

Source: U.S. Census Bureau

See margin.

Additional Answer

29. Illinois, South Carolina, Kentucky

CHAPTER 1

Study Guide and Review

1-6 Round Whole Numbers (pp. 36–39)

Example 6
Round 587 to the nearest ten.

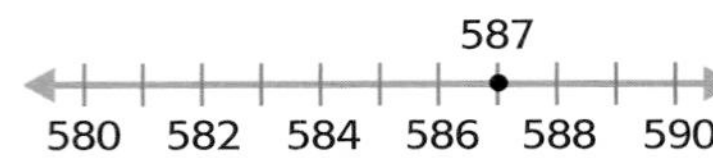

On the number line, 587 is closer to 590 than 580. Therefore, round 587 to 590.

Round each number to the given place-value position.

30. 874; hundred **900**

31. 12,025; ten thousands **10,000**

32. 617,589; ten thousands **620,000**

33. 547,203; thousands **547,000**

34. In 1790, the population of the United States was 3,929,214. To the nearest million, what was the population in 1790? **4,000,000**

1-7 Problem-Solving Investigation: Choose a Strategy (pp. 40–41)

Example 7
Each time Esteban goes to the grocery store for his grandmother, she gives him $4. He has $12. How many times has Esteban gone to the grocery store?

Esteban has $12, and he gets $4 each time he goes to the store. You need to find how many times he has gone to the store. Use addition.

$4	1 trip
$4	1 trip
+ $4	1 trip
$12	

So, Esteban has gone to the store 3 times.

Use the four-step plan to solve.

35. Lindsay earns $5 for every A she gets on her report card and $3 for every B. On her last report card, she received a total of $19 for 5 subjects. How many As and Bs did she get? **2 As and 3 Bs**

36. Precious spends 35 hours in school every five-day week. How many five-day weeks will she have been in school if she has been in school for 175 hours? **5 wk**

37. In 1916, Jeannette Rankin of Montana became the first woman elected to Congress. Use rounding to estimate how many years ago the first woman was elected to Congress. **Accept answers from 90–100 years.**

Chapter Test

For Exercises 1 and 2, tell whether each statement is *true* or *false*.

1. The four steps of the four-step problem-solving plan in order are Plan, Understand, Solve, Check. false
2. The standard form of nine hundred seventy is 970. true

Write the value of the underlined digit.

3. 18,765 8,000
4. 301,936 300,000
5. Students voted on their favorite frozen yogurt flavors. The results are shown. Order the results from most favorite to least favorite. 410, 401, 240, 99

Flavor	Number of Students
Vanilla	410
Chocolate	240
Strawberry	99
Chocolate chip	401

6. **MULTIPLE CHOICE** Which of these is 7,201,446? B
   - **A** seven thousand, two hundred one, four hundred forty-six
   - **B** seven million, two hundred one thousand, four hundred forty-six
   - **C** seven hundred two thousand, one hundred forty-six
   - **D** seven million, two hundred ten thousand, four hundred forty-six

Order the numbers from greatest to least.

7. 1,002; 1,037; 1,200; 1,102 1,200; 1,102; 1,037; 1,002
8. 7,613; 7,702; 8,045; 7,499 8,045, 7,702; 7,613; 7,499
9. A computer costs $1,295. Round this price to the nearest hundred. $1,300

Compare. Use >, <, or =.

10. 6,782 ● 6,702 >
11. 2,487 ● 2,784 <
12. **MULTIPLE CHOICE** What is 7,620,113 rounded to the nearest hundred thousand? F
    - **F** 7,600,000
    - **G** 7,620,000
    - **H** 7,700,000
    - **J** 8,000,000
13. Sora earned a score of 98 on a test. Ryan earned a score of 89. Who earned a higher score? Sora

14–16. See Ch.1 Answer Appendix.

Write each number in word form.

14. 3,476
15. 97,602
16. WRITING IN MATH Andrew rounded 647,963 to the nearest hundred thousand. Is his answer correct? Explain.

700,000

Chapter Test

Summative Assessment

Use these alternate leveled chapter tests to differentiate assessment for the specific needs of your students.

Leveled Chapter 1 Tests			
Form	Type	Level	CRM Pages
1	Multiple Choice	BL	57–58
2A	Multiple Choice	OL	59–60
2B	Multiple Choice	OL	61–62
2C	Free Response	OL	63–64
2D	Free Response	OL	65–66
3	Free Response	AL	67–68

BL = below/approaching grade level
OL = on grade level
AL = above/beyond grade level

Vocabulary Test

CRM **Chapter 1 Resource Masters** (p. 52)

Customize and create multiple versions of your chapter test and the test answer keys.

Data-Driven Decision Making

Based on the results of the Chapter Test, use the following to review concepts that continue to present students with problems.

Exercises	State/Local Standards	What's the Math?	Error Analysis	Resources for Review
2–4, 6, 14–15		Read and write whole numbers to hundred thousands.	Does not understand "expanded form." Does not understand "standard form." Does not know correct words for place value.	Strategic Intervention Guide (pp. 2, 6, 8, 10) CRM Chapter 1 Resource Masters (Reteach Worksheets) Math Adventures My Math Zone Chapter 1 Math Online Extra Examples • Personal Tutor • Concepts in Motion
1		Use four-step plan to solve a problem. Write whole numbers in word form.	Does not know words "altogether," "total." Adds or multiplies incorrectly.	
10–11, 13		Compare whole numbers.	Reverses "less than" and "greater than" signs. Does not know place value.	
5, 7–9		Orders whole numbers.	Does not know place value. Does not know place value words, word "value," or use of commas in writing numbers.	

Chapter 1 Test Practice

Formative Assessment

- Use Student Edition pp. 50–51 as practice and cumulative review. The questions are written in the same style as many state tests.
- You can also use these two pages to benchmark student progress, or as an alternate homework assignment.

Additional practice pages can be found in the Chapter 1 Resource Masters.

CRM **Chapter 1 Resource Masters**
Cumulative Test Practice

- Multiple Choice format (pp. 57–62)
- Free Response format (pp. 63–68)

ExamView Assessment Suite Create practice worksheets or tests that align to your state standards.

Math Online Have students visit macmillanmh.com for additional practice to reinforce your state standards.

Test Practice gives students an opportunity to practice the kinds of questions found on state assessments.

Chapter 1 Test Practice

Cumulative, Chapter 1

Math Online macmillanmh.com
- Test Practice

TEST Example

What is four hundred sixty-one thousand, eight hundred five in standard form?

A 416,805 **C** 461,805

B 461,580 **D** 461,850

Read the Test Question

You need to find the number in standard form.

Solve the Test Question

Make a place-value chart to help you find the standard form of the number.

Thousands			Ones		
hundreds	tens	ones	hundreds	tens	ones
4	6	1,	8	0	5

As you read the numbers, listen to the place value.

The answer is C.

TEST-TAKING TIP

You can use place value to help you read and write numbers in the millions.

PART 1 Multiple Choice

Read each question. Then fill in the correct answer on the answer sheet provided by your teacher or on a sheet of paper.

1. What is 54,678,491 rounded to the nearest hundred thousand? D

A 54,000,000 **C** 54,680,000

B 54,600,000 **D** 54,700,000

2. What is the standard form for sixteen million, three hundred twenty-seven thousand, four hundred three? H

F 16,723,043 **H** 16,327,403

G 16,372,430 **J** 16,237,340

Test-Taking Tip

Share with students that it is best to examine all the answer choices to determine which one is correct.

Preparing for Standardized Tests

For test-taking strategies and practice, see pages R42–R55.

3. The table shows the number of coupons mailed out by four large grocery store chains.

Grocery Store Coupons	
Store	**Number of Coupons**
Fast Mart	35,411
Saver Center	35,408
Gardens	35,416
Big Value	35,420

Which store mailed out the most coupons? A

A Big Value **C** Gardens

B Fast Mart **D** Saver Center

4. Which symbol makes the following true? G

12,935,374 ■ 12,953,748

F > **H** =

G < **J** +

5. Which is the value of the digit 7 in 273,158? D

A 70 **C** 7,000

B 700 **D** 70,000

PART 2 Short Response

Record your answers on the answer sheet provided by your teacher or on a sheet of paper.

6. What is $4,775,000 rounded to the nearest million? $5,000,000

7. What is the word form for 724,385? See margin.

8. Which point on the number line represents 22? C

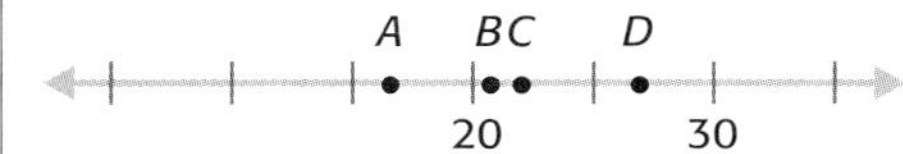

PART 3 Extended Response

Record your answers on the answer sheet provided by your teacher or on a sheet of paper.

9. What is the value of the digit 9 in 349,865? Create a place-value chart to support your answer.

10. Explain how to round $3,876,342 to the nearest million.

9, 10. See margin.

NEED EXTRA HELP?										
If You Missed Question...	1	2	3	4	5	6	7	8	9	10
Go to Lesson...	1-6	1-2	1-5	1-4	1-1	1-6	1-1	1-4	1-1	1-6

Summative Assessment 51

Answer Sheet Practice

Have students simulate taking a state test by recording their answers on a practice recording sheet.

CRM **Chapter 1 Resource Masters**
Student Recording Sheet (p. 73)

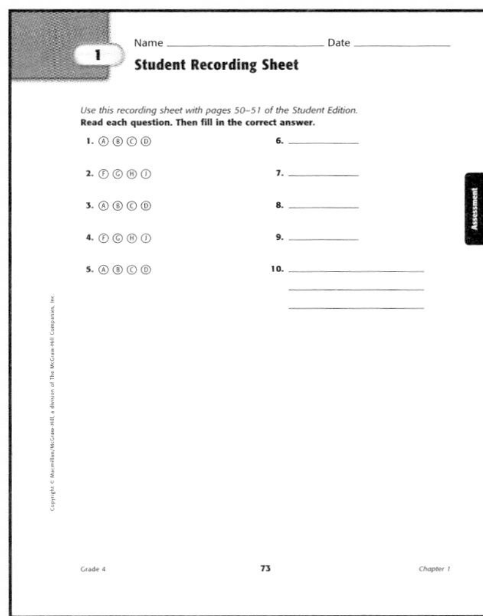

Name ______ Date ______

1 **Student Recording Sheet**

Use this recording sheet with pages 50–51 of the Student Edition.
Read each question. Then fill in the correct answer.

1. Ⓐ Ⓑ Ⓒ Ⓓ 6. ______
2. Ⓕ Ⓖ Ⓗ Ⓙ 7. ______
3. Ⓐ Ⓑ Ⓒ Ⓓ 8. ______
4. Ⓕ Ⓖ Ⓗ Ⓙ 9. ______
5. Ⓐ Ⓑ Ⓒ Ⓓ 10. ______

Grade 4 73 Chapter 1

A Student Recording Sheet for the Test Practice is provided for each chapter in the Chapter Resource Masters.

7. seven hundred twenty-four thousand, three hundred eighty-five

9. Sample answer: The digit nine is written in the thousands place in the place-value chart. So, the value of the digit 9 is 9,000.

Thousands			Ones		
hundreds	tens	ones	hundreds	tens	ones
3	4	9	8	6	5

10. Sample answer: Identify the digit to be rounded, 3. Look at the digit to the right of 3, which is 8. Since 8 is greater than 5, add one to 3. Then replace all digits after 3 with zeros. So, the answer is $4,000,000.

Page 16, Are You Ready

3. seventy-nine; 70 + 9
4. thirty; 30
5. ninety, 90
6. one hundred sixty-five; 100 + 60 + 5
7. three hundred forty-seven; 300 + 40 + 7
8. six hundred ninety-two; 600 + 90 + 2
9. one thousand, eight hundred forty; 1,000 + 800 + 40
10. four thousand, five hundred five; 4,000 + 500 + 5

Page 19, Lesson 1-1

20. five thousand, fifty; 5,000 + 50
21. three thousand, seven hundred ninety-one; 3,000 + 700 + 90 + 1
22. fifty-seven thousand, four hundred two; 50,000 + 7,000 + 400 + 2
23. eighty-nine thousand, seventy-four; 80,000 + 9,000 + 70 + 4
24. two hundred forty-three thousand, eight hundred ninety-five; 200,000 + 40,000 + 3,000 + 800 + 90 + 5
25. four hundred eighty-five thousand, eight hundred thirty; 400, 000 + 80,000 + 5,000 + 800 + 30
26. six hundred forty-nine thousand, three hundred twenty; 600,000 + 40,000 + 9,000 + 300 + 20
27. seven hundred eighty-four thousand, one hundred thirty-two; 700,000 + 80,000 + 4,000 + 100 + 30 + 2
31. seven thousand, six hundred thirty-five; 7,635
32. twenty thousand, nine hundred seventy-six; 20,976
33. sixty thousand, eighty-four; 60,084

Page 23, Lesson 1-2

11. two million, six hundred seventeen thousand; 2,000,000 + 600,000 + 10,000 + 7,000
12. Sample answer: Write the number in a place-value chart to find that the digit 5 has a value of 50,000.

Page 27, Lesson 1-3

1. Addition was used because multiplication is repeated addition.
2. A child's ticket costs $12. So an adult's ticket would cost $20. Three adult tickets would cost $20 + $20 + $20 or $60.
3. The model shows that 20 + 20 + 20 = 60.

Page 30, Lesson 1-4

28. Show an example. Stack the numbers, lining up the ones place. Then look at the greatest place. Compare the digits. If the digits are different, the number with the greater digit has the greater value. If they are the same, look at the second greatest place and compare the digits. Continue the process until the relationship between the numbers is found.

Page 31, Mid-Chapter Check

1. two thousand, three hundred eighty-four; 2,000 + 300 + 80 + 4
2. nine hundred seventeen thousand, twenty-two; 900,000 + 10,000 + 7,000 + 20 + 2
3. 19,206; 10,000 + 9,000 + 200 + 6
4. 272; 200 + 70 + 2
9. 90,000 + 8,000 + 400 + 10
10. 28,306,037, twenty-eight million, three hundred six thousand, thirty-seven
16. Neither, they traveled the same distance.
18. Sample answer: No number is given for the hundred thousands place, so a place holder is needed. So, the missing digit is zero.

Page 41, Lesson 1-7

7. yes; 3 hours burns 350 + 350 + 350 or 1,050 Calories. Since Turi burned 1,200 Calories, he skied more than 3 hours.
11. Sample answer: Think of all of the different possible combinations of five bills to find which five total $37.

Page 49, Chapter Test

14. three thousand, four hundred seventy-six
15. ninety-seven thousand, six hundred two
16. Sample answer: no; The 4 in the ten thousands place does not cause the 6 to round up to a seven.

NOTES

Chapter Overview

Chapter-at-a-Glance

In Chapter 2, students learn how to add, subtract, and estimate sums and differences of whole numbers.

Lesson		Math Objective	State/Local Standards
2-1	**Algebra: Addition Properties and Subtraction Rules** (pp. 55–57)	Use addition properties and subtraction rules to add and subtract.	
2-2	**Estimate Sums and Differences** (pp. 58–61)	Estimate sums and differences of numbers.	
2-3	**Problem-Solving Skill: Estimate or Exact Answer** (pp. 62–63)	Determine when to estimate or find an exact answer.	
2-4	**Add Whole Numbers** (pp. 64–67)	Add numbers, including multi-digit numbers.	
EXTEND	**Techlink** (p. 68)	Use technology to explore addition.	
EXPLORE 2-5	**Subtract Whole Numbers** (pp. 70–71)	Explore how to subtract whole numbers.	
2-5	**Subtract Whole Numbers** (pp. 72–75)	Subtract multi-digit numbers.	
2-6	**Problem-Solving Investigation: Choose a Strategy** (pp. 76–77)	Choose the best strategy to solve a problem.	
2-7	**Subtract Across Zeros** (pp. 80–83)	Subtract multi-digit numbers, when some digits are zero.	

Solve Addition and Subtraction Problems

BIG Idea As students advance through grade levels, their computational abilities progress. Some students may still need to use manipulatives to help them understand addition and subtraction of five- and six-digit numbers. Although students have been learning subtraction since Grade 2, some may still find it difficult to regroup when necessary and subtract the smaller digit from the larger digit. Lesson 2-7 addresses this troublesome topic.

Teachers should continue to remind students that estimation provides a quick way to determine the reasonableness of their sums or differences.

Algebra Students learn to use addition properties with whole numbers. This concept will help prepare them for algebra concepts, such as solving equations. (Lesson 2-1)

G4-FP4C *Algebra:* Students continue identifying, describing, and extending numeric patterns involving all operations and nonnumeric growing or repeating patterns. Through these experiences, they develop an understanding of the use of a rule to describe a sequence of numbers or objects.

G4-FP8C *Number and Operations:* Building on their work in grade 3, students extend their understanding of place value and ways of representing numbers to 100,000 in various contexts. They use estimation in determining the relative sizes of amounts or distances. Students develop understandings of strategies for multidigit division by using models that represent division as the inverse of multiplication, as partitioning, or as successive subtraction. By working with decimals, students extend their ability to recognize equivalent fractions. Students' earlier work in grade 3 with models of fractions and multiplication and division facts supports their understanding of techniques for generating equivalent fractions and simplifying fractions.

Skills Trace

Vertical Alignment

Third Grade

In third grade, students learned to:

- Find the sum and difference of two whole numbers between 0 and 10,000.
- Use estimation to verify the reasonableness of calculated results.

Fourth Grade

During this chapter, students learn to:

- Add, subtract, and estimate the sum or difference of numbers.
- Demonstrate an understanding of, and the ability to add multi-digit numbers.
- Add and subtract using addition properties and subtraction rules.

After this chapter, students learn to:

- Add and subtract decimals.

Fifth Grade

In fifth grade, students learn to:

- Add, subtract, and estimate fractions with like denominators.
- Add, subtract, and estimate sums and differences of fractions and mixed numbers.

Backmapping and Vertical Alignment **McGraw-Hill's *Math Connects*** program was conceived and developed with the final results in mind: student success in Algebra 1 and beyond. The authors, using the **NCTM Focal Points and Focal Connections** as their guide, developed this brand-new series by backmapping from Algebra 1 concepts, and vertically aligning the topics so that they build upon prior skills and concepts and serve as a foundation for future topics.

Math Vocabulary

The following math vocabulary words for Chapter 2 are listed in the glossary of the **Student Edition**. You can find interactive definitions in 13 languages in the **eGlossary** at macmillanmh.com.

Associative Property of Addition The property that states that the grouping of the addends does not change the sum. (p. 55A)
Example: $(4 + 5) + 2 = 4 + (5 + 2)$

Commutative Property of Addition The property that states that the order in which two numbers are added does not change the sum. (p. 55A)
Example: $12 + 15 = 15 + 12$

difference The answer to a subtraction problem. (p. 72A)

estimate A number close to an exact value; an estimate indicates about how much. (p. 58A)
Example: 47 + 22 (estimate 50 + 20) about 70

Identity Property of Addition The property that states that the sum of any number and 0 is the number.
Example: $7 + 0 = 7$ $0 + 7 = 7$

minuend The first number in a subtraction sentence from which a second number is to be subtracted. (p. 72A)
Example: 8 − 3 = 5 (8 = minuend, 3 = subtrahend, 5 = difference)

subtrahend The second number in a subtraction sentence that is subtracted from a number or minuend. (p. 72A)

Visual Vocabulary Cards
Use Visual Vocabulary Card 15 to reinforce the vocabulary in this lesson. (The Define/Example/Ask routine is printed on the back of each card.)

estimate

CHAPTER 2

Chapter Planner

Suggested Pacing		
Instruction	Review & Assessment	TOTAL
9 days	1 day	**10 days**

Diagnostic Assessment
Quick Check (p. 54)

	Lesson 2-1 (Pacing: 1 day)	Lesson 2-2 (Pacing: 1 day)	Lesson 2-3 (Pacing: 1 day)
Lesson/ Objective	**Algebra: Addition Properties and Subtraction Rules** (pp. 55–57) **Objective:** Use addition properties and subtraction rules to add and subtract.	**Estimate Sums and Differences** (pp. 58–61) **Objective:** Estimate sums and differences of numbers.	**Problem-Solving Skill** **Estimate or Exact Answer** (pp. 62–63) **Objective:** Determine when to estimate or find an exact answer.
State/Local Standards			
Math Vocabulary	**Commutative Property of Addition**, **Associative Property of Addition**, **Identity Property of Addition**	**estimate**	
Lesson Resources	**Materials** index cards, construction paper **Manipulatives** connecting cubes **Other Resources** CRM Leveled Worksheets (pp. 8–12) Daily Reteach • 5-Minute Check • Problem of the Day	**Manipulatives** number cubes **Other Resources** CRM Leveled Worksheets (pp. 13–17) Daily Reteach • 5-Minute Check • Problem of the Day	**Materials** self sticking notes **Other Resources** CRM Leveled Worksheets (pp. 18–22) Daily Reteach • 5-Minute Check • Problem of the Day *The Olympic Games*
Technology		Math Adventures	
Math Online	Personal Tutor	Personal Tutor	
Reaching All Learners	English Learners, p. 55B ELL Gifted and Talented, p. 55B AL Early Finishers, p. 55B OL AL	English Learners, p. 58B ELL Gifted and Talented, p. 58B AL Early Finishers, p. 58B OL AL	English Learners, p. 62B ELL Below Level, p. 62B BL Early Finishers, p. 62B OL AL
Alternate Lesson		*IMPACT Mathematics:* Unit C	

KEY

BL Below/Approaching Level
OL On Level
AL Above/Beyond Level
ELL English Learners
SE Student Edition
TE Teacher Edition
CRM Chapter 2 Resource Masters
CD-Rom
Transparency
Real-World Problem Solving Library

	Lesson 2-4 Pacing: 1 day	Extend 2-4 Pacing: 1 day	Explore 2-5 Pacing: 1 day
Lesson/ Objective	**Add Whole Numbers** (pp. 64–67) **Objective:** Add numbers, including multi-digit numbers.	**Explore Composing and Decomposing Numbers** (p. 68) Tech Link **Objective:** Use technology to explore addition.	**Subtract Whole Numbers** (pp. 70–71) **Objective:** Explore how to subtract whole numbers.
State/Local Standards			
Math Vocabulary			
Lesson Resources	**Manipulatives** base-ten blocks **Other Resources** CRM Leveled Worksheets (pp. 23–27) Daily Reteach • 5-Minute Check • Problem of the Day		**Manipulatives** base-ten blocks
Technology	Math Adventures	Math Tool Chest	
Math Online	Personal Tutor		Concepts in Motion
Reaching All Learners	English Learners, p. 64B ELL Gifted and Talented, p. 64B AL Early Finishers, p. 64B OL AL		
Alternate Lesson			

Formative Assessment
Mid-Chapter Check (p. 69)

CHAPTER 2

Chapter Planner

	Lesson 2-5 (Pacing: 1 day)	Lesson 2-6 (Pacing: 1 day)	Lesson 2-7 (Pacing: 1 day)
Lesson/ Objective	**Subtract Whole Numbers** (pp. 72–75) **Objective:** Subtract multi-digit numbers.	**Problem-Solving Investigation** **Choose a Strategy** (pp. 76–77) **Objective:** Choose the best strategy to solve a problem.	**Subtract Across Zeros** (pp. 80–83) **Objective:** Subtract multi-digit numbers, when some digits are zero.
State/Local Standards			
Math Vocabulary	**difference**, **minuend**, **subtrahend**		
Lesson Resources	**Materials** grid paper **Manipulatives** base-ten blocks **Other Resources** CRM Leveled Worksheets (pp. 28–32) Daily Reteach • 5-Minute Check • Problem of the Day	**Other Resources** CRM Leveled Worksheets (pp. 33–37) Daily Reteach • 5-Minute Check • Problem of the Day *The Olympic Games*	**Manipulatives** play money, base-ten blocks **Other Resources** CRM Leveled Worksheets (pp. 38–42)  Daily Reteach • 5-Minute Check • Problem of the Day
Technology	Math Adventures		 Math Adventures
Math Online	Personal Tutor		Personal Tutor
Reaching All Learners	English Learners, p. 72B ELL Below Level, p. 72B BL Early Finishers, p. 72B OL AL	English Learners, p. 76B ELL Below Level, p. 76B BL Early Finishers, p. 76B OL AL	English Learners, p. 80B ELL Below Level, p. 80B BL Early Finishers, p. 80B OL AL
Alternate Lesson			
	Game Time Make a Big Difference (p. 75)	**Problem Solving in Science** (p. 78)	**Summative Assessment** • Study Guide and Review (p. 84) • Chapter Test (p. 89) • Test Practice (p. 90)

Assessment Options

Diagnostic Assessment

- SE *Option 1:* Quick Check (p. 54)
- *Option 2:* Online Quiz macmillanmh.com
- CRM *Option 3:* Diagnostic Test (p. 44)
- CRM *Option 4:* Chapter Pretest (p. 45)

Formative Assessment

- TE Alternate Teaching Strategies (in every lesson)
- SE Talk About It (in every lesson)
- SE Writing in Math (in every lesson)
- SE Check What You Know (in every lesson)
- TE Ticket Out the Door (pp. 57, 74)
- TE Into the Future (p. 61)
- TE Yesterday's News (p. 83)
- SE Mid-Chapter Check (p. 69)
- CRM Lesson Quizzes (pp. 46–48)
- CRM Mid-Chapter Test (p. 49)

Summative Assessment

- SE Chapter Test (p. 89)
- SE Test Practice (p. 90)
- CRM Vocabulary Test (p. 50)
- CRM Leveled Chapter Tests (pp. 55–66)
- CRM Cumulative Test Practice (pp. 69–71)
- CRM Oral Assessment (pp. 51–52)
- ExamView® Assessment Suite
- Advance Tracker

Mc Graw Hill Professional Development

Targeted professional development has been articulated throughout **McGraw-Hill's *Math Connects*** program. The **McGraw-Hill Professional Development Video Library** provides short videos that support the **NCTM Focal Points and Focal Connections.** For more information visit macmillanmh.com.

Model Lessons

Instructional Strategies

What the Research Says ...

Refer to these resources for additional information on addition and subtraction.

- A. Baroody, *Children's Difficulties in Subtraction: Some Causes and Questions,* Journal for Research in Mathematics Education, 1985, pp. 203–213.
- T. P. Carpenter, M. L. Franke, V. R. Jacobs, E. Fennema, and S. B. Empson, *A Longitudinal Study of Invention and Understanding in Children's Multidigit Addition and Subtraction,* Journal for Research in Mathematics Education, 1998, pp. 3–20.
- The 1998 Yearbook of the National Council of Teachers of Mathematics, entitled *The Teaching and Learning of Algorithms in School Mathematics,* contains several research and general articles on algorithms.
- Lorna J. Morrow, *Whither Algorithms?* Mathematics Educators Express Their Views, pp. 1–6.
- Zalman Usiskin, *Paper-and-Pencil Algorithms in a Calculator-and-Computer Age,* pp. 7–20.
- Patricia F. Campbell, Thomas E. Rowan, and Anna R. Suarez, *What Criteria for Student-Invented Algorithms?,* pp. 49–55.

Teacher Notes

Learning Stations

Cross-Curricular Links

Writing

 individual | LINGUISTIC 

How Much Time?

- How many minutes do you spend each day getting back and forth to school? Write an explanation of how you can calculate your total travel time using addition.
- Explain how you can use addition to calculate how much time you spend traveling back and forth to school in one week. How about in one month?

Materials:

- paper
- pencil

Art

  individual | VISUAL 

Add Up Your Impressions

Pointillism is a technique to create paintings using hundreds of dots of paint. If you stand far away from a pointillist painting, you can see the subject of the painting rather than the dots of paint.

- Make a painting using dots of different colors of paint to create your image. Keep track of how many dots you make with each color.
- How many dots of each color did you use? How many dots in total did you use? How many more dots did you make for the color you used the most than the color you used the least?

Materials:

- paint
- round brush
- access to water
- paper
- pencil

Reading

 group | SOCIAL 

A Penny a Year

- Read *The Hundred Penny Box* by Sharon Bell Mathis by yourself or with a group and make your own Penny Box.
- For each year of your life, tape a penny with that year on it to an index card, and write one sentence about something that happened in your life that year. If you cannot find a penny with the right year on it, write the correct year below the penny on the card. Put the cards in your box.
- Add the total of pennies your group has on the chalkboard. Then use addition to find out how many pennies the whole class has.

I learned to add multi-digit numbers

Materials:

- *The Hundred Penny Box* by Sharon Bell Mathis
- index cards
- tape
- pennies
- small cardboard boxes

Solve Addition and Subtraction Problems

Science

group | LOGICAL

Measure the Difference

- Each person in the group measures his or her height in inches. Write down the heights of all the students in your group on a chart from tallest to shortest.
- What is the combined height of everyone in your group? How much taller is the tallest person than each person in the group?
- Make a poster showing your heights in your group, and your subtraction equations for finding the differences between the tallest person and each member of the group on the chart.

Materials:

- measuring stick or measuring tape
- markers
- paper
- pencils

Health

group | SOCIAL

Add Up Sit-Ups

- Each person in your group does as many sit-ups as possible before getting tired. Write down the total number of sit-ups for each member of your group. How many sit-ups did your group do altogether? Add up the totals to find out.
- Compare your group total with the other groups in your class. Which group did the most sit-ups?
- Write all the group totals on the blackboard. How many sit-ups did the whole class do? Add up the totals to find your class's grand sit-up total.

Erica 15 sit-ups
Angel 25 sit-ups
Kesia 20 sit-ups
15
25
+20
60

Materials:

- paper
- pencils

Social Studies

pair | LOGICAL

Climb Every Mountain

- Make one card for each of the following mountains:
  Lookout Mountain, Alabama: 2,392 feet
  Black Mountain, Kentucky: 4,145 feet
  Mt. McKinley, Alaska: 20,320 feet
  Dome Peak, Texas: 5,360 feet
  Mt. Lincoln, Colorado: 14,269 feet
  Mt. Rainier, Washington: 14,410 feet
- Shuffle the cards. Each partner picks one card.
- Subtract the smaller mountain height from the larger one to find the difference in height. Play until there are no cards left. Then add the heights.

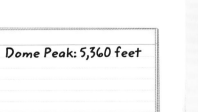

Dome Peak: 5,360 feet

Materials:

- index cards
- markers
- paper
- pencils

CHAPTER 2

Introduce the Chapter

Real World: Pluses and Minuses

Materials: pencils and paper

Share with students that they will be learning about adding and subtracting large numbers during the lessons of this chapter.

Have students divide into small groups. One student in each group will record student contributions under the headings:

- What We Know About Addition
- Where Addition Is Used
- What We Know About Subtraction
- Where Subtraction Is Used.

Give students several minutes to discuss and record at least three items under each category.

Invite students to share their lists orally. Lists can be posted for later use in writing real-world word problems.

Direct students to Student Edition p. 52. Have students read the paragraph at the top of the page.

- **How are addition and subtraction different?** In addition you put things together to make a larger number, and in subtraction you take things away, which results in a smaller number.

WRITING IN MATH

Starting the Chapter

Ask students to write a short paragraph about addition and subtraction, where they have seen it used, and where they have used it themselves. Have them include reasons why adding and subtracting accurately could be important.

Key Vocabulary Introduce the key vocabulary in the chapter using the routine below.

<u>Define:</u> An estimate is a number close to the exact amount.
<u>Example:</u> 47 + 22 (estimate 50 + 20) about 70
<u>Ask:</u> Can you estimate how many students go to this school?

Read-Aloud Anthology For an optional reading activity to introduce this chapter's math concepts, see the Read-Aloud Anthology on p. TR25.

CHAPTER 2

Solve Addition and Subtraction Problems

BIG Idea **What is addition? What is subtraction?**

Addition is an operation on two or more numbers that tells how many in all. Subtraction is an operation on two numbers that tells how many are left when some are taken away.

Example Celeste and her parents are painting a fence. The fence has three sides. To find the total length of the fence, use addition.

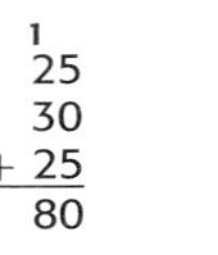

The total length of the fence is 80 feet.

What will I learn in this chapter?

- Use addition properties and subtraction rules.
- Estimate sums and differences.
- Determine when to estimate or find an exact answer.
- Add and subtract whole numbers, including multi-digit numbers.

Key Vocabulary

Commutative Property of Addition
Associative Property of Addition
estimate

Math Online **Student Study Tools at** macmillanmh.com

52 **Chapter 2** Solve Addition and Subtraction Problems

Chapter 2 Project

Recycle It!

Students create a drive to recycle cans and bottles, and they keep records of their success.

- Students make posters to publicize a drive to collect cans and bottles for recycling. Students keep records, adding up how many bottles and cans they collect each week. Students estimate how many they will collect in one month and then compare their actual collections with their estimates.
- Students add up how much money they will get for returning the cans and bottles for deposit. They can use the money they collect to have a class party or give a donation to a charity they select.

CRM *Refer to Chapter 2 Resource Masters, p. 53, for a rubric to assess students' progress on this project.*

FOLDABLES® Study Organizer

Make this Foldable to help you organize information about addition and subtraction. Begin with one sheet of 11″ × 17″ paper.

1. **Fold** lengthwise about 3″ from the bottom.
2. **Fold** the paper in thirds.
3. **Open** and staple to form 3 pockets.
4. **Label** as shown. Place 2 index cards in each pocket.

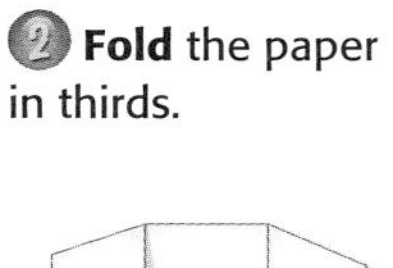
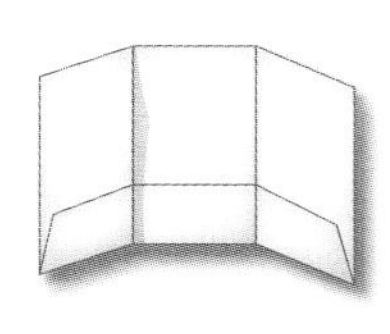
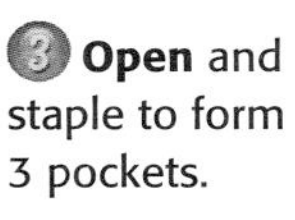
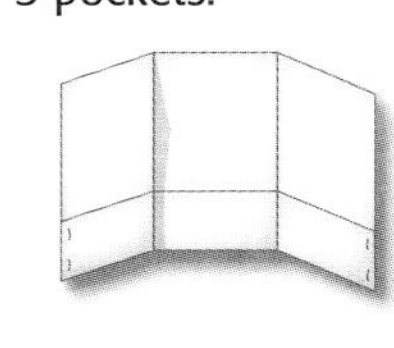
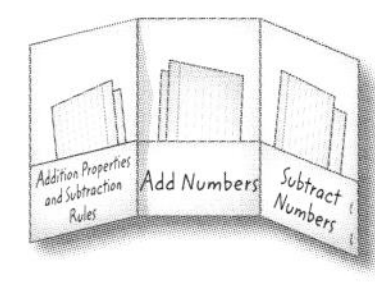

ELL National ESL Standards Alignment for Chapter 2			
Lesson, Page	ESL Standard	Modality	Level
2-1, p. 55B	Goal 2, Standard 3, g	Visual	Beginning
2-2, p. 58B	Goal 1, Standard 3, g	Kinesthetic	Beginning
2-3, p. 62B	Goal 2, Standard 1, d	Linguistic, Visual	Advanced
2-4, p. 64B	Goal 1, Standard 2, d	Visual, Auditory	Beginning
2-5, p. 72B	Goal 2, Standard 1, f	Kinesthetic, Linguistic	Advanced
2-6, p. 76B	Goal 1, Standard 3, k	Interpersonal, Linguistic	Intermediate
2-7, p. 80B	Goal 3, Standard 3, d	Linguistic, Logical	Intermediate

The National ESL Standards can be found in the Teacher Reference Handbook.

FOLDABLES® Dinah Zike's Foldables

Guide students through the directions on p. 53 to create their own Foldable graphic organizers for adding and subtracting numbers. Students may also use their Foldables to study and review for chapter assessments.

When to Use It Lessons 2-1, 2-2, 2-4, 2-5, and 2-7. (Additional instructions for using the Foldable with these lessons are found on pp. 69 and 84.)

Chapter 2 Literature List

Lesson	Book Title
2-1	**MATHterpieces** Greg Tang
2-2	**Alexander, Who Used to Be Rich Last Sunday** Judith Viorst
2-3	**Ten Mile Day: The Building of the Transcontinental Railroad** Mary Ann Fraser
2-4	**Earth Day—Hooray!** Stuart J. Murphy
2-5	**Elevator Magic** Stuart J. Murphy
2-7	**Shark Swimathon** Stuart J. Murphy
Any	**Midnight Math: Twelve Terrific Math Games** Peter Lewdon

- Read the Math at Home letter found in the Chapter 2 Resource Masters, p. 4, with the class and have each student sign it. (A Spanish version is found on p. 5.)
- Send home copies of the Math at Home letter with each student.

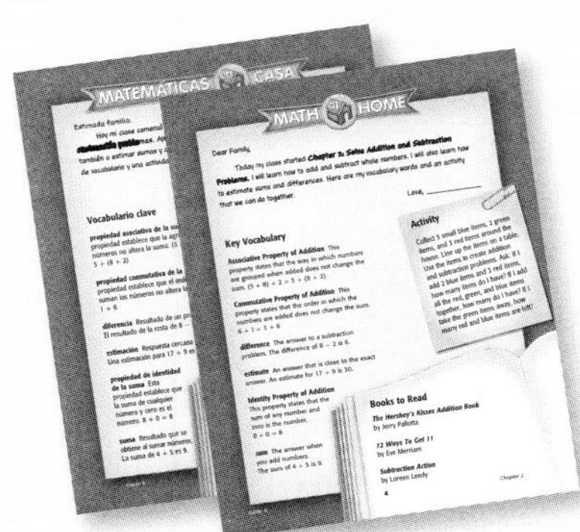

Diagnostic Assessment

Check for students' prerequisite skills before beginning the chapter.

- **Option 1:** ***Quick Check***
  SE Student Edition, p. 54
- **Option 2:** ***Online Assessment***
  Math Online macmillanmh.com
- **Option 3:** ***Diagnostic Test***
  CRM Chapter 2 Resource Masters, p. 44

RTI (Response to Intervention)

Apply the Results Based on the results of the diagnostic assessment on Student Edition p. 54, use the chart below to address individual needs before beginning the chapter.

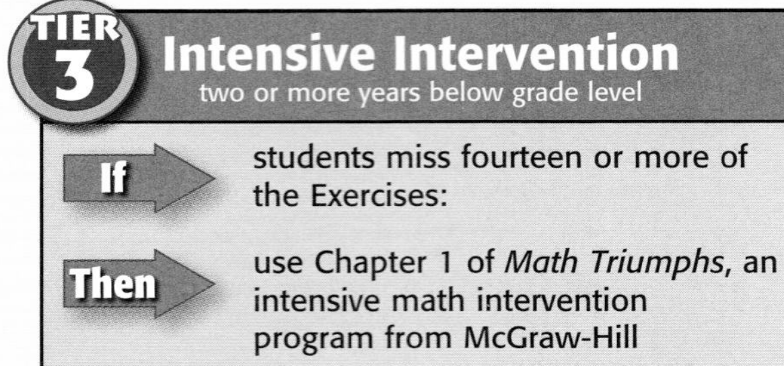

TIER 3 Intensive Intervention
two or more years below grade level

If students miss fourteen or more of the Exercises:

Then use Chapter 1 of *Math Triumphs*, an intensive math intervention program from McGraw-Hill

ARE YOU READY for Chapter 2?

You have two ways to check prerequisite skills for this chapter.

Option 2
Math Online Take the Chapter Readiness Quiz at macmillanmh.com.

Option 1
Complete the Quick Check below.

QUICK Check

Estimate. Round to the tens place. (Lesson 1-6) (Used in Lesson 2-2)

1. 65 + 23 — $70 + 20 = 90$
2. 58 + 31 — $60 + 30 = 90$
3. \$64 − \$21 — \$60 − \$20 = \$40
4. 98 − 22 — $100 - 20 = 80$
5. \$60 + \$29 — \$60 + \$30 = \$90
6. 88 − 26 — $90 - 30 = 60$
7. Kavel wants to buy a pair of swimming goggles and a snorkel. Kavel has \$22. About how much more money does he need to buy the items? about \$30 more

\$28 \$19

Add. (Prior Grade) (Used in Lessons 2-1 and 2-4)

8. 24 + 47 71
9. 36 + 57 93
10. 67 + 24 91
11. \$56 + \$25 \$81
12. 46 + 78 124
13. \$89 + \$53 \$142
14. Zita read an 82-page book. Then she read a 69-page book. How many pages did she read in all? 151 pages

Subtract. (Prior Grade) (Used in Lessons 2-5 and 2-7)

15. 26 − 9 17
16. \$31 − \$ 7 \$24
17. 47 − 19 28
18. 42 − 19 23
19. 64 − 27 37
20. \$73 − \$45 \$28
21. **Algebra** Omar took 34 pictures on Monday and some more on Tuesday. He took 71 pictures in all. How many did Omar take on Tuesday? 37 pictures

54 **Chapter 2** Solve Addition and Subtraction Problems

TIER 2 Strategic Intervention below/approaching grade level	TIER 1 On-Level	Above/Beyond Level
If students miss seven to thirteen in: **Exercises 1–21**	**If** students miss three to six in: **Exercises 1–21**	**If** students miss two or less in: **Exercises 1–21**
Then choose a resource:	**Then** choose a resource:	**Then** choose a resource:
Strategic Intervention Guide (pp. 36, 38, 40, 42, 44, 46, 48) CRM Chapter 1 Resource Masters Reteach Worksheets Math Online Extra Examples • Personal Tutor • Concepts in Motion	TE Learning Stations (pp. 52G–52H) TE Chapter Project (p. 52) CRM Game: Right Price Race Math Adventures My Math Zone Chapter 1 Math Online Fact Dash	TE Learning Stations (pp. 52G–52H) TE Chapter Project (p. 52) Real-World Problem-Solving: *The Olympic Games* My Math Zone Chapters 1, 2 Math Online Games

LESSON 2-1

Algebra: Addition Properties and Subtraction Rules

Lesson Planner

Objective

Use addition properties and subtraction rules to add and subtract.

Vocabulary

Commutative Property of Addition, **Associative Property of Addition**, **Identity Property of Addition**

Resources

Materials: index cards, construction paper

Manipulatives: connecting cubes

Literature Connection: *MATHterpieces* by Greg Tang

Teacher Technology
TeacherWorks • Interactive Classroom

Daily Routine

Use these suggestions before beginning the lesson on p. 55.

5-Minute Check

(Reviews Lesson 1-7)

Use the four-step plan to solve.
Lee Ann's family travels 60 miles in one hour. Roberto's family travels 40 miles in one hour. How many hours would it take for Lee Ann's family to travel as far as Roberto's family travels in 6 hours? Roberto's family travels 240 miles in 6 hours; it will take Lee Ann's family 4 hours to travel 240 miles.

Problem of the Day

Alba is learning about numbers. She thinks that 6,438 is greater than 6,452 since 8 is greater than 2. Is she correct? Explain. Alba is not correct. She is only looking at the ones place, but she needs to look at the tens place. 52 is greater than 38.

Focus on Math Background

Knowing and understanding the basic properties of operations help students develop operation sense. The Commutative Property of Addition says you can add in any order, for example, $a + b = b + a$. This property is very useful to students as they learn their basic addition facts. The Associative Property says you can change the grouping of the addends when you add, for example, $(a + b) + c = a + (b + c)$. This property helps students as they do column addition. Students should be aware that subtraction is not commutative, for example, $7 - 3 \neq 3 - 7$. The rules that do apply to subtraction say that when you subtract 0 from a number, the result is the number ($n - 0 = n$) and when you subtract a number from itself, the result is 0 ($n - n = 0$).

Building Math Vocabulary

Write the lesson vocabulary words and their definitions on the board.

Divide students into groups. Assign each group one vocabulary term. Have one student write the term and its definition on the top of piece of a construction paper. Each member of the group will give an example to illustrate the term. Hang the papers around the room.

Differentiated Instruction

Small Group Options

Option 1 Gifted and Talented AL

LOGICAL

Materials: paper and pencil

- Tell students to find the missing digits in the following number sentences and identify the property used.
- If time permits, instruct students to create 3 more problems of their own.
- Once accuracy has been verified, share these problems with other students.

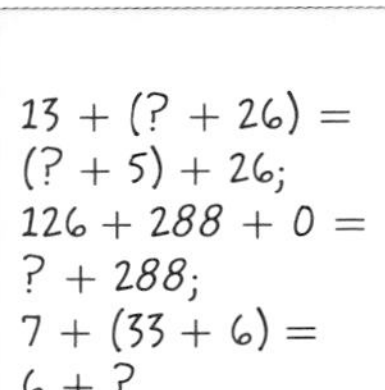

Option 2 English Language Learners ELL

VISUAL

Materials: pictures of various items, people, animals
Core Vocabulary: switch, total is unchanged, does not matter
Common Use Verb: changed
See Math This strategy uses visuals to show the Commutative and Associative Properties.

- Post "Commutative Property."
- With the pictures, create a simple equation with an equals sign and a sum (two fish + two dogs = 4). Count aloud to demonstrate how to find the sum.
- Switch the order of pictures and repeat, emphasizing that the sum is still 4.
- Repeat with more complex addition and then subtraction equations.
- Post "Associative Property."
- Model the picture with 3 numbers.
- Allow students to repeat as time permits.

Use this worksheet to provide additional support for English Language Learners.

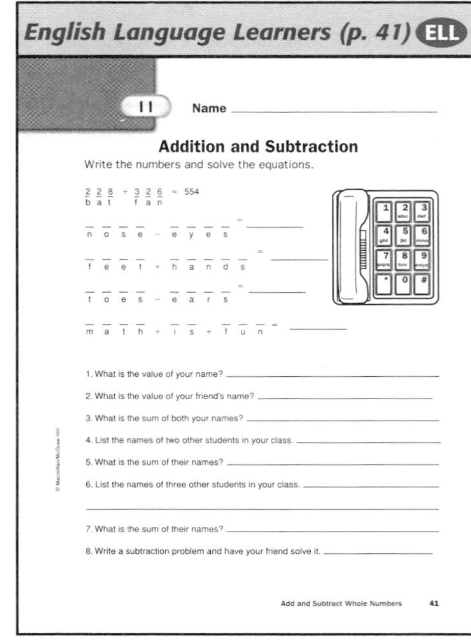

English Language Learners (p. 41) ELL

11 Name ____________

Addition and Subtraction

Write the numbers and solve the equations.

2 2 8 + 3 2 6 = 554
b a t   f a n

n o s e − e y e s = ______

f e e t + h a n d s = ______

t o e s − e a r s = ______

m a t h + i s + f u n = ______

1. What is the value of your name? ______
2. What is the value of your friend's name? ______
3. What is the sum of both your names? ______
4. List the names of two other students in your class. ______
5. What is the sum of their names? ______
6. List the names of three other students in your class. ______
7. What is the sum of their names? ______
8. Write a subtraction problem and have your friend solve it. ______

© Macmillan/McGraw-Hill

Add and Subtract Whole Numbers 41

Independent Work Options

Option 1 Early Finishers OL AL

KINESTHETIC

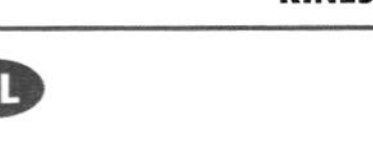

Materials: number cubes, color counters

- Have students roll a number cube twice and use the numbers rolled to model an addition sentence using color counters, one color for each number.
- Have them model the Commutative Property using the addition sentence they generated with color counters.
- Next, have students roll the cube to generate three numbers and create a new addition model with the counters, one color for each number.

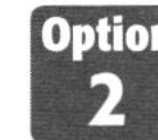

Option 2 Student Technology

Math Online macmillanmh.com

Personal Tutor • Extra Examples

Option 3 Learning Station: Art (p. 52G)

Direct students to the Art Learning Station for opportunities to explore and extend the lesson concept.

Option 4 Problem-Solving Practice

Reinforce problem-solving skills and strategies with the Problem-Solving Practice worksheet.

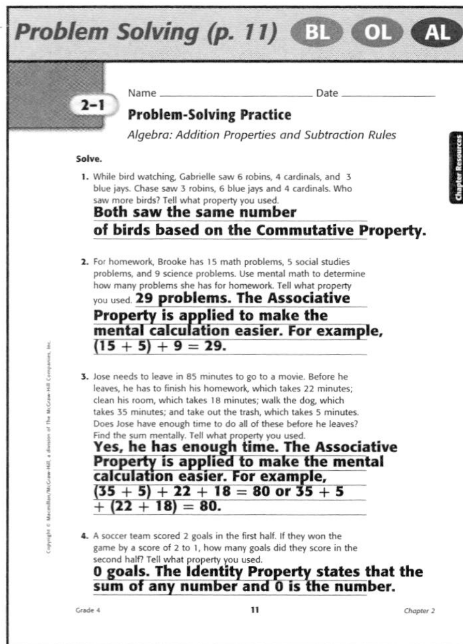

Problem Solving (p. 11) BL OL AL

2–1 Name ____________ Date ____________

Problem-Solving Practice

Algebra: Addition Properties and Subtraction Rules

Chapter Resources

Solve.

1. While bird watching, Gabrielle saw 6 robins, 4 cardinals, and 3 blue jays. Chase saw 3 robins, 6 blue jays and 4 cardinals. Who saw more birds? Tell what property you used. **Both saw the same number of birds based on the Commutative Property.**
2. For homework, Brooke has 15 math problems, 5 social studies problems, and 9 science problems. Use mental math to determine how many problems she has for homework. Tell what property you used. **29 problems. The Associative Property is applied to make the mental calculation easier. For example, (15 + 5) + 9 = 29.**
3. Jose needs to leave in 85 minutes to go to a movie. Before he leaves, he has to finish his homework, which takes 22 minutes; clean his room, which takes 18 minutes; walk the dog, which takes 35 minutes; and take out the trash, which takes 5 minutes. Does Jose have enough time to do all of these before he leaves? Find the sum mentally. Tell what property you used. **Yes, he has enough time. The Associative Property is applied to make the mental calculation easier. For example, (35 + 5) + 22 + 18 = 80 or 35 + 5 + (22 + 18) = 80.**
4. A soccer team scored 2 goals in the first half. If they won the game by a score of 2 to 1, how many goals did they score in the second half? Tell what property you used. **0 goals. The Identity Property states that the sum of any number and 0 is the number.**

Copyright © Macmillan/McGraw-Hill, a division of The McGraw-Hill Companies, Inc.

Grade 4 11 Chapter 2

Algebra: Addition Properties and Subtraction Rules

GET READY to Learn

Carlos is buying the items shown. Does the order in which the cashier scans the items change the total cost?

MAIN IDEA

I will use addition properties and subtraction rules to add and subtract.

New Vocabulary

Commutative Property of Addition
Associative Property of Addition
Identity Property of Addition

Math Online
macmillanmh.com
- Extra Examples
- Personal Tutor
- Self-Check Quiz

Addition Properties — Key Concepts

Words	**Commutative Property of Addition** The order in which numbers are added does not change the sum.
Examples	4 + 1 = 5 1 + 4 = 5
Words	**Associative Property of Addition** The way in which numbers are grouped when added does not change the sum.
Examples	(5 + 2) + 3 → 7 + 3 → 10 5 + (2 + 3) → 5 + 5 → 10 Parentheses ( ) show which numbers are added first.
Words	**Identity Property of Addition** The sum of any number and 0 is the number.
Examples	8 + 0 = 8 0 + 8 = 8

Real-World EXAMPLE — Use Addition Properties

1. **MONEY Does the order in which the camping supplies are scanned change the total cost?**

The Associative Property tells us that the way in which numbers are grouped when added does not change the sum.

($20 + $15) + $10 = $20 + ($15 + $10)
($35 + $10) = $20 + $25
$45 = $45

2-1 Algebra: Addition Properties and Subtraction Rules

1 Introduce

Activity Choice 1 • Hands-On

- Write 3 + 5 on the board. Have students model the addition sentence using connecting cubes. **What is the sum of this problem?** 8
- **Can you use the same cubes to show the addition sentence in another order? Does the sum change?** Students should change the order of the cubes to show 5 + 3; no.
- Write 5 + 3 + 4 = ? on the board. Have students model 5 cubes and 3 cubes grouped and 4 cubes separate. **What is the sum?** 12
- Ask students to separate the 5 cubes and group the 3 and 4 cubes. **What is the sum?** 12
- **Does changing how the numbers are grouped change the sum? Explain.** No; the number of cubes used is the same.

Activity Choice 2 • Literature

Introduce the lesson with *MATHterpieces* by Greg Tang. For a related math activity, see p. TR43.

2 Teach

Scaffolding Questions

Write 4 + 5 + 6 on the board.

- **What is the sum of these numbers when I write 5 + 6 + 4? 6 + 5 + 4?** 15; 15
- **Does the order of the addends make a difference in the sum?** no
- Write (4 + 5) + 6. **What do the parentheses tell you to do? What is the sum?** Add 4 + 5 first; 15.
- **If I group the addends to show 4 + (5 + 6), what do I do first? Does the sum change?** Add 5 + 6 first; no.

GET READY to Learn

Have students open their books and read the information in **Get Ready to Learn**. Introduce **Commutative Property of Addition**, **Associative Property of Addition**, and **Identity Property of Addition**. As a class, work through **Examples 1–3**.

Use Addition Properties

Example 2 Encourage students to look at both sides of the problem to find the missing numbers and to identify the property.

ADDITIONAL EXAMPLES

1. Pedro has 18 slot cars. Max has 25 slot cars. Does the order in which you add the number of cars change the total number of cars? no; 18 + 25 = 43 and 25 + 18 = 43
2. Complete 9 + ■ = 6 + 9. Identify the property used. 6; Commutative Property of Addition
3. Find the missing number in 5 − ■ = 5. The missing number is 0.

CHECK What You Know

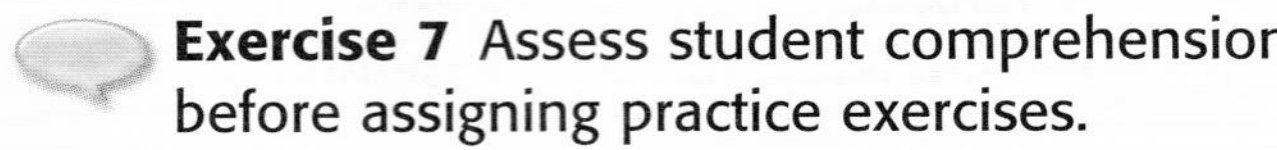

As a class, have students complete Exercises 1–7 in **Check What You Know** as you observe their work.

Exercise 7 Assess student comprehension before assigning practice exercises.

BL Alternate Teaching Strategy

If students have trouble using addition and subtraction properties…

Then use one of these reteach options:

1. CRM **Daily Reteach Worksheet** (p. 8)
2. Have students use index cards to make flash cards with the name of the property on one side and an example on the other.
   - **What hints might you use to remember the property?** Accept all reasonable answers.
   - Have students also write hints.

7. Sample answer: The Subtraction Rule that results in a 0; The Identity Property of Addition results in a sum that is equal to the original non-zero number.

COMMON ERROR!

Exercise 2 Students may mix up the Commutative and Associative Properties in labeling the problems. Relate the familiar words "commuting," meaning to go from one place to another, and "associating," meaning to be grouped with or to be friends with, to help students use the labels more accurately.

EXAMPLE Use Addition Properties

Remember
Use parentheses ( ) to show the two numbers you are adding first.

2. **Complete 0 + ■ = 6. Identify the property used.**

   Zero is added to a number, and the sum is 6. So, the missing number is 6. 0 + 6 = 6

   This is the Identity Property of Addition.

The following rules apply to subtraction.

Subtraction Rules — Key Concepts

Words	When you subtract 0 from any number, the result is the number.
Examples	6 − 0 = 6 4 − 0 = 4
Words	When you subtract any number from itself, the result is 0.
Examples	6 − 6 = 0 5 − 5 = 0

EXAMPLE Use Subtraction Rules

3. **Find the missing number in 10 − ■ = 10.**

   When you subtract 0 from 10, the result is 10.

   10 − 0 = 10   So, the missing number is 0.

1. 0; Subtraction Rule
2. 9; Associative Property of Addition
3. 68; Commutative Property of Addition

CHECK What You Know

Copy and complete each number sentence. Identify the property or rule used. See Examples 1–3 (pp. 55–56)

1. 19 − ■ = 19
2. (5 + ■) + 2 = 5 + (9 + 2)
3. 74 + 68 = ■ + 74

Add mentally. See Example 1 (p. 55)

4. 12 + 13 + 28 53
5. 21 + 16 + 19 56
6. 24 + 17 + 36 77
7. Talk About It — What subtraction rule is like the opposite of the Identity Property of Addition? Explain your reasoning. See margin.

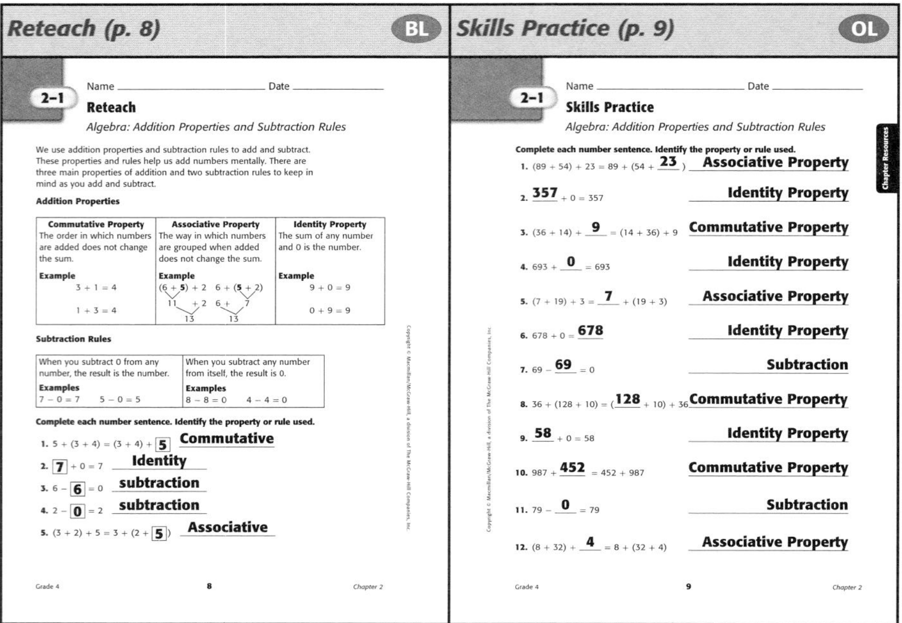

Reteach (p. 8) BL

2-1 Name ____________ Date ____________

Reteach

Algebra: Addition Properties and Subtraction Rules

We use addition properties and subtraction rules to add and subtract. These properties and rules help us add numbers mentally. There are three main properties of addition and two subtraction rules to keep in mind as you add and subtract.

Addition Properties

Commutative Property	Associative Property	Identity Property
The order in which numbers are added does not change the sum.	The way in which numbers are grouped when added does not change the sum.	The sum of any number and 0 is the number.
Example 3 + 1 = 4, 1 + 3 = 4	**Example** (6 + **5**) + 2 → 11 + 2 → 13; 6 + (**5** + 2) → 6 + 7 → 13	**Example** 9 + 0 = 9, 0 + 9 = 9

Subtraction Rules

When you subtract 0 from any number, the result is the number.	When you subtract any number from itself, the result is 0.
Examples 7 − 0 = 7 5 − 0 = 5	**Examples** 8 − 8 = 0 4 − 4 = 0

Complete each number sentence. Identify the property or rule used.

1. 5 + (3 + 4) = (3 + 4) + **5** Commutative
2. **7** + 0 = 7 Identity
3. 6 − **6** = 0 subtraction
4. 2 − **0** = 2 subtraction
5. (3 + 2) + 5 = 3 + (2 + **5**) Associative

Grade 4 8 Chapter 2

Skills Practice (p. 9) OL

2-1 Name ____________ Date ____________

Skills Practice

Algebra: Addition Properties and Subtraction Rules

Complete each number sentence. Identify the property or rule used.

1. (89 + 54) + 23 = 89 + (54 + **23**) Associative Property
2. **357** + 0 = 357 Identity Property
3. (36 + 14) + **9** = (14 + 36) + 9 Commutative Property
4. 693 + **0** = 693 Identity Property
5. (7 + 19) + 3 = **7** + (19 + 3) Associative Property
6. 678 + 0 = **678** Identity Property
7. 69 − **69** = 0 Subtraction
8. 36 + (128 + 10) = (**128** + 10) + 36 Commutative Property
9. **58** + 0 = 58 Identity Property
10. 987 + **452** = 452 + 987 Commutative Property
11. 79 − **0** = 79 Subtraction
12. (8 + 32) + **4** = 8 + (32 + 4) Associative Property

Grade 4 9 Chapter 2

Chapter Resources

Practice and Problem Solving

EXTRA PRACTICE See page R4.

Copy and complete each number sentence. Identify the property or rule used. See Examples 1–3 (pp. 55–56) 8–13. See Ch. 2 Answer Appendix.

8. $(\blacksquare + 8) + 7 = 9 + (8 + 7)$ **9.** $4 + 3 + 1 = 3 + 1 + \blacksquare$ **10.** $\blacksquare + 0 = 9$

11. $5 - \blacksquare = 0$ **12.** $7 + (1 + 8) = (7 + \blacksquare) + 8$ **13.** $15 - \blacksquare = 15$

Add mentally. See Example 1 (p. 55)

14. $17 + 24 + 13$ 54 **15.** $35 + 22 + 15$ 72 **16.** $13 + 11 + 27$ 51

17. $22 + 16 + 28$ 66 **18.** $14 + 33 + 26$ 73 **19.** $31 + 22 + 29$ 82

20. **Measurement** There are 24 minutes left in Alicia's class. Then she has 2 more classes before lunch that are each 35 minutes. How many minutes does Alicia have before lunch? 94 min

21. **Measurement** Paco has 75 minutes before practice. He cleans his room for 40 minutes and reads for 30 minutes. Can he do both of these activities before his baseball practice? Explain. yes; 70 min < 75 min

Write a number sentence. Then identify the property or rule used.

22. Susan ate 1 hot dog and 2 apples. Amelia ate 2 hot dogs and 1 apple. Who ate more food items?

23. Carla has 4 triangles, 3 squares, and 5 circles. Ethan has 3 circles, 4 squares, and 5 triangles. Who has more shapes?

22, 23. See Ch. 2 Answer Appendix.

H.O.T. Problems

24. **OPEN ENDED** Copy and complete the number sentence $(23 + \blacksquare) + 19 = 23 + (\blacksquare + 19)$. Can any number complete the number sentence? Explain. 15; yes, The same numbers will be on each side.

25. **FIND THE ERROR** Trey and Mika are showing an example of the Identity Property of Addition. Who is correct? Explain.

Sample answer: Trey; According to the Identity Property of Addition, the sum of any number and 0 is the number.

26. WRITING IN MATH Explain how you could group $775 + 639 + 225$ to find the sum mentally. Sample answer: Group 775 and 225 together to get 1,000. Then add 639 to get 1,639.

Enrich (p. 12) AL

2–1 Name ______ Date ______

Enrich

Alpha Math

A	B	C	D	E	F	G	H	I	J
9	4	0	8	1	5	2	6	3	7

Each letter in these addition and subtraction problems stands for a different numeral. Use the clues given to substitute the correct numerals in the problems below. As you study the problems, you will discover the correct numerals for each letter in the chart. Rewrite each problem and fill in the chart.

1. IEC + DED = EEGD; 310 + 818 = 1,128
2. FFD + IBH = ACB; 558 + 346 = 904
3. DAE + HGH = EFEJ; 891 + 626 = 1,517
4. IEC − EGF = EDF; 310 − 125 = 185
5. DAA − JEF = EDB; 899 − 715 = 184
6. EHHB − BEG = EGFG; 1664 − 412 = 1,252

Grade 4 12 Chapter 2

Homework Practice (p. 10) OL

2–1 Name ______ Date ______

Homework Practice

Algebra: Addition Properties and Subtraction Rules

Complete each number sentence. Identify the property or rule used.

1. 85 + 0 = **85** — **Identity Property**
2. 96 + 13 = 13 + **96** — **Commutative Property**
3. **37** − 0 = 37 — **Subtraction**
4. (15 + 23) + 7 = 15 + (**23** + 7) — **Associative Property**
5. 67 + (29 + 31) = (29 + 31) + **67** — **Commutative Property**
6. 452 − **0** = 452 — **Subtraction**

Spiral Review

Round each number to the given place-value position.

7. 582; ten **580**
8. 391; hundred **400**
9. 749; ten **750**
10. 248; ten **250**
11. 8,763; thousand **9,000**
12. 1,421; hundred **1,400**
13. 5,717; thousand **6,000**
14. 38,954; thousand **39,000**
15. 1,579; hundred **1,600**
16. 1,337; ten **1,340**
17. 40, 397; thousand **40,000**
18. 58,852; hundred **58,900**

Grade 4 10 Chapter 2

3 Practice

Differentiate practice using these leveled assignments for Exercises 8–26.

Level	Assignment
BL Below/Approaching Level	8–10, 14–16, 20, 22
OL On Level	9–13, 15–18, 20–23, 25
AL Above/Beyond Level	9–23 odd, 24–26

Have students discuss and complete the Higher Order Thinking problems. For Exercise 24 have students carefully compare the addends on each side of the problem.

WRITING IN MATH Have students complete Exercise 26 in their Math Journals. You may choose to use this exercise as an optional formative assessment.

4 Assess

Formative Assessment

Write the following on the board:

A. $(1 + 3) + 9 = 1 + (3 + 9)$
B. $4 + 5 = 5 + 4$
C. $19 + 0 = 19$

- **What property is shown in A? Explain.** Associative Property of Addition; the addends' grouping is changed.
- **What property is shown in B? Explain.** Commutative Property of Addition; the order of the addends is changed.
- **What property is shown in C? Explain.** Identity Property of Addition; adding zero does not change the original number.

Quick Check **Are students continuing to struggle with using addition properties and subtraction rules?**

If Yes → Strategic Intervention Guide (p. 38)

If No → Independent Work Options (p. 55B)
CRM Skills Practice Worksheet (p. 9)
CRM Enrich Worksheet (p. 12)

Ticket Out the Door Have students write a number sentence that uses one of the properties or rules they learned. Then, have them write the solution and identify the property or rule.

LESSON 2-2

Estimate Sums and Differences

Lesson Planner

Objective

Estimate sums and differences of numbers.

Vocabulary

estimate

Resources

Manipulative: number cubes

Literature Connection: *Alexander, Who Used to Be Rich Last Sunday* by Judith Viorst

Alternate Lesson: Use *IMPACT Mathematics:* Unit C to provide practice with estimation.

Teacher Technology
TeacherWorks • Interactive Classroom

Daily Routine

Use these suggestions before beginning the lesson on p. 58.

5-Minute Check

(Reviews Lesson 2-1)

Copy and complete each number sentence. Identify the property or rule used.

1. 7 + ■ = 7 0; Identity Property of Addition
2. (9 + 2) + 7 = 9 + (■ + 7) 2; Associative Property of Addition
3. 4 − ■ = 0 4; Subtraction Rule
4. 385 + 22 = 22 + ■ 385; Commutative Property of Addition

Problem of the Day

Talisha needs a total of 189 red, white, and blue beads. She has 86 blue and 69 white beads. How many red beads does she need? 34 red beads; 69 + 86 = 155, 189 − 155 = 34

Focus on Math Background

As students learn to add and subtract two- and three-digit numbers, it is important that they learn to estimate sums and differences. Estimation helps students avoid errors that occur as a result of rote procedures. For students to be good estimators, they need to be able to change numbers to manageable forms. In this lesson, students use the strategy of rounding to estimate. For example, to estimate the sum of 498 + 115, you can round each number to the nearest hundred (500 + 100) and get an estimate of 600.

Building Math Vocabulary

Write the lesson vocabulary word and its definition on the board.

Have students write the word and its definition in their Math Journals. As a class, make a list of situations when estimating would be useful. Using the list, ask students when it would be best to overestimate and when it would be best to underestimate. Ask students to explain their reasoning.

Visual Vocabulary Cards

Use Visual Vocabulary Card 15 to reinforce the vocabulary introduced in this lesson. (The Define/Example/Ask routine is printed on the back of each card.)

Differentiated Instruction

Small Group Options

Option 1 — LINGUISTIC, SOCIAL 

Gifted and Talented AL

Materials: pencil and paper

- Students work in pairs. One writes a word problem where the answer is an exact sum. The other writes a word problem in which the answer can be an estimated sum.
- Repeat, switching roles, with each student solving word problems.

Option 2 — KINESTHETIC 

English Language Learners ELL

Materials: masking tape, note cards
Core Vocabulary: near, jump, closer
Common Use Verb: reach

Do Math This strategy allows students to understand estimating as a way to find a close answer.

- Create a number line on the board or on the floor.
- Write a 50 on the left end of the line and a 60 on the right end. Place 53 on the line closer to the 50.
- Ask: "Which number is 53 **closer** to?"
- Ask students to jump from one end to the other or try to reach one of the numbers. Ask: "Which one is **closer**?"
- Say: "Estimating is like ***reaching*** the **closer** number, not the exact number."
- Repeat for other numbers between 50–60.

Independent Work Options

Option 1 — SOCIAL 

Early Finishers 

Materials: number cube, pencil, paper

- Have students use number cubes to generate 2 four-digit numbers. Record the numbers.
- Students will estimate both the sum and the difference of the two numbers and record their answers.
- Have students repeat as time permits.

Option 2 

Student Technology

Math Online macmillanmh.com

Personal Tutor • Extra Examples

 Math Adventures

Option 3

Learning Station: Writing (p. 52G)

Direct students to the Writing Learning Station for opportunities to explore and extend the lesson concept.

Option 4

Problem-Solving Practice

Reinforce problem-solving skills and strategies with the Problem-Solving Practice worksheet.

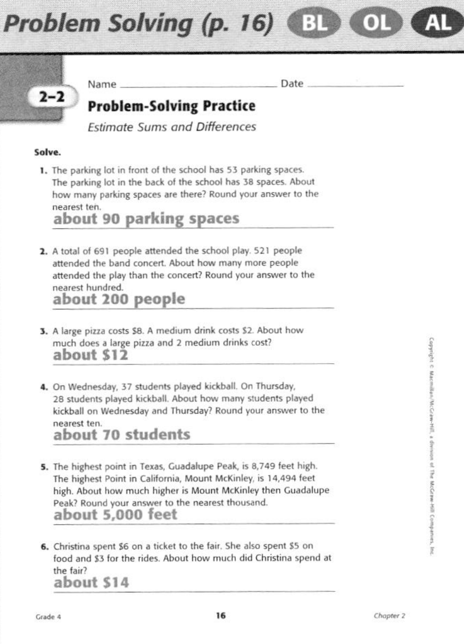

Problem Solving (p. 16) BL OL AL

2–2 Name ______________ Date ______________

Problem-Solving Practice

Estimate Sums and Differences

Solve.

1. The parking lot in front of the school has 53 parking spaces. The parking lot in the back of the school has 38 spaces. About how many parking spaces are there? Round your answer to the nearest ten.
   about 90 parking spaces
2. A total of 691 people attended the school play. 521 people attended the band concert. About how many more people attended the play than the concert? Round your answer to the nearest hundred.
   about 200 people
3. A large pizza costs $8. A medium drink costs $2. About how much does a large pizza and 2 medium drinks cost?
   about $12
4. On Wednesday, 37 students played kickball. On Thursday, 28 students played kickball. About how many students played kickball on Wednesday and Thursday? Round your answer to the nearest ten.
   about 70 students
5. The highest point in Texas, Guadalupe Peak, is 8,749 feet high. The highest Point in California, Mount McKinley, is 14,494 feet high. About how much higher is Mount McKinley then Guadalupe Peak? Round your answer to the nearest thousand.
   about 5,000 feet
6. Christina spent $6 on a ticket to the fair. She also spent $5 on food and $3 for the rides. About how much did Christina spend at the fair?
   about $14

Grade 4 16 Chapter 2

2-2 Estimate Sums and Differences

1 Introduce

Activity Choice 1 • Hands-On

- Write the number 2,362 on the board. **What is this number rounded to the nearest hundred? Explain.** 2,400; 362 is closer to 400 than 300.
- Have students work with a partner to generate several more two-, three-, and four-digit numbers by rolling a number cube. Have students round to a different place for each number generated.
- **If a number is rounded to the nearest hundred, how many zeros will there be to the right of the hundreds place?** two zeros
- **If a number is rounded to the nearest thousand, how many zeros will there be to the right of the thousands place?** three zeros

Activity Choice 2 • Literature

Introduce the lesson with *Alexander, Who Used to Be Rich Last Sunday* by Judith Viorst. For a related math activity, see p. TR43.

2 Teach

Scaffolding Questions

Tell students that you have $129 in one account and $74 in another.

- **I want to know about how much money I have. What could I do to estimate about how much I have?** round each number and add
- **What could $129 be rounded to?** either $130 or $100
- **What could $74 be rounded to?** $70 or $100
- **About how much money is $129 + $74 if you round both numbers to the nearest 10? nearest 100?** about $200

GET READY to Learn

Have students open their books and read the information in **Get Ready to Learn**. Introduce **estimate**. As a class, work through **Examples 1–4**.

2-2 Estimate Sums and Differences

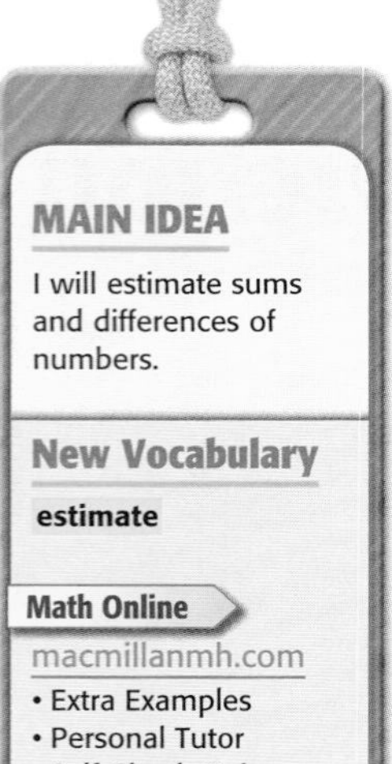

MAIN IDEA

I will estimate sums and differences of numbers.

New Vocabulary

estimate

Math Online

macmillanmh.com

- Extra Examples
- Personal Tutor
- Self-Check Quiz

GET READY to Learn

Natalie has been saving her money so that she can buy snowboarding equipment. She wants to buy the items shown. About how much money does she need?

Sometimes you do not need an exact answer. When the word *about* is used in a problem, you can find an estimate. An **estimate** is an answer close to the exact answer.

Real-World EXAMPLE Estimate Sums

1 **MONEY About how much money does Natalie need to buy a snowboard and boots? Round to the tens place.**

Round each amount to the nearest tens. Then add.

$119 — rounds to → $120
+$ 67 — rounds to → +$ 70
$190

So, Natalie needs to save about $190.

When estimating, you can also round to the nearest hundred or thousand.

EXAMPLE Estimate Sums

2 **Estimate 2,342 + 637. Round to the hundreds place.**

Round each number to the nearest hundreds. Then add.

2,342 — rounds to → 2,300
+ 637 — rounds to → + 600
2,900

So, 2,342 + 637 is about 2,900.

58 Chapter 2 Solve Addition and Subtraction Problems

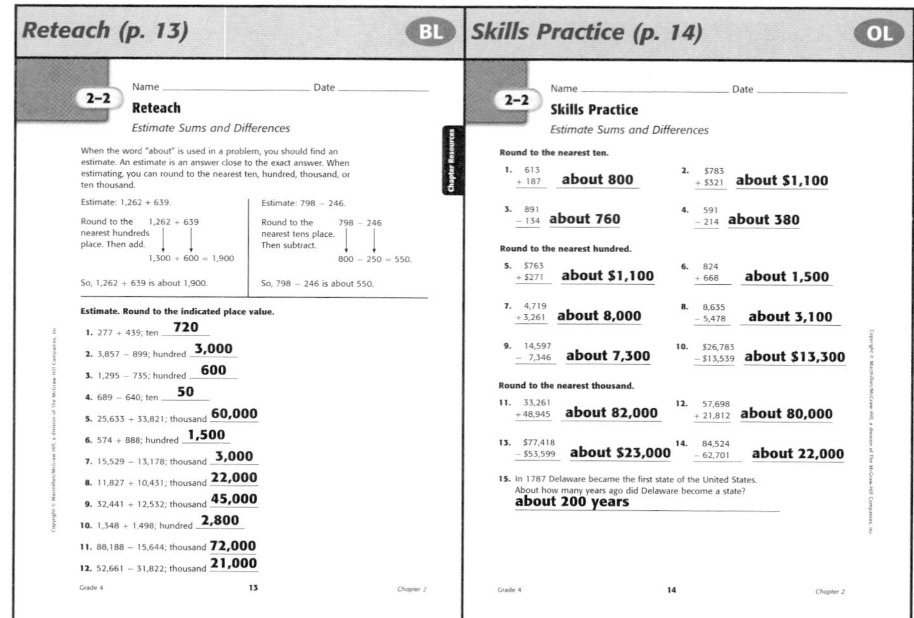

Reteach (p. 13) BL

2-2 Name ________ Date ________

Reteach

Estimate Sums and Differences

When the word "about" is used in a problem, you should find an estimate. An estimate is an answer close to the exact answer. When estimating, you can round to the nearest ten, hundred, thousand, or ten thousand.

Estimate: 1,262 + 639.

Round to the nearest hundreds place. Then add.

1,262 + 639
1,300 + 600 = 1,900

So, 1,262 + 639 is about 1,900.

Estimate: 798 − 246.

Round to the nearest tens place. Then subtract.

798 − 246
800 − 250 = 550.

So, 798 − 246 is about 550.

Estimate. Round to the indicated place value.

1. 277 + 439; ten **720**
2. 3,857 − 899; hundred **3,000**
3. 1,295 − 735; hundred **600**
4. 689 − 640; ten **50**
5. 25,633 + 33,821; thousand **60,000**
6. 574 + 888; hundred **1,500**
7. 15,529 − 13,178; thousand **3,000**
8. 11,827 + 10,431; thousand **22,000**
9. 32,441 + 12,532; thousand **45,000**
10. 1,348 + 1,498; hundred **2,800**
11. 88,188 − 15,644; thousand **72,000**
12. 52,661 − 31,822; thousand **21,000**

Chapter Resources

Grade 4 13 Chapter 2

Skills Practice (p. 14) OL

2-2 Name ________ Date ________

Skills Practice

Estimate Sums and Differences

Round to the nearest ten.

1. 613 + 187 **about 800**
2. $783 + $321 **about $1,100**
3. 891 − 134 **about 760**
4. 591 − 214 **about 380**

Round to the nearest hundred.

5. $763 + $271 **about $1,100**
6. 824 + 668 **about 1,500**
7. 4,719 + 3,261 **about 8,000**
8. 8,635 − 5,478 **about 3,100**
9. 14,597 − 7,346 **about 7,300**
10. $26,783 − $13,539 **about $13,300**

Round to the nearest thousand.

11. 33,261 + 48,945 **about 82,000**
12. 57,698 + 21,812 **about 80,000**
13. $77,418 − $53,599 **about $23,000**
14. 84,524 − 62,701 **about 22,000**
15. In 1787 Delaware became the first state of the United States. About how many years ago did Delaware become a state? **about 200 years**

Grade 4 14 Chapter 2

EXAMPLE Estimate Differences

Remember

Use place value to help you round whole numbers.

3 Estimate $7,542 − $3,225. Round to the tens place.

Round each amount to the nearest ten dollars. Then subtract.

$7,542	rounds to →	$7,540
− $3,225	rounds to →	− $3,230
		$4,310

So, $7,542 − $3,225 is about $4,310.

Real-World EXAMPLE Estimate Differences

4 MEASUREMENT The table shows populations for two cities in Kentucky. About how many more people live in Covington than in Ashland?

City Populations	
City	**Population**
Ashland	21,510
Covington	42,811

Source: U.S. Census Bureau

Round each population to the nearest thousand. Then subtract.

42,811	rounds to →	43,000
− 21,510	rounds to →	− 22,000
		21,000

So, Covington has about 21,000 more people.

CHECK What You Know

Estimate. Round to the indicated place value. See Examples 1–4 (pp. 58–59)

1. $21 + $73; tens $20 + $70 = $90
2. 312 + 27; tens 310 + 30 = 340
3. 383 + 122; hundreds 400 + 100 = 500
4. 1,561 − 305; hundreds 1,600 − 300 = 1,300
5. $2,746 − $1,529; tens $2,750 − $1,530 = $1,220
6. 37,215 − 6,972; thousands 37,000 − 7,000 = 30,000
7. The Davis family will buy the camping equipment shown. About how much will the equipment cost? $400 + $200 = $600

Camping Equipment	
Item	**Cost**
Family-size tent	$399
Camping stove	$179

8. **Talk About It** Estimate 829 + 1,560 to the nearest hundred and the nearest thousand. Compare both estimates to the actual sum. What do you notice? See Ch. 2 Answer Appendix.

Enrich (p. 17) AL

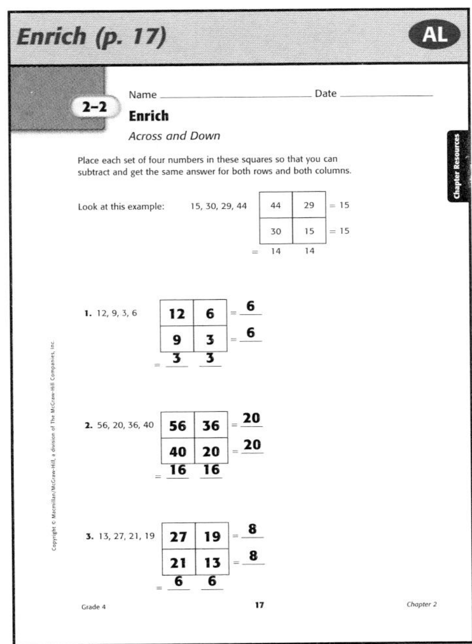

2–2 Name ______________ Date ______________

Enrich

Across and Down

Place each set of four numbers in these squares so that you can subtract and get the same answer for both rows and both columns.

Look at this example: 15, 30, 29, 44

44	29	= 15
30	15	= 15
= 14	14	

1. 12, 9, 3, 6

12	6	= 6
9	3	= 6
= 3	3	

2. 56, 20, 36, 40

56	36	= 20
40	20	= 20
= 16	16	

3. 13, 27, 21, 19

27	19	= 8
21	13	= 8
= 6	6	

Chapter Resources

Grade 4 17 Chapter 2

Estimate Sums

Example 2 Be certain students understand that all addends of an estimated sum will be rounded to the same place, usually the greatest place in the smallest number.

ADDITIONAL EXAMPLES

1. Genoveva wanted to buy a bicycle for $239 and a helmet for $37. About how much money will Genoveva need to buy the bicycle and helmet? Round to the tens place. $280
2. Estimate 6,243 + 942. Round to the hundreds place. 7,100
3. Estimate 5,845 − 2,312. Round to the tens place. about 3,540
4.

World's Tallest Mountains	
Mountain	**Height (feet)**
Mt. Everest	**29,028**
K2	**28,250**
Kangchenjunga	**28,208**
Lhotse	**27,923**

About how much taller is Mt. Everest than Lhotse? Round to the thousands place. about 1,000 feet taller

CHECK What You Know

As a class, have students complete Exercises 1–8 in **Check What You Know** as you observe their work.

Exercise 8 Assess student comprehension before assigning practice exercises.

BL Alternate Teaching Strategy

If students have trouble estimating sums and differences of whole numbers…

Then use one of these reteach options:

1 CRM **Daily Reteach Worksheet** (p. 13)

2 Have students write 4,321 + 589. Have them circle the hundreds place in each number. Then they underline the digits to look at to decide which hundred the number is closer to.

- **What will be to the right of the rounded place in each number?** two zeros
- **What will you add?** 4,300 + 600

3 Practice

Differentiate practice using these leveled assignments for Exercises 9–30.

Level	Assignment
BL Below/Approaching Level	9–11, 15–16, 21–22, 25–27
OL On Level	10–19, 22–27, 29
AL Above/Beyond Level	10–26 even, 28–30

Have students discuss and complete the Higher Order Thinking problems. Direct students to show examples that support their answers.

WRITING IN MATH Have students complete Exercise 30 in their Math Journals. You may choose to use this exercise as an optional formative assessment.

COMMON ERROR!

Exercises 21–24 Students may round to a different place value. Remind them when rounding to the thousands place there will be zeros in the hundreds, tens, and ones places.

Practice and Problem Solving

EXTRA PRACTICE See page R4.

Estimate. Round to the indicated place value. See Examples 1–4 (pp. 58–59)

9. \$34 + \$23; tens \$30 + \$20 = \$50

10. \$35 + \$42; tens \$40 + \$40 = \$80

11. \$636 + \$27; tens \$640 + \$30 = \$670

12. \$687 + \$331; hundreds \$700 + \$300 = \$1,000

13. \$455 + \$229; tens \$460 + \$230 = \$690

14. 1,624 + 534; hundreds 1,600 + 500 = 2,100

15. \$772 − \$593; hundreds \$800 − \$600 = \$200

16. 985 − 639; tens 990 − 640 = 350

17. 2,647 − 256; hundreds 2,600 − 300 = 2,300

18. 27,629 − 5,364; thousands 28,000 − 5,000 = 23,000

19. \$48,986 − \$7,664; thousands \$49,000 − \$8,000 = \$41,000

20. \$47,236 − \$20,425; thousands \$47,000 − \$20,000 = \$27,000

Solve. Round to the nearest thousand.

21. The largest NBA arena can seat 22,076 people. Suppose two games are sold out. About how many people will attend the two games? 22,000 + 22,000 = 44,000 people

22. Luz is going to buy a car that costs \$18,460 new and \$15,788 used. About how much money would Luz save if she bought the car used? \$18,000 − \$16,000 = \$2,000

23. **Measurement** A mountain climber is climbing Mt. Everest. It is 29,035 feet tall. About how many feet will the climber have traveled after going up and down the mountain? 29,000 ft + 29,000 ft = 58,000 ft

24. Jupiter and Saturn are the two largest planets in our solar system. Jupiter is 88,846 miles across and Saturn is 74,898 miles across. What is the approximate difference in the distance across these two planets? 89,000 − 75,000 = 14,000 miles

Real-World PROBLEM SOLVING

Buildings This table shows the tallest buildings in the world. Round to the nearest hundred.

25. About how much taller is the Sears Tower than the Jin Mao Building? 100 ft

26. Estimate the difference between the height of the Taipai 101 Building and the Empire State Building. 400 ft

27. About how much taller is Petronas Towers than the Empire State Building? 200 ft

Tallest Buildings in the World

Building	Location	Height (ft)
Taipai 101	Taiwan	1,669
Petronas Towers	Malaysia	1,482
Sears Tower	United States	1,450
Jin Mao Building	China	1,381
CITIC Plaza	China	1,282
Shun Hing Square	China	1,259
Empire State Building	United States	1,250

Source: *The Ultimate Book of Lists*

H.O.T. Problems

28. OPEN ENDED Write two numbers that when rounded to the thousands place have an estimated sum of 10,000. Sample answer: 4,749 and 5,246

29. NUMBER SENSE If both addends are rounded down, will the sum of the numbers be greater or less than the actual sum? Explain.

29, 30. See margin.

30. WRITING IN MATH When rounding to estimate the sum or difference of numbers, explain a situation where less exact answers would be better than more exact answers.

31. What number completes the number sentence below? (Lesson 2-1) C

(24 + ■) + 18 = 24 + (36 + 18)

A 18 **C** 36

B 24 **D** 38

32. The Casey family traveled last week. They drove 182 miles on Friday, 138 miles on Saturday, and 119 miles on Sunday. Approximately how many miles did they travel? (Lesson 2-2) J

F 200 miles **H** 320 miles

G 300 miles **J** 400 miles

Spiral Review

Algebra **Copy and complete each number sentence. Identify the property or rule used.** (Lesson 2-1)

33. 35 − ■ = 35 0; Subtraction Rule

34. (57 + ■) + 36 = 57 + (25 + 36) 25; Associative Property (+)

Round each number to the given place-value position. (Lesson 1-6)

35. 354; ten 350

36. 4,396; thousand 4,000

37. 257,468; hundred 257,500

Compare. Use >, <, or =. (Lesson 1-4)

38. 8,650 ● 8,623 >

39. 44,068 ● 44,086 <

40. 248,632 ● 284,632 <

41. Jameson's basketball team scored a total of 58 points. Jameson scored 18 points, and his sister scored 12 points. How many points did the rest of the team score? (Lesson 1-3) 28 points

42. Teresa's cell phone bill is $32 each month. About how much money does she spend on cell phone service every two months? (Lesson 1-3) $60

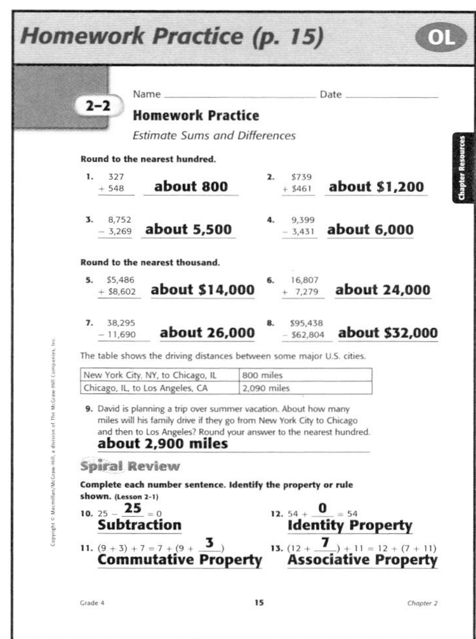

Homework Practice (p. 15) OL

Name ____________ Date ____________

2-2 Homework Practice

Estimate Sums and Differences

Round to the nearest hundred.

1. 327 + 548 **about 800**
2. $739 + $461 **about $1,200**
3. 8,752 − 3,269 **about 5,500**
4. 9,399 − 3,431 **about 6,000**

Round to the nearest thousand.

5. $5,486 + $8,602 **about $14,000**
6. 16,807 + 7,279 **about 24,000**
7. 38,295 − 11,690 **about 26,000**
8. $95,438 − $62,804 **about $32,000**

The table shows the driving distances between some major U.S. cities.

New York City, NY, to Chicago, IL	800 miles
Chicago, IL, to Los Angeles, CA	2,090 miles

9. David is planning a trip over summer vacation. About how many miles will his family drive if they go from New York City to Chicago and then to Los Angeles? Round your answer to the nearest hundred. **about 2,900 miles**

Spiral Review

Complete each number sentence. Identify the property or rule shown. (Lesson 2-1)

10. 25 − **25** = 0 **Subtraction**
11. (9 + 3) + 7 = 7 + (9 + **3**) **Commutative Property**
12. 54 + **0** = 54 **Identity Property**
13. (12 + **7**) + 11 = 12 + (7 + 11) **Associative Property**

Chapter Resources

Grade 4 15 Chapter 2

4 Assess

Formative Assessment

Write 4,378 − 1,237 on the board.

- **How would you estimate the difference?** Round 4,378 to the nearest thousand, 4,000. Round 1,237 to the nearest thousand, 1,000. Subtract 4,000 − 1,000 = 3,000.
- **Would rounding to the nearest hundred or nearest thousand give a better estimate? Explain.** to the nearest hundred, because the nearest hundred would be close to the original number

Quick Check **Are students continuing to struggle with estimating sums and differences of whole numbers?**

If Yes → Strategic Intervention Guide (p. 52)

If No → Independent Work Options (p. 58B)
CRM Skills Practice Worksheet (p. 14)
CRM Enrich Worksheet (p. 17)

Into the Future Ask students to write about how today's lesson on estimating sums and differences might help them with determining when to estimate or find an exact answer in tomorrow's lesson.

Reviews Lessons 2-1 and 2-2

Assign the Test Practice problems to provide daily reinforcement of test-taking skills.

Spiral Review

Reviews Lessons 1-3, 1-4, 1-6, and 2-1

Review and assess mastery of skills and concepts from previous chapters.

Additional Answers

29. Sample answer: less; When both addends are rounded down, their value is less than before. Therefore, when they are added together, the estimated sum is less than the exact sum.

30. Sample answer: A situation where a person does not have enough time to find an exact answer. Example: estimating total cost of items in a checkout line at a store.

2-3 Problem-Solving Skill
Estimate or Exact Answer

Lesson Planner

Objective

Determine when to estimate or find an exact answer.

Resources

Materials: index cards, transparent tape

Manipulatives: play money, square pattern blocks

Literature Connection: *Ten Mile Day: The Building of the Transcontinental Railroad* by Mary Ann Fraser

Teacher Technology
TeacherWorks • Interactive Classroom

Real-World Problem Solving Library
Math and Social Studies: *The Olympic Games*
Use these leveled books to reinforce and extend problem-solving skills and strategies.

Leveled for:
- OL On Level
- ELL Sheltered English
- SP Spanish

For additional support, see the Real-World Problem Solving Teacher Guide.

Daily Routine

Use these suggestions before beginning the lesson on p. 62.

5-Minute Check

(Reviews Lesson 2-2)

Estimate. Round to the indicated place value.

1. $24 + $32; tens $20 + $30 = $50
2. $60 − $17; tens $60 − $20 = $40
3. 2,466 − 1,377; hundreds
   2,500 − 1,400 = 1,100
4. 19,556 + 14,789; thousands
   20,000 + 15,000 = 35,000

Problem of the Day

Darren earns $15 a week babysitting, but he spends $3 a week on snacks. If he has saved $48, how many more weeks will it be until he saves $125? 7 more weeks

Differentiated Instruction

Small Group Options

Option 1 LOGICAL

Below Level BL

Materials: paper and pencil

Hand this problem to students to solve:

Anna and her classmates are going on a Saturday field trip. So far, Anna has earned $25 babysitting to help her way. The bus costs $9, the event ticket costs $10, and food will cost $7. Has she earned enough to pay for the trip? no

If the souvenirs cost $6, how much more must she earn for this trip? $7

Option 2 LINGUISTIC, VISUAL

English Language Learners ELL

Materials: magazine pictures, cubes, bucket
Core Vocabulary: estimates, exact, here
Common Use Verb: can/can't see

Talk Math This strategy illustrates why math uses both exact and estimated answers and allows students to practice their acquired language as they act out problems.

- Spread out a handful of cubes. Ask: "How many ***can*** you ***see here***?" Accept responses.
- Repeat for cubes in a bucket. Ask: "How many ***can*** you ***see here***?"
- Do not allow students to touch or separate the cubes as you accept answers.
- Discuss why you cannot give an exact answer.
- Allow students to find pictures that show things that can have exact answers and pictures that require estimates. Have students act out things that should be estimated and things that need to be exact answers. Discuss.
- Repeat for remaining groups.

Independent Work Options

Option 1 LINGUISTIC

Early Finishers OL AL

Materials: paper and pencil

- Have students find the greatest sum they can for 2 two-digit odd numbers. They cannot use any digit more than once.
- Then have them find the least sum, using two-digit even numbers.

Option 2

Student Technology

Math Online macmillanmh.com

Personal Tutor • Extra Examples

Option 3

Learning Station: Health (p. 52H)

Direct students to the Health Learning Station for opportunities to explore and extend the lesson concept.

1 Introduce

Activity Choice 1 • Review

- Present the following problem to students:
  Marta has 125 baseball cards. Yasir has 36 fewer cards than Marta. How many cards do they have in all?
- **What strategy would you use to solve the problem?** four-step plan
- **What information is important to understand to find the answer?** Marta has 125 cards and Yasir has 36 less than Marta.
- **What is a possible plan to solve the problem?** Subtract 125 − 36 = 89 to find Yasir's total. Then add 125 + 89 to find the total number of cards. They have 214 cards in all.

Activity Choice 2 • Literature

Introduce the lesson with *Ten Mile Day: The Building of the Transcontinental Railroad* by Mary Fraser. For a related math activity, see p. TR44.

2 Teach

Have students read the problem. Guide them through the problem-solving steps.

Understand Using the questions, review what students know and need to find.

Plan Have them discuss their strategy.

Solve Guide students to choose an estimate or exact answer to solve the problem.

- **Is an estimate or exact answer needed? Explain.** Estimate; "about" tells you it is not exact.
- **Will $170 be enough to build the tree house? How do you know?** Yes; all amounts of money were rounded up, which means that there is more money in the estimate than needed.

Check Have students look back at the problem to make sure that the answer fits the facts given.

2-3 Problem-Solving Skill

MAIN IDEA I will determine when to estimate or find an exact answer.

Keith and his brother are going to build a tree house. They will need $12 for nails, $95 for tools, and $46 for wood. About how much money do they need to build the tree house?

Understand

What facts do you know?

- Nails cost $12.
- Tools cost $95.
- Wood costs $46.

What do you need to find?

- Find about how much money they need to build the tree house.

Plan

Since the question says *about* how much money is needed, you can estimate the sum.

Solve

Round each amount to each greatest place value. Then add.

$$\begin{array}{rcr} \$12 & \longrightarrow & \$\ 10 \\ \$95 & \longrightarrow & \$100 \\ +\ \$46 & \longrightarrow & +\ \$\ 50 \\ \hline & & \$160 \end{array}$$

Round each number to its greatest place value.

So, about $160 is needed to build the tree house.

Check

Look back. Suppose the question asked for an exact answer. Add $12, $95, and $46.

$$\begin{array}{r} {}^{1}\ \ \\ \$12 \\ \$95 \\ +\ \$46 \\ \hline \$153 \end{array}$$

Since $153 is close to $160, an estimate of $160 is correct.

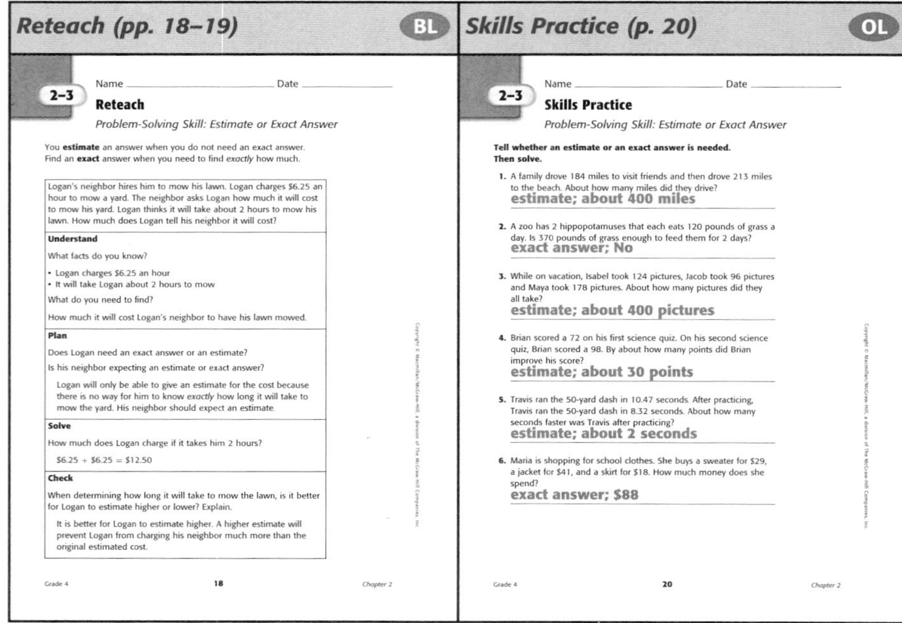

Reteach (pp. 18–19) BL

2-3 Name ______ Date ______

Reteach

Problem-Solving Skill: Estimate or Exact Answer

You **estimate** an answer when you do not need an exact answer.
Find an **exact** answer when you need to find *exactly* how much.

Logan's neighbor hires him to mow his lawn. Logan charges $6.25 an hour to mow a yard. The neighbor asks Logan how much it will cost to mow his yard. Logan thinks it will take about 2 hours to mow his lawn. How much does Logan tell his neighbor it will cost?

Understand

What facts do you know?

- Logan charges $6.25 an hour
- It will take Logan about 2 hours to mow

What do you need to find?

How much it will cost Logan's neighbor to have his lawn mowed.

Plan

Does Logan need an exact answer or an estimate?

Is his neighbor expecting an estimate or exact answer?

Logan will only be able to give an estimate for the cost because there is no way for him to know *exactly* how long it will take to mow the yard. His neighbor should expect an estimate.

Solve

How much does Logan charge if it takes him 2 hours?

$6.25 + $6.25 = $12.50

Check

When determining how long it will take to mow the lawn, is it better for Logan to estimate higher or lower? Explain.

It is better for Logan to estimate higher. A higher estimate will prevent Logan from charging his neighbor much more than the original estimated cost.

Grade 4 18 Chapter 2

Skills Practice (p. 20) OL

2-3 Name ______ Date ______

Skills Practice

Problem-Solving Skill: Estimate or Exact Answer

Tell whether an estimate or an exact answer is needed. Then solve.

1. A family drove 184 miles to visit friends and then drove 213 miles to the beach. About how many miles did they drive? **estimate; about 400 miles**
2. A zoo has 2 hippopotamuses that each eats 120 pounds of grass a day. Is 370 pounds of grass enough to feed them for 2 days? **exact answer; No**
3. While on vacation, Isabel took 124 pictures, Jacob took 96 pictures and Maya took 178 pictures. About how many pictures did they all take? **estimate; about 400 pictures**
4. Brian scored a 72 on his first science quiz. On his second science quiz, Brian scored a 98. By about how many points did Brian improve his score? **estimate; about 30 points**
5. Travis ran the 50-yard dash in 10.47 seconds. After practicing, Travis ran the 50-yard dash in 8.32 seconds. About how many seconds faster was Travis after practicing? **estimate; about 2 seconds**
6. Maria is shopping for school clothes. She buys a sweater for $29, a jacket for $41, and a skirt for $18. How much money does she spend? **exact answer; $88**

Grade 4 20 Chapter 2

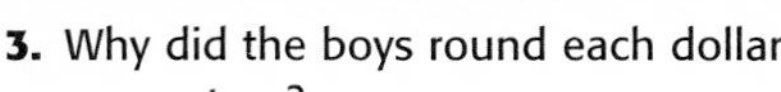

ANALYZE the Skill

Refer to the problem on the previous page. 1–4. See Ch. 2 Answer Appendix.

1. Why does it make sense to round in this situation?
2. Suppose it costs $16 for nails, $109 for tools, and $62 for wood. What would a good estimate be? Explain.
3. Why did the boys round each dollar amount up?
4. Why is it a good idea to round up when dealing with money even if the number would be rounded down?

★ indicates multi-step problem

PRACTICE the Skill

EXTRA PRACTICE See page R5.

Tell whether an estimate or exact answer is needed. Then solve.

5. Determine if Tammy, Anessa, and Jaleesa have more than 110 CDs. exact answer; no; $96 < 110$

6. Samuel bought a sweater for $36 and paid with a $50 bill. About how much change should he get back? estimate; $10
7. A theater can hold 200 people. Two groups rented out the theater. The first group has 92 people and the other has 107 people. Are there enough seats for everyone? Explain. exact answer; yes; $92 + 107 = 199$
8. ★ Carissa pays $2 each day for lunch. Her money is in an account that is deducted each time she buys a lunch. There are 6 days until the end of the school year and her account has $13 in it. How much money will she get back at the end of the year? exact answer; $1
9. Jacob is taking a test at school. The question is shown below. What is the answer?

23 + 34 + 17

    exact answer; 74
10. Tracy is allowed to watch 2 hours of television each night. About how much television does she watch in a year? estimate; about 740 hours a year
11. **Measurement** Rodney needs to measure the distance around his garden. How much fencing should Rodney buy?

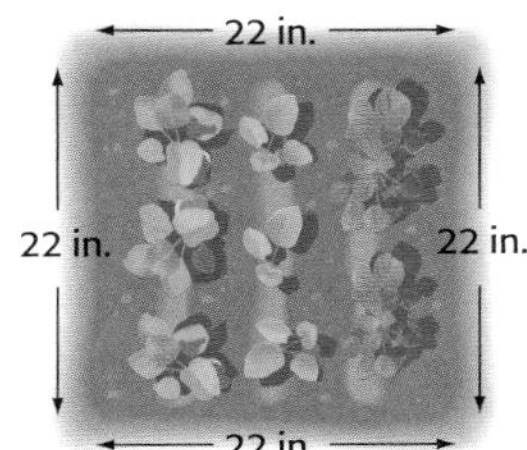

exact answer; 88 in.

12. WRITING IN MATH A newspaper stated that the population of California was 33,871,600. Explain why this is probably an estimate. See Ch. 2 Answer Appendix.

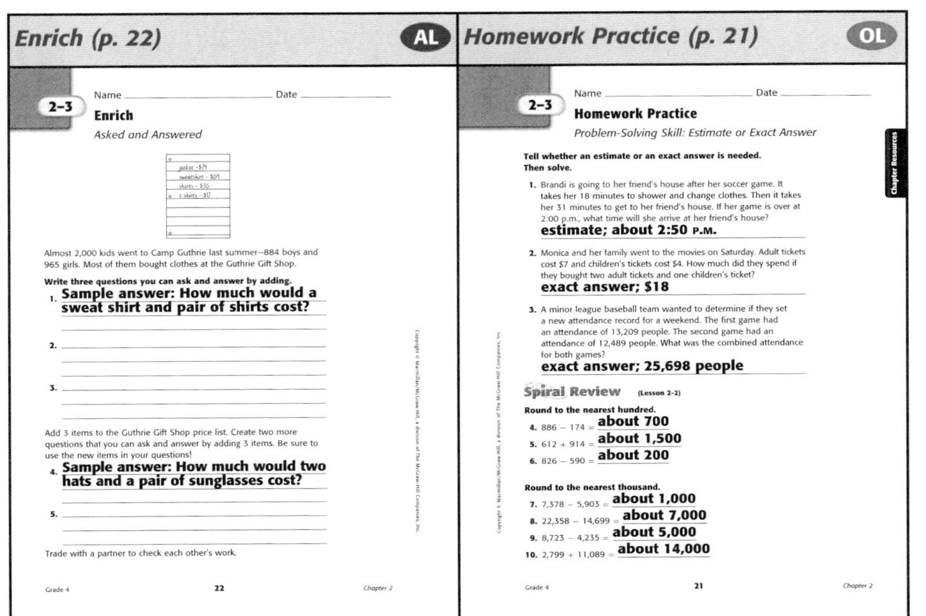

Enrich (p. 22) AL

2–3 Name ______ Date ______

Enrich

Asked and Answered

jacket - $79
sweatshirt - $59
shorts - $35
t-shirts - $17

Almost 2,000 kids went to Camp Guthrie last summer—884 boys and 965 girls. Most of them bought clothes at the Guthrie Gift Shop.

Write three questions you can ask and answer by adding.

1. **Sample answer: How much would a sweat shirt and pair of shirts cost?**
2. ______
3. ______

Add 3 items to the Guthrie Gift Shop price list. Create two more questions that you can ask and answer by adding 3 items. Be sure to use the new items in your questions!

4. **Sample answer: How much would two hats and a pair of sunglasses cost?**
5. ______

Trade with a partner to check each other's work.

Grade 4 22 *Chapter 2*

Homework Practice (p. 21) OL

2–3 Name ______ Date ______

Homework Practice

Problem-Solving Skill: Estimate or Exact Answer

Chapter Resources

Tell whether an estimate or an exact answer is needed. Then solve.

1. Brandi is going to her friend's house after her soccer game. It takes her 18 minutes to shower and change clothes. Then it takes her 31 minutes to get to her friend's house. If her game is over at 2:00 p.m., what time will she arrive at her friend's house? **estimate; about 2:50 P.M.**
2. Monica and her family went to the movies on Saturday. Adult tickets cost $7 and children's tickets cost $4. How much did they spend if they bought two adult tickets and one children's ticket? **exact answer; $18**
3. A minor league baseball team wanted to determine if they set a new attendance record for a weekend. The first game had an attendance of 13,209 people. The second game had an attendance of 12,489 people. What was the combined attendance for both games? **exact answer; 25,698 people**

Spiral Review (Lesson 2-2)

Round to the nearest hundred.

4. $886 - 174 =$ **about 700**
5. $612 + 914 =$ **about 1,500**
6. $826 - 590 =$ **about 200**

Round to the nearest thousand.

7. $7{,}378 - 5{,}903 =$ **about 1,000**
8. $22{,}358 - 14{,}699 =$ **about 7,000**
9. $8{,}723 - 4{,}235 =$ **about 5,000**
10. $2{,}799 + 11{,}089 =$ **about 14,000**

Grade 4 21 *Chapter 2*

Analyze the Skill Use Exercises 1–4 to analyze and discuss the problem-solving skill.

BL Alternate Teaching Strategy

If students have trouble determining when an estimate or exact answer is needed…

Then use one of these reteach options:

1. CRM **Daily Reteach Worksheet** (pp. 18–19)
2. Have them write a series of statements about themselves with the word "about" in them. Examples might include: I am about 10 years old. **What does "about" mean?** almost or close to, but not exact

   Students might want to use small self-sticking notes to call out the word "about".

3 Practice

Using the Exercises

Exercise 7 requires students to know that there must be a seat for every person and no fewer.

Exercise 12 may be difficult for students because the number does not appear to be rounded. Help students understand that some numbers may be estimates because they are so large.

4 Assess

Formative Assessment

Write the following on the board:

Jasmine has $3, Deepak has $2, and Ramira has $4. If a pizza costs $12, do they have enough money to buy a pizza? no; they have $9

- **Is an exact answer needed?** no
- **To know if they have enough money, should the amounts be rounded up or down?** down

Quick Check

Are students continuing to struggle with determining when to estimate or find an exact answer?

If Yes → Small Group Options (p. 62B)

If No → Independent Work Options (p. 62B)
CRM Skills Practice Worksheet (p. 20)
CRM Enrich Worksheet (p. 22)

LESSON 2-4

Add Whole Numbers

Lesson Planner

Objective

Add numbers, including multi-digit numbers.

Review Vocabulary

regroup

Resources

Manipulatives: base-ten blocks

Literature Connection: *Earth Day–Hooray!* by Stuart J. Murphy

Teacher Technology
TeacherWorks • Interactive Classroom

Focus on Math Background

As students begin to add multi-digit numbers, the concept of place value becomes extremely important. Students who have learned how to regroup when they add two-digit numbers will find that they can use the same algorithm to add multi-digit numbers. A new algorithm is not necessary. Estimating the sum *before* adding and checking for reasonableness will help students avoid errors.

Daily Routine

Use these suggestions before beginning the lesson on p. 64.

5-Minute Check

(Reviews Lesson 2-3)

Solve. Explain why you gave an estimate or an exact answer.

A turkey sandwich costs $4 and a bottle of juice costs $1. If Diego buys two sandwiches and a bottle of juice, how much change will he receive from $10.00? $1; exact answer because the question asks about an exact amount of change.

Problem of the Day

Nicki has $37. Does she have enough money to buy two videos that cost $18 each? Explain.
yes; $18 + 18 = 36$; $\$37 > \$36$

Review Math Vocabulary

Write the review vocabulary word and its definition on the board.

Have students record the word and its definition in their Math Journals. Ask them to write what they know about regrouping in addition and examples of when it is used.

Differentiated Instruction

Small Group Options

SPATIAL, KINESTHETIC 

Option 1 Gifted and Talented AL

Materials: number cubes

- Have students roll a number cube to create three-, four-, or five-digit numbers.
- Then have students create two addends, find the sum, and check their answers.

$$\begin{array}{r} 4{,}861 \\ +\ 329 \\ \hline 5{,}190 \end{array} \qquad \begin{array}{r} 12{,}963 \\ +\ 5{,}782 \\ \hline 18{,}745 \end{array}$$

VISUAL, AUDITORY

Option 2 English Language Learners ELL

Materials: colored markers, chart paper
Core Vocabulary: line them up, move them, again
Common Use Verb: regroup

Do Math This strategy uses a song and color to draw attention to the order of adding or subtracting multi-digit numbers while regrouping.

- Model writing a problem vertically with each place value in a different color.
- Guide students through the problem as you repeat the song.
- Sing to the tune of "Three Blind Mice":

  Line them up. Move to regroup. (repeat)
  If you have 10 ones, then regroup again.
  If you have 10 tens, then regroup again.
  If you have 10 hundreds then regroup again
  and line them up.

- Allow student to repeat as time permits.

Independent Work Options

SOCIAL, LOGICAL 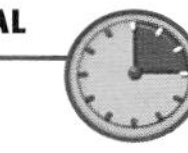

Option 1 Early Finishers OL AL

Materials: number cubes, base-ten blocks, pencil, paper

- Have students roll the number cube three times with the first number hundreds, the second tens, and the third ones.
- Students use base-ten blocks to model the number rolled. Repeat for a second number.
- Students add the numbers and regroup as needed using the blocks. Students write the numbers rolled and add to check. Roll the cube three more times and build a third number to add to the existing sum.
- Repeat as time permits.

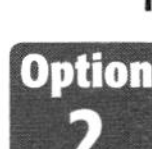

Option 2 Student Technology

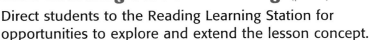

Math Online macmillanmh.com

Personal Tutor • Extra Examples

 Math Adventures

Option 3 Learning Station: Reading (p. 52G)

Direct students to the Reading Learning Station for opportunities to explore and extend the lesson concept.

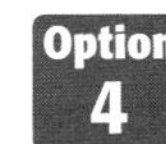

Option 4 Problem-Solving Practice

Reinforce problem-solving skills and strategies with the Problem-Solving Practice worksheet.

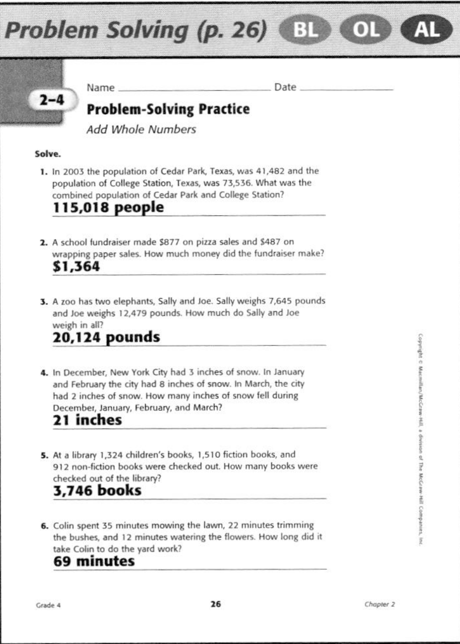

Problem Solving (p. 26) BL OL AL

2–4 Name ______ Date ______

Problem-Solving Practice

Add Whole Numbers

Solve.

1. In 2003 the population of Cedar Park, Texas, was 41,482 and the population of College Station, Texas, was 73,536. What was the combined population of Cedar Park and College Station?
   115,018 people
2. A school fundraiser made $877 on pizza sales and $487 on wrapping paper sales. How much money did the fundraiser make?
   $1,364
3. A zoo has two elephants, Sally and Joe. Sally weighs 7,645 pounds and Joe weighs 12,479 pounds. How much do Sally and Joe weigh in all?
   20,124 pounds
4. In December, New York City had 3 inches of snow. In January and February the city had 8 inches of snow. In March, the city had 2 inches of snow. How many inches of snow fell during December, January, February, and March?
   21 inches
5. At a library 1,324 children's books, 1,510 fiction books, and 912 non-fiction books were checked out. How many books were checked out of the library?
   3,746 books
6. Colin spent 35 minutes mowing the lawn, 22 minutes trimming the bushes, and 12 minutes watering the flowers. How long did it take Colin to do the yard work?
   69 minutes

Grade 4 26 Chapter 2

2-4 Add Whole Numbers

1 Introduce

Activity Choice 1 • Hands-On 

- Write 351 + 432 on the board. Have small groups use base-ten blocks to model the problem.
- **How many ones, tens, and hundreds are there in all?** 3 ones, 8 tens, 7 hundreds
- Write 46 + 521 on the board. Have students model the problem using base-ten blocks. Have them arrange the blocks to model the problem in vertical form, lining up ones, tens, and hundreds.
- **When writing problems, why is it important to line up the ones with ones, tens with tens, and hundreds with hundreds?** You can only add ones together, tens together, and hundreds together.
- Have students practice with several addition problems that do not have regrouping. Have them model the problems with blocks as well as write the problems in vertical form.

Activity Choice 2 • Literature

Introduce the lesson with *Earth Day—Hooray!* by Stuart J. Murphy. For a related math activity, see p. TR44.

2 Teach

Scaffolding Questions

Write 3,567 + 328 on the board. Use base-ten blocks to show the problem in vertical form.

- **What is a first step in finding the sum?** Add ones.
- **How many ones are there?** 15 ones
- **When there are ten or more ones, what should you do?** Regroup or exchange ten ones for one ten.
- Exchange 10 ones for one ten. Place the new rod above the tens.
- **How many tens are there now?** 9 tens

GET READY to Learn

Hands-On Mini Activity Distribute base-ten blocks to students. Guide them through each step of the activity.

2-4 Add Whole Numbers

MAIN IDEA

I will add numbers, including multi-digit numbers.

Math Online

macmillanmh.com
- Extra Examples
- Personal Tutor
- Self-Check Quiz

GET READY to Learn

Hands-On Mini Activity

The model shows 135 + 127.

Hundreds	Tens	Ones
1	3	5
+ 1	2	7

1. Estimate 135 + 127. 100 + 100 = 200
2. To find 135 + 127, is it necessary to regroup the ones? How do you know? yes; 5 + 7 > 9
3. Is it necessary to regroup the tens? How do you know? no; 1 + 3 + 2 < 9

When you add whole numbers, it may be necessary to regroup.

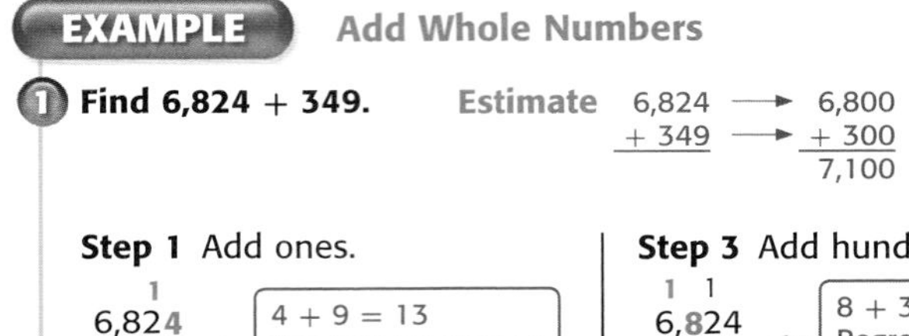

EXAMPLE Add Whole Numbers

1 **Find 6,824 + 349.**

Estimate 6,824 → 6,800; + 349 → + 300; 7,100

Step 1 Add ones.

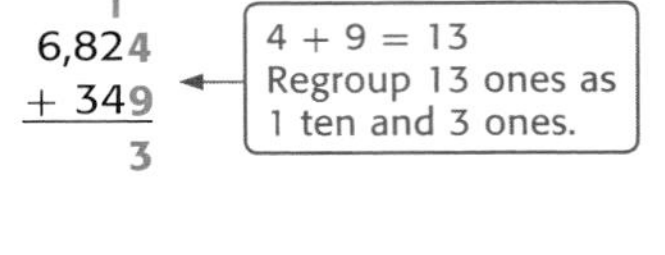

$$\begin{array}{r} \scriptstyle 1 \\ 6{,}824 \\ +\ 349 \\ \hline 3 \end{array}$$

4 + 9 = 13 Regroup 13 ones as 1 ten and 3 ones.

Step 2 Add tens.

$$\begin{array}{r} \scriptstyle 1 \\ 6{,}824 \\ +\ 349 \\ \hline 73 \end{array}$$

1 + 2 + 4 = 7

Step 3 Add hundreds.

$$\begin{array}{r} \scriptstyle 1\ 1 \\ 6{,}824 \\ +\ 349 \\ \hline 173 \end{array}$$

8 + 3 = 11 Regroup 11 hundreds as 1 thousand and 1 hundred.

Step 4 Add thousands.

$$\begin{array}{r} \scriptstyle 1\ 1 \\ 6{,}824 \\ +\ 349 \\ \hline 7{,}173 \end{array}$$

6 + 1 = 7

Check for Reasonableness

The estimate is 7,100. Since 7,173 is close to the estimate, the answer is reasonable. ✓

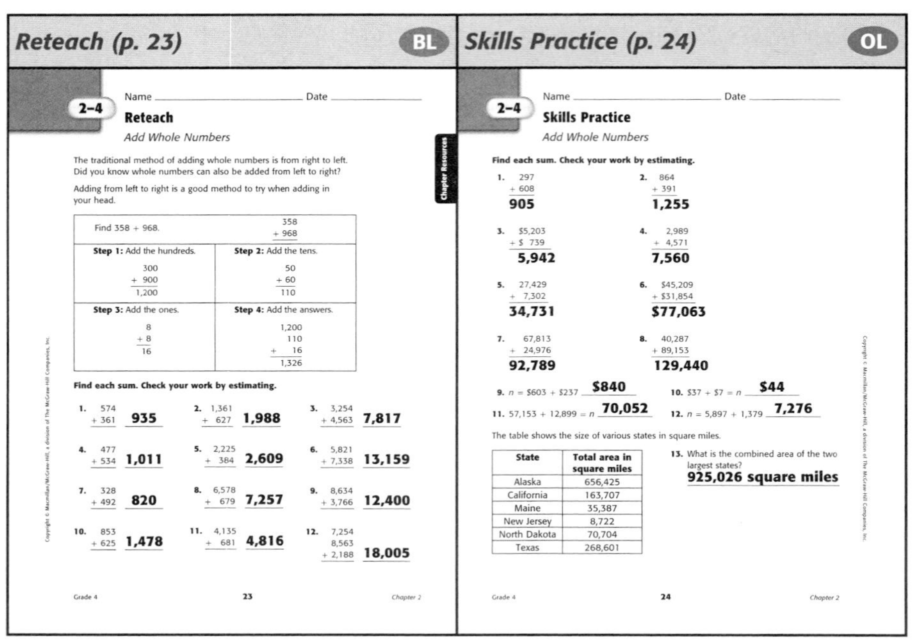

Reteach (p. 23) BL

2-4 Name ________ Date ________

Reteach

Add Whole Numbers

The traditional method of adding whole numbers is from right to left. Did you know whole numbers can also be added from left to right?

Adding from left to right is a good method to try when adding in your head.

Find 358 + 968.	358 + 968
Step 1: Add the hundreds. 300 + 900 = 1,200	**Step 2:** Add the tens. 50 + 60 = 110
Step 3: Add the ones. 8 + 8 = 16	**Step 4:** Add the answers. 1,200 + 110 + 16 = 1,326

Find each sum. Check your work by estimating.

1. 574 + 361 **935**
2. 1,361 + 627 **1,988**
3. 3,254 + 4,563 **7,817**
4. 477 + 534 **1,011**
5. 2,225 + 384 **2,609**
6. 5,821 + 7,338 **13,159**
7. 328 + 492 **820**
8. 6,578 + 679 **7,257**
9. 8,634 + 3,766 **12,400**
10. 853 + 625 **1,478**
11. 4,135 + 681 **4,816**
12. 7,254 + 8,563 + 2,188 **18,005**

Grade 4 23 Chapter 2

Skills Practice (p. 24) OL

2-4 Name ________ Date ________

Skills Practice

Add Whole Numbers

Find each sum. Check your work by estimating.

1. 297 + 608 **905**
2. 864 + 391 **1,255**
3. $5,203 + $ 739 **5,942**
4. 2,989 + 4,571 **7,560**
5. 27,429 + 7,302 **34,731**
6. $45,209 + $31,854 **$77,063**
7. 67,813 + 24,976 **92,789**
8. 40,287 + 89,153 **129,440**
9. n = $603 + $237 **$840**
10. $37 + $7 = n **$44**
11. 57,153 + 12,899 = n **70,052**
12. n = 5,897 + 1,379 **7,276**

The table shows the size of various states in square miles.

State	Total area in square miles
Alaska	656,425
California	163,707
Maine	35,387
New Jersey	8,722
North Dakota	70,704
Texas	268,601

13. What is the combined area of the two largest states? **925,026 square miles**

Grade 4 24 Chapter 2

Add Multi-Digit Numbers

2 TICKETS Weekend ticket sales for a play are shown in the table. What was the total?

Ticket Sales	
Day	**Amount**
Saturday	$5,713
Sunday	$4,827

Estimate

$5,713 → $6,000
+ $4,827 → + $5,000
$11,000

Vocabulary Link
prefixes The prefix *re-* means *again*. Examples: *regroup* means *to group again; review* means *to view again*

Step 1 Add ones.

```
     1
 $5,713
+ $4,827
      0
```
3 + 7 = 10
Regroup 10 ones as 1 ten and 0 ones.

Step 2 Add tens.

```
    1
 $5,713
+ $4,827
     40
```
1 + 1 + 2 = 4

Step 3 Add hundreds.

```
  1  1
 $5,713
+ $4,827
    540
```
7 + 8 = 15
Regroup 15 hundreds as 1 thousand and 5 hundreds.

Step 4 Add thousands. Place $ sign.

```
  1  1
 $5,713
+ $4,827
$10,540
```
1 + 5 + 4 = 10
Place $ in front.

So, the total ticket sales were $10,540.

Check for Reasonableness

The estimate is $11,000. Since $10,540 is close to the estimate, the answer is reasonable. ✓

Lesson 2-4 Add Whole Numbers **65**

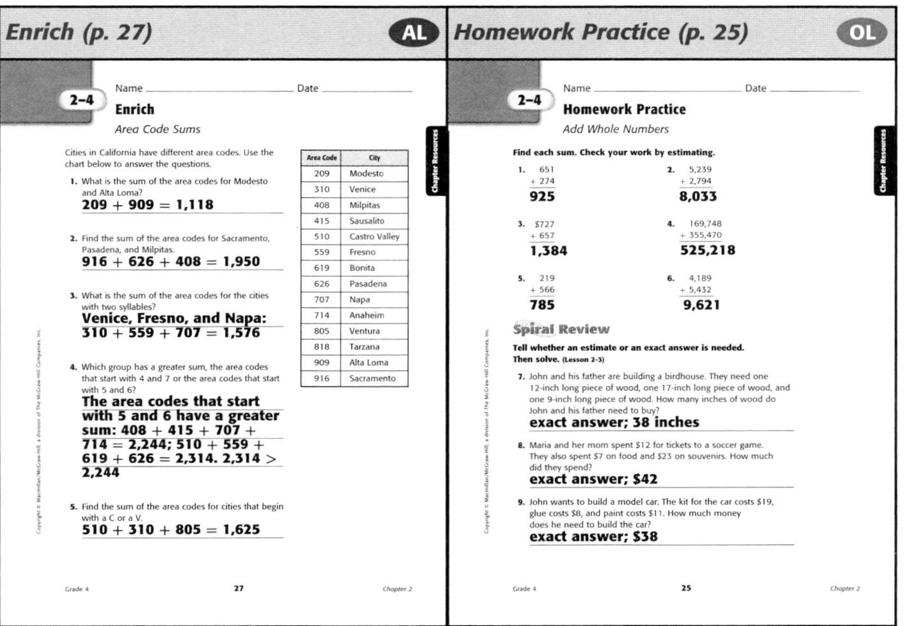

Enrich (p. 27) AL

2–4 Name ______________ Date ______________

Enrich

Area Code Sums

Cities in California have different area codes. Use the chart below to answer the questions.

Area Code	City
209	Modesto
310	Venice
408	Milpitas
415	Sausalito
510	Castro Valley
559	Fresno
619	Bonita
626	Pasadena
707	Napa
714	Anaheim
805	Ventura
818	Tarzana
909	Alta Loma
916	Sacramento

1. What is the sum of the area codes for Modesto and Alta Loma?
209 + 909 = 1,118

2. Find the sum of the area codes for Sacramento, Pasadena, and Milpitas.
916 + 626 + 408 = 1,950

3. What is the sum of the area codes for the cities with two syllables?
Venice, Fresno, and Napa: 310 + 559 + 707 = 1,576

4. Which group has a greater sum, the area codes that start with 4 and 7 or the area codes that start with 5 and 6?
The area codes that start with 5 and 6 have a greater sum: 408 + 415 + 707 + 714 = 2,244; 510 + 559 + 619 + 626 = 2,314. 2,314 > 2,244

5. Find the sum of the area codes for cities that begin with a C or a V.
510 + 310 + 805 = 1,625

Grade 4 27 *Chapter 2*

Homework Practice (p. 25) OL

2–4 Name ______________ Date ______________

Homework Practice

Add Whole Numbers

Find each sum. Check your work by estimating.

1. 651 + 274 = **925**
2. 5,239 + 2,794 = **8,033**
3. $727 + 657 = **1,384**
4. 169,748 + 355,470 = **525,218**
5. 219 + 566 = **785**
6. 4,189 + 5,432 = **9,621**

Spiral Review

Tell whether an estimate or an exact answer is needed. Then solve. (Lesson 2-3)

7. John and his father are building a birdhouse. They need one 12-inch long piece of wood, one 17-inch long piece of wood, and one 9-inch long piece of wood. How many inches of wood do John and his father need to buy?
exact answer; 38 inches

8. Maria and her mom spent $12 for tickets to a soccer game. They also spent $7 on food and $23 on souvenirs. How much did they spend?
exact answer; $42

9. John wants to build a model car. The kit for the car costs $19, glue costs $8, and paint costs $11. How much money does he need to build the car?
exact answer; $38

Grade 4 25 *Chapter 2*

Add Multi-Digit Numbers

Example 2 Point out that it is sometimes necessary to regroup several times in a problem.

ADDITIONAL EXAMPLES

1 Add 4,568 + 2,429. 6,997

2 Two farm sizes are listed in the table below. What is the total size of the two farms?

Farm	Size (acres)
Smith Family	**12,879**
Frank Family	**5,732**

18,611 acres

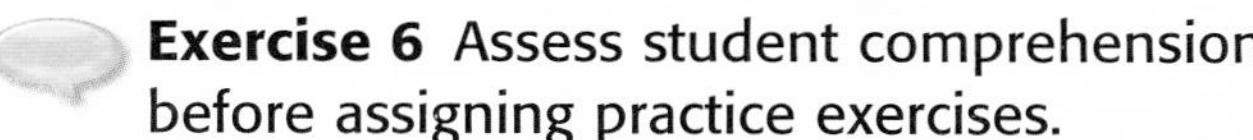

CHECK What You Know

As a class, have students complete Exercises 1–6 in **Check What You Know** as you observe their work.

Exercise 6 Assess student comprehension before assigning practice exercises.

BL Alternate Teaching Strategy

If students have trouble adding multidigit whole numbers…

Then use one of these reteach options:

1 CRM **Daily Reteach Worksheet** (p. 23)

2 Write several addition problems with ones, tens, and hundreds on the board. Have students use base-ten blocks to regroup by exchanging 10 ones for a ten and 10 tens for a hundred. Have them record each step.

- **What must always happen if there are 10 or more ones?** Exchange 10 ones for 1 ten.
- **What must always happen if there are more than 10 tens?** Exchange 10 tens for a hundred.

3 Practice

Differentiate practice using these leveled assignments for Exercises 7–21.

Level	Assignment
BL Below/Approaching Level	8–12, 16–17
OL On Level	8–12, 14–15, 17–18, 20
AL Above/Beyond Level	7–19 odd, 20–21

Have students discuss and complete the Higher Order Thinking problems. Encourage them to try more than one addition problem before deciding on their answers for each problem.

WRITING IN MATH Have students complete Exercise 21 in their Math Journals. You may choose to use this exercise as an optional formative assessment.

COMMON ERROR!

Exercise 19 Students may have trouble adding three or more numbers. Remind them to line up the digits by place value in all the numbers.

CHECK What You Know

Find each sum. Check your work by estimating. See Examples 1 and 2 (pp. 64–65)

1–4. See margin.

1. 397 + 84
2. 1,592 + 429
3. \$2,971 + \$ 864
4. \$29,380 + \$ 8,253

5. Mr. Russo's class is collecting bottles to recycle. The class collected 178 bottles in March and 236 bottles in April. How many bottles were collected? 414 bottles

6. Talk About It Explain why it is important to line up digits in numbers when you add. See margin.

Practice and Problem Solving

EXTRA PRACTICE See page R5.

Find each sum. Check your work by estimating. See Examples 1 and 2 (pp. 64–65)

7–14. See margin.

7. 364 + 58
8. 290 + 693
9. 6,742 + 975
10. 8,346 + 7,208
11. \$23,824 + \$ 7,346
12. 82,828 + 4,789
13. \$37,178 + \$82,370
14. \$693,782 + \$ 47,816

15. There are 4,585 students who rode the bus to school today. There were 3,369 students who came to school another way. How many students were there in all at school? 7,954 students

16. Becky wants to buy a new bike that costs \$150 and a pair of roller blades that costs \$30. She made \$200 baby-sitting. If she buys a book that is \$15, will she have enough money for the bike and roller blades? yes; \$195 < \$200

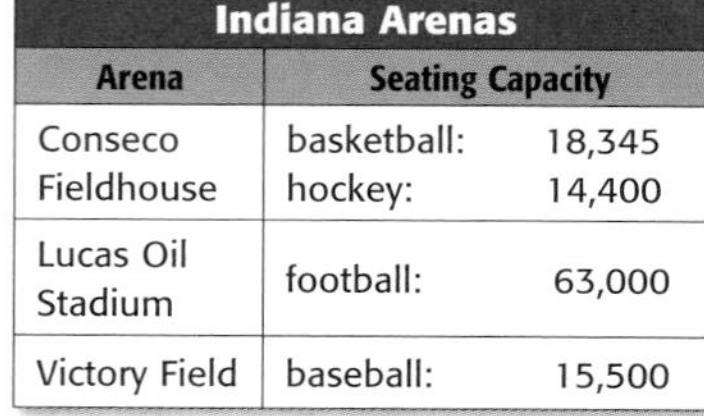

Data File

Indiana has several professional sports teams. The capacities of the arenas they play in are shown in the table.

Indiana Arenas

Arena	Seating Capacity	
Conseco Fieldhouse	basketball:	18,345
	hockey:	14,400
Lucas Oil Stadium	football:	63,000
Victory Field	baseball:	15,500

Source: Marchex, Inc.

17. What is the greatest number of people that could attend two basketball games? 36,690 people

18. Could more than 30,000 people attend two hockey games? Explain. Sample answer: no; 14,400 + 14,400 = 28,800

19. What is the least number of baseball games that must be played to allow more than 50,000 fans to attend? Explain. Sample answer: 4; 3 games = 46,500 fans and 4 games = 62,000 fans

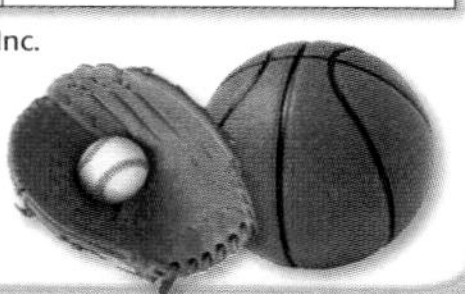

Additional Answers

1. 481; 400 + 80 = 480
2. 2,021; 1,600 + 400 = 2,000
3. \$3,835; 3,000 + 900 = 3,900
4. \$37,633; 29,000 + 8,000 = 37,000
6. Sample answer: You need to add the digits in the same place value position.
7. 422; 360 + 60 = 420
8. 983; 300 + 700 = 1,000
9. 7,717; 6,700 + 1,000 = 7,700
10. 15,554; 8,000 + 7,000 = 15,000
11. \$31,170; 24,000 + 7,000 = 31,000
12. 87,617; 83,000 + 5,000 = 88,000
13. \$119,548; 37,000 + 82,000 = 119,000
14. \$741,598; 694,000 + 48,000 = 742,000

H.O.T. Problems

20. **OPEN ENDED** Write two 5-digit addends whose sum would give an estimate of 60,000. Sample answer: 32,985 and 29,592

21. **WRITING IN MATH** Explain why an addition problem that has 4-digit addends could have a 5-digit sum. See margin.

TEST Practice

22. Jackson is buying a new board game. It costs $26. If he has 2 ten-dollar bills and 5 one-dollar bills, which of the following statements is true? (Lesson 2-3) B

A He will have less than $5 left over.

B He does not have enough money.

C He has the exact amount of money.

D He will have more than $5 left over.

23. There are 17 extra chairs in the library and 45 extra chairs in the cafeteria. Which of the following shows how to find the total number of extra chairs? (Lesson 2-4) F

F 17 + 45

G 17 − 45

H 17 × 45

J 17 ÷ 45

Spiral Review

Tell whether an estimate or exact answer is needed. Then solve.

24. A school collected 189 cans of corn, 500 cans of soup, 168 cans of beans, and 269 jars of spaghetti sauce in a food drive. How many items did the school collect? (Lesson 2-3) exact answer; 1,126

Estimate. Round to the indicated place value. (Lesson 2-2)

25. 137 + 192; tens 140 + 190 = 330

26. 489 + 1,963; hundreds 500 + 2,000 = 2,500

Add mentally. (Lesson 2-1)

27. 10 + 25 + 18 53

28. 26 + 14 + 3 43

29. 15 + 12 + 30 57

Round each number to the given place-value position. (Lesson 1-6)

30. 987; ten 990

31. 2,159; hundred 2,200

32. 78,368; thousand 78,000

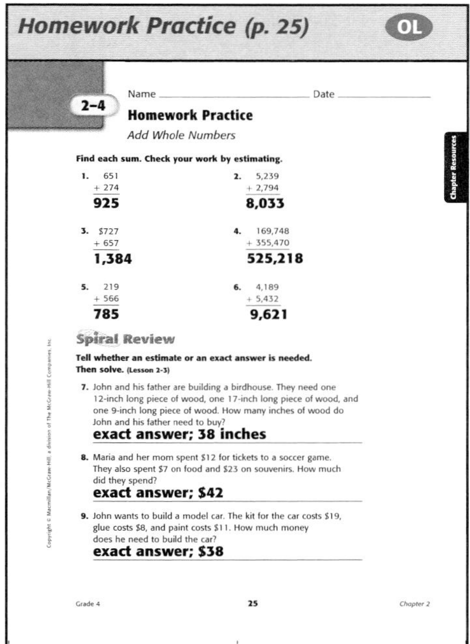

Homework Practice (p. 25) OL

2-4

Name ______________ Date ______________

Homework Practice

Add Whole Numbers

Chapter Resources

Find each sum. Check your work by estimating.

1. 651 + 274 = **925**
2. 5,239 + 2,794 = **8,033**
3. $727 + 657 = **1,384**
4. 169,748 + 355,470 = **525,218**
5. 219 + 566 = **785**
6. 4,189 + 5,432 = **9,621**

Spiral Review

Tell whether an estimate or an exact answer is needed. Then solve. (Lesson 2-3)

7. John and his father are building a birdhouse. They need one 12-inch long piece of wood, one 17-inch long piece of wood, and one 9-inch long piece of wood. How many inches of wood do John and his father need to buy?
exact answer; 38 inches

8. Maria and her mom spent $12 for tickets to a soccer game. They also spent $7 on food and $23 on souvenirs. How much did they spend?
exact answer; $42

9. John wants to build a model car. The kit for the car costs $19, glue costs $8, and paint costs $11. How much money does he need to build the car?
exact answer; $38

Grade 4 25 Chapter 2

4 Assess

Formative Assessment

Write 6,572 + 4,259 on the board.

- **In what places will regrouping be needed?** ones, tens, and thousands places
- **How many tens will be added together?** 13 tens
- **What is the sum?** 10,831

Quick Check **Are students continuing to struggle with adding multi-digit whole numbers?**

If Yes → Strategic Intervention Guide (p. 40)

If No → Independent Work Options (p. 64B)
CRM Skills Practice Worksheet (p. 24)
CRM Enrich Worksheet (p. 27)

Name the Math Write 916 + 475 on the board. Have students write the step-by-step process for finding 916 + 475.

TEST Practice

Reviews Lessons 2-3 and 2-4

Assign the Test Practice problems to provide daily reinforcement of test-taking skills.

Spiral Review

Reviews Lessons 1-6, 2-2, and 2-3

Review and assess mastery of skills and concepts from previous chapters.

Additional Answer

21. Sample answer: If the digits in the ten thousands place have a sum that is greater than 9, the sum will be 5 digits.

Extend Technology Activity for 2-4

Lesson Planner

Objective

Use technology to explore addition.

Resources

Math Tool Chest *(accessible in three ways)*

- **Math Online** macmillanmh.com
- StudentWorks Plus
- Interactive Classroom

Getting Started

- The activities and exercises on p. 68 use the Place-Value Tool Box in *Math Tool Chest*. They may be completed as a class, in pairs, or individually.
- Have students read the example on p. 68.
- As a class, work through the activity in the example following the instructions on the page.

Using Math Tool Chest

Place Value The in *Math Tool Chest* provides opportunities for students to make place-value models quickly and easily.

- The number in the box at the bottom left-hand corner shows the digits stamped out.

Technology Activity for 2-4

Explore Composing and Decomposing Numbers

Tech Link

You can use *Math Tool Chest* to compose and decompose numbers.

MAIN IDEA

I will use technology to explore addition.

EXAMPLE

1 There are 275 books. Each book is either non-fiction or fiction. How many of each type might there be?

Click on place-value tool box from the *Math Tool Chest.*

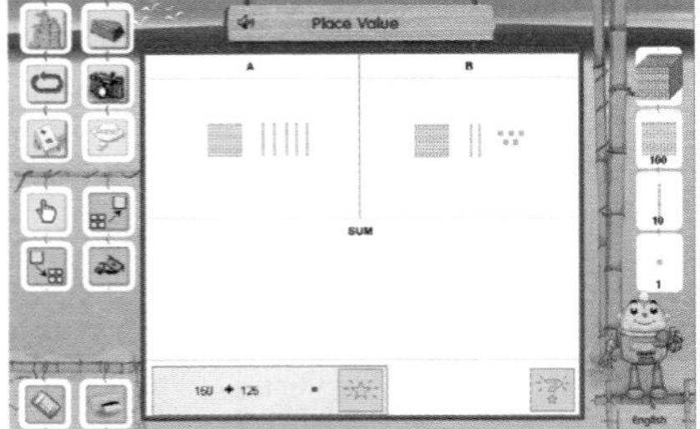

- Click on the addition mat.
- In section A, use hundreds and tens to stamp out 150.
- In section B, use hundreds, tens, and ones to stamp out 125.
- Click on sum. The models show that $150 + 125 = 275$.
- Click on the star at the bottom to check the sum.
- Explore different ways to make 275.

CHECK What You Know

Use the *Math Tool Chest* to explore different ways to compose and decompose each amount. Name two different ways.

1. There are 895 students in the 4th grade at South Elementary. How might this population be divided between boys and girls? Sample answer: 400 + 495 or 450 + 445
2. There are 1,750 freshwater and saltwater fish at a pet store. How many of each type of fish might the pet store have? Sample answer: 1,000 and 750 or 1,200 and 550
3. **WRITING IN MATH** Describe how different combinations of numbers can have the same sum. You can compose and decompose numbers different ways but will still get the same sum.

Math Tool Chest: Place Value Button Bar

The Place Value Button Bar offers buttons that perform functions specific to the Place Value Button Bar tool.

Erase Students use to remove place-value models from the mat.

Trade Up/Trade Down Students use and to automatically convert place-value models to larger or smaller models of equal value.

Move Students use to move the place value models to help arrange them for ease in counting.

Start Over The allows the student to start over with the same work mat.

Mid-Chapter Check

CHAPTER 2

Lessons 2-1 through 2-4

Algebra Copy and complete each number sentence. Identify the property or rule. (Lesson 2-1)

1. 136 + 0 = ■ 136; Identity Property of Addition
2. (4 + ■)+ 7 = 4 + (2 + 7) 2; Associative Property of Addition
3. 58 + 98 = ■ + 58 98; Commutative Property of Addition

Algebra Write a number sentence. Identify the property or rule used. (Lesson 2-1)

4. Andrea's pencil box has 3 pencils, 2 pencil-top erasers, and 1 red pen. Max's pencil box has 2 pencils, 1 pencil-top eraser, and 3 red pens. Whose pencil box contains more items? Explain. See Ch. 2 Answer Appendix.
5. **MULTIPLE CHOICE** What number completes the number sentence below? (Lesson 2-1) C

   (21 + ■) + 12 = 21 + (17 + 12)

   A 11 **C** 17

   B 12 **D** 21

Estimate. Round to the indicated place value. (Lesson 2-2)

6. \$22 + \$63; tens
   \$20 + \$60 = \$80
7. 567 − 203; hundreds
   600 − 200 = 400
8. 5,825 − 551; hundreds
   5,800 − 600 = 5,200
9. **MULTIPLE CHOICE** About how many miles did a soccer team travel during the weekend? (Lesson 2-2) G

Distance Traveled	
Day	Distance (miles)
Friday	146
Saturday	175
Sunday	206

   F 400 miles **H** 600 miles

   G 500 miles **J** 700 miles

Tell whether an estimate or exact answer is needed. Then solve. (Lesson 2-3)

10. Celia needs to make a fence in her yard for her puppy. She wants it to be square. One side measures 20 feet. How much fence should she buy? exact answer; 80 ft

Find each sum. Check your work by estimating. (Lesson 2-4)

11. 28,180 + 7,233
12. 63,456 + 37,425

11, 12. See Ch. 2 Answer Appendix.

13. Gina's brother is starting college in the fall. The cost of tuition for one year will be \$5,491. All the other expenses for the year will cost \$10,065. What will the total cost of one year of college be for Gina's brother? (Lesson 2-4) \$15,556
14. **WRITING IN MATH** Explain how you could add 175 + 139 + 225 mentally. (Lesson 2-1) See Ch. 2 Answer Appendix.

Formative Assessment 69

Mid-Chapter Check

CHAPTER 2

Lessons 2-1 through 2-4

Formative Assessment

Use the Mid-Chapter Check to assess students' progress in the first half of the chapter.

ExamView Assessment Suite Customize and create multiple versions of your Mid-Chapter Check and the test answer keys.

Dinah Zike's Foldables

Use these lesson suggestions to incorporate the Foldables during this chapter.

Lesson 2-1 Have students define and provide examples of the Associative Property, Commutative Property, Identity Property, and the Subtraction Rule on quarter sheets of paper or index cards and store their work in the first pocket of the Foldable.

Lesson 2-4 Students use the second pocket to store work demonstrating that they understand how to add multi-digit numbers.

Data-Driven Decision Making

Based on the results of the Mid-Chapter Check, use the following resources to review concepts that continue to give students problems.

Exercises	State/Local Standards	What's the Math?	Error Analysis	Resources for Review
1–5, 14 Lesson 2-1		Solve addition problems and understand relationships among operations.	Does not understand word "property." Does not know "rules." Adds or subtracts incorrectly. Does not understand "number sentence."	Strategic Intervention Guide (pp. 36, 38, 40, 42, 44, 46) CRM Chapter 2 Resource Masters (Reteach Worksheets) Math Adventures My Math Zone Chapter 2 Math Online Extra Examples • Concepts in Motion
6–9 Lesson 2-2		Estimate and compute the sum or difference of whole numbers. Explain mathematical reasoning.	Does not know difference between estimate and exact answer.	
10 Lesson 2-3		Understand when an estimate or an exact answer is needed to solve a problem.	Adds incorrectly. Does not understand "square."	
11–13 Lesson 2-4		Compute the sum of whole numbers.	Adds incorrectly.	

Math Activity for 2-5

Lesson Planner

Objective

Explore how to subtract whole numbers.

Resources

Manipulatives: base-ten blocks

Teacher Technology

 macmillanmh.com

Concepts in Motion

1 Introduce

Introduce the Concept

- Have students use the base-ten blocks to show addition with regrouping in the problem 349 + 278. **How are the blocks used to show regrouping in the ones place? In the tens place?** Exchange 10 ones for 1 ten; exchange 10 tens for 1 hundred.
- Have students discuss the differences between addition and subtraction. Guide them to the idea that they are opposite or inverse operations. Write 467 − 124 on the board and have students use blocks to demonstrate.
- **How do you show this problem with blocks?** Set up 4 hundreds, 6 tens, and 7 ones, then remove 4 ones, 2 tens, and 1 hundred.
- Tell students that they will be using base-ten blocks to show regrouping in subtraction.

2 Teach

Activity As students subtract using base-ten blocks, make sure they understand to set out blocks that show only the minuend and then remove blocks from that number. Since there are not enough tens in 421, students should exchange 1 hundred for 10 tens. Have them record their steps in writing as they work through each problem.

Explore

Math Activity for 2-5

Subtract Whole Numbers

When subtracting whole numbers, you may need to regroup.

MAIN IDEA

I will explore how to subtract whole numbers.

You Will Need
base-ten blocks

New Vocabulary

minuend
subtrahend
difference

Math Online macmillanmh.com
• Concepts in Motion

ACTIVITY **Use models to find 421 − 241.**

Step 1 **Model 421.** Use base-ten blocks to model 421.

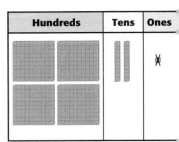

Hundreds	Tens	Ones

Step 2 **Subtract the ones.** Subtract.

$$\begin{array}{r} 421 \\ -\ 241 \\ \hline 0 \end{array}$$

Step 3 **Subtract the tens.** Since you cannot take 4 tens from 2 tens, you need to regroup. Regroup one hundreds flat as 10 tens. You now have 12 tens.

$$\begin{array}{r} {}^{3\,12} \\ \not4\not21 \\ -\ 241 \\ \hline 80 \end{array}$$

Step 4 **Subtract the hundreds.**

Take 2 hundreds flats away from the 3 hundreds flats.

```
 3 12
 421  ← minuend
−241  ← subtrahend
 180  ← difference
```

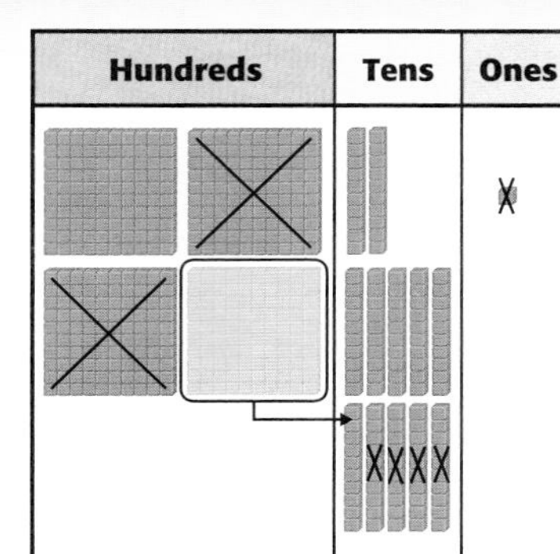

Check

You can use addition to check your subtraction.

```
 421      180
−241     +241
 180  →   421
```

So, the answer is correct. ✓

Think About It

1. How did you subtract 241 from 421 using base-ten blocks? See margin.
2. Describe how you regrouped the tens place. Sample answer: 1 hundreds flat was exchanged for 10 tens. The result was 3 hundreds flats, 12 tens, and 1 one.

Subtract. Check by adding.

3. 357 − 98 259

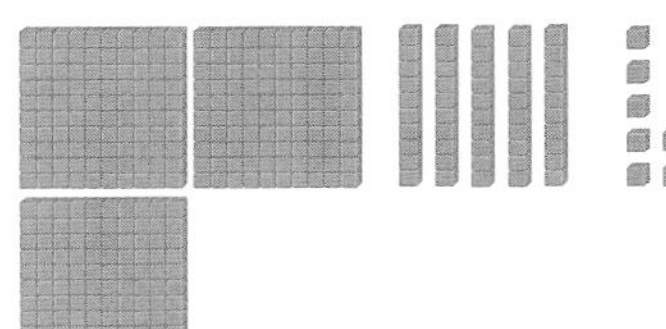

4. 679 − 345 334

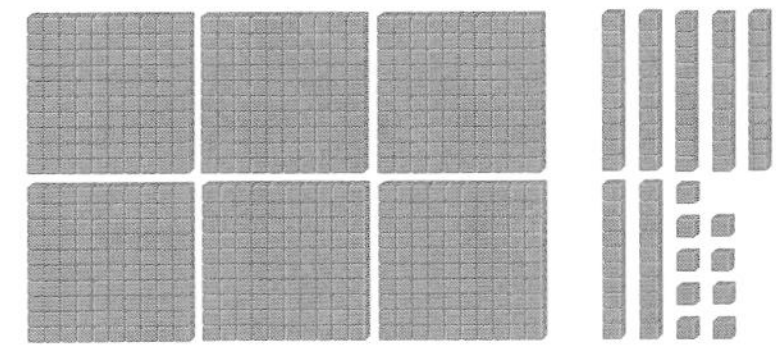

5. 287 − 195 92
6. 525 − 385 140
7. 632 − 248 384
8. 727 − 469 258
9. 861 − 593 268
10. 948 − 729 219
11. WRITING IN ▶MATH Why is it important to line up the digits in each place-value position when subtracting? See margin.

Formative Assessment

Use the **Think About It** Exercises 1 and 2 to assess whether students comprehend how to subtract greater whole numbers.

Assess

Formative Assessment

Use **Check What You Know** Exercises 3–11 to assess whether students comprehend subtracting greater whole numbers.

From Concrete to Abstract Use Exercises 5–10 to bridge the gap between using a model and using pencil-and-paper computation of subtraction problems.

Extending the Concept

- **How can you tell where regrouping is necessary in the problem 456 − 268?** in the ones place because you cannot subtract 8 from 6, and in the tens place because you cannot subtract 6 from 5 without regrouping

Additional Answers

1. Sample answer: First, take away the single unit. Then, regroup a hundreds flat so that there are enough tens to subtract. Subtract the tens place. Finally, subtract the hundreds place.
11. Sample answer: It is important to align each place value so that you know the value of each digit to help with regrouping if needed.

LESSON 2-5

Subtract Whole Numbers

Lesson Planner

Objective

Subtract multi-digit numbers.

Review Vocabulary

minuend, subtrahend, difference

Resources

Materials: grid paper

Manipulatives: base-ten blocks

Literature Connection: *Elevator Magic* by Stuart J. Murphy

Teacher Technology
TeacherWorks • Interactive Classroom

Daily Routine

Use these suggestions before beginning the lesson on p. 72.

5-Minute Check

(Reviews Lesson 2-4)

Find each sum. Check your work by estimating.

1. 568 + 29 597
2. 478 + 245 723
3. 8,238 + 676 8,914
4. 4,765 + 3,482 8,247
5. 54,763 + 2,788 57,551

Problem of the Day

A tree was planted 43 years before 1979. How old will the tree be in 2015? 79 years old

Review Math Vocabulary

Write the review vocabulary words and their definitions on the board.

Have students record the words and their definitions in their Math Journals. Have them write a subtraction problem and label each part correctly.

Differentiated Instruction

Small Group Options

LOGICAL

Option 1 Below Level BL

Materials: paper and pencil

- Write the following information on the board:

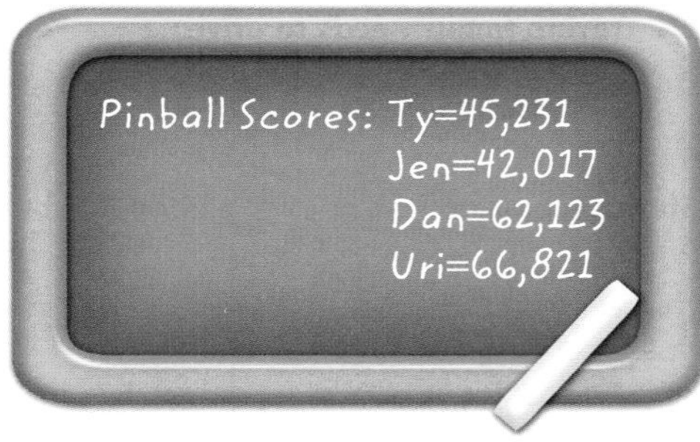

Pinball Scores: Ty=45,231
Jen=42,017
Dan=62,123
Uri=66,821

- Have students list in order the points scored by the pinball players. Students choose a method to calculate the difference in the points between the highest-scoring and the lowest scoring player. Uri, 66,821; Dan, 62,123; Ty, 45,231; Jen, 42,017. Uri scored 24,804 points more than Jen.

KINESTHETIC, LINGUISTIC

Option 2 English Language Learners ELL

Materials: index cards with 0–9 written on them, one per card, chairs
Core Vocabulary: give away, are going, will
Common Use Verb: give/gave
Talk Math This strategy uses visuals and kinesthetic movement to understand subtraction and connect it to background knowledge.

- Say: "Do you remember a time when you ***gave*** something to a friend?"
- Accept responses as you give students a number card. Give one number to each student.
- Write 184 − 66 on the board. Have students with "1," "8," and "4" stand behind the chairs. Students with "66" cards should sit on the chairs.
- As you walk through the problem, have the "answer" students sit on the floor in the appropriate place.
- Say, "We have 184 dollars. We are going to give away 66 dollars. How much will we have left?"
- Repeat with other problems as time permits.

Independent Work Options

SPATIAL, LOGICAL

Option 1 Early Finishers OL AL

Materials: base-ten blocks, number cubes, pencil and paper

- Have students use base-ten blocks to show the number 999. Students roll two number cubes and subtract the number generated from the blocks. Have them record the subtraction. Roll again and subtract from the remaining blocks and on paper. Have them roll and subtract until they have reached 0.
- After using the blocks, have students complete the activity using pencil and paper only.

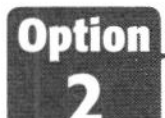

Option 2 Student Technology

Math Online macmillanmh.com

Personal Tutor • Extra Examples

 Math Tool Chest Counters •  Math Adventures

Option 3 Learning Station: Social Studies (p. 52H)

Direct students to the Social Studies Learning Station for opportunities to explore and extend the lesson concept.

Option 4 Problem-Solving Practice

Reinforce problem-solving skills and strategies with the Problem-Solving Practice worksheet.

Problem Solving (p. 31) BL OL AL

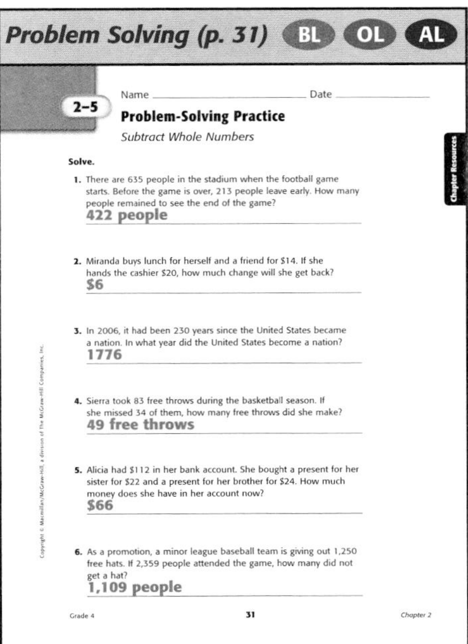

Name ______________ Date ______________

2–5 **Problem-Solving Practice**

Subtract Whole Numbers

Chapter Resources

Solve.

1. There are 635 people in the stadium when the football game starts. Before the game is over, 213 people leave early. How many people remained to see the end of the game?
   422 people
2. Miranda buys lunch for herself and a friend for $14. If she hands the cashier $20, how much change will she get back?
   $6
3. In 2006, it had been 230 years since the United States became a nation. In what year did the United States become a nation?
   1776
4. Sierra took 83 free throws during the basketball season. If she missed 34 of them, how many free throws did she make?
   49 free throws
5. Alicia had $112 in her bank account. She bought a present for her sister for $22 and a present for her brother for $24. How much money does she have in her account now?
   $66
6. As a promotion, a minor league baseball team is giving out 1,250 free hats. If 2,359 people attended the game, how many did not get a hat?
   1,109 people

Grade 4 31 Chapter 2

2-5 Subtract Whole Numbers

1 Introduce

Activity Choice 1 • Hands-On

- Write 562 on the board. Have students use base-ten blocks to model the number.
- **What is this number using place-value terms?** 5 hundreds, 6 tens, and 2 ones
- Remind students that numbers can change in the way they look without changing in value.
- **What can I do to the model of 562 without changing the value?** exchange 1 ten for 10 ones to make 5 hundreds, 5 tens, and 12 ones
- Have students model several numbers and make one change in each place without changing the value. Have them write the numbers as hundreds, tens, and ones before and after the changes are made.

Activity Choice 2 • Literature

Introduce the lesson with *Elevator Magic* by Stuart J. Murphy. For a related math activity, see p. TR44.

2 Teach

Scaffolding Questions

Draw a place-value model showing 563.
Write 563 − 299 on the board.

- **Do you need to regroup the ones? Explain.** Yes; you cannot subtract 9 ones from 3 ones.
- **How would you change 563 so that you have enough ones?** Regroup to make 5 hundreds, 5 tens, and 13 ones.
- Subtract the ones. **Do you need to regroup the tens?** yes
- **How will you change the number of tens?** Regroup 1 hundred to make 10 tens.
- **What are the last two steps in this problem?** Subtract the tens and subtract the hundreds for a difference of 264.

GET READY to Learn

Have students open their books and read the information in **Get Ready to Learn**. Review **minuend**, **subtrahend**, and **difference**. As a class, work through **Examples 1 and 2**.

2-5 Subtract Whole Numbers

MAIN IDEA

I will subtract multi-digit numbers.

Math Online

macmillanmh.com

- Extra Examples
- Personal Tutor
- Self-Check Quiz

GET READY to Learn

The Trevino family is moving to a new city. They have driven 957 miles out of the 3,214 miles that they need to drive. How many more miles do they need to drive?

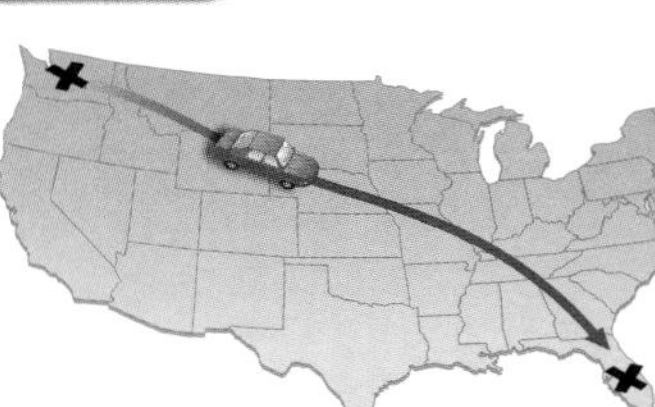

Subtraction of whole numbers is similar to addition of whole numbers in that you may need to regroup.

Real-World EXAMPLE Subtract Whole Numbers

1 MEASUREMENT Find 3,214 − 957 to find how many miles the Trevino family needs to drive.

Estimate 3,214 − 957 → 3,200 − 1,000 = 2,200

Step 1 Subtract ones.

3,214 − 957: regroup 14 → 0 tens 14 ones; 14 − 7 = 7

Regroup a ten as 10 ones.

Step 2 Subtract tens.

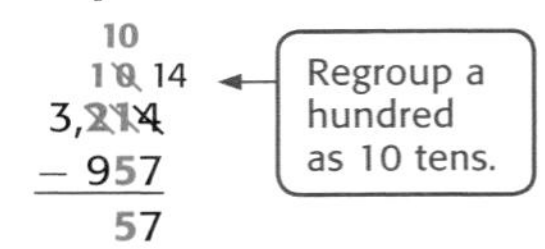

3,214 − 957 = ...57

Regroup a hundred as 10 tens.

Step 3 Subtract hundreds.

3,214 − 957 = ...257

Regroup a thousand as 10 hundreds.

Step 4 Subtract thousands.

3,214 − 957 = 2,257

So, the Trevino family needs to drive 2,257 more miles.

Check You can use addition to check your subtraction.

3,214 − 957 = 2,257 → 2,257 + 957 = 3,214 ✓

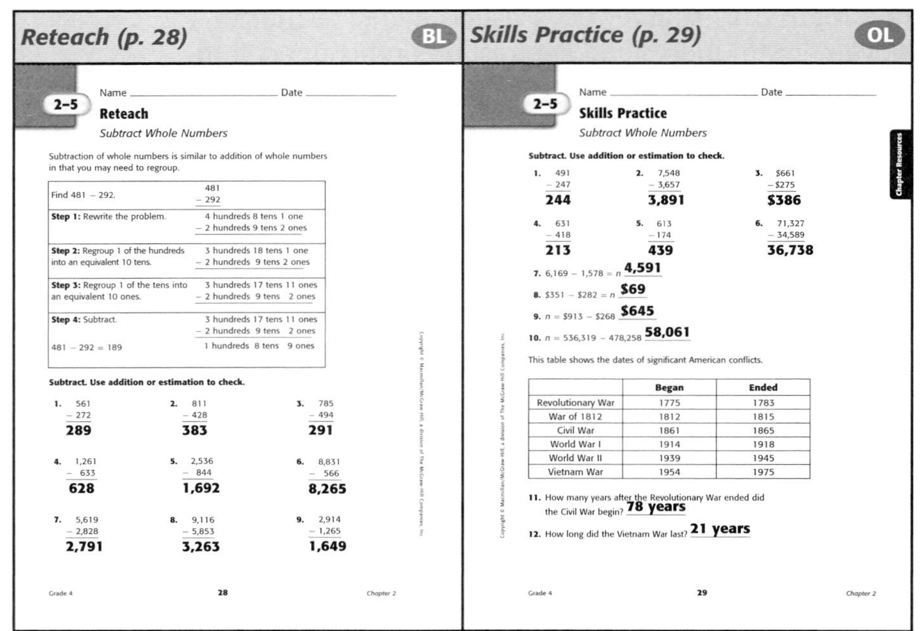

Reteach (p. 28) BL

2-5 Name ______ Date ______

Reteach

Subtract Whole Numbers

Subtraction of whole numbers is similar to addition of whole numbers in that you may need to regroup.

Find 481 − 292.	481 − 292
Step 1: Rewrite the problem.	4 hundreds 8 tens 1 one − 2 hundreds 9 tens 2 ones
Step 2: Regroup 1 of the hundreds into an equivalent 10 tens.	3 hundreds 18 tens 1 one − 2 hundreds 9 tens 2 ones
Step 3: Regroup 1 of the tens into an equivalent 10 ones.	3 hundreds 17 tens 11 ones − 2 hundreds 9 tens 2 ones
Step 4: Subtract. 481 − 292 = 189	3 hundreds 17 tens 11 ones − 2 hundreds 9 tens 2 ones = 1 hundreds 8 tens 9 ones

Subtract. Use addition or estimation to check.

1. 561 − 272 = **289**
2. 811 − 428 = **383**
3. 785 − 494 = **291**
4. 1,261 − 633 = **628**
5. 2,536 − 844 = **1,692**
6. 8,831 − 566 = **8,265**
7. 5,619 − 2,828 = **2,791**
8. 9,116 − 5,853 = **3,263**
9. 2,914 − 1,265 = **1,649**

Grade 4 28 Chapter 2

Skills Practice (p. 29) OL

2-5 Name ______ Date ______

Skills Practice

Subtract Whole Numbers

Chapter Resources

Subtract. Use addition or estimation to check.

1. 491 − 247 = **244**
2. 7,548 − 3,657 = **3,891**
3. $661 − $275 = **$386**
4. 631 − 418 = **213**
5. 613 − 174 = **439**
6. 71,327 − 34,589 = **36,738**
7. 6,169 − 1,578 = n **4,591**
8. $351 − $282 = n **$69**
9. n = $913 − $268 **$645**
10. n = 536,319 − 478,258 **58,061**

This table shows the dates of significant American conflicts.

	Began	Ended
Revolutionary War	1775	1783
War of 1812	1812	1815
Civil War	1861	1865
World War I	1914	1918
World War II	1939	1945
Vietnam War	1954	1975

11. How many years after the Revolutionary War ended did the Civil War begin? **78 years**
12. How long did the Vietnam War last? **21 years**

Grade 4 29 Chapter 2

Real-World EXAMPLE Subtract Money

2 MONEY The parent-teacher organization at an elementary school has raised $1,345 toward new playground equipment. If the goal is to raise $4,275, how much money must still be raised?

Estimate

$4,275 → $4,300
− $1,345 → − $1,300
$3,000

Step 1 Subtract ones.

$4,275
− $1,345
0

Step 2 Subtract tens.

$4,275
− $1,345
30

Step 3 Subtract hundreds.

3 12
$4,275
− $1,345
930

Regroup a thousand as 10 hundreds.

Step 4 Subtract thousands.

3 12
$4,275
− $1,345
$2,930

So, the amount of money that must still be raised is $2,930.

Check

$4,275	$2,930
− $1,345	+ $1,345
$2,930	$4,275

The answer is correct and close to the estimate. ✓

★ indicates multi-step problem

CHECK What You Know

Subtract. Use addition or estimation to check. See Examples 1 and 2 (pp. 72–73)

1. 526 − 403 = **123**
2. $937 − $729 = **$208**
3. 2,962 − 845 = **2,117**
4. $4,785 − $2,293 = **$2,492**
5. Kerri had $95 in her bank account. She bought her mom a bottle of perfume for her birthday for $25. How much money does she have left? **$70**
6. Talk About It Explain how to check the answer to a subtraction problem by using addition. **Add the difference to the subtrahend. The answer is the minuend.**

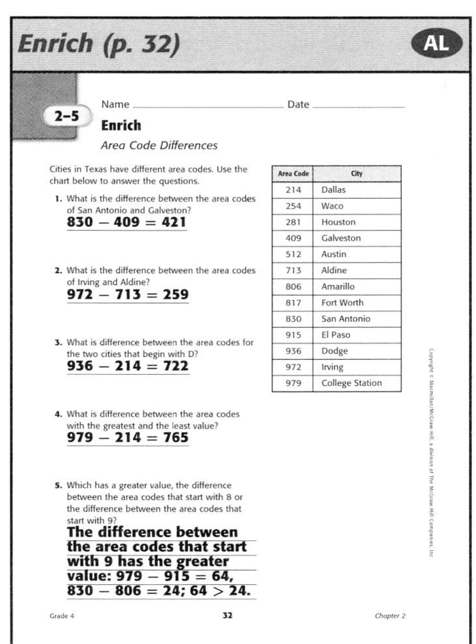

Enrich (p. 32) AL

2–5 Name ____ Date ____

Enrich

Area Code Differences

Cities in Texas have different area codes. Use the chart below to answer the questions.

Area Code	City
214	Dallas
254	Waco
281	Houston
409	Galveston
512	Austin
713	Aldine
806	Amarillo
817	Fort Worth
830	San Antonio
915	El Paso
936	Dodge
972	Irving
979	College Station

1. What is the difference between the area codes of San Antonio and Galveston? **830 − 409 = 421**
2. What is the difference between the area codes of Irving and Aldine? **972 − 713 = 259**
3. What is difference between the area codes for the two cities that begin with D? **936 − 214 = 722**
4. What is difference between the area codes with the greatest and the least value? **979 − 214 = 765**
5. Which has a greater value, the difference between the area codes that start with 8 or the difference between the area codes that start with 9? **The difference between the area codes that start with 9 has the greater value: 979 − 915 = 64, 830 − 806 = 24; 64 > 24.**

Grade 4 32 Chapter 2

Subtract Whole Numbers

Example 1 Be sure students record each regrouping as they subtract. Since problems can have regrouping in several places, it can become difficult to remember what digits have been regrouped.

ADDITIONAL EXAMPLES

1. The Hernandez family flies 9,635 miles to visit some cousins. Next year, they fly 3,867 miles to visit their grandmother. How much farther did they travel to see their cousins? 5,768 miles
2. Elija's dad had $9,643 in his checking account. He wrote a check for $6,720 to buy a car. How much money did he have left? $2,923

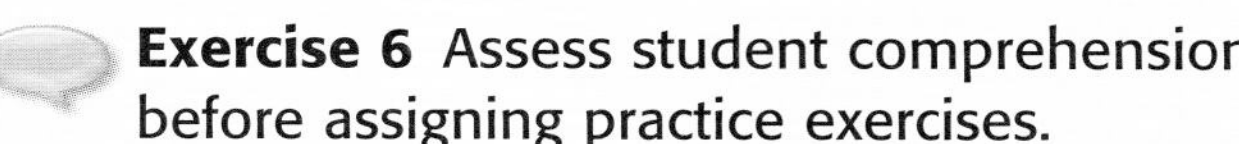

As a class, have students complete Exercises 1–6 in **Check What You Know** as you observe their work.

Exercise 6 Assess student comprehension before assigning practice exercises.

BL Alternate Teaching Strategy

If students have trouble subtracting multi-digit numbers…

Then use one of these reteach options:

1. CRM **Daily Reteach Worksheet** (p. 28)
2. Write 724 – 381 on the board. Have students subtract using grid paper. Place each digit of the number in a separate box. Have them ask themselves, "Can I subtract?" for each digit in the minuend. If yes, subtract without regrouping. If no, then show the regrouping and subtract.
3. Have students use Math Tool Chest to help complete the problem-solving exercise.

COMMON ERROR!

Exercises 7–20 Students may think that regrouping will be necessary for every place in a minuend. Remind them that they should only regroup if the digit in the subtrahend is greater than the digit above it in the minuend.

3 Practice

Differentiate practice using these leveled assignments for Exercises 7–23.

Level	Assignment
BL Below/Approaching Level	7–10, 15–17, 19–21
OL On Level	8–13, 17, 19–21, 22
AL Above/Beyond Level	8–20 even, 22–23

Have students discuss and complete the Higher Order Thinking problems. For Exercise 22, have students work each subtraction problem.

WRITING IN MATH Have students complete Exercise 23 in their Math Journals. You may choose to use this exercise as an optional formative assessment.

4 Assess

Formative Assessment

Write the following on the board: 3,624 – 857.

- **Where is regrouping needed in this problem? Explain.** ones, tens, and hundreds places; 3,624 has fewer ones, tens, and hundreds than 857.
- **What is the difference?** 2,767

Quick Check **Are students continuing to struggle with subtracting multi-digit numbers?**

If Yes → Small Group Options (p. 72B)
Strategic Intervention Guide (p. 60)

If No → Independent Work Options (p. 72B)
CRM Skills Practice Worksheet (p. 29)
CRM Enrich Worksheet (p. 32)

Ticket Out the Door Write \$96 – \$44 on the board. Have students use the numbers to write and solve a real-world problem.

Additional Answer

23. Sample answer: Sam is hiking on a path that is 4 miles or 21,120 feet long. He has already hiked 1 mile, or 5,280 feet. How many feet are left to hike?

Practice and Problem Solving

See page R5.

Subtract. Use addition or estimation to check. See Examples 1 and 2 (pp. 72–73)

7. 479 – 292 = 187
8. \$924 – \$837 = \$87
9. \$524 – \$246 = \$278
10. \$986 – \$339 = \$647
11. 4,273 – 365 = 3,908
12. 8,845 – 627 = 8,218
13. \$5,751 – \$4,824 = \$927
14. \$8,327 – \$5,709 = \$2,618
15. 39,536 – 18,698 20,838
16. \$64,779 – \$42,788 \$21,991

★17. Ramon is buying a DVD that costs \$14, a book that costs \$15, and pays \$2 in tax. If he hands the cashier \$40, how much change will he get back? \$9

★18. Mount Everest is 29,035 feet tall. From base camp at 17,600 feet, a climber hiked 2,300 feet. How much farther does the climber have before reaching the top of the mountain? 9,135 ft

Real-World PROBLEM SOLVING

History This table shows information about former Presidents of the United States.

19. ★ Who was older when he became President, John Adams or Harry S. Truman? John Adams

20. ★ Who was the youngest person on this list to become President? How old was he? John F. Kennedy; 44

21. How old was Ronald Reagan when John F. Kennedy died? 52

United States Presidents

President	Born	Year became President	Death
John Adams	1732	1797	1801
James K. Polk	1795	1845	1849
Harry S. Truman	1884	1945	1972
John F. Kennedy	1917	1961	1963
Ronald Reagan	1911	1981	2004

Source: The White House

H.O.T. Problems

22. **WHICH ONE DOESN'T BELONG?** Which subtraction problem does not require regrouping? Explain. third problem; The number in each place value in the subtrahend is greater than the number in the minuend.

67,457 – 40,724 | 70,639 – 39,607 | 89,584 – 57,372 | 95,947 – 26,377

23. **WRITING IN MATH** Write a real-world problem that involves subtraction and regrouping to solve. The numbers used in the problem must have at least three digits. See margin.

74 Chapter 2 Solve Addition and Subtraction Problems

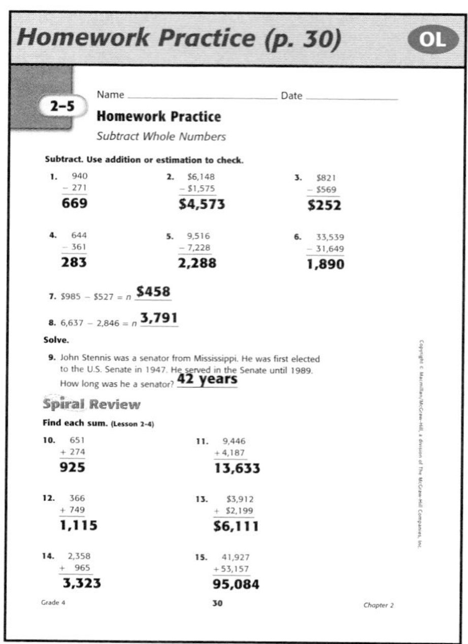
Homework Practice (p. 30) OL

2-5 Name ________ Date ________

Homework Practice

Subtract Whole Numbers

Subtract. Use addition or estimation to check.

1. 940 – 271 = **669**
2. \$6,148 – \$1,575 = **\$4,573**
3. \$821 – \$569 = **\$252**
4. 644 – 361 = **283**
5. 9,516 – 7,228 = **2,288**
6. 33,539 – 31,649 = **1,890**
7. \$985 – \$527 = *n* **\$458**
8. 6,637 – 2,846 = *n* **3,791**

Solve.

9. John Stennis was a senator from Mississippi. He was first elected to the U.S. Senate in 1947. He served in the Senate until 1989. How long was he a senator? **42 years**

Spiral Review

Find each sum. (Lesson 2-4)

10. 651 + 274 = **925**
11. 9,446 + 4,187 = **13,633**
12. 366 + 749 = **1,115**
13. \$3,912 + \$2,199 = **\$6,111**
14. 2,358 + 965 = **3,323**
15. 41,927 + 53,157 = **95,084**

Grade 4 30 Chapter 2

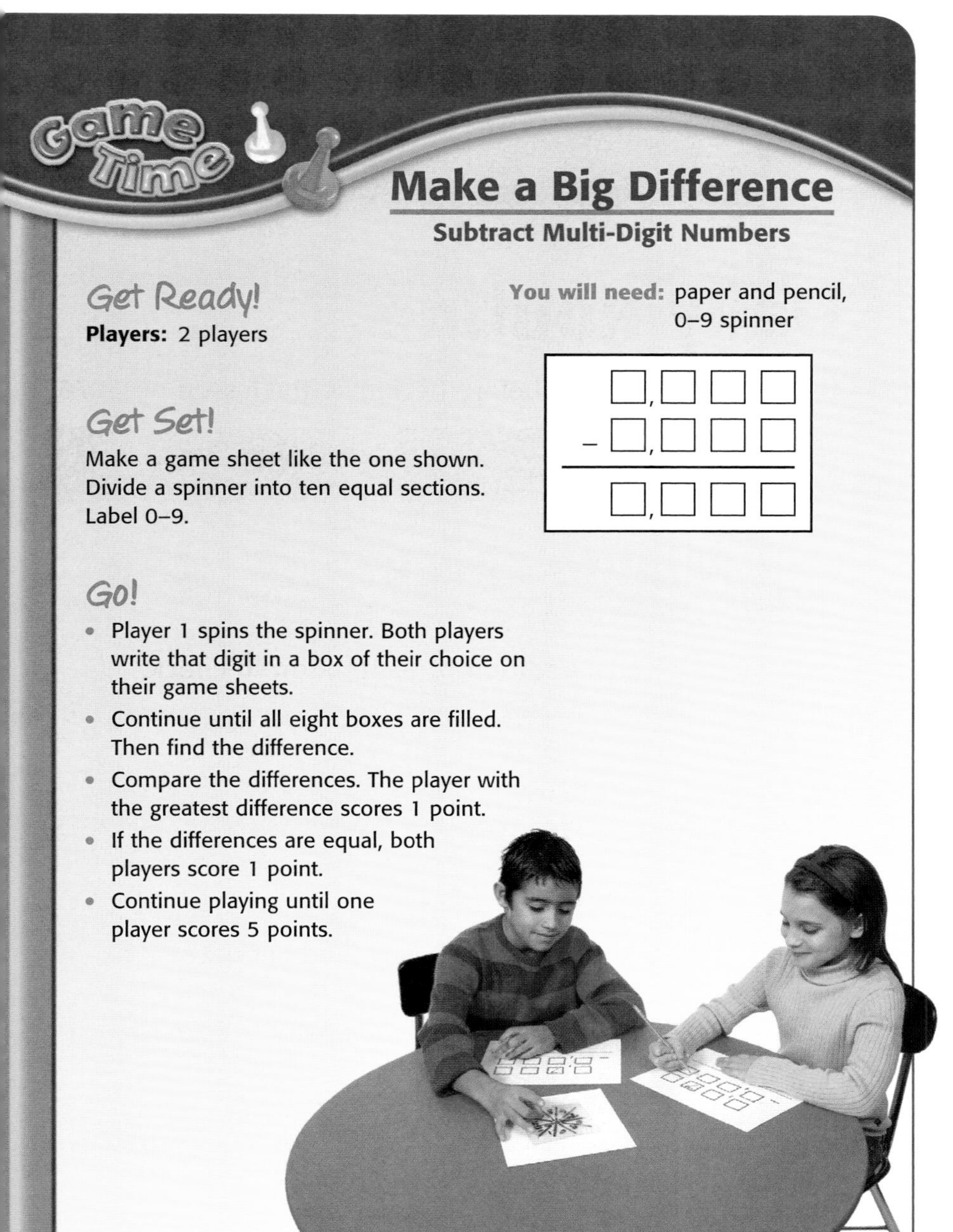

Make a Big Difference

Subtract Multi-Digit Numbers

Get Ready!

Players: 2 players

You will need: paper and pencil, 0–9 spinner

Get Set!

Make a game sheet like the one shown. Divide a spinner into ten equal sections. Label 0–9.

Go!

- Player 1 spins the spinner. Both players write that digit in a box of their choice on their game sheets.
- Continue until all eight boxes are filled. Then find the difference.
- Compare the differences. The player with the greatest difference scores 1 point.
- If the differences are equal, both players score 1 point.
- Continue playing until one player scores 5 points.

Game Time Make a Big Difference 75

Make a Big Difference

Math Concept: Subtract Multi-Digit Numbers

Materials: paper and pencils, 0–9 spinners

Introduce the game on p. 75 to your students to play as a class, in small groups, or at a learning station to review concepts introduced in this chapter.

Instructions

- Students each make a game sheet, as shown on p. 75.
- Students take turns spinning the spinner, and write each digit they get in a box of their choice on their sheets.
- Students continue to spin the spinner until they have filled their eight boxes. Then they find the difference.
- Players compare their differences. The player with the greatest difference gets 1 point. If the differences are equal, both players get 1 point.
- Play continues until one player scores 5 points.

Extend the Game

Have students make the game using sums, and the lowest sum wins.

Differentiated Practice

Use these leveled suggestions to differentiate the game for all learners.

Level	Assignment
BL Below/Approaching Level	Students may make a game sheet subtracting three-digit numbers.
OL On Level	Have students play the game with the rules as written.
AL Above/Beyond Level	Students create the game using 5-digit numbers.

2-6 Problem-Solving Investigation
Choose a Strategy

Lesson Planner

Objective
Choose the best strategy to solve a problem.

Resources
Teacher Technology
TeacherWorks • Interactive Classroom

Real-World Problem Solving Library
Math and Social Studies: *The Olympic Games*
Use these leveled books to reinforce and extend problem-solving skills and strategies.

Leveled for:
- OL On Level
- ELL Sheltered English
- SP Spanish

For additional support, see the Real-World Problem Solving Teacher Guide.

Daily Routine

Use these suggestions before beginning the lesson on p. 76.

5-Minute Check

(Reviews Lesson 2-5)

Subtract. Use addition or estimation to check.

1. 839 – 573 266
2. 1,495 – 988 507
3. 9,546 – 5,969 3,577
4. \$837 – \$475 \$362

Problem of the Day

Kenya sells bracelets for \$3 each and necklaces for \$5 each. If he made \$35, what are three possible combinations of bracelets and necklaces Kenya sold? 1 necklace and 10 bracelets, 4 necklaces and 5 bracelets, 7 necklaces and 0 bracelets

Differentiated Instruction

Small Group Options

LOGICAL

Option 1 Below Level BL

Materials: paper and pencil

- Pair students. Hand each one of these problems.

  On a normal weekday afternoon, 25 students visit the town library. On Saturday, twice as many students visit because the library is closed on Sunday. How many students use the library each week? 175 students

  School shirts sell for $8, a matching cap is $6, and a school water bottle costs $4. If Mom gives you $20, will you have enough money to buy all three items? yes
- Ask them to solve and show their work.
- When both members have finished, have them share their strategy and answers.

INTERPERSONAL, LINGUISTIC

Option 2 English Language Learners ELL

Materials: teacher-made number cards with + or − equations with the operation symbol missing (about 2–5 cards per player)

Core Vocabulary: fist, center, flat hand

Common Use Verb: throw

Talk Math This strategy helps students use and internalize language and recognize the correct operation.

- Flip a card to the center of the table.
- Students must say (at the same time) either "addition" as they throw their fists, or say "subtraction" as they throw their hands flat on the table.
- Encourage the students to speak as fast as they can.
- If everyone recognizes the correct operation, the card stays in the center. If anyone is wrong, return the card to your deck to be thrown again.
- Play continues until all the cards are in the center of the table.
- Allow students to discuss their strategy for recognizing the operation.

Independent Work Options

LINGUISTIC

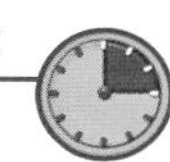

Option 1 Early Finishers OL AL

Materials: index cards

- Have students write a real-world word problem that uses addition or subtraction on the front of an index card. Place the word problem cards in a pile.

  > 1,536 − 937
  >
  > In September, my mother drove 1,536 miles. In October, she drove 937 miles. How many more miles did she drive in September than October?
- Students then draw a word problem card and solve the problem on it.

Option 2 Student Technology

Math Online macmillanmh.com

Personal Tutor • Extra Examples

Option 3 Learning Station: Art (p. 52G)

Direct students to the Art Learning Station for opportunities to explore and extend the lesson concept.

2-6 Problem-Solving Investigation

1 Introduce

Activity • Review

- There are 14 ducks at an animal habitat. This is 6 fewer than twice the number of squirrels at the habitat. How many squirrels are at the habitat?
- **What strategy would you use to find the answer?** act it out
- **Solve.** There are 10 squirrels at the habitat.

2 Teach

Have students read the problem on downloading music. Guide them through the problem-solving steps.

Understand Using the questions, review what students know and need to find.

Plan Have them discuss their strategy.

Solve Guide students to use a table and repeated addition to solve the problem.

- **How could you find the number of songs on 2 CDs?** use repeated addition to add; 14 + 14
- **How could you find the number of songs on 3 CDs? 4 CDs?** add 14 + 14 + 14; add 14 + 14 + 14 + 14

Check Have students look back at the problem to make sure that the answer fits the facts given.

- **Why will repeated subtraction help you check your answer?** Subtraction is the inverse of addition.

! COMMON ERROR!

Exercise 9 Students may have trouble finding the three numbers in this problem. Suggest students think of one addend. Subtract that number from 14. Then think of two numbers that add up to the result of what they got when they subtracted.

2-6 Problem-Solving Investigation

MAIN IDEA I will choose the best strategy to solve a problem.

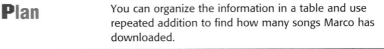

P.S.I. TEAM +

MARCO: I am downloading music. So far, I have downloaded 4 CDs. Each CD has 14 songs.

YOUR MISSION: Find how many songs Marco has downloaded.

Understand Marco has downloaded 4 CDs, and each CD has 14 songs. Find how many songs Marco has downloaded.

Plan You can organize the information in a table and use repeated addition to find how many songs Marco has downloaded.

Solve Start with 14, the number of songs on the first CD. Then continue to add 14 for each additional CD.

$$\begin{array}{r} 14 \\ +\ 14 \\ \hline 28 \end{array}$$ ← first CD, second CD

$$\begin{array}{r} \overset{1}{28} \\ +\ 14 \\ \hline 42 \end{array}$$ ← third CD

$$\begin{array}{r} 42 \\ +\ 14 \\ \hline 56 \end{array}$$ ← fourth CD

CDs	Songs
1	14
2	28
3	42
4	56

So, he downloaded a total of 56 songs.

Check Look back. 56 − 14 = 42, 42 − 14 = 28, 28 − 14 = 14, and 14 − 14 = 0. The answer is correct.

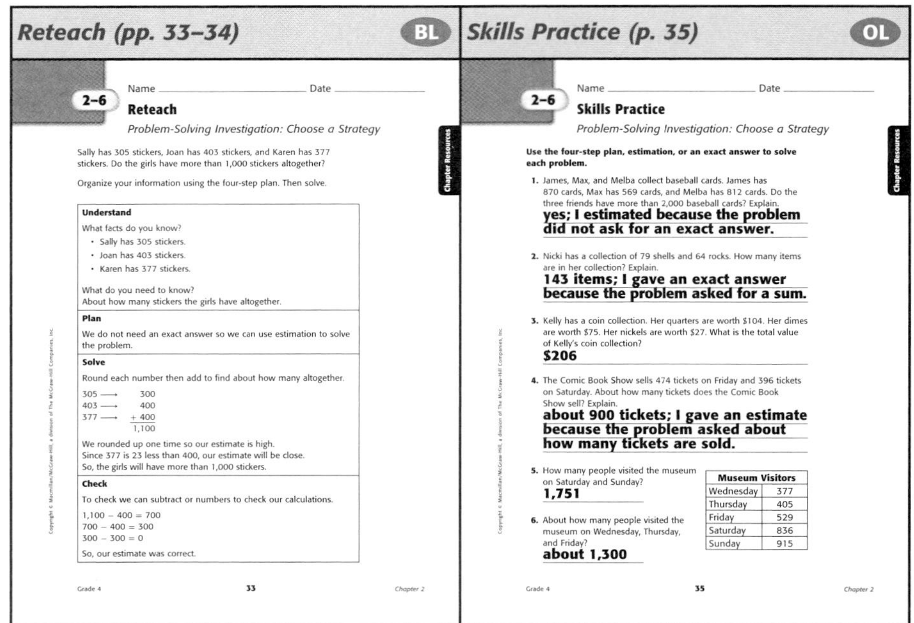

Reteach (pp. 33–34) BL

2-6 Name ______ Date ______

Reteach

Problem-Solving Investigation: Choose a Strategy

Sally has 305 stickers, Joan has 403 stickers, and Karen has 377 stickers. Do the girls have more than 1,000 stickers altogether?

Organize your information using the four-step plan. Then solve.

Understand

What facts do you know?

- Sally has 305 stickers.
- Joan has 403 stickers.
- Karen has 377 stickers.

What do you need to know?
About how many stickers the girls have altogether.

Plan

We do not need an exact answer so we can use estimation to solve the problem.

Solve

Round each number then add to find about how many altogether.

305 → 300
403 → 400
377 → + 400
1,100

We rounded up one time so our estimate is high.
Since 377 is 23 less than 400, our estimate will be close.
So, the girls will have more than 1,000 stickers.

Check

To check we can subtract or numbers to check our calculations.

1,100 − 400 = 700
700 − 400 = 300
300 − 300 = 0

So, our estimate was correct.

Skills Practice (p. 35) OL

2-6 Name ______ Date ______

Skills Practice

Problem-Solving Investigation: Choose a Strategy

Use the four-step plan, estimation, or an exact answer to solve each problem.

1. James, Max, and Melba collect baseball cards. James has 870 cards, Max has 569 cards, and Melba has 812 cards. Do the three friends have more than 2,000 baseball cards? Explain.
   yes; I estimated because the problem did not ask for an exact answer.
2. Nicki has a collection of 79 shells and 64 rocks. How many items are in her collection? Explain.
   143 items; I gave an exact answer because the problem asked for a sum.
3. Kelly has a coin collection. Her quarters are worth $104. Her dimes are worth $75. Her nickels are worth $27. What is the total value of Kelly's coin collection?
   $206
4. The Comic Book Show sells 474 tickets on Friday and 396 tickets on Saturday. About how many tickets does the Comic Book Show sell? Explain.
   about 900 tickets; I gave an estimate because the problem asked about how many tickets are sold.
5. How many people visited the museum on Saturday and Sunday?
   1,751
6. About how many people visited the museum on Wednesday, Thursday, and Friday?
   about 1,300

Museum Visitors	
Wednesday	377
Thursday	405
Friday	529
Saturday	836
Sunday	915

★ indicates multi-step problem

Mixed Problem Solving

See page R6.

Use any strategy to solve each problem.

1. Mrs. Thomas had $85. She bought a toaster. She now has $43. How much was the toaster? **$42**

2. **Measurement** The Nile River is 4,145 miles long. The Mississippi River is 405 miles shorter than the Nile River. How long is the Mississippi River? **3,740 miles**

3. Rosana has $9 left over after buying a movie ticket. If she buys a soft pretzel, what other item can she buy?

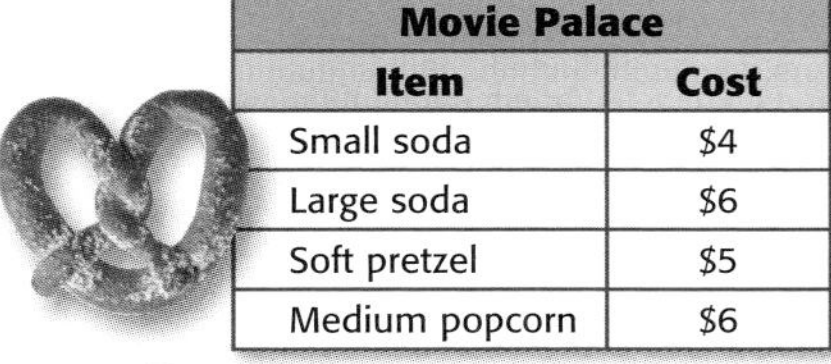

Movie Palace	
Item	**Cost**
Small soda	$4
Large soda	$6
Soft pretzel	$5
Medium popcorn	$6

small soda

4. Alonso has 139 comic books. Maggie has 72 comic books. Do they have a total of about 225 comic books? Explain. **No, they have about 210.**

5. A piñata is $36, and party decorations are $18. A gift is $28. About how much is spent altogether? **$90**

★6. There are 58 third graders and 62 fourth graders going on a field trip. Each bus can carry 40 people. How many buses are needed? **3**

7. Marcel earns $5 a week for doing his chores. About how many weeks will he have to save his money in order to buy the sports equipment below? **16**

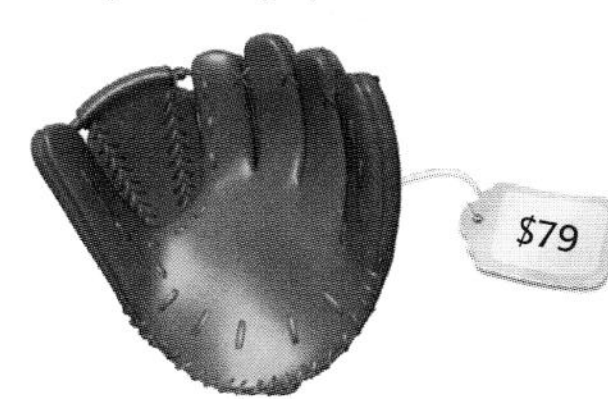

★8. Greta earns $5 each week walking dogs. Her portion of the family cell phone bill each month is $15. How much does she have left after paying her cell phone bill for a month that has four weeks? **$5**

9. Prem is thinking of three numbers from 1 to 10. The sum of the numbers is 14. Find the numbers. **Sample answer: 1, 5, and 8**

10. **Measurement** About how much farther does the willow warbler migrate than the barn swallow?

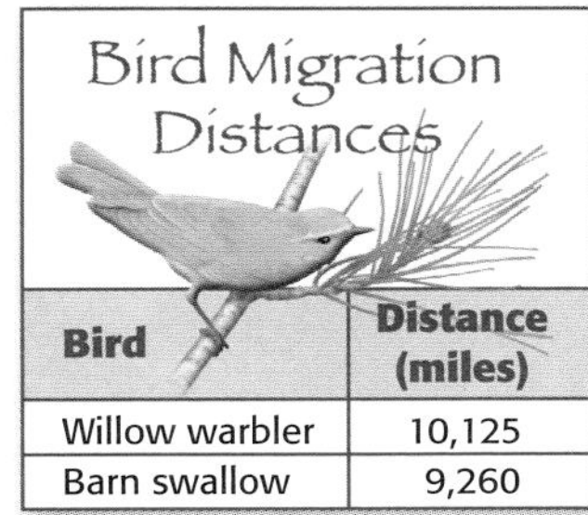

Bird Migration Distances

Bird	Distance (miles)
Willow warbler	10,125
Barn swallow	9,260

1,000 miles

11. **WRITING IN MATH** Juan bowls 133 in his first game. He bowls 148 in his second game. The answer is 280. What is the question? **See Ch. 2 Answer Appendix.**

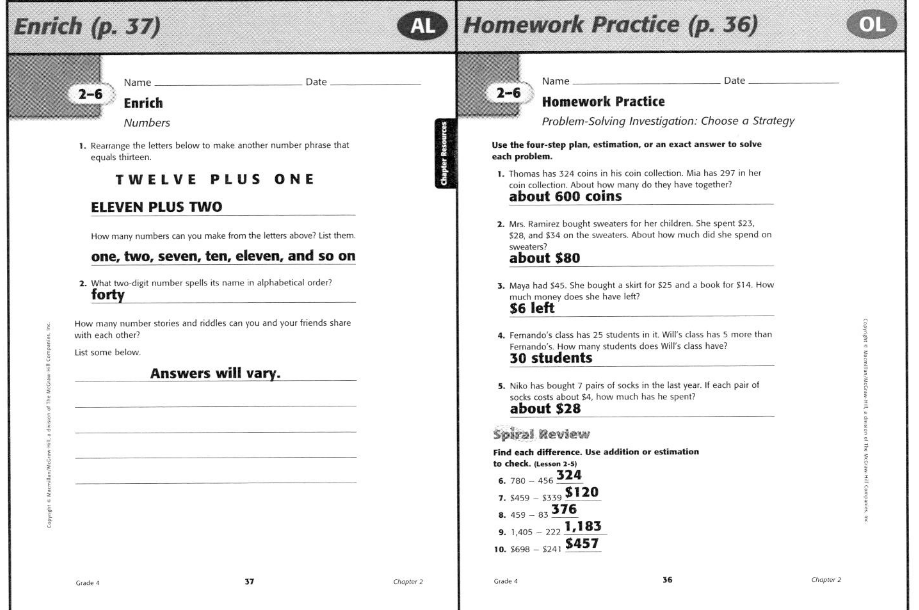

Enrich (p. 37) AL

Name ______ Date ______

2-6 **Enrich**

Numbers

1. Rearrange the letters below to make another number phrase that equals thirteen.

TWELVE PLUS ONE

ELEVEN PLUS TWO

How many numbers can you make from the letters above? List them.

one, two, seven, ten, eleven, and so on

2. What two-digit number spells its name in alphabetical order?
forty

How many number stories and riddles can you and your friends share with each other?

List some below.

Answers will vary.

Chapter Resources

Grade 4 37 *Chapter 2*

Homework Practice (p. 36) OL

Name ______ Date ______

2-6 **Homework Practice**

Problem-Solving Investigation: Choose a Strategy

Use the four-step plan, estimation, or an exact answer to solve each problem.

1. Thomas has 324 coins in his coin collection. Mia has 297 in her coin collection. About how many do they have together?
about 600 coins

2. Mrs. Ramirez bought sweaters for her children. She spent $23, $28, and $34 on the sweaters. About how much did she spend on sweaters?
about $80

3. Maya had $45. She bought a skirt for $25 and a book for $14. How much money does she have left?
$6 left

4. Fernando's class has 25 students in it. Will's class has 5 more than Fernando's. How many students does Will's class have?
30 students

5. Niko has bought 7 pairs of socks in the last year. If each pair of socks costs about $4, how much has he spent?
about $28

Spiral Review

Find each difference. Use addition or estimation to check. (Lesson 2-5)

6. 780 − 456 **324**
7. $459 − $339 **$120**
8. 459 − 83 **376**
9. 1,405 − 222 **1,183**
10. $698 − $241 **$457**

Grade 4 36 *Chapter 2*

BL Alternate Teaching Strategy

If students have trouble choosing a strategy…

Then assign one of these reteach options:

1. CRM **Daily Reteach Worksheet** (pp. 33–34)
2. Have them talk about each problem using the four-step plan and possible strategies to solve each one. Also review key words that let them know whether their answer should be exact or an estimate.

3 Practice

Using the Exercises

Exercises 1–11 give practice in using the four-step plan and choosing an appropriate strategy to solve a problem.

Exercise 9 has several correct answers. Encourage students to find more than one combination.

4 Assess

Formative Assessment

Write the following on the board:

2,148 people participated in a marathon last year. 682 more people participated this year than last. About how many people participated this year?

- **Is an estimate or exact answer needed? Explain.** An estimate is needed because of the words "about how many."
- **Explain how you would solve the problem.** Round 2,148 to 2,100 and 682 to 700. 2,100 + 700 = 2,800

Quick Check **Are students continuing to struggle with choosing the best strategy?**

If Yes → Small Group Options (p. 76B)

If No → Independent Work Options (p. 76B)
CRM Skills Practice Worksheet (p. 35)
CRM Enrich Worksheet (p. 37)

Lesson Planner

Objective

Interpret information and data to solve problems.

National Standard 

Students should develop an understanding about science and technology.

Activate Prior Knowledge

Before you turn students' attention to the pages, ask them to discuss photography.

- **What type of cameras have you or people you know used?** digital, flash, disposable, cell phone
- **Before the digital process, how were photographs developed?** using chemicals

Using the Student Page

Ask students to read the information on pp. 78–79 and answer these questions:

- **How long has it been since the start of the digital revolution?** Sample answer: 27 years; $2008 - 1981 = 27$
- **Suppose you buy one of each type of disposable camera with two bills. What two bills would you use? How much change would you receive?** Sample answer: 2 twenty-dollar bills; $6

Problem Solving in Science
Ready, Set, Click!
The first photographers had difficult jobs. They carried separate pieces of film in large metal containers. Each container was 12 inches wide and 16 inches long.
Taking a picture was first a chemical process. Today, taking a picture is a digital process, too. Digital cameras take pictures like a television records images.
There are now many different types of cameras that are affordable. Some cameras that scientists have invented are used only once. There are many different kinds of these cameras, including digital disposable cameras.
Did You Know?
The digital camera revolution started in 1981.
78 Chapter 2 Solve Addition and Subtraction Problems

Real-World Math

Use the information on pages 78 and 79 to solve each problem.

1. Hanna paid $35 for 4 disposable cameras. Which ones did she buy? See margin.
2. Coty buys two digital cameras, three outdoor cameras, and three flash cameras. How much money does Coty spend? $2 \times \$10 + 3 \times \$4 + 3 \times \$6$; $50
3. Suppose you buy an outdoor disposable camera and a flash disposable camera. If you pay with $30, how much change will you get? $20
4. Which two cameras cost the same as one underwater camera? outdoor and black-and-white
5. If you buy 2 underwater cameras, you get a $3 discount. How much money will you spend? $15
6. What two cameras can you buy with $9? black-and-white and outdoor
7. Emily has $30. Identify two ways she can spend her money on individual cameras without having any change. See margin.

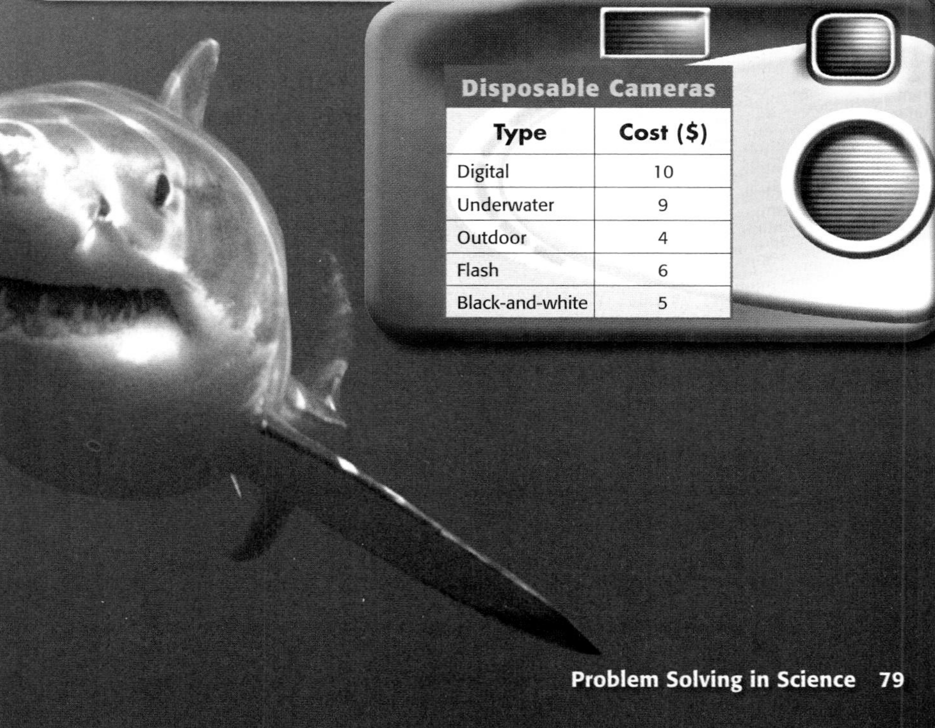

Disposable Cameras

Type	Cost ($)
Digital	10
Underwater	9
Outdoor	4
Flash	6
Black-and-white	5

Real-World Math

Assign the exercises on p. 79. Encourage students to choose a problem-solving strategy before beginning each exercise. If necessary, review the strategies suggested in Lesson 2-6, p. 77.

Exercise 1 Point out to students that there is more than one way to spend $35, but not more than one way to spend $35 on 4 disposable cameras.

Exercise 3 Remind students that they must first figure out the cost of the purchases before calculating how much change they will get.

Exercise 6 Tell students that there is more than one right answer to this question.

WRITING IN MATH Have students create a word problem that uses the information found in the text and in the chart on pp. 78–79.

Extend the Activity

Have students figure out the most number of cameras they can buy for $50.

Additional Answers

1. Sample answer: 2 digital, 1 underwater and 1 flash
7. Sample answer: Emily can buy 3 digital cameras or she can buy 6 black-and-white cameras.

LESSON 2-7

Subtract Across Zeros

Lesson Planner

Objective

Subtract multi-digit numbers, when some digits are zeros.

Review Vocabulary

minuend, **subtrahend**

Resources

Manipulatives: play money, base-ten blocks

Literature Connection: *Shark Swimathon* by Stuart J. Murphy

Teacher Technology
TeacherWorks • Interactive Classroom

Daily Routine

Use these suggestions before beginning the lesson on p. 80.

5-Minute Check

(Reviews Lesson 2-6)

Tell whether an estimate or exact answer is needed. Then solve.

Jade has 246 baseball cards. Tiana has 183 baseball cards. How many cards do they have altogether? exact; 429 cards

Problem of the Day

Jin wants to buy 1 dozen pens. Pencils are on sale 4 for $2. How much will Jin pay for 1 dozen pencils? Show your work. $6; 1 dozen = 12 pencils. There are 3 groups of 4 in 12, so $2 + $2 + $2 = $6.

Focus on Math Background

Even students who have a sound understanding of regrouping may have difficulty with zeros in subtraction. Consider 800 − 324. This problem requires double regrouping:

$$\begin{array}{r} \scriptstyle 9 \\ \scriptstyle 7\;\not{10}\;10 \\ \not{8}\;\not{0}\;\not{0} \\ -3\;2\;4 \\ \hline 4\;7\;6 \end{array}$$

Another way to view this subtraction is to think of 800 as 80 tens and 0 ones. If you think of 800 this way, you need only one regrouping:

$$\begin{array}{rcl} 800 = 80 \text{ tens } 0 \text{ ones} & = & 79 \text{ tens } 10 \text{ ones} \\ -324 = 32 \text{ tens } 4 \text{ ones} & = & 32 \text{ tens } \;\; 4 \text{ ones} \\ \hline & = & 47 \text{ tens } \;\; 6 \text{ ones} = 476 \end{array}$$

Review Math Vocabulary

Write the review vocabulary words and their definitions on the board.

Have students use each word in sentences of their own. Check to see that the sentences show understanding of the meaning of each. Ask volunteers to share their sentences with the class.

Differentiated Instruction

Small Group Options

Option 1 Below Level BL

INTRAPERSONAL

Materials: paper and pencil

- Share this problem with students:
  The twins, Sherry and Terry, are having a disagreement. Sherry solved this problem: 3,000 − 568 = 2,432. Terry solved the problem: 3,000 − 568 = 3,532.
- **Who is correct? What mistake did one twin make?**
  Sherry is correct; Terry forgot to change the hundreds and thousands.

Option 2 English Language Learners ELL

LINGUISTIC, LOGICAL

Materials: paper, pencil
Core Vocabulary: flow chart, step, from here to there
Common Use Verb: sequence
Write Math This strategy uses writing and a graphic organizer to help students understand the process behind subtracting when some digits are zeros.

- Demonstrate how to make a flow chart labeled "first," "then," and "next."
- Write a multi-digit subtraction problem on the board with zero as some of the digits.
- Talk through the problem with students, using the flow chart to write out the steps of solving the problem as you model the problem on the board.
- Allow students to use their native language, phrases, or numbers as necessary.
- Repeat as time permits or allow students to extend the strategy by writing the steps in a flow chart in their native language, and teaching it to English-only speakers.

Independent Work Options

Option 1 Early Finishers OL AL

LOGICAL

Materials: grocery ads, pencil and paper

- Have students write $1,000 at the top of their paper. Tell them that they have $1,000 to "spend" at an electronics store.
- Ask students to look through the electronics ad and choose an item to buy. They will list the item with its price below the $1,000 and then subtract.
- Tell students to continue to list and subtract the cost of each item until they have "spent" all of the $1,000.

Option 2 Student Technology

Tech Link

Math Online macmillanmh.com

Personal Tutor • Extra Examples

Math Adventures

Option 3 Learning Station: Science (p. 52H)

Direct students to the Science Learning Station for opportunities to explore and extend the lesson concept.

Option 4 Problem-Solving Practice

Reinforce problem-solving skills and strategies with the Problem-Solving Practice worksheet.

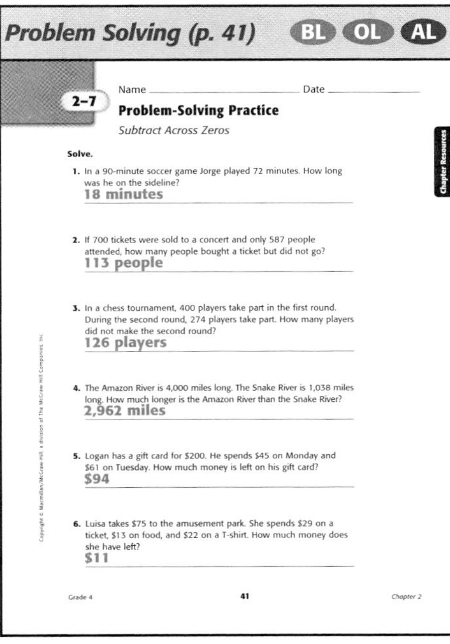

Problem Solving (p. 41) BL OL AL

2–7 Name ______ Date ______

Problem-Solving Practice

Subtract Across Zeros

Solve.

1. In a 90-minute soccer game Jorge played 72 minutes. How long was he on the sideline?
   18 minutes
2. If 700 tickets were sold to a concert and only 587 people attended, how many people bought a ticket but did not go?
   113 people
3. In a chess tournament, 400 players take part in the first round. During the second round, 274 players take part. How many players did not make the second round?
   126 players
4. The Amazon River is 4,000 miles long. The Snake River is 1,038 miles long. How much longer is the Amazon River than the Snake River?
   2,962 miles
5. Logan has a gift card for $200. He spends $45 on Monday and $61 on Tuesday. How much money is left on his gift card?
   $94
6. Luisa takes $75 to the amusement park. She spends $29 on a ticket, $13 on food, and $22 on a T-shirt. How much money does she have left?
   $11

Chapter Resources

Grade 4 41 Chapter 2

2-7 Subtract Across Zeros

1 Introduce

Activity Choice 1 • Hands-On

- Write 407 on the board.
- **What is another way of writing 4 hundreds, 0 tens, and 7 ones without changing the value?** 3 hundreds, 10 tens, and 7 ones
- Have students work in pairs with several more numbers that have a 0 in the tens place. Remind students that they can make changes in all three place-value places, but the value of the numbers must not change.
- **How can 407 be changed in all places but retain its value?** 3 hundreds, 9 tens, and 17 ones
- **Where did the 17 come from?** There were 7 ones in 407 and there were 10 more ones added when a ten was regrouped as 10 ones.

Activity Choice 2 • Literature

Introduce the lesson with *Shark Swimathon* by Stuart J. Murphy. For a related math activity, see p. TR44.

2 Teach

Scaffolding Questions

Write 506 − 367 on the board. Use base-ten blocks to show the subtraction step-by-step.

- **Do we need to regroup the ones?** yes
- **If there are no tens, what place will we regroup?** hundreds place
- **How will you regroup 1 hundred?** Regroup 1 hundred as 10 tens; regroup 1 ten as 10 ones.
- Tell the students that you can regroup the hundred in one step as 9 tens and 10 ones because that is equal to 1 hundred.
- **What does the minuend look like after regrouping? What is the difference?** 4 hundreds, 9 tens, and 16 ones; 139

GET READY to Learn

Have students open their books and read the information in **Get Ready to Learn**. Review **minuend** and **subtrahend**. As a class, work through **Examples 1 and 2**.

2-7 Subtract Across Zeros

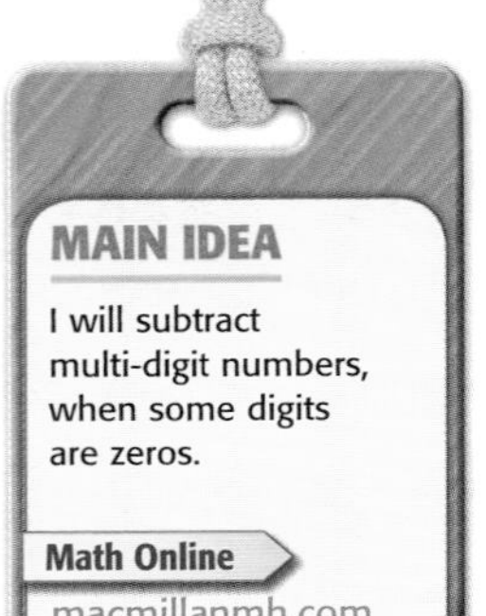

MAIN IDEA
I will subtract multi-digit numbers, when some digits are zeros.
Math Online
macmillanmh.com
• Extra Examples
• Personal Tutor
• Self-Check Quiz

GET READY to Learn

The bar graph shows the number of movies produced by five countries. What is the difference in the greatest and least number of movies produced?

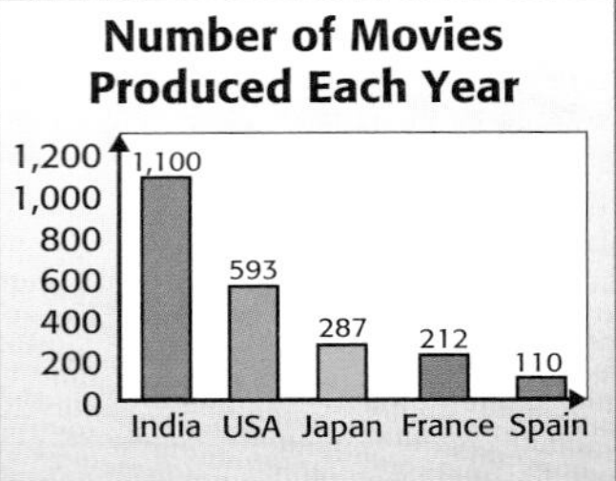

Source: *The Top 10 of Everything*

Subtraction that involves digits that are zeros uses the same steps as subtraction that involves digits that are not zeros.

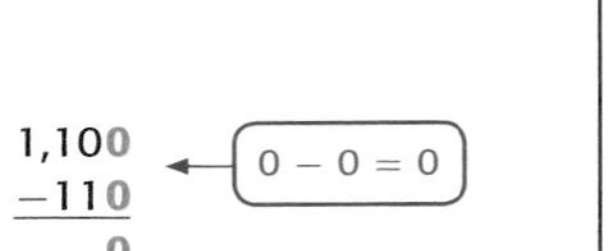

Real-World EXAMPLE Subtract Across Zeros

1 **MOVIES** **Refer to the graph. How many more movies does India produce than Spain?**

Step 1 Subtract ones.

$$\begin{array}{r} 1{,}100 \\ -110 \\ \hline 0 \end{array} \quad 0 - 0 = 0$$

Step 2 Subtract tens.

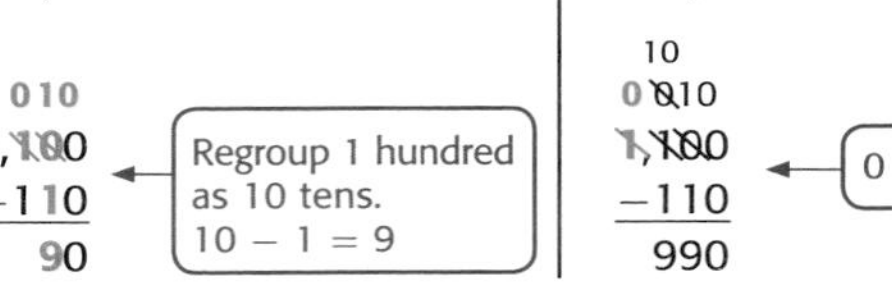

$$\begin{array}{r} 0\,10 \\ 1{,}\not{1}\not{0}0 \\ -110 \\ \hline 90 \end{array}$$

Regroup 1 hundred as 10 tens. 10 − 1 = 9

Step 3 Subtract hundreds.

$$\begin{array}{r} 10 \\ 0\,\not{0}10 \\ \not{1},\not{1}\not{0}0 \\ -110 \\ \hline 990 \end{array}$$

Regroup 1 thousand as 10 hundreds. 10 − 1 = 9

Step 4 Subtract thousands.

$$\begin{array}{r} 10 \\ 0\,\not{0}10 \\ \not{1},\not{1}\not{0}0 \\ -110 \\ \hline 990 \end{array} \quad 0 - 0 = 0$$

So, India produces 990 more movies a year than Spain.

Check 990 + 110 = 1,100. So, the answer is correct. ✓

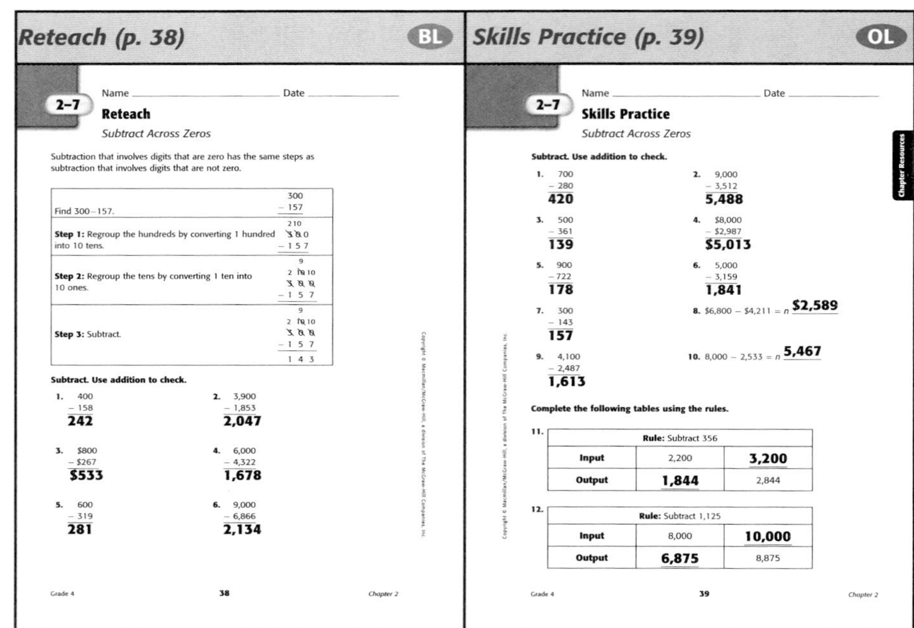

Reteach (p. 38) BL

2–7 Name ____________ Date ____________

Reteach

Subtract Across Zeros

Subtraction that involves digits that are zero has the same steps as subtraction that involves digits that are not zero.

Find 300 − 157.	300 − 157
Step 1: Regroup the hundreds by converting 1 hundred into 10 tens.	2 10 / ~~3~~ ~~0~~ 0 − 1 5 7
Step 2: Regroup the tens by converting 1 ten into 10 ones.	9 / 2 ~~10~~ 10 / ~~3~~ ~~0~~ ~~0~~ − 1 5 7
Step 3: Subtract.	9 / 2 ~~10~~ 10 / ~~3~~ ~~0~~ ~~0~~ − 1 5 7 = 1 4 3

Subtract. Use addition to check.

1. 400 − 158 = **242**
2. 3,900 − 1,853 = **2,047**
3. $800 − $267 = **$533**
4. 6,000 − 4,322 = **1,678**
5. 600 − 319 = **281**
6. 9,000 − 6,866 = **2,134**

Grade 4 38 Chapter 2

Copyright © Macmillan/McGraw-Hill, a division of The McGraw-Hill Companies, Inc.

Skills Practice (p. 39) OL

2–7 Name ____________ Date ____________

Skills Practice

Subtract Across Zeros

Chapter Resources

Subtract. Use addition to check.

1. 700 − 280 = **420**
2. 9,000 − 3,512 = **5,488**
3. 500 − 361 = **139**
4. $8,000 − $2,987 = **$5,013**
5. 900 − 722 = **178**
6. 5,000 − 3,159 = **1,841**
7. 300 − 143 = **157**
8. $6,800 − $4,211 = n **$2,589**
9. 4,100 − 2,487 = **1,613**
10. 8,000 − 2,533 = n **5,467**

Complete the following tables using the rules.

11.

Rule: Subtract 356		
Input	2,200	**3,200**
Output	**1,844**	2,844

12.

Rule: Subtract 1,125		
Input	8,000	**10,000**
Output	**6,875**	8,875

Grade 4 39 Chapter 2

Copyright © Macmillan/McGraw-Hill, a division of The McGraw-Hill Companies, Inc.

Real-World EXAMPLE Subtract Across Zeros

2 MONEY A school bought music equipment for $5,004. The drums cost $2,815. How much money was spent on music equipment other than the drums?

Remember
When you subtract, start at the place farthest to the right.

Step 1 Subtract ones.

```
   9 9
  4 10 10 14
  $5,0 0 4
– $2,8 1 5
         9
```

Regroup 1 thousand as 10 hundreds.
Regroup 1 hundred as 10 tens.
Regroup 1 ten as 10 ones.
14 – 9 = 5

Step 2 Subtract tens.

```
   9 9
  4 10 10 14
  $5,0 0 4
– $2,8 1 5
       8 9
```

9 – 8 = 1

Step 3 Subtract hundreds.

```
   9 9
  4 10 10 14
  $5,0 0 4
– $2,8 1 5
     1 8 9
```

9 – 8 = 1

Step 4 Subtract thousands.

```
   9 9
  4 10 10 14
  $5,0 0 4
– $2,8 1 5
  $2,1 8 9
```

4 – 2 = 2

So, $2,189 was spent on music equipment other than drums.

★ indicates multi-step problem

CHECK What You Know

Subtract. Use addition to check. See Examples 1 and 2 (pp. 80–81) 1–6. See margin.

1. 309 – 57
2. 608 – 45
3. $707 – $535
4. 903 – 791
5. 2,006 – 536
6. $8,005 – $4,423
7. On Saturday, there were 1,000 balloons at a hot air balloon festival. On Sunday, there were 350 balloons. How many more balloons were there on Saturday than on Sunday? 650
8. **Talk About It** Explain where you would start regrouping to find the difference in the problem below. See margin.
   66,000 – 23,475

Enrich (p. 42) AL

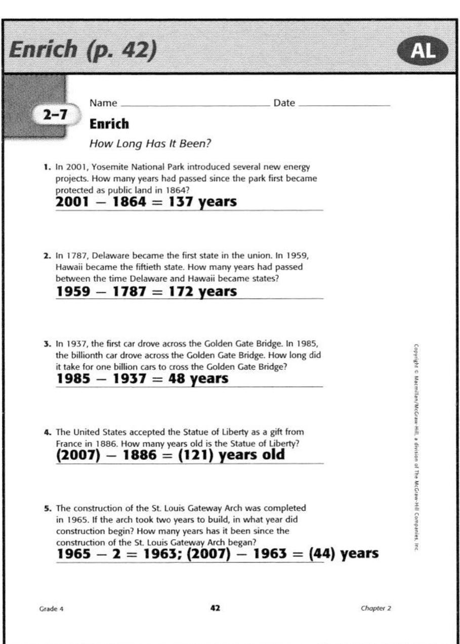

Name ______ Date ______

2-7 **Enrich**

How Long Has It Been?

1. In 2001, Yosemite National Park introduced several new energy projects. How many years had passed since the park first became protected as public land in 1864?
   2001 – 1864 = 137 years
2. In 1787, Delaware became the first state in the union. In 1959, Hawaii became the fiftieth state. How many years had passed between the time Delaware and Hawaii became states?
   1959 – 1787 = 172 years
3. In 1937, the first car drove across the Golden Gate Bridge. In 1985, the billionth car drove across the Golden Gate Bridge. How long did it take for one billion cars to cross the Golden Gate Bridge?
   1985 – 1937 = 48 years
4. The United States accepted the Statue of Liberty as a gift from France in 1886. How many years old is the Statue of Liberty?
   (2007) – 1886 = (121) years old
5. The construction of the St. Louis Gateway Arch was completed in 1965. If the arch took two years to build, in what year did construction begin? How many years has it been since the construction of the St. Louis Gateway Arch began?
   1965 – 2 = 1963; (2007) – 1963 = (44) years

Grade 4 42 Chapter 2

Subtract Across Zeros

Example 2 Encourage students to work in a step-by-step fashion when subtracting large numbers, recording carefully as they regroup. Be sure they understand that they must examine each digit of the minuend to know if regrouping is necessary.

ADDITIONAL EXAMPLES

1. Refer to the table. How much larger is Jupiter than Earth?

Planets	Diameter km
Earth	12,756
Saturn	119,300
Jupiter	142,200

129,444 km

2. Maricel gave the store clerk $50 for her purchase. She received $13 in change. How much did she spend? $37

Additional Answers

1. 252; 57 + 252 = 309
2. 563; 45 + 563 = 608
3. 172; 535 + 172 = 707
4. 112; 791 + 112 = 903
5. 1,470; 536 + 1,470 = 2,006
6. $3,582; $4,423 + 3,582 = $8,005
8. Sample answer: thousands place; Always start regrouping from the next place value that has a digit other than 0 in it.

As a class, have students complete Exercises 1–8 in **Check What You Know** as you observe their work.

Exercise 8 Assess student comprehension before assigning practice exercises.

BL Alternate Teaching Strategy

If students have trouble subtracting across zeroes...

Then use one of these reteach options:

1 CRM **Daily Reteach Worksheet** (p. 38)

2 Have them use play money and give change from amounts that include zeros. Tell students to record the exchanges they make.

- **If you need more ones, what will you do?** Exchange 1 ten-dollar bill for 10 one-dollar bills.

3 Practice

Differentiate practice using these leveled assignments for Exercises 9–26.

Level	Assignment
BL Below/Approaching Level	9–12, 17–18, 22–23
OL On Level	10–16, 18–20, 22–23, 25
AL Above/Beyond Level	9–23 odd, 24–26

Have students discuss and complete the Higher Order Thinking problems. For Exercise 25, have students find the difference, then analyze what mistake was made.

WRITING IN MATH Have students complete Exercise 26 in their Math Journals. You may choose to use this exercise as an optional formative assessment.

Practice and Problem Solving

Subtract. Use addition to check. See Examples 1 and 2 (pp. 80–81) 9–19. See margin.

9. 408 − 36

10. 805 − 75

11. 604 − 492

12. \$502 − \$130

13. \$708 − \$222

14. 809 − 566

15. \$8,001 − \$6,930

16. 9,006 − 7,474

17. 8,007 − 4,836

18. \$9,003 − \$5,295

19. 30,070 − 14,021

20. Ava guessed that there were 1,007 marbles in a jar for a contest. There were actually 972 marbles in the jar. How far off was Ava's guess? 35

21. **Measurement** Dillan hiked one and a half miles or 7,920 feet. If Sato hiked two miles or 10,560 feet, how many more feet did Sato hike? 2,640 ft

Real-World PROBLEM SOLVING

Travel The length of paved and unpaved roads in four countries is shown.

22. How many more miles of road does Australia have than Spain? 91,844 miles

23. Which two countries have the greatest difference in miles of roads? France and Australia, Australia and Spain, or Spain and Russia? 23. Australia and Spain

Countries' Roads

Country	Length (miles)
France	555,506
Australia	504,307
Spain	412,463
Russia	330,814

Source: *The Top 10 of Everything*

H.O.T. Problems

24. **OPEN ENDED** Identify a number that results in a 3-digit number when 35,475 is subtracted from it. Sample answer: 35,987

25. **FIND THE ERROR** Jim and Sabrina are solving the subtraction problem shown. Who is correct? Explain. See margin.

26. **WRITING IN MATH** Explain how you would regroup to subtract 3,406 from 5,000. Sample answer: Regroup 1 thousand as 9 hundreds, 9 tens, and 10 ones.

Additional Answers

9. 372; 36 + 372 = 408

10. 730, 75 + 730 = 805

11. 112; 492 + 112 = 604

12. \$372; \$130 + \$372 = \$502

13. \$486; \$222 + \$486 = \$708

14. 243; 566 + 243 = 809

15. \$1,071; \$6,930 + \$1,071 = \$8,001

16. 1,532; 7,474 + 1,532 = 9,006

17. 3,171; 4,836 + 3,171 = 8,007

18. \$3,708; \$5,295 + \$3,708 = \$9,003

19. 16,049; 14,021 + 16,049 = 30,070

25. Sample answer: Sabrina; Jim forgot to regroup the 3 in the ten thousands place. Therefore, his answer is ten thousand too much

TEST Practice

27. There were 4,668 people at the fair on Saturday and 3,816 people on Sunday. How many more people were at the fair on Saturday? B (Lesson 2-5)

A 842 **C** 942

B 852 **D** 952

28. There were 34,007 visitors at the amusement park last week. There were 21,829 visitors this week. How many fewer visitors were there this week? F (Lesson 2-7)

F 12,178 **H** 13,108

G 12,912 **J** 13,112

Spiral Review

Solve. (Lesson 2-6)

29. Measurement On Friday, Nida drove 178 miles. On Saturday, she drove 129 miles. On Sunday, she drove 205 miles. How many miles did she drive in the three days? 512 miles

★**30.** Henri is going to buy a football that costs $10, a shirt that costs $8, and a hat that costs $6. If he has $30, about how much change can he expect to get back? about $6

Subtract. Use addition or estimation to check. (Lesson 2-5)

31. 952 − 624 = 328

32. $8,961 − $1,258 = $7,703

33. 19,034 − 1,617 = 17,417

Find each sum. Check your work by estimating. (Lesson 2-4)

34. 6,922 + 24,367 = 31,289

35. $8,738 + $2,253 = $10,991

36. 36,640 + 14,255 = 50,895

Measurement For Exercises 37–39, use the table shown. (Lesson 1-3)

Area of Great Lakes	
Lake	**Area (square miles)**
Erie	9,922
Huron	23,011
Michigan	22,316
Ontario	7,320
Superior	31,698

Source: World Atlas Travel

37. What is the difference between the lakes with the greatest and least area? 24,378 square miles

38. Which two lakes have the least difference in area? Lake Huron and Lake Michigan

39. Is the combined area of Lake Erie and Lake Michigan greater than the area of Lake Superior? Explain. yes; 32,238 > 31,698

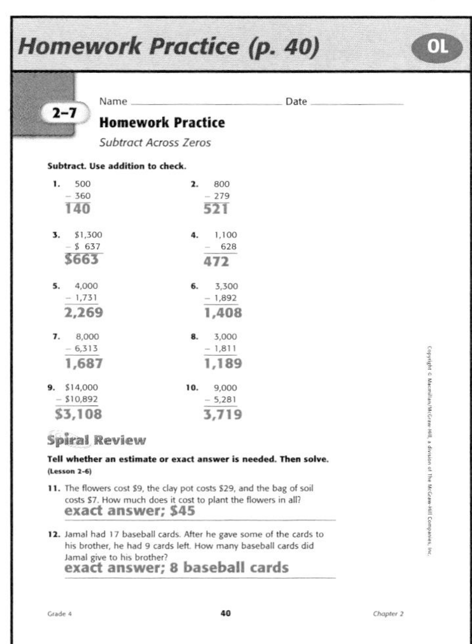

Homework Practice (p. 40) OL

2-7 Name ____________ Date ____________

Homework Practice

Subtract Across Zeros

Subtract. Use addition to check.

1. 500 − 360 = 140

2. 800 − 279 = 521

3. $1,300 − $ 637 = $663

4. 1,100 − 628 = 472

5. 4,000 − 1,731 = 2,269

6. 3,300 − 1,892 = 1,408

7. 8,000 − 6,313 = 1,687

8. 3,000 − 1,811 = 1,189

9. $14,000 − $10,892 = $3,108

10. 9,000 − 5,281 = 3,719

Spiral Review

Tell whether an estimate or exact answer is needed. Then solve. (Lesson 2-6)

11. The flowers cost $9, the clay pot costs $29, and the bag of soil costs $7. How much does it cost to plant the flowers in all? exact answer; $45

12. Jamal had 17 baseball cards. After he gave some of the cards to his brother, he had 9 cards left. How many baseball cards did Jamal give to his brother? exact answer; 8 baseball cards

Grade 4 **40** *Chapter 2*

4 Assess

Formative Assessment

Write 2,501 – 542 on the board.

- **How would you regroup in this problem?** Take 1 hundred from the 5 hundreds and regroup it to be 9 tens and 10 ones.
- **How many thousands, hundreds, tens, and ones are there after regrouping 2,501?** 2 thousands, 4 hundreds, 9 tens, and 11 ones.
- **What is 2,501 − 542?** 1,959

Quick Check **Are students continuing to struggle with subtracting multi-digit numbers, when some digits are zero?**

If Yes → Small Group Options (p. 80B)

If No → Independent Work Options (p. 80B)

CRM Skills Practice Worksheet (p. 39)

CRM Enrich Worksheet (p. 42)

Yesterday's News Ask students to explain how what they learned about subtracting whole numbers helped them with what they learned about subtracting across zeros in today's lesson.

TEST Practice

Reviews Lessons 2-5 and 2-7

Assign the Test Practice problems to provide daily reinforcement of test-taking skills.

Spiral Review

Reviews Lessons 1-3, 2-4, 2-5, and 2-6

Review and assess mastery of skills and concepts from previous chapters.

COMMON ERROR!

Exercise 19 Students may have trouble remembering to regroup the tens and hundreds places after regrouping the hundreds or thousands places. Have students regroup from the hundreds place as 9 tens and 10 ones or from the thousands place as 9 hundreds, 9 tens, and 10 ones in one step.

CHAPTER 2

Study Guide and Review

FOLDABLES Dinah Zike's Foldables

Use these lesson suggestions to incorporate the Foldable during the chapter. Students can then use their Foldables to review for the test.

Lessons 2-5, 2-6 The third pocket of the Foldable is used to store student work demonstrating that they understand how to subtract multi-digit numbers.

Key Vocabulary

The page references after each word denote where that term was first introduced. If students have difficulty answering Exercises 1–5, remind them they can use the page references to review the vocabulary terms.

Vocabulary Review

Review chapter vocabulary using one of the following options.

- **Visual Vocabulary Cards** (15)
- **eGlossary** at macmillanmh.com

CHAPTER 2

Study Guide and Review

Math Online macmillanmh.com
- STUDY TO GO
- Vocabulary Review

FOLDABLES Study Organizer GET READY to Study

Be sure the following Key Vocabulary words and Key Concepts are written in your Foldable.

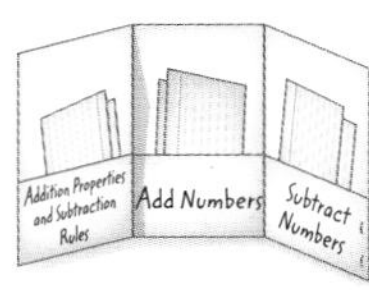

Key Concepts

Addition Properties and Subtraction Rules (p. 55)

- Addition properties and subtraction rules can help you to add and subtract.

Estimate Sums and Differences (p. 58)

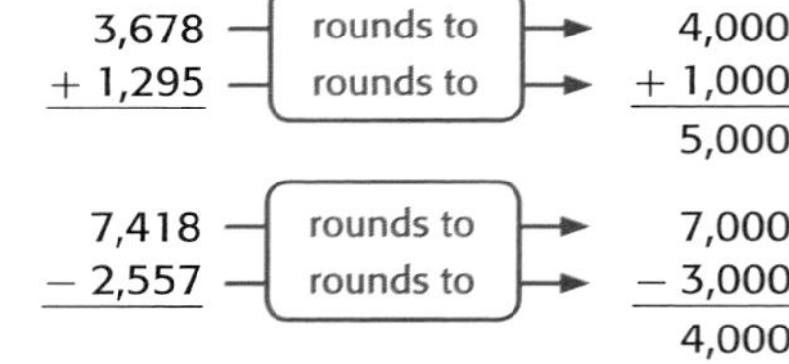

3,678 — rounds to → 4,000
+ 1,295 — rounds to → + 1,000
= 5,000

7,418 — rounds to → 7,000
− 2,557 — rounds to → − 3,000
= 4,000

Add and Subtract Whole Numbers (pp. 64, 72)

- To add or subtract whole numbers, add or subtract each place, starting with the place farthest to the right. Regroup when needed.

$$\begin{array}{r} {\scriptstyle 1\,1} \\ 3,752 \\ +\ 481 \\ \hline 4,233 \end{array} \qquad \begin{array}{r} {\scriptstyle 8\,13} \\ 9,368 \\ -\ 827 \\ \hline 8,541 \end{array}$$

Key Vocabulary

Associative Property of Addition (p. 55)
Commutative Property of Addition (p. 55)
estimate (p. 58)

Vocabulary Check

Complete each sentence with the correct vocabulary word.

1. The number sentence $3 + 7 = 7 + 3$ represents the ___?___. Commutative Property of Addition
2. If you do not need an exact answer, you can ___?___. estimate
3. The ___?___ says you can change the grouping without changing the sum. Associative Property of Addition
4. The ___?___ says the order in which numbers are added does not change the sum. Commutative Property of Addition
5. When the word *about* is used in a problem, you should find a(n) ___?___. estimate

Chapter 2 Project

Recycle It!

Alone, in pairs, or in small groups, have students discuss the results of their completed chapter project with the class. Assess their work using the Chapter Project rubric found in Chapter 2 Resource Masters, p. 53.

Lesson-by-Lesson Review

2-1 Algebra: Addition Properties and Subtraction Rules (pp. 55–57)

Example 1
Complete 4 + ■ = 6 + 4. Identify the property or rule.

The right side of the sentence shows 6 + 4. The left side shows a 4. So, the missing number is 6.

$$4 + 6 = 6 + 4$$

This is the Commutative Property of Addition.

Copy and complete each number sentence. Identify the property or rule used. 6–10. See margin.

6. ■ + 0 = 11 **7.** 12 − ■ = 12

8. (■ + 9) + 2 = 9 + (9 + 2)

9. 5 + 4 + 3 = 4 + 3 + ■

10. Lamont has 3 red pencils and 2 yellow pencils. Aida has 2 yellow pencils and 3 red pencils. Who has more pencils? Identify the property used.

2-2 Estimate Sums and Differences (pp. 58–61)

Example 2
Estimate 1,352 + 487. Round to the hundreds place.

Round. Then add.

1,352	rounds to →	1,400
+ 487	rounds to →	+ 500
		1,900

So, 1,352 + 487 is about 1,900.

Example 3
Estimate \$53 − \$27. Round to the tens place.

Round. Then subtract.

\$53	rounds to →	\$50
− \$27	rounds to →	− \$30
		\$20

So, \$53 − \$27 is about \$20.

Estimate. Round to the indicated place value. 11–13. See margin.

11. \$519 + \$368; tens

12. 3,436 + 597; hundreds

13. 8,728 − 6,493; thousands

14. \$17 − \$12; tens
\$20 − \$10 = \$10

15. Neka wants to buy a book that costs \$32 and a bookmark that costs \$3. Approximately how much will these items cost?
\$30 + \$3 = \$33

16. **Measurement** Derek is 3,285 days old. Tionna is 4,015 days old. About how much older is Tionna?
4,000 − 3,300 = 700

Lesson-by-Lesson Review

Have students complete the Lesson-by-Lesson Review on pp. 85–88. Then you can use ExamView® Assessment Suite to customize another review worksheet that practices all the objectives of this chapter or only the objectives on which your students need more help.

Intervention If the given examples are not sufficient to review the topics covered by the questions, use the page references next to the exercises to review that topic in the Student Edition.

Additional Answers

6. 11 + 0 =1; Identity Property of Addition

7. 12 − 0 = 12; Subtraction Rule

8. (9 + 9) + 2 = 9 + (9 + 2); Associative Property of Addition

9. 5 + 4 + 3 = 4 + 3 + 5 = Commutative Property of Addition

10. They are equal; Commutative Property of Addition

11. \$520 + \$370 = 890

12. 3,400 + 600 = 4,000

13. 9,000 − 6,000 = 3,000

Study Guide and Review

2-3 Problem-Solving Skill: Estimate or Exact Answer (pp. 62–63)

Example 4

Jenelle and her sister are going to build a bookcase. They will need $9 for nails, $18 for tools, and $38 for wood. About how much money do they need to build the bookcase?

Understand

What facts do you know?

- Nails cost $9.
- Tools cost $18.
- Wood costs $38.

What do you need to find?

- Find about how much money they need to build the bookcase.

Plan Since the question asks *about* how much money is needed, you can estimate the sum.

Solve

$ 9	→	$10
$18	→	$20
+ $38	→	+ $40
		$70

So, about $70 is needed to build the bookcase.

Check Look back at the problem. If the question asked for an exact answer, the result would be $9 + $18 + $38 or $65. Since $70 is close to $65, you know that an estimate of $70 makes sense.

17. **Measurement** There are 365 days in a year. Tess's younger brother is 3 years old. About how many days old is he?
estimate; 1,200 days old

18. Benton needs to buy the items shown. He has $20. Does Benton have enough money? exact answer; no

$5

$3

$13

19. Admission to a water park is $21 for adults and $14 for children. How much will admission cost for two adults and three children?
exact answer; $84

20. **Measurement** Rebeca will go to the park when her chores are complete. How many minutes before she will go to the park?
exact answer; 85 min

List of Chores

Chore	Time (min)
Clean room	45
Dust	15
Sweep	25

21. Chet has $7 after buying skates for $62 and a helmet for $22. How much money did he have?
exact answer; $91

2-4 Add Whole Numbers (pp. 64–67)

Example 5
Find 714 + 249.

Step 1 Add ones.

```
   1
  714
+ 249
    3
```
4 + 9 = 13
Regroup 13 ones as 1 ten and 3 ones.

Step 2 Add tens.

```
   1
  714
+ 249
   63
```
1 + 1 + 4 = 6

Step 3 Add hundreds.

```
   1
  714
+ 249
  963
```
7 + 2 = 9

Find each sum. Check your work by estimating. 22–27. See margin.

22. 564 + 308
23. 2,875 + 496
24. $4,691 + $ 872
25. $6,467 + $5,237
26. 61,248 + 47,229
27. 82,267 + 21,037

28. **Measurement** Rick drove 12,363 miles in his new car the first year he owned it. He drove 15,934 miles in his car the second year. How many miles did Rick drive these two years? 28,297 miles

2-5 Subtract Whole Numbers (pp. 72–74)

Example 6
Find 4,274 – 857.

Step 1 Subtract ones.

```
       6 14
4, 2  7  4
 – 8  5  7
         7
```
Regroup 1 ten as 10 ones.

Step 2 Subtract each place.

```
 3 12 6 14
 4, 2  7  4
  – 8  5  7
 3, 4  1  7
```
Regroup if necessary.

Subtract. Use addition or estimation to check. 29–34. See margin.

29. 478 – 293
30. 872 – 694
31. 5,524 – 2,346
32. $54,751 – $43,226
33. 7,367 – 2,128
34. 73,979 – 63,485

35. **Measurement** A moose weighs 1,820 pounds. A camel weighs 1,521 pounds. How much more does a moose weigh than a camel? 299 lb

Additional Answers

22. 872; 600 + 300 = 900
23. 3,371; 2,900 + 500 = 3,400
24. $5,563; $4,700 + $900 = $5,600
25. $11,704; $6,500 + $5,200 = $11,700
26. 108,477; 60,000 + 50,000 = 110,000
27. 103,304; 80,000 + 20,000 = 100,000
29. 185; 500 – 300 = 200
30. 178; 694 + 178 = 872
31. 3,178; 6,000 – 2,000 = 4,000
32. $11,525; $50,000 – $40,000 = $10,000
33. 5,239; 7,000 – 2,000 = 5,000
34. 10,494; 63,485 + 10,494 = 73,979

CHAPTER 2 Study Guide and Review

Additional Answers

39. 94; 206 + 94 = 300
40. $408; $392 + $408 = $800
41. 3,366; 642 + 3,366 = 4,008
42. $8473; $531 + $8473 = $9004
43. 4,164; 3,836 + 4,164 = 8,000
44. $105; $1,195 + $105 = $1,300
45. $704; $1,299 + $704 = $2,003

2-6 Problem-Solving Investigation: Choose a Strategy (pp. 76–77)

Example 7
Naomi had $125. She bought rollerblades. She now has $19. How much were the rollerblades?

Understand Naomi had $125. She now has $19. You need to find the cost of the rollerblades.

Plan Solve $125 – $19 to find the cost of the rollerblades.

Solve

```
   115
  $125
– $ 19
  $106
```

So, the cost was $106.

Check $19 + $106 = $125.
So, the answer is correct.

Use any strategy to solve.

36. Jase earned $125 last month for delivering newspapers. He will earn $185 this month. How much money will Jase earn from delivering newspapers for the two months? **$310**

37. **Measurement** A cheetah can run up to 71 miles per hour. A horse can run up to 45 miles per hour. Suppose both animals ran at these speeds for two hours. How much farther would a cheetah have run? **52 miles**

38. **Measurement** The highest elevation in the United States is 20,320 feet. The second highest elevation is 14,494. What is the difference in these heights? **5,826 ft**

2-7 Subtract Across Zeros (pp. 80–83)

Example 8
Find 2,005 – 593.

Step 1 Subtract ones.

```
  2, 0 0 5
–    5 9 3     ← 5 – 3 = 2
         2
```

Step 2 Subtract each place.

```
      9
  1 10 10
  2, 0 0 5     ← Regroup.
–    5 9 3
  1, 4 1 2
```

39–45. See margin.

Subtract. Use addition to check.

39. 300 – 206

40. $800 – $392

41. 4,008 – 642

42. $9,004 – $531

43. 8,000 – 3,836

44. $1,300 – $1,195

45. Mr. Acosta had $2,003 in his bank account. He bought a laptop computer for $1,299. How much money does he have left?

Chapter Test

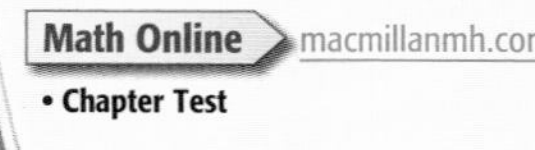

• Chapter Test

For Exercises 1–3, tell whether each statement is *true* or *false*.

1. Always start with the ones place when subtracting. false
2. When asked to find the sum, you are to subtract. false
3. To regroup means to add again. false

Algebra **Copy and complete each number sentence. Identify the property or rule used.**

4. ▪ + 73 + 79 = 73 + 79 + 65
   65; Commutative Property of Addition
5. ▪ − 389 = 0 389; Subtraction Rule
6. 2 + (3 + 9) = (2 + ▪) + 9
   3; Associative Property of Addition
7. **MULTIPLE CHOICE** What number completes this number sentence? A

   23 + ▪ = 17 + 23

   A 17 **C** 36
   B 23 **D** 38

Estimate. Round to the indicated place value.

8. 5,364 + 482; hundreds
   5,400 + 500 = 5,900
9. 89,325 − 80,236; ten thousands
   90,000 − 80,000 = 10,000

Tell whether an estimate or exact answer is needed. Then solve.

10. Mr. Murphy had $92. He bought a watch. Now he has $36. How much was the watch? exact answer; $56
11. **MULTIPLE CHOICE** What is the sum of 212,048 and 37,251? F
    F 249,299
    G 289,299
    H 289,399
    J 299,289

Subtract. Use addition or estimation to check.

12. 612 − 430 = 182
13. 8,547 − 6,391 = 2,156
14. 4,005 − 273 = 3,732
15. 6,007 − 317 = 5,690
16. Vickie had $87 in her bank account. She bought her sister a doll for her birthday for $15. How much money does she have left in her account? $72
17. **Measurement** The lengths of the longest rivers in the world are shown in the table.

World's Longest Rivers	
River	Length (miles)
Nile	4,145
Amazon	4,000
Mississippi-Missouri	3,740

Source: *The Top 10 of Everything*

Find the difference in the lengths of the Nile and the Mississippi-Missouri Rivers. 405 miles

18. **WRITING IN MATH** Explain how you would regroup to subtract 2,317 from 4,000. See Ch. 2 Answer Appendix.

Summative Assessment 89

Chapter 2 Chapter Test

Summative Assessment

Use these alternate leveled chapter tests to differentiate assessment for the specific needs of your students.

Leveled Chapter 2 Tests			
Form	Type	Level	CRM Pages
1	Multiple Choice	BL	55–56
2A	Multiple Choice	OL	57–58
2B	Multiple Choice	OL	59–60
2C	Free Response	OL	61–62
2D	Free Response	OL	63–64
3	Free Response	AL	65–66

BL = below/approaching grade level
OL = on grade level
AL = above/beyond grade level

Vocabulary Test

CRM **Chapter 2 Resource Masters** (p. 50)

ExamView Assessment Suite Customize and create multiple versions of your Chapter Test and the test answer keys.

Data-Driven Decision Making

Based on the results of the Chapter Test, use the following to review concepts that continue to present students with problems.

Exercises	State/Local Standards	What's the Math?	Error Analysis	Resources for Review
1–6		Solve addition and subtraction problems and understand relationships among operations.	Does not understand word "property." Does not know "rules." Adds/subtracts incorrectly. Does not understand "number sentence."	Strategic Intervention Guide (pp. 56, 58, 60, 62, 64) CRM Chapter 2 Resource Masters (Reteach Worksheets) Math Adventures My Math Zone Chapter 2 Math Online Extra Examples • Concepts in Motion
8–10		Estimate and compute the sum or difference of whole numbers. Explain mathematical reasoning.	Does not know difference between estimate and exact answer.	
12–16, 18		Subtract multi-digit whole numbers and understand relationships among operations.	Does not understand "difference." Incorrectly subtracts and adds.	

CHAPTER 2

Test Practice

Formative Assessment

- Use Student Edition pp. 90–92 as practice and cumulative review. The questions are written in the same style as many state tests.
- You can also use these two pages to benchmark student progress, or as an alternate homework assignment.

Additional practice pages can be found in the Chapter 2 Resource Masters.

CRM **Chapter 2 Resource Masters**
Cumulative Test Practice

- Multiple Choice format (pp. 55–60)
- Free Response format (pp. 61–66)

Create practice worksheets or tests that align to your state standards.

Math Online Have students visit macmillanmh.com for additional practice to reinforce your state standards.

CHAPTER 2

Test Practice

Cumulative, Chapters 1–2

Math Online macmillanmh.com
• Test Practice

PART 1 Multiple Choice

Read each question. Then fill in the correct answer on the answer sheet provided by your teacher or on a sheet of paper.

1. On Saturday, a store had 218 customers. On Sunday, the store had 24 fewer customers. How many customers did the store have on Sunday? B

A 188 **C** 236
B 194 **D** 242

2. Which point on the number line represents 8? H

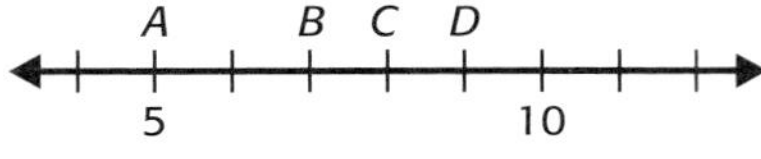

F point *A* **H** point *C*
G point *B* **J** point *D*

3. Which number is 10,000 more than 312,884? C

A 302,884 **C** 322,884
B 319,884 **D** 324,882

4. Which symbol makes the following true? F

76,153 ■ 76,149

F > **H** =
G < **J** +

5. Which of the following is another way to write *nine million, three hundred thirty-one thousand, one-hundred eight*? B

A 9,313,180 **C** 9,331,180
B 9,331,108 **D** 90,331,108

6. Silvio says his street address has a 3 in the hundreds place. Which of the following could be his address? F

F 1368 **H** 2437
G 1483 **J** 3865

7. Kayla used a catalog to make a list of the clothes she wants to buy. Her list is shown below.

Kayla's Wish List

Item	Cost
Shorts	$20
T-shirt	$15
Hooded sweatshirt	$35
Sneakers	$43

If Kayla orders all the clothing items, about how much will she spend? D

A $70 **C** $110
B $100 **D** $120

Test-Taking Tip

Remind students to be sure that they are answering the problem that is being asked.

Preparing for Standardized Tests
For test-taking strategies and practice, see pages R42–R55.

8. What is the difference in height of Angel Falls and Yosemite Falls? J

Highest Waterfalls	
Waterfall	**Height (feet)**
Angel	3,212
Yosemite	2,425

Source: *Scholastic Book of World Records*

F 1,000 ft **H** 887 ft
G 900 ft **J** 787 ft

9. Which is the value of the digit 5 in 1,853,742? C

A 50 **C** 50,000
B 500 **D** 500,000

10. A hobby store has sold 15,871 kites since the store opened 25 years ago. What is the number rounded to the nearest thousand? J

F 15,000 **H** 15,900
G 15,800 **J** 16,000

11. What is $7,959 rounded to the nearest hundred? C

A $700 **C** $8,000
B $7,900 **D** $9,000

PART 2 Short Response

Record your answers on the answer sheet provided by your teacher or on a sheet of paper.

12. What is the value of the digit 3 in 805,312? 300

13. What is the difference in width of Earth's moon and Jupiter's moon? 1,110 miles

Largest Moons	
Moon	**Width (miles)**
Jupiter's moon	3,270
Saturn's moon	3,200
Earth's moon	2,160

Source: *Scholastic Book of World Records*

PART 3 Extended Response

Record your answers on the answer sheet provided by your teacher or on a sheet of paper.

14. What number is 1,000 more than 456,987? Explain your reasoning.
14, 15. See margin.

15. What is the standard form for twelve million, two hundred thirty-five thousand, one hundred twelve? Explain your reasoning.

NEED EXTRA HELP?															
If You Missed Question...	1	2	3	4	5	6	7	8	9	10	11	12	13	14	15
Go to Lesson...	2-5	1-4	2-4	1-4	1-2	1-1	2-4	2-5	1-2	1-6	1-6	1-1	2-5	2-5	1-2

Answer Sheet Practice

Have students simulate taking a state test by recording their answers on a practice recording sheet.

CRM **Chapter 2 Resource Masters**
Student Recording Sheet (p. 71)

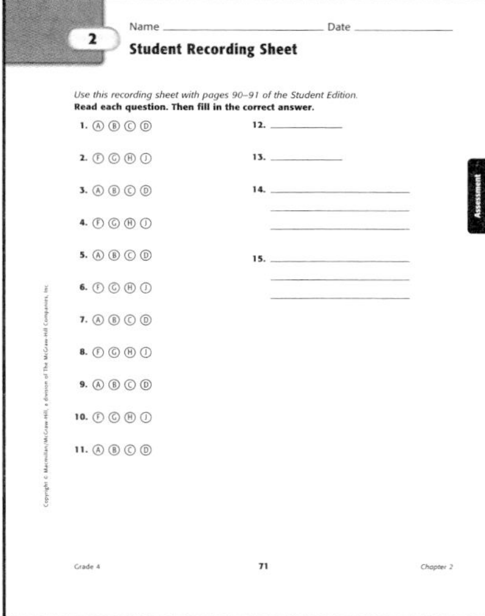
Name Date
2 Student Recording Sheet
Use this recording sheet with pages 90–91 of the Student Edition.
Read each question. Then fill in the correct answer.

Additional Answers

14. Sample answer: 457,987; 456,987 + 1,000 = 457,987

15. Sample answer: 12,235,112; Standard form is the usual way to write a number using digits. So, read the number in word form and write down the digits as you read them.

Pages 57, Lesson 2-1

8. $(9 + 8) + 7 = 9 + (8 + 7)$;
Associative Property of Addition

9. $4 + 3 + 1 = 3 + 1 + 4$;
Commutative Property of Addition

10. $9 + 0 = 9$;
Identity Property of Addition

11. $5 - 5 = 0$;
Subtraction rule

12. $7 + (1 + 8) = (7 + 1) + 8$;
Associative Property of Addition

13. $15 - 0 = 15$;
Subtraction rule

22. Sample answer: $2 + 1 = 1 + 2$; They ate the same amount; Commutative Property of Addition.

23. $(4 + 3) + 5 = (3 + 4) + 5$; They had the same number of shapes; Commutative Property of Addition.

Page 59, Lesson 2-2

8. Sample answer:
Nearest hundred: $800 + 1{,}600 = 2{,}400$;
Nearest thousand: $1{,}000 + 2{,}000 = 3{,}000$;
Actual sum: 2,389;
Choosing a place further to the right gives a more exact answer.

Page 63, Lesson 2-3

1. Sample answer: The boys need an estimate to determine about how much money will be enough for the supplies.

2. Sample answer: $20 + $110 + $60 = $190; The exact cost is $187, so $190 is a good estimate.

3. Sample answer: The numbers are closer to the next ten then the previous ten.

4. Sample answer: By rounding up you are ensuring that you have enough money to buy the items you want.

12. Sample answer: Population counts such as with California are generally estimations because it is difficult to account for a large number of people.

Page 69, Mid-Chapter Check

4. $3 + 2 + 1 = 2 + 1 + 3$; Commutative Property of Addition

11. 35,413; $28{,}000 + 7{,}000 = 35{,}000$

12. 100,881; $60{,}000 + 40{,}000 = 100{,}000$

14. Sample answer: Add $175 + 225 = 400$, then $400 + 139 = 539$.

Page 77, Lesson 2-6

11. Sample answer: What is the approximate total score of Juan's two games?

Page 89, Chapter Test

18. Sample answer: Regroup 1 thousand as 9 hundreds, 9 tens, and 10 ones. Then subtract. The result is 1,683.

NOTES

Chapter Overview

Chapter-at-a-Glance

In Chapter 3, the emphasis is on collecting and organizing data, making and reading graphs, and finding measures of central tendency.

Lesson		Math Objective	State/Local Standards
3-1	**Collect and Organize Data** (pp. 95–97)	Take a survey and collect and organize data.	
3-2	**Find Mode, Median, and Outliers** (pp. 98–101)	Identify the mode, median, and outliers of a set of data.	
3-3	**Problem-Solving Strategy: Make a Table** (pp. 102–103)	Solve problems by making a table.	
3-4	**Line Plots** (pp. 104–107)	Present and interpret data in a line plot.	
3-5	**Bar Graphs** (pp. 108–110)	Interpret a bar graph.	
3-6	**Bar and Double Bar Graphs** (pp. 112–114)	Interpret bar graphs to answer questions.	
EXTEND 3-6	**Make Double Bar Graphs** (pp. 116–117)	Display data in double bar graphs.	
3-7	**Problem Solving Investigation: Choose a strategy** (pp. 118–119)	Choose the best strategy to solve a problem.	
EXPLORE 3-8	**Possible Outcomes** (pp. 122–123)	Determine the possible outcomes of an experiment.	
3-8	**Determine Possible Outcomes** (pp. 124–127)	Use pictures to find all the possible outcomes in a problem situation.	
3-9	**Probability** (pp. 128–130)	Describe probability with words and numbers.	
EXTEND 3-9	**Find Probability** (p. 131)	Use technology to find probability.	

Organize, Display, and Interpret Data

BIG Idea On a daily basis, students and adults are confronted with information that they must organize, process, analyze, and act upon. They use data-analysis skills to make important decisions and predictions. How much time will it take to finish this task? What are the injury rates for fourth graders using skateboards?

Students must grasp decision-making concepts early and that these ideas are reinforced throughout their mathematics education. In this chapter, students will record, analyze, and organize data using tally charts and graphs that can be used to make predictions.

Algebra Students learn to use the make a table problem-solving strategy. This will help prepare them for algebra concepts, such as function tables and using rules to write equations. (Lesson 3-3)

G4-FP7C *Data Analysis:* Students continue to use tools from grade 3, solving problems by making frequency tables, bar graphs, picture graphs, and line plots. They apply their understanding of place value to develop and use stem-and-leaf plots.

Skills Trace

Vertical Alignment

Third Grade

In third grade, students learned to:

- Collect, organize, record, and display data in pictographs and bar graphs.
- Interpret data in pictographs and bar graphs.
- Describe data as more likely than, less likely than, or equally likely as.

Fourth Grade

During this chapter, students learn to:

- Take a survey, and collect and represent data on line plots, graphs, tables, and charts.
- Identify the mode, median, and outliers of a set of data.
- Interpret a bar graph.

After this chapter, students learn to:

- Use grids and tree diagrams to show outcomes.

Fifth Grade

In fifth grade, students learn to:

- List outcomes of a probability experiment and determine the likelihood of an event.

Backmapping and Vertical Alignment McGraw-Hill's *Math Connects* program was conceived and developed with the final results in mind: student success in Algebra 1 and beyond. The authors, using the **NCTM Focal Points and Focal Connections** as their guide, developed this brand-new series by backmapping from Algebra 1 concepts, and vertically aligning the topics so that they build upon prior skills and concepts and serve as a foundation for future topics.

Math Vocabulary

The following math vocabulary words for Chapter 3 are listed in the glossary of the ***Student Edition***. You can find interactive definitions in 13 languages in the ***eGlossary*** at macmillanmh.com.

data Information collected from a survey or experiment. (p. 95A)

double bar graph A bar graph that compares two related groups of data. (p. 112A)

frequency table A table for organizing a set of data that shows the number of times each results has occurred. (p. 95A)

line plot A graph that uses columns of Xs above a number line to show frequency of data. (p. 104A)

median The middle number in a group of numbers arranged in numerical order. (p. 98A)
Example: 3, 5, 6, 7, 8 (The median is 6).

mode The number(s), that occurs most often in a set of numbers. A set can have more than one mode. (p. 98A)
Example: 7, 4, 7, 10, 7, and 2 (The mode is 7).

outlier A number in a set of data that is much larger or much smaller than most of the other numbers in the set. (p. 98A)

probability A number between 0 and 1 that measures the likelihood of an event happening. (p. 128)

survey A method of collecting data. (p. 95A)

tally chart A way to keep track of data. (p. 95A)

Visual Vocabulary Cards
Use Visual Vocabulary Cards 4 and 40 to reinforce the vocabulary in this chapter. (The Define/Example/Ask routine is printed on the back of each card.)

bar graph

Chapter Planner

Suggested Pacing		
Instruction	Review & Assessment	TOTAL
12 days	1 day	**13 days**

Diagnostic Assessment
Quick Check (p. 94)

	Lesson 3-1 (Pacing: 1 day)	Lesson 3-2 (Pacing: 1 day)	Lesson 3-3 (Pacing: 1 day)
Lesson/ Objective	**Collect and Organize Data** (pp. 95–97) **Objective:** Take a survey and collect and organize data.	**Find Mode, Median, and Outliers** (pp. 98–101) **Objective:** Identify the mode, median, and outliers of a set of data.	**Problem-Solving Strategy Make a Table** (pp. 102–103) **Objective:** Solve problems by making a table.
State/Local Standards			
Math Vocabulary	**survey**, **data**, **tally chart**, **frequency table**	**mode**, **median**, **outlier**	
Lesson Resources	**Materials** index cards, construction paper or poster board **Other Resources** CRM Leveled Worksheets (pp. 8–12) Daily Reteach • 5-Minute Check • Problem of the Day	**Other Resources** CRM Leveled Worksheets (pp. 13–17) Daily Reteach • 5-Minute Check • Problem of the Day	**Materials** grid paper **Other Resources** CRM Leveled Worksheets (pp. 18–22) Daily Reteach • 5-Minute Check • Problem of the Day *Americans On the Move*
Technology		Math Adventures	
Math Online	Personal Tutor	Personal Tutor	
Reaching All Learners	English Learners, p. 95B ELL Below Level, p. 95B BL Early Finishers, p. 95B OL AL	English Learners, p. 98B ELL Below Level, p. 98B BL Early Finishers, p. 98B AL	English Learners, p. 102B ELL Below Level, p. 102B BL Early Finishers, p. 102B OL AL
Alternate Lesson	*IMPACT Mathematics:* Unit I		

KEY

BL Below/Approaching Level · OL On Level · AL Above/Beyond Level · ELL English Learners
SE Student Edition · TE Teacher Edition · CRM Chapter 3 Resource Masters · CD-Rom
Transparency · Real-World Problem Solving Library

	Lesson 3-4 (Pacing: 1 day)	Lesson 3-5 (Pacing: 1 day)	Lesson 3-6 (Pacing: 1 day)
Lesson/ Objective	**Line Plots** (pp. 104–107) **Objective:** Represent and interpret data in a line plot.	**Bar Graphs** (pp. 108–110) **Objective:** Interpret a bar graph.	**Bar and Double Bar Graphs** (pp. 112–115) **Objective:** Interpret bar graphs to answer questions.
State/Local Standards			
Math Vocabulary	**line plot**	**bar graph**	**double bar**
Lesson Resources	**Materials** 9-foot long piece of paper, lined paper, index cards **Other Resources** CRM Leveled Worksheets (pp. 23–27) Daily Reteach • 5-Minute Check • Problem of the Day	**Materials** newspapers, magazines, scissors paper, pencil **Other Resources** CRM Leveled Worksheets (pp. 28–32) Daily Reteach • 5-Minute Check • Problem of the Day	**Materials** two blank transparencies **Other Resources** CRM Leveled Worksheets (pp. 33–37) Daily Reteach • 5-Minute Check • Problem of the Day
Technology	Math Adventures	Math Adventures	
Math Online	Personal Tutor	Personal Tutor	Personal Tutor
Reaching All Learners	English Learners, p. 104B ELL Below Level, p. 104B BL Early Finishers, p. 104B AL	English Learners, p. 108B ELL Below Level, p. 108B BL Early Finishers, p. 108B AL	English Learners, p. 112B ELL Gifted and Talented, p. 112B BL Early Finishers, p. 112B AL
Alternate Lesson		*IMPACT Mathematics:* Unit I	*IMPACT Mathematics:* Unit I
		Formative Assessment Mid-Chapter Check (p. 111)	**Game Time** Graph Race (p. 115)

Chapter Planner

	Extend 3-6 (Pacing: 1 day)	Lesson 3-7 (Pacing: 1 day)	Explore 3-8 (Pacing: 1 day)
Lesson/ Objective	**Make Double Bar Graphs** (pp. 116–117) **Objective:** Display data in a double bar graph.	**Problem-Solving Investigation** **Choose a Strategy** (pp. 118–119) **Objective:** Choose the best strategy to solve a problem.	**Possible Outcomes** (pp. 122–123) **Objective:** Determine the possible outcomes of an experiment.
State/Local Standards			
Math Vocabulary			
Lesson Resources	**Materials** colored pencils, graph paper	**Manipulatives** coins **Other Resources** CRM Leveled Worksheets (pp. 38–42) Daily Reteach • 5-Minute Check • Problem of the Day *Americans On the Move*	**Manipulatives** 4 number cubes labeled 0–5
Technology			
Math Online	Concepts in Motion		Personal Tutor
Reaching All Learners		English Learners, p. 118B ELL Gifted and Talented, p. 118B AL Early Finishers, p. 118B OL AL	
Alternate Lesson			

Problem Solving in Science
A Head Above the Rest (p. 120)

	Lesson 3-8 Pacing: 1 day	Lesson 3-9 Pacing: 1 day	Extend 3-9 Pacing: 1 day
Lesson/ Objective	**Determine Possible Outcomes** (pp. 124–127) **Objective:** Use pictures to find all the possible outcomes in a problem situation.	**Probability** (pp. 128–130) **Objective:** Describe probability with words and numbers.	**Find Probability** (p. 131) **Objective:** Use technology to find probability.
State/Local Standards			
Math Vocabulary	**tree diagram**	**outcome**, **probability**,	
Lesson Resources	**Materials** grid paper, index cards **Other Resources** CRM Leveled Worksheets (pp. 43–47) Daily Reteach • 5-Minute Check • Problem of the Day	**Materials** marbles and small bowls **Manipulatives** connecting cubes **Other Resources** CRM Leveled Worksheets (pp. 48–52) Daily Reteach • 5-Minute Check • Problem of the Day	
Technology / **Math Online**	Personal Tutor	Personal Tutor	Math Tool Chest
Reaching All Learners	English Learners, p. 124B ELL Below Level, p. 124B BL Early Finishers, p. 124B AL	English Learners, p. 128B ELL Below Level, p. 128B BL Early Finishers, p. 128B OL AL	
Alternate Lesson			

Summative Assessment
- Study Guide/Review (p. 132)
- Chapter Test (p. 139)
- Test Practice (p. 140)

Chapter Planner

Assessment Options

Diagnostic Assessment

- SE *Option 1:* Quick Check (p. 94)
- *Option 2:* Online Quiz macmillanmh.com
- CRM *Option 3:* Diagnostic Test (p. 54)
- CRM *Option 4:* Chapter Pretest (p. 55)

Formative Assessment

- TE Alternate Teaching Strategy (every lesson)
- SE Talk About It (every lesson)
- SE Writing in Math (every lesson)
- SE Check What You Know (every lesson)
- TE Ticket Out the Door (p. 110)
- TE Into the Future (pp. 107, 127)
- TE Yesterday's News (p. 101, 114)
- SE Mid-Chapter Check (p. 111)
- CRM Lesson Quizzes (pp. 56–58)
- CRM Mid-Chapter Test (p. 59)

Summative Assessment

- SE Chapter Test (p. 139)
- SE Standards Practice (p. 140)
- CRM Vocabulary Test (p. 60)
- CRM Leveled Chapter Tests (pp. 65–76)
- CRM Cumulative Test Practice (pp. 78–79)
- CRM Oral Assessment (pp. 61–62)
- ExamView® Assessment Suite
- Advance Tracker

From Our Authors

It is essential that students develop data-driven decision-making concepts and skills early and that the concepts and skills be reinforced throughout students' school mathematics experiences. In this chapter, students develop and use data-driven decision-making concepts and skills through exploration of familiar settings. Students will:

- record and organize data using tally charts and frequency charts,
- generate data pictures with line plots and bar graphs,
- determine measures of central tendency, including median and mode,
- determine possible outcomes from simple experiments to make predictions.

The lesson progression in this chapter leads you and your students to culminating activities in data-driven analysis and prediction, skills that will continue to be essential in our homes, our work, our communities, our nation, and our world.

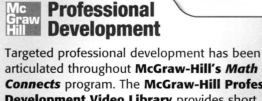

Targeted professional development has been articulated throughout **McGraw-Hill's *Math Connects*** program. The **McGraw-Hill Professional Development Video Library** provides short videos that support the **NCTM Focal Points and Focal Connections.** For more information visit macmillanmh.com.

Model Lessons

Instructional Strategies

Teacher Notes

Learning Stations

Cross-Curricular Links

Writing

individual | LOGICAL

Family Counts

- Write a paragraph detailing who is in your family, back to your grandparents' generation. You can include cousins, aunts, uncles, step-parents—every family is different. Then make a tally chart of females and males in your family.
- Use your tally chart to create a bar graph showing how many people in your family are female and how many are male.

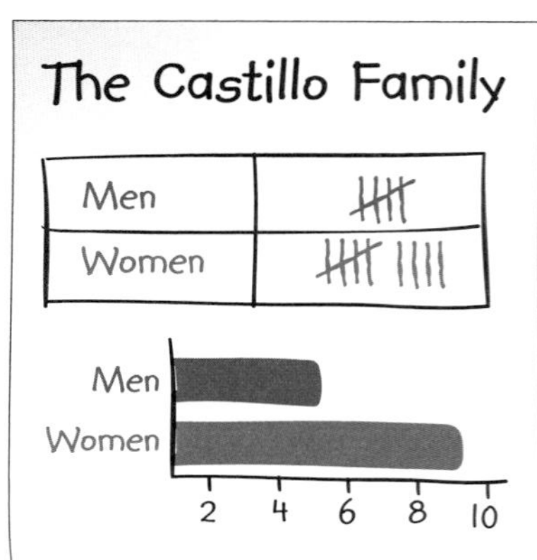

Materials:

- paper
- pencil

Social Studies

pair | VISUAL

What Is in Your Wallet?

Take a look at your play money and figure out how much of each type of coin or bill you have.

- Each partner separates his or her money into piles of pennies, nickels, dimes, quarters, and dollar bills. Make a bar graph showing how much each of you has in each pile.
- You both have the same amount of money, but how is it divided among the types of coins and bills? Compare your bar graphs and see.

Materials:

- $10 play money per person, different denominations for each partner
- paper
- pencils

Science

How Is the Weather?

Write down what the weather was like every day for the past week. Then graph it.

- Try to remember what the weather was like each day last week, and put each day into the following categories: sunny, cloudy, rainy. How many days fall into each category? Make a bar graph showing the three categories and graph the week's weather.
- Now look at the weather prediction for the next seven days. Make a similar bar graph showing what the weather will be like.
- How do your two bar graphs compare? Explain.

Materials:

- newspaper with weather report for the next week
- paper
- pencil

Organize, Display, and Interpret Data

Music

group | VISUAL

Bars of Music

How many music CDs do each of you own? Make a poster showing your group's musical data.

- Collect data of how many CDs each group member owns. If you cannot think of the exact number off the top of your head, use the tally chart method to estimate the number of CDs you have. Create a bar graph on a poster, showing a bar for each student's CD collection.
- At the bottom of your poster, write the median, the mode (if there is one), and any outliers for your data.

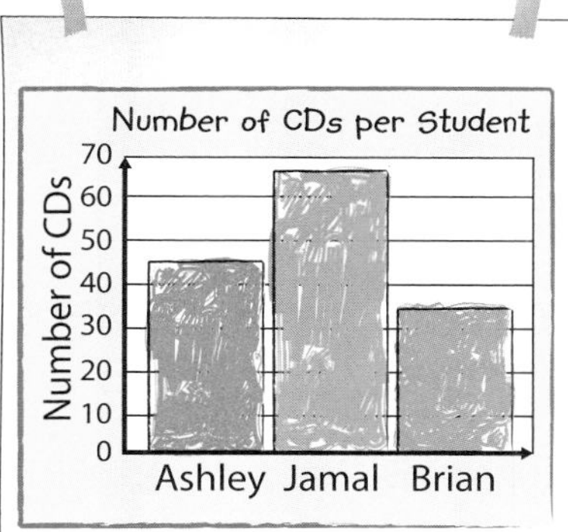

Materials:
- markers
- paper
- pencils

Health

individual | VISUAL

Fruit and Veggie Plots

How many servings of fruit and vegetables do you get a day? Find out if you are getting enough.

- Make two tally charts. Then survey the class to find how many servings of fruit each person had yesterday. Instead of marking each person's score in the tally chart with a tick mark, mark it with an apple. Do the same for vegetables in the second tally chart, and mark each person's score with a carrot.
- Use the tally charts to create frequency tables for fruits and vegetables. How many people ate the recommended number of servings?

Fruit Servings	
Number of Servings	Number of People
1	🍎 🍎 🍎
2	🍎
3	🍎 🍎 🍎 🍎
4	🍎 🍎
5	🍎

Materials:
- markers
- paper

Reading

group | LOGICAL

A Terrible Storm

- Read *Night of the Twisters* by Ivy Ruckman by yourself or with a group.
- Take a survey of your group to see if anyone has ever experienced a big storm or weather event. Make a bar graph showing your group's weather experience.
- The seven twisters in this story were rated on the Fujita Scale, a scale of storm strength. F0–F1 is Weak, F2–F3 is Strong, and F4–F5 is Violent. There were three F1 tornados, one F2, two F3s, and one F4. Make a bar graph showing this storm data.

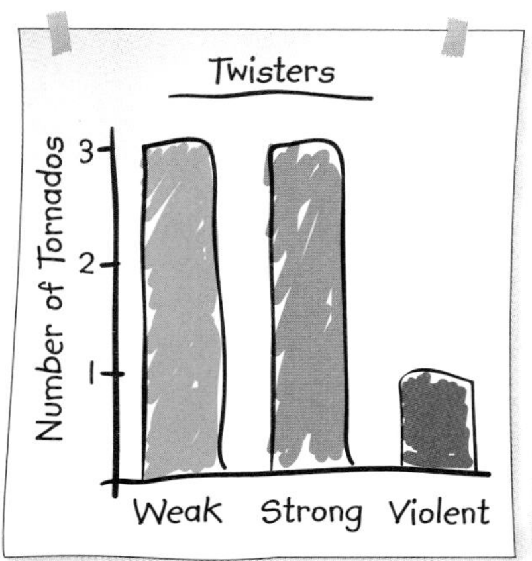

Materials:
- *Night of the Twisters* by Ivy Ruckman
- markers
- paper
- pencils

CHAPTER 3

Introduce the Chapter

 Real World: What's the Score?

Materials: sports sections of newspapers

Share with students that in this chapter they are going to learn about organizing data and displaying sets of data in different types of graphs.

Home	0	2	1	0	4	0
Visitor	1	0	3	0	0	2

Point out that there are many ways to organize and display data, and that the table above is just one of these ways.

- Have students divide into small groups.
- Ask them to search the sports sections of newspapers and make tables that show scores by inning or by quarter.
- Have students share their tables with the class. Ask them why it is helpful to organize data in tables.

Direct students to Student Edition p. 92. Have students read the paragraph at the top of the page.

- **Why is information sometimes displayed in tables and graphs?** Graphs and tables are good visual tools that can help us analyze and interpret data.
- **What kinds of data can you think of that are displayed in tables and graphs?** Answers will vary.

WRITING IN ►MATH

Starting the Chapter

Have students write a short paragraph in their Math Journals explaining how they think tables and graphs could be used in other school subjects such as social studies and science. Suggest that they give specific examples.

Key Vocabulary Introduce the key vocabulary in the chapter using the routine below.

<u>Define:</u> Data is information collected from a survey or experiment.

<u>Example:</u> I used the data from the survey to make a chart.

<u>Ask:</u> What are some ways that we use data in math?

Read-Aloud Anthology For an optional reading activity to introduce this chapter's math concepts, see the Read-Aloud Anthology on p. TR27.

CHAPTER 3

Organize, Display, and Interpret Data

BIG Idea What are data and graphs?

Data is a set of information. When data is displayed in a **graph**, it is easier to read and interpret.

Example The graph shows the number of children in the United States. About 35 million children are 5 to 13 years old.

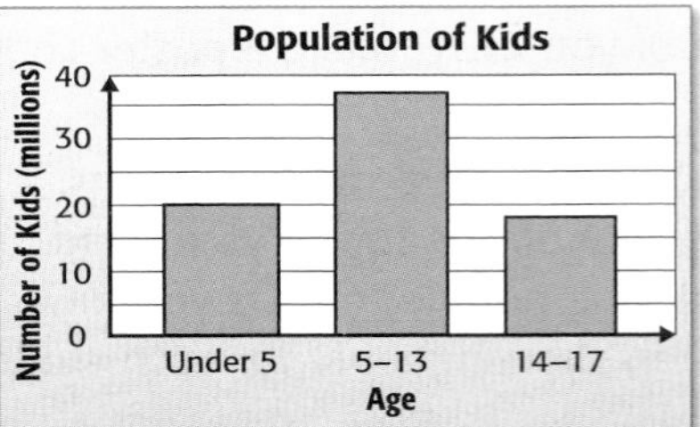

Source: U.S. Census Bureau

What will I learn in this chapter?

- Collect and represent data on a number line, and in graphs, tables, and charts.
- Read and interpret data.
- Determine all possible outcomes of a situation.
- Solve problems by making a table.

Key Vocabulary

data
survey
bar graph
probability
tree diagram

Math Online Student Study Tools at macmillanmh.com

 Chapter 3 Project

Choosing to Help

Students hold a clothing and canned food drive, and make a bar graph showing their progress for both items.

- Students ask fellow students, friends, and family to donate clothing and canned food for them to collect and give to a charity.
- Students make a bar graph showing one bar for clothing and another for canned goods. Each piece of clothing counts as 1 item and each can counts as 1 item. The bar graph can not only show the students' progress, but also allow them to compare the amounts of clothing and food they collect.
- Challenge students to add the amounts they collect each day for one month to the bar graph.

CRM *Refer to Chapter 3 Resource Masters, p. 63, for a rubric to assess students' progress on this project.*

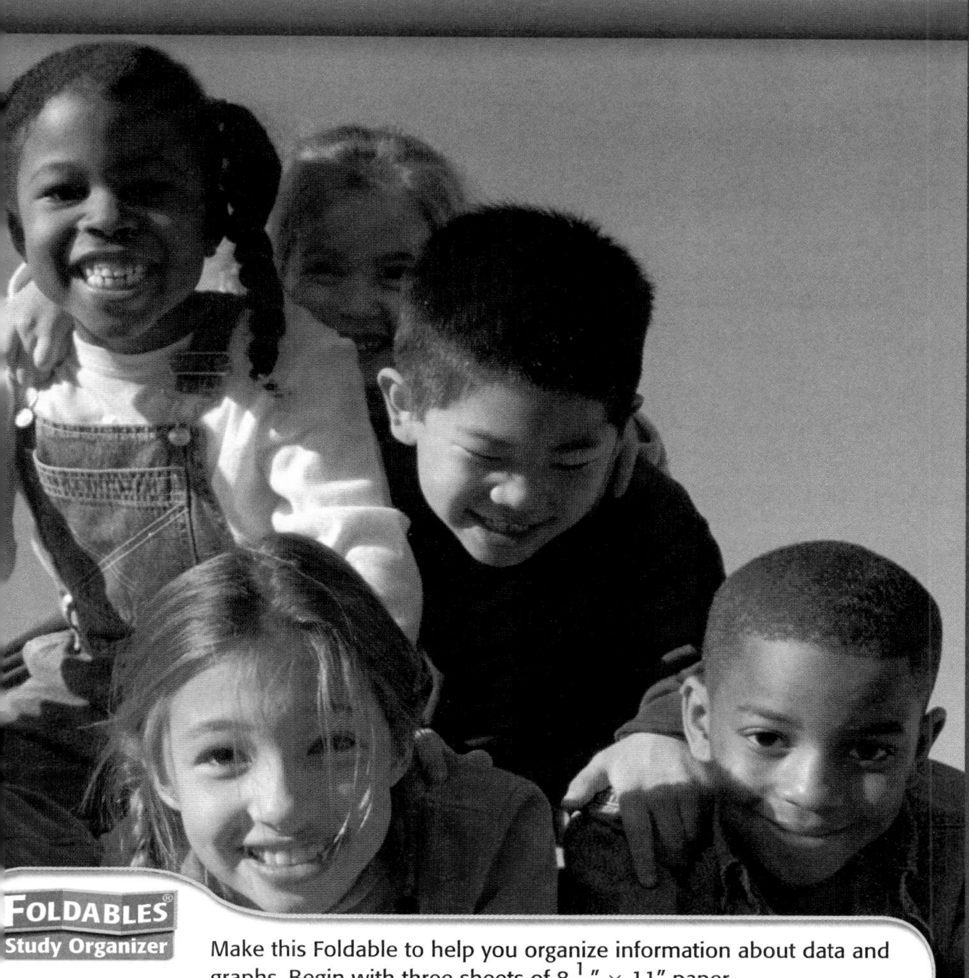

FOLDABLES Study Organizer

Make this Foldable to help you organize information about data and graphs. Begin with three sheets of $8\frac{1}{2}" \times 11"$ paper.

1 **Stack** the paper about 3 inches apart.

2 **Roll** up the bottom so all tabs are the same size.

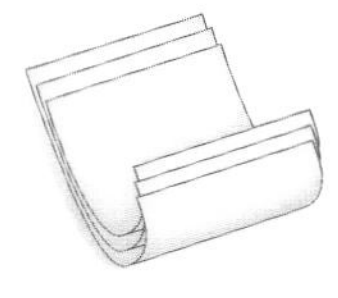

3 **Crease** and staple along the fold as shown.

4 **Label.** Take notes as you move through the chapter.

National ESL Standards Alignment for Chapter 3			
Lesson, Page	ESL Standard	Modality	Level
3-1, p. 95B	Goal 1, Standard 3, b	Linguistic	Beginning
3-2, p. 99B	Goal 2, Standard 2, b	Kinesthetic, Social	Intermediate
3-3, p. 102B	Goal 1, Standard 1, f	Intrapersonal, Visual	Advanced
3-4, p. 104B	Goal 2, Standard 1, g	Logical, Social	Advanced
3-5, p. 108B	Goal 3, Standard 3, e	Linguistic	Intermediate
3-6, p. 112B	Goal 1, Standard 3, f	Social, Linguistic	Beginning
3-7, p. 118B	Goal 1, Standard 2, f	Linguistic, Social	Beginning
3-8, p. 124B	Goal 3, Standard 3, a	Auditory	Intermediate
3-9, p. 128B	Goal 2, Standard 2, h	Auditory	Intermediate

The National ESL Standards can be found in the Teacher Reference Handbook.

FOLDABLES Dinah Zike's Foldables

Guide students through the directions on p. 93 to create their own Foldables graphic organizers for data and graphs. Students may also use their Foldables graphic organizers to study and review for chapter assessments.

When to Use It Lessons 3-1, 3-3, 3-4, 3-6, and 3-7. (Additional instructions for using the Foldables with these lessons are found on pp. 111 and 132.)

Chapter 3 Literature List

Lesson	Book Title
3-1	**The War Between the Vowels and the Consonants** Pricilla Turner
3-2	**A Day's Work** Eve Bunting
3-3	**A Day's Work** Eve Bunting
3-4	**Heat Wave** Helen Ketteman
3-5	**Tiger Math: Learning to Graph from a Baby Tiger** Ann Whitehead Nagda and Cindy Bickel
3-6	**Tiger Math: Learning to Graph from a Baby Tiger** Ann Whitehead Nagda and Cindy Bickel
3-8	**Do You Wanna Bet? Your Chance to Find Out About Probability** Jean Cushman and Martha Westman
3-9	**Same Old Horse** Stuart J. Murphy

Before you begin Chapter 3:

- Read the Math at Home letter found in the Chapter 3 Resource Masters, p. 4, with the class and have each student sign it. (A Spanish version is found on p. 5.)
- Send home copies of the Math at Home letter with each student.

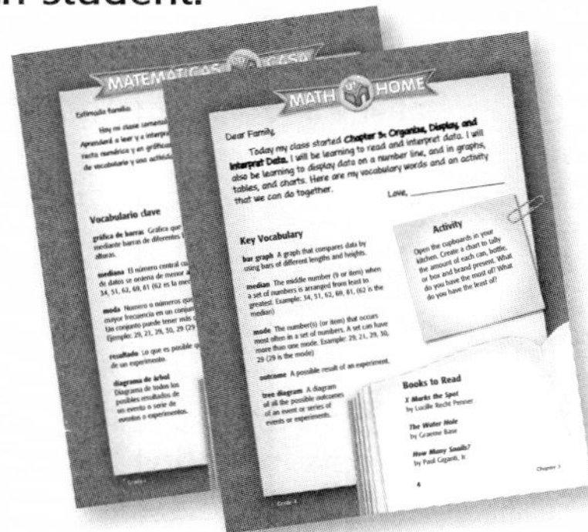

Diagnostic Assessment

Check for students' prerequisite skills before beginning the chapter.

- **Option 1:** ***Quick Check***
  SE Student Edition, p. 94
- **Option 2:** ***Online Assessment***
  Math Online macmillanmh.com
- **Option 3:** ***Diagnostic Tests***
  CRM Chapter 3 Resource Masters, p. 54–55

RTI (Response to Intervention)

Apply the Results Based on the results of the diagnostic assessment on Student Edition p. 94, address individual needs before beginning the chapter.

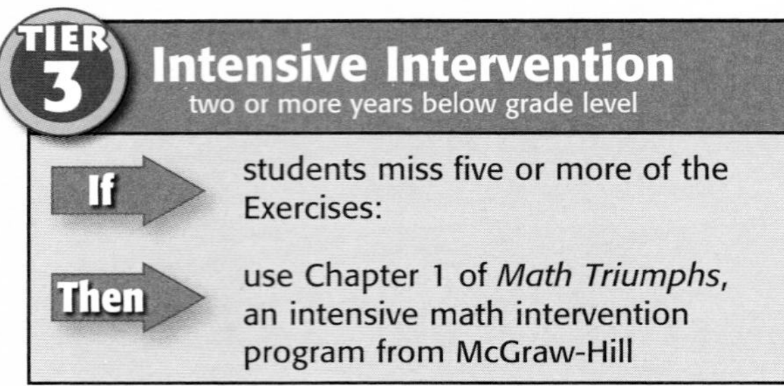

TIER 3 Intensive Intervention
two or more years below grade level

If students miss five or more of the Exercises:

Then use Chapter 1 of *Math Triumphs*, an intensive math intervention program from McGraw-Hill

ARE YOU READY for Chapter 3?

You have two ways to check prerequisite skills for this chapter.

Option 2
Math Online Take the Chapter Readiness Quiz at macmillanmh.com

Option 1
Complete the Quick Check below.

QUICK Check

Make a tally chart for each situation. (Prior Grade) (Used in Lesson 3-1)

1. Alexi took a survey to find out her friends' favorite colors.

Favorite Colors		
red	yellow	green
blue	pink	red
green	blue	pink
red	blue	blue

2. Mr. Bailey recorded the ages of the students on the basketball team.

Ages of Basketball Players		
10	11	9
9	10	11
10	9	10
10	10	10

1, 2. See Ch. 3 Answer Appendix.

Order from least to greatest. (Lesson 1-5) (Used in Lesson 3-2)

3. 12, 17, 19, 15, 13 12,13,15,17,19

4. 87, 56, 72, 34, 94 34, 56, 72, 87, 94

5. 31, 60, 23, 87, 91 23, 31, 60, 87, 91

Use the graph to answer each question. (Prior Grade) (Used in Lessons 3-5 and 3-6)

6. How many more students like art than gym? 4 students

7. How do the number of students who like music and gym compare to the number of students who like art? Sample answer: More students like gym and music than art.

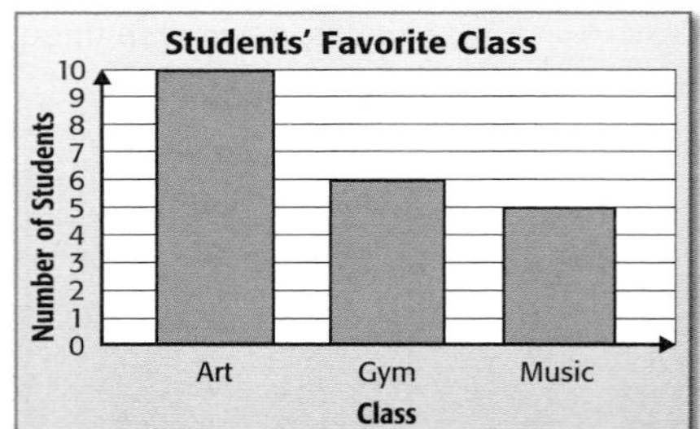

TIER 2 Strategic Intervention
below/approaching grade level

If students miss three or four in: **Exercises 1–7**

Then choose a resource:

- Strategic Intervention Guide (p. 130)
- TE Start Smart 6: Probability and Statistics (p. 12)
- **Math Online** Extra Examples • Personal Tutor • Concepts in Motion

TIER 1 On-Level

If students miss two in: **Exercises 1–7**

Then choose a resource:

- TE Learning Stations (pp. 92I–92J)
- TE Chapter Project (p. 92)
- CRM Game: Hit the Grid!
- Math Adventures
- My Math Zone Chapter 2
- **Math Online** Fact Dash

Above/Beyond Level

If students miss one or less in: **Exercises 1–7**

Then choose a resource:

- TE Learning Stations (pp. 92I–92J)
- TE Chapter Project (p. 92)
- Real-World Problem Solving: *Americans On the Move*
- My Math Zone Chapter 2, Chapter 3
- **Math Online** Games

LESSON 3-1 Collect and Organize Data

Lesson Planner

Objective

Take a survey and collect and organize data.

Vocabulary

survey, **data**, **tally chart**, **frequency table**

Resources

Materials: index cards, construction paper or poster board

Literature Connection: *The War Between the Vowels and the Consonants* by Priscilla Turner

Alternate Lesson: Use *IMPACT Mathematics:* Unit I to provide practice with collecting and organizing data.

Teacher Technology

TeacherWorks • Interactive Classroom

Daily Routine

Use these suggestions before beginning the lesson on p. 95.

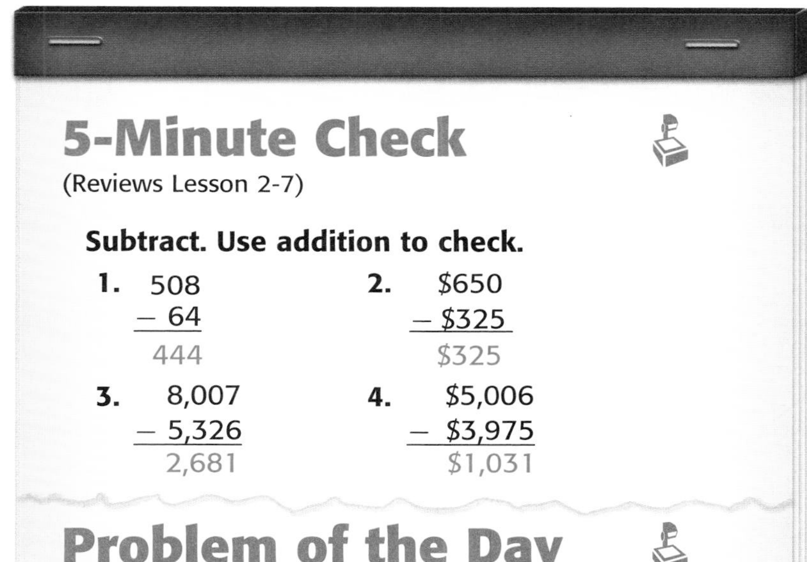

5-Minute Check

(Reviews Lesson 2-7)

Subtract. Use addition to check.

1. 508 − 64 = 444

2. \$650 − \$325 = \$325

3. 8,007 − 5,326 = 2,681

4. \$5,006 − \$3,975 = \$1,031

Problem of the Day

Mr. Jackson asked his students which of three fruits they prefer. Twice as many students chose apples as chose bananas, six chose bananas, and the remaining six students chose oranges. How many students did Mr. Jackson survey? 24

Focus on Math Background

Students enjoy taking surveys, collecting data, and organizing data. When they collect data in a survey, they have ownership of the data along with a vested interest in the problem. Data collection and organization begins in the primary grades. As students design questions and conduct surveys, they will need to remember to obtain unbiased results, or results that do not favor a particular outcome. To do this, they may need to change the questions asked or change whom they are asking.

Tally marks and tally charts are probably not new to students at this level, but frequency tables may be. Moving from a tally chart to a frequency table is simply a matter of adding the tally marks.

Building Math Vocabulary

Write the lesson vocabulary words and their definitions on the board.

Have students work in small groups to draw an illustration for each definition. Have each group label their illustrations with the appropriate word and its definition. As a class, make a poster and hang it in the room with the words, definitions, and pictures to help students as they work through the chapter.

Differentiated Instruction

Small Group Options

SOCIAL

Option 1 Below Level BL

Materials: paper and pencil, poster board

- Challenge students to survey their classmates for their favorite kind of pet.
- Students should limit the choices to no more than 5 pets. Make a tally chart of student choices.
- Students will then convert their data into a frequency table and share their findings with the class.

Pets	Tally
Dog	~~IIII~~ II
Bird	II
Hamster	IIII
Lizard	III
Cat	~~IIII~~

LINGUISTIC

Option 2 English Language Learners ELL

Materials: blocks
Core Vocabulary: do you like? Yes, I do. No, I don't
Common Use Verb: ask

Hear Math This strategy scaffolds organizing data with simple *yes* or *no* questions and answers.

- Write a simple *yes* or *no* question on the board or transparency. Circle the helping verb and underline the verb. Repeat using the same helping verb "Do."
- Script a survey question to assist non-productive ELL students in taking a survey. Read the question aloud several times, asking students to chorally read.
- Say: "A survey is asking questions and then adding the total number of answers."
- Have ELL students ask the questions to other ELL students.
- Tell students to give their classmate a certain colored block or rod when the classmate answers *yes*. Choose another color to represent *no*.
- As a group, tally the results.

Independent Work Options

LINGUISTIC

Option 1 Early Finishers OL AL

- Have students develop a survey question.
  *Remind students to design a question that will have an unbiased result.
- Students should make a blank tally chart they can later fill in with their results.
- Allow a few minutes of class time for students to survey the class and record the data. (This data can be used later as a classroom example in various graphs.)

Option 2 Student Technology

Math Online macmillanmh.com

Personal Tutor • Extra Examples

Option 3 Learning Station: Writing (p. 92I)

Direct students to the Writing Learning Station for opportunities to explore and extend the lesson concept.

Option 4 Problem-Solving Practice

Reinforce problem-solving skills and strategies with the Problem-Solving Practice worksheet.

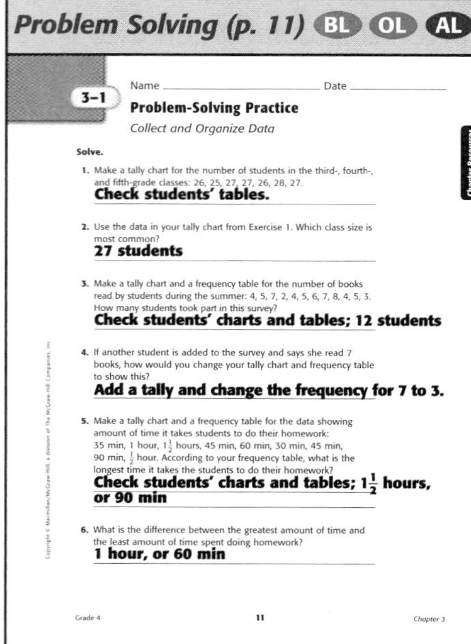

Problem Solving (p. 11) BL OL AL

3–1 Name ______ Date ______

Problem-Solving Practice

Collect and Organize Data

Chapter Resources

Solve.

1. Make a tally chart for the number of students in the third-, fourth-, and fifth-grade classes: 26, 25, 27, 27, 26, 28, 27.
   Check students' tables.
2. Use the data in your tally chart from Exercise 1. Which class size is most common?
   27 students
3. Make a tally chart and a frequency table for the number of books read by students during the summer: 4, 5, 7, 2, 4, 5, 6, 7, 8, 4, 5, 3. How many students took part in this survey?
   Check students' charts and tables; 12 students
4. If another student is added to the survey and says she read 7 books, how would you change your tally chart and frequency table to show this?
   Add a tally and change the frequency for 7 to 3.
5. Make a tally chart and a frequency table for the data showing amount of time it takes students to do their homework: 35 min, 1 hour, $1\frac{1}{2}$ hours, 45 min, 60 min, 30 min, 45 min, 90 min, $\frac{1}{2}$ hour. According to your frequency table, what is the longest time it takes the students to do their homework?
   Check students' charts and tables; $1\frac{1}{2}$ hours, or 90 min
6. What is the difference between the greatest amount of time and the least amount of time spent doing homework?
   1 hour, or 60 min

Grade 4 11 Chapter 3

3-1 Collect and Organize Data

GET READY to Learn

Ms. Alvarez asked each of her students, "What is your favorite after school activity?" The results are shown.

Playing a Sport	Reading	Watching T.V.
Staci	Alita	Julian
Eric	Sue	Chen
Melisa	Omar	Sarita
Kensey	Nicolas	
Alano		

MAIN IDEA

I will take a survey, and collect and organize data.

New Vocabulary

survey
data
tally chart
frequency table

Math Online
macmillanmh.com
- Extra Examples
- Personal Tutor
- Self-Check Quiz

Ms. Alvarez took a survey. A **survey** is a way to collect **data** or information that answers a question. You can use a **tally chart** or a **frequency table** to record data.

Real-World EXAMPLE Organize Data

1 SCHOOL **Look at the data Ms. Alvarez collected. Organize the data in a tally chart and a frequency table.**

Step 1 Draw a table with two columns. Include a title.

Step 2 List each activity in the first column.

Step 3 Use tally marks or numbers to record the results.

Tally Chart

Favorite After School Activities	
Activity	**Tally**
Playing a sport	𝍸
Reading	||||
Watching T.V.	|||

Each tally mark represents a student.

Frequency Table

Favorite After School Activities	
Activity	**Frequency**
Playing a sport	5
Reading	4
Watching T.V.	3

Numbers are used to record the results.

3-1 Collect and Organize Data

1 Introduce

Activity Choice 1 • Hands-On

- Hand out a blank index card to each student.
- Have students draw a line down the middle of their cards. Write their two favorite fruits.
- Gather around a table and have all students place their cards in front of them.
- Guide students toward the idea that unorganized data is hard to use.
- Help students organize the data. Cards may be taped on the board instead.

Activity Choice 2 • Literature

Introduce the lesson with *The War Between the Vowels and the Consonants* by Priscilla Turner. For a related math activity, see p. TR44.

2 Teach

Scaffolding Questions

Use the results from Activity 1 to answer the following questions.

- **What is the class favorite fruit? the least favorite?** Answers will vary.
- **How many more students like the class favorite than the runner-up? than the least favorite?** Answers will vary.
- **How might the results change if all the students were in line to buy apples?** more students would choose apples.
- **How are tally charts and frequency charts alike? How are they different?** Sample answer: They both tell how many people like a certain type of fruit; one uses tally marks and the other uses numbers.

GET READY to Learn

Have students open their books and read the information in **Get Ready to Learn**. Introduce **survey**, **data**, **tally chart**, and **frequency table**. As a class, work through **Example 1**.

Organize Data

Example 1 Make sure students translate the same number of data from their tally charts to their frequency tables.

ADDITIONAL EXAMPLE

1 Mrs. Patel asks her students what their favorite vegetable is. Organize the data given in a tally table and a frequency chart.

Corn: Noah, Pedro, Lilly, David, Emilio
Peas: Nathan, Jack
Carrots: Keisha, Mike, Christopher
Broccoli: Lidia, Rama, Nicholas
Potatoes: Wes, Tucker, Ruth, Kenya

Vegetable	Tally
Broccoli	|||
Carrots	|||
Corn	~~||||~~
Peas	||
Potatoes	||||

Vegetable	Frequency
Broccoli	3
Carrots	3
Corn	5
Peas	2
Potatoes	4

CHECK What You Know

As a class, have students complete **Exercises 1–4** in **Check What You Know** as you observe their work.

Exercise 4 Assess student comprehension before assigning practice exercises.

BL Alternate Teaching Strategy

If students have trouble recording data in their tally table or frequency chart...

Then use one of these reteach options:

1 CRM **Daily Reteach Worksheet** (p. 8)

2 Draw a line across the board and write the numbers 1–12 below the line. Have students make an X above the number of their favorite month.

- **How many students chose June? How many students are represented in the data?** Answers will vary.

You can take a survey and collect and represent data on charts and tables.

Remember
The tally marks used to represent a value of 5 are ~~||||~~, not |||||.

Hands-On Mini Activity

Step 1 Write a survey question you can ask your classmates. An example is shown.

What type of pet is your favorite?

a) Dog b) Cat

c) Fish d) I do not like pets.

Step 2 Create a tally chart to record your results.

Step 3 Ask the question to each of your classmates. Organize the data as you collect it.

Step 4 Use the information on your tally chart to create a frequency table.

Analyze the data. 1, 2. See students' work.

1. Write two sentences that describe your survey results.
2. Were the survey results what you expected? Explain.

CHECK What You Know

1. The data shows the ways Mrs. Jackson's students travel to school. Organize the data in a tally chart. See Example 1 (p. 95)

How Do You Travel to School?	
Method	**Frequency**
Bicycle	3
Bus	6
Car	9
Walk	5

2. Refer to Exercise 1. What is the most popular way to travel to school? What is the least popular? See Example 1 (p. 95) most popular: car; least popular: bicycle

3. Mary lists all of the fish in her fish tank. Organize the data below in a frequency table. See Example 1 (p. 95)

Mary's Fish Tank	
angelfish	damsel
angelfish	damsel
angelfish	damsel
clown fish	eel
clown fish	eel

1, 2. See Ch. 3 Answer Appendix.

4. Talk About It What are three different questions that you could use to conduct a survey?

4. Sample answer: How much time do you spend studying the night before a test? How many siblings do you have? What is your favorite type of restaurant?

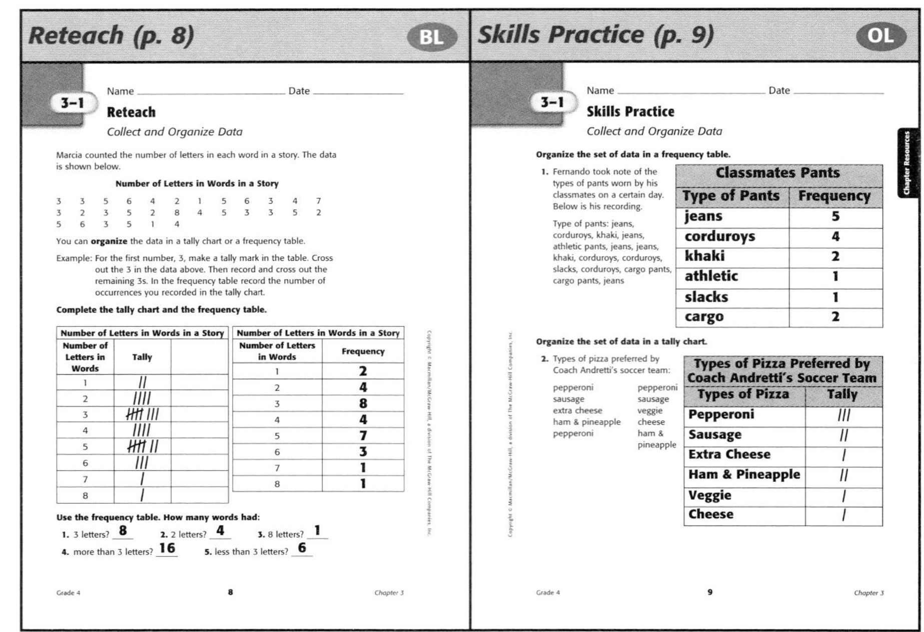

Reteach (p. 8) BL

3-1 Name ________ Date ________

Reteach

Collect and Organize Data

Marcia counted the number of letters in each word in a story. The data is shown below.

Number of Letters in Words in a Story

3 3 5 6 4 2 1 5 6 3 4 7
3 2 3 5 2 8 4 5 3 3 5 2
5 6 3 5 1 4

You can **organize** the data in a tally chart or a frequency table.

Example: For the first number, 3, make a tally mark in the table. Cross out the 3 in the data above. Then record and cross out the remaining 3s. In the frequency table record the number of occurrences you recorded in the tally chart.

Complete the tally chart and the frequency table.

Number of Letters in Words in a Story		
Number of Letters in Words	**Tally**	
1	||	
2	||||	
3	~~||||~~ |||	
4	||||	
5	~~||||~~ ||	
6	|||	
7	|	
8	|	

Number of Letters in Words in a Story	
Number of Letters in Words	**Frequency**
1	2
2	4
3	8
4	4
5	7
6	3
7	1
8	1

Use the frequency table. How many words had:

1. 3 letters? 8 2. 2 letters? 4 3. 8 letters? 1
4. more than 3 letters? 16 5. less than 3 letters? 6

Grade 4 8 Chapter 3

Skills Practice (p. 9) OL

3-1 Name ________ Date ________

Skills Practice

Collect and Organize Data

Chapter Resources

Organize the set of data in a frequency table.

1. Fernando took note of the types of pants worn by his classmates on a certain day. Below is his recording.

Type of pants: jeans, corduroys, khaki, jeans, athletic pants, jeans, jeans, khaki, corduroys, corduroys, slacks, corduroys, cargo pants, cargo pants, jeans

Classmates Pants	
Type of Pants	**Frequency**
jeans	5
corduroys	4
khaki	2
athletic	1
slacks	1
cargo	2

Organize the set of data in a tally chart.

2. Types of pizza preferred by Coach Andretti's soccer team:

pepperoni, sausage, extra cheese, ham & pineapple, pepperoni, pepperoni, sausage, veggie, cheese, ham & pineapple

Types of Pizza Preferred by Coach Andretti's Soccer Team	
Types of Pizza	**Tally**
Pepperoni	|||
Sausage	||
Extra Cheese	|
Ham & Pineapple	||
Veggie	|
Cheese	|

Grade 4 9 Chapter 3

Practice and Problem Solving

Organize each set of data in a tally chart. See Example 1 (p. 95)

5. Mr. Ortega records the type of pizza that his science club members like.

Favorite Type of Pizza		
cheese	cheese	sausage
cheese	pepperoni	sausage
cheese	pepperoni	
cheese	pepperoni	

6. Elisa took a survey to find out which movie to rent for her party.

Type of Movie	
action	comedy
action	comedy
action	comedy
animated	comedy

5–8. See Ch. 3 Answer Appendix.

Organize each set of data in a frequency table. See Example 1 (p. 95)

7. Measurement Damián recorded the temperatures in one week.

Weekly Temperatures	
Temperature (°F)	**Days**
70–75	||
76–80	|||
81–85	|
86–90	|

8. A survey was taken to see how students spend their time at recess.

Recess Activities		
kickball	drawing	swing
kickball	drawing	swing
kickball	swing	tag
kickball	swing	tag
drawing	swing	tag

For Exercises 9–12, use the tally chart that shows items sold at a school store.

Items Sold at School Store	
Item	**Tally**
Eraser	𝍸
Bottle of glue	
Pencil	𝍸 |||
Scissors	|

9. Which item was the top seller? How many were sold? pencils; 8

10. Which item sold once? scissors

11. How many items were sold altogether? 14

12. Organize the data in a frequency table. See margin.

H.O.T. Problems

13. OPEN ENDED Explain how a frequency table differs from a tally chart. How are they alike? 13, 14. See Ch. 3 Answer Appendix.

14. WRITING IN ▶MATH Suppose you are collecting and organizing data about the population of your city. Would it be better to use a frequency table or a tally chart? Explain.

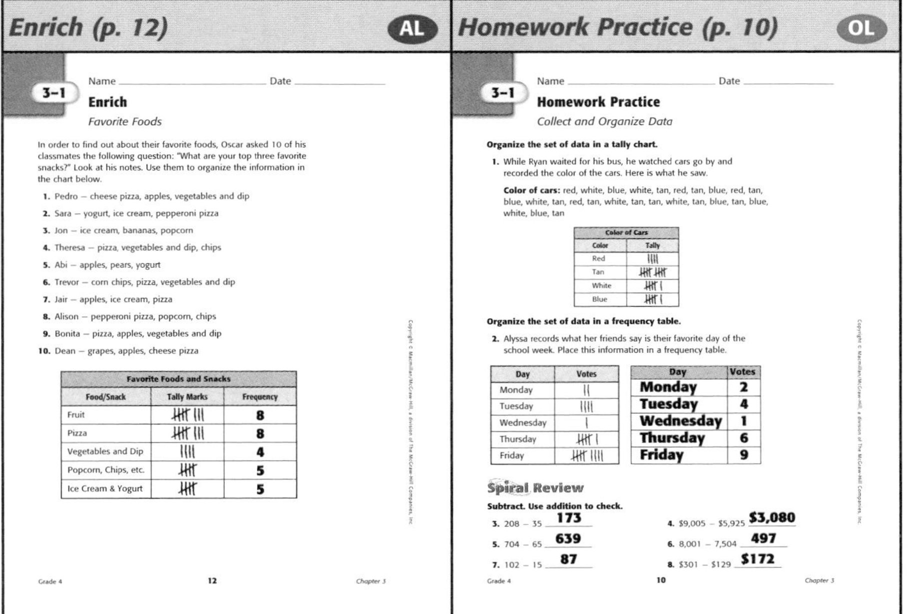

Enrich (p. 12) AL

3-1 Name ______ Date ______

Enrich

Favorite Foods

In order to find out about their favorite foods, Oscar asked 10 of his classmates the following question: "What are your top three favorite snacks?" Look at his notes. Use them to organize the information in the chart below.

1. Pedro – cheese pizza, apples, vegetables and dip
2. Sara – yogurt, ice cream, pepperoni pizza
3. Jon – ice cream, bananas, popcorn
4. Theresa – pizza, vegetables and dip, chips
5. Abi – apples, pears, yogurt
6. Trevor – corn chips, pizza, vegetables and dip
7. Jair – apples, ice cream, pizza
8. Alison – pepperoni pizza, popcorn, chips
9. Bonita – pizza, apples, vegetables and dip
10. Dean – grapes, apples, cheese pizza

Favorite Foods and Snacks		
Food/Snack	**Tally Marks**	**Frequency**
Fruit	𝍸 |||	**8**
Pizza	𝍸 |||	**8**
Vegetables and Dip	||||	**4**
Popcorn, Chips, etc.	𝍸	**5**
Ice Cream & Yogurt	𝍸	**5**

Grade 4 12 Chapter 3

Homework Practice (p. 10) OL

3-1 Name ______ Date ______

Homework Practice

Collect and Organize Data

Organize the set of data in a tally chart.

1. While Ryan waited for his bus, he watched cars go by and recorded the color of the cars. Here is what he saw.

Color of cars: red, white, blue, white, tan, red, tan, blue, red, tan, blue, white, tan, red, tan, white, tan, tan, white, tan, blue, tan, blue, white, blue, tan

Color of Cars	
Color	**Tally**
Red	||||
Tan	𝍸 𝍸
White	𝍸 |
Blue	𝍸 |

Organize the set of data in a frequency table.

2. Alyssa records what her friends say is their favorite day of the school week. Place this information in a frequency table.

Day	Votes
Monday	||
Tuesday	||||
Wednesday	|
Thursday	𝍸 |
Friday	𝍸 ||||

Day	Votes
Monday	**2**
Tuesday	**4**
Wednesday	**1**
Thursday	**6**
Friday	**9**

Spiral Review

Subtract. Use addition to check.

3. 208 – 35 **173**
4. $9,005 – $5,925 **$3,080**
5. 704 – 65 **639**
6. 8,001 – 7,504 **497**
7. 102 – 15 **87**
8. $301 – $129 **$172**

Grade 4 10 Chapter 3

3 Practice

Differentiate practice using these leveled assignments for Exercises 5–14.

Level	Assignment
BL Below/Approaching Level	5, 7, 9–12
OL On Level	6, 8–14
AL Above/Beyond Level	5–11 odd, 13–14

Have students discuss and complete the Higher Order Thinking problems. Have students explain how the data are related in a tally chart and a frequency table.

WRITING IN ▶MATH Have students complete Exercise 14 in their Math Journals. You may choose to use this exercise as an optional formative assessment.

4 Assess

Formative Assessment

Write the following problem on the board:

beets green beans beets green beans
corn green beans corn peas
corn mixed vegetables

- **What is the frequency of the data shown?** beets 2; corn 3; green beans 3; mixed vegetables 1; peas 1

Quick Check **Are students continuing to struggle with collecting and organizing data?**

If Yes → Small Group Options (p. 95B)

If No → Independent Work Options (p. 95B)
CRM Skills Practice Worksheet (p. 9)
CRM Enrich Worksheet (p. 12)

Additional Answer

12.

Items Sold at School Store	
Item	**Frequency**
Eraser	5
Bottle of glue	0
Pencil	8
Scissors	1

LESSON 3-2

Find Mode, Median, and Outliers

Lesson Planner

Objective

Identify the mode, median, and outliers of a set of data.

Vocabulary

mode, **median**, **outlier**

Resources

Literature Connection: *A Day's Work* by Eve Bunting

Teacher Technology

TeacherWorks • Interactive Classroom

Daily Routine

Use these suggestions before beginning the lesson on p. 98.

5-Minute Check

(Reviews Lesson 3-1)

1. Carla took a survey to find which sports her friends liked best. Organize the data into a tally table. See students' work.
2. Identify the most popular sport. soccer

Favorite Sport		
baseball	soccer	track
baseball	soccer	track
baseball	soccer	track
basketball	soccer	track
basketball	soccer	

Problem of the Day

Kim, Rey, Hannah, and Taye ran a race. Kim finished before Rey but after Taye. Hannah finished after Kim and did not finish last. Arrange these friends in order of who finished the race first to last.
Taye, Kim, Hannah, Rey

Focus on Math Background

Students are introduced to two measures of central tendency (median and mode) in this lesson. The concept of outlier is also introduced. Outliers are individual observations that fall well outside the overall pattern of the data. These data items may be much larger or smaller than the other data items. The median is always the middle measure when the data are listed in order, so outliers have little influence on the median. Likewise, the mode depends on frequency of occurrence and is not influenced by extremes. To expand upon different interpretations of data, you may wish to refer to page *R74* to teach minimum and maximum values and range.

Building Math Vocabulary

Write the lesson vocabulary words and their definitions on the board.

Have students write the words and their definitions in their Math Journals. Ask them to include an example of each. Once they have completed Lesson 3-2, have them look back at their examples and make any corrections that may be needed.

Visual Vocabulary Cards

Use Visual Vocabulary Cards 24 and 26 to reinforce the vocabulary introduced in this lesson. (The Define/Example/Ask routine is printed on the back of each card.)

Differentiated Instruction

Small Group Options

LOGICAL

Option 1 Below Level BL

Materials: paper and pencil

- Hand students a piece of paper with the following scores written on it:

  75, 68, 75, 95, 84
- Tell students that Rafael received these scores on his spelling tests.
- Have students help Rafael find his median score. 75
- Then ask students to determine the mode and any outliers for Rafael's tests. 75; there are no outliers.

KINESTHETIC, SOCIAL

Option 2 English Language Learners ELL

Materials: notebook paper
Core Vocabulary: middle, more than once, different
Common Use Verb: is/are
Hear Math This strategy attaches movement with concept to make the math input more comprehensible to ELL students.

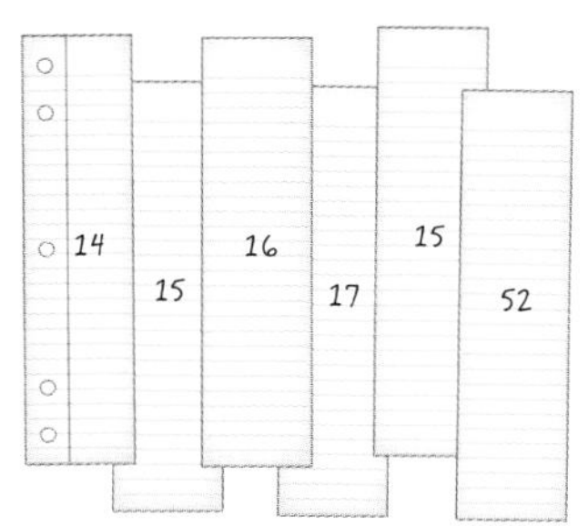

- Have students write a number between 10 and 20 so that it can be seen on a piece of paper and have the students line up.
- Say: "What number do you see **more than once**?" Identify this as the mode.
- Put the numbers in order. Say: "Which number is in the **middle**? This is the median."
- Have students find similarities between the sound and look of mode/more and middle/median.

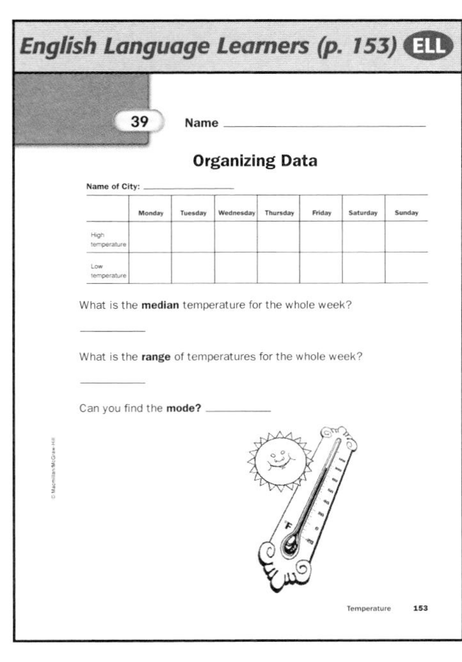

English Language Learners (p. 153) ELL

39 Name ____________

Organizing Data

Name of City: ____________

	Monday	Tuesday	Wednesday	Thursday	Friday	Saturday	Sunday
High temperature							
Low temperature							

What is the **median** temperature for the whole week?

____

What is the **range** of temperatures for the whole week?

____

Can you find the **mode?** ____________

© Macmillan/McGraw-Hill

Temperature 153

Use this worksheet to provide additional support for English Language Learners.

Independent Work Options

LOGICAL

Option 1 Early Finishers AL

Materials: index cards with sets of data written on them

- For each card, have students find the mode, median, and any outliers of the given data.
- Next, have students choose one card and write out a realistic problem or survey question for the set of data on the back. For example, if the set of data is 12, 5, 30, 28, 15, 18, 22, 1, 4, 9, 18, 6, the survey could have been the day of a month on which a person was born.

Option 2 Student Technology

Math Online macmillanmh.com

Personal Tutor • Extra Examples

 Math Adventures

Option 3 Learning Station: Science (p. 92I)

Direct students to the Science Learning Station for opportunities to explore and extend the lesson concept.

Option 4 Problem-Solving Practice

Reinforce problem-solving skills and strategies with the Problem-Solving Practice worksheet.

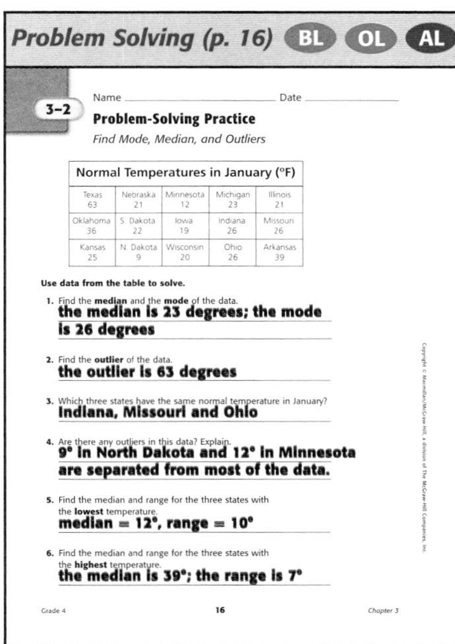

Problem Solving (p. 16) BL OL AL

3–2 Name ____________ Date ____________

Problem-Solving Practice

Find Mode, Median, and Outliers

Normal Temperatures in January (°F)				
Texas 63	Nebraska 21	Minnesota 12	Michigan 23	Illinois 21
Oklahoma 36	S. Dakota 22	Iowa 19	Indiana 26	Missouri 26
Kansas 25	N. Dakota 9	Wisconsin 20	Ohio 26	Arkansas 39

Use data from the table to solve.

1. Find the **median** and the **mode** of the data.
   the median is 23 degrees; the mode is 26 degrees
2. Find the **outlier** of the data.
   the outlier is 63 degrees
3. Which three states have the same normal temperature in January?
   Indiana, Missouri and Ohio
4. Are there any outliers in this data? Explain.
   9° in North Dakota and 12° in Minnesota are separated from most of the data.
5. Find the median and range for the three states with the **lowest** temperature.
   median = 12°, range = 10°
6. Find the median and range for the three states with the **highest** temperature.
   the median is 39°; the range is 7°

Copyright © Macmillan/McGraw-Hill, a division of The McGraw-Hill Companies, Inc.

Grade 4 16 Chapter 3

3-2 Find Mode, Median, and Outliers

1 Introduce

Activity Choice 1 • Hands-On

- Give each student 6 feet of ribbon. Tell each student to cut their ribbon to represent his or her height.
- Then have students arrange their ribbons according to height.
- Point out the mode (if there is one) and the median.
- Tell students that the mode and median of a data set tell us important information about the data set.

Activity Choice 2 • Literature

Introduce the lesson with *A Day's Work* by Eve Bunting. For a related math activity, see p. TR44.

2 Teach

Scaffolding Questions

To introduce the idea of outliers, ask students to consider the ribbons again. Introduce a new ribbon that is much taller than the others.

- **Does this change the mode?** no
- **Does this change the median?** Possibly. If there are several students of the same height in the middle of the group, then the median won't change.

GET READY to Learn

Have students read the information in **Get Ready to Learn**. Introduce **mode**, **median**, and **outlier**. As a class, work through **Examples 1 and 2**.

3-2 Find Mode, Median, and Outliers

MAIN IDEA

I will identify the mode, median, and outliers of a set of data.

New Vocabulary

mode
median
outlier

Math Online

macmillanmh.com
- Extra Examples
- Personal Tutor
- Self-Check Quiz

GET READY to Learn

The largest spider in the world is almost one foot long. Look at the table. Which spider's length appears most often? Which length is in the middle?

World's Largest Spiders	
Spider	**Length (in.)**
Goliath birdeater	11
Slate red ornamental	9
King baboon	8
Salmon pink birdeater	10
Colombian giant redleg	8

Source: *Scholastic Book of World Records*

The **mode** of a set of data is the number or numbers that occur(s) most often. If no number occurs more than once, there is no mode. The **median** is the number in the middle when the numbers have been arranged from least to greatest.

Real-World EXAMPLE — Identify Mode and Median

1 **SCIENCE Use the spider data above. What are the mode and the median of the data?**

To find the mode, find the number that occurs most often.

11, 9, 8, 10, 8 ← 8 appears twice.

So, the mode is 8.

To find the median, first arrange the numbers in order from least to greatest. Then, find the middle number.

8, 8, 9, 10, 11 ← 9 is the middle number.

So, the median is 9.

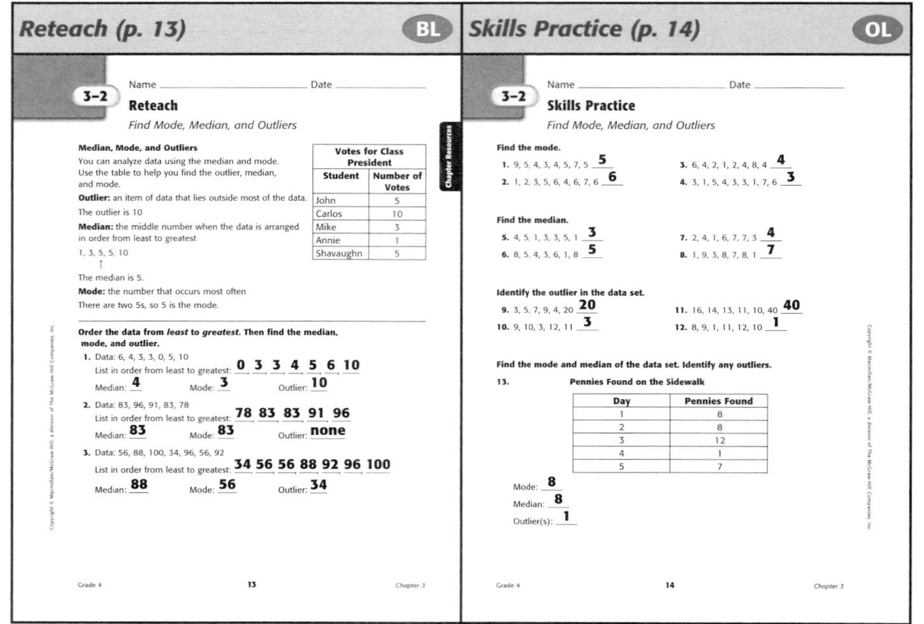

Reteach (p. 13) BL

3-2 Name ______ Date ______

Reteach

Find Mode, Median, and Outliers

Median, Mode, and Outliers

You can analyze data using the median and mode. Use the table to help you find the outlier, median, and mode.

Votes for Class President	
Student	**Number of Votes**
John	5
Carlos	10
Mike	3
Annie	1
Shavaughn	5

Outlier: an item of data that lies outside most of the data.

The outlier is 10

Median: the middle number when the data is arranged in order from least to greatest

1, 3, 5, 5, 10
↑

The median is 5.

Mode: the number that occurs most often

There are two 5s, so 5 is the mode.

Order the data from *least* to *greatest*. Then find the median, mode, and outlier.

1. Data: 6, 4, 3, 3, 0, 5, 10
   List in order from least to greatest: **0**, **3**, **3**, **4**, **5**, **6**, **10**
   Median: **4** Mode: **3** Outlier: **10**
2. Data: 83, 96, 91, 83, 78
   List in order from least to greatest: **78**, **83**, **83**, **91**, **96**
   Median: **83** Mode: **83** Outlier: **none**
3. Data: 56, 88, 100, 34, 96, 56, 92
   List in order from least to greatest: **34**, **56**, **56**, **88**, **92**, **96**, **100**
   Median: **88** Mode: **56** Outlier: **34**

Grade 4 13 Chapter 3

Skills Practice (p. 14) OL

3-2 Name ______ Date ______

Skills Practice

Find Mode, Median, and Outliers

Find the mode.

1. 9, 5, 4, 3, 4, 5, 7, 5 **5**
2. 1, 2, 3, 5, 6, 4, 6, 7, 6 **6**
3. 6, 4, 2, 1, 2, 4, 8, 4 **4**
4. 3, 1, 5, 4, 3, 3, 1, 7, 6 **3**

Find the median.

5. 4, 5, 1, 3, 3, 5, 1 **3**
6. 8, 5, 4, 3, 6, 1, 8 **5**
7. 2, 4, 1, 6, 7, 7, 3 **4**
8. 1, 9, 3, 8, 7, 8, 1 **7**

Identify the outlier in the data set.

9. 3, 5, 7, 9, 4, 20 **20**
10. 9, 10, 3, 12, 11 **3**
11. 16, 14, 13, 11, 10, 40 **40**
12. 8, 9, 1, 11, 12, 10 **1**

Find the mode and median of the data set. Identify any outliers.

13. **Pennies Found on the Sidewalk**

Day	Pennies Found
1	8
2	8
3	12
4	1
5	7

Mode: **8**
Median: **8**
Outlier(s): **1**

Grade 4 14 Chapter 3

An **outlier** is an item of data that is either much larger or much smaller than the rest of the data. A data set may not have outliers.

Remember
In some cases, when no numbers repeat in a data set, there is no mode. There can also be more than one mode.

Real-World EXAMPLE Identify Outliers

2 MOVIES What is the outlier of the data?

Movie Tickets Sold							
Day	Sun.	Mon.	Tues.	Wed.	Thurs.	Fri.	Sat.
Tickets	285	110	232	236	235	252	306

Look for the number that is either much larger or much smaller than the rest of the data items.

The number of tickets sold on Monday was 110. The number 110 is an outlier because it is much less than the other data items, which were between 235 and 306.

CHECK What You Know

Find the mode and median of the set of data. Identify any outliers. See Examples 1 and 2 (pp. 98–99) 2. no mode; 4; no outliers

1.

Shells Found on a Beach	
Name	**Shells Found**
Margo	9
Eva	7
Dani	9
Sondra	8
Louis	7

7 and 9; 8; no outliers

2.

Fish Caught While Camping	
Day	**Fish Caught**
Monday	3
Tuesday	6
Wednesday	2
Thursday	4
Friday	7

3.

Tall Mammals							
Mammal	Antelope	Camel	Gorilla	Giraffe	Okapi	Wallaby	Takin
Height (ft)	6	7	5	18	5	3	4

5; 5; outlier: 18

The table shows the time spent studying by 4th grade students each day.

Time Spent Studying					
Day	Mon.	Tues.	Wed.	Thurs.	Fri.
Time (min)	15	20	18	40	10

4. Identify the outlier. 40

5. 

Give a possible explanation for an outlier in this situation. Sample answer: There may have been a quiz or test on Friday for which the students had to study.

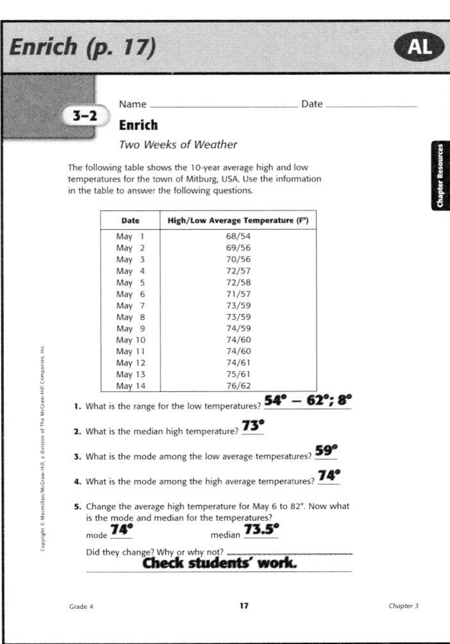

Enrich (p. 17) AL

3–2 Name ______________ Date ______________

Enrich

Two Weeks of Weather

The following table shows the 10-year average high and low temperatures for the town of Mitburg, USA. Use the information in the table to answer the following questions.

Date	High/Low Average Temperature (F°)
May 1	68/54
May 2	69/56
May 3	70/56
May 4	72/57
May 5	72/58
May 6	71/57
May 7	73/59
May 8	73/59
May 9	74/59
May 10	74/60
May 11	74/60
May 12	74/61
May 13	75/61
May 14	76/62

1. What is the range for the low temperatures? **54° – 62°; 8°**
2. What is the median high temperature? **73°**
3. What is the mode among the low average temperatures? **59°**
4. What is the mode among the high average temperatures? **74°**
5. Change the average high temperature for May 6 to 82°. Now what is the mode and median for the temperatures?
   mode **74°** median **73.5°**
   Did they change? Why or why not? **Check students' work.**

Chapter Resources

Grade 4 17 Chapter 3

Identify Outliers

Example 2 Point out to students that in many sets of data, there will be no outliers.

ADDITIONAL EXAMPLES

1. Find the mode and median of the following set of data: 8, 2, 3, 4, 9, 2, 4, 6, 5, 1, 4. 4; 4
2. Identify any outliers in the set of data: 12, 10, 20, 11, 9, 14, 12. 20

CHECK What You Know

As a class, have students complete Exercises 1–5 in **Check What You Know** as you observe their work.

Exercise 5 Assess student comprehension before assigning practice exercises.

BL Alternate Teaching Strategy

If students have trouble remembering to order the data to find the median…

Then use one of these reteach options:

1. CRM **Daily Reteach Worksheet** (p. 13)
2. Have students find the middle number of a set of data where the middle number in the unordered set of data is an outlier. They should clearly see that this number is not a good representative of the data. Once the data is in numerical order, show them that this middle number is the actual median.

Tips for New Teachers

You may wish to write this helpful hint for students on the board:

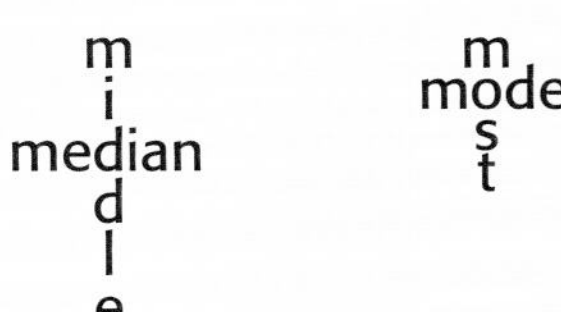

3 Practice

Differentiate practice using these leveled assignments for Exercises 6–18.

Level	Assignment
BL Below/Approaching Level	6–8, 10, 14–15
OL On Level	6–16, 17
AL Above/Beyond Level	8–16 even, 17–18

Have students discuss and complete the Higher Order Thinking problems. If students fail to find the error in Exercise 17, ask them what is the first thing that needs to be done with a set of data before finding the median.

WRITING IN MATH Have students complete Exercise 18 in their Math Journals. You may choose to use this exercise as an optional formative assessment.

COMMON ERROR!

Exercises 1 and 2 Students may have trouble identifying the mode. In Exercise 1, there are two modes, and in Exercise 2 there is no mode. Point out that a set of data can have many modes. Also, remind them that in some cases, no numbers repeat in the data set, so there is no mode.

Practice and Problem Solving

See page R7.

Find the mode and median of the set of data. Identify any outliers. See Examples 1 and 2 (pp. 98–99)

6.

Pints of Strawberries Sold	
Day	**Pints Sold**
Monday	18
Tuesday	14
Wednesday	11
Thursday	16
Friday	3

no mode 14; outlier: 3

7.

Faces Painted at a Fair	
Day	**Faces Painted**
Wednesday	8
Thursday	23
Friday	25
Saturday	24
Sunday	28

no mode; 24; outlier: 8

8.

Scores in Golf Tournament	
Player	**Scores**
Trisha	58
Marita	42
Aashi	64
Ted	49
Ciro	56

no mode; 56; no outlier

9.

Arts Festival Visitors	
Day	**Visitors**
Wednesday	46
Thursday	40
Friday	35
Saturday	12
Sunday	40

40; 40; outlier: 12

10.

Theme Park Ticket Prices							
Theme Park	A	B	C	D	E	F	G
Adult Ticket	$39	$59	$49	$45	$20	$50	$35

10. no mode, $45, outlier: $20 11. 45; 50; no outlier

11.

Average High Temperatures for Each Month (°F)							
Month	August	September	October	November	December	January	February
Temp. (°F)	85	78	68	50	45	42	45

12. Look at Exercise 10. What is the difference in cost of one adult ticket for parks C and G? $14

13. **Measurement** Look at Exercise 11. How much warmer was it in August than in September? 7°F

Real-World PROBLEM SOLVING

Science The table at the right shows the number of rings for five planets. 14. no mode; 6

14. Identify the mode and median of the data.

15. Identify the outlier. 1,000

16. How many more rings does Saturn have than Uranus? Neptune? 989; 994

Planets with Rings	
Planet	**Rings**
Uranus	11
Jupiter	1
Saturn	1,000
Neptune	6
Earth	0

Source: The Nine Planets

H.O.T. Problems

17. FIND THE ERROR Jasmine and Grady are finding the median of the data set 34, 51, 49, 27, and 38. Who is correct? Explain.

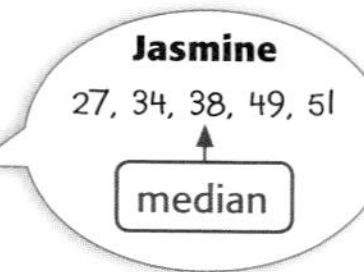

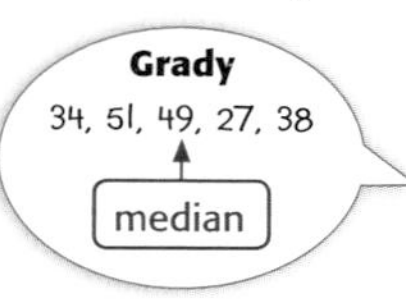

17, 18. See Ch. 4 Answer Appendix.

18. WRITING IN MATH Explain a way that you can remember the difference between median and mode.

TEST Practice

19. Which sentence best descibes the data? (Lesson 3-1) D

Favorite Animals	
Animal	**Number of Students**
Dolphin	𝍷𝍷𝍷𝍷
Elephant	𝍷𝍷
Lion	𝍸
Snake	𝍷𝍷𝍷

A Thirteen students were surveyed.

B Lions are the least popular.

C Elephants are most popular.

D Three students like snakes.

20. What is the median of the data set? (Lesson 3-2) H

Math Test Scores	
Student	**Score**
Angela	89
Carmen	93
Edgardo	85
Rafiq	78
Justin	89

F 78

G 85

H 89

J 93

Spiral Review

21. Miss Moore recorded the jersey sizes for the girls' volleyball team. Organize the information in a frequency table. (Lesson 3-1) See margin.

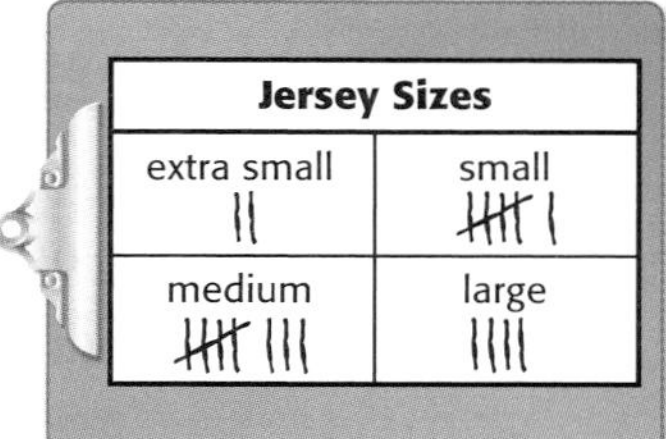

Jersey Sizes	
extra small 𝍷𝍷	small 𝍸𝍷
medium 𝍸𝍷𝍷𝍷	large 𝍷𝍷𝍷𝍷

22. Find the missing number in the equation 5,007 − 3,746 = ■. (Lesson 2-7) 1,261

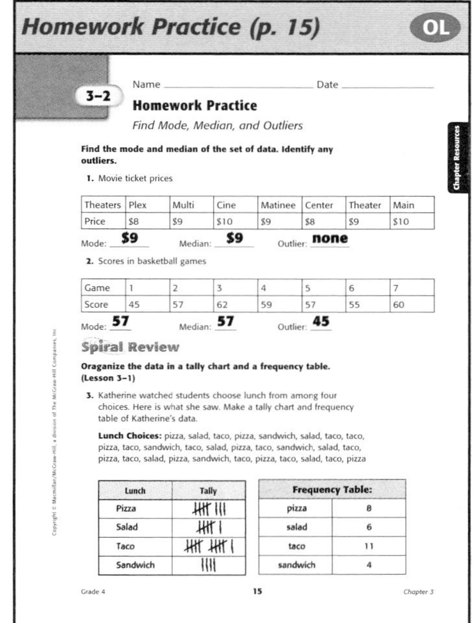

Homework Practice (p. 15) OL

3-2 Name ____________ Date ____________

Homework Practice

Find Mode, Median, and Outliers

Chapter Resources

Find the mode and median of the set of data. Identify any outliers.

1. Movie ticket prices

Theaters	Plex	Multi	Cine	Matinee	Center	Theater	Main
Price	$8	$9	$10	$9	$8	$9	$10

Mode: **$9** Median: **$9** Outlier: **none**

2. Scores in basketball games

Game	1	2	3	4	5	6	7
Score	45	57	62	59	57	55	60

Mode: **57** Median: **57** Outlier: **45**

Spiral Review

Oraganize the data in a tally chart and a frequency table. (Lesson 3–1)

3. Katherine watched students choose lunch from among four choices. Here is what she saw. Make a tally chart and frequency table of Katherine's data.

Lunch Choices: pizza, salad, taco, pizza, sandwich, salad, taco, taco, pizza, taco, sandwich, taco, salad, pizza, taco, sandwich, salad, taco, pizza, taco, salad, pizza, sandwich, taco, pizza, taco, salad, taco, pizza

Lunch	Tally
Pizza	𝍸𝍷𝍷𝍷
Salad	𝍸𝍷
Taco	𝍸𝍸𝍷
Sandwich	𝍷𝍷𝍷𝍷

Frequency Table:	
pizza	8
salad	6
taco	11
sandwich	4

Grade 4 15 Chapter 3

4 Assess

Formative Assessment

Provide the following list of ages of passengers on a boat trip. The seven passengers are 25, 28, 27, 26, 30, 2, and 2.

- Compute the median and the mode. 26; 2
- Explain which value better represents the data and why. The median of 26, because the mode is an outlier.

Quick Check **Are students continuing to struggle with finding median, mode and outliers?**

If Yes → Small Group Options (p. 130B)

If No → Independent Work Options (p. 130B)
CRM Skills Practice Worksheet (p. 14)
CRM Enrich Worksheet (p. 17)

Yesterday's News Ask students to write how learning about organizing data yesterday helped them learn about the median, mode, and outliers in today's lesson.

Reviews Lessons 3-1 and 3-2

Assign the Test Practice problems to provide daily reinforcement of test-taking skills.

Spiral Review

Reviews Lessons 2-7 and 3-1

Review and assess mastery of skills and concepts from previous chapters.

Additional Answer

21.

Jersey Sizes	
Size	**Number of Jerseys**
Extra small	2
Small	6
Medium	8
Large	4

3-3 Problem-Solving Strategy
Make a Table

Lesson Planner

Objective
Solve problems by making a table.

Resources
Materials: grid paper

Literature Connection: *A Day's Work* by Eve Bunting

Teacher Technology
TeacherWorks • Interactive Classroom

Real-World Problem Solving Library
Math and Science: *Americans On the Move*
Use these leveled books to reinforce and extend problem-solving skills and strategies.

Leveled for:
- OL On Level
- ELL Sheltered English
- SP Spanish

For additional support, see the Real-World Problem Solving Teacher Guide.

Daily Routine

Use these suggestions before beginning the lesson on p. 102.

5-Minute Check

(Reviews Lesson 3-2)

Find the median and mode of each set of data.

1. 12, 15, 10, 6, 15 median 12; mode 15
2. 5, 6, 4, 5, 7, 5, 2 median 5; mode 5

Find any outlier(s) of each set of data.

3. Ticket prices: \$52, \$46, \$62, \$57, \$22, \$49 \$22
4. Ages of team members: 9, 8, 10, 9, 8, 9, 20,10, 8 20

Problem of the Day

I am thinking of a number that is greater than 30, less than 40, and can be divided by both 3 and 6. What number is it? 36

Differentiated Instruction

Small Group Options

LOGICAL

Option 1 Below Level BL

Materials: paper and pencil

Give students a written copy of this problem:

A discount store gave $2 off for every $20 spent.

- *Emma's mother bought her some new clothes that cost $60. How much did they save?* $6
- *Ilan's family bought a table and chairs for $110. How much did they save? Show how you solved.*

Making a table is the easiest way to solve this problem. Since $110 is between $100 and $120, the answer is $11.

Amount Spent	20	40	60	80	100	120
Discount	2	4	6	8	10	12

INTRAPERSONAL, VISUAL

Option 2 English Language Learners ELL

Materials: art or manila paper

Core Vocabulary: table, eat, contents

Common Use Verb: recognize

See Math This strategy helps students recognize the word *table* and the context in which it is used.

- Explain that some words may have more than one meaning. *Table* is a word with more than one meaning.
- Show students a *table of contents*. Explain what it is used for.
- Show students a *math table*. Go over how it is used and how to figure out the *in* and *out* numbers.
- Have students fold their papers in 3 parts and illustrate a mathematical table, a table of contents, and a dining table.

Use this worksheet to provide additional support for English Language Learners.

English Language Learners (p. 189) **ELL**

51 Name ____________

Collecting Data

Write the names of five famous people.
Then tally the votes for each famous person.

Celebrities

Name of Famous Person	Tally

Which celebrity got the **most** votes?

Which celebrity got the **least** number of votes?

Tables and Graphs 189

Independent Work Options

LOGICAL

Option 1 Early Finishers OL AL

Materials: grid paper, recipe cards

- Each student selects a recipe. Have students make a table to show how many eggs (or another ingredient) will be needed to feed their class, their grade, or the whole school.
- Once students have calculated the number of eggs for their recipe, have them write a similar question for a classmate. For example, how much granola will be needed to make enough granola bars for the entire fourth grade?

Grandma's Eggs

6 eggs	hard cooked
1 tbsp.	light sour cream
1 tbsp.	light mayonnaise
3/4 tsp.	prepared mustard
1 tsp.	green relish
1/8 tsp.	onion powder
1/4 tsp.	sea salt (optional)
1/8 tsp.	pepper

Option 2 Student Technology

Tech Link

Math Online macmillanmh.com

Personal Tutor • Extra Examples

Option 3 Learning Station: Writing (p. 92I)

Direct students to the Writing Learning Station for opportunities to explore and extend the lesson concept.

3-3 Problem-Solving Strategy

1 Introduce

Activity Choice 1 • Review

- Ask students to solve this problem:

  A group of five friends had $11 to buy salads. Did they have enough money to each get a small salad? The problem can't be solved, as there is not enough information given.
- Ask students what information they need to solve the problem. Students need to know the price of the salads.
- Tell students that a small salad costs $2. Now have them answer the question. Yes, they have enough money.

Activity Choice 2 • Literature

Introduce the lesson with *A Day's Work* by Eve Bunting. For a related math activity, see p. TR44.

2 Teach

Have students read the problem on how many students are going to the concert. Guide them through the problem-solving steps.

Understand Using the questions, review what students know and need to find.

Plan Have them discuss their strategy.

Solve Guide students to use tables to solve the problem.

- **Since 2 teachers are going to the concert for every 9 students, if 4 teachers go, how many students are going? Explain.** 18; double each number
- **So if there are 16 teachers going, how many students are going to the concert?** 72

Check Have students look back at the problem to make sure that the answer fits the facts given.

COMMON ERROR!

Exercise 9 Call attention to the fact that Elki is paid every two weeks.

3-3 Problem-Solving Strategy

MAIN IDEA I will solve problems by making a table.

The music club at Steven's school is going to a concert. There are 2 teachers going to the concert for every 9 students going. If there are 16 teachers going, how many students are going to the concert?

Understand

What facts do you know?

- There are 2 teachers going for every 9 students going to the concert.
- The total number of teachers going is 16.

What do you need to find?

- Find how many students are going to the concert.

Plan

You can make a table to solve the problem.

Solve

Make a table to show that there are 2 teachers going for every 9 students going.

	+2	+2	+2	+2	+2	+2	+2
Teachers	2	4	6	8	10	12	14	16
Students	9	18	27	36	45	54	63	72

+9 +9 +9 +9 +9 +9 +9

So, 72 students are going to the concert.

Check

Divide the total number of teachers by the number of teachers per group.

$16 \div 2 = 8$

There are 8 groups. There are 9 students in each group. So, there are $8 \times 9 = 72$ students going altogether. The answer is correct. ✓

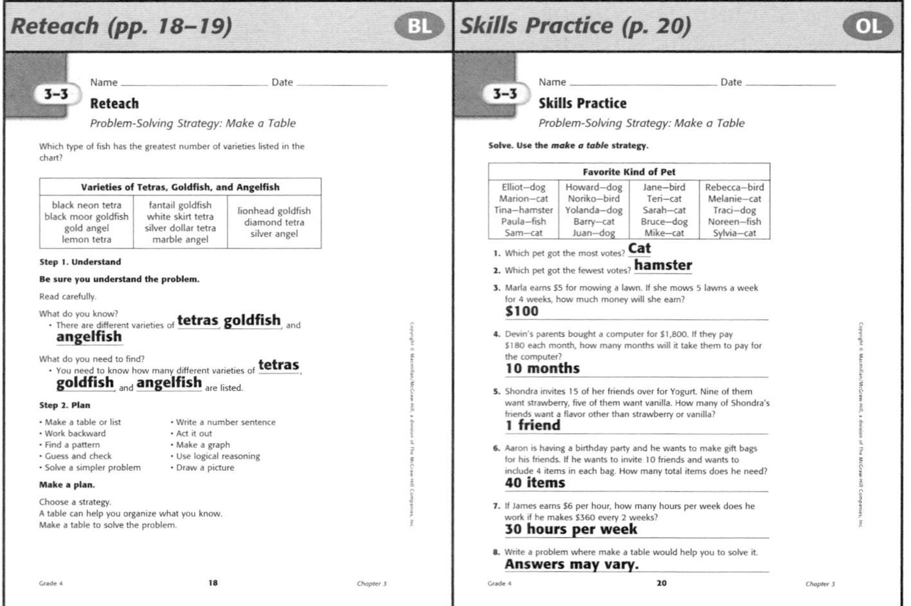

Reteach (pp. 18–19) BL

3–3 Name ______ Date ______

Reteach

Problem-Solving Strategy: Make a Table

Which type of fish has the greatest number of varieties listed in the chart?

Varieties of Tetras, Goldfish, and Angelfish		
black neon tetra black moor goldfish gold angel lemon tetra	fantail goldfish white skirt tetra silver dollar tetra marble angel	lionhead goldfish diamond tetra silver angel

Step 1. Understand

Be sure you understand the problem.

Read carefully.

What do you know?

- There are different varieties of **tetras**, **goldfish**, and **angelfish**

What do you need to find?

- You need to know how many different varieties of **tetras**, **goldfish**, and **angelfish** are listed.

Step 2. Plan

- Make a table or list
- Work backward
- Find a pattern
- Guess and check
- Solve a simpler problem
- Write a number sentence
- Act it out
- Make a graph
- Use logical reasoning
- Draw a picture

Make a plan.

Choose a strategy.
A table can help you organize what you know.
Make a table to solve the problem.

Grade 4 18 Chapter 3

Skills Practice (p. 20) OL

3–3 Name ______ Date ______

Skills Practice

Problem-Solving Strategy: Make a Table

Solve. Use the *make a table* strategy.

Favorite Kind of Pet			
Elliot–dog Marion–cat Tina–hamster Paula–fish Sam–cat	Howard–dog Noriko–bird Yolanda–dog Barry–cat Juan–dog	Jane–bird Teri–cat Sarah–cat Bruce–dog Mike–cat	Rebecca–bird Melanie–cat Traci–dog Noreen–fish Sylvia–cat

1. Which pet got the most votes? **Cat**
2. Which pet got the fewest votes? **hamster**
3. Marla earns $5 for mowing a lawn. If she mows 5 lawns a week for 4 weeks, how much money will she earn? **$100**
4. Devin's parents bought a computer for $1,800. If they pay $180 each month, how many months will it take them to pay for the computer? **10 months**
5. Shondra invites 15 of her friends over for Yogurt. Nine of them want strawberry, five of them want vanilla. How many of Shondra's friends want a flavor other than strawberry or vanilla? **1 friend**
6. Aaron is having a birthday party and he wants to make gift bags for his friends. If he wants to invite 10 friends and wants to include 4 items in each bag. How many total items does he need? **40 items**
7. If James earns $6 per hour, how many hours per week does he work if he makes $360 every 2 weeks? **30 hours per week**
8. Write a problem where make a table would help you to solve it. **Answers may vary.**

Grade 4 20 Chapter 3

ANALYZE the Strategy

Refer to the problem on the previous page. 1, 2, 4. See Ch. 3 Answer Appendix.

1. Explain how a table was used to find the number of students going to the concert.
2. What pattern is shown on the table?
3. Suppose 1 teacher was going for every 3 students. How many teachers would be going on the trip? Make a table. 24 teachers
4. Refer to Exercise 3. Check your answer. How do you know that it is correct?

★ indicates multi-step problem

PRACTICE the Strategy

See page R7.

Solve. Use the make a table strategy.

5. **Algebra** Kenya's school day is 6 hours long. Copy and complete the table to find if her school day is more or less than 300 minutes. more than 300 min

Hours	1	2	3	4	5	6
Minutes	60	120	■	■	■	■

180; 240; 300; 360

6. Malik buys a $2 lunch every day at school. How many lunches can Malik purchase for $17? 8 lunches
7. Martín sold some of his old toys on the Internet. The cost of shipping each item is shown. If he paid $32 in shipping, how many of his toys did he ship? 8 toys

★8. Jenna scored 24 points in her last basketball game. She made 2 baskets for every 5 shots she took. If one basket is equal to 2 points, how many shots did she take for the entire game? 30 shots

★9. Elki received her first paycheck from a job. She earns $150 every 2 weeks. How many weeks will it take her to earn more than $1,000? 14 wks

10. ★ The state sales tax is $7 for every $100 spent on certain items. Takara's mother is charged $21 in tax at the store. What was the total cost of all the items she purchased? $300

11. **Algebra** Don spends 40 minutes on homework every night. How many minutes of homework does he complete in 5 days? 200 min

Day	Total Homework Time (min)
Monday	40
Tuesday	80
Wednesday	120
Thursday	160 ■
Friday	200 ■

12. **WRITING IN MATH** Explain why the make a table strategy is a good problem-solving strategy to use for Exercise 10. See Ch. 3 Answer Appendix.

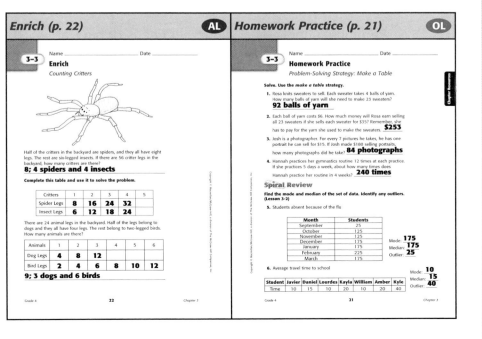

Enrich (p. 22) AL

3-3 Name ______ Date ______

Enrich

Counting Critters

Half of the critters in the backyard are spiders, and they all have eight legs. The rest are six-legged insects. If there are 56 critter legs in the backyard, how many critters are there?

8; 4 spiders and 4 insects

Complete this table and use it to solve the problem.

Critters	1	2	3	4	5
Spider Legs	**8**	**16**	**24**	**32**	
Insect Legs	**6**	**12**	**18**	**24**	

There are 24 animal legs in the backyard. Half of the legs belong to dogs and they all have four legs. The rest belong to two-legged birds. How many animals are there?

Animals	1	2	3	4	5	6
Dog Legs	**4**	**8**	**12**			
Bird Legs	**2**	**4**	**6**	**8**	**10**	**12**

9; 3 dogs and 6 birds

Grade 4 22 Chapter 3

Homework Practice (p. 21) OL

3-3 Name ______ Date ______

Homework Practice

Problem-Solving Strategy: Make a Table

Chapter Resources

Solve. Use the *make a table* strategy.

1. Rosa knits sweaters to sell. Each sweater takes 4 balls of yarn. How many balls of yarn will she need to make 23 sweaters? **92 balls of yarn**
2. Each ball of yarn costs $6. How much money will Rosa earn selling all 23 sweaters if she sells each sweater for $35? Remember, she has to pay for the yarn she used to make the sweaters. **$253**
3. Josh is a photographer. For every 7 pictures he takes, he has one portrait he can sell for $15. If Josh made $180 selling portraits, how many photographs did he take? **84 photographs**
4. Hannah practices her gymnastics routine 12 times at each practice. If she practices 5 days a week, about how many times does Hannah practice her routine in 4 weeks? **240 times**

Spiral Review

Find the mode and median of the set of data. Identify any outliers. (Lesson 3-2)

5. Students absent because of the flu

Month	Students
September	25
October	125
November	125
December	175
January	175
February	225
March	175

Mode: **175**
Median: **175**
Outlier: **25**

6. Average travel time to school

Student	Javier	Daniel	Lourdes	Kayla	William	Amber	Kyle
Time	10	15	10	20	10	20	40

Mode: **10**
Median: **15**
Outlier: **40**

Grade 4 21 Chapter 3

Analyze the Strategy Use Exercises 1–4 to analyze and discuss the problem-solving strategy.

BL Alternate Teaching Strategy

If students have trouble finding the patterns in the tables…

Then use one of these reteach options:

1. CRM **Daily Reteach Worksheet** (pp. 18–19)
2. Pose a simpler problem and help students make a table: **If Enrique's guitar lessons are twice a week, how many lessons does he have in 6 weeks?** 12

   Ask students to choose an activity they participate in at least once a week and have them calculate the number of times this activity will occur in 10 weeks.

3 Practice

Using the Exercises

Exercises 5–11 are assigned for students to practice making and using tables to solve.

Exercise 12 requires students to write an explanation.

4 Assess

Formative Assessment

Ask students to make a table to solve:
The Miller family drives to Tule Lake National Wildlife Refuge. For every 50 miles traveled, it takes one hour.

- **How far did they travel in 2 hours?** 100 mi
- **If the trip takes 4 hours in all, how far did they drive?** 200 mi

Quick Check **Are students continuing to struggle with making tables to solve problems?**

If Yes → Small Group Options (p. 98B)
Strategic Intervention Guide (p. 130)

If No → Independent Work Options (p. 98B)
CRM Skills Practice Worksheet (p. 20)
CRM Enrich Worksheet (p. 22)

LESSON 3-4

Line Plots

Lesson Planner

Objective

Represent and interpret data in a line plot.

Vocabulary

line plot

Resources

Materials: 9-foot long piece of paper, lined paper, index cards

Literature Connection: *Heat Wave* by Helen Ketteman

Teacher Technology

TeacherWorks • Interactive Classroom

Daily Routine

Use these suggestions before beginning the lesson on p. 104.

5-Minute Check

(Reviews Lesson 3-3)

Solve. Use the make a table strategy.

Jamilla is running laps around a track. She runs a lap in 4 minutes. If she runs for 24 minutes, how many laps has she run? How long would it take her to run 9 laps? 6 laps; 36 minutes

Problem of the Day

Pia eats an apple each weekday and a pear each weekend day. How many more apples than pears will she eat in three weeks? in four weeks? in five weeks? Describe the pattern that you see. 9, 12, 15; three more apples per week

Focus on Math Background

Once students survey, collect, and organize their data, they must find a way to display the data. Graphs are a logical choice. There are many types of graphs: pictographs, bar graphs, line plots, line graphs, etc. Graphs that show data groupings are usually called *plots*. A line plot is used to show the spread of the data. When you look at a line plot, you can quickly see the mode and identify any outliers. The mode is the number with the most Xs above it, and outliers appear as numbers that are separated from the clusters of Xs formed by the rest of the data.

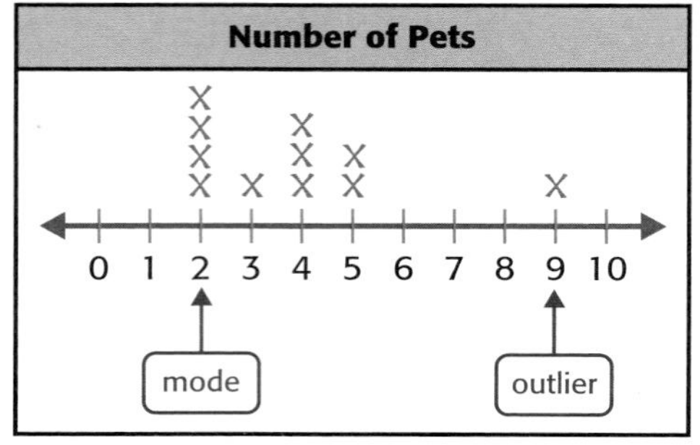

Building Math Vocabulary

Write the lesson vocabulary term and its definition on the board.

- Remind students what a number line is or have a volunteer come draw one on the board.
- Next, have students make a tally chart with Xs instead of tally marks. Ask students how many siblings each has.
- Have them record the class results in a tally table as described, then ask them to turn the table on its side as you draw the corresponding line plot.

Differentiated Instruction

Small Group Options

Option 1 Below Level BL

LOGICAL

Materials: paper, pencil

- Draw a line across the board and write the numbers 1 to 12 below the line.
- Ask students to come to the board and make an X above the number of the month in which they were born.
- **How many students were born in the 4th month? How many were born in June? How many students are represented in the data?** Answers will vary.
- Have students graph the results using a frequency table or tally charts.

Option 2 English Language Learners ELL

LOGICAL, SOCIAL

Core Vocabulary: at a glance, quickly, slowly
Common Use Verb: read
Write Math This strategy allows students to practice an integrate math and acquired language.

- Activate background knowledge by asking students what a book can give us and then explain that books give us information.
- Pass out varying amounts of money to students. Say, "How many pennies do you have?"
- Pass out index cards with an X on the card and draw a number line on the board to allow students to place an X above the number of pennies they have.
- While the students are plotting their quantities, write out sentences describing the line plot and fold into a book (see book fold, foldables).
- Tell them that both the line plot and the book have the same information.
- Ask which form they can read quickly and which one they have to read slowly. Discuss.

Independent Work Options

Option 1 Early Finishers AL

LOGICAL

Materials: pencil, paper

- Provide students with the following example and corresponding line plot.
- Have students make up and write a set of clues to be used in a line plot.
- Have students challenge classmates to solve their problem.

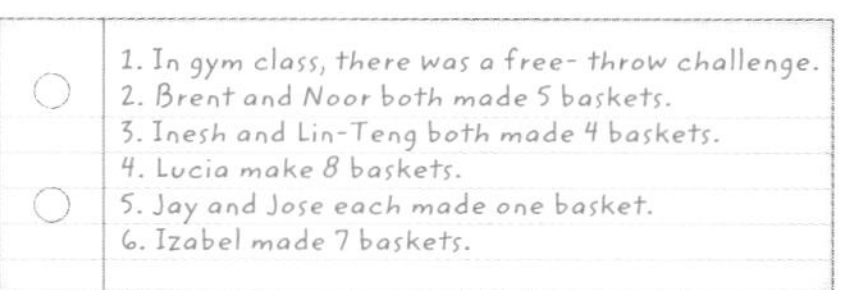
1. In gym class, there was a free- throw challenge.
2. Brent and Noor both made 5 baskets.
3. Inesh and Lin-Teng both made 4 baskets.
4. Lucia make 8 baskets.
5. Jay and Jose each made one basket.
6. Izabel made 7 baskets.

Option 2 Student Technology

Math Online macmillanmh.com

Personal Tutor • Extra Examples

Math Adventures

Option 3 Learning Station: Health (p. 92J)

Direct students to the Health Learning Station for opportunities to explore and extend the lesson concept.

Option 4 Problem-Solving Practice

Reinforce problem-solving skills and strategies with the Problem-Solving Practice worksheet.

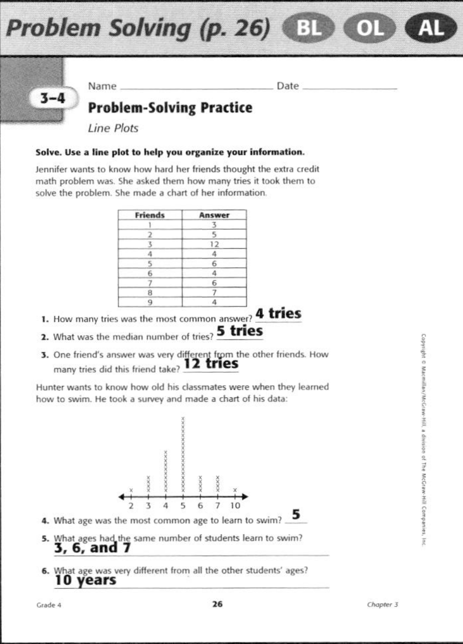
Problem Solving (p. 26) BL OL AL

3–4

Name ______________ Date ______________

Problem-Solving Practice

Line Plots

Solve. Use a line plot to help you organize your information.

Jennifer wants to know how hard her friends thought the extra credit math problem was. She asked them how many tries it took them to solve the problem. She made a chart of her information.

Friends	Answer
1	3
2	5
3	12
4	4
5	6
6	4
7	6
8	7
9	4

1. How many tries was the most common answer? **4 tries**
2. What was the median number of tries? **5 tries**
3. One friend's answer was very different from the other friends. How many tries did this friend take? **12 tries**

Hunter wants to know how old his classmates were when they learned how to swim. He took a survey and made a chart of his data:

4. What age was the most common age to learn to swim? **5**
5. What ages had the same number of students learn to swim? **3, 6, and 7**
6. What age was very different from all the other students' ages? **10 years**

Grade 4 26 Chapter 3

3-4 Line Plots

1 Introduce

Activity Choice 1 • Hands-On

- Draw and display a number line on a 9-foot long piece of paper with the numbers 1–9 evenly spaced.
- Give each student an index card with a large X on it. Ask them to tape their cards, one above another, over their favorite number. Explain the concept of a line plot, pointing out that line plots are labeled with numbers instead of words. Line plots include every number written in order even if no data exists for some of the numbers. The least and greatest numbers included in a line plot should fit the data being displayed.

Activity Choice 2 • Literature

Introduce the lesson with *Heat Wave* by Helen Ketteman. For a related math activity, see p. TR44.

2 Teach

Scaffolding Questions

Ask students to interpret the results of the data from Activity Choice 1.

- **What is the mode?** Answers will vary depending on class results; it will be the most popular number.
- **What does the mode represent?** the most popular number
- **Identify the median of the data set.** Answers will vary depending on class results; it will be the middle number.

GET READY to Learn

Have students open their books and read the information in **Get Ready to Learn**. Introduce **line plot**. As a class, work through **Examples 1 and 2**.

3-4 Line Plots

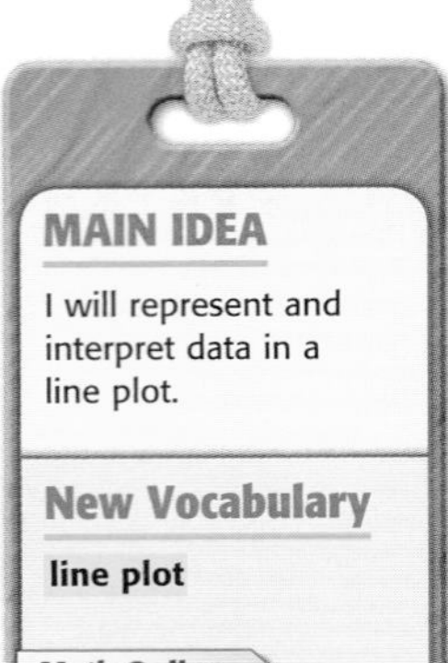

MAIN IDEA

I will represent and interpret data in a line plot.

New Vocabulary

line plot

Math Online

macmillanmh.com

- Extra Examples
- Personal Tutor
- Self-Check Quiz

GET READY to Learn

Vijay went camping in Pennsylvania Wilds. He recorded the number of elk he saw in a tally chart.

Elk Observed	
Day	**Tally**
Monday	𝍷𝍷
Tuesday	𝍸
Wednesday	𝍷𝍷𝍷𝍷
Thursday	𝍷𝍷
Friday	𝍷𝍷𝍷𝍷
Saturday	𝍸 𝍷𝍷
Sunday	𝍷𝍷

You have used tally charts and frequency tables to show data. A **line plot** is a way to show data using Xs above a number line.

Real-World EXAMPLE Make a Line Plot

1 **SCIENCE** **Represent Vijay's elk data in a line plot.**

Step 1 Draw and label a number line.

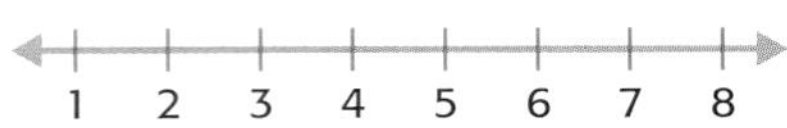

Step 2 Mark an X above the number line to show each data item. Add a title.

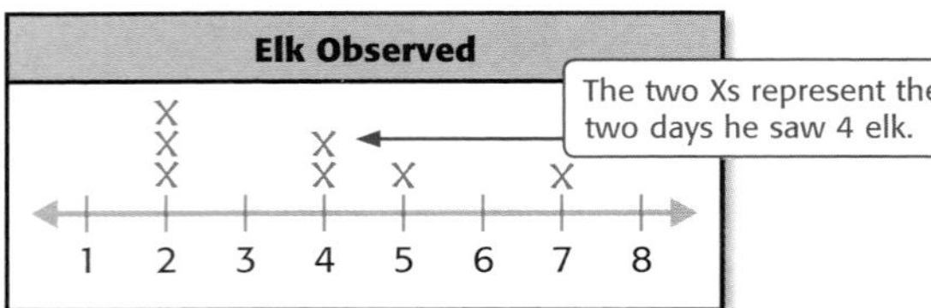

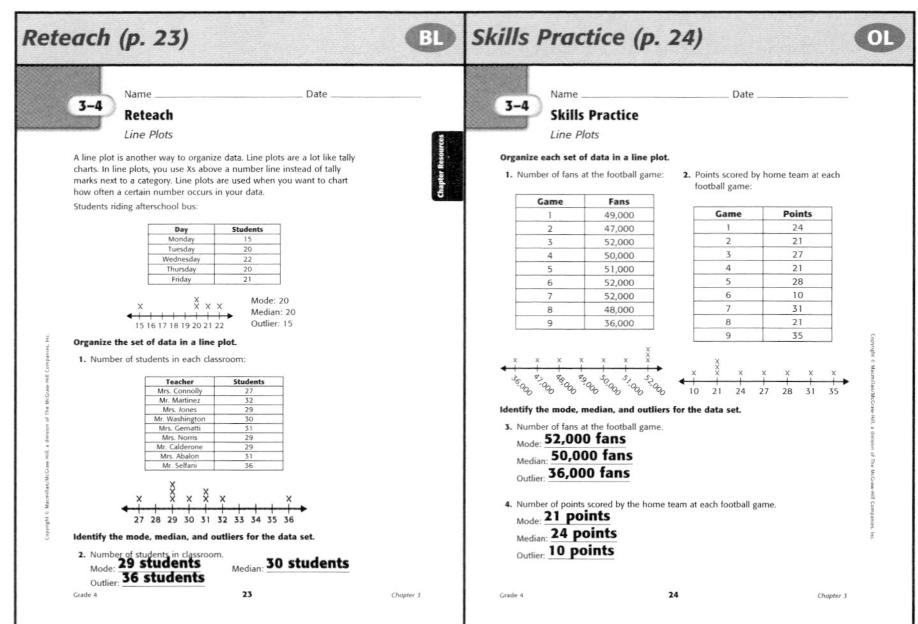

Reteach (p. 23) BL

3–4 Name ______ Date ______

Reteach

Line Plots

A line plot is another way to organize data. Line plots are a lot like tally charts. In line plots, you use Xs above a number line instead of tally marks next to a category. Line plots are used when you want to chart how often a certain number occurs in your data.

Students riding afterschool bus:

Day	Students
Monday	15
Tuesday	20
Wednesday	22
Thursday	20
Friday	21

15 16 17 18 19 20 21 22

Mode: 20
Median: 20
Outlier: 15

Organize the set of data in a line plot.

1. Number of students in each classroom:

Teacher	Students
Mrs. Connolly	27
Mr. Martinez	32
Mrs. Jones	29
Mr. Washington	30
Mrs. Gematti	31
Mrs. Norris	29
Mr. Calderone	29
Mrs. Abalon	31
Mr. Selfani	36

27 28 29 30 31 32 33 34 35 36

Identify the mode, median, and outliers for the data set.

2. Number of students in classroom.
Mode: **29 students** Median: **30 students**
Outlier: **36 students**

Grade 4 23 Chapter 3

Chapter Resources

Skills Practice (p. 24) OL

3–4 Name ______ Date ______

Skills Practice

Line Plots

Organize each set of data in a line plot.

1. Number of fans at the football game:

Game	Fans
1	49,000
2	47,000
3	52,000
4	50,000
5	51,000
6	52,000
7	52,000
8	48,000
9	36,000

36,000 47,000 48,000 49,000 50,000 51,000 52,000

2. Points scored by home team at each football game:

Game	Points
1	24
2	21
3	27
4	21
5	28
6	10
7	31
8	21
9	35

10 21 24 27 28 31 35

Identify the mode, median, and outliers for the data set.

3. Number of fans at the football game.
Mode: **52,000 fans**
Median: **50,000 fans**
Outlier: **36,000 fans**

4. Number of points scored by the home team at each football game.
Mode: **21 points**
Median: **24 points**
Outlier: **10 points**

Grade 4 24 Chapter 3

You can also read a line plot to answer questions about the data.

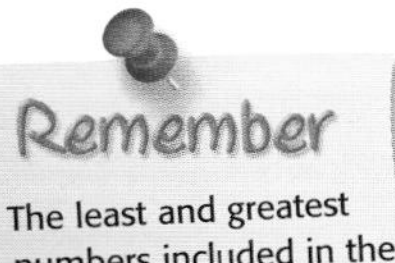

The least and greatest numbers included in the line plot should fit the data being displayed.

Real-World EXAMPLE Read a Line Plot

2 **READING** **Bianca's class took part in a reading competition. The results are shown below. Identify the mode, median, and any outliers for the data set.**

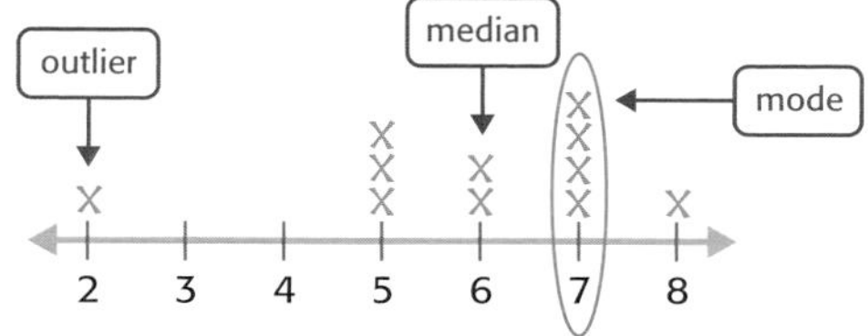

So, the mode is 7, the median is 6, and 2 is an outlier.

★ indicates multi-step problem

CHECK What You Know

Organize each set of data in a line plot. See Example 1 (p. 104)

1.

Ages of Students			
11	11	10	12
10	11	11	11
10	11	11	10

2.

Time Spent on Chores	
Student	**Time (hr)**
Mac	3
Julio	1
Tala	2
Peyton	3

1, 2. See Ch. 3 Answer Appendix.

Identify the mode, median, and any outliers for each data set. See Example 2 (p. 105)

3.

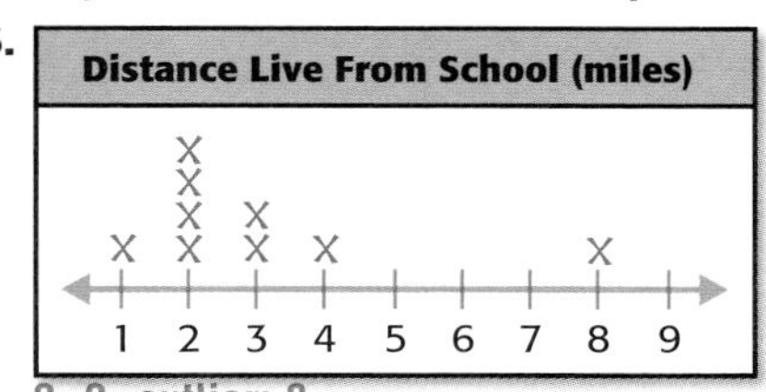

2, 2, outlier: 8

4.

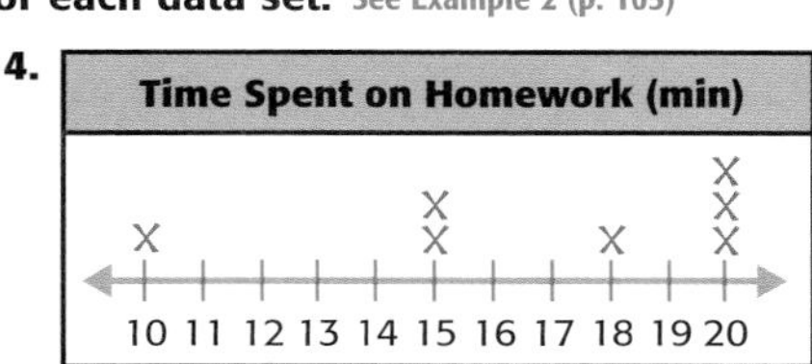

20, 18, outlier: 10

The line plot shows weekly allowances.

Friends' Allowances

$5 $6 $7 $8 $9 $10

5. What is the most money a person receives? $10

6. Talk About It Sumi's weekly allowance is $4. Should she use the line plot to convince her parents to increase her allowance? Explain. yes; Her friends receive more money.

Enrich (p. 27) AL

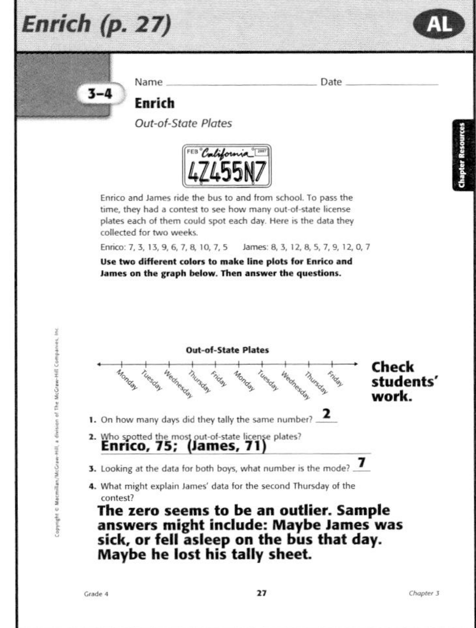
3-4 Name ______ Date ______

Enrich

Out-of-State Plates

Enrico and James ride the bus to and from school. To pass the time, they had a contest to see how many out-of-state license plates each of them could spot each day. Here is the data they collected for two weeks.

Enrico: 7, 3, 13, 9, 6, 7, 8, 10, 7, 5   James: 8, 3, 12, 8, 5, 7, 9, 12, 0, 7

Use two different colors to make line plots for Enrico and James on the graph below. Then answer the questions.

Out-of-State Plates

Monday Tuesday Wednesday Thursday Friday Monday Tuesday Wednesday Thursday Friday

Check students' work.

1. On how many days did they tally the same number? **2**
2. Who spotted the most out-of-state license plates? **Enrico, 75; (James, 71)**
3. Looking at the data for both boys, what number is the mode? **7**
4. What might explain James' data for the second Thursday of the contest? **The zero seems to be an outlier. Sample answers might include: Maybe James was sick, or fell asleep on the bus that day. Maybe he lost his tally sheet.**

Grade 4 27 Chapter 3

Read a Line Plot

Example 2 Tell students they can identify the mode on a line plot by finding the tallest column of Xs. Remind them that an outlier is a piece of data that lies outside of the data.

ADDITIONAL EXAMPLES

1 Organize the information below in a line plot. Check students' line plots.

Miles hiked on a weeklong camping trip.			
Day	**Miles Hiked**	**Day**	**Miles Hiked**
Sat.	2	Wed.	2
Sun.	4	Thurs.	8
Mon.	5	Fri.	5
Tues.	0		

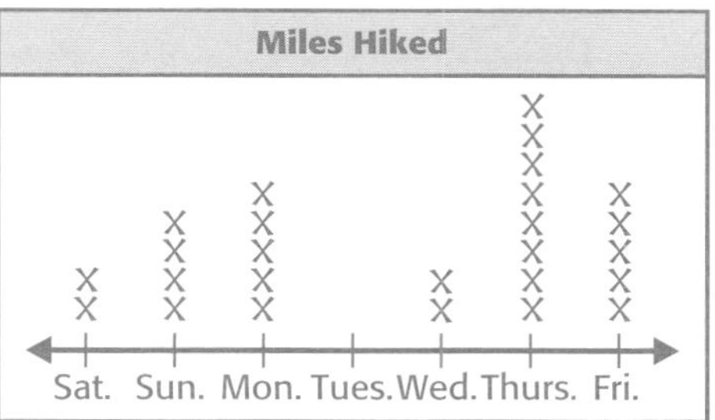

2 Identify the mode, median, and outliers of the data shown.

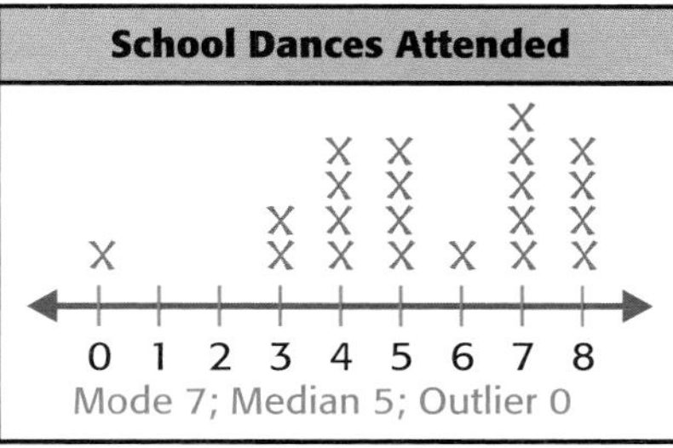

Mode 7; Median 5; Outlier 0

CHECK What You Know

As a class, have students complete Exercises 1–6 in **Check What You Know** as you observe their work.

Exercise 6 Assess student comprehension before assigning practice exercises.

BL Alternate Teaching Strategy

If students have trouble making a line plot…

Then use one of these reteach options:

1 CRM **Daily Reteach Worksheet** (p. 23)

2 Allow students to make their line plots on lined paper and turn the lined paper sideways to use the lines as a guide for drawing Xs.

3 Practice

Differentiate practice using these leveled assignments for Exercises 7–17.

Level	Assignment
BL Below/Approaching Level	7, 9, 11, 13–14
OL On Level	7–9, 11–13, 15
AL Above/Beyond Level	7–15 odd, 16–17

Have students discuss and complete the Higher Order Thinking problems. For Exercise 16, have students brainstorm a list of survey questions before they begin.

WRITING IN MATH Have students complete Exercise 17 in their Math Journals. You may choose to use this exercise as an optional formative assessment.

COMMON ERROR!

Exercise 17 Watch for students who make up a question that can be answered "yes" or "no." Suggest that the survey questions have at least four possible answers.

Practice and Problem Solving

See page R7.

Organize each set of data in a line plot. See Example 1 (p. 104) 7–10. See Ch. 3 Answer App

7.

Crickets Caught	
Day	**Crickets**
Monday	6
Tuesday	3
Wednesday	8
Thursday	6
Friday	6

8.

Test Scores	
Student	**Score**
Darin	95
Janna	91
Grace	90
Arnoldo	95
Lali	86

9.

Points Scored per Game			
4	4	6	10
8	3	4	5
6	5	2	4

10.

Magazine Subsciptions Sold			
12	15	9	16
11	10	12	8
15	11	10	11

Identify the mode, median, and any outliers for each data set. See Example 2 (p. 105)

11. Shoe Sizes

4 5 6 7 8 9 10 11

4 and 6; 6; outlier: 11

12.

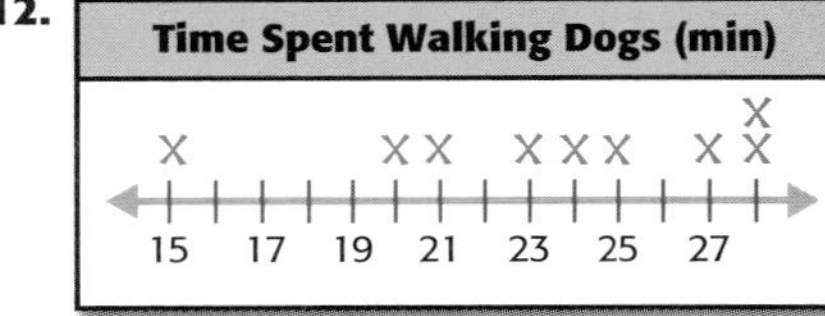

28; 24; outlier: 15

13.

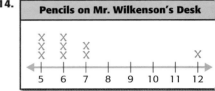

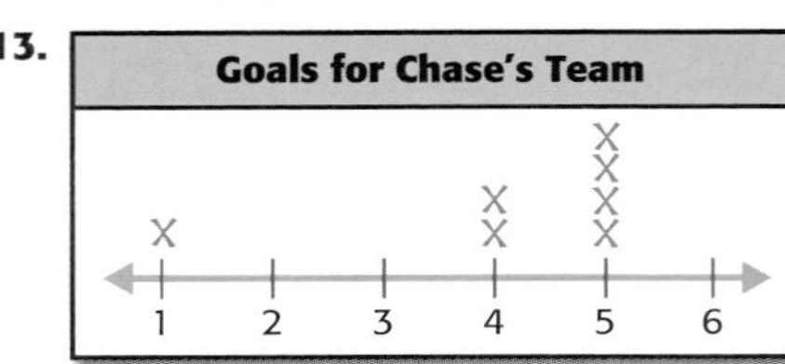

5; 5; outlier: 1

14. Pencils on Mr. Wilkenson's Desk

5 6 7 8 9 10 11 12

5 and 6; 6; outlier: 12

Real-World PROBLEM SOLVING

Measurement Mr. Simmons recorded the height of each player on his basketball team.

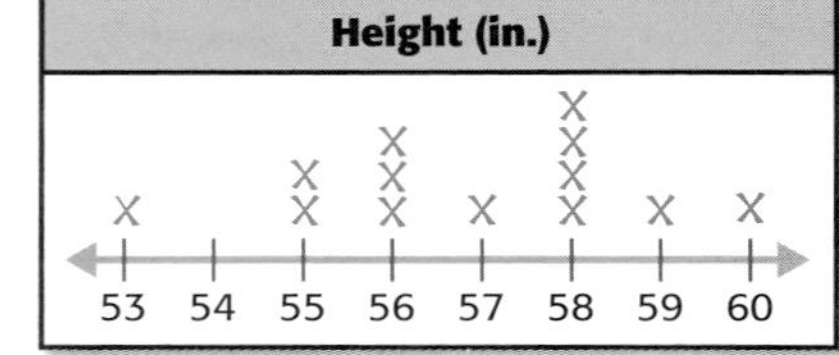

15. How many players are 58 inches tall? 4

16. ★ The median height of the Los Angeles Clippers is 80 inches. Compare this height to the median height of the players on Mr. Simmons's team. See Ch. 3 Answer Appendix.

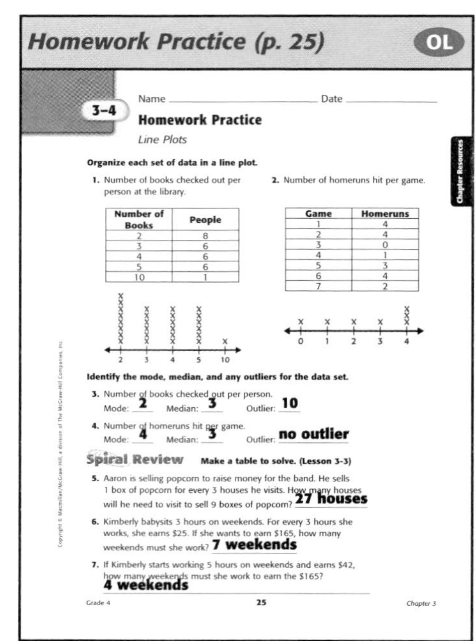

Homework Practice (p. 25) OL

3–4

Name ______ Date ______

Homework Practice

Line Plots

Organize each set of data in a line plot.

1. Number of books checked out per person at the library.

Number of Books	People
2	8
3	6
4	6
5	6
10	1

2. Number of homeruns hit per game.

Game	Homeruns
1	4
2	4
3	0
4	1
5	3
6	4
7	2

Identify the mode, median, and any outliers for the data set.

3. Number of books checked out per person.
Mode: **2** Median: **3** Outlier: **10**

4. Number of homeruns hit per game.
Mode: **4** Median: **3** Outlier: **no outlier**

Spiral Review **Make a table to solve. (Lesson 3-3)**

5. Aaron is selling popcorn to raise money for the band. He sells 1 box of popcorn for every 3 houses he visits. How many houses will he need to visit to sell 9 boxes of popcorn? **27 houses**

6. Kimberly babysits 3 hours on weekends. For every 3 hours she works, she earns $25. If she wants to earn $165, how many weekends must she work? **7 weekends**

7. If Kimberly starts working 5 hours on weekends and earns $42, how many weekends must she work to earn the $165? **4 weekends**

H.O.T. Problems

17. OPEN ENDED Create a survey question to ask your classmates. Ask your question. Collect and represent the data on a line plot. See students' work.

18. WRITING IN MATH How would the median change if the lowest score in Exercise 8 was replaced with 93? Sample answer: The median would increase to 93.

TEST Practice

19. What is the median of the data shown in the frequency table below? (Lesson 3-2) C

Garden Vegetables	
Vegetable	**Frequency**
Carrots	49
Celery	25
Cucumbers	28
Lettuce	32
Onions	44

A 49 **C** 32

B 44 **D** 28

20. What is the mode of the data shown on the line plot? (Lesson 3-4) G

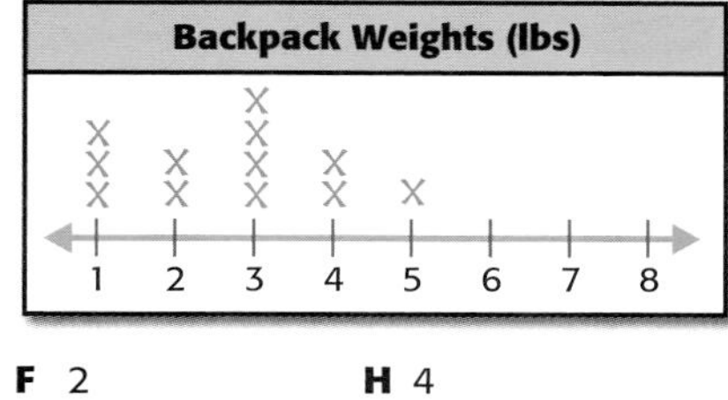

F 2 **H** 4

G 3 **J** 8

Spiral Review

21. There are eight hamburger buns in a package. How many packages of hamburger buns should Mr. Green buy to make 43 hamburgers? (Lesson 3-3) 6 packages

For Exercises 22–24, use the table to the right. It lists the items in Ella's school supply box. (Lesson 3-2)

Ella's School Supply Box	
Supply	**Frequency**
Crayons	36
Erasers	5
Glue	1
Pencils	7
Scissors	1

22. Find the mode of the set of data. 1

23. Find the median of the set of data. 5

24. Identify any outliers in the set of data. 36

4 Assess

Formative Assessment

Make a line plot of the number of pets owned by Kalila and her friends: 0, 1, 3, 2, 1, 9, 3, 2, 1

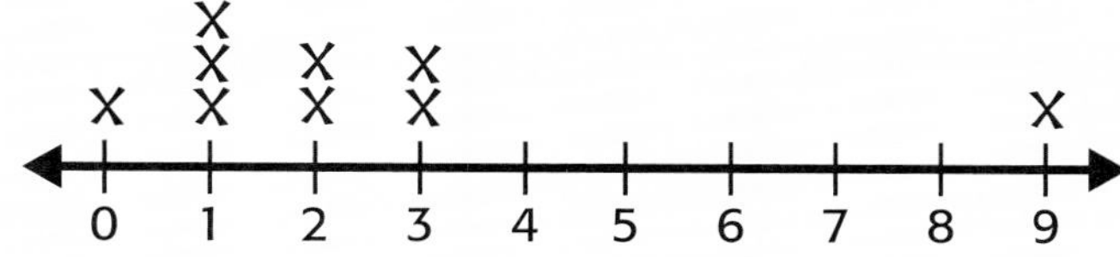

- **Identify the mode.** 1
- **Identify the median.** 2

Quick Check **Are students continuing to struggle with line plots?**

If Yes → Small Group Options (p. 136B)

If No → Independent Work Options (p. 136B)
CRM Skills Practice Worksheet (p. 24)
CRM Enrich Worksheet (p. 27)

Into the Future Ask students to write about how what they learned today about line plots will help them in tomorrow's lesson on bar graphs and double bar graphs.

TEST Practice

Reviews Lessons 3-2 and 3-4

Assign the Test Practice problems to provide daily reinforcement of test-taking skills.

Spiral Review

Reviews Lessons 3-2 and 3-3

Review and assess mastery of skills and concepts from previous chapters.

LESSON 3-5

Bar Graphs

Lesson Planner

Objective

Interpret a bar graph.

Vocabulary

bar graph

Resources

Materials: newspapers, magazines, scissors, paper, pencil

Literature Connection: *Tiger Math: Learning to Graph from a Baby Tiger* by Ann Whitehead Nagda and Cindy Bickel

Alternate Lesson: Use *IMPACT Mathematics:* Unit I to provide practice with bar graphs.

Teacher Technology
TeacherWorks • Interactive Classroom

Daily Routine

Use these suggestions before beginning the lesson on p. 108.

5-Minute Check

(Reviews Lesson 3-4)

Identify the mode, median, and outlier for each data set.

1. 2, 3, 3, 5, 8, 9, 22 mode: 3; median: 5; outlier: 22
2. 0, 12, 14, 12, 15 mode: 12; median: 12; outlier: 0

Problem of the Day

The elevation of Mt. Everest in Asia is 29,035 feet. The elevation of Mt. McKinley in Alaska is 20,320 feet. How much higher is Mt. Everest than Mt. McKinley? 8,715 ft

Focus on Math Background

Single bar graphs use solid bars of different lengths to represent data. This type of graph allows you to compare quantities at a glance. They are best used with the data that are qualitative, such as colors, activities, foods, animals, etc. In Grade 3, students learned to compare the lengths of bars to identify and compare the largest and smallest quantities represented in a bar graph. In this lesson, they perform more sophisticated comparisons. Since bar lengths are proportional to the sizes of the quantities they represent, knowledge of ratio can be used to estimate relative amounts displayed in the graphs. Adding up the amounts represented by several bars provides answers to questions such as "How many in the class are taller than (or shorter than) 48 inches?"

Building Math Vocabulary

Write the lesson vocabulary term and its definition on the board.

Have students write the new term in their Math Journals. Brainstorm where students have seen bar graphs used in real life. Have a volunteer record the responses on the board. Discuss how bar graphs help you interpret data.

Visual Vocabulary Cards

Use Visual Vocabulary Card 4 to reinforce the vocabulary introduced in this lesson. (The Define/Example/Ask routine is printed on the back of each card.)

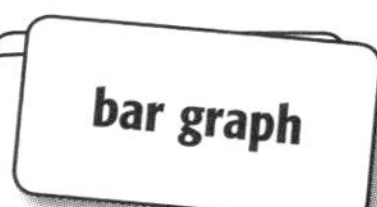

Differentiated Instruction

Small Group Options

Option 1 Below Level BL

LOGICAL

Materials: centimeter grid paper, chart paper, markers, pencils

- Copy the following information on the chart paper: robins 5, blue jays 8, cardinals 4, chickadees 7
- Tell the students that their task is to make a bar graph of the data gathered while watching the birds in the yard.
- Remind them that they need to include a title, labels on both axes, and numbers that work well for the data given.
- Early finishers can write a question for others in the group that can only be answered by using the bar graph they have created.

Option 2 English Language Learners ELL

LINGUISTIC

Materials: various number lines, bar graphs, and line graphs
Core Vocabulary: this graph, we can see, it tells us
Common Use Verb: shows

Talk Math This strategy uses cooperative work to shelter student vocalization and understanding of bar graphs.

- Divide students into pairs.
- Give each group a different type of graph and list core vocabulary.
- Prompt the groups with the following question: "What can you and your partner see from your **graph**? Write about what the information **tells us**."
- Ask each group to talk about the information to the class.

Independent Work Options

Option 1 Early Finishers AL

VISUAL/LOGICAL

Materials: newspapers, magazines, scissors, paper, pencil

- Students search print media to find and record an example of how bar graphs are used in real life.
- If possible, students cut out the bar graph for display. Otherwise, they trace the bar graph.
- Students write three word problems about the bar graph.
- Allow students to display the bar graph and challenge classmates to answer the questions.

Option 2 Student Technology

Math Online macmillanmh.com

Personal Tutor • Extra Examples

Option 3 Learning Station: Social Studies

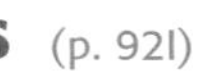

(p. 92I)

Direct students to the Social Studies Learning Station for opportunities to explore and extend the lesson concept.

Option 4 Problem-Solving Practice

Reinforce problem-solving skills and strategies with the Problem-Solving Practice worksheet.

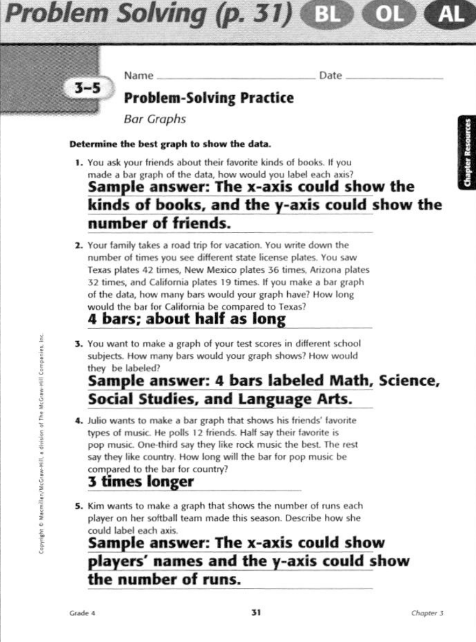

Problem Solving (p. 31) BL OL AL

3–5

Name ________________ Date ________________

Problem-Solving Practice

Bar Graphs

Chapter Resources

Determine the best graph to show the data.

1. You ask your friends about their favorite kinds of books. If you made a bar graph of the data, how would you label each axis?
Sample answer: The x-axis could show the kinds of books, and the y-axis could show the number of friends.

2. Your family takes a road trip for vacation. You write down the number of times you see different state license plates. You saw Texas plates 42 times, New Mexico plates 36 times, Arizona plates 32 times, and California plates 19 times. If you make a bar graph of the data, how many bars would your graph have? How long would the bar for California be compared to Texas?
4 bars; about half as long

3. You want to make a graph of your test scores in different school subjects. How many bars would your graph shows? How would they be labeled?
Sample answer: 4 bars labeled Math, Science, Social Studies, and Language Arts.

4. Julio wants to make a bar graph that shows his friends' favorite types of music. He polls 12 friends. Half say their favorite is pop music. One-third say they like rock music the best. The rest say they like country. How long will the bar for pop music be compared to the bar for country?
3 times longer

5. Kim wants to make a graph that shows the number of runs each player on her softball team made this season. Describe how she could label each axis.
Sample answer: The x-axis could show players' names and the y-axis could show the number of runs.

Grade 4 31 Chapter 3

3-5 Bar Graphs

1 Introduce

Activity Choice 1 • Hands-On

- Make a tally chart that shows these five types of music: jazz, Latin, country, pop, rock and roll.
- Have students vote by raising a hand to show which type of music they prefer. Have a volunteer record the information in the tally chart.
- Have another volunteer make a frequency table from the tally chart. **Which kind of music is preferred? Which kind is least preferred?** Answers will vary.
- **How do you think we can visually represent this data?** in a graph

Activity Choice 2 • Literature

Introduce the lesson with *Tiger Math: Learning to Graph from a Baby Tiger* by Ann Whitehead Nagda and Cindy Bickel. For a related math activity, see p. TR45.

2 Teach

Scaffolding Questions

Use the data from Activity Choice 1 to create a bar graph. Do not put the titles on the graph, the horizontal axis, or the vertical axis.

- Have students look at the horizontal axis. **What label would you give this axis?** Sample answer: Types of Music
- Have students look at the vertical axis. **What label would you give this axis?** Sample answer: Number of Students
- **What label would you give the graph?** Sample answer: Favorite Type of Music Write all labels on the graph.
- Point out the highest bar on the graph. **What do you think this bar represents?** Sample answer: the type of music most students prefer

GET READY to Learn

Have students open their books and read the information in **Get Ready to Learn.** Introduce **bar graph.** As a class, work through **Examples 1 and 2.**

3-5 Bar Graphs

MAIN IDEA

I will interpret a bar graph.

New Vocabulary

bar graph

Math Online

macmillanmh.com
- Extra Examples
- Personal Tutor
- Self-Check Quiz

GET READY to Learn

The students in Mrs. Smith's class measured their heights in inches. What was the most common height?

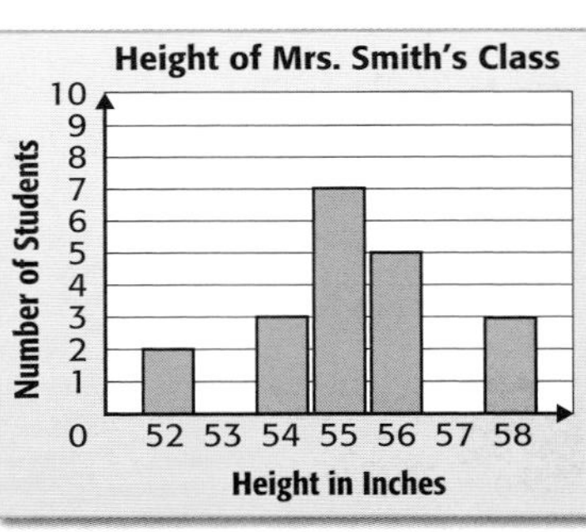

A **bar graph** is used to compare data by using bars of different heights to represent values. You can interpret data that is displayed in a bar graph.

EXAMPLE Interpret a Bar Graph

1 **MEASUREMENT** **What was the most common height?**

The longest bar represents the height of the most students.

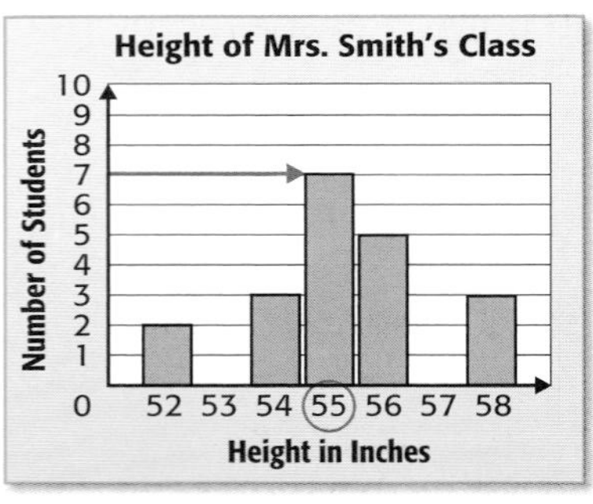

So, the most common height was 55 inches tall.

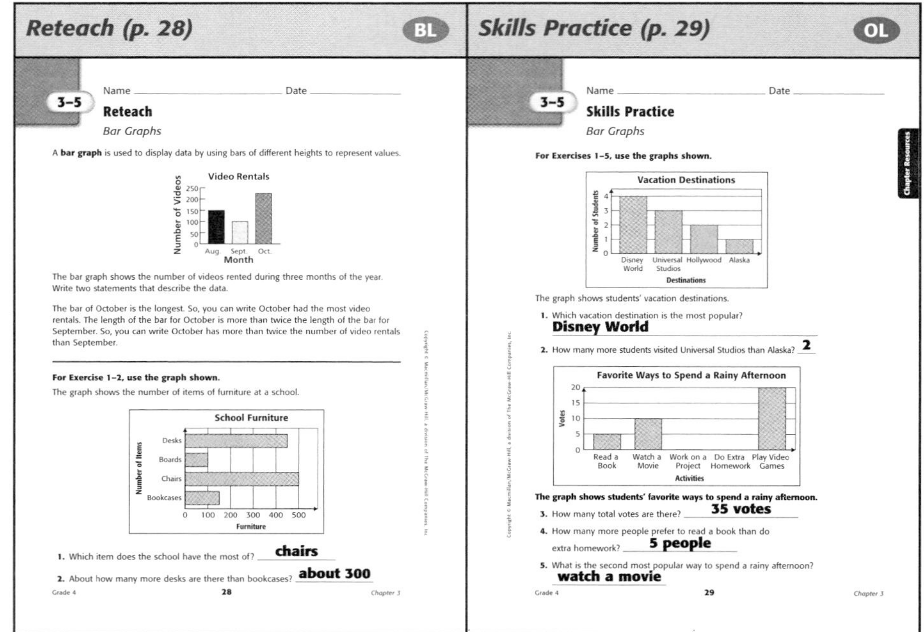

Reteach (p. 28) BL

3–5 Name ________ Date ________

Reteach

Bar Graphs

A **bar graph** is used to display data by using bars of different heights to represent values.

Video Rentals (Number of Videos: 0, 50, 100, 150, 200, 250; Month: Aug., Sept., Oct.)

The bar graph shows the number of videos rented during three months of the year. Write two statements that describe the data.

The bar of October is the longest. So, you can write October had the most video rentals. The length of the bar for October is more than twice the length of the bar for September. So, you can write October has more than twice the number of video rentals than September.

For Exercise 1–2, use the graph shown.

The graph shows the number of items of furniture at a school.

School Furniture (Number of Items: Desks, Boards, Chairs, Bookcases; Furniture: 0, 100, 200, 300, 400, 500)

1. Which item does the school have the most of? **chairs**
2. About how many more desks are there than bookcases? **about 300**

Grade 4 28 Chapter 3

Skills Practice (p. 29) OL

3–5 Name ________ Date ________

Skills Practice

Bar Graphs

For Exercises 1–5, use the graphs shown.

Vacation Destinations (Number of Students: 0, 1, 2, 3, 4; Destinations: Disney World, Universal Studios, Hollywood, Alaska)

The graph shows students' vacation destinations.

1. Which vacation destination is the most popular? **Disney World**
2. How many more students visited Universal Studios than Alaska? **2**

Favorite Ways to Spend a Rainy Afternoon (Votes: 0, 5, 10, 15, 20; Activities: Read a Book, Watch a Movie, Work on a Project, Do Extra Homework, Play Video Games)

The graph shows students' favorite ways to spend a rainy afternoon.

3. How many total votes are there? **35 votes**
4. How many more people prefer to read a book than do extra homework? **5 people**
5. What is the second most popular way to spend a rainy afternoon? **watch a movie**

Grade 4 29 Chapter 3

Chapter Resources

Remember

In grade 3 you learned that a scale is a set of numbers that represents data.

EXAMPLE Interpret a Bar Graph

2 MEASUREMENT **The bar graph shows the land area of four cities in North Carolina. Write a statement that describes the data.**

To write a statement that describes the data in a bar graph, you need to compare the lengths of the bars in the graph.

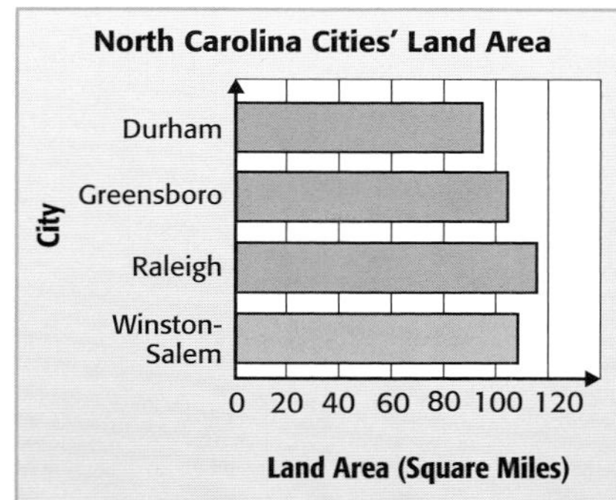

Source: North Carolina Bigger Cities

The bar for Raleigh is the longest. So, you can write that Raleigh has the largest land area of the four cities shown.

CHECK What You Know

For Exercises 1–6, use the graph shown. See Examples 1–2 (pp. 108–109)

Janet's School Absences

Grade Level: 3, 2, 1, K

Number of Days Absent: 0, 2, 4, 6, 8, 10, 12

1. During which grade was Janet absent the most days? second grade
2. What grade was Janet in when she was absent for 3 days? first grade
3. How many more days was Janet absent in second grade than in third grade? 2 days
4. How many days has Janet been absent since she finished the first grade? 14 days
5. Write a statement that describes the data in the graph. See margin.
6. **Talk About It** Refer back to Exercise 4. How did you find the answer? Sample answer: I added the number of days absent for grades 2 and 3 to get 14.

Enrich (p. 32) AL

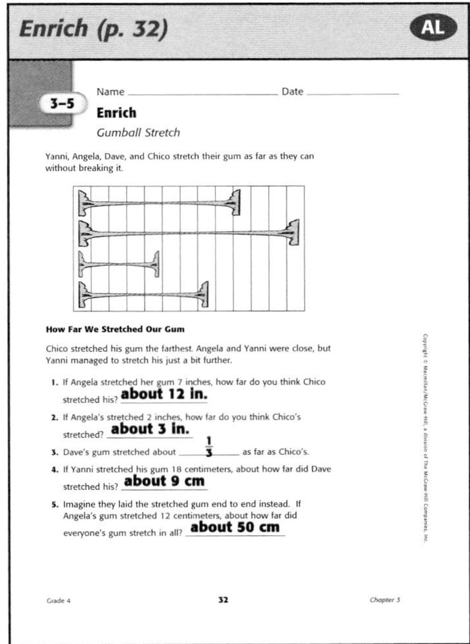

Name ______ Date ______

3-5 **Enrich**

Gumball Stretch

Yanni, Angela, Dave, and Chico stretch their gum as far as they can without breaking it.

How Far We Stretched Our Gum

Chico stretched his gum the farthest. Angela and Yanni were close, but Yanni managed to stretch his just a bit further.

1. If Angela stretched her gum 7 inches, how far do you think Chico stretched his? **about 12 in.**
2. If Angela's stretched 2 inches, how far do you think Chico's stretched? **about 3 in.**
3. Dave's gum stretched about **$\frac{1}{3}$** as far as Chico's.
4. If Yanni stretched his gum 18 centimeters, about how far did Dave stretch his? **about 9 cm**
5. Imagine they laid the stretched gum end to end instead. If Angela's gum stretched 12 centimeters, about how far did everyone's gum stretch in all? **about 50 cm**

Grade 4 32 Chapter 3

Interpret a Bar Graph

Example 1 Emphasize the importance of labeling the two axes correctly. Remind students that an axis is a horizontal or vertical number line on a graph.

ADDITIONAL EXAMPLES

1. Use the graph from Example 1 on p. 108. What was the least common height? 52 inches
2. Use the graph from Example 1 on p. 108. Write two statements that describe the data. Sample answers: More students are 55 inches than 56 inches; The same number of students are 54 inches tall as are 58 inches tall.

CHECK What You Know

As a class, have students complete Exercises 1–6 in **Check What You Know** as you observe their work.

Exercise 6 Assess student comprehension before assigning practice exercises.

BL Alternate Teaching Strategy

If students have trouble interpreting bar graphs...

Then use one of these reteach options:

1. CRM **Daily Reteach Worksheet** (p. 28)
2. Display the bar graph from the Scaffolding Questions. Point out the labels for the axes. **Which bar is the longest? the shortest? How many students prefer rock and roll? How many prefer pop? How many more prefer one than the other?** Answers will vary with class data.

Additional Answer

5. Sample answer: Janet was absent the most during second grade and the least during first grade.

COMMON ERROR!

Exercises 7–14 Some students may have trouble associating the top of a bar with the correct number. Allow these students to use a ruler to align the top of the bar with the correct number on the vertical scale.

3 Practice

Differentiate practice using these leveled assignments for Exercises 7–17.

Level	Assignment
BL Below/Approaching Level	7–10
OL On Level	8–10, 11–13, 16
AL Above/Beyond Level	8–14 even, 15–17

Have students discuss and complete the Higher Order Thinking problems. For Exercise 17, challenge students to suggest how the vertical scale for a graph should be chosen.

Have students complete Exercise 17 in their Math Journals. You may choose to use this exercise as an optional formative assessment.

4 Assess

Formative Assessment

Refer students to the land-area bar graph in Example 2.

- **About how much greater is the land area of Raleigh than that of Durham?** 20 sq mi
- **About what is the land area of Durham and Greensboro combined?** 200 sq mi
- **What is the order of the cities if they are listed from least to greatest land area?** Durham, Greensboro, Winston-Salem, Raleigh

Quick Check **Are students continuing to struggle with interpreting bar graphs?**

If Yes → Small Group Options (p. 108B)

If No → Independent Work Options (p. 108B)
CRM Skill Practice Worksheet (p. 29)
CRM Enrich Worksheet (p. 32)

Exercise Alert!

Exercises 9 and 17 In grade 3, students learned that a scale is a set of numbers that represents data.

Practice and Problem Solving

For Exercises 7–14, use the graphs shown. See Examples 1–2 (pp. 108–109)

Measurement The graph shows the lengths of certain whales.

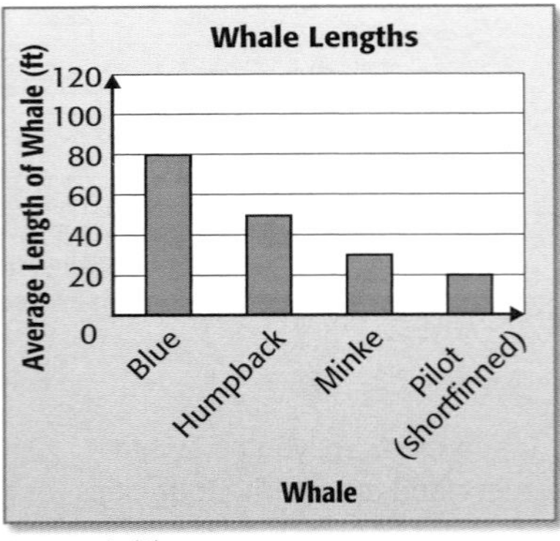

Source: Animal Planet

7. Which type of whale is the shortest? pilot
8. Which whale is about 50 feet long? humpback
9. Why is the scale set in intervals of 20 feet? 9, 10. See Ch. 3 Answer Appendix.
10. Can you find the exact difference between the length of a humpback whale and a minke whale by using this bar graph? Explain.

The graph shows the states with the most tornadoes in a recent year.

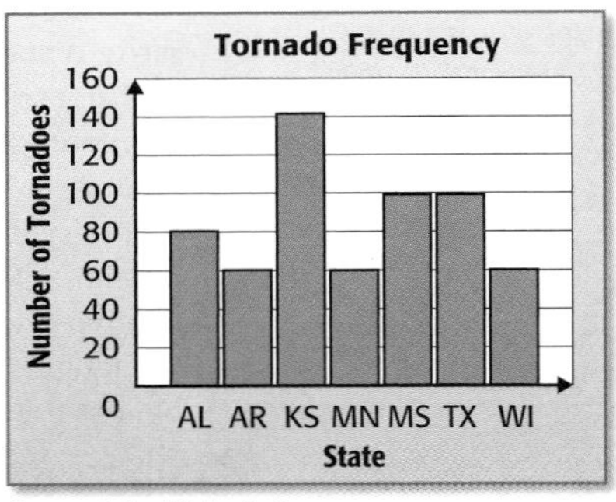

Source: National Weather Service

11. Which states appear to have had the same number of tornadoes? See Ch. 3 Answer Appendix.
12. About how many more tornadoes were in Texas than in Alabama? about 20
13. About how many more tornadoes were in Kansas than in Wisconsin? about 80
14. Which two states had a combined total of about 220 tornadoes? Explain how you found your answer. See Ch. 3 Answer Appendix.

H.O.T. Problems

15. **OPEN ENDED** Where have you seen bar graphs used outside of the classroom? What information was being described? Sample answer: I have seen bar graphs in newspapers describing population differences from year to year.
16. **NUMBER SENSE** Why is it sometimes necessary to estimate when reading a bar graph? Sample answer: Finding exact numbers may be difficult due to the intervals between the markings.
17. **WRITING IN MATH** Refer to the graph used for Exercises 11–14. Would this graph be easier to read if the scale was changed to intervals of 100? Explain. Sample answer: No, if the scale on this graph increases, the graph will be more difficult to read because the bars will look very similar

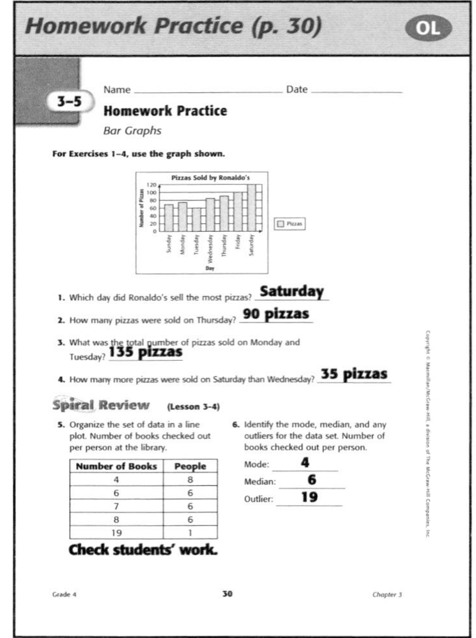

Homework Practice (p. 30) OL

Name ____________ Date ____________

3–5 **Homework Practice**
Bar Graphs

For Exercises 1–4, use the graph shown.

1. Which day did Ronaldo's sell the most pizzas? **Saturday**
2. How many pizzas were sold on Thursday? **90 pizzas**
3. What was the total number of pizzas sold on Monday and Tuesday? **135 pizzas**
4. How many more pizzas were sold on Saturday than Wednesday? **35 pizzas**

Spiral Review (Lesson 3-4)

5. Organize the set of data in a line plot. Number of books checked out per person at the library.

Number of Books	People
4	8
6	6
7	6
8	6
19	1

Check students' work.

6. Identify the mode, median, and any outliers for the data set. Number of books checked out per person.

Mode: **4**
Median: **6**
Outlier: **19**

Grade 4 30 Chapter 3

Mid-Chapter Check

Lessons 3-1 through 3-5

1. See Ch. 3 Answer Appendix.

1. Organize the set of data in a tally chart and in a frequency table. (Lesson 3-1)

Sandwiches for a Picnic		
Peanut butter	Ham	Turkey
Turkey	Turkey	Peanut butter
Ham	Ham	Ham

For Exercises 2 and 3, use the tally chart below. (Lesson 3-1)

Where Do You Read?	
Place	**Tally**
Outside	卌 |
Bedroom	卌 ||
Library	卌
Living room	|||

2. Where do most students like to read? bedroom

3. How many students read in their bedroom or at the library? 12

4. **MULTIPLE CHOICE** What is the mode of the data set {4, 5, 8, 8, 4, 3, 4}? (Lesson 3-2) B

A 3 **C** 5

B 4 **D** 8

5. Find the mode and median of the data. Identify any outliers. (Lesson 3-2)

Movies Rented During a Week					
Day	1	2	3	4	5
Movies	29	58	62	55	64

no mode; 58; 29

Solve. Use the make a table strategy. (Lesson 3-3)

6. It costs $32 for 2 admissions to a museum. Ebony and her father invite 10 friends for opening night. At this rate, how much would it cost for everyone to go to the museum? $192

7. Organize the set of data in a line plot. (Lesson 3-4)

Time it Takes to Walk Home (min)			
10	11	12	15
12	15	8	7
10	8	10	9

7, 9. See Ch. 3 Answer Appendix.

8. **MULTIPLE CHOICE** About how much farther did Greg travel than Joy? (Lesson 3-5) G

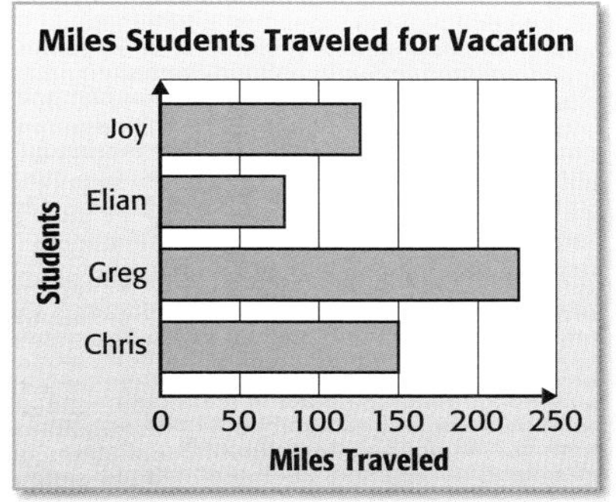

F 50 miles **H** 200 miles

G 100 miles **J** 300 miles

9. **WRITING IN MATH** Explain the difference between median and mode. (Lesson 3-2)

Mid-Chapter Check

Lessons 3-1 through 3-5

Formative Assessment

Use the Mid-Chapter Check to assess students' progress in the first half of the chapter.

ExamView Assessment Suite Customize and create multiple versions of your Mid-Chapter Check and the test answer keys.

FOLDABLES Dinah Zike's Foldables

Use these lesson suggestions to incorporate the Foldables during this chapter.

Lesson 3-2 Students record information and definitions, and demonstrate their ability to find the modes, median, and any outliers for a number set on the first layer of the Foldable.

Lesson 3-4 Have students collect data and use a number line, table, or chart to present a visual representation of the data on the second layer of the Foldable.

Data-Driven Decision Making

Based on the results of the Mid-Chapter Check, use the following resources to review concepts that continue to give students problems.

Exercises	State/Local Standards	What's the Mathematics?	Error Analysis	Resources for Review
1–3, 7 Lessons 3-1 and 3-4		Collect and organize data.	Does not know how to make a tally chart or a frequency chart. Does not know how to make or read a line plot.	Strategic Intervention Guide (p. 132) CRM Chapter 4 Resource Masters (Reteach Worksheets) Math Adventures My Math Zone Chapter 3 Math Online Extra Examples • Concepts in Motion
4, 5, 9 Lessons 3-2 and 3-4		Find mode, median, and outliers.	Does not know "mean," "median," "mode," or "outlier." Cannot explain difference between median and mode.	
6 Lesson 3-3		Make a table to solve problems.	Does not know how to make a table.	
8 Lesson 3-5		Read and interpret a bar graph.	Does not know how to read and interpret a bar graph.	

LESSON 3-6

Bar and Double Bar Graphs

Lesson Planner

Objective

Interpret bar graphs to answer questions.

Vocabulary

double bar graph

Resources

Materials: two blank transparencies

Literature Connection: *Tiger Math: Learning to Graph from a Baby Tiger* by Ann Whitehead Nagda and Cindy Bickel

Alternate Lesson: Use *IMPACT Mathematics:* Unit I to provide practice with bar graphs.

Teacher Technology

TeacherWorks • Interactive Classroom

Daily Routine

Use these suggestions before beginning the lesson on p. 112.

5-Minute Check

(Reviews Lesson 3-5)

The graph shows the musical instruments preferred by students in one Grade 4 classroom.

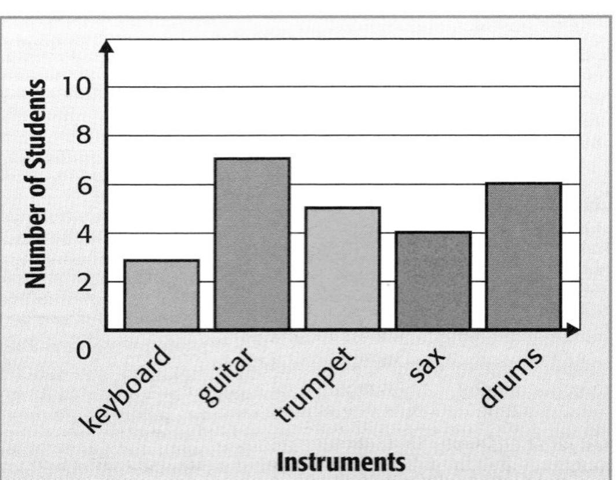

1. Which instrument was least preferred? keyboard
2. How many more students prefer the guitar to the sax? 3
3. How many students were surveyed? 25

Problem of the Day

What is the *difference* between the *sum* of the even numbers between 1–15 and the *sum* of the odd numbers between 0–14? 7

Focus on Math Background

A double bar graph with pairs of bars allows you to compare related sets of data, such as time spent on homework and time spent watching T.V. for each night of the week. As with single bar graphs, the bars may be oriented either horizontally or vertically.

Double bar graphs must have legends (or keys). These are important when reading and interpreting double bar graphs, as they tell you which set of bars represents which data set.

Building Math Vocabulary

Write the lesson vocabulary word and its definition on the board.

After discussing Example 3, have students brainstorm and record situations where a double bar graph would be useful (e.g., comparing favorite kinds of music between boys and girls in two classrooms).

Differentiated Instruction

Small Group Options

Option 1 Gifted and Talented AL

LINGUISTIC

Materials: paper, pencil, 1-inch grid paper

- Hand students the following set of data:

Subject	# of boys	# of girls
Math	3	5
Science	4	4
Social Studies	5	2
English	2	3

- Ask students to construct a double bar graph using the data set and the grid paper. Remind students to include a main title and subtitles for the axes.
- Then have students write two or three questions about their double bar graphs. Questions might include: Which subject is least popular? Which subject is liked equally?

Option 2 English Language Learners ELL

SOCIAL, LINGUISTIC

Materials: chalkboard, chalk
Core Vocabulary: what language, we (speak), at home
Common Use Verb: speak

Talk Math This strategy uses students as sources of information to help students relate to the concepts of bar graphs.

- Design a bar graph with the numbers 0–10 to the right. Label the bottom with the different languages spoken by students in the class. Ask: "What **language** do you **speak at home**?"
- As students answer, construct a bar graph.
- Once each student has been questioned, prompt students to answer "How many people ***speak*** Spanish, Japanese, etc."

Use this worksheet to provide additional support for English Language Learners.

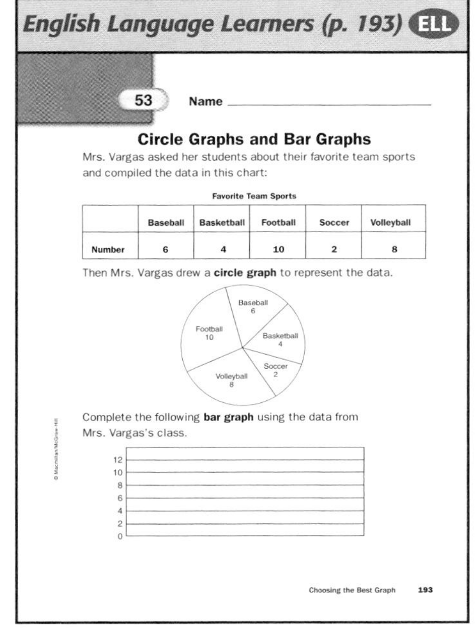

English Language Learners (p. 193) ELL

53 Name ________

Circle Graphs and Bar Graphs

Mrs. Vargas asked her students about their favorite team sports and compiled the data in this chart:

Favorite Team Sports

	Baseball	Basketball	Football	Soccer	Volleyball
Number	6	4	10	2	8

Then Mrs. Vargas drew a **circle graph** to represent the data.

Complete the following **bar graph** using the data from Mrs. Vargas's class.

Choosing the Best Graph 193

Independent Work Options

Option 1 Early Finishers OL AL

LINGUISTIC

Materials: grid paper, colored pencils

- Ask each student to make a bar graph to show how much time they spend doing each of the following activities during the average week of summer vacation. Activities: swimming, bike riding, reading, watching TV, playing ball games, playing with friends.

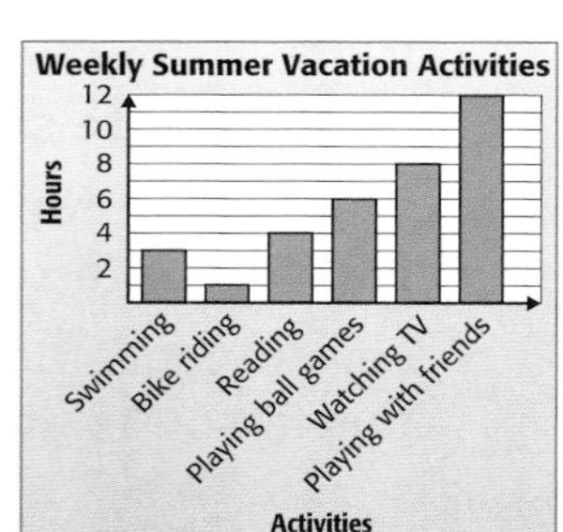

- With a partner, create a double bar graph.

Option 2 Student Technology

Tech Link

Personal Tutor • Extra Examples

Option 3 Learning Station: Reading (p. 92J)

Direct students to the Reading Learning Station for opportunities to explore and extend the lesson concept.

Option 4 Problem-Solving Practice

Reinforce problem-solving skills and strategies with the Problem-Solving Practice worksheet.

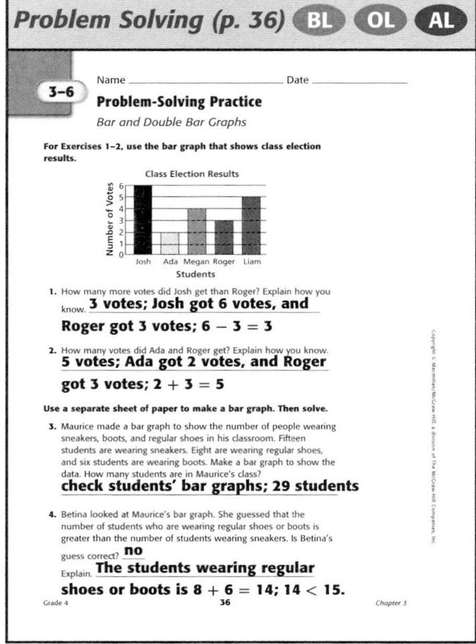

Problem Solving (p. 36) BL OL AL

3–6 Name ________ Date ________

Problem-Solving Practice

Bar and Double Bar Graphs

For Exercises 1–2, use the bar graph that shows class election results.

1. How many more votes did Josh get than Roger? Explain how you know. **3 votes; Josh got 6 votes, and Roger got 3 votes; $6 - 3 = 3$**
2. How many votes did Ada and Roger get? Explain how you know. **5 votes; Ada got 2 votes, and Roger got 3 votes; $2 + 3 = 5$**

Use a separate sheet of paper to make a bar graph. Then solve.

3. Maurice made a bar graph to show the number of people wearing sneakers, boots, and regular shoes in his classroom. Fifteen students are wearing sneakers. Eight are wearing regular shoes, and six students are wearing boots. Make a bar graph to show the data. How many students are in Maurice's class? **check students' bar graphs; 29 students**
4. Betina looked at Maurice's bar graph. She guessed that the number of students who are wearing regular shoes or boots is greater than the number of students wearing sneakers. Is Betina's guess correct? **no** Explain. **The students wearing regular shoes or boots is $8 + 6 = 14$; $14 < 15$.**

Grade 4 36 Chapter 3

Bar and Double Bar Graphs

1 Introduce

Activity Choice 1

- Draw two tally charts on board with titles of Boys' Favorite Season and Girls' Favorite Season. List choices of Spring, Summer, Fall, and Winter.
- Have each student come up and place tally mark by their favorite season.
- **What is the favorite season for the girls? least favorite season?** Answers will vary.
- **What is the favorite season for the boys? least favorite season?** Answers will vary.
- Tell students they will interpret bar graphs in this lesson to answer questions.

Activity Choice 2 • Literature

Introduce the lesson with *Tiger Math: Learning to Graph from a Baby Tiger* by Ann Whitehead Nagda and Cindy Bickel. For a related math activity, see p. TR45.

2 Teach

Scaffolding Questions

- **How does a bar graph help you interpret data?** It organizes data visually.
- **What does a bar represent?** a number amount
- **How does a bar graph communicate information?** It uses the lengths of the bars to compare number amounts.

GET READY to Learn

Have students open their books and read the information in **Get Ready to Learn**. Review **double bar graph**. As a class, work through **Examples 1–3**.

3-6 Bar and Double Bar Graphs

MAIN IDEA

I will interpret bar graphs to answer questions.

New Vocabulary

double bar graph

Math Online

macmillanmh.com
- Extra Examples
- Personal Tutor
- Self-Check Quiz

GET READY to Learn

The graph shows the amount of time four astronauts spent in space during a single mission. You can use the graph to compare the time spent in space.

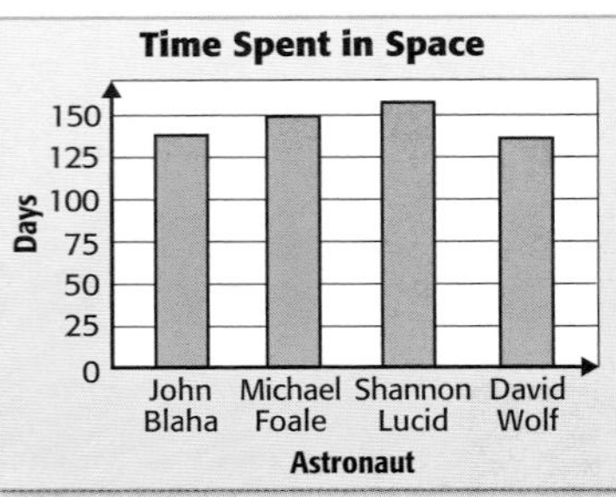

Source: *Time for Kids*

A bar graph allows you to compare data easily.

Real-World EXAMPLES Read Bar Graphs

BOOKS The bar graph shows the number of books checked out of a school library.

1 What is the most popular book?

To find the most popular kind of book, look for the longest bar.

Sports books are most popular.

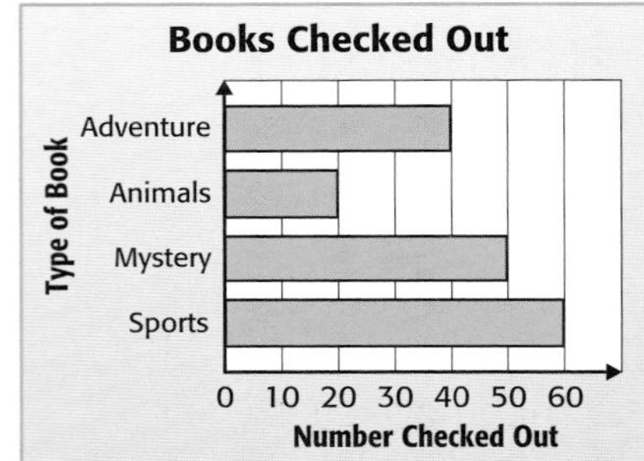

2 How many sports and animal books were checked out?

60 sports books and 20 animal books were checked out.

$60 + 20 = 80$

So, there were 80 sports and animal books checked out.

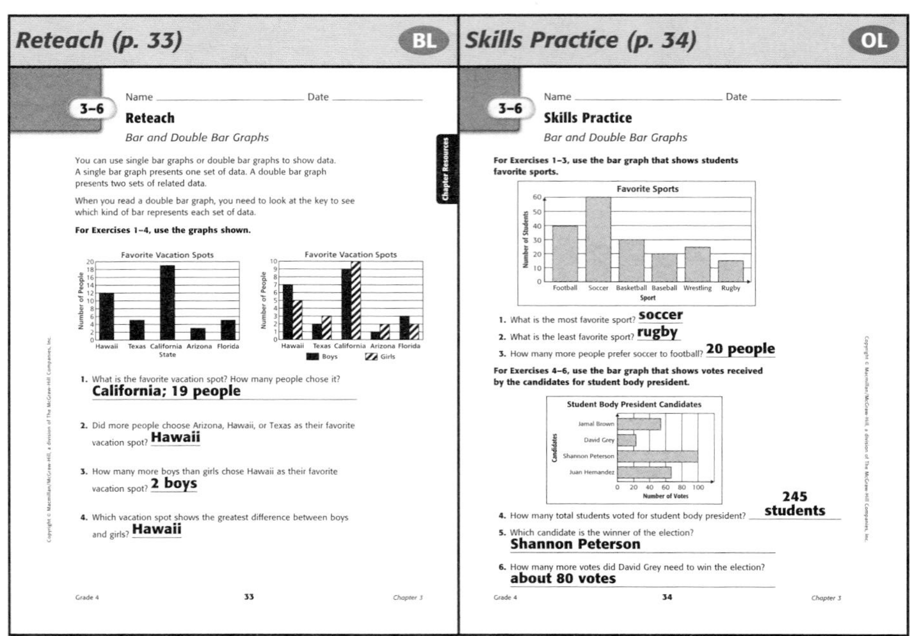

Reteach (p. 33) BL

3–6
Name ______ Date ______

Reteach

Bar and Double Bar Graphs

You can use single bar graphs or double bar graphs to show data. A single bar graph presents one set of data. A double bar graph presents two sets of related data.

When you read a double bar graph, you need to look at the key to see which kind of bar represents each set of data.

For Exercises 1–4, use the graphs shown.

1. What is the favorite vacation spot? How many people chose it? **California; 19 people**
2. Did more people choose Arizona, Hawaii, or Texas as their favorite vacation spot? **Hawaii**
3. How many more boys than girls chose Hawaii as their favorite vacation spot? **2 boys**
4. Which vacation spot shows the greatest difference between boys and girls? **Hawaii**

Grade 4 33 *Chapter 3*

Skills Practice (p. 34) OL

3–6
Name ______ Date ______

Skills Practice

Bar and Double Bar Graphs

For Exercises 1–3, use the bar graph that shows students favorite sports.

1. What is the most favorite sport? **soccer**
2. What is the least favorite sport? **rugby**
3. How many more people prefer soccer to football? **20 people**

For Exercises 4–6, use the bar graph that shows votes received by the candidates for student body president.

4. How many total students voted for student body president? **245 students**
5. Which candidate is the winner of the election? **Shannon Peterson**
6. How many more votes did David Grey need to win the election? **about 80 votes**

Grade 4 34 *Chapter 3*

A **double bar graph** displays two sets of related data using bars of different colors and heights.

Remember

When reading a double bar graph, always look at the scale and the key.

5. Sample answer: A double bar graph compares two sets of data. A bar graph is used to display one set of data.

Real-World EXAMPLE Read Double Bar Graphs

3 **SCHOOL** **Students are selling magazines for a fundraiser. About how many students will sell magazines in the second grade?**

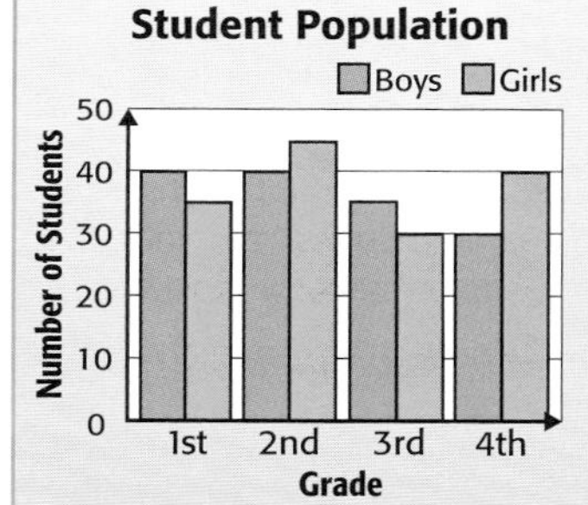

There are about 40 boys and about 45 girls in the second grade.

$40 + 45 = 85$

So, about 85 students will sell magazines in second grade.

★ indicates multi-step problem

CHECK What You Know

For Exercises 1–4, use the graphs shown. See Examples 1–3 (pp. 112–113)

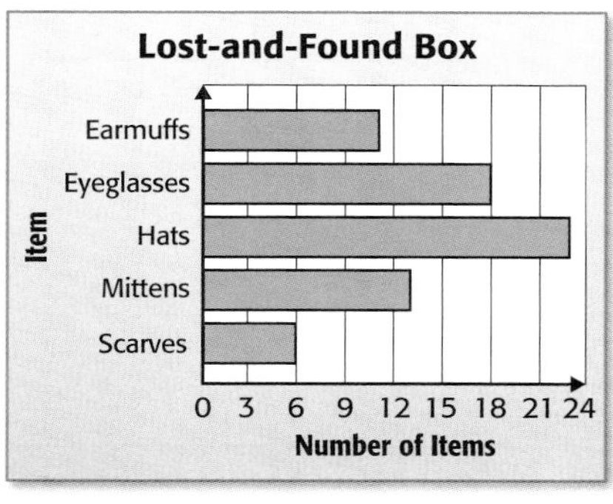

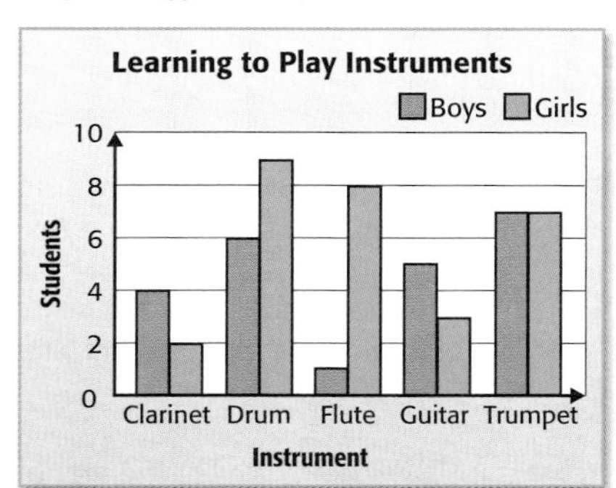

1. What is the most common item in the lost-and-found box? hats
2. How many more eyeglasses are in the box than scarves? 12 eyeglasses
3. What is the least popular instrument for boys? flute
4. What is the total number of students surveyed? 52
5. **Talk About It** Describe when you would use a bar graph and a double bar graph to display sets of data.

Read Double Bar Graphs

Example 3 Call attention to the keys on the graph.

ADDITIONAL EXAMPLES

1–2

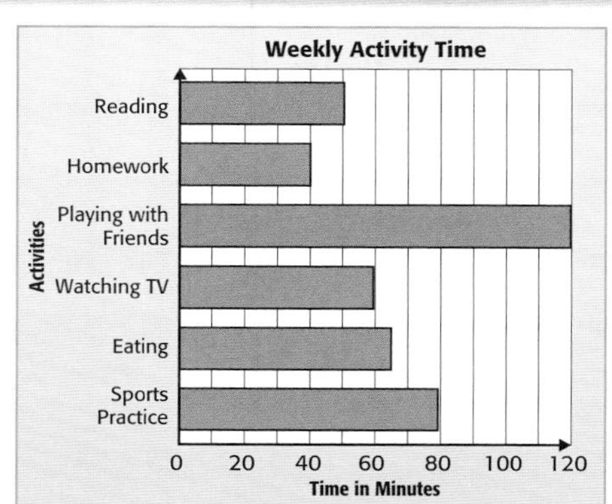

On which activity does Sanji spend the most time? How long does Sanji spend doing homework and reading? playing with friends; 90 minutes or $1\frac{1}{2}$ hours

3

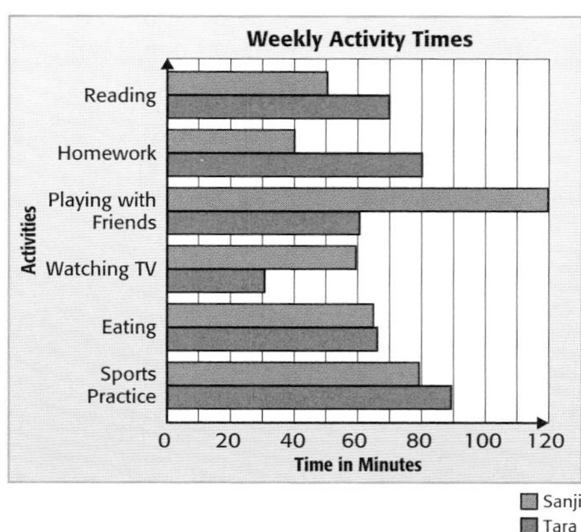

Who spends more time watching TV? Who spends more time reading? For which activity do they spend the same amount of time? Sanji; Tara; eating

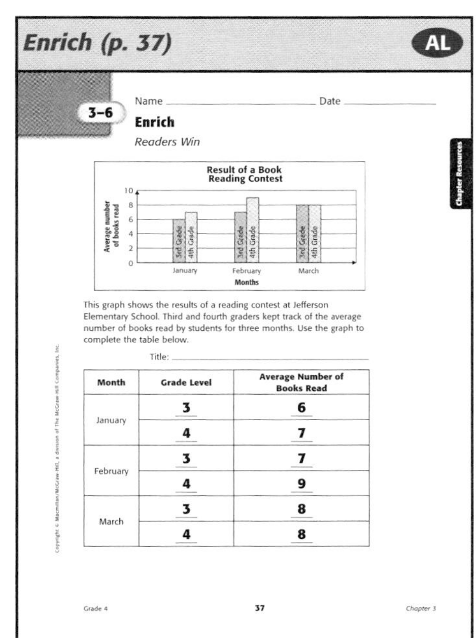

Enrich (p. 37) AL

3–6

Name ______________ Date ______________

Enrich

Readers Win

Result of a Book Reading Contest

This graph shows the results of a reading contest at Jefferson Elementary School. Third and fourth graders kept track of the average number of books read by students for three months. Use the graph to complete the table below.

Title: ______________

Month	Grade Level	Average Number of Books Read
January	3	6
	4	7
February	3	7
	4	9
March	3	8
	4	8

Grade 4 37 Chapter 3

CHECK What You Know

As a class, have students complete Exercises 1–5 in **Check What You Know** as you observe their work.

Exercise 5 Assess student comprehension before assigning practice exercises.

BL Alternate Teaching Strategy

If students have trouble interpreting bar graphs and double bar graphs…

Then use one of these reteach options:

1 CRM **Daily Reteach Worksheet** (p. 33)

2 Display two bar graphs on transparencies. Have students merge the two transparencies to show a double bar graph.

3 Practice

Differentiate practice using these leveled assignments for Exercises 6–15.

Level	Assignment
BL Below/Approaching Level	6–7, 10–11
OL On Level	6–9, 10–12, 14
AL Above/Beyond Level	7–13 odd, 14–15

Have students discuss and complete the Higher Order Thinking problems. For Exercise 15, suggest that students make a list of the different types of data sets they can think of and decide whether a double bar graph would be an appropriate display.

MATH Have students complete Exercise 14 in their Math Journals. You may choose to use this exercise as an optional formative assessment.

4 Assess

Formative Assessment

- **Describe when a double bar graph is the best choice to display data.** to compare two related sets of data

Quick Check **Are students continuing to struggle with bar and double bar graphs?**

If Yes → CRM Reteach Worksheet (p. 33)

If No → Independent Work Options (p. 112B)
CRM Skills Practice Worksheet (p. 34)
CRM Enrich Worksheet (p. 37)

Yesterday's News Ask students to write a few sentences in their Math Journals about how yesterday's lesson on bar graphs helped them with today's lesson.

Exercise Alert!

Exercise 14 Point out the break in the bar graph in the *y*-axis to students. Explain that a break in a graph means that an axis of the graph contains a change in the interval of the scale.

Practice and Problem Solving

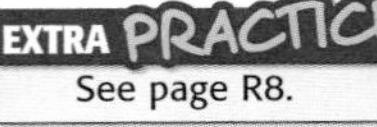

See page R8.

For Exercises 6–9, use the bar graph that shows the number of Little League Championship wins. See Examples 1–2 (p. 112)

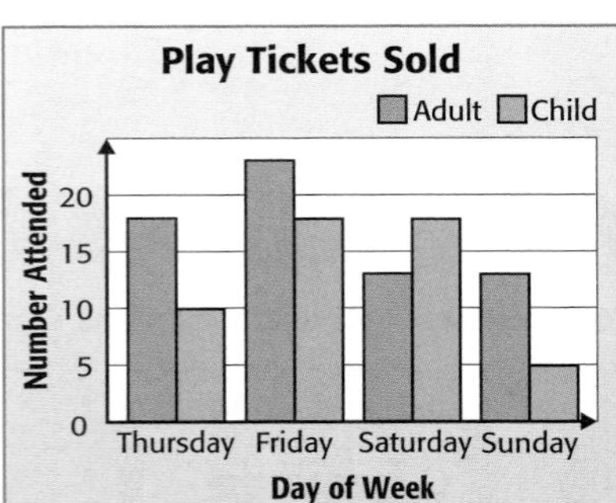

Source: *Scholastic Book of World Records*

6. Which team has the most wins? United States
7. Which team has the least wins? Mexico
8. How many more wins does the United States have than the team that has the second most wins? 13
9. ★ If the wins for Japan, Mexico, and Taiwan were added together, would they have as many wins as the United States? Explain. no; 22 < 26

For Exercises 10–13, use the double bar graph that shows the number of tickets sold for a high school play. See Example 3 (p. 113)

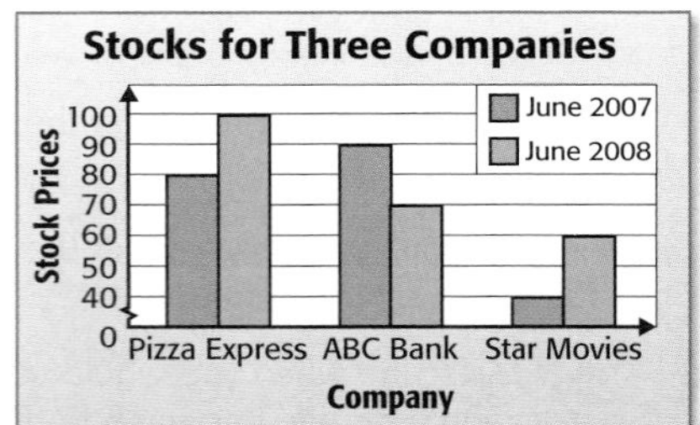

10. Which day had the highest total attendance? Friday
11. Did more adults or children attend on Friday? adults
12. About how many adults attended in all? about 60–65 adults
13. ★ Suppose adult tickets cost \$4 and children tickets cost \$2. On which day was more than \$100 made in ticket sales? Friday

14. Sample answer: Each company's stock increased except ABC bank. The stock prices of both Pizza Express and Star Movies increased by 20.

H.O.T. Problems

14. WRITING IN MATH The graph shows the value of stocks for three companies. Write 2 sentences that describe the data.
15. **OPEN ENDED** Describe a set of data that could not be shown in a double bar graph. Sample answer: Compare the cost of hamburgers at five different restaurants.

Stocks for Three Companies
June 2007
June 2008
Stock Prices
0
40
50
60
70
80
90
100
Pizza Express
ABC Bank
Star Movies
Company

Homework Practice (p. 35) OL

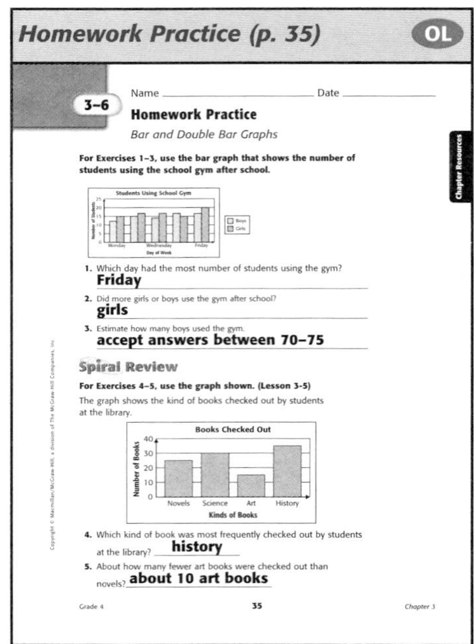
Name ______ Date ______

3–6 **Homework Practice**
Bar and Double Bar Graphs

For Exercises 1–3, use the bar graph that shows the number of students using the school gym after school.

1. Which day had the most number of students using the gym? **Friday**
2. Did more girls or boys use the gym after school? **girls**
3. Estimate how many boys used the gym. **accept answers between 70–75**

Spiral Review

For Exercises 4–5, use the graph shown. (Lesson 3-5)
The graph shows the kind of books checked out by students at the library.

4. Which kind of book was most frequently checked out by students at the library? **history**
5. About how many fewer art books were checked out than novels? **about 10 art books**

Grade 4 35 Chapter 3

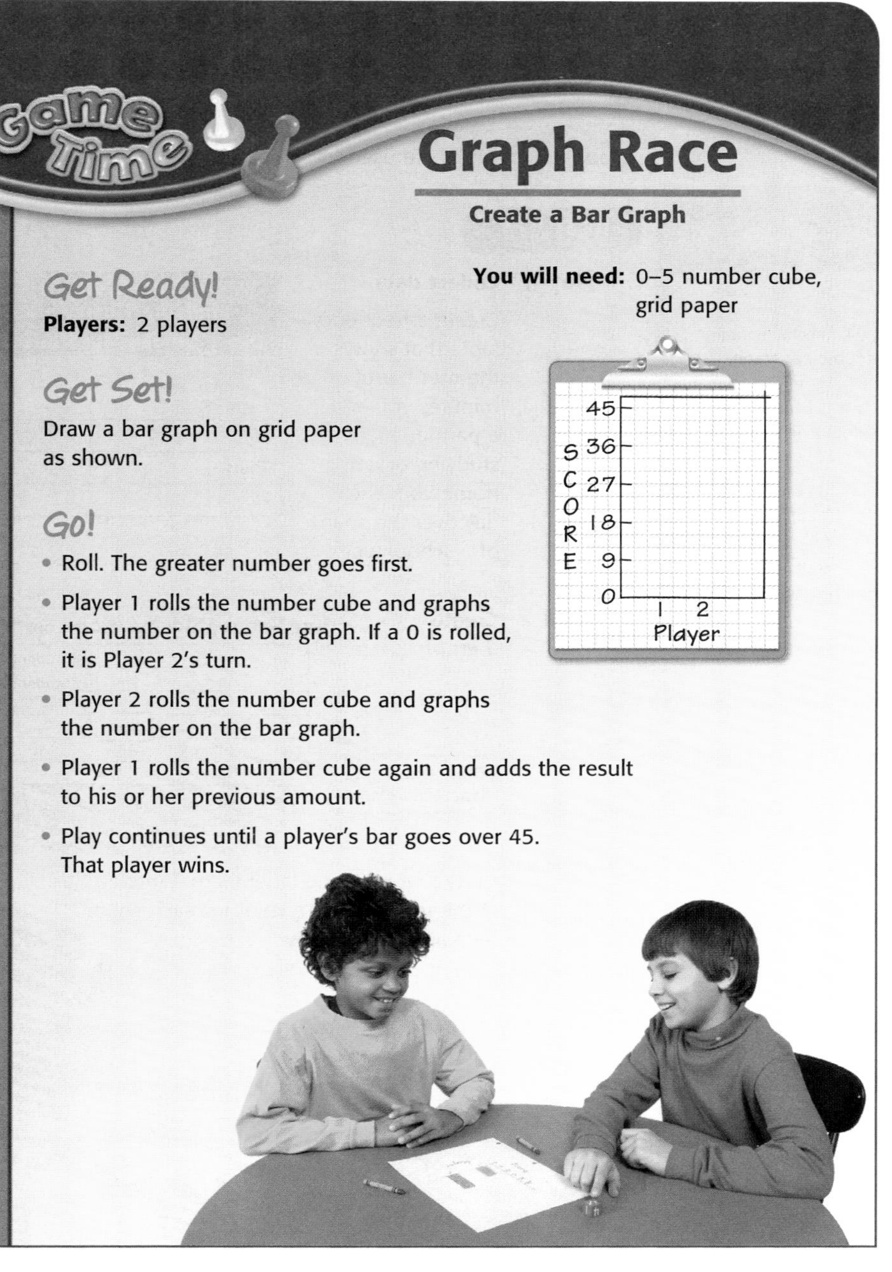

Game Time

Graph Race

Create a Bar Graph

You will need: 0–5 number cube, grid paper

Get Ready!

Players: 2 players

Get Set!

Draw a bar graph on grid paper as shown.

Go!

- Roll. The greater number goes first.
- Player 1 rolls the number cube and graphs the number on the bar graph. If a 0 is rolled, it is Player 2's turn.
- Player 2 rolls the number cube and graphs the number on the bar graph.
- Player 1 rolls the number cube again and adds the result to his or her previous amount.
- Play continues until a player's bar goes over 45. That player wins.

Game Time Graph Race **115**

Differentiated Practice

Use these leveled suggestions to differentiate the game for all learners.

Level	Assignment
BL Below/Approaching Level	Students use grid paper, using the squares on the paper to help them add each roll of the number cube to their bar graphs.
OL On Level	Have students play the game with the rules as written.
AL Above/Beyond Level	Students play using a 5–10 number cube and play to 100.

Graph Race

Math Concept: Create A Bar Graph

Materials: 0–5 number cube, grid paper, pencils

Introduce the game on p. 115 to your students to play as a class, in small groups, or at a learning workstation to review concepts introduced in this chapter.

Instructions

- Students draw the outline of a bar graph on a sheet of paper, as shown on p. 115.
- Students take turns rolling the number cube to see who goes first. The high roller starts the game.
- Player 1 rolls the number cube and graphs the number on his or her space on the bar graph. Player 2 does the same.
- Player 1 rolls the number cube and adds the number to the previous amount rolled, extending his or her bar by the amount rolled. If a 0 is rolled, the turn passes to Player 2.
- Players continue to take turns rolling the number cube and adding the result to their bar graphs until one player's bar reaches or surpasses 45. The first player to reach or surpass 45 wins.

Extend the Game

Have students make the game using a larger bar graph, playing until 60, or playing with more than two players.

Statistics Activity for 3-6

Lesson Planner

Objective

Display data in double bar graphs.

Resources

Materials: transparency, colored pencils, graph paper

1 Introduce

Introduce the Concept

- Draw a blank tally table labeled *Favorite Sports* on the board or an overhead transparency. Label 3 columns *Sport, Girls, Boys.* In the column labeled *Sport,* list several sports such as softball, baseball, basketball, and swimming. Poll the class about their favorite sport and record the results in the tally chart.
- Evaluate the results with students. Ask questions such as: **Which sport is the girls' favorite? Which sport is the boys' least favorite? Is there one sport that boys and girls like equally?** Answers will vary.
- Remind students that tables and graphs help them to organize and interpret a set of data. A double bar graph helps them compare two sets of related data.

2 Teach

Activity 1 Be sure that students pay careful attention to the title, the labels, and the keys on their graphs. Emphasize that these pieces of information must correspond to the data sets they are graphing.

Extend

Statistics Activity for 3-6

Make Double Bar Graphs

Double bar graphs are used to compare two sets of related data.

MAIN IDEA

I will display data in double bar graph.

You Will Need

colored pencils
graph paper

Math Online

macmillanmh.com
• Concepts in Motion

ACTIVITY

Step 1 Collect data.

Create a frequency table that shows the number of minutes you and a partner spend studying or doing homework each day over the span of a school week.

Time Spent Studying/Homework		
Day	**Student 1**	**Student 2**
Mon.		
Tues.		
Wed.		
Thurs.		
Fri.		

Step 2 Create a graph.

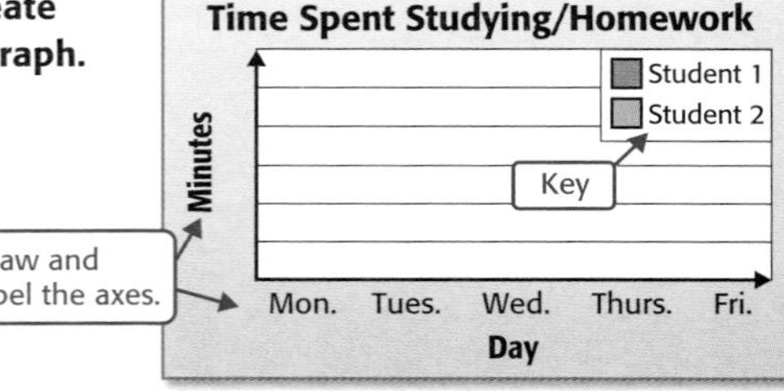

Draw two axes and label them. Write a title at the top. Choose a color for each set of data and make a **key**.

Step 3 **Choose a scale.**

The scale should include the least and the greatest number from your data.

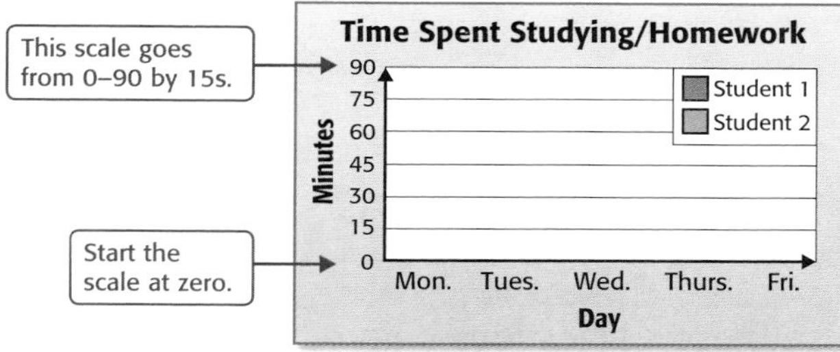

Step 4 **Draw bars.**

Draw the bars for your data on the graph. Then draw the bars for your partner's data on the graph.

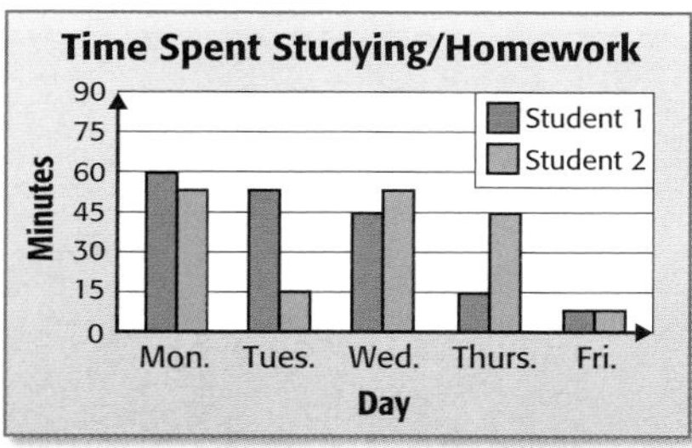

Think About It

1. Tell how you can use a double bar graph to compare data. Sample answer: Examine the heights of both bars and compare the data shown.
2. Explain how you choose a scale and intervals. 2–5. See margin.

CHECK What You Know

Represent each set of data in a double bar graph.

3.

Books Read		
Month	**Miki**	**Alicia**
May	3	2
June	5	6
July	4	5
August	6	4

4.

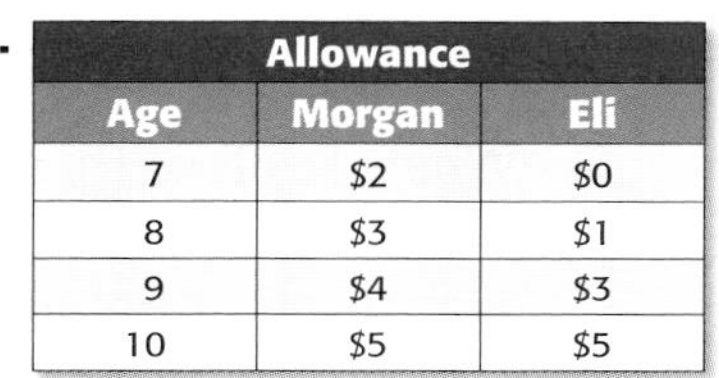

Allowance		
Age	**Morgan**	**Eli**
7	\$2	\$0
8	\$3	\$1
9	\$4	\$3
10	\$5	\$5

5. **WRITING IN MATH** Look at Exercises 3 and 4. Write a comparison sentence that describes the data in each table.

Step 3 Emphasize the importance of starting the scales at zero and counting by the same amount for each interval.

Step 4 Remind students to start their bars at zero and to place the top of each bar carefully.

Formative Assessment

Use **Think About It** Exercises 1–2 to assess whether students comprehend how to make a double bar graph to compare two sets of related data.

Assess

Formative Assessment

Use the **Check What You Know** Exercises to assess whether students comprehend how to make a double bar graph to compare two sets of data.

From Concrete to Abstract Use Exercise 5 to bridge making double bar graphs and using them to interpret a given set of data.

Extending the Concept Ask students to think back to the survey of students' favorite sports.

- **If you were going to make a double bar graph using the data from that survey, what scale would you choose? How would you decide?** Answers will vary; Use the data set to determine the best fit.

Additional Answers

2. Sample answer: Define the range of numbers within the data being compared. Determine an interval that will show all the data and create bars that are easily measurable.

3.

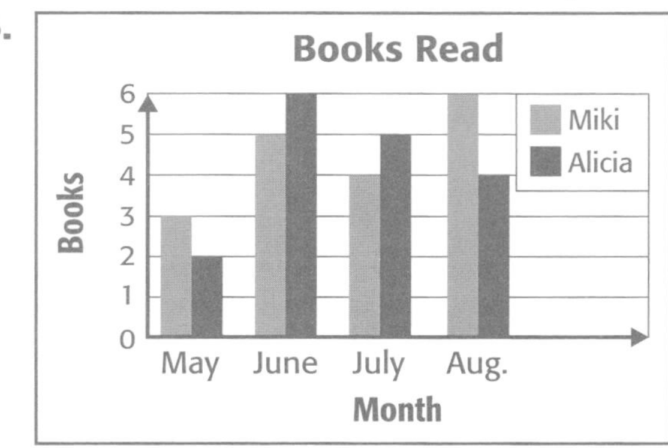

4.

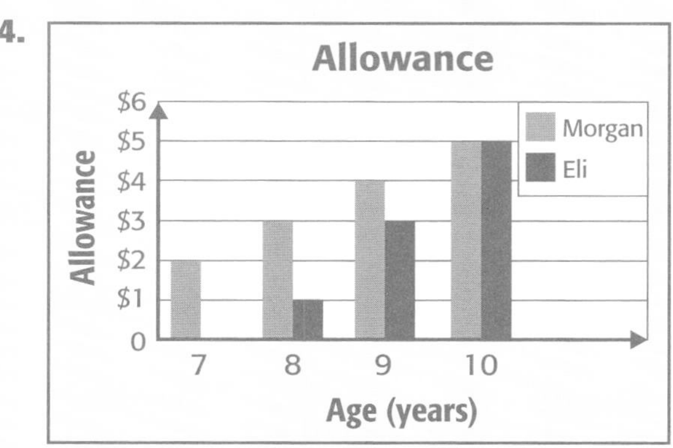

5. Sample answer: Exercise 3: Miki read one more book than Alicia; Exercise 4: Morgan had a greater allowance than Eli from ages 7 through 9. Then they received the same allowance at age 10.

3-7 Problem-Solving Investigation
Choose a Strategy

Lesson Planner

Objective

Choose the best strategy to solve a problem.

Resources

Manipulatives: money

Teacher Technology

TeacherWorks • Interactive Classroom

Real-World Problem Solving Library
Math and Science: *Americans On the Move*
Use these leveled books to reinforce and extend problem-solving skills and strategies.

Leveled for:

- OL On Level
- ELL Sheltered English
- SP Spanish

For additional support, see the Real-World Problem Solving Teacher Guide.

Daily Routine

Use these suggestions before beginning the lesson on p. 118.

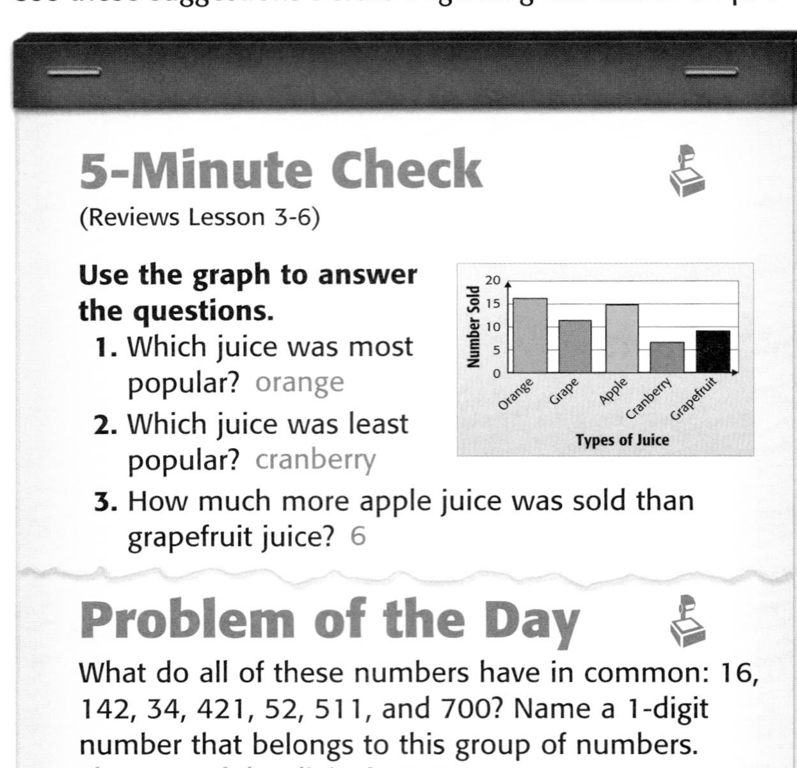

5-Minute Check

(Reviews Lesson 3-6)

Use the graph to answer the questions.

1. Which juice was most popular? orange
2. Which juice was least popular? cranberry
3. How much more apple juice was sold than grapefruit juice? 6

Problem of the Day

What do all of these numbers have in common: 16, 142, 34, 421, 52, 511, and 700? Name a 1-digit number that belongs to this group of numbers. The sum of the digits is 7; 7.

Differentiated Instruction

Small Group Options

LOGICAL

Option 1 Gifted and Talented AL

Materials: paper and pencil

Have students refer back to Exercise 4 of this lesson. Then hand them this problem to solve:

- *Ricardo mailed the invitations. Only 25 of the people responded to say they were coming to his party. He wants to serve pizza and soda. A large pizza serves 8 and costs $7. A large bottle of soda serves 9 and costs $2.*
- **If Ricardo plans 2 pieces of pizza and 1 glass of soda for each person, what will the party food cost?** 25 guests + Ricardo will need 52 servings; Seven pizzas will be needed because 6 pizzas = 48 servings, which is not enough. 52 servings of pizza = 7 pizzas × $7 = $49; 26 servings of soda = 3 bottles × $2 = $6; Total = $55

LINGUISTIC, LOGICAL

Option 2 English Language Learners ELL

Materials: phone card (if available) or picture of one
Core Vocabulary: pay for, credit, run out of money
Common Use Verb: gets used up

Hear Math This strategy uses background knowledge to help students understand the concept of subtraction.

- Show a phone. Prompt students to explain what they know about them and what they have in common: that you must pay to use them.
- Say: "You **pay** money **for** a card and every time you use it, the card's credit **gets used up**."
- Have students pantomime calling home, deducting different amounts of time, on a graphic organizer or graph that will keep track of how much is left on the card.
- Students repeat until they "run out of money."

Independent Work Options

LOGICAL, SOCIAL

Option 1 Early Finishers OL AL

Materials: paper, pencil, sets of data from previous lessons' Activity Choice 1 (pp. 95, 100, 104)

- Give students sets of data from earlier activities and have them organize the information in tables and graphs.
- Then have them write a series of questions based on the data in the tables and graphs.
- They can challenge classmates to answer the questions.

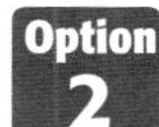

Option 2 Student Technology

Math Online macmillanmh.com

Personal Tutor • Extra Examples

Option 3 Learning Station: Music (p. 92J)

Direct students to the Music Learning Station for opportunities to explore and extend the lesson concept.

3-7 Problem-Solving Investigation

1 Introduce

Activity • Review

- Write the following problem on the board:

  Peter and Mai are saving to buy softball mitts. They have $22. They need $87 to buy two mitts. About how much more money do Peter and Mai need?
- Ask students to recall the strategies they have used in previous lessons. **Which problem-solving strategy would you use to solve this problem?** estimation vs. exact answers
- **Do you need an estimate or exact answer?** estimate **Why?** uses *about*
- **Solve.** $90 − $20 = $70, need about $70

2 Teach

Have students read the problem on taking the subway. Guide them through the problem-solving steps.

Understand Using the questions, review what students know and need to find.

Plan Have them discuss their strategy.

Solve Guide students to use the make a table strategy to solve the problem.

- **What is the pattern in the table?** Add $2.
- **How many round trips can Seth make?** 5
- **How much money will be left on his subway card?** $1

Check Have students look back at the problem to make sure that the answer fits the facts given.

COMMON ERROR!

Exercise 1 Students sometimes fail to see a pattern once they have made a table. Remind them to look for a connection between the numbers in the columns or to look for a way to get from one number in a row to the next number in that same row.

3-7 Problem-Solving Investigation

MAIN IDEA I will choose the best strategy to solve a problem.

P.S.I. TEAM +

SETH: I take the subway to get to school and back. Each round trip costs $2. My subway card has a value of $11.

YOUR MISSION: Find how many round trips Seth can make with $11.

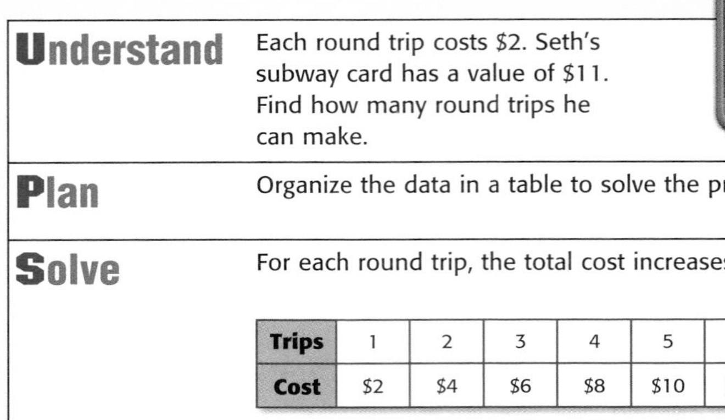

Understand Each round trip costs $2. Seth's subway card has a value of $11. Find how many round trips he can make.

Plan Organize the data in a table to solve the problem.

Solve For each round trip, the total cost increases by $2.

Trips	1	2	3	4	5	6
Cost	$2	$4	$6	$8	$10	$12

+2 +2 +2 +2 +2

Seth's card has a value of $11. He cannot make a sixth trip because after making 5 trips he has only $1 left. This is not enough for another trip. So, he can make 5 trips to school and back.

Check Use a set of play money that is in piles of $2. Add the money until you have more than $11.

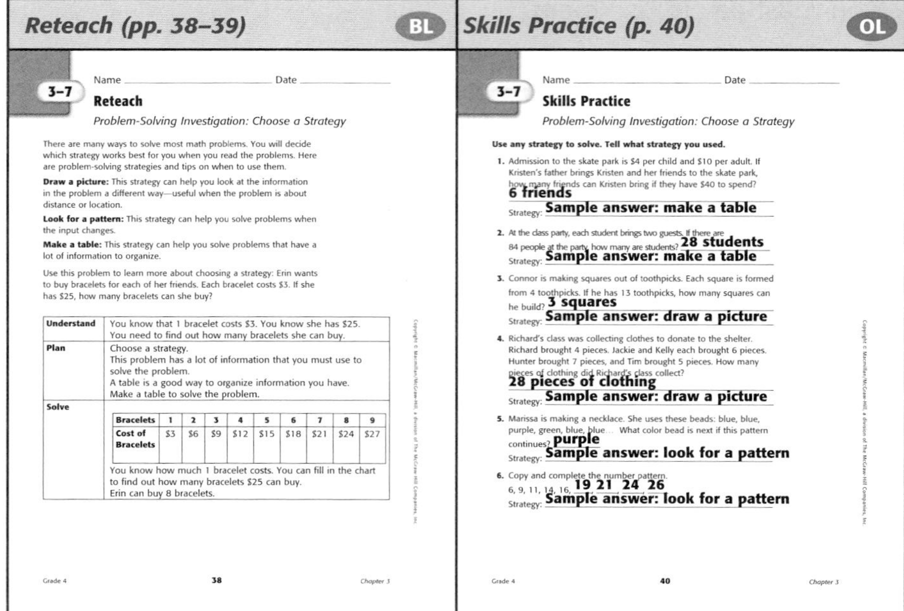

Reteach (pp. 38–39) BL

3-7 Name ______ Date ______

Reteach

Problem-Solving Investigation: Choose a Strategy

There are many ways to solve most math problems. You will decide which strategy works best for you when you read the problems. Here are problem-solving strategies and tips on when to use them.

Draw a picture: This strategy can help you look at the information in the problem a different way—useful when the problem is about distance or location.

Look for a pattern: This strategy can help you solve problems when the input changes.

Make a table: This strategy can help you solve problems that have a lot of information to organize.

Use this problem to learn more about choosing a strategy: Erin wants to buy bracelets for each of her friends. Each bracelet costs $3. If she has $25, how many bracelets can she buy?

Understand You know that 1 bracelet costs $3. You know she has $25. You need to find out how many bracelets she can buy.

Plan Choose a strategy. This problem has a lot of information that you must use to solve the problem. A table is a good way to organize information you have. Make a table to solve the problem.

Solve

Bracelets	1	2	3	4	5	6	7	8	9
Cost of Bracelets	$3	$6	$9	$12	$15	$18	$21	$24	$27

You know how much 1 bracelet costs. You can fill in the chart to find out how many bracelets $25 can buy. Erin can buy 8 bracelets.

Grade 4 38 Chapter 3

Skills Practice (p. 40) OL

3-7 Name ______ Date ______

Skills Practice

Problem-Solving Investigation: Choose a Strategy

Use any strategy to solve. Tell what strategy you used.

1. Admission to the skate park is $4 per child and $10 per adult. If Kristen's father brings Kristen and her friends to the skate park, how many friends can Kristen bring if they have $40 to spend? **6 friends**
   Strategy: **Sample answer: make a table**
2. At the class party, each student brings two guests. If there are 84 people at the party, how many are students? **28 students**
   Strategy: **Sample answer: make a table**
3. Connor is making squares out of toothpicks. Each square is formed from 4 toothpicks. If he has 13 toothpicks, how many squares can he build? **3 squares**
   Strategy: **Sample answer: draw a picture**
4. Richard's class was collecting clothes to donate to the shelter. Richard brought 4 pieces. Jackie and Kelly each brought 6 pieces. Hunter brought 7 pieces, and Tim brought 5 pieces. How many pieces of clothing did Richard's class collect? **28 pieces of clothing**
   Strategy: **Sample answer: draw a picture**
5. Marissa is making a necklace. She uses these beads: blue, blue, purple, green, blue, blue... What color bead is next if this pattern continues? **purple**
   Strategy: **Sample answer: look for a pattern**
6. Copy and complete the number pattern.
   6, 9, 11, 14, 16, **19**, **21**, **24**, **26**
   Strategy: **Sample answer: look for a pattern**

Grade 4 40 Chapter 3

★ indicates multi-step problem

Mixed Problem Solving

EXTRA PRACTICE See page R8.

Use any strategy to solve.

1. **Algebra** Mrs. Vargas is making costumes for a play. She needs 4 buttons for each costume. Copy and complete the table to find how many buttons she will need for 14 costumes. 56 buttons

Costumes	Buttons
1	4
2	8
4	16
6	24
8	32
10	40
12	48
14	56

2. It costs $12 for 2 admissions to miniature golf. Marcus wants to invite 9 friends. At this rate, how much would it cost for 10 people? $60

★3. Paz is making granola bars for her scout meeting. There are 8 girls in her troop including herself. If she makes 2 dozen granola bars, how many will each girl get? 3 bars

★4. Ricardo has to mail 27 party invitations. The invitations come in packs of 8 that cost $3. How much will he spend on invitations? $12

5. **Measurement** Pete spends 30 minutes a night reading. About how many hours does he spend reading each month? 15 hrs

★6. Tomas has $49. He wants to buy as many video games as he can. How many can he get at the yard sale?

21 games

★7. A parent-teacher organization sells bottled water at elementary school basketball games. They sold three cases in 20 minutes. If they continue selling bottled water at this rate, how many cases of bottled water would they sell in two hours? 18 cases

8. **Measurement** The Castros drove 64 miles to a water park. The Baxters drove 81 miles. The Klines drove 19 miles. How much farther did the Castros have to drive than the Klines? 45 miles

9. During a basketball game, Faith and Brandy each scored 4 points. Maria and Jo each scored 7 points. Dena scored 12 points. Find the total points scored by this team. 34 points

10. **WRITING IN MATH** Explain when to use the make a table strategy to solve a word problem. See Ch. 3 Answer Appendix.

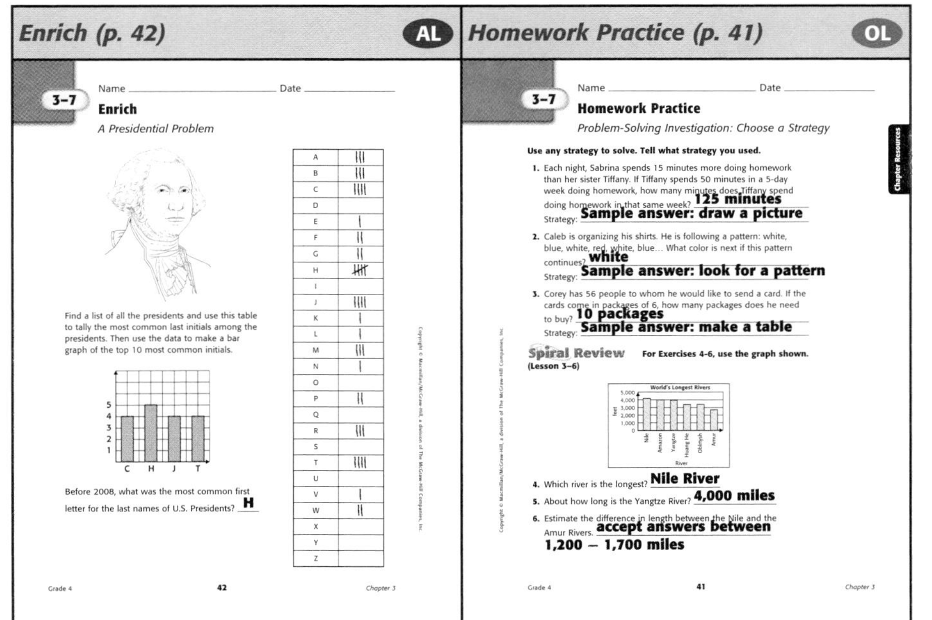

Enrich (p. 42) AL

Name ______ Date ______

3–7 **Enrich**

A Presidential Problem

A	𝍷𝍷𝍷
B	𝍷𝍷𝍷
C	𝍷𝍷𝍷𝍷
D	
E	𝍷
F	𝍷𝍷
G	𝍷𝍷
H	𝍸
I	
J	𝍷𝍷𝍷𝍷
K	𝍷
L	𝍷
M	𝍷𝍷𝍷
N	𝍷
O	
P	𝍷𝍷
Q	
R	𝍷𝍷𝍷
S	
T	𝍷𝍷𝍷𝍷
U	
V	𝍷
W	𝍷𝍷
X	
Y	
Z	

Find a list of all the presidents and use this table to tally the most common last initials among the presidents. Then use the data to make a bar graph of the top 10 most common initials.

Before 2008, what was the most common first letter for the last names of U.S. Presidents? H

Grade 4 42 Chapter 3

Homework Practice (p. 41) OL

Name ______ Date ______

3–7 **Homework Practice**

Problem-Solving Investigation: Choose a Strategy

Use any strategy to solve. Tell what strategy you used.

1. Each night, Sabrina spends 15 minutes more doing homework than her sister Tiffany. If Tiffany spends 50 minutes in a 5-day week doing homework, how many minutes does Tiffany spend doing homework in that same week? **125 minutes**
Strategy: **Sample answer: draw a picture**

2. Caleb is organizing his shirts. He is following a pattern: white, blue, white, red, white, blue… What color is next if this pattern continues? **white**
Strategy: **Sample answer: look for a pattern**

3. Corey has 56 people to whom he would like to send a card. If the cards come in packages of 6, how many packages does he need to buy? **10 packages**
Strategy: **Sample answer: make a table**

Spiral Review (Lesson 3–6) **For Exercises 4-6, use the graph shown.**

4. Which river is the longest? **Nile River**

5. About how long is the Yangtze River? **4,000 miles**

6. Estimate the difference in length between the Nile and the Amur Rivers. **accept answers between 1,200 – 1,700 miles**

Grade 4 41 Chapter 3

Chapter Resources

BL Alternate Teaching Strategy

If students have trouble making a table to solve the problem…

Then use one of these reteach options:

1 CRM **Daily Reteach Worksheet** (pp. 38–39)

2 Have students try another method, such as skip counting on a number line or using money manipulatives to work through the problem.

3 Practice

Using the Exercises

Exercises 1–9 ask students to use the four-step plan and make a table to solve the problems.

Exercise 5 may be confusing to some students. They may wonder whether they should use 28, 30, or 31 days in a month. Suggest that they use 30 days.

4 Assess

Formative Assessment

Write the following problem on the board:

Sofia is collecting cans for her school's recycling drive. She collects 8 cans on her first day. If she collects 5 more cans every day, how many days will she have to collect until she has at least 40 cans?

- **Which strategy would you use to solve this problem?** Answers may vary; Sample answer: make a table
- **What is the pattern in the table?** Add 5.
- **How many days does Sofia have to collect cans to reach 40?** 8

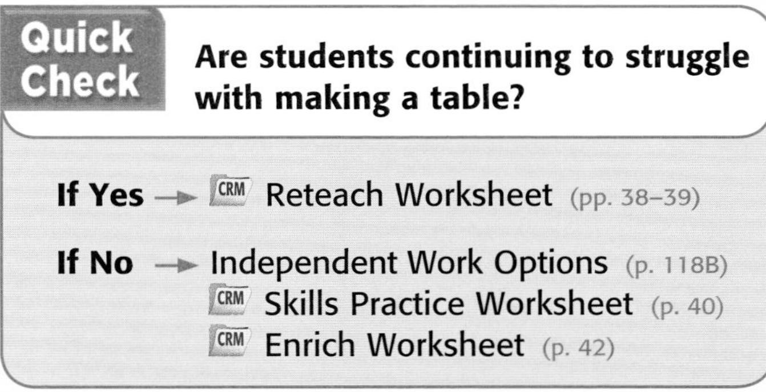

Quick Check Are students continuing to struggle with making a table?

If Yes → CRM Reteach Worksheet (pp. 38–39)

If No → Independent Work Options (p. 118B)
CRM Skills Practice Worksheet (p. 40)
CRM Enrich Worksheet (p. 42)

Lesson Planner

Objective

Interpret information and data from science to solve problems.

National Standard 

Students should develop understanding of the characteristics of organisms.

Activate Prior Knowledge

Before you turn students' attention to the pages, ask them to discuss sunflowers.

- **What quality makes the sunflower stand out among other flowers?** its height
- **Name something edible that comes from a sunflower.** sunflower seeds

Using the Student Page

Ask students to read the information on pp. 120–121 and answer these questions:

- **What is the difference between the height of a door and the height of the tallest sunflower on record?** 18 feet
- **What is the difference between the height of a fourth grade student and the width of the biggest sunflower head on record?** about 2 feet

Sunflowers are giants in the plant world. The tallest sunflower grew to a total height of 25 feet 5 inches. The size of the largest sunflower head is 32 inches across. This is almost three feet across!

Sunflowers can be used for decoration, but they are also an important source of food.

Sunflower oil is a valued and healthy vegetable oil. In addition, sunflower seeds are enjoyed as a healthy, tasty snack and nutritious ingredient in many foods.

Did You Know? The shortest sunflower on record measured just over 2 inches tall.

Real-World Math

Use the information on page 120 to solve each problem.

1. What is the tallest object on the bar graph? How tall is this object? sunflower; 25 ft
2. What is the difference in height of a sunflower and a giraffe? about 7 ft
3. What is the shortest object on the bar graph? How tall is this object? fourth grade student; almost 5 ft
4. Look at Exercise 3. Explain how you found the answer. See margin.
5. What is the difference between the tallest and shortest objects on the bar graph? about 20 ft
6. The height of how many fourth grade students equals the height of a sunflower? about 6 students

Real-World Math

Assign the exercises on p. 120. Encourage students to choose a problem-solving strategy before beginning each exercise. If necessary, review the strategies suggested in Lesson 3-7, p. 118.

Exercise 1 Tell students that for the purposes of this graph, heights are rounded to the nearest foot.

Exercise 4 Tell students to describe how they used the graph on p. 120 to give them the answer to Exercise 3.

Exercise 6 Tell students that they will need to multiply or divide to get their answer.

WRITING IN MATH Have students create a word problem that uses the information found in the text and in the chart on pp. 120–121.

Extend the Activity

Have students make a bar graph that compares heights of other objects around them to the height of a sunflower.

Additional Answer

4. Sample answer: The one with the shortest bar was the shortest object; Used estimation to solve.

Lesson Planner

Objective

Determine the possible outcomes of an experiment.

Resources

Materials: paper, pencil

Manipulatives: spinner

Teacher Technology

 macmillanmh.com

Concepts in Motion

1 Introduce

Introduce the Concept

- Assign groups of four. Provide each group with a spinner divided in 4 equal sections. Label the sections 1, 2, 3, and 4.
- **What digits are on the spinner?** 1, 2, 3, 4
- **What is the greatest sum when you spin the spinner twice?** 8 **the least sum?** 2
- Students take turns spinning and naming the sum of the digits showing.

2 Teach

Activity Be sure students understand what "multi-digit numbers" means.

Step 3 Remind students they will use the first two digits that were spun. They will need to spin again if the number is the same.

Explore Math Activity for 3-8

Possible Outcomes

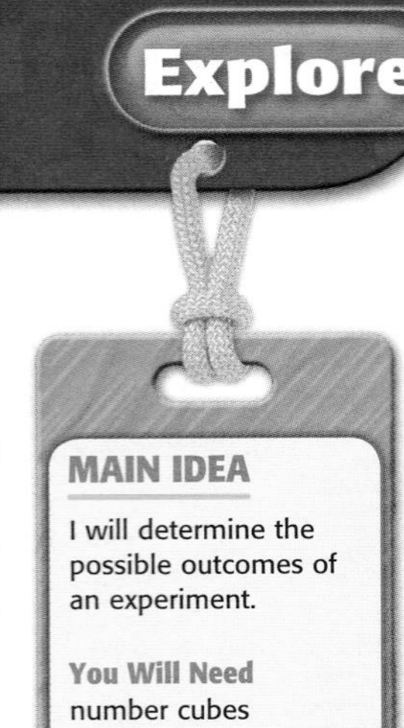

MAIN IDEA

I will determine the possible outcomes of an experiment.

You Will Need

number cubes labeled 0–5

spinner labeled 1–4

Math Online macmillanmh.com

Possible **outcomes** are all of the results that could occur from an experiment. In this activity, you will explore the possible outcomes of an experiment.

ACTIVITY

1 **Use a spinner to create multi-digit numbers.**

Step 1 **Spin a spinner like the one shown two times.**

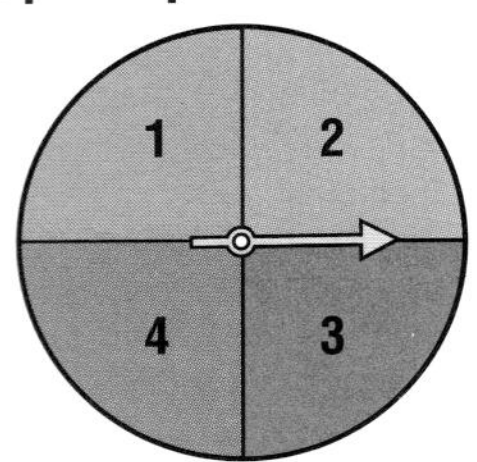

Step 2 **Create two-digit numbers.**

Use each digit once to make as many two-digit numbers as possible. Record the numbers.

Step 3 **Create three-digit numbers.**

Spin the spinner a third time. If it lands on a digit already spun, spin again. Use the two digits spun in step 1 and the digit you just spun to make as many three-digit numbers as possible. Remember to use each digit only once. Record the numbers you made.

Step 4 **Create four-digit numbers.**

Spin a fourth digit to go with the three digits you previously spun. If the spinner lands on a digit you already have, spin again. Use the fourth digit to create as many numbers as possible.

Think About It

1. How many two-digit numbers can be made with two digits, if each digit is used only once? 2

2. How many three-digit numbers can be made with three digits, if each digit is used only once? 6

3. How many four-digit numbers can be made with four digits, if each digit is used only once? 24

4. Describe the strategy you used to find the numbers you made. Sample answer: I used number cubes. I moved one number cube at a time until I found all the possible outcomes.

CHECK What You Know

Determine all the possible outcomes for each situation.

5. What are all the possible outcomes if the spinner is spun twice?

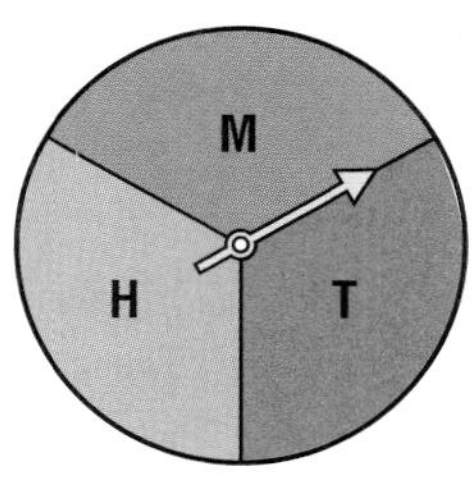

6. Describe an outcome that is not possible if two connecting cubes are chosen from the bag at a time.

5, 6. See Ch. 3 Answer Appendix.

7. What are all the possible outcomes if the coin is flipped twice?

Head Head, Tail Tail, Head Tail, Tail Head

8. What are all the possible outcomes if two counters are each flipped once?

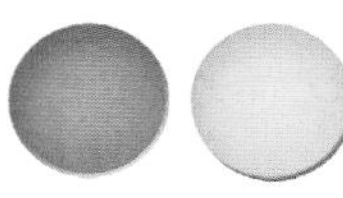

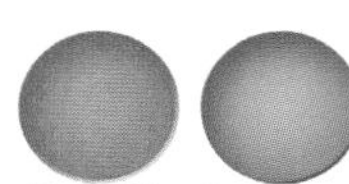

8, 9. See Ch. 3 Answer Appendix.

9. WRITING IN MATH Create an experiment using two spinners. What are all the possible outcomes for that experiment? How did you find all the possible outcomes? What predictions can you make?

Think About It

Assign Exercises 1–4 in the **Think About It** section to assess student comprehension of the concept presented in the Activity.

3 Assess

Formative Assessment

Use **Check What You Know** Exercises 5–8 to assess whether students comprehend how to determine the possible outcomes that could occur from an experiment.

From Concrete to Abstract Use Exercise 9 to determine if students have made the transition from using manipulatives to understanding the concept of possible outcomes.

Extending the Concept

- Have three volunteers line up side by side on the left side of the classroom, each holding one object: a book, a piece of paper, or a ruler.
- Have three other volunteers line up on the right side of the room, each holding one object: a pen, a pencil, or a crayon.
- Have the volunteers model the possible outcomes of choosing an object from the left and one from the right by having one student from each group step forward to show each possible outcome.
- Have another student record the outcomes on the board.

LESSON 3-8

Determine Possible Outcomes

Lesson Planner

Objective

Use pictures to find all the possible outcomes in a problem situation.

Vocabulary

outcome, **tree diagram**

Resources

Materials: index cards

Manipulates: coins, spinners

Literature Connection: *Do You Wanna Bet? Your Chance to Find Out About Probability* by Jean Cushman and Martha Westman

Teacher Technology
TeacherWorks • Interactive Classroom

Daily Routine

Use these suggestions before beginning the lesson on p. 124.

5-Minute Check

(Reviews Lesson 3-7)

Use any strategy to solve. Tell what strategy you used.
Ted is buying fishing rods at a sale. The first rod he buys costs $25. Each additional rod costs $2 less than the previous rod. How much does the fourth fishing rod cost? $19; make a table

Problem of the Day

Miss Jones has to drive 700 miles to a sales conference. If she drives 320 miles on the first day and 245 miles on the second day, how far must she drive on the third day? 135 mi

Focus on Math Background

Drawing a tree diagram is another technique that shows outcomes. This method is especially useful when the grid method cannot be used, i.e., there are more than two steps to an experiment. Students will list outcomes for one step. Then, all the outcomes for the second step are listed for each outcome for the first step. They do the same for the next step. One limitation is that a tree diagram can expand quickly.

Building Math Vocabulary

Write the lesson vocabulary word and its definition on the board.

Have students write the new term in their Math Journals. Have students describe a tree, stating the fact that a tree has a trunk and branches. As you work through the lesson, relate the tree diagram to this description.

Differentiated Instruction

Small Group Options

LOGICAL, VISUAL, SPATIAL

Option 1 Below Level BL

Materials: one number cube for each student and one spinner for each student that is equally divided in four parts, with each part colored red, blue, green, and yellow respectively, paper, pencils

- Ask the students to determine how many different outcomes they can make with the number cube and the spinner. 24 different outcomes
- Give an example by rolling the number cube once and spinning the spinner once and recording your answer on a piece of paper.
- Encourage the students to make an organized list.

AUDITORY

Option 2 English Language Learners ELL

Core Vocabulary: maybe, yes, no
Common Use Verb: happen
Hear Math This strategy asks students questions about events in their life to introduce the concept of probability.

- Say: "Probability means if something will ***happen*** or not. I am going to ask you questions about your life and you should answer **yes**, **no**, or **maybe**."
- Demonstrate using thumbs up for yes, thumbs down for no, and a thumb sideways for maybe.
- Ask: "Who is going to eat lunch? Who is going to go to college? Who is going to sleep after school?"
- Remind students of the definition if answers reflect a lack of understanding.

Independent Work Options

LINGUISTIC, VISUAL

Option 1 Early Finishers AL

Materials: index card, paper, pencil

- On the front of the index card, each student writes the names of three types of pants such as blue jeans, denim shorts, sweat pants and the colors of four pairs of socks, such as white, brown, black, red.
- On the other side, the student draws a tree diagram to show all the possible combinations of clothing.
- Students exchange cards, draw tree diagrams for the card received. Partners discuss the tree diagrams and must agree that they are correct.

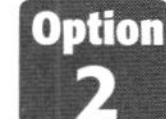

Option 2 Student Technology

Math Online macmillanmh.com

Personal Tutor • Extra Examples

Option 3 Learning Station Science (p. 92I)

Direct students to the Science Learning Station for opportunities to explore and extend the lesson concept.

Option 4 Problem-Solving Practice

Reinforce problem-solving skills and strategies with the Problem-Solving Practice worksheet.

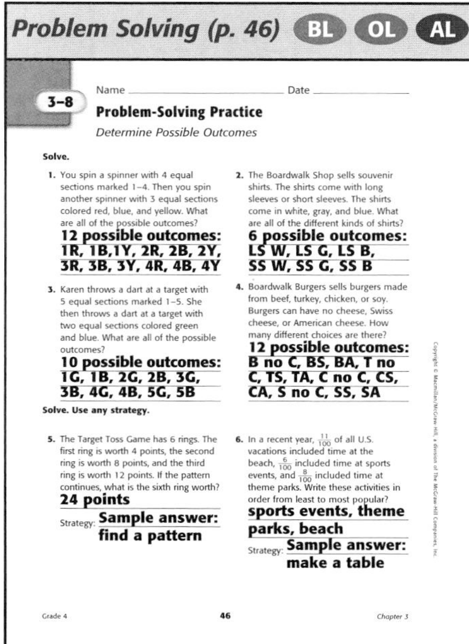

Problem Solving (p. 46) BL OL AL

3–8

Name ____________ Date ____________

Problem-Solving Practice

Determine Possible Outcomes

Solve.

1. You spin a spinner with 4 equal sections marked 1–4. Then you spin another spinner with 3 equal sections colored red, blue, and yellow. What are all of the possible outcomes?
12 possible outcomes: 1R, 1B,1Y, 2R, 2B, 2Y, 3R, 3B, 3Y, 4R, 4B, 4Y

2. The Boardwalk Shop sells souvenir shirts. The shirts come with long sleeves or short sleeves. The shirts come in white, gray, and blue. What are all of the different kinds of shirts?
6 possible outcomes: LS W, LS G, LS B, SS W, SS G, SS B

3. Karen throws a dart at a target with 5 equal sections marked 1–5. She then throws a dart at a target with two equal sections colored green and blue. What are all of the possible outcomes?
10 possible outcomes: 1G, 1B, 2G, 2B, 3G, 3B, 4G, 4B, 5G, 5B

4. Boardwalk Burgers sells burgers made from beef, turkey, chicken, or soy. Burgers can have no cheese, Swiss cheese, or American cheese. How many different choices are there?
12 possible outcomes: B no C, BS, BA, T no C, TS, TA, C no C, CS, CA, S no C, SS, SA

Solve. Use any strategy.

5. The Target Toss Game has 6 rings. The first ring is worth 4 points, the second ring is worth 8 points, and the third ring is worth 12 points. If the pattern continues, what is the sixth ring worth?
24 points
Strategy: **Sample answer: find a pattern**

6. In a recent year, $\frac{11}{100}$ of all U.S. vacations included time at the beach, $\frac{6}{100}$ included time at sports events, and $\frac{8}{100}$ included time at theme parks. Write these activities in order from least to most popular?
sports events, theme parks, beach
Strategy: **Sample answer: make a table**

Grade 4 46 Chapter 3

Determine Possible Outcomes

1 Introduce

Activity Choice 1 • Hands-On

- Give each pair of students three index cards labeled "sausage," "mushrooms," and "pepperoni." Also give them two small triangles labeled "thick" and "thin."
- Tell them that they are going to make pizzas that consist of one type of crust (triangle) and one topping (square). Have them make as many different types of pizzas as they can and record the results.
- **What is one type of pizza you could make?** Sample answer: thick crust with mushrooms
- **How many different outcomes of pizza are possible?** 6

Activity Choice 2 • Literature

Introduce the lesson with *Do You Wanna Bet? Your Chance to Find Out About Probability* by Jean Cushman and Martha Westman. For a related math activity, see p. TR45.

2 Teach

Scaffolding Questions

Display a coin.

- **How many sides are there for this coin?** 2
- **If you flip this coin, what are the possible outcomes?** H, T
- **Suppose you flip this coin twice? What is the outcome for the first flip?** H or T **For the second flip?** H or T
- **How many possible outcomes are there for flipping a coin twice? Explain.** 4; accept and record all answers on the board. Discuss the explanations

GET READY to Learn

Have students open their books and read the information in **Get Ready to Learn**. Introduce **tree diagram**. As a class, work through **Examples 1 and 2**.

3-8 Determine Possible Outcomes

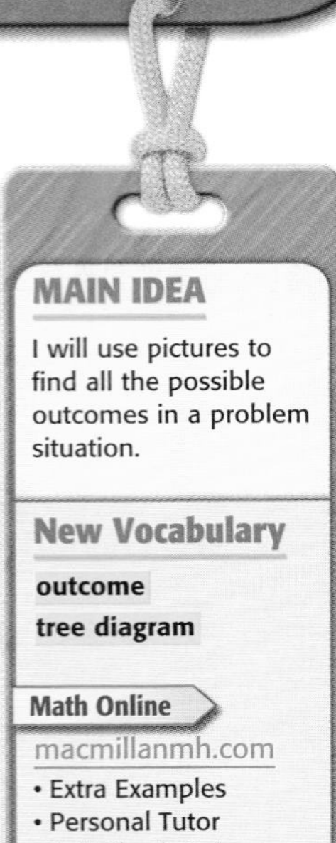

MAIN IDEA

I will use pictures to find all the possible outcomes in a problem situation.

New Vocabulary

outcome
tree diagram

Math Online

macmillanmh.com
- Extra Examples
- Personal Tutor
- Self-Check Quiz

GET READY to Learn

In a basketball game, Samantha went to the free-throw line. She attempted to make a basket twice. What are all the possible combinations of her free throws?

In the previous Explore Activity, you learned that an **outcome** is a result in an experiment. You can use a grid to help you find outcomes.

EXAMPLE Determine Outcomes

1 **SPORTS How many possible outcomes does Samantha have for her two free throws?**

You know that Samantha attempted to make a basket twice.

One way to find the possible outcomes is by making a grid. On a grid, each outcome is shown where each row and column intersect.

First Shot	Second Shot: Make	Second Shot: Miss
Make	Make, Make	Make, Miss
Miss	Miss, Make	Miss, Miss

These are Samantha's possible outcomes.

So, there are 4 possible outcomes.

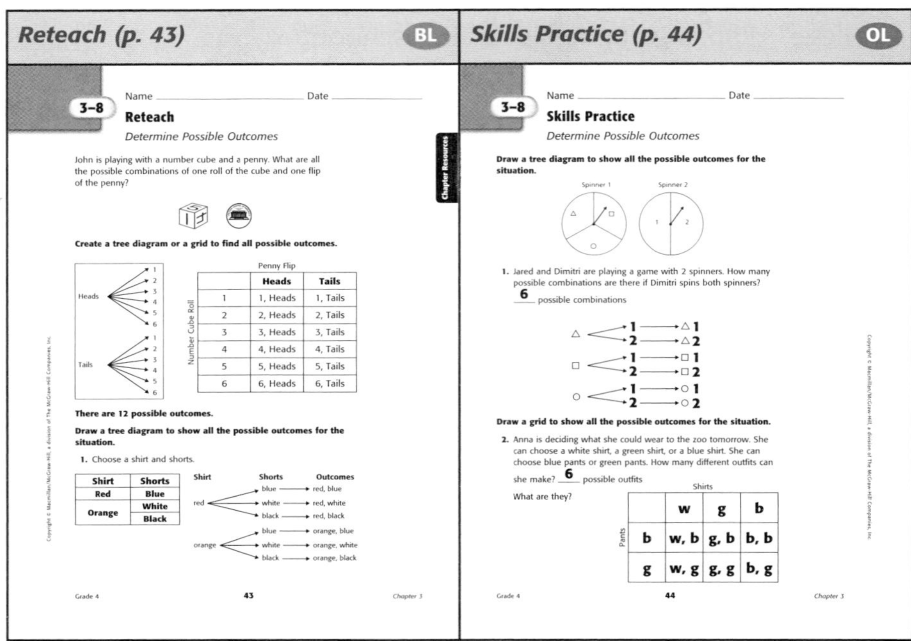

Reteach (p. 43) BL

3–8 Name ______ Date ______

Reteach

Determine Possible Outcomes

John is playing with a number cube and a penny. What are all the possible combinations of one roll of the cube and one flip of the penny?

Create a tree diagram or a grid to find all possible outcomes.

Heads → 1, 2, 3, 4, 5, 6
Tails → 1, 2, 3, 4, 5, 6

Penny Flip

Number Cube Roll	Heads	Tails
1	1, Heads	1, Tails
2	2, Heads	2, Tails
3	3, Heads	3, Tails
4	4, Heads	4, Tails
5	5, Heads	5, Tails
6	6, Heads	6, Tails

There are 12 possible outcomes.

Draw a tree diagram to show all the possible outcomes for the situation.

1. Choose a shirt and shorts.

Shirt	Shorts
Red	Blue
Orange	White
	Black

Shirt	Shorts	Outcomes
red	blue	red, blue
	white	red, white
	black	red, black
orange	blue	orange, blue
	white	orange, white
	black	orange, black

Grade 4 43 Chapter 3

Chapter Resources

Skills Practice (p. 44) OL

3–8 Name ______ Date ______

Skills Practice

Determine Possible Outcomes

Draw a tree diagram to show all the possible outcomes for the situation.

Spinner 1: △, □, ○
Spinner 2: 1, 2

1. Jared and Dimitri are playing a game with 2 spinners. How many possible combinations are there if Dimitri spins both spinners?
   6 possible combinations

△ → 1 → △1; 2 → △2
□ → 1 → □1; 2 → □2
○ → 1 → ○1; 2 → ○2

Draw a grid to show all the possible outcomes for the situation.

2. Anna is deciding what she could wear to the zoo tomorrow. She can choose a white shirt, a green shirt, or a blue shirt. She can choose blue pants or green pants. How many different outfits can she make? **6** possible outfits
   What are they?

Shirts

Pants	w	g	b
b	w, b	g, b	b, b
g	w, g	g, g	b, g

Grade 4 44 Chapter 3

Another way to find the possible outcomes is by using a **tree diagram**. A tree diagram uses "branches" to show all the possible outcomes.

EXAMPLE Possible Outcomes

2 **A student is spinning two spinners. How many possible outcomes are there?**

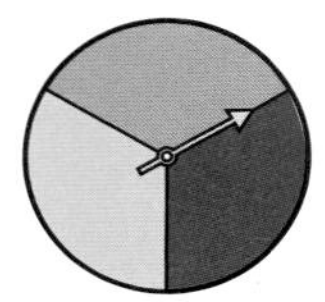

A tree diagram can be used to find all the possible outcomes for spinning both spinners.

First Spinner	Second Spinner	Outcomes
Orange	Red →	Orange, Red
	Blue →	Orange, Blue
Purple	Red →	Purple, Red
	Blue →	Purple, Blue
Yellow	Red →	Yellow, Red
	Blue →	Yellow, Blue

So, there are 6 possible outcomes.

CHECK What You Know

1. Draw a grid to find the number of possible outcomes if the spinner is spun twice. See Example 1 (p. 124)
   1–3. See Ch. 3 Answer Appendix.

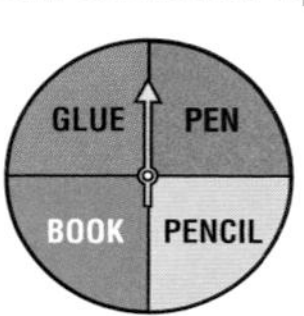

2. Draw a tree diagram to find the number of possible outcomes if the coin is tossed and the spinner is spun. See Example 2 (p. 125)

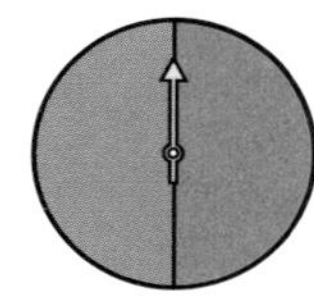

3. Talk About It In Exercise 2, what generalization can be made about determining all possible outcomes?

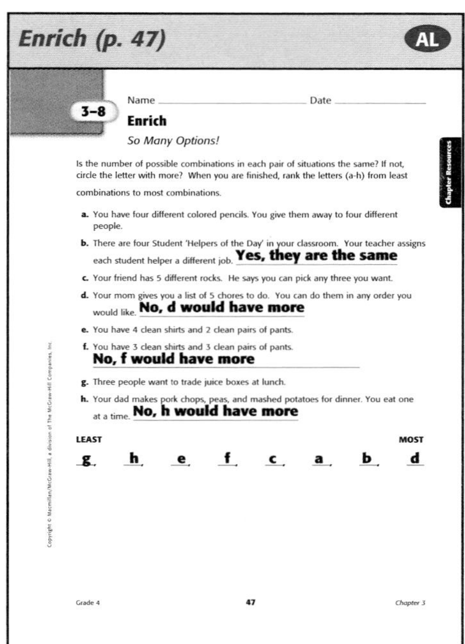

Enrich (p. 47) AL

3–8

Name ______________ Date ______________

Enrich

So Many Options!

Is the number of possible combinations in each pair of situations the same? If not, circle the letter with more? When you are finished, rank the letters (a-h) from least combinations to most combinations.

a. You have four different colored pencils. You give them away to four different people.

b. There are four Student 'Helpers of the Day' in your classroom. Your teacher assigns each student helper a different job. **Yes, they are the same**

c. Your friend has 5 different rocks. He says you can pick any three you want.

d. Your mom gives you a list of 5 chores to do. You can do them in any order you would like. **No, d would have more**

e. You have 4 clean shirts and 2 clean pairs of pants.

f. You have 3 clean shirts and 3 clean pairs of pants. **No, f would have more**

g. Three people want to trade juice boxes at lunch.

h. Your dad makes pork chops, peas, and mashed potatoes for dinner. You eat one at a time. **No, h would have more**

LEAST g. h. e. f. c. a. b. d MOST

Chapter Resources

Grade 4 47 Chapter 3

Determine Outcomes

Example 1 Be sure students understand they are counting the outcomes in the cells, and that this does not include all of the cells in the grid.

ADDITIONAL EXAMPLES

1 Nicole flipped a coin twice. Make a grid to show the possible outcomes.

First flip / Second flip	HEADS	TAILS
HEADS	H, H	H, T
TAILS	T, H	T, T

2 Suppose you have one spinner with 3 sections: sandwich, hot dog, hamburger. You have another spinner with four sections: mustard, ketchup, salsa, mayonnaise. How many possible combinations are there? 12

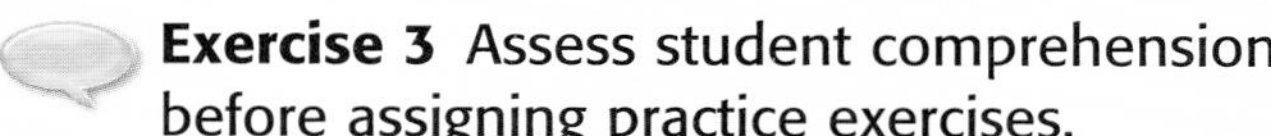

As a class, have students complete Exercises 1–3 in **Check What You Know** as you observe their work.

Exercise 3 Assess student comprehension before assigning practice exercises.

BL Alternate Teaching Strategy

If students have trouble finding all possible outcomes in a problem situation…

Then use one of these reteach options:

1. CRM **Daily Reteach Worksheet** (p. 43)
2. Have volunteers make two spinners to model Example 2. Have students take turns spinning and recording the results in a grid.

- **How can you fill in the grid without any more spinning?** Accept all reasonable answers.

3 Practice

Differentiate practice using these leveled assignments for Exercises 4–11.

Level	Assignment
BL Below/Approaching Level	4–5, 8–9
OL On Level	5–9, 11
AL Above/Beyond Level	4–8 even, 10–11

Have students discuss and complete the Higher Order Thinking problems. Have students estimate the number of possible outcomes before they make to a grid or draw a tree diagram.

WRITING IN ▶MATH Have students complete Exercise 11 in their Math Journals. You may choose to use this as an optional formative assessment.

! COMMON ERROR!

Exercise 9 Students may be confused by this question. Have students look at their tree diagram. Point out that for this question, the combination Banded Tulip-Horse Conch is considered the same as Horse Conch-Banded Tulip.

Practice and Problem Solving

See page R9.

Draw a grid to find the number of possible outcomes for each situation. See Example 1 (p. 124) 4–7. See Ch. 3 Answer Appendix.

4. How many outcomes are possible if the spinner below is spun twice?

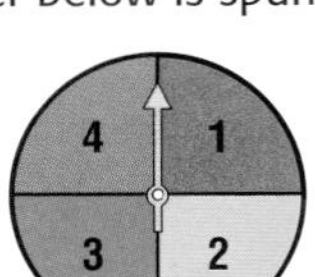

5. How many outcomes are possible if the 5–10 number cube is rolled twice?

Draw a tree diagram to find the number of possible outcomes for each situation. See Example 2 (p. 125)

6. How many outcomes are possible if the spinners are spun?

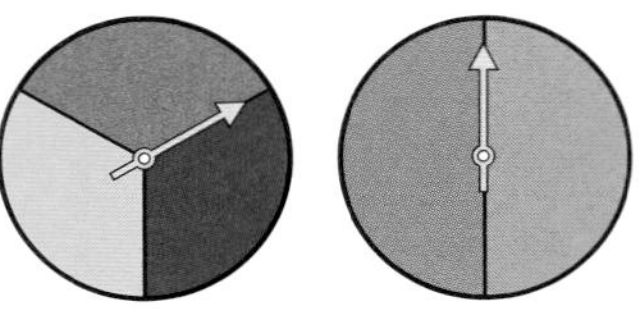

7. How many outcomes are possible if the 0–5 number cube is rolled and the spinner is spun?

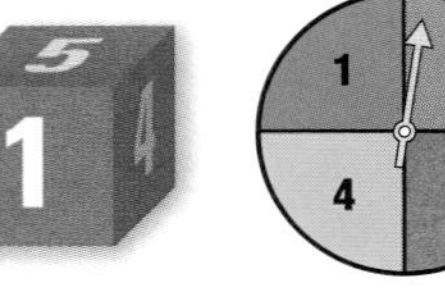

Data File

The shells in the table are found in Louisiana and other states along the Gulf Coast.

Shells of the Gulf Coast
Atlantic Shark Eye
Banded Tulip
Horse Conch
Lightning Whelk

Source: *Sea Shells of the World*

8. Make a tree diagram to show all the two-shell combinations that are possible from the shells listed in the table if each shell is used once. See Ch. 3 Answer Appendix.

9. After you take out shell combinations that are the same, how many combinations are left? 6

H.O.T. Problems

10. **OPEN ENDED** Create two spinners with at least three different colors on each spinner. The possible combinations of the spinners must include red more often than any other color. See margin.

11. **WRITING IN ▶MATH** In Exercise 10, what generalization can you make about determining all possible combinations? See Ch. 3 Answer Appendix.

Additional Answer

10.

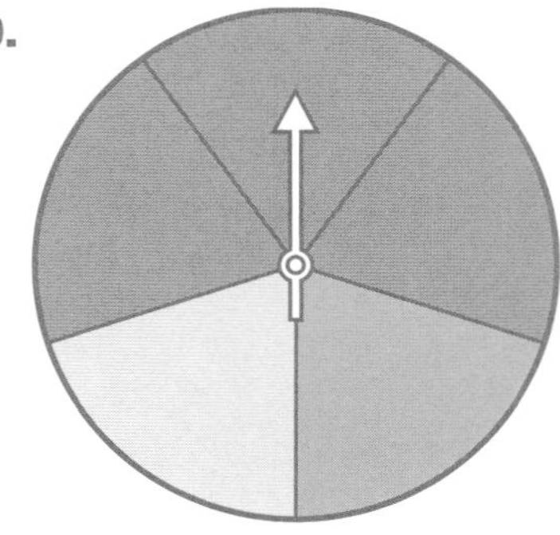

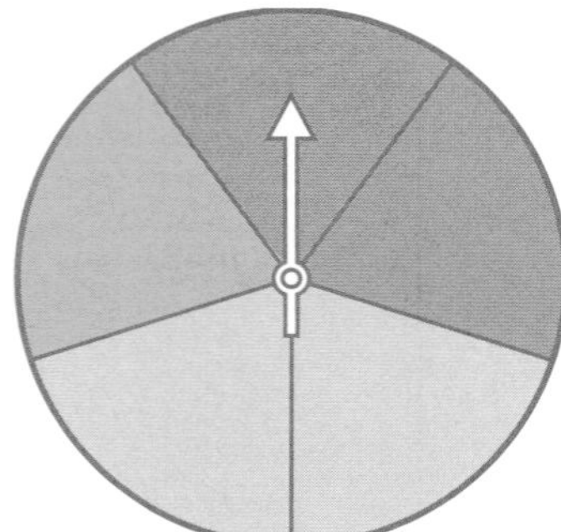

12. About how many more moons does Saturn have than Uranus? (Lesson 3-6)

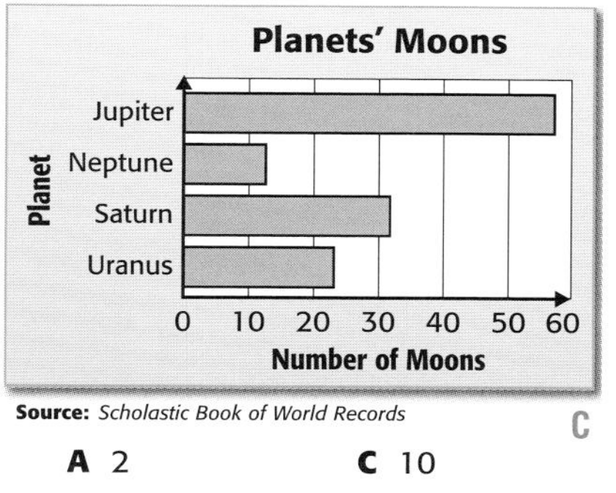

Source: *Scholastic Book of World Records* C

A 2   C 10

B 5   D 15

13. If Ellis spins the arrow twice, which of these is **NOT** a possible outcome? (Lesson 3-8) G

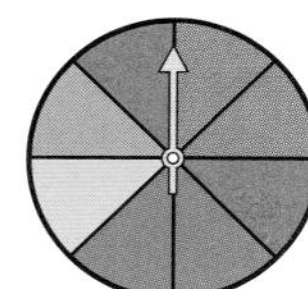

F Blue, blue

G Red, purple

H Yellow, red

J Green, blue

Spiral Review

14. There were 2,367 students buying lunch on Monday. On Wednesday there were 2,745 buying lunch. If 45 more students bought lunch on Tuesday than Monday, how many lunches were sold on those three days in all? (Lesson 3-7) 7,524 lunches

For Exercises 15–18, use the graph that shows speeds of land animals. (Lesson 3-6)

Speeds of Land Animals

Antelope, Cheetah, Elephant, Lion (Animal)

0 10 20 30 40 50 60 70 80

Speed (miles per hour)

15. How fast can an antelope run? 60 mph

16. Which animal can run 35 miles per hour faster than an elephant? antelope

17. How much faster can a cheetah run than a lion? 20 mph

18. Which animal can run twice as fast as an elephant? lion

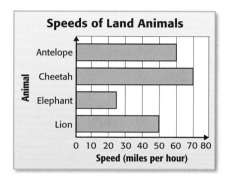

Compare. Use >, <, or =. (Lesson 1-4)

19. 2,483 ● 2,438 >   **20.** 42,395 ● 42,935 <   **21.** 739,305 ● 739,305 =

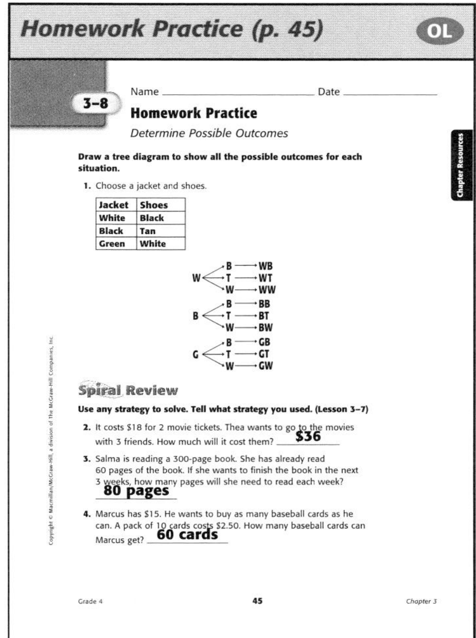

Homework Practice (p. 45) OL

3-8 Name ______ Date ______

Homework Practice

Determine Possible Outcomes

Draw a tree diagram to show all the possible outcomes for each situation.

1. Choose a jacket and shoes.

Jacket	Shoes
White	Black
Black	Tan
Green	White

W — B → WB, T → WT, W → WW

B — B → BB, T → BT, W → BW

G — B → GB, T → GT, W → GW

Spiral Review

Use any strategy to solve. Tell what strategy you used. (Lesson 3-7)

2. It costs $18 for 2 movie tickets. Thea wants to go to the movies with 3 friends. How much will it cost them? $36

3. Salma is reading a 300-page book. She has already read 60 pages of the book. If she wants to finish the book in the next 3 weeks, how many pages will she need to read each week? 80 pages

4. Marcus has $15. He wants to buy as many baseball cards as he can. A pack of 10 cards costs $2.50. How many baseball cards can Marcus get? 60 cards

Grade 4   45   Chapter 3

Formative Assessment

Display two spinners: one spinner with 3 sections, labeled with the names of 3 boys; the other spinner labeled with names of 4 playground items, such as swing, slide, merry-go-round, and climbing gym.

- **Make a grid to show all the possible outtcomes of boys and playground items.** 12 outcomes; Check students' grids.
- **Make a tree diagram to show all the possible outcomes.** 12 outcomes; Check students' diagrams.

Quick Check **Are students continuing to struggle with using pictures to find all possible outcomes in a problem situation?**

If Yes → Small Group Options (p. 124B)
Strategic Intervention Guide (p. 130)

If No → Independent Work Options (p. 124B)
CRM Skills Practice Worksheet (p. 44)
CRM Enrich Worksheet (p. 47)

Into the Future Tell students that in the next lesson, they will need to find all possible outcomes in a problem situation in order to calculate probability. Have them write about how they think what they learned about grids and tree diagrams will help them with the next lesson.

TEST Practice

Reviews Lessons 3-6 and 3-8

Assign the Test Practice problems to provide daily reinforcement of test-taking skills.

Spiral Review

Reviews Lessons 1-4, 3-6, and 3-7

Review and assess mastery of skills and concepts from previous chapters.

LESSON 3-9

Probability

Lesson Planner

Objective

Describe probability with words and numbers.

Vocabulary

probability

Resources

Materials: marbles and small bowls

Manipulatives: connecting cubes

Literature Connection: *Same Old Horse* by Stuart J. Murphy

Teacher Technology

TeacherWorks • Interactive Classroom

Focus on Math Background

Students need to explore a variety of situations involving chance or uncertainty to gain an understanding of probability, as well as a sense of what kinds of things are usual or unusual. Informal descriptions help them develop a "probability vocabulary" that is essential to later quantitative study. In listing all possible outcomes of a process, they identify a *sample space* for a probability *experiment*. At the same time, they lay the groundwork for identifying a *probability distribution*, which is a list of all outcomes and their associated probabilities. They will also later learn that an *event* consists of a collection of one or more outcomes.

In this lesson, students will describe probability with words and numbers. Later in the book, on page *R76*, students will use fractions to describe probability.

Daily Routine

Use these suggestions before beginning the lesson on p. 128.

5-Minute Check

(Reviews Lesson 3-8)

A bag holds 4 marbles: yellow, red, green, blue. A box holds 3 marbles: purple, brown, white. Draw a tree diagram to show all the possible outcomes of picking one marble from each container.

Bag	Box	Outcomes
Y	P	Y, P
	B	Y, B
	W	Y, W
R	P	R, P
	B	R, B
	W	R, W
G	P	G, P
	B	G, B
	W	G, W
B	P	B, P
	B	B, B
	W	B, W

Problem of the Day

Rafael leaves home and walks 5 blocks west, then 3 blocks north, and then 2 blocks east. How many blocks is the shortest walk back home? 6 blocks

Building Math Vocabulary

Write the lesson vocabulary word and its definition on the board.

Ask students to write the word in a sentence. Ask them to then write a third sentence using both words. Have students take turns reading this third sentence aloud. Discuss any misunderstandings of the definitions if they arise.

Visual Vocabulary Cards

Use Visual Vocabulary Card 40 to reinforce the vocabulary reviewed in this lesson. (The Define/Example/Ask routine is printed on the back of each card.)

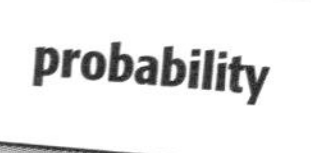

Differentiated Instruction

Small Group Options

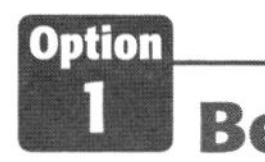

LOGICAL, SOCIAL

Below Level BL

Materials: copies for each student of a blank yearly calendar from any year, pencils, paper

- Review the terms *impossible, certain, likely,* and *unlikely*.
- Tell students that their task is to write one statement for each term using the calendar to help them.
- They may work in pairs. Give them an example or two to get them started.

"It is unlikely we will have snow in July."
"If today is Monday, it is impossible for tomorrow to be Wednesday."

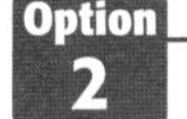

AUDITORY

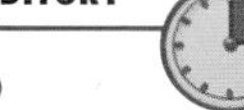

English Language Learners ELL

Core Vocabulary: maybe, whether or not, future
Common Use Verb: will happen
Hear Math This strategy asks students questions about events in their life to extend the concept of probability.

- Review probability as something that will or might happen.
- Tell students you are going to ask them questions about their life and they should answer yes, no, or maybe.
- Draw a line with yes and no on either end, and maybe in the center. Model asking a question and placing your hand near the most probable answer.
- Repeat, allowing students to create their own questions to answer.

English Language Learners (p. 203) ELL

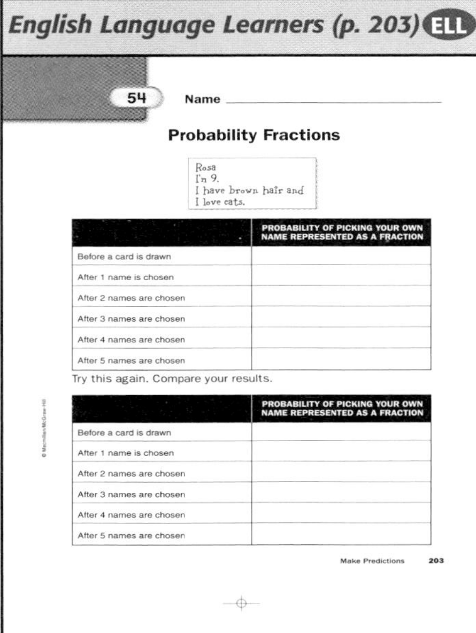

54 Name

Probability Fractions

Rosa
I'm 9.
I have brown hair and
I love cats.

	PROBABILITY OF PICKING YOUR OWN NAME REPRESENTED AS A FRACTION
Before a card is drawn	
After 1 name is chosen	
After 2 names are chosen	
After 3 names are chosen	
After 4 names are chosen	
After 5 names are chosen	

Try this again. Compare your results.

	PROBABILITY OF PICKING YOUR OWN NAME REPRESENTED AS A FRACTION
Before a card is drawn	
After 1 name is chosen	
After 2 names are chosen	
After 3 names are chosen	
After 4 names are chosen	
After 5 names are chosen	

Make Predictions 203

Use this worksheet to provide additional support for English Language Learners.

Independent Work Options

Option 1

LINGUISTIC, SOCIAL

Early Finishers OL AL

Materials: pre-made index cards describing spinners

- Students will need to make spinners according to the directions on the card. For example, their index card may say: 6 equal sections; possible colors—red, yellow, blue, and green; likely—blue; unlikely—yellow; impossible—green. The result could be a spinner with 4 blue sections, 1 yellow, and 1 red.
- Provide each pair of students with two index cards describing the spinners they should make. Have them work together and discuss their results.

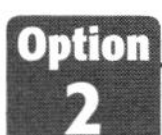

Student Technology

Math Online macmillanmh.com

Personal Tutor • Extra Examples

Option 3

Learning Station: Music (p. 92J)

Direct students to the Music Learning Station for opportunities to explore and extend the lesson concept.

Option 4

Problem-Solving Practice

Reinforce problem-solving skills and strategies with the Problem-Solving Practice worksheet.

Problem Solving (p. 51) BL OL AL

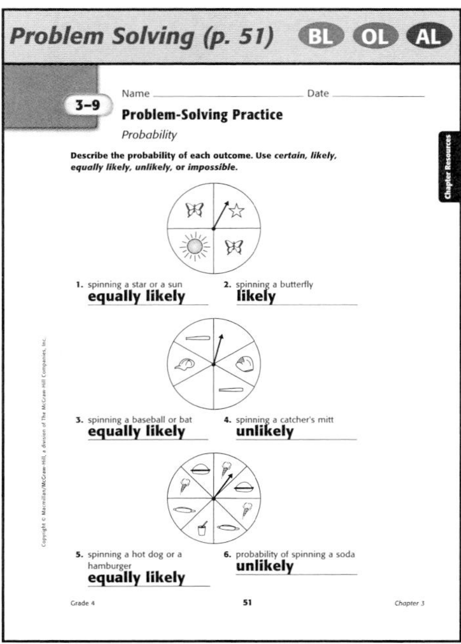

3–9 Name Date

Problem-Solving Practice

Probability

Describe the probability of each outcome. Use *certain, likely, equally likely, unlikely,* or *impossible*.

1. spinning a star or a sun **equally likely**
2. spinning a butterfly **likely**
3. spinning a baseball or bat **equally likely**
4. spinning a catcher's mitt **unlikely**
5. spinning a hot dog or a hamburger **equally likely**
6. probability of spinning a soda **unlikely**

Grade 4 51 Chapter 3

3-9 Probability

1 Introduce

Activity Choice 1 • Hands-On 

- Show students 20 red and 5 green connecting cubes. **If I reach into the bowl without looking, do you think I will get a red or green cube? Why?** red; Sample answer: There are many more red cubes than green cubes.
- Show students 10 orange, 5 purple, and 5 green cubes. **What are the chances I will get a white cube?** None, it is impossible.
- Show students a dozen yellow cubes. **What are the chances I will get a yellow cube?** It is a sure thing; it is certain.
- Using these and other examples, help students use the words *likely, unlikely, equally likely, certain,* and *impossible* to describe probability.

Activity Choice 2 • Literature

Introduce the lesson with *Same Old Horse* by Stuart J. Murphy. For a related math activity, see p. TR45.

2 Teach

Scaffolding Questions

Divide the class into pairs or small groups. Provide each group with 8 red, 2 green, 2 orange, 1 yellow, and 3 purple gumballs.

- **If you were to pick one without looking, what color are you most likely to get?** red
- **It is equally likely you will pick green and what color?** orange
- **Do you think you will pick yellow?** Sample answer: It is unlikely.
- Explain that in this example, no outcome is certain.
- **What are the chances you will choose a white gumball?** impossible

GET READY to Learn

Have students open their books and read the information in **Get Ready to Learn**. Introduce **probability**. As a class, work through **Examples 1 and 2**.

3-9 Probability

MAIN IDEA

I will describe probability with words and numbers.

New Vocabulary

probability

Math Online

macmillanmh.com

- Extra Examples
- Personal Tutor
- Self-Check Quiz

GET READY to Learn

Only Sophie knew the colors of the marbles in the bag. She asked Marta to reach in and choose a marble without looking. What color do you think Marta will grab?

The chance that an outcome will occur is its **probability**. The words *certain, likely, equally likely, unlikely,* and *impossible* can describe probability.

certain to choose red

likely to choose red

equally likely to choose red or blue

unlikely to choose red

impossible to choose red

EXAMPLE Use Words to Describe Probability

1 **Describe how likely it is that Marta will choose a yellow marble from Sophie's bag.**

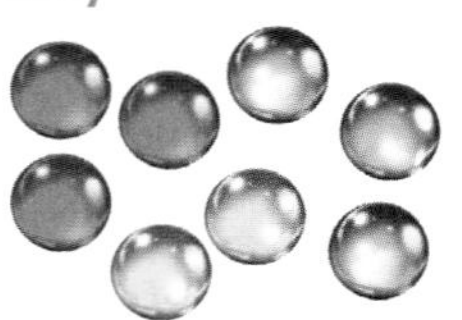

There are 8 marbles in the bag, and 2 are yellow.

In the bag, less than half of the marbles are yellow. So, it is *unlikely* that Marta will choose a yellow marble.

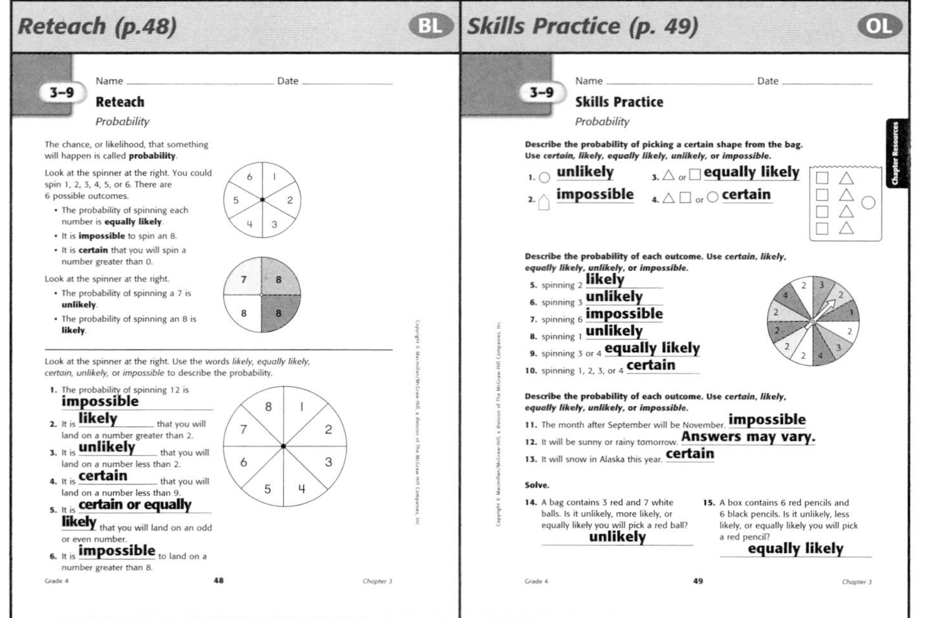

Reteach (p.48) BL

3-9 Name ____ Date ____

Reteach

Probability

The chance, or likelihood, that something will happen is called **probability**.

Look at the spinner at the right. You could spin 1, 2, 3, 4, 5, or 6. There are 6 possible outcomes.

- The probability of spinning each number is **equally likely**.
- It is **impossible** to spin an 8.
- It is **certain** that you will spin a number greater than 0.

Look at the spinner at the right.

- The probability of spinning a 7 is **unlikely**.
- The probability of spinning an 8 is **likely**.

Look at the spinner at the right. Use the words *likely, equally likely, certain, unlikely,* or *impossible* to describe the probability.

1. The probability of spinning 12 is **impossible**
2. It is **likely** that you will land on a number greater than 2.
3. It is **unlikely** that you will land on a number less than 2.
4. It is **certain** that you will land on a number less than 9.
5. It is **certain or equally likely** that you will land on an odd or even number.
6. It is **impossible** to land on a number greater than 8.

Grade 4 48 Chapter 3

Skills Practice (p. 49) OL

3-9 Name ____ Date ____

Skills Practice

Probability

Chapter Resources

Describe the probability of picking a certain shape from the bag. Use *certain, likely, equally likely, unlikely,* or *impossible*.

1. ○ **unlikely**
2. ⌂ **impossible**
3. △ or □ **equally likely**
4. △ □ or ○ **certain**

Describe the probability of each outcome. Use *certain, likely, equally likely, unlikely,* or *impossible*.

5. spinning 2 **likely**
6. spinning 3 **unlikely**
7. spinning 6 **impossible**
8. spinning 1 **unlikely**
9. spinning 3 or 4 **equally likely**
10. spinning 1, 2, 3, or 4 **certain**

Describe the probability of each outcome. Use *certain, likely, equally likely, unlikely,* or *impossible*.

11. The month after September will be November. **impossible**
12. It will be sunny or rainy tomorrow. **Answers may vary.**
13. It will snow in Alaska this year. **certain**

Solve.

14. A bag contains 3 red and 7 white balls. Is it unlikely, more likely, or equally likely you will pick a red ball? **unlikely**
15. A box contains 6 red pencils and 6 black pencils. Is it unlikely, less likely, or equally likely you will pick a red pencil? **equally likely**

Grade 4 49 Chapter 3

Real-World EXAMPLE — Use Words to Describe Probability

2 **MONEY The table shows the coins Tucker has in his pocket. Suppose he drops a coin on the ground. Describe the probability that the coin he dropped is a dime.**

Coin	Frequency
Quarter	1
Dime	5
Penny	2
TOTAL	8

Of the 8 coins in Tucker's pocket, 5 are dimes.

So, it is *likely* that Tucker dropped a dime.

You can also use numbers to describe probability.

EXAMPLE — Use Numbers to Describe Probability

3 **The letter tiles below spell out mathematics. Use numbers to describe the probability of choosing a vowel without looking.**

Four out of eleven letters are vowels.

So, the probability of choosing a vowel is 4 out of 11.

CHECK What You Know

The spinner is spun. Describe the probability of each outcome. Write *certain, likely, equally likely, unlikely,* or *impossible*.
See Examples 1 and 2 (pp. 128–129)

1. odd number certain

2. even number impossible

3. number less than 3 impossible

4. the number 5, 11, or 13 equally likely

For Exercises 5 and 6, use the cubes at the right. See Example 3 (p. 129)

5. Use numbers to describe the probability of choosing a cube that is not yellow without looking. 8 out of 10

6. Talk About It Omar reaches into the bag and chooses one cube without looking. Are there any colors that are more likely to be chosen? Explain.

6. Sample answer: of the 10 cubes, blue is more likely to be chosen than any other color.

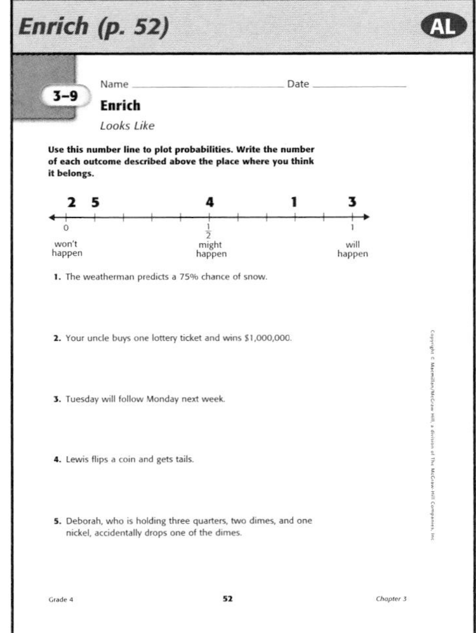

Enrich (p. 52) AL

3–9

Name ______ Date ______

Enrich

Looks Like

Use this number line to plot probabilities. Write the number of each outcome described above the place where you think it belongs.

2 5 (at 0, won't happen) — 4 (at 1/2, might happen) — 1 — 3 (at 1, will happen)

1. The weatherman predicts a 75% chance of snow.

2. Your uncle buys one lottery ticket and wins $1,000,000.

3. Tuesday will follow Monday next week.

4. Lewis flips a coin and gets tails.

5. Deborah, who is holding three quarters, two dimes, and one nickel, accidentally drops one of the dimes.

Grade 4 — 52 — Chapter 3

Describe Outcomes

Example 2 Point out that the numbers in the *Frequency* column of the table correspond to the numbers of each type of coin Tucker has.

ADDITIONAL EXAMPLES

1 Kimmela has 8 green and 2 white marbles. Describe how likely it is that Kimmela will choose a green marble. likely

2 Jeremiah has 15 coins in his pocket. 10 are dimes, 5 are nickels. If he drops a coin on the ground, describe the probability that the coin is a penny. impossible

CHECK What You Know

As a class, have students complete Exercises 1–9 in **Check What You Know** as you observe their work.

Exercise 1–2 Remind students of the difference between odd and even numbers.

Exercise 9 Assess student comprehension before assigning practice exercises.

BL Alternate Teaching Strategy

If students have trouble determining if an outcome is likely or unlikely…

Then use one of these reteach options:

1 CRM **Daily Reteach Worksheet** (p. 48)

2 Provide students with manipulatives such as connecting cubes. Show them 5 green cubes and 1 red cube.

- **Which is more likely to be chosen?** green
- **Describe the probability that a red cube is chosen.** unlikely

Allow students to use manipulatives as they work through the exercises.

COMMON ERROR!

Exercises 3 through 8 Most students will already have a sense of probability, but some may have difficulty using words to describe what they know. Suggest that they draw models or use manipulatives to represent each situation.

3 Practice

Differentiate practice using these leveled assignments for Exercises 9–21.

Level	Assignment
BL Below/Approaching Level	9–10, 12–15, 17
OL On Level	9–16, 18, 20
AL Above/Beyond Level	9–17 odd, 19–21

Have students discuss and complete the Higher Order Thinking problems. Remind students that more than half the outcomes must produce the desired outcome in order for it to be considered likely.

WRITING IN MATH Have students complete Exercise 23 in their Math Journals. You may choose to use this exercise as an optional formative assessment.

4 Assess

Formative Assessment

Ask students to draw 10 circles to represent 10 marbles in a bowl, and imagine some are red, some are white, and some are blue.

- **How do you tell how to describe the probability of a certain color being chosen?** Answers will vary. It is likely if it represents more than half the marbles; it is certain if all marbles are that color; it is unlikely if there are less than half of that color; it is impossible if no marbles are of that color.

Quick Check **Are students continuing to struggle with probability and outcomes?**

If Yes → Small Group Options (p. 127B)
Strategic Intervention Guide (p. 132)

If No → Independent Work Options (p. 127B)
CRM Skills Practice Worksheet (p. 49)
CRM Enrich Worksheet (p. 52)

Practice and Problem Solving

See page R9.

A marble is chosen from the bag without looking. Describe the probability of each outcome. Write *certain, likely, equally likely, unlikely,* or *impossible.* See Examples 1 and 2 (pp. 128–129)

7. green unlikely
8. yellow likely
9. red, yellow, or green certain
10. blue impossible
11. not green likely
12. red or green unlikely

The spinner is spun. Use numbers to describe the probability of each outcome. See Example 3 (p. 129)

13. A 1 out of 5
14. not E 4 out of 5
15. consonant 3 out of 5
16. vowel 2 out of 5
17. not A or B 3 out of 5
18. letter in the name LILY 0 out of 5

19. Sancho spun a spinner 21 times. The table shows his results.

Color	Results
Blue	卌 ||
Green	卌 卌 ||
Orange	||

Suppose Sancho spins the spinner one more time. Describe the probability that the spinner will land on orange. unlikely

20. Erin dropped a stack of 32 plastic cups. The table shows how the cups landed.

How Cup Landed	Number
	10
	18
	4

Suppose Erin drops one more cup. Describe the probability that the cup will land on its side. likely

H.O.T. Problems

21. **OPEN ENDED** Make a spinner with 8 equal parts in which green is most *likely* to be landed on and so that red and blue are *unlikely* to occur. See Ch. 3 Answer Appendix.

22. **WRITING IN MATH** Describe a probability situation in which an outcome is certain to happen. Sample answer: Spinning a B on a spinner in which all sections are labeled B.

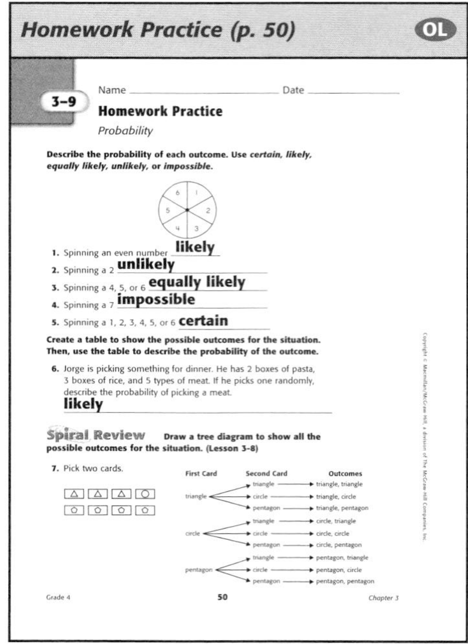

Homework Practice (p. 50) OL

Name ____________ Date ____________

3–9 **Homework Practice**

Probability

Describe the probability of each outcome. Use *certain, likely, equally likely, unlikely,* or *impossible.*

1. Spinning an even number likely
2. Spinning a 2 unlikely
3. Spinning a 4, 5, or 6 equally likely
4. Spinning a 7 impossible
5. Spinning a 1, 2, 3, 4, 5, or 6 certain

Create a table to show the possible outcomes for the situation. Then, use the table to describe the probability of the outcome.

6. Jorge is picking something for dinner. He has 2 boxes of pasta, 3 boxes of rice, and 5 types of meat. If he picks one randomly, describe the probability of picking a meat.
likely

Spiral Review **Draw a tree diagram to show all the possible outcomes for the situation. (Lesson 3-8)**

7. Pick two cards.

First Card	Second Card	Outcomes
triangle	triangle	triangle, triangle
	circle	triangle, circle
	pentagon	triangle, pentagon
circle	triangle	circle, triangle
	circle	circle, circle
	pentagon	circle, pentagon
pentagon	triangle	pentagon, triangle
	circle	pentagon, circle
	pentagon	pentagon, pentagon

Grade 4 50 Chapter 3

Technology Activity for 3-9

Find Probability

You can use the *Math Tool Chest* to explore probability.

MAIN IDEA

I will use technology to find probability.

ACTIVITY

Angelo is using a spinner with four sections: one green, one red, one yellow, and one blue, to conduct an experiment. He spins the spinner 100 times and draws a bar graph of the results. Try the experiment.

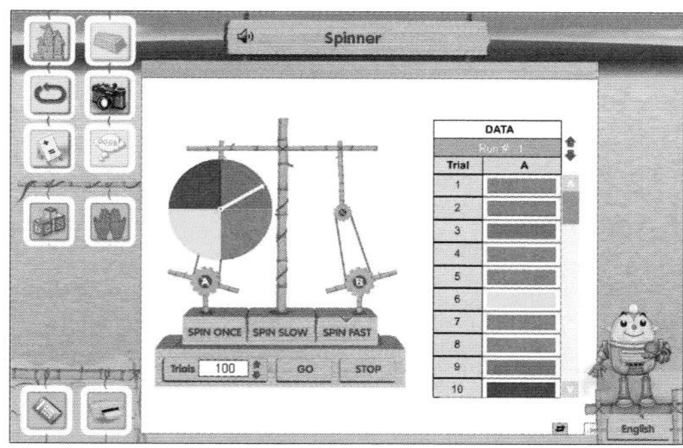

- Click on the spinner toolchest.
- Set the number of trials at 100.
- Click on SPIN FAST.
- Click on the links icon ( ) below the data table.
- Click on Bar Graph to display the data.
- Use numbers to tell on which color the spinner landed.

CHECK What You Know

For Exercises 1–4, repeat the activity above. Change the number of trials for each exercise. Use numbers to describe the probability of landing on each color, red, yellow, green, and blue. 1–5. See students' work.

1. 15 times **2.** 25 times **3.** 30 times **4.** 50 times

5. Spin a spinner with three sections 25 times. Draw a bar graph to display the results. Use numbers to tell what color was spun most.

Math Tool Chest: Spinner Button Bar

The Spinner Button Bar offers two buttons that perform functions specific to the Spinners tool.

Setting Up Spinners Students click Setup on the Button Bar to change Spinner settings.

Hide Data Students click Hide Data to hide the Data area that displays to the right of the Spinner. To redisplay the Data area, students click Hide Data again.

Extend

Technology Activity for 3-9

Lesson Planner

Objective

Use technology to find probability.

Resources

Math Tool Chest *(accessible in three ways)*

- **Math Online** macmillanmh.com
- StudentWorks Plus
- Interactive Classroom

Getting Started

- Share with students that this activity requires them to use Math Tool Chest, a computer program that allows them to explore mathematical concepts and develop math skills.
- As a class, work through the each activity in each example following the instructions on the page.

Using Math Tool Chest

Spinners The provides opportunities for students to work on probability quickly and easily.

- Students choose one or two spinners and use a number or color spinner.
- Students can also change the size of spinner wedges and display the probability of landing on each segment in percents, decimals, or fractions.
- Students click Go to start a Spinner run.
- Students click Stop to suspend the run, with the results up to that point displayed in the Data area.
- The most recent run results appear in the Data window. Students can see other results by using the arrows on the right of the Run # box.

Chapter 3 Study Guide and Review

FOLDABLES Dinah Zike's Foldables

Use these lesson suggestions to incorporate the Foldables during the chapter. Students can then use their Foldables to review for the test.

Lessons 3-5, 3-6 On the Foldable layer titled "Bar and Double Bar Graphs," ask students to make, read, and use data in a bar graph and a double bar graph.

Lesson 3-8 Students define *tree diagram* beneath the bottom tab of the Foldable.

Lesson 3-9 Students define *probability* and *grid* beneath the bottom tab of the Foldable.

Key Vocabulary

The page references after each word denote where that term was first introduced. If students have difficulty answering Exercises 1–6, remind them they can use the page references to review the vocabulary terms.

Vocabulary Review

Review chapter vocabulary using one of the following options.

- **Visual Vocabulary Card** (4)
- **eGlossary** at macmillanmh.com

Chapter 3 Study Guide and Review

FOLDABLES Study Organizer GET READY to Study

Be sure the following Key Vocabulary words and Key Concepts are written in your Foldable.

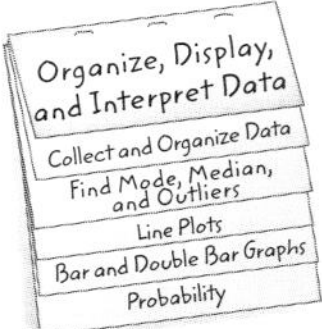

Key Concepts

Displaying Data

- A **survey** is a way to collect data. **Data** can be organized in different ways, such as a tally chart and a frequency table. (p. 95)
- A **bar graph** is used to compare data by using bars of different heights to represent data. (p. 108)

Probability describes the likelihood of an event taking place. (p. 128)

The probability of two coins landing on heads after being tossed can be found by using the grid.

		Second Coin	
		Heads	**Tails**
First Coin	**Heads**	heads, heads	heads, tails
	Tails	tails, heads	tails tails

The probability of two coins landing on heads is unlikely, or 1 out of 4.

Key Vocabulary

bar graph (p. 108)
data (p. 95)
probability (p. 128)
survey (p. 95)
tree diagram (p. 125)

Vocabulary Check

Match each phrase with the correct vocabulary word above.

1. A survey is a way to collect ___?___ . data
2. ___?___ describes the likelihood of an event taking place. probability
3. A ___?___ is used to compare data by using bars of different heights to represent values. bar graph
4. A ___?___ is a way to collect information that answers a question. survey
5. A ___?___ uses "branches" to show all possible combinations of a probability situation. tree diagram
6. A grid can be used to find the ___?___ of a situation. probability

Chapter 3 Project

Choosing to Help

Alone, in pairs, or in small groups, have students discuss the results of their completed chapter project with the class. Assess their work using the Chapter Project rubric found in Chapter 3 Resource Masters, p. 63.

Lesson-by-Lesson Review

3-1 Collect and Organize Data (pp. 95–97)

Example 1
Organize the data shown in a tally chart and frequency table.

Favorite Sports		
basketball	basketball	track
basketball	softball	volleyball
basketball	softball	volleyball
basketball	softball	volleyball
basketball	track	volleyball

Favorite Sports	
Sport	**Tally**
Softball	|||
Track	||
Basketball	~~||||~~ |
Volleyball	||||

Favorite Sports	
Sport	**Frequency**
Softball	3
Track	2
Basketball	6
Volleyball	4

7, 8. See margin.

Organize the data shown in a tally chart and frequency table.

7. Family members were asked what they wanted to do after dinner.

After Dinner Activity		
nap	read	game
game	nap	read
game	game	read
read	game	game

8. Fourth graders voted for Student Council President.

Votes for President		
Tom	Monica	Lamar
Monica	Tom	Tom
Tom	Monica	Monica
Lamar	Monica	Lamar

3-2 Find Mode, Median, and Outliers (pp. 98–101)

Example 2
Find the mode and median for the data set 50, 50, 51, 53, 95. Identify any outliers.

Order from least to greatest.

50, 50, 51, 53, 95

The mode occurs most often: 50.
The median is the number in the middle: 51. The outlier is the number that lies outside of the data: 95.

Find the mode and median of the set of data. Identify any outliers.

9. Hours of practice each week: 3, 8, 2, 4, 3 3; 3; 8

10. Wild birds seen at a state park: 54, 17, 15, 16, 15 15; 16; 54

11. The number of students in Mr. Parker's class who brought lunches this week: 8, 6, 5, 7, 17 no mode; 7; 17

Lesson-by-Lesson Review

Have students complete the Lesson-by-Lesson Review on pp. 133–138. Then you can use ExamView® Assessment Suite to customize another review worksheet that practices all the objectives of this chapter or only the objectives on which your students need more help.

Intervention If the given examples are not sufficient to review the topics covered by the questions, use the page references next to the exercises to review that topic in the Student Edition.

Additional Answers

7.

After Dinner Activity	
Activity	**Tally**
Game	~~||||~~ |
Nap	||
Read	||||

After Dinner Activity	
Activity	**Frequency**
Game	6
Nap	2
Read	4

8.

Votes for President	
Classmate	**Tally**
Tom	||||
Monica	~~||||~~
Lamar	|||

Votes for President	
Classmate	**Frequency**
Tom	4
Monica	5
Lamar	3

CHAPTER 3 Study Guide and Review

3-3 Problem-Solving Strategy: Make a Table (pp. 102–103)

Example 3
Students are going on a class trip. There are 140 students going, and 28 students fit on each bus. How many buses are needed?

Understand You know that 140 students are going, and each bus holds 28 students. Find the number of buses needed.

Plan You can make a table.

Solve

Bus	Students
1	28
2	56
3	84
4	112
5	140

+28 +28 +28 +28

So, 5 buses are needed.

Check Use subtraction to check.

$$\begin{array}{rl} 140 & \\ -\ 28 & \text{one bus} \\ \hline 112 & \\ -\ 28 & \text{one bus} \\ \hline 84 & \\ -\ 28 & \text{one bus} \\ \hline 56 & \\ -\ 28 & \text{one bus} \\ \hline 28 & \\ -\ 28 & \text{one bus} \\ \hline 0 & \end{array}$$

Subtracting 28 from 140 five times equals 0. So, the answer makes sense.

Solve the problems using a table.

12. **Algebra** Jordan has to read a 125-page book by Friday. It is Sunday, and Jordan plans to read 25 pages each night. Will he finish reading the book by Friday? Explain.

Day	Pages Read
Sunday	25
Monday	50
Tuesday	75
Wednesday	■ 100
Thursday	■ 125

yes

13. There are 26 cars waiting on the on-ramp to the freeway. A green light lets 2 cars on at a time. How many lights will it take before all the cars enter the freeway? 13 lights

14. At Riverside Elementary, there are 346 students in the school who take the bus each day.

1 bus = 40 students

What is the least number of buses the school will need to transport children to and from the school? 9 buses

15. Thirty-six students are going rafting. Each raft holds 7 students. How many more students are needed to fill each raft with 7 people? 6 students

134 Chapter 3 Organize, Display, and Interpret Data

3-4 Line Plots (pp. 104–107)

Example 4
Organize the information from the frequency table in a line plot.

Children at the Park				
1	5	6	6	3
3	2	3	4	2
2	4	5	2	
6	3	6	7	
7	2	1	6	
5	6	6	5	

Children at the Park

1 2 3 4 5 6 7

Organize each set of data in a line plot. 16, 17. See margin.

16.

Phone Calls Made Each Day	
Day	Calls
Monday	3
Tuesday	2
Wednesday	5
Thursday	7
Friday	4

17.

Canned Goods Collected Each Month			
27	26	24	24
30	33	28	26
25	29	30	28

3-5 Bar Graphs (pp. 108–110)

Example 5
Which sport was played twice as long as another sport?

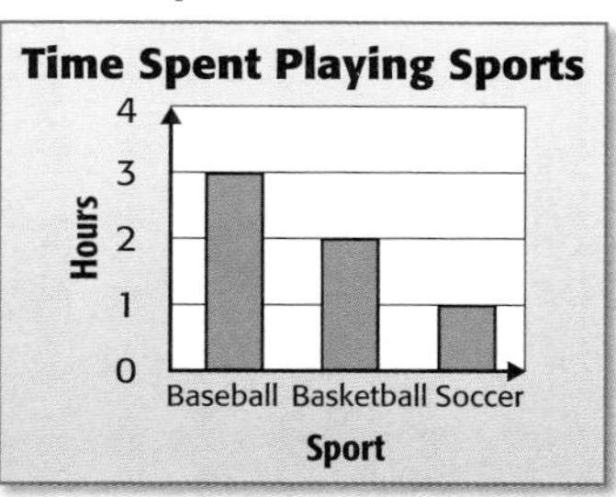

Basketball was played for 2 hours. Soccer was played for one hour. So, basketball was played twice as long as soccer. $1 \times 2 = 2$.

For Exercises 18 and 19, use the graph.

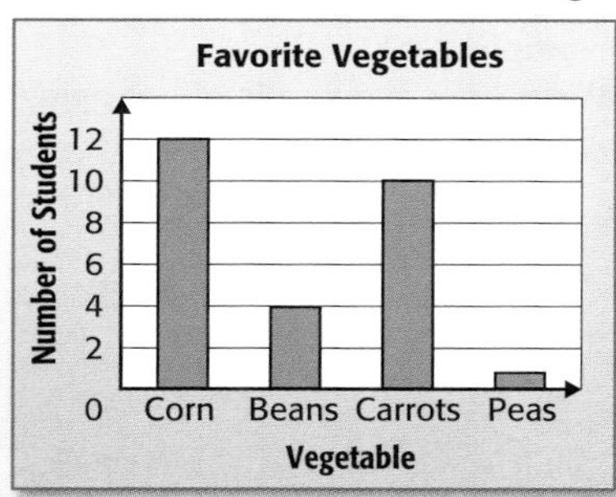

18. Which vegetable is the class's least favorite? peas

19. What is the sum of students who liked beans and corn? 16

Additional Answers

16.

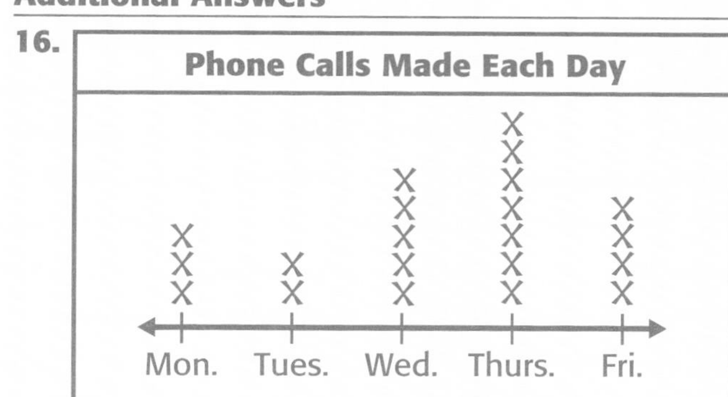

17.

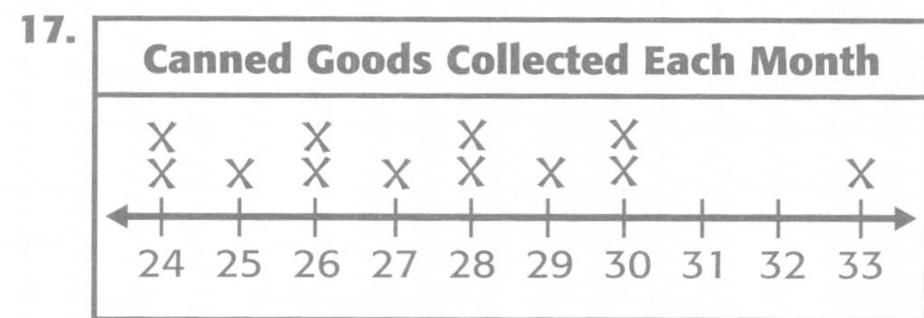

Study Guide and Review

Study Guide and Review

3-6 Bar and Double Bar Graphs (pp. 112–114)

Example 6
About how many new members joined the school choir in 2007?

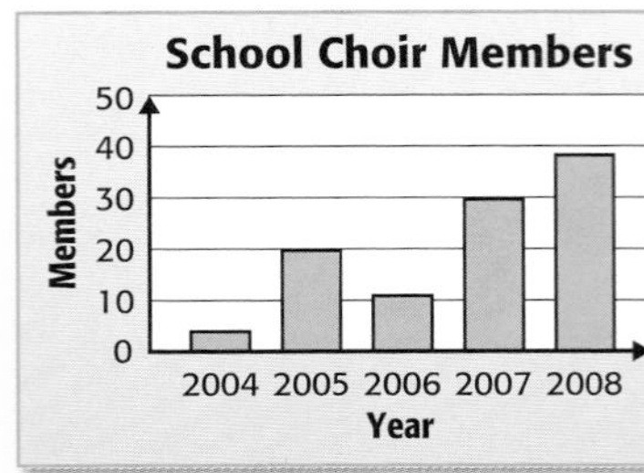

To find the answer, subtract the number of 2006 choir members from the number of 2007 choir members.

30	−	10	=	20
2007 choir members		2006 choir members		new members

So, about 20 members joined the school choir in 2007.

Example 7
About how many rolls of wrapping paper did the third grade sell?

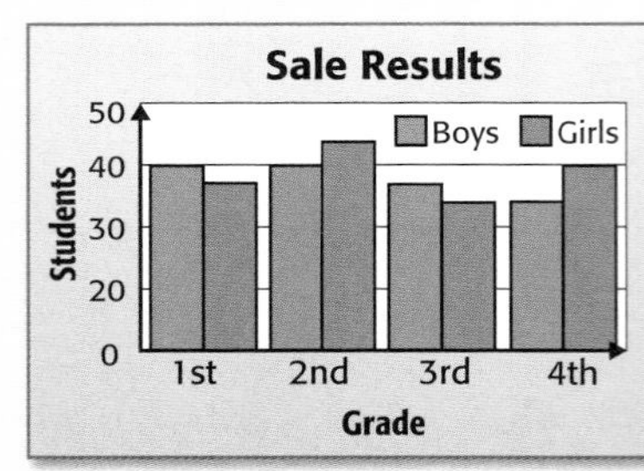

35 + 40 = 75. So, about 75 rolls of wrapping paper were sold.

For Exercises 20 and 21, use the graph that shows the type of music dog owners play for their dogs while they are not home.

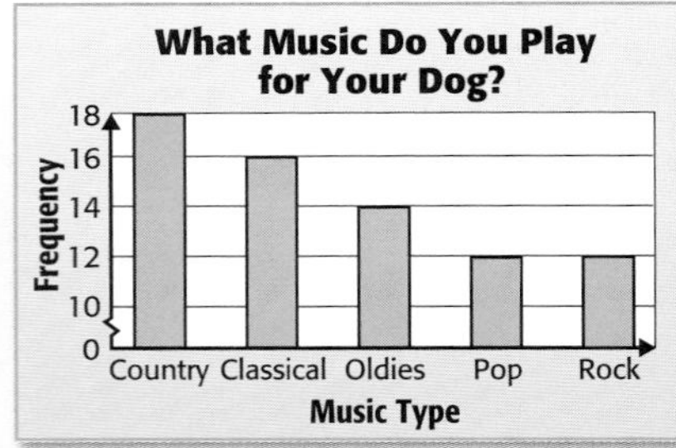

Source: *USA Today*

20. How many dogs listened to oldies? 14

21. What is the total number of dogs that listened to pop and rock music? 24

For Exercises 22 and 23, use the graph.

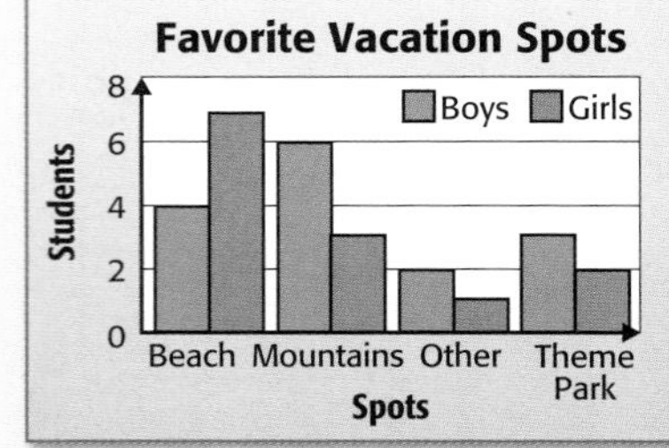

22. What is the most popular spot? beach

23. What is the difference in number of students who liked the most popular and least popular vacation spots? 8

3-7 Problem-Solving Investigation: Choose a Strategy (pp. 118–119)

Example 8

Pia wants to earn $75. If she earns $15 each time she babysits, how many times will she have to babysit in order to earn $75?

Understand Pia earns $15 each time she babysits. She wants to earn $75. Find the number of days Pia needs to babysit to earn $75.

Plan Organize the data in a table to solve the problem.

Solve

Day	Money Earned
1	$15
2	$30
3	$45
4	$60
5	$75

Pia will have to babysit 5 times to earn $75.

Check $75 – $15 = $60
$60 – $15 = $45
$45 – $15 = $30
$30 – $15 = $15
$15 – $15 = $0

Subtracting $15 from $75 five times equals 0. So, the answer makes sense.

Use any strategy to solve.

24. Bruce has 19 baseball hats. Rashid has 5 more than Bruce. Shelly has 2 less than Rashid. How many baseball hats does Shelly have? 22 hats

25. **Algebra** What four shapes come next in the pattern if it continues?

See margin.

26. The sum of two numbers is 14. The difference between those same two numbers is 0. What are the two numbers? 7, 7

27. **Algebra** What shape will be tenth in the pattern if it continues?

See margin.

28. **Measurement** Grant's favorite video game takes him 132 minutes to win. Each level takes Grant about 22 minutes to clear. About how many levels does his video game have? 6 levels

29. Doria works at a sandwich shop. There are 3 different kinds of bread and 5 different kinds of meat to choose from. How many different sandwiches can be made using one bread and one meat? 15 sandwiches

Additional Answers

25.

27.

Chapter 3 Study Guide and Review

Additional Answer

30.

Coin	Spinner	Outcome
heads	red	heads, red
	orange	heads, orange
	blue	heads, blue
	purple	heads, purple
tails	red	tails, red
	orange	tails, orange
	blue	tails, blue
	purple	tails, purple

3-8 Determine Possible Outcomes (pp. 124–127)

Example 9
Angie can use clay or paper for an art project. Her project can be blue or yellow. What are all the outcomes of the art project?

Use a tree diagram.

Material	Color	Outcome
clay	blue	clay, blue
	yellow	clay, yellow
paper	blue	paper, blue
	yellow	paper, yellow

There are four possible outcomes.

Draw a tree diagram to find the number of possible outcomes for the situation.

30. How many outcomes are possible if the coin is tossed and the spinner is spun? See margin.

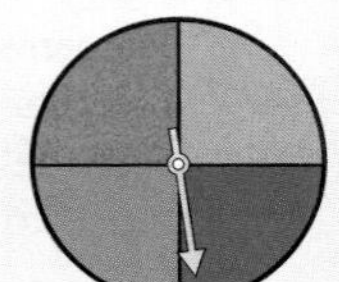

3-9 Probability (pp. 128–130)

Example 10
A marble is chosen without looking. Describe the probability that the chosen marble will be red.

There are 10 marbles in the bag, and 6 are red.

In the bag, more than half of the marbles are red. So, it is likely that a red marble will be chosen.

The spinner is spun. Describe the probability of each outcome. Write *certain, likely, equally likely, unlikely,* or *impossible*.

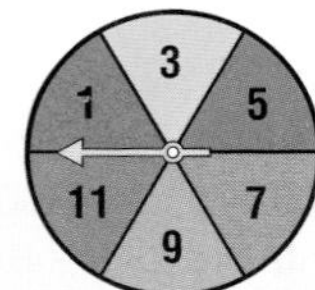

31. 3 or 5 unlikely

32. even number impossible

33. a number greater than 7 unlikely

34. prime number likely

35. Identify an outcome that is certain to take place when the spinner is spun. Sample answer: odd number

Chapter Test

Math Online macmillanmh.com
• Chapter Test

For Exercises 1–2, tell whether each statement is *true* or *false*.

1. A double bar graph displays two sets of related data using bars of different colors. true

2. A tree diagram uses "branches" to show all possible combinations of a probability situation. true

3. **MULTIPLE CHOICE** Reggie will spin the arrow on a spinner like the one shown below. C

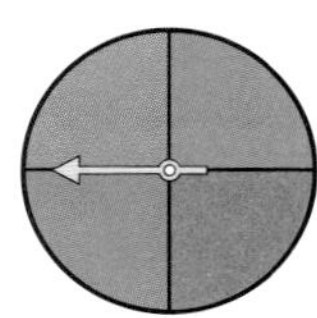

If the spinner lands on two different sections, which of the following is NOT a possible outcome?

A Red, Blue

B Green, Green

C Red, Red

D Green, Red

Make a table to solve each problem.

4. A car needs an oil change every 3 months. Joe's car has had 4 oil changes so far. How many months have passed? 12 months

5. How much money will Kendall save if he saves $35 a month for a year? $420

One piece of fruit is chosen without looking. Use words and a number to describe the probability of each outcome.

6. orange unlikely; 1 out of 4

7. apple or peach likely; 3 out of 4

8. **MULTIPLE CHOICE** The graph below shows the number of touchdowns made in four different games. F

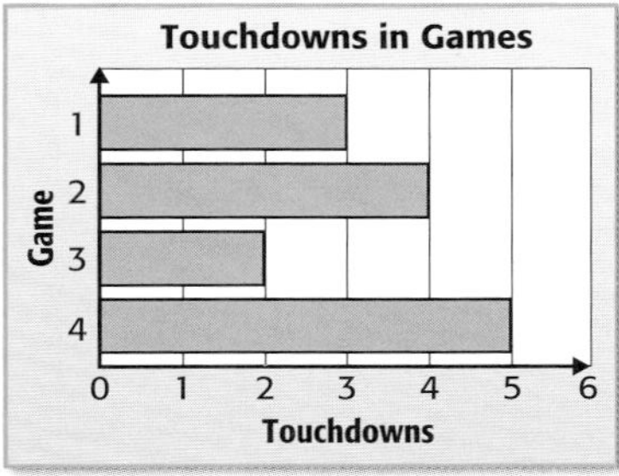

According to the graph, how many more touchdowns were made in game 4 than in game 1?

F 2 **H** 4

G 3 **J** 5

9. WRITING IN MATH Write two sentences to describe the graph in Exercise 8. See Ch. 3 Answer Appendix.

Chapter 3 Chapter Test

Summative Assessment

Use these alternate leveled chapter tests to differentiate assessment for the specific needs of your students.

Leveled Chapter 3 Tests			
Form	**Type**	**Level**	**CRM Pages**
1	Multiple Choice	BL	65–66
2A	Multiple Choice	OL	67–68
2B	Multiple Choice	OL	69–70
2C	Free Response	OL	71–72
2D	Free Response	OL	73–74
3	Free Response	AL	75–76

BL = below/approaching grade level
OL = on grade level
AL = above/beyond grade level

Vocabulary Test

CRM **Chapter 3 Resource Masters** (p. 60)

ExamView Assessment Suite Customize and create multiple versions of your Chapter Test and the test answer keys.

Data-Driven Decision Making

Based on the results of the Chapter Test, use the following to review concepts that continue to present students with problems.

Exercises	State/Local Standards	What's the Math?	Error Analysis	Resources for Review
1–2, 4–7		Understand ways to represent data.	Does not understand "bar graph" or "double bar graph." Does not know how to make a table.	Strategic Intervention Guide (p. 130) CRM Chapter 3 Resource Masters (Reteach Worksheets) Math Adventures My Math Zone Chapter 3 Math Online Extra Examples • Concepts in Motion
8		Interpret a bar graph.	Misreads graph or chart. Does not add or subtract correctly.	

CHAPTER 3

Test Practice

Formative Assessment

- Use Student Edition pp. 130–131 as practice and cumulative review. The questions are written in the same style as many state tests.
- You can also use these two pages to benchmark student progress, or as an alternate homework assignment.

Additional practice pages can be found in the Chapter 3 Resource Masters.

CRM **Chapter 3 Resource Masters**
Cumulative Test Practice

- Multiple Choice format (pp. 65–70)
- Free Response format (pp. 71–76)

Create practice worksheets or tests that align to your state standards.

Math Online Have students visit macmillanmh.com for additional practice to reinforce your state standards.

CHAPTER 3

Test Practice

Cumulative, Chapters 1–3

Math Online macmillanmh.com
• Test Practice

PART I Multiple Choice

Read each question. Then fill in the correct answer on the answer sheet provided by your teacher or on a sheet of paper.

1. Marla asked her class about their favorite class trip. She made a bar graph to show the results.

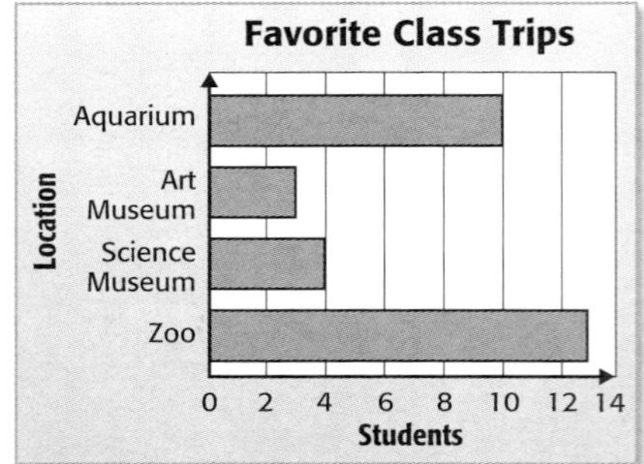

How many more students prefer going to the zoo than to the science museum? D

A 3 **C** 7
B 6 **D** 9

2. What is the median of the shoe sizes shown in the data set shown below?

{6, 4, 5, 7, 8, 5, 6} J

F 3
G 4
H 5
J 6

3. Which number is 1,000 more than 82,753? B

A 82,853 **C** 92,735
B 83,753 **D** 92,753

4. A mountain is 9,485 feet tall. A climber has hiked 6,208 feet. How many more feet does the climber need to hike to reach the top of the mountain? H

F 15,693 **H** 3,277
G 15,267 **J** 3,183

5. What is the mode of the data set {3, 5, 7, 2, 2, 4, 6}? A

A 2 **C** 4
B 3 **D** 5

6. What is the value of the digit 9 in 169,328,457? G

F 900,000 **H** 90,000,000
G 9,000,000 **J** 900,000,000

7. Kari has a bag of 20 blocks. Six are blue, 4 are red, 7 are green, and 3 are yellow. If Kari chooses a block without looking, which color is most likely to be chosen? A

A green **C** red
B blue **D** yellow

Test-Taking Tip

Tell students that as they examine a multiple-choice test item, they should eliminate answer choices they know to be incorrect.

Preparing for Standardized Tests
For test-taking strategies and practice, see pages R42–R55.

8. What is 736,249 rounded to the nearest hundred? G

F 736,000 H 736,250
G 736,200 J 740,000

9. Ron sold lemonade at soccer practice. On which two days did he sell the least amount of lemonade? C

Lemonade Sales	
Day	**Tally**
Monday	𝍸 IIII
Tuesday	IIII
Wednesday	𝍸 I
Thursday	IIII
Friday	𝍸 III

A Monday and Friday
B Wednesday and Friday
C Tuesday and Thursday
D Thursday and Friday

10. Nadia tossed a number cube labeled 0–5. What is the probability that she will toss an even number? G

F 2 out of 6 H 4 out of 6
G 3 out of 6 J 5 out of 6

PART 2 Short Response

Record your answers on the answer sheet provided by your teacher or on a sheet of paper.

11. A piggy bank has the coins shown below in it. If a coin is selected at random, what is the probability in numbers that the coin will be a penny? 3 out of 14

PART 3 Extended Response

Record your answers on the answer sheet provided by your teacher or on a sheet of paper.

12. Larisa has three pairs of pants and three sweaters.

Larisa's Outfits	
Pants	tan, black, navy
Sweaters	red, stripe, white

a. Draw a tree diagram to show the possible outfits Larisa can wear. See margin.

b. How many different outfits can Larisa wear? 9

NEED EXTRA HELP?												
If You Missed Question...	1	2	3	4	5	6	7	8	9	10	11	12
Go to Lesson...	3-5	3-2	2-4	2-5	3-2	1-2	3-9	1-6	3-1	3-9	3-9	3-8

Summative Assessment 141

Answer Sheet Practice

Have students simulate taking a state test by recording their answers on a practice recording sheet.

CRM **Chapter 3 Resource Masters**
Student Recording Sheet (p. 81)

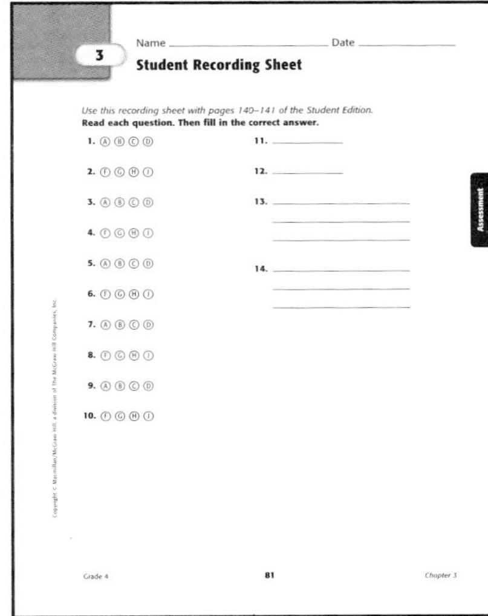
3 Name ______ Date ______
Student Recording Sheet
Use this recording sheet with pages 140–141 of the Student Edition.
Read each question. Then fill in the correct answer.
1. Ⓐ Ⓑ Ⓒ Ⓓ 11. ______
2. Ⓕ Ⓖ Ⓗ Ⓙ 12. ______
3. Ⓐ Ⓑ Ⓒ Ⓓ 13. ______
4. Ⓕ Ⓖ Ⓗ Ⓙ
5. Ⓐ Ⓑ Ⓒ Ⓓ 14. ______
6. Ⓕ Ⓖ Ⓗ Ⓙ
7. Ⓐ Ⓑ Ⓒ Ⓓ
8. Ⓕ Ⓖ Ⓗ Ⓙ
9. Ⓐ Ⓑ Ⓒ Ⓓ
10. Ⓕ Ⓖ Ⓗ Ⓙ
Grade 4 81 Chapter 3

Additional Answers

12a.

Pants	Sweater	Outcome
tan	red	tan, red
	stripe	tan, stripe
	white	tan, white
black	red	black, red
	stripe	black, stripe
	white	black, white
navy	red	navy, red
	stripe	navy, stripe
	white	navy, white

Page 94

1.

Favorite Colors	
Color	**Tally**
Red	𝍷𝍷𝍷
Yellow	𝍷
Green	𝍷𝍷
Blue	𝍷𝍷𝍷𝍷
Pink	𝍷𝍷

2.

Ages of Basketball Players	
Age	**Tally**
9	𝍷𝍷𝍷
10	𝍸 𝍷𝍷
11	𝍷𝍷

Page 96, Lesson 3-1

1.

How Do You Travel to School?	
Method	**Tally**
Bicycle	𝍷𝍷𝍷
Bus	𝍸 𝍷
Car	𝍸 𝍷𝍷𝍷𝍷
Walk	𝍸

2.

Mary's Fish Tank	
h	**re e y**
Angelfish	3
Clownfish	2
Damsel	3
Eel	2

5.

Favorite Type of Pizza	
Pizza Topping	**Tally**
Cheese	𝍸
Pepperoni	𝍷𝍷𝍷
Sausage	𝍷𝍷

6.

Type of Movie	
Movie Type	**Tally**
Action	𝍷𝍷𝍷
Animated	𝍷
Comedy	𝍷𝍷𝍷𝍷

7.

Weekly Temperatures	
Temperature (°F)	**Days**
70–75	2
76–80	3
81–85	1
86–90	1

8.

Recess Activity	
Activity	**Frequency**
Kickball	4
Drawing	3
Swing	5
Tag	3

13. Sample answer: A frequency table and a tally chart both display data. A frequency table uses numbers to display data. A tally chart uses tally marks.

14. Sample answer: It would be better to use a frequency table. For larger numbers, it is easier to record the frequency rather than tally marks.

Page 101, Lesson 3-2

17. Sample answer: Jasmine; she lined up the numbers from least to greatest, and then found the middle number. Grady did not line up the numbers from least to greatest, so the middle number he found was incorrect.

18. Sample answer: Median is the one in the middle as in the median of the road. The letters m and o in mode can mean most often.

Page 103, Lesson 3-3

1. The table was used to find the pattern between the number of students and teachers.

2. The number of teachers increases by 2. The number of students increase by 9.

4. Sample answer: The pattern changes by increasing the number of students by 3 for every 1 teacher.

Teachers	1	2	4	8	16	20	24
Students	3	6	12	24	48	60	72

12. Sample answer: The numbers involved in Exercise 10 are large. Also, there are many numbers to keep in order, which can be done by using the make a table strategy.

Page 105–106, Lesson 3-4

1.

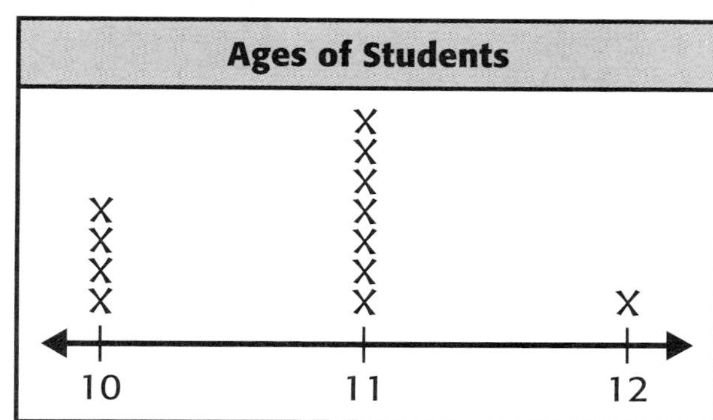

2.

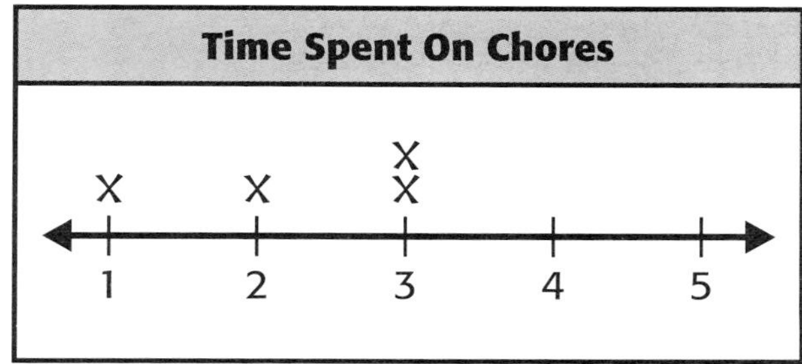

7.

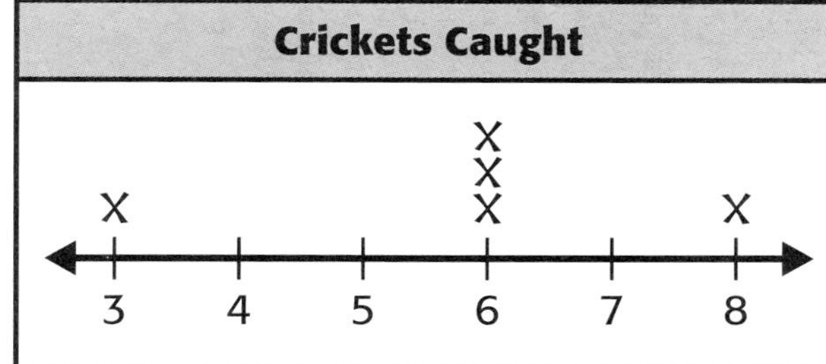

8.

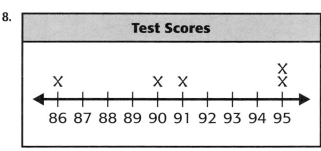

Test Scores

86 87 88 89 90 91 92 93 94 95

9.

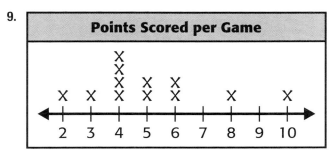

Points Scored per Game

2 3 4 5 6 7 8 9 10

10.

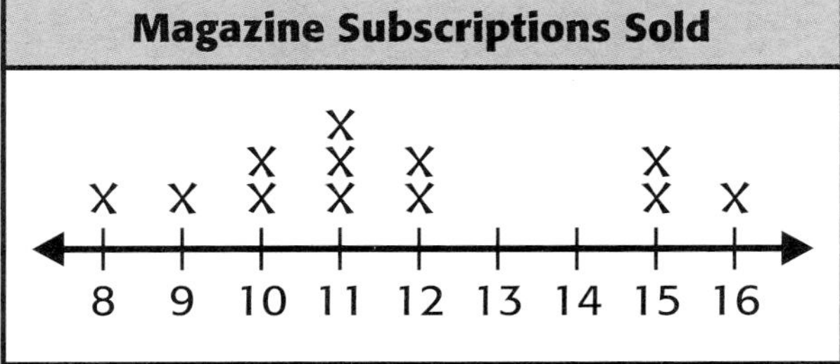

16. Sample answer: The Los Angeles Clippers have a median height that is 23 inches taller.

Page 110, Lesson 3-5

9. Sample answer: If the scale were in intervals of less than 20 feet, the graph would be very large.

10. Sample answer: Since the scale is set at 20 feet, finding an exact calculation of the difference between the lengths of the whales is difficult.

11. Mississippi and Texas, and Arkansas, Minnesota, and Wisconsin

14. Sample answer: Kansas and Alabama; I found the answer by estimating. If KS had about 140 and TX or MS had 100 that would be too much so AL must be the other state.

Page 111, Mid-Chapter Check

1.

Sandwiches for a Picnic	
Sandwich	Tally
Ham	||||
Peanut Butter	||
Turkey	|||

Sandwiches for a Picnic	
Ham	4
Peanut Butter	2
Turkey	3

7.

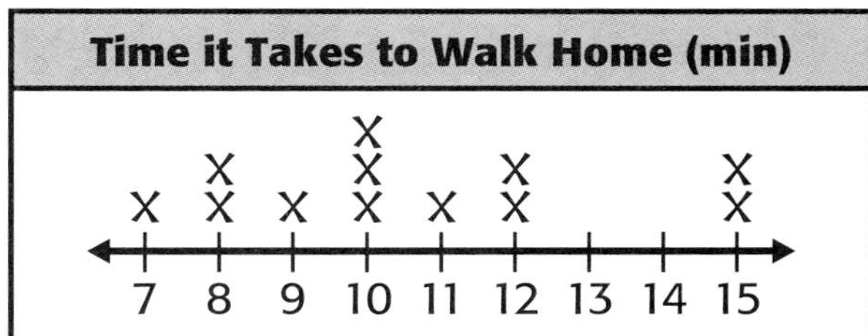

9. Sample answer: A median is in the middle of a data set, a mode is the number that occurs most often.

Page 119, Lesson 3-7

10. Sample answer: Use the make a table strategy when a word problem involves two patterns of numbers. One pattern acts as the input numbers in the table. The other pattern acts as the output numbers in the table.

Page 123, Explore 3-8

5. MM, MT, MH, TT, TM, TH, HH, HM, HT
6. Sample answer: It would be impossible to pull a blue and an yellow connecting cube from the bag.
8. red red, red yellow, red green, yellow green
9. Sample answer: Two spinners; one is divided into thirds and the other is divided in half. The first spinner has the colors orange, blue, and red. The second spinner has the letters A and E. All the possible combinations if each spinner is spun one time is; A orange, A blue, A red, E orange, E blue, E red. I found all the possible combinations by moving the arrow on a spinner and recording the result and then moving the arrow again. I did this until combinations started to repeat.

Page 125–126, Lesson 3-8

1. Second Spin

First Spin	Pen	Glue	Book	Pencil
Pen	Pen, Pen	Pen, Glue	Pen, Book	Pen, Pencil
Glue	Glue, Pen	Glue, Glue	Glue, Book	Glue, Pencil
Book	Book, Pen	Book, Glue	Book, Book	Book, Pencil
Pencil	Pencil, Pen	Pencil, Glue	Pencil, Book	Pencil, Pencil

2. 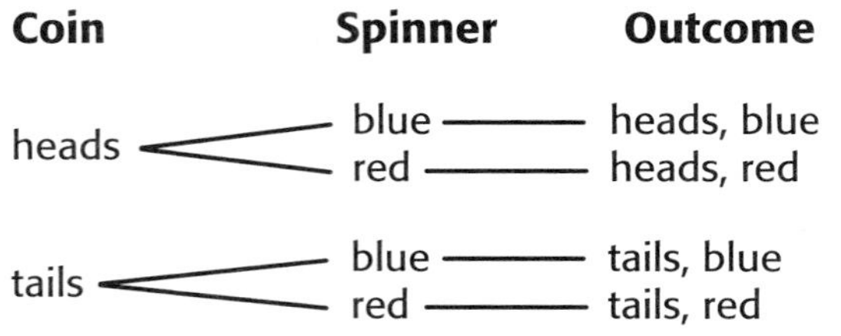 **Coin** **Spinner** **Outcome**

heads — blue — heads, blue
heads — red — heads, red
tails — blue — tails, blue
tails — red — tails, red

3. Sample answer: If you multiply the number of colors in the spinner by the number of sides to the quarter you will get the total number of combinations, $2 \times 2 = 4$.

4. **Second Spinner**

First Spinner	1	2	3	4
1	1,1	1,2	1,3	1,4
2	2,1	2,2	2,3	2,4
3	3,1	3,2	3,3	3,4
4	4,1	4,2	4,3	4,4

5. **Second Roll**

First Roll	5	6	7	8	9	10
5	5,5	5,6	5,7	5,8	5,9	5,10
6	6,5	6,6	6,7	6,8	6,9	6,10
7	7,5	7,6	7,7	7,8	7,9	7,10
8	8,5	8,6	8,7	8,8	8,9	8,10
9	9,5	9,6	9,7	9,8	9,9	9,10
10	10,5	10,6	10,7	10,8	10,9	10,10

6. 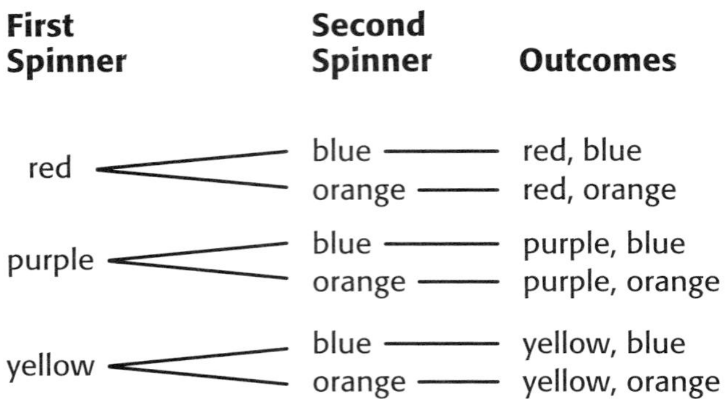 **First Spinner** **Second Spinner** **Outcomes**

red — blue — red, blue
red — orange — red, orange
purple — blue — purple, blue
purple — orange — purple, orange
yellow — blue — yellow, blue
yellow — orange — yellow, orange

7. 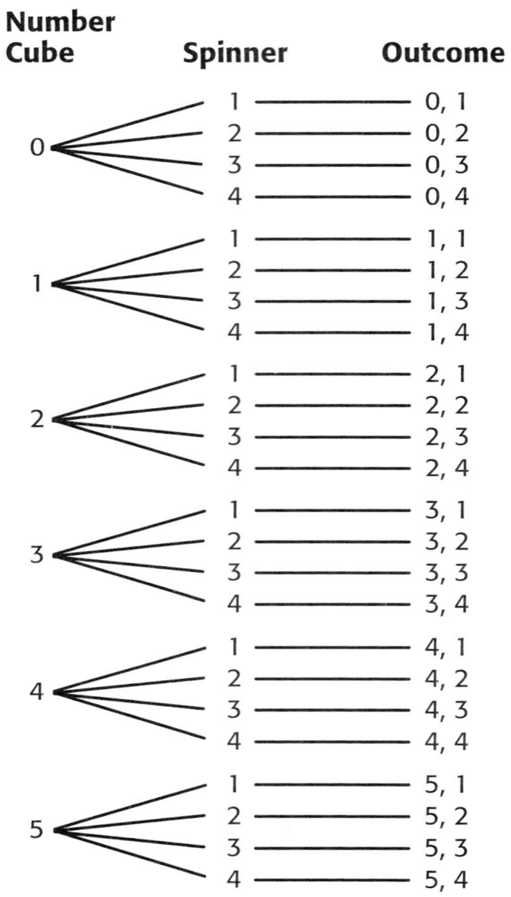 **Number Cube** **Spinner** **Outcome**

0 — 1 — 0, 1
0 — 2 — 0, 2
0 — 3 — 0, 3
0 — 4 — 0, 4
1 — 1 — 1, 1
1 — 2 — 1, 2
1 — 3 — 1, 3
1 — 4 — 1, 4
2 — 1 — 2, 1
2 — 2 — 2, 2
2 — 3 — 2, 3
2 — 4 — 2, 4
3 — 1 — 3, 1
3 — 2 — 3, 2
3 — 3 — 3, 3
3 — 4 — 3, 4
4 — 1 — 4, 1
4 — 2 — 4, 2
4 — 3 — 4, 3
4 — 4 — 4, 4
5 — 1 — 5, 1
5 — 2 — 5, 2
5 — 3 — 5, 3
5 — 4 — 5, 4

8. 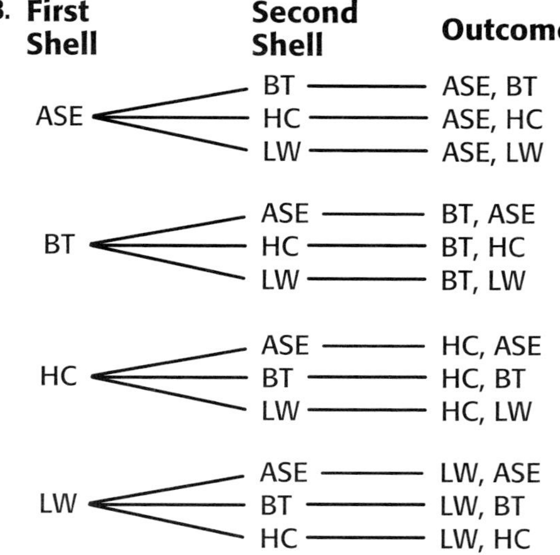

11. Sample answer: More of the combinations will have red in the outcome.

Page 130, Lesson 3-9

21. Sample answer:

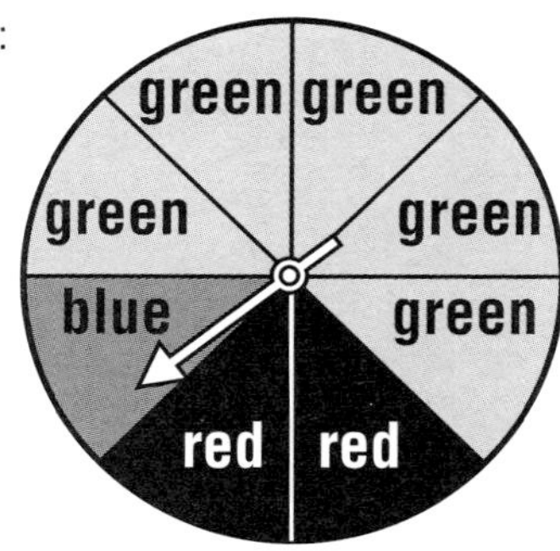

Page 139, Chapter Test

9. Sample answer: The bar graph shows the number of touchdowns scored in four football games; more touchdowns were scored in the fourth game than in any other games.

Chapter 3 Answer Appendix

Chapter Overview

Chapter-at-a-Glance

In Chapter 4, the emphasis is on multiplication and division facts, the properties of multiplication, and division rules.

Lesson	Math Objective	State/Local Standards
EXPLORE 4-1 **Meaning of Multiplication and Division** (pp. 145–146)	Use models to represent multiplication and division.	
4-1 **Relate Multiplication and Division** (pp. 147–149)	Understand how multiplication and division are related.	
4-2 **Algebra: Multiplication Properties and Division Rules** (pp. 150–153)	Use multiplication properties and division rules.	
4-3 **Multiply and Divide Facts Through 5** (pp. 154–157)	Recall multiplication and division facts 0 through 5.	
4-4 **Problem-Solving Skill: Choose an Operation** (pp. 158–169)	Choose an operation to solve a problem.	
4-5 **Multiply and Divide Facts Through 10** (pp. 160–162)	Recall multiplication and division facts through 10.	
4-6 **Multiply with 11 and 12** (pp. 166–169)	Recall and apply multiplication facts for 11 and 12.	
4-7 **Problem-Solving Investigation: Choose a Strategy** (pp. 170–171)	Choose the best strategy to solve a problem.	
4-8 **Algebra: Multiply Three Numbers** (pp. 172–174)	Multiply 3 factors.	
4-9 **Factors and Multiples** (pp. 176–179)	Find factors and multiples of whole numbers.	

Apply Multiplication and Division Facts

BIG Idea Students review basic multiplication and division facts, then focus on the relationship between the multiplication and division operations.

Using patterns is the key to simplifying the task of recalling facts with fluency. Opportunities should be provided to practice these strategies and promote discussions so students can communicate their thinking. The emphasis is to further develop number sense in order for students to become competent and confident in their understanding of multiplication and division facts.

Algebra Students learn about the relationship between multiplication properties and division rules. These concepts provide a foundation for developing algebra concepts, such as solving equations and inequalities. (Lessons 4-1 and 4-2)

G4-FP1 *Number and Operations* **and** *Algebra:* **Developing quick recall of multiplication facts and related division facts and fluency with whole number multiplication**

Students use understandings of multiplication to develop quick recall of the basic multiplication facts and related division facts. They apply their understanding of models for multiplication (i.e., equal sized groups, arrays, area models, equal intervals on the number line), place value, and properties of operations (in particular, the distributive property) as they develop, discuss, and use efficient, accurate, and generalizable methods to multiply multidigit whole numbers. They select appropriate methods and apply them accurately to estimate products or calculate them mentally, depending on the context and numbers involved. They develop fluency with efficient procedures, including the standard algorithm, for multiplying whole numbers, understand why the procedures work (on the basis of place value and properties of operations), and use them to solve problems.

Skills Trace
Vertical Alignment

Third Grade
In third grade, students learned to:
- Explore and memorize the multiplication table and look for patterns in it.

Fourth Grade
During this chapter, students learn to:
- Find factors and multiples of whole numbers.
- Recall multiplication and division facts through 12.
- Understand how multiplication and division are related and use multiplication properties and division rules.

After this chapter, students learn to:
- Multiply and divide by 1- and 2-digit numbers. Chapters 6 and 7

Fifth Grade
In fifth grade, students learn to:
- Use basic facts and patterns to multiply and divide multiples of 10, 100, and 1,000 mentally.
- Estimate products and quotients using rounding, clustering, and compatible numbers.

Backmapping and Vertical Alignment **McGraw-Hill's *Math Connects*** program was conceived and developed with the final results in mind: student success in Algebra 1 and beyond. The authors, using the **NCTM Focal Points and Focal Connections** as their guide, developed this brand-new series by backmapping from Algebra 1 concepts, and vertically aligning the topics so that they build upon prior skills and concepts and serve as a foundation for future topics.

Math Vocabulary
The following math vocabulary words for Chapter 4 are listed in the glossary of the ***Student Edition***. You can find interactive definitions in 13 languages in the ***eGlossary*** at macmillanmh.com.

Associative Property of Multiplication The property that states that the grouping of the factors does not change the product. (p. 150A)
Example: $3 \times (6 \times 2) = (3 \times 6) \times 2$

Commutative Property of Multiplication The property that states that the order in which two numbers are multiplied does not change the product. (p. 150A)
Example: $7 \times 2 = 2 \times 7$

Distributive Property of Multiplication To multiply a sum by a number, you can multiply each addend by the same number and add the products. (p. 166)
Example: $4 \times (1 + 3) = (4 \times 1) + (4 \times 3) = 16$

fact family A group of related facts using the same numbers. (p. 147A)
Example: $5 + 3 = 8$, $3 + 5 = 8$, $8 - 3 = 5$, $8 - 5 = 3$, or $5 \times 3 = 15$, $3 \times 5 = 15$, $15 \div 5 = 3$, $15 \div 3 = 5$

factor A number that divides into a whole number evenly. Also a number that is multiplied by another number. (p. 176A)

multiple A multiple of a number is the product of that number and any whole number. (p. 176A)
Example: 15 is a multiple of 5 because $3 \times 5 = 15$.

Visual Vocabulary Cards
Use Visual Vocabulary Cards 17, 18, and 27 to reinforce the vocabulary in this lesson. (The Define/Example/Ask routine is printed on the back of each card.)

factor

Chapter Planner

Suggested Pacing		
Instruction	Review & Assessment	TOTAL
10 days	1 day	**11 days**

Diagnostic Assessment
Quick Check (p. 144)

	Explore 4-1 (Pacing: 1 day)	Lesson 4-1 (Pacing: 1 day)	Lesson 4-2 (Pacing: 1 day)
Lesson/ Objective	**Meaning of Multiplication and Division** (pp. 145–146) **Objective:** Use models to represent multiplication and division.	**Relate Multiplication and Division** (pp. 147–149) **Objective:** Understand how multiplication and division are related.	**Algebra: Multiplication Properties and Division Rules** (pp. 150–153) **Objective:** Use multiplication properties and division rules.
State/Local Standards			
Math Vocabulary		**fact family**	**Commutative Property of Multiplication**, **Associative Property of Multiplication**, **Identity Property of Multiplication**, **Zero Property of Multiplication**
Lesson Resources	**Materials** cups **Manipulatives** counters	**Materials** egg cartons and beans, or a simple 2 × 6 grid used with any small objects **Manipulatives** counters **Other Resources** CRM Leveled Worksheets (pp. 8–12) Daily Reteach • 5-Minute Check • Problem of the Day	**Materials** red, green, and blue cards or pieces of paper **Other Resources** CRM Leveled Worksheets (pp. 13–17) Daily Reteach • 5-Minute Check • Problem of the Day
Technology			Math Song Track #3
Math Online	Concepts in Motion	Personal Tutor	Personal Tutor
Reaching All Learners		English Learners, p. 147B ELL Below Level, p. 147B BL Early Finishers, p. 147B OL AL	English Learners, p. 150B ELL Gifted and Talented, p. 150B AL Early Finishers, p. 150B OL AL
Alternate Lesson		*IMPACT Mathematics:* Unit A	*IMPACT Mathematics:* Unit A

KEY

BL Below/Approaching Level; OL On Level; AL Above/Beyond Level; ELL English Learners
SE Student Edition; TE Teacher Edition; CRM Chapter 4 Resource Masters; CD-Rom
Transparency; Real-World Problem Solving Library

	Lesson 4-3 (Pacing: 1 day)	Lesson 4-4 (Pacing: 1 day)	Lesson 4-5 (Pacing: 1 day)
Lesson/Objective	**Multiply and Divide Facts Through 5** (pp. 154–157) **Objective:** Recall multiplication and division facts 0 through 5.	**Problem-Solving Skill Choose an Operation** (pp. 158–159) **Objective:** Choose an operation to solve a problem.	**Multiply and Divide Facts Through 10** (pp. 160–162) **Objective:** Recall multiplication and division facts through 10.
State/Local Standards			
Math Vocabulary			
Lesson Resources	**Materials** hundreds charts **Manipulatives** number lines **Other Resources** CRM Leveled Worksheets (pp. 18–22) Daily Reteach • 5-Minute Check • Problem of the Day	**Other Resources** CRM Leveled Worksheets (pp. 23–27) Daily Reteach • 5-Minute Check • Problem of the Day *Class Project*	**Manipulatives** counters **Other Resources** CRM Leveled Worksheets (pp. 28–32) Daily Reteach • 5-Minute Check • Problem of the Day
Technology (Math Online)	Math Adventures Math Song Track #8 Personal Tutor	Personal Tutor	Math Adventures Math Song Track #8 Personal Tutor
Reaching All Learners	English Learners, p. 154B ELL Gifted and Talented, p. 154B AL Early Finishers, p. 154B OL AL	English Learners, p. 158 ELL Below Level, p. 158 BL Early Finishers, p. 158 OL AL	English Learners, p. 160B ELL Below Level, p. 160B BL Early Finishers, p. 160B OL AL
Alternate Lesson	*IMPACT Mathematics:* Unit A		*IMPACT Mathematics:* Unit A

Formative Assessment
Mid-Chapter Check (p. 163)

Problem Solving in History (p. 164)

Chapter Planner

	Lesson 4-6 (Pacing: 1 day)	Lesson 4-7 (Pacing: 1 day)	Lesson 4-8 (Pacing: 1 day)
Lesson/ Objective	**Multiply with 11 and 12** (pp. 166–169) **Objective:** Recall and apply multiplication facts for 11 and 12.	**Problem-Solving Investigation** **Choose a Strategy** (pp. 170–171) **Objective:** Choose the best strategy to solve a problem.	**Algebra: Multiply Three Numbers** (pp. 172–174) **Objective:** Multiply 3 factors.
State/Local Standards			
Math Vocabulary	**Distributive Property of Multiplication**		
Lesson Resources	**Materials** hundreds charts, crayons or markers **Manipulatives** counters **Other Resources** CRM Leveled Worksheets (pp. 33–37) Daily Reteach • 5-Minute Check • Problem of the Day	**Other Resources** CRM Leveled Worksheets (pp. 38–42) Daily Reteach • 5-Minute Check • Problem of the Day *Class Project*	**Manipulatives** counters **Other Resources** CRM Leveled Worksheets (pp. 43–47) Daily Reteach • 5-Minute Check • Problem of the Day
Technology Math Online	Math Adventures Math Song Track #8 Personal Tutor		Math Adventures Math Song Track #3 Personal Tutor
Reaching All Learners	English Learners, p. 166B ELL Gifted and Talented, p. 166B AL Early Finishers, p. 166B OL AL	English Learners, p. 170B ELL Gifted and Talented, p. 170B AL Early Finishers, p. 170B OL AL	English Learners, p. 172B ELL Gifted and Talented, p. 172B AL Early Finishers, p. 172B OL AL
Alternate Lesson	*IMPACT Mathematics:* Unit A		

Game Time
Multiplication Bingo (p. 175)

Lesson 4-9

Pacing: 1 day

Factors and Multiples
(pp. 176–179)

Objective: Find factors and multiples of whole numbers.

factor, **multiple**

Materials
multiplication tables, grid paper

Manipulatives
counters

Other Resources

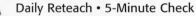

CRM Leveled Worksheets (pp. 48–52)

Daily Reteach • 5-Minute Check • Problem of the Day

Math Adventures

Math Song Track #4

Personal Tutor

English Learners, p. 176B ELL

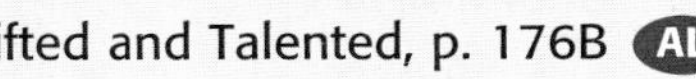
Gifted and Talented, p. 176B AL

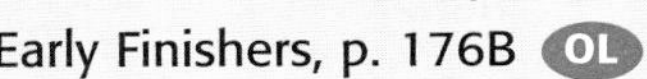
Early Finishers, p. 176B OL AL

IMPACT Mathematics: Unit A

Summative Assessment
- Study Guide/Review (pp. 181–186)
- Chapter Test (p. 187)
- Test Practice (pp. 188–189)

Assessment Options

Diagnostic Assessment

- SE *Option 1:* Quick Check (p. 144)
- *Option 2:* Online Quiz macmillanmh.com
- CRM *Option 3:* Diagnostic Test (p. 54)
- CRM *Option 4:* Chapter Pretest (p. 55)

Formative Assessment

- TE Alternate Teaching Strategy (every lesson)
- SE Talk About It (every lesson)
- SE Writing in Math (every lesson)
- SE Check What You Know (every lesson)
- TE Ticket Out the Door (pp. 153, 174)
- TE Name the Math (pp. 157, 169, 179)
- SE Mid-Chapter Check (p. 163)
- CRM Lesson Quizzes (pp. 56–58)
- CRM Mid-Chapter Test (p. 59)

Summative Assessment

- SE Chapter Test (p. 187)
- SE Test Practice (p. 188)
- CRM Vocabulary Test (p. X)
- CRM Leveled Chapter Tests (pp. 65–77)
- CRM Cumulative Test Practice (pp. 78–80)
- CRM Oral Assessment (pp. 61–62)
- ExamView® Assessment Suite
- Advance Tracker

McGraw Hill Professional Development

Targeted professional development has been articulated throughout **McGraw-Hill's *Math Connects*** program. The **McGraw-Hill Professional Development Video Library** provides short videos that support the **NCTM Focal Points and Focal Connections.** For more information visit macmillanmh.com.

Model Lessons

Instructional Strategies

Learning Stations

Cross-Curricular Links

Writing

individual | LINGUISTIC

Field Trip

- Write a paragraph about a fictional field trip. You can use details from a trip your class actually took. How many students will go on the trip? How much does the trip cost for each person?
- How much does it cost your class to go on the trip?
- How will you get there? How is your class arranged in an array on the transport you will take? Are there any other parts of the trip when your class is arranged in an array?

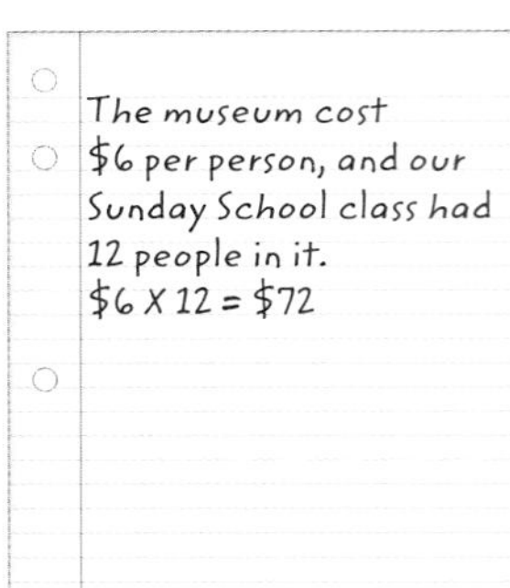

The museum cost
$6 per person, and our
Sunday School class had
12 people in it.
$6 X 12 = $72

Materials:
- paper
- pencil

Art

individual | VISUAL

Paint an Array

- Start with red, yellow, and blue paints. Then make orange, green, and violet using these colors. Now paint a one-row array of circles of the colors you have.
- Set aside enough paint to make a lighter array by adding white to each color and paint it above your one-row array. Then paint a darker array below by adding black to each color.
- What does your array look like now? How many rows and how many columns does it have? What would the fact family be for this array?

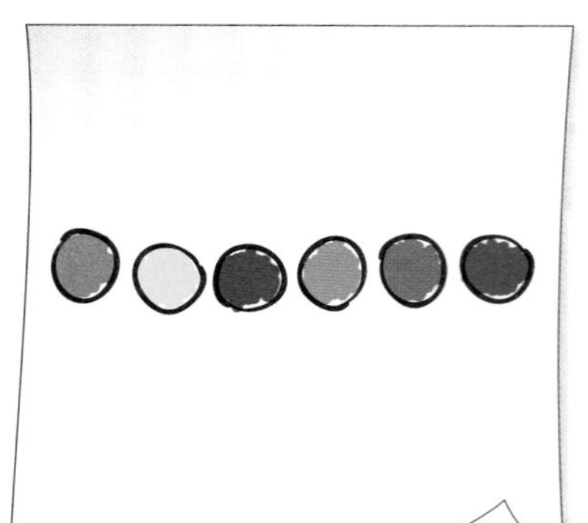

Materials:
- poster paints
- brushes
- rinsing water for brushes
- plastic cups for mixing paints
- paper

Health

individual | VISUAL

A Healthy Equation

Plan a walking program and get moving.

- Health experts say that everyone needs at least 30 minutes of exercise each day. Try walking for a month. If you use one blank square for each day of the week for four weeks, how many squares will you need?
- If you check off 30 minutes of walking for each day in this array, how many minutes per week have you walked?

Teacher note: Answers: $7 \times 4 = 28$ squares; $7 \times 30 = 210$ minutes

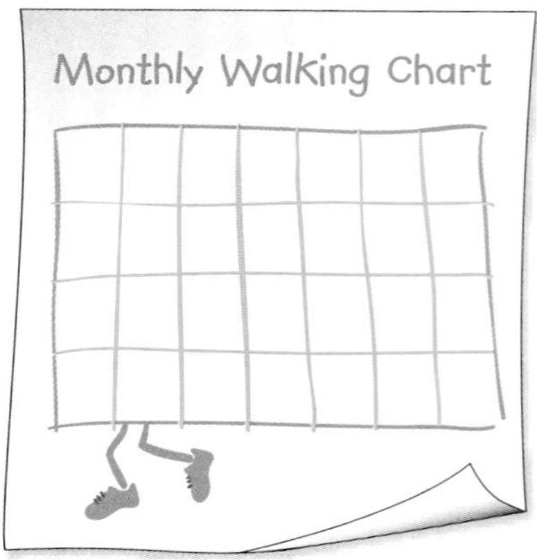

Materials:
- markers
- paper

Apply Multiplication and Division Facts

Science

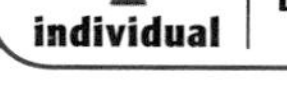
individual | LOGICAL

Factor Sifter

- Write down the following sets: numbers between 1–10; below that set, write down 11–20; then beneath that set, 21–30; next 31–40; and 41–50.
- 1 has only one factor. Anything divisible by 2 has more than two factors. Cross out numbers greater than 2 that are divisible by 2.
- Do numbers greater than 3 and divisible by 3 have more than one factor? If so, cross them out. Then do the same with numbers greater than 5 and divisible by 5.
- Are there any numbers left? Explain why or why not.

Materials:
- markers
- paper

Music

group | VISUAL

Do You Download?

Estimate how many songs you will download in one week.

- Each person reports how many songs they downloaded in one day. Everyone must use the same day to get his or her data.
- Make a chart of the data. The chart should have one row per person and two columns. The first column shows how many songs each person downloaded on that one day. In the second column, put the estimated weekly amount for each person. If you know how many songs were downloaded in one day, how can you estimate the weekly amount?

Downloaded Songs

Name	Downloaded Songs on Monday	Estimated Weekly Download Songs
Ayashe	4	28
Carla	7	49

Materials:
- markers
- paper
- pencils

Social Studies

pair | VISUAL

Rearrange the Senate

Part of each state legislature is the Senate. The Senate usually meets in the Senate Chamber. Suppose a certain state senate has 32 senators.

- Draw your own version of a Senate Chamber. Each partner should use a different array, using factors of 32. Factors of 32 are 1, 2, 4, 8, 16, and 32.
- How many different arrays could you make? What if four senators had to speak at the podium and the rest had to sit in rows in front of the podium? How would you arrange your array now for the rest of the Senate? Factors of 28 are 1, 2, 4, 7, 14 and 28.

Senate Chamber

Materials:
- markers
- paper
- pencils

CHAPTER 4

Introduce the Chapter

Real World: Into the Future!

Materials: a variety of fruits and vegetables, play money (dollar bills)

Tell students that they are going to look into the future and shop at a store in the year 3008.

Set up a fruit and vegetable counter. If you do not wish to use real food items, find or draw pictures of a variety of food types. Suggestions include apples, carrots, potatoes, and oranges.

Label the food with prices ranging from \$1 to \$5.

- How much will 8 carrots cost? Answers will vary.
- If you spent \$20 on oranges, how many did you buy? Answers will vary.

Have students act out the various scenarios to use multiplication and division skills.

Direct students to Student Edition p. 142. Have students read the paragraph at the top of the page.

- **How can repeated subtraction help you figure out Andrés' age in Mars years?** Sample answer: subtract by 2s five times (up to 10).
- **How old would a 12-year-old be in Mars years?** 6 Mars years

WRITING IN MATH

Starting the Chapter
Multiplication and division are skills that most people use daily. Have students write in their Math Journal how they used multiplication or division recently.

Key Vocabulary Introduce the key vocabulary in the chapter using the routine below.

Define: The Commutative Property of Multiplication states that the order in which two numbers are multiplied does not change the product.
Example: $5 \times 6 = 6 \times 5$
Ask: How does the Commutative Property help make multiplication easier?

Read-Aloud Anthology For an optional reading activity to introduce this chapter's math concepts, see the Read-Aloud Anthology on p. TR28.

CHAPTER 4 Apply Multiplication and Division Facts

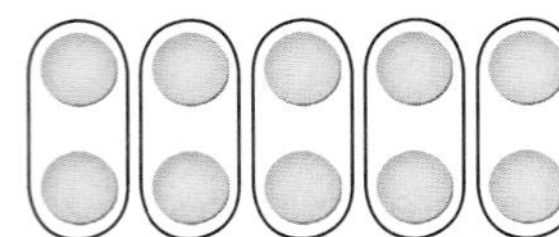

BIG Idea What are multiplication and division?

Multiplication means to find the total of equal groups.
Division means to separate an amount into equal groups.

Example Two years on Earth is about one year on Mars. Andrés is 10 years old. If he lived on Mars, he would be $10 \div 2$ or 5 years old.

$10 \div 2$ means to separate 10 into equal groups of 2.
$10 \div 2 = 5$

What will I learn in this chapter?

- Understand how multiplication and division are related.
- Use multiplication properties and division rules.
- Multiply and divide facts through 12.
- Identify factors and multiples.
- Choose an operation to solve problems.

Key Vocabulary

Commutative Property of Multiplication
Associative Property of Multiplication
factor
multiple
Distributive Property of Multiplication

Math Online Student Study Tools at macmillanmh.com

Chapter 4 Project

Daily Multiples Book

Throughout the chapter, students should identify any items or events that occur or appear in various multiples. They will assemble their multiples in a picture book format.

- Students should put together a book for younger students (like kindergarteners) to show things that occur in different multiples.
- One could be an only child, a lone tree, just about anything. Hands and feet occur in pairs. For three, some students may have 3 dogs, or 2 siblings, etc. There are four wheels on cars, five toes on a foot, etc.
- Students should use their imaginations and illustrate each page of their book.

CRM *Refer to Chapter 4 Resource Masters, p. 63, for a rubric to assess students' progress on this project.*

FOLDABLES® Study Organizer Make this Foldable to help you organize information about multiplication and division. Begin with four sheets of $8\frac{1}{2}'' \times 11''$ paper.

1. **Stack** 4 sheets of paper. Place each sheet $\frac{3}{4}$ inch apart.
2. **Roll** up the edges, so all tabs are the same size.
3. **Crease** and staple along the fold.
4. **Label** the tabs with the topics from the chapter.

FOLDABLES® Dinah Zike's Foldables

Guide students through the directions on p. 143 to create their own Foldable graphic organizer for multiplication and division facts. Students may also use their Foldable to study and review for chapter assessments.

When to Use It Lessons 4-1, 4-2, 4-3, 4-4, 4-5, 4-6, and 4-8. (Additional instructions for using the Foldable with these lessons are found on pp. 163 and 180.)

Chapter 4 Literature List

Lesson	Book Title
4-1	**Math Curse** John Scieszka and Lane Smith
4-2	**A Place for Zero: A Math Adventure** Angeline Sparagna LoPresti
4-3	**Math Appeal** Greg Tang
4-4	**Amanda Bean's Amazing Dream** Cindy Neuschwander
4-5	**Spaghetti and Meatballs for All!** Marilyn Burns
4-6	**The Grapes of Math** Greg Tang
4-8	**Anno's Mysterious Multiplying Jar** Masaichiro and Mitsumasa Anno
4-9	**The Man Who Counted: A Collection of Mathematical Adventures** Malba Tahan

ELL National ESL Standards Alignment for Chapter 4

Lesson, Page	ESL Standard	Modality	Level
4-1, p. 147B	Goal 2, Standard 2, f	Kinesthetic, Visual, Spatial	Intermediate
4-2, p. 150B	Goal 2, Standard 3, e	Social	Beginning
4-3, p. 154B	Goal 2, Standard 2, g	Visual, Spatial	Intermediate
4-4, p. 158B	Goal 2, Standard 3, d	Logical	Intermediate
4-5, p. 160B	Goal 1, Standard 3, d	Auditory	Beginning
4-6, p. 166B	Goal 2, Standard 2, h	Logical, Intrapersonal	Intermediate
4-7, p. 170B	Goal 1, Standard 3, k	Linguistic	Beginning
4-8, p. 172B	Goal 2, Standard 1, h	Linguistic	Intermediate
4-9, p. 176B	Goal 2, Standard 3, h	Linguistic	Intermediate

The National ESL Standards can be found in the Teacher Reference Handbook.

- Read the Math at Home letter found in the Chapter 4 Resource Masters, p. 4, with the class and have each student sign it. (A Spanish version is found on p. 5.)
- Send home copies of the Math at Home letter with each student.

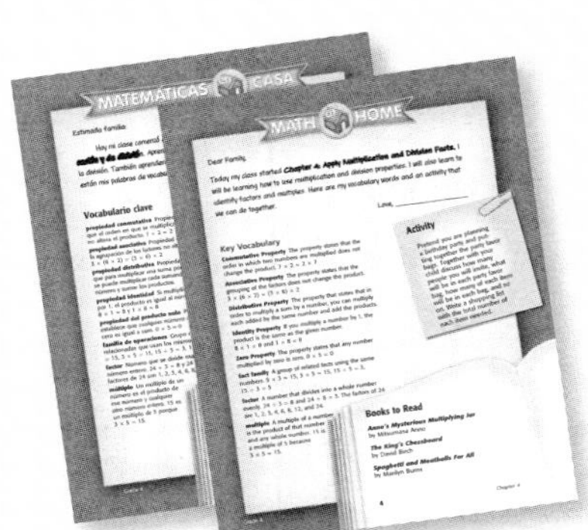

Diagnostic Assessment

Check for readiness before beginning the chapter.

- **Option 1:** ***Quick Check***
  SE Student Edition, p. 144
- **Option 2:** ***Online Assessment***
  Math Online macmillanmh.com
- **Option 3:** ***Diagnostic Tests***
  CRM Chapter 4 Resource Masters, p. 44–45

RTI (Response to Intervention)

Apply the Results Based on the results of the diagnostic assessment on Student Edition p. 144, use the chart below to address individual needs before beginning the chapter.

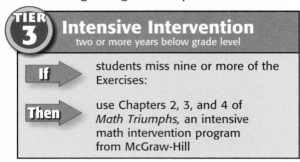

TIER 3 Intensive Intervention

two or more years below grade level

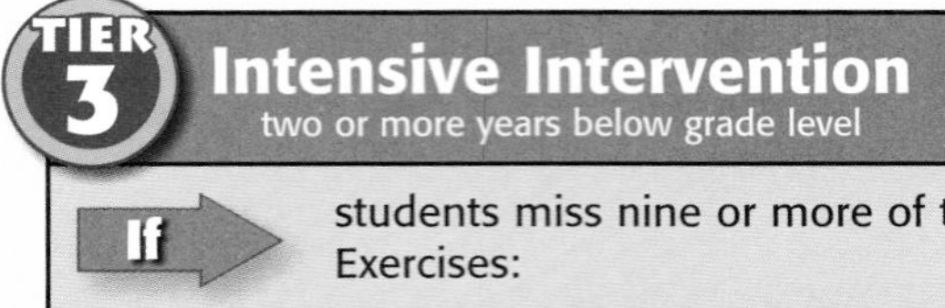

If students miss nine or more of the Exercises:

Then use Chapters 2, 3, and 4 of *Math Triumphs*, an intensive math intervention program from McGraw-Hill

ARE YOU READY for Chapter 4?

You have two ways to check prerequisite skills for this chapter.

Option 2

Math Online Take the Chapter Readiness Quiz at macmillanmh.com.

Option 1

Complete the Quick Check below.

QUICK Check

Algebra Complete each number sentence. (Prior Grade) (Used in Lesson 4-1)

1. $4 + 4 + 4 = \blacksquare$ 12

2. $6 + 6 + \blacksquare + 6 = 24$ 6

3. $9 + 9 + 9 = 3 \times \blacksquare$ 9

4. $11 + 11 + 11 + 11 = \blacksquare \times 11$ 4

5. Write the multiplication fact modeled by the array at the right. 2×4

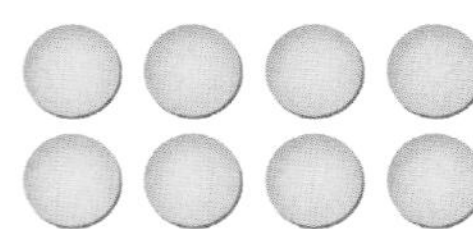

Copy each array. Then circle equal groups of 3. (Prior Grade) (Used in Lesson 4-3)

6.

7.

8. Marcia has 15 action figures. If Marcia places the figures in 3 equal rows, how many figures will be in each row? 5

Algebra The number patterns below are formed by skip counting. Copy and complete each pattern. (Prior Grade) (Used in Lessons 4-3 and 4-9)

9. 2, 4, 6, ■, 10, ■, 14 8, 12

10. 4, 8, 12, ■, 20, 24, ■ 16, 28

11. 5, ■, 15, 20, ■, 30, ■ 10, 25, 35

12. ■, 18, 27, ■, 45, 54, ■ 9, 36, 63

13. Write a number pattern that involves skip counting forward by 25.
Sample answer: 50, 75, 100, 125, 150, 175, 200

14. Write a number pattern that involves skip counting backward by 4.
Sample answer: 36, 32, 28, 24, 20, 16, 12

144 **Chapter 4** Apply Multiplication and Division Facts

TIER 2 Strategic Intervention below/approaching grade level	TIER 1 On-Level	Above/Beyond Level
If students miss five to eight in: **Exercises 1–13**	**If** students miss three or four in: **Exercises 1–13**	**If** students miss two or less in: **Exercises 1–13**
Then choose a resource:	**Then** choose a resource:	**Then** choose a resource:
Strategic Intervention Guide (pp. 70, 72, 74, 76, 78, 82) TE Start Smart 2: Number and Operations (p. 4)	TE Learning Stations (pp. 142G–142H) TE Chapter Project (p. 142) CRM Game: Dealing Dividends and Divisions Math Adventures My Math Zone Chapter 3	TE Learning Stations (pp. 142G–142H) TE Chapter Project (p. 142) Real-World Problem Solving: *Class Project* My Math Zone Chapters 2 and 3
Math Online Extra Examples • Personal Tutor • Concepts in Motion	**Math Online** Fact Dash	**Math Online** Games

Math Activity for 4-1

Meaning of Multiplication and Division

You can use models to represent multiplication and division.

MAIN IDEA

I will use models to represent multiplication and division.

You Will Need
counters
cups

Math Online
macmillanmh.com
• Concepts in Motion

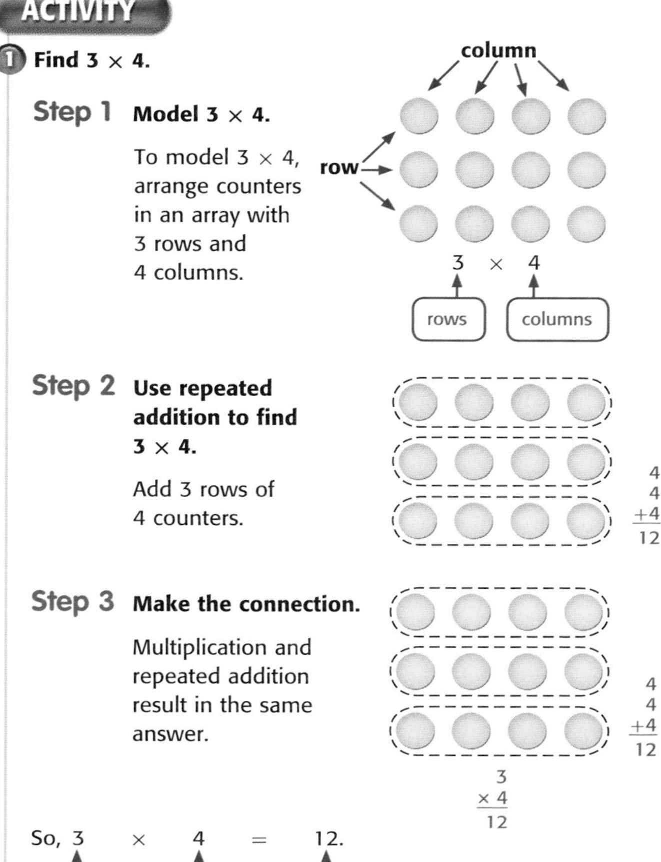

ACTIVITY

1 **Find 3 × 4.**

Step 1 **Model 3 × 4.**

To model 3 × 4, arrange counters in an array with 3 rows and 4 columns.

Step 2 **Use repeated addition to find 3 × 4.**

Add 3 rows of 4 counters.

Step 3 **Make the connection.**

Multiplication and repeated addition result in the same answer.

So, 3 × 4 = 12.

Math Activity for 4-1

Lesson Planner

Objective

Use models to represent multiplication and division.

Resources

Manipulatives: cups and counters

Teacher Technology

Math Online macmillanmh.com

Concepts in Motion

1 Introduce

Introduce the Concept

- Have students use counters to model addition and subtraction problems.
- Ask students to use counters to find the sum of 12 and 9. 21
- **Find 25 − 8.** 17
- Guide students to discover the connection between repeated addition and multiplication by asking them to model 4 + 4 + 4 + 4 + 4.
- **What is the sum?** 20
- **Is there an easier way to find the sum than by counting each one individually?** Sample answer: Count by 4s.

2 Teach

Activity 1 Show students how to use an array to model 3 × 4. Explain that the first number (3) shows the number of rows, while the second number (4) is the number of columns. They can add three rows of 4 or multiply 3 × 4. Be sure to point out that repeated addition and multiplication result in the same total.

Activity 2 Explain that students should distribute the counters equally to the cups. This will help them understand that all cups need to have the same number of counters. Once all counters are put into the cups, ask students if it matters which cup they use to count.

Think About It

Assign Exercises 1 and 2 to assess student comprehension of the concept presented in the Activity.

3 Assess

Formative Assessment

Use **Check What You Know** Exercises 3–6 to assess whether students comprehend how to use models to represent multiplication and division.

From Concrete to Abstract Use Exercise 7 to bridge the idea of modeling multiplication with physical models such as counters and with number sentences.

Extending the Concept

- **Why do 3 × 5 and 5 × 3 have the same product?** Sample answer: Because they have the same factors, even if the order is different.

ACTIVITY

2 Find 15 ÷ 3.

Step 1 Model 15 ÷ 3.

Use 15 counters. Put the counters in 3 rows since the divisor is 3.

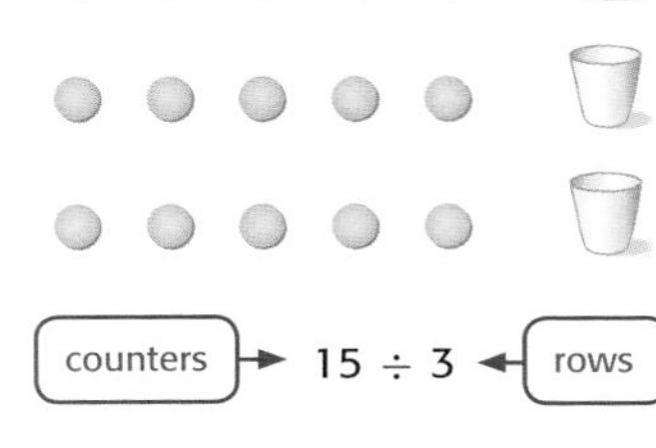

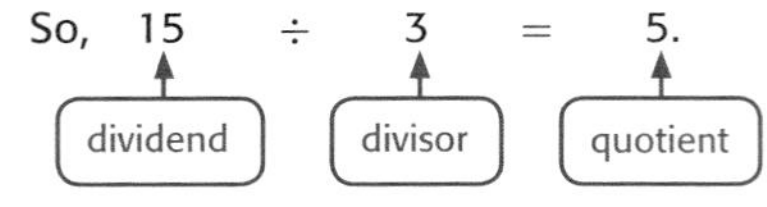

Step 2 Place the counters in the cups.

Divide the counters equally one by one into the cups until all 15 counters are gone.

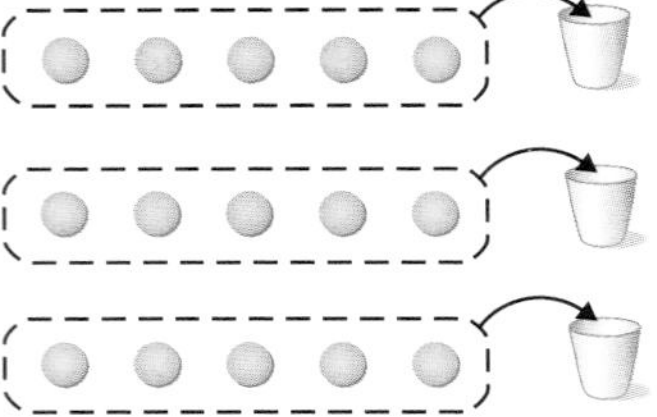

Step 3 Find 15 ÷ 3.

There are 5 counters in each cup.

So, 15 (dividend) ÷ 3 (divisor) = 5 (quotient).

Think About It

1. How would you model 2 × 8? 2 rows of 8 counters
2. How would you model 10 ÷ 5? 10 counters and 5 cups

CHECK What You Know

Draw pictures to model. Then multiply or divide.

3. 3 × 7 21
4. 6 ÷ 3 2
5. 6 × 8 48
6. 24 ÷ 6 4

For Exercises 3–6, see students' work for pictures.

7. WRITING IN MATH Explain how to model 4 groups of 9. Write a number sentence to show the total amount in 4 groups of 9. Show 4 rows with 9 counters in each row. 4 × 9 = 36

Relate Multiplication and Division

Lesson Planner

Objective

Understand how multiplication and division are related.

New Vocabulary

fact family

Resources

Materials: egg cartons, beans. If not available, a simple 2 × 6 grid can be drawn and any small objects can be substituted.

Manipulatives: counters

Literature Connection: *Math Curse* by Jon Scieszka and Lane Smith

Teacher Technology
TeacherWorks • Interactive Classroom

Alternate Lesson: Use *IMPACT Mathematics:* Unit A to provide practice with multiplication.

Daily Routine

Use these suggestions before beginning the lesson on p. 147.

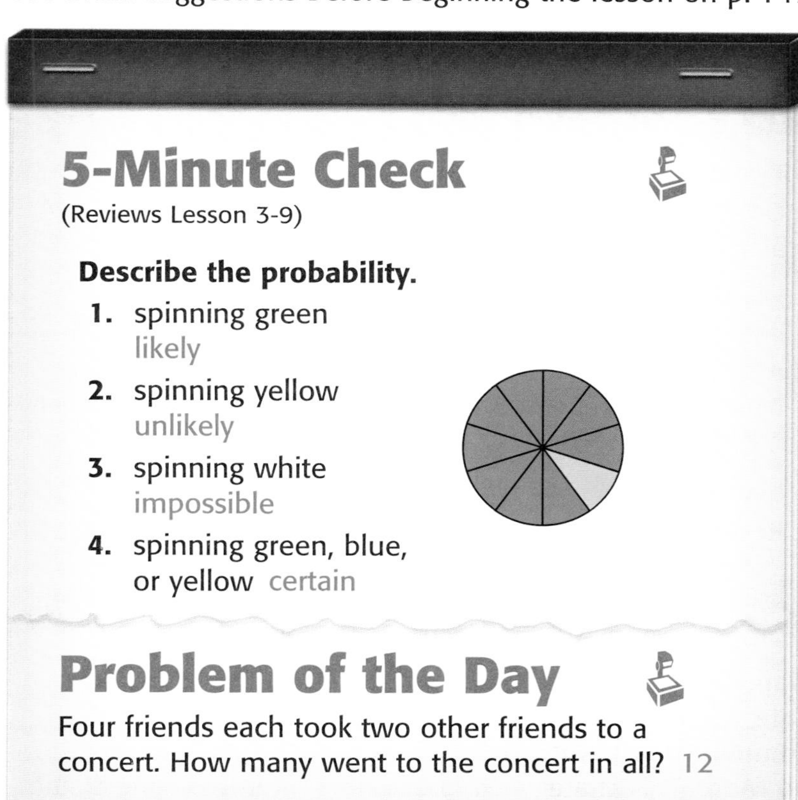

5-Minute Check

(Reviews Lesson 3-9)

Describe the probability.

1. spinning green likely
2. spinning yellow unlikely
3. spinning white impossible
4. spinning green, blue, or yellow certain

Problem of the Day

Four friends each took two other friends to a concert. How many went to the concert in all? 12

Focus on Math Background

Division has a similar relationship to multiplication as subtraction has to addition. Multiplication and division are inverse operations. You can think of division as "undoing" what multiplication "does." A set of four related multiplication and division facts known as a fact family can be used to illustrate this relationship. In general, the fact family that can be written for the relationship that "factor 1 × factor 2 = product" are:

factor 1 × factor 2 = product
factor 2 × factor 1 = product
product ÷ factor 1 = factor 2
product ÷ factor 2 = factor 1

Building Math Vocabulary

Write the lesson vocabulary word and its definition on the board.

Write 15, 3, and 5 on the board. Have students write the fact family that uses multiplication and division sentences to relate these three numbers. Have students write the fact family in their Math Journals.

Visual Vocabulary Cards

Use Visual Vocabulary Card 17 to reinforce the vocabulary introduced in this lesson. (The Define/Example/Ask routine is printed on the back of each card.)

Differentiated Instruction

Small Group Options

Option 1 Below Level BL

VISUAL, SPATIAL

Materials: two-colored counters

- Give each student 12 counters. Ask them to arrange the counters yellow side up in a 4×3 array.
- **What is the division fact that goes with this array?** $12 \div 4 = 3$
- Ask students to turn the counters over 3 at a time to demonstrate repeated subtraction. They should turn over 4 groups of 3 to get 12.
- Repeat this process with an array to show $3 \times 4 = 12$.
- Repeat this process with an array to show $6 \times 2 = 12$.

Option 2 English Language Learners ELL

KINESTHETIC, VISUAL

Materials: egg cartons
Core Vocabulary: into, in half, ways to divide
Common Use Verb: rip

Do Math This strategy explores division through kinesthetic movement and introduces new action vocabulary.

- Divide students into pairs, giving each pair an egg carton.
- Demonstrate that the egg carton is 2×6, and equals 12.
- Ask half the students to rip the egg carton in half.
- Discuss methods. Say: "12 divided by 2 is 6."
- Ask the other half of the students to rip the egg carton into six pieces, two pieces in each.
- Discuss other number sentences.

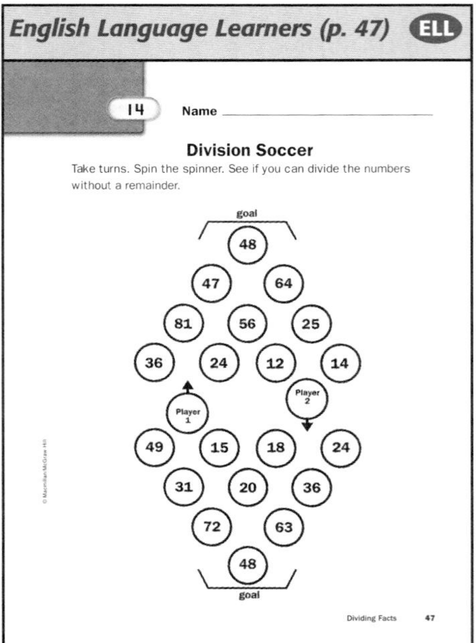

English Language Learners (p. 47) ELL

14 Name ____________

Division Soccer

Take turns. Spin the spinner. See if you can divide the numbers without a remainder.

Dividing Facts 47

Use this worksheet to provide additional support for English Language Learners.

Independent Work Options

Option 1 Early Finishers OL AL

VISUAL, SPATIAL

Materials: number cubes, paper, pencil

- In groups of 2 to 4, have students take turns rolling the number cubes. One student will be the scorekeeper. The roller will say the fact family for the numbers rolled. One point is awarded per fact given.
- Depending on the roll, there may be two fact families per pair. For example, if a 2 and a 5 are rolled, there is only one fact family (2, 5, 10) If a 2 and a 6 are rolled, then two fact families are possible (2, 6, 12 and 2, 3, 6).
- The person with the highest score wins.

Option 2 Student Technology

Tech Link

Math Online > macmillanmh.com

Personal Tutor • Extra Examples

Option 3 Learning Station: Writing (p. 142)

Direct students to the Writing Learning Station for opportunities to explore and extend the lesson concept.

Option 4 Problem-Solving Practice

Reinforce problem-solving skills and strategies with the Problem-Solving Practice worksheet.

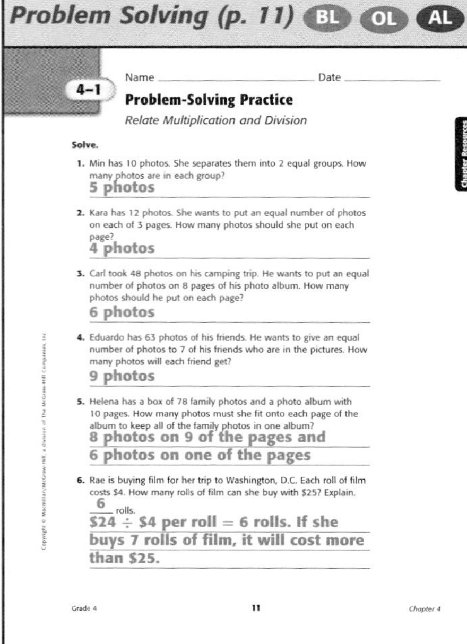

Problem Solving (p. 11) BL OL AL

4–1 Name ____________ Date ____________

Problem-Solving Practice

Relate Multiplication and Division

Chapter Resources

Solve.

1. Min has 10 photos. She separates them into 2 equal groups. How many photos are in each group?
   5 photos
2. Kara has 12 photos. She wants to put an equal number of photos on each of 3 pages. How many photos should she put on each page?
   4 photos
3. Carl took 48 photos on his camping trip. He wants to put an equal number of photos on 8 pages of his photo album. How many photos should he put on each page?
   6 photos
4. Eduardo has 63 photos of his friends. He wants to give an equal number of photos to 7 of his friends who are in the pictures. How many photos will each friend get?
   9 photos
5. Helena has a box of 78 family photos and a photo album with 10 pages. How many photos must she fit onto each page of the album to keep all of the family photos in one album?
   8 photos on 9 of the pages and 6 photos on one of the pages
6. Rae is buying film for her trip to Washington, D.C. Each roll of film costs $4. How many rolls of film can she buy with $25? Explain.
   6 rolls.
   $24 ÷ $4 per roll = 6 rolls. If she buys 7 rolls of film, it will cost more than $25.

Grade 4 11 Chapter 4

Relate Multiplication and Division

GET READY to Learn

Latanya and her father are baking a cake. Her father asks her how many eggs they have. The eggs in the carton are arranged in an array.

MAIN IDEA

I will understand how multiplication and division are related.

New Vocabulary

fact family

Math Online

macmillanmh.com

- Extra Examples
- Personal Tutor
- Self-Check Quiz

You can write related multiplication and division sentences to describe the array of eggs. You can think of this array as 2 rows and 3 columns or 3 rows and 2 columns.

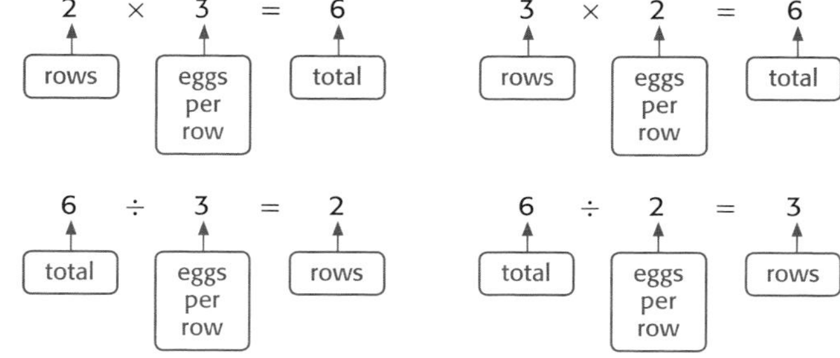

The number sentences above show a fact family. A **fact family** is a set of four related multiplication and division facts that use the same three numbers. The fact family follows a pattern.

Write a Fact Family

1 Write a fact family for the array.

There are 3 rows, 4 columns, and a total of 12 objects.

$3 \times 4 = 12$ $4 \times 3 = 12$

$12 \div 3 = 4$ $12 \div 4 = 3$

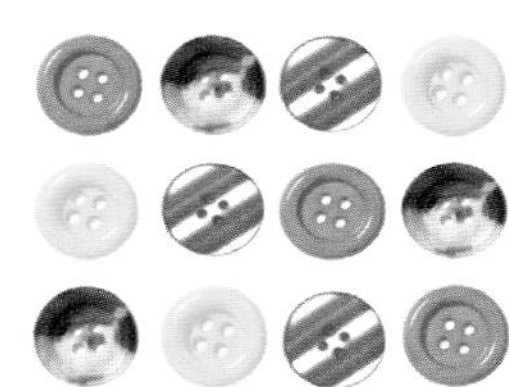

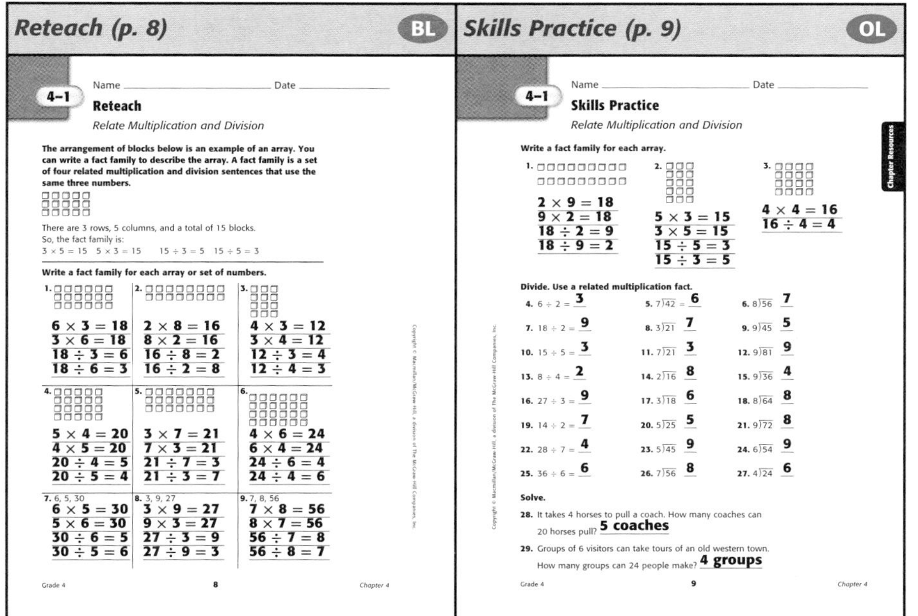

Reteach (p. 8) BL

4-1 Name ______ Date ______

Reteach

Relate Multiplication and Division

The arrangement of blocks below is an example of an array. You can write a fact family to describe the array. A fact family is a set of four related multiplication and division sentences that use the same three numbers.

There are 3 rows, 5 columns, and a total of 15 blocks.
So, the fact family is:
$3 \times 5 = 15$ $5 \times 3 = 15$ $15 \div 3 = 5$ $15 \div 5 = 3$

Write a fact family for each array or set of numbers.

1. $6 \times 3 = 18$, $3 \times 6 = 18$, $18 \div 3 = 6$, $18 \div 6 = 3$
2. $2 \times 8 = 16$, $8 \times 2 = 16$, $16 \div 8 = 2$, $16 \div 2 = 8$
3. $4 \times 3 = 12$, $3 \times 4 = 12$, $12 \div 3 = 4$, $12 \div 4 = 3$
4. $5 \times 4 = 20$, $4 \times 5 = 20$, $20 \div 4 = 5$, $20 \div 5 = 4$
5. $3 \times 7 = 21$, $7 \times 3 = 21$, $21 \div 7 = 3$, $21 \div 3 = 7$
6. $4 \times 6 = 24$, $6 \times 4 = 24$, $24 \div 6 = 4$, $24 \div 4 = 6$
7. 6, 5, 30: $6 \times 5 = 30$, $5 \times 6 = 30$, $30 \div 6 = 5$, $30 \div 5 = 6$
8. 3, 9, 27: $3 \times 9 = 27$, $9 \times 3 = 27$, $27 \div 3 = 9$, $27 \div 9 = 3$
9. 7, 8, 56: $7 \times 8 = 56$, $8 \times 7 = 56$, $56 \div 7 = 8$, $56 \div 8 = 7$

Grade 4 8 Chapter 4

Skills Practice (p. 9) OL

4-1 Name ______ Date ______

Skills Practice

Relate Multiplication and Division

Chapter Resources

Write a fact family for each array.

1. $2 \times 9 = 18$, $9 \times 2 = 18$, $18 \div 2 = 9$, $18 \div 9 = 2$
2. $5 \times 3 = 15$, $3 \times 5 = 15$, $15 \div 5 = 3$, $15 \div 3 = 5$
3. $4 \times 4 = 16$, $16 \div 4 = 4$

Divide. Use a related multiplication fact.

4. $6 \div 2 =$ **3**
5. $7\overline{)42}$ = **6**
6. $8\overline{)56}$ **7**
7. $18 \div 2 =$ **9**
8. $3\overline{)21}$ **7**
9. $9\overline{)45}$ **5**
10. $15 \div 5 =$ **3**
11. $7\overline{)21}$ **3**
12. $9\overline{)81}$ **9**
13. $8 \div 4 =$ **2**
14. $2\overline{)16}$ **8**
15. $9\overline{)36}$ **4**
16. $27 \div 3 =$ **9**
17. $3\overline{)18}$ **6**
18. $8\overline{)64}$ **8**
19. $14 \div 2 =$ **7**
20. $5\overline{)25}$ **5**
21. $9\overline{)72}$ **8**
22. $28 \div 7 =$ **4**
23. $5\overline{)45}$ **9**
24. $6\overline{)54}$ **9**
25. $36 \div 6 =$ **6**
26. $7\overline{)56}$ **8**
27. $4\overline{)24}$ **6**

Solve.

28. It takes 4 horses to pull a coach. How many coaches can 20 horses pull? **5 coaches**
29. Groups of 6 visitors can take tours of an old western town. How many groups can 24 people make? **4 groups**

Grade 4 9 Chapter 4

Relate Multiplication and Division

1 Introduce

Activity Choice 1 • Hands-On

- Hand out empty egg cartons and a dozen beans to small groups of students. They can choose how many of their beans to use, but only one bean can go in each compartment.
- Students now have a simple array of beans.
- **How can you determine how many beans you used?** Sample answer: Count the beans.
- Draw an array of 6 rows of 8 beans on the board. Tell students that one way to figure out how many beans are here is to count.
- **Is there an easier way?** Yes; multiply 6×8.
- Fact families represent inverse operations. **What division sentence would show the same fact family?** $48 \div 6 = 8$

Activity Choice 2 • Literature

Introduce the lesson with *Math Curse* by Jon Scieszka and Lane Smith. For a related math activity, see p. TR46.

2 Teach

Scaffolding Questions

Students continue using egg cartons and beans.

- **How many rows are in the carton? How many columns?** 2; 6
- **What multiplication sentence shows the number of beans in the egg carton?** $2 \times 6 = 12$
- **Suppose you place two egg cartons side-by-side, with a bean in each compartment. What multiplication sentence shows the number of beans in the 2 cartons?** $2 \times 12 = 24$

GET READY to Learn

Have students open their books and read the information in **Get Ready to Learn**. Introduce **fact family**. As a class, work through **Examples 1 and 2**.

Use Related Facts

Example 2 Remind students they can use fact families to find the related multiplication facts.

ADDITIONAL EXAMPLES

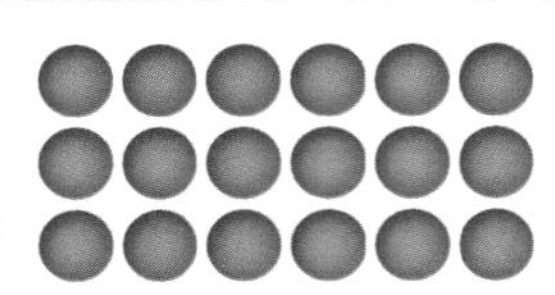

1. Write a fact family for the array. $3 \times 6 = 18$; $6 \times 3 = 18$; $18 \div 3 = 6$; $18 \div 6 = 3$

2. Jorge has 42 pictures he wants to place in an album. If six pictures fit on each page, how many pages will he fill? 7 pages

CHECK What You Know

As a class, have students complete Exercises 1–10 in **Check What You Know** as you observe their work.

Exercise 10 Assess student comprehension before assigning practice exercises.

BL Alternate Teaching Strategy

If students have trouble with division facts…

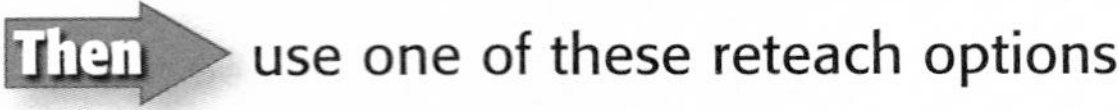

Then use one of these reteach options:

1 CRM **Daily Reteach Worksheet** (p. 8)

2 Use counters to model the division problems. For example, to model $18 \div 6$, give students 18 counters and have them arrange the counters into 6 groups.

- **How many counters are in each group?** 3
- **How many are in each group if you divide the 18 counters into 3 groups?** 6

Help students make the connection among the four related facts for 3, 6, and 18.

COMMON ERROR!

Exercises 11–14 Students may not find the correct numbers in the fact family. Remind them to count (or multiply) to find the total in the array.

You can use a related multiplication fact to help you divide.

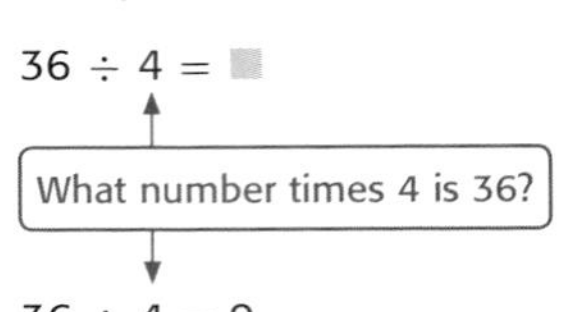

Remember

Multiplication and division are opposite, or *inverse*, operations.

Real-World EXAMPLE Use Related Facts

2 **BOOKS Vanesa has 36 books to put on 4 shelves. The same number of books will be placed on each shelf. How many books will be on each shelf?**

Find $36 \div 4$. You can use a related multiplication fact to help you divide.

$36 \div 4 = ■$

What number times 4 is 36?

$36 \div 4 = 9$

So, Vanesa will place 9 books on each shelf.

10. Sample answer: Multiplication and division are opposite, or inverse, operations. Example: $2 \times 4 = 8$ and $8 \div 4 = 2$.

CHECK What You Know

Write a fact family for each array or set of numbers. See Example 1 (p. 147)

1.  $3 \times 7 = 21$, $7 \times 3 = 21$, $21 \div 3 = 7$, $21 \div 7 = 3$

2. $5 \times 5 = 25$, $25 \div 5 = 5$

3. 6, 8, 48 $6 \times 8 = 48$, $8 \times 6 = 48$, $48 \div 6 = 8$, $48 \div 8 = 6$

4. 3, 12, 4 $4 \times 3 = 12$, $3 \times 4 = 12$, $12 \div 3 = 4$, $12 \div 4 = 3$

Algebra Copy and complete each fact family. See Example 1 (p. 147)

5. $3 \times 6 = ■$ $3 \times 6 = 18$ $6 \times ■ = 18$ $6 \times 3 = 18$ $18 \div ■ = 3$ $18 \div 6 = 3$ $18 \div 3 = ■$ $18 \div 3 = 6$

6. $5 \times 7 = ■$ $5 \times 7 = 35$ $■ \times 5 = 35$ $7 \times 5 = 35$ $35 \div ■ = 7$ $35 \div 5 = 7$ $35 \div 7 = ■$ $35 \div 7 = 5$

Algebra Divide. Use a related multiplication fact. See Example 2 (p. 148)

7. $22 \div 2 = ■$ 11; $2 \times 11 = 22$

8. $81 \div 9 = ■$ 9; $9 \times 9 = 81$

9. Ed wants to share 18 grapes equally among himself and two friends. How many grapes will each get? 6 grapes

10. Talk About It How are multiplication and division related? Use examples to support your answer.

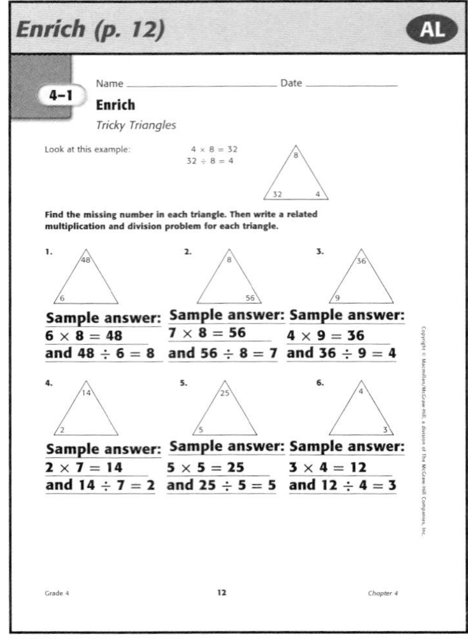

Enrich (p. 12) AL

4-1 Name ______ Date ______

Enrich

Tricky Triangles

Look at this example: $4 \times 8 = 32$ $32 \div 8 = 4$ (triangle: 8, 32, 4)

Find the missing number in each triangle. Then write a related multiplication and division problem for each triangle.

1. (48, 6) Sample answer: $6 \times 8 = 48$ and $48 \div 6 = 8$
2. (8, 56) Sample answer: $7 \times 8 = 56$ and $56 \div 8 = 7$
3. (36, 9) Sample answer: $4 \times 9 = 36$ and $36 \div 9 = 4$
4. (14, 2) Sample answer: $2 \times 7 = 14$ and $14 \div 7 = 2$
5. (25, 5) Sample answer: $5 \times 5 = 25$ and $25 \div 5 = 5$
6. (4, 3) Sample answer: $3 \times 4 = 12$ and $12 \div 4 = 3$

Grade 4 12 Chapter 4

Practice and Problem Solving

See page R9.

Write a fact family for each array or set of numbers. See Example 1 (p. 147)

11.  $2 \times 3 = 6$, $3 \times 2 = 6$, $6 \div 3 = 2$, $6 \div 2 = 3$

12.  $3 \times 5 = 15$, $5 \times 3 = 15$, $15 \div 3 = 5$, $15 \div 5 = 3$

13. $6 \times 6 = 36$, $36 \div 6 = 6$

14. $5 \times 8 = 40$, $8 \times 5 = 40$, $40 \div 5 = 8$, $40 \div 8 = 5$

15. 6, 9, 54 **16.** 7, 8, 56 **17.** 9, 11, 99 **18.** 11, 12, 132

15–18. See Ch. 4 Answer Appendix.

Algebra **Copy and complete each fact family.** See Example 1 (p. 147)

19. $4 \times 8 = ■$ $■ \times 4 = 32$ $32 \div ■ = 8$ $32 \div 8 = ■$
$4 \times 8 = 32$, $8 \times 4 = 32$, $32 \div 4 = 8$, $32 \div 8 = 4$

20. $■ \times 9 = 72$ $9 \times 8 = ■$ $72 \div ■ = 8$ $72 \div 8 = ■$
$8 \times 9 = 72$, $9 \times 8 = 72$, $72 \div 9 = 8$, $72 \div 8 = 9$

Algebra **Divide. Use a related multiplication fact.** See Example 2 (p. 148)

21. $18 \div 2 = ■$ 9; $2 \times 9 = 18$

22. $36 \div 6 = ■$ 6; $6 \times 6 = 36$

23. $63 \div 7 = ■$ 9; $7 \times 9 = 63$

24. $64 \div 8 = ■$ 8; $8 \times 8 = 64$

Data File

The cardinal is the state bird in seven states. It became Kentucky's state bird in 1926.

25. Cardinals can weigh up to 2 ounces. Suppose a flock of cardinals weighs a total of 24 ounces. How many cardinals are in this flock? at least 12 cardinals

26. A cardinal lays 3 or 4 eggs in each clutch (a set of eggs laid at one time). Suppose 18 eggs are found in nests throughout a park. There are three eggs in each nest. How many nests contained eggs? 6 nests

H.O.T. Problem

27. WRITING IN MATH Explain how fact families and multiplication facts can help you solve division problems.
See Ch. 4 Answer Appendix.

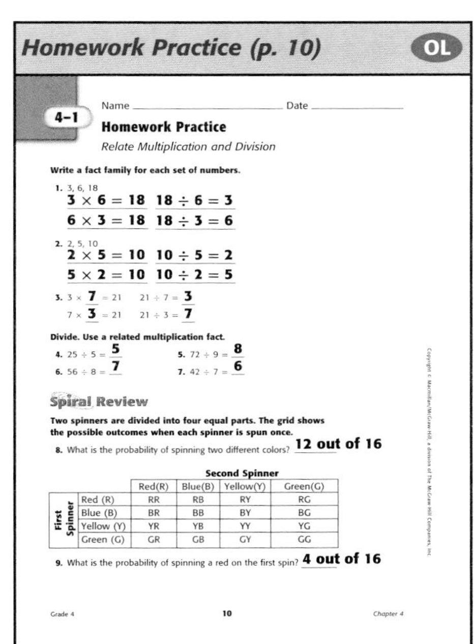

Homework Practice (p. 10) OL

4–1 Name ______ Date ______

Homework Practice

Relate Multiplication and Division

Write a fact family for each set of numbers.

1. 3, 6, 18
$3 \times 6 = 18$ $18 \div 6 = 3$
$6 \times 3 = 18$ $18 \div 3 = 6$

2. 2, 5, 10
$2 \times 5 = 10$ $10 \div 5 = 2$
$5 \times 2 = 10$ $10 \div 2 = 5$

3. $3 \times$ **7** $= 21$ $21 \div 7 =$ **3**
$7 \times$ **3** $= 21$ $21 \div 3 =$ **7**

Divide. Use a related multiplication fact.

4. $25 \div 5 =$ **5** 5. $72 \div 9 =$ **8**
6. $56 \div 8 =$ **7** 7. $42 \div 7 =$ **6**

Spiral Review

Two spinners are divided into four equal parts. The grid shows the possible outcomes when each spinner is spun once.

8. What is the probability of spinning two different colors? **12 out of 16**

	Second Spinner			
First Spinner	Red(R)	Blue(B)	Yellow(Y)	Green(G)
Red (R)	RR	RB	RY	RG
Blue (B)	BR	BB	BY	BG
Yellow (Y)	YR	YB	YY	YG
Green (G)	GR	GB	GY	GG

9. What is the probability of spinning a red on the first spin? **4 out of 16**

Grade 4 10 Chapter 4

3 Practice

Differentiate practice using these leveled assignments for Exercises 11–27.

Level	Assignment
BL Below/Approaching Level	11–12, 15–16, 19, 21–22, 25
OL On Level	12–17, 20–23, 26, 27
AL Above/Beyond Level	12–26 even, 27

Have students discuss and complete the Higher Order Thinking problems. For Exercise 27, suggest that students draw an array to illustrate the fact family.

WRITING IN MATH Have students complete Exercise 27 in their Math Journals. You may choose to use this exercise as an optional formative assessment.

4 Assess

Formative Assessment

Ask your students how they would explain the following questions to a third-grader.

- **How are multiplication and division related?** Sample answer: Division and multiplication are opposite or inverse operations.
- **Do all fact families contain three different numbers? Explain.** No; Some fact families, such as 5, 25, have only two numbers.

Quick Check **Are students continuing to struggle with relating multiplication and division?**

If Yes → Small Group Options (p. 147)
Strategic Intervention Guide (p. 70)

If No → Independent Work Options (p. 147)
CRM Skills Practice Worksheet (p. 9)
CRM Enrich Worksheet (p. 12)

LESSON 4-2

Algebra: Multiplication Properties and Division Rules

Lesson Planner

Objective

Use multiplication properties and division rules.

Vocabulary

Commutative Property of Multiplication, **Associative Property of Multiplication**, **Identity Property of Multiplication**, **Zero Property of Multiplication**

Resources

Materials: red, green, and blue cards or pieces of paper

Literature Connection: *A Place for Zero: A Math Adventure* by Angeline Sparagna LoPresti

Alternate Lesson: Use *IMPACT Mathematics*: Unit A to provide practice with multiplication.

Teacher Technology
TeacherWorks • Interactive Classroom • Math Song Track #3 Lesson Plan

Daily Routine

Use these suggestions before beginning the lesson on p. 150.

5-Minute Check

(Reviews Lesson 4-1)

Write a fact family for each set of numbers.

1. 2, 4, 8 $2 \times 4 = 8, 4 \times 2 = 8, 8 \div 4 = 2, 8 \div 2 = 4$
2. 5, 8, 40 $5 \times 8 = 40, 8 \times 5 = 40, 40 \div 8 = 5, 40 \div 5 = 8$

Divide. Use a related multiplication fact.

3. $10 \div 5 =$ ___ 2
4. $48 \div 6 =$ ___ 8

Problem of the Day

Estella and Sherman are skip counting by 3s. If Estella starts with 3, Sherman says 6, Estella says 9, etc. What is the 7th number each says?
Estella says 39; Sherman says 42

Focus on Math Background

In this lesson, students are introduced to the properties of multiplication and the division rules.

- The Commutative Property of Multiplication says that you can multiply in any order: $a \times b = b \times a$. Notice that division is not commutative.
- The Associative Property of Multiplication says that you can change the grouping of the factors when you multiply: $(a \times b) \times c = a \times (b \times c)$.
- The Identify Property of Multiplication says that any number times 1 is that number ($a \times 1 = a$).

Building Math Vocabulary

Write the lesson vocabulary words and their definition on the board.

Have students make a chart or poster that shows the definitions of these four properties along with at least two examples of each property.

Differentiated Instruction

Small Group Options

Option 1 Gifted and Talented AL

LOGICAL

Materials: pencil, paper

- Ask the students to write an equation that equals zero using any of the four operations (+, −, ×, ÷) and the digits 4 and 5.
- Remind them to use the properties to help them.
- Challenge the students to continue to use only 4 and 5 to write equations that equal 1 through 5.

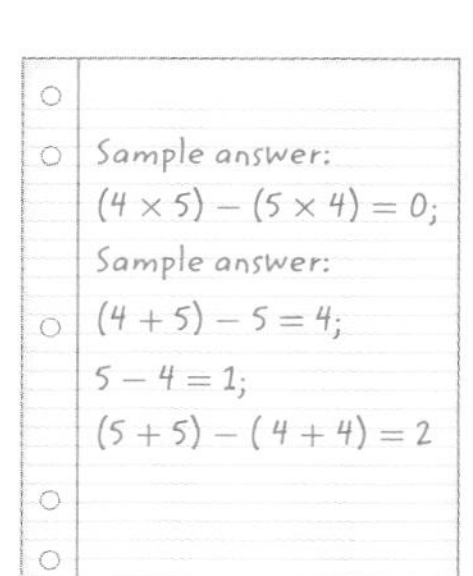

Option 2 English Language Learners ELL

SOCIAL

Materials: index cards
Core Vocabulary: shuffle, correct/incorrect, match
Common Use Verb: take turns
See Math This strategy uses games and peer tutoring groups to practice multiplication and division facts.

- Give pairs index cards.
- Draw four large squares labeled with each different property on the board.
- Post 4 problem cards in the square that demonstrates each of the four properties.
- Allow pairs to shuffle the cards so they are with the correct property. Other students should show thumbs up if all 4 are correct, thumbs down if not.
- If the placement is incorrect, another pair should re-shuffle the placement.
- Repeat as time permits.

Use this worksheet to provide additional support for English Language Learners.

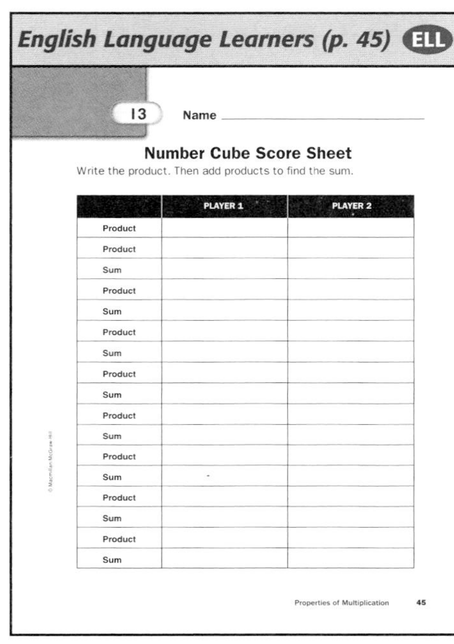

English Language Learners (p. 45) ELL

13 Name ______

Number Cube Score Sheet

Write the product. Then add products to find the sum.

	PLAYER 1	PLAYER 2
Product		
Product		
Sum		
Product		
Sum		
Product		
Sum		
Product		
Sum		
Product		
Sum		
Product		
Sum		
Product		
Sum		
Product		
Sum		

Properties of Multiplication 45

Independent Work Options

Option 1 Early Finishers OL AL

LOGICAL

Materials: index cards, pencil

- Give each student three index cards. On the front of each card, have them write a problem similar to those in Exercises 15–20. On the back, have them write the answer.
- Have students exchange cards with classmates and solve the problems.

Option 2 Student Technology

Math Online macmillanmh.com

Personal Tutor • Extra Examples

Math Songs, "Multiplication Association" Track #3

Option 3 Learning Station: Art (p. 142G)

Direct students to the Art Learning Station for opportunities to explore and extend the lesson concept.

Option 4 Problem-Solving Practice

Reinforce problem-solving skills and strategies with the Problem-Solving Practice worksheet.

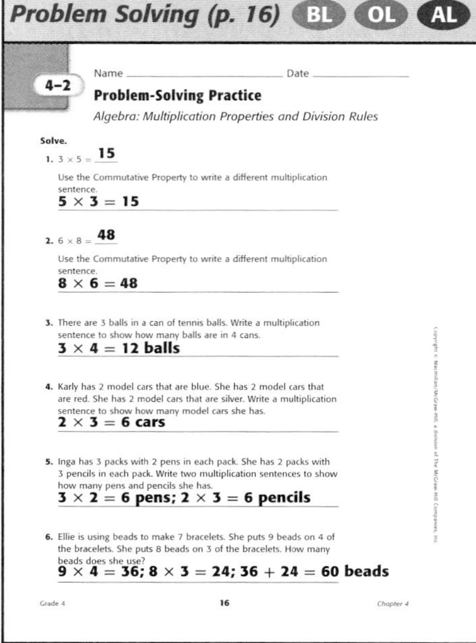

Problem Solving (p. 16) BL OL AL

4–2 Name ______ Date ______

Problem-Solving Practice

Algebra: Multiplication Properties and Division Rules

Solve.

1. $3 \times 5 =$ **15**

   Use the Commutative Property to write a different multiplication sentence.

   $5 \times 3 = 15$

2. $6 \times 8 =$ **48**

   Use the Commutative Property to write a different multiplication sentence.

   $8 \times 6 = 48$

3. There are 3 balls in a can of tennis balls. Write a multiplication sentence to show how many balls are in 4 cans.

   $3 \times 4 = 12$ balls

4. Karly has 2 model cars that are blue. She has 2 model cars that are red. She has 2 model cars that are silver. Write a multiplication sentence to show how many model cars she has.

   $2 \times 3 = 6$ cars

5. Inga has 3 packs with 2 pens in each pack. She has 2 packs with 3 pencils in each pack. Write two multiplication sentences to show how many pens and pencils she has.

   $3 \times 2 = 6$ pens; $2 \times 3 = 6$ pencils

6. Ellie is using beads to make 7 bracelets. She puts 9 beads on 4 of the bracelets. She puts 8 beads on 3 of the bracelets. How many beads does she use?

   $9 \times 4 = 36$; $8 \times 3 = 24$; $36 + 24 = 60$ beads

Grade 4 16 Chapter 4

Algebra: Multiplication Properties and Division Rules

Introduce

Activity Choice 1 • Hands-On

Hand out 10 red, 7 blue, and 4 green cards, one per student. First, have the students with the blue and green cards come up to the front of the class. Arrange them in 2 groups according to color.

- **How many cards are there?** 11 cards
- Switch the position of the blue and green cards and repeat the question.
- **Does the sum change when the order changes?** no
- **Which property supports your answer?** Commutative Property of Addition
- Have the red students join the green group.
- **What is the new total?** 21
- **If the red group joins the blue group instead, does it change the total?** no
- **Which property supports your answer?** Associative Property of Addition

Activity Choice 2 • Literature

Introduce the lesson with *A Place for Zero* by Angeline Sparagna LoPresti. For a related math activity, see p. TR46.

Teach

Scaffolding Questions

Refer to Activity Choice 1 and explain that these same properties are also used in multiplication. Write $2 \times 6 = 6 \times 2$ on the board.

- **What property of multiplication is shown by this number sentence? Explain.** Commutative Property of Multiplication; the order in which you multiply has been changed.

Write $2 \times (4 \times 5) = (2 \times 4) \times 5$.

- **What property of multiplication is shown by this number sentence? Explain.** Associative Property of Multiplication; the grouping has been changed.

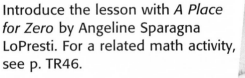

GET READY to Learn

Have students open their books and read the information in **Get Ready to Learn**. Introduce the properties of multiplication. As a class, work through **Examples 1–3**.

4-2 Algebra: Multiplication Properties and Division Rules

MAIN IDEA

I will use multiplication properties and division rules.

New Vocabulary

- Commutative Property of Multiplication
- Associative Property of Multiplication
- Identity Property of Multiplication
- Zero Property of Multiplication

Math Online

macmillanmh.com
- Extra Examples
- Personal Tutor
- Self-Check Quiz

GET READY to Learn

The table shows Jenny and Cliff's chores. Jenny earns $3 for each chore and Cliff earns $2 for each chore. How much does each person earn for completing chores?

Jenny	Cliff
Pack lunches	Set table
Take out trash	Clean room
Laundry	Walk dog
Clean room	Wash dishes
	Sweep floor

Multiplication has properties similar to addition. You can use the patterns and relationships in these properties.

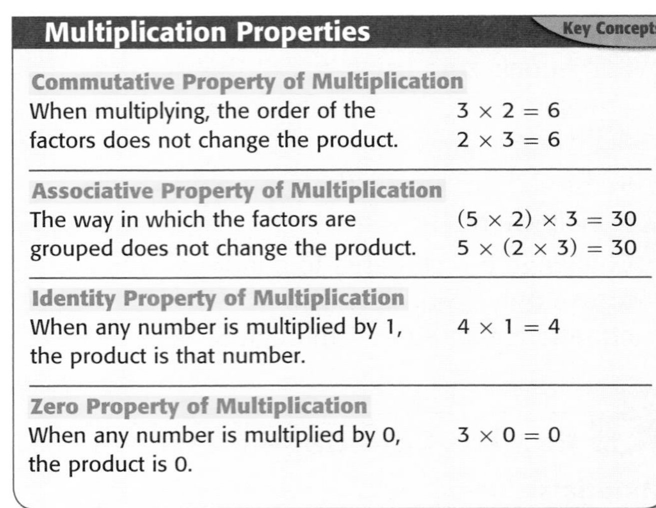

Multiplication Properties — Key Concepts

Commutative Property of Multiplication
When multiplying, the order of the factors does not change the product. $3 \times 2 = 6$, $2 \times 3 = 6$

Associative Property of Multiplication
The way in which the factors are grouped does not change the product. $(5 \times 2) \times 3 = 30$, $5 \times (2 \times 3) = 30$

Identity Property of Multiplication
When any number is multiplied by 1, the product is that number. $4 \times 1 = 4$

Zero Property of Multiplication
When any number is multiplied by 0, the product is 0. $3 \times 0 = 0$

EXAMPLE Identify Properties

1. **Identify the property shown by $8 \times 1 = 8$.**

   A number is multiplied by 1, and the product is that number. This is the Identity Property of Multiplication.

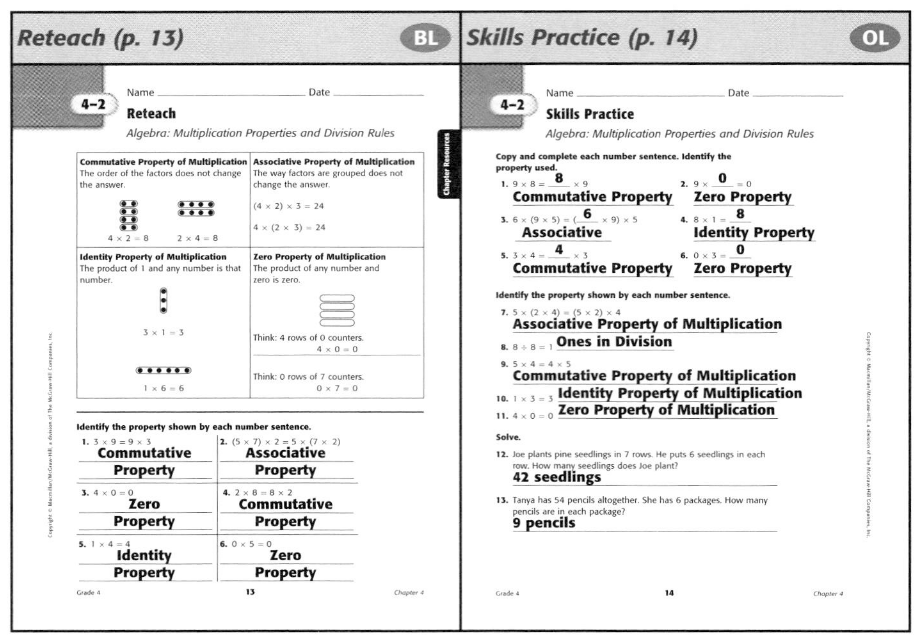

Reteach (p. 13) BL

4-2 Name ______ Date ______

Reteach

Algebra: Multiplication Properties and Division Rules

Commutative Property of Multiplication The order of the factors does not change the answer. $4 \times 2 = 8$ $2 \times 4 = 8$	**Associative Property of Multiplication** The way factors are grouped does not change the answer. $(4 \times 2) \times 3 = 24$ $4 \times (2 \times 3) = 24$
Identity Property of Multiplication The product of 1 and any number is that number. $3 \times 1 = 3$ $1 \times 6 = 6$	**Zero Property of Multiplication** The product of any number and zero is zero. Think: 4 rows of 0 counters. $4 \times 0 = 0$ Think: 0 rows of 7 counters. $0 \times 7 = 0$

Identify the property shown by each number sentence.

1. $3 \times 9 = 9 \times 3$ **Commutative Property**
2. $(5 \times 7) \times 2 = 5 \times (7 \times 2)$ **Associative Property**
3. $4 \times 0 = 0$ **Zero Property**
4. $2 \times 8 = 8 \times 2$ **Commutative Property**
5. $1 \times 4 = 4$ **Identity Property**
6. $0 \times 5 = 0$ **Zero Property**

Grade 4 13 Chapter 4

Chapter Resources

Skills Practice (p. 14) OL

4-2 Name ______ Date ______

Skills Practice

Algebra: Multiplication Properties and Division Rules

Copy and complete each number sentence. Identify the property used.

1. $9 \times 8 =$ **8** $\times 9$ **Commutative Property**
2. $9 \times$ **0** $= 0$ **Zero Property**
3. $6 \times (9 \times 5) = ($**6** $\times 9) \times 5$ **Associative**
4. $8 \times 1 =$ **8** **Identity Property**
5. $3 \times 4 =$ **4** $\times 3$ **Commutative Property**
6. $0 \times 3 =$ **0** **Zero Property**

Identify the property shown by each number sentence.

7. $5 \times (2 \times 4) = (5 \times 2) \times 4$ **Associative Property of Multiplication**
8. $8 \div 8 = 1$ **Ones in Division**
9. $5 \times 4 = 4 \times 5$ **Commutative Property of Multiplication**
10. $1 \times 3 = 3$ **Identity Property of Multiplication**
11. $4 \times 0 = 0$ **Zero Property of Multiplication**

Solve.

12. Joe plants pine seedlings in 7 rows. He puts 6 seedlings in each row. How many seedlings does Joe plant? **42 seedlings**
13. Tanya has 54 pencils altogether. She has 6 packages. How many pencils are in each package? **9 pencils**

Grade 4 14 Chapter 4

EXAMPLE Use Properties

2 **Complete $(4 \times 3) \times 2 = 4 \times (\blacksquare \times 2)$. Identify the property used.**

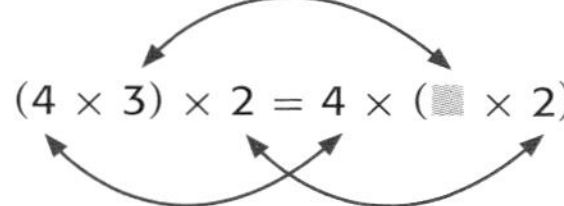

A 3 completes the number sentence. The way in which the factors are grouped does not change the product. This is the Associative Property of Multiplication.

The following facts can help you with division.

Division Rules

Key Concepts

Zeros in Division

When you divide 0 by any number other than 0, the quotient is 0.	$0 \div 5 = 0$
It is not possible to divide a number by 0.	7 ÷ 0 (crossed out)

Ones in Division

When you divide any number by 1, the quotient is always the dividend.	$8 \div 1 = 8$
When you divide any number by itself, the quotient is always 1. This is true for all numbers except 0.	$9 \div 9 = 1$

Remember

Quotient is the name of the answer for division problems.

Use a Division Rule

3 **PARTIES There are 9 party favors and 9 guests. How many party favors will each guest get?**

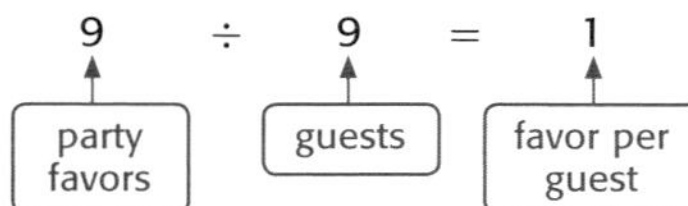

A non-zero number divided by the same number is 1. So, each guest will get 1 party favor.

Enrich (p. 17) AL

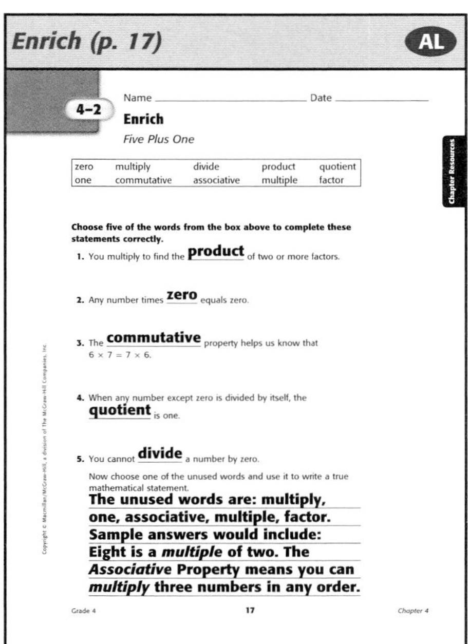

4–2

Name ________ Date ________

Enrich

Five Plus One

zero	multiply	divide	product	quotient
one	commutative	associative	multiple	factor

Choose five of the words from the box above to complete these statements correctly.

1. You multiply to find the **product** of two or more factors.
2. Any number times **zero** equals zero.
3. The **commutative** property helps us know that $6 \times 7 = 7 \times 6$.
4. When any number except zero is divided by itself, the **quotient** is one.
5. You cannot **divide** a number by zero.

Now choose one of the unused words and use it to write a true mathematical statement.

The unused words are: multiply, one, associative, multiple, factor. Sample answers would include: Eight is a *multiple* of two. The *Associative* Property means you can *multiply* three numbers in any order.

Grade 4 17 Chapter 4

Chapter Resources

Use Properties

Example 2 Be sure students understand that they do *not* have to work out the multiplication problem in order to solve the number sentence. Using the Associative Property gives them the answer.

ADDITIONAL EXAMPLES

1. Identify the property or rule shown by $9 \times 0 = 0$. Zero Property of Multiplication
2. Complete $(5 \times 6) \times 2 = 5 \times (6 \times \blacksquare)$. Identify the property used. 2; Associative Property of Multiplication
3. Rafi went to the park with his brother and his sister. Together they had three kites. How many kites did each person have? 1 kite

CHECK What You Know

As a class, have students complete Exercises 1–8 in **Check What You Know** as you observe their work.

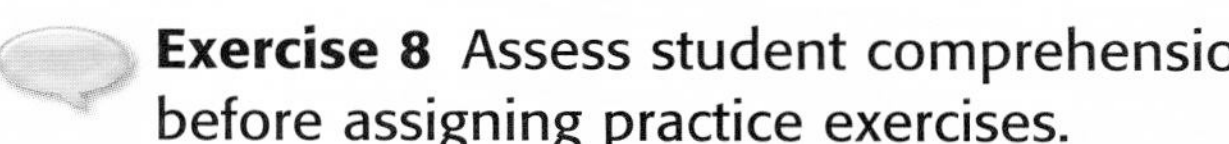

Exercise 8 Assess student comprehension before assigning practice exercises.

BL Alternate Teaching Strategy

If students have trouble identifying which property or rule is shown…

Then use one of these reteach options:

1. CRM **Daily Reteach Worksheet** (p. 13)
2. Have students refer back to the chart they made in the Building Math Vocabulary activity. Help them add several more examples for each property and rule. Have students look for clues that indicate which property or rule is shown, such as the Associative Property of Multiplication usually involves parentheses.

3 Practice

Differentiate practice using these leveled assignments for Exercises 9–25.

Level	Assignment
BL Below/Approaching Level	9–12, 15–17, 22
OL On Level	9–20, 22
AL Above/Beyond Level	9–22 odd, 23–25

Have students discuss and complete the Higher Order Thinking problems. For Exercise 23, remind them that the product should be the same for both orders.

WRITING IN MATH Have students complete Exercise 25 in their Math Journals. You may choose to use this exercise as an optional formative assessment.

Additional Answers

8. Sample answer: A number times 1 is itself. A number plus 0 is itself.
15. 3; Divide a number by itself.
16. 4; Commutative Property of Multiplication
17. 0; Zero divided by a non-zero number is 0.
18. 3; Associative Property of Multiplication
19. 1; Identity Property of Multiplication
20. 0; Zero Property of Multiplication

COMMON ERROR!

Exercise 10 If students think that this number sentence shows the Commutative Property, ask them to look at both sides of the equation to see if the order has been changed.

CHECK What You Know

Identify the property or rule shown by each number sentence.
See Examples 1–3 (pp. 150–151)

1. $12 \times 0 = 0$ Zero Prop. (×)
2. $8 \times 5 = 5 \times 8$ Comm. Prop. (×)
3. $6 \div 1 = 6$ Divide by 1.

Algebra Copy and complete each number sentence. Identify the property or rule used. See Example 2 (p. 151)

4. $7 \times ■ = 7$ 1; Identity Prop. (×)
5. $5 \div ■ = 1$ 5; Divide by the same number.
6. $(7 \times 2) \times 3 = 7 \times (■ \times 3)$ 2; Assoc. Prop. (×)
7. Brenda has 4 rows of 6 stickers. What is another way she can arrange the stickers? Write a number sentence. 6 rows of 4 stickers; $6 \times 4 = 24$
8. Talk About It Explain why the Identity Property of Multiplication uses 1 while the Identity Property of Addition uses 0. See margin.

Practice and Problem Solving

EXTRA PRACTICE See page R10.

Identify the property or rule shown by each number sentence.
See Examples 1–3 (pp. 150–151)

9. $10 \div 10 = 1$ Divide a number by itself.
10. $6 \times (3 \times 4) = (6 \times 3) \times 4$ Assoc. Prop. (×)
11. $8 \times 0 = 0$ Zero Property (×)
12. $0 \div 12 = 0$ Divide 0 by a number.
13. $(6 \times 3) \times 4 = 6 \times (3 \times 4)$ Assoc. Prop. (×)
14. $22 \times 1 = 22$ Identity Prop. (×)

Algebra Copy and complete each number sentence. Identify the property or rule used. See Example 2 (p. 151) 15–20. See margin.

15. $3 \div ■ = 1$
16. $■ \times 8 = 8 \times 4$
17. $■ \div 11 = 0$
18. $3 \times (■ \times 6) = (3 \times 3) \times 6$
19. $15 \times ■ = 15$
20. $28 \times ■ = 0$

Real-World PROBLEM SOLVING

Hiking Write a number sentence for each situation. Then solve.

21. On their first hiking trip, Tamika and Brian hiked 7 miles a day. They hiked for 5 days. Kurt and Suki hiked 5 miles a day. How many days did it take Kurt and Suki to hike the same distance as Tamika and Brian? $7 \times 5 = 5 \times 7$; 7 days
22. On their second trip, Tamika and Brian hiked twice as long as they did on their first trip. How many days will Kurt and Suki need to hike to go the same distance as Tamika and Brian? $(7 \times 5) \times 2 = (5 \times 7) \times 2$; 14 days

H.O.T. Problems

23. OPEN ENDED Using the same three numbers, write two different multiplication expressions with a product of 60. $(2 \times 6) \times 5$ and $2 \times (6 \times 5)$

24. NUMBER SENSE When finding the value of $(2 \times 9) \times 5$, is it easier to find 2×9 or 2×5 first? Explain. 24, 25. See Ch. 4 Answer Appendix.

25. WRITING IN ▶MATH Marcie thinks it is easier to find $(7 \times 6) \times 2$ than to find $7 \times (6 \times 2)$. What property tells her that the number sentences are equal? Why might Marcie think it is easier to find the answer to the first number sentence?

TEST Practice

26. Which number sentence is in the same fact family as $42 \div 7 = ■$? (Lesson 4-1) C

A $7 + ■ = 42$

B $■ - 7 = 42$

C $7 \times ■ = 42$

D $42 \times 7 = 42$

27. Luther's photo album has 6 pages with 8 photos on each page. Identify the number sentence that describes this situation. (Lesson 4-2) F

F $8 \times 6 = 6 \times 8$

G $8 \times 6 > 6 \times 8$

H $8 \times 6 < 6 \times 8$

J $8 \times 8 > 6 \times 6$

Spiral Review

Algebra **Divide. Use a related multiplication fact.** (Lesson 4-1)

28. $12 \div 3 = ■$ 4; $3 \times 4 = 12$

29. $16 \div 4 = ■$ 4; $4 \times 4 = 16$

30. $20 \div 5 = ■$ 4; $5 \times 4 = 20$

For Exercises 31 and 32, use the graph. (Lesson 3-6)

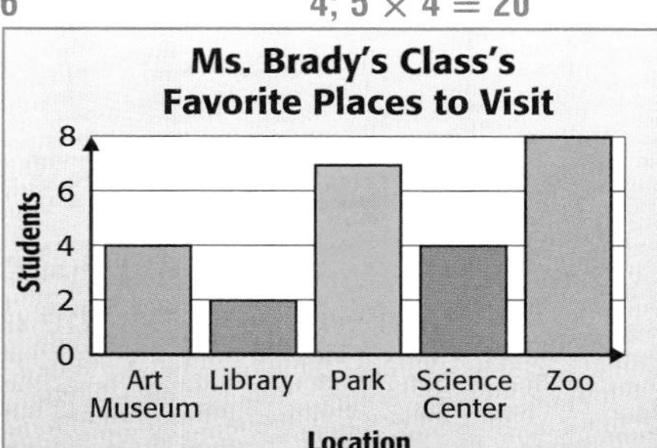

31. What is the most and least favorite place to visit? most: zoo; least: library

32. Identify which two places to visit received a difference in votes of 5. park and library

33. Fernando's two dogs eat 3 cups of food each day. How much food do his dogs eat in a week? (Lesson 3-3) 21 cups

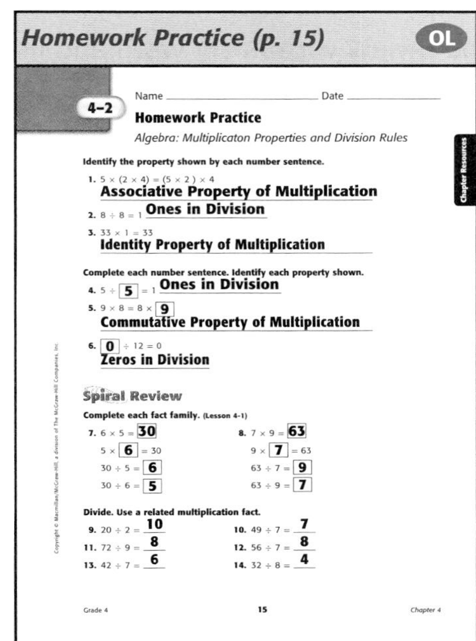

Homework Practice (p. 15) OL

4–2 Name ______ Date ______

Homework Practice

Algebra: Multiplicaton Properties and Division Rules

Identify the property shown by each number sentence.

1. $5 \times (2 \times 4) = (5 \times 2) \times 4$ **Associative Property of Multiplication**
2. $8 \div 8 = 1$ **Ones in Division**
3. $33 \times 1 = 33$ **Identity Property of Multiplication**

Complete each number sentence. Identify each property shown.

4. $5 \div$ **5** $= 1$ **Ones in Division**
5. $9 \times 8 = 8 \times$ **9** **Commutative Property of Multiplication**
6. **0** $\div 12 = 0$ **Zeros in Division**

Spiral Review

Complete each fact family. (Lesson 4-1)

7. $6 \times 5 =$ **30**; $5 \times$ **6** $= 30$; $30 \div 5 =$ **6**; $30 \div 6 =$ **5**
8. $7 \times 9 =$ **63**; $9 \times$ **7** $= 63$; $63 \div 7 =$ **9**; $63 \div 9 =$ **7**

Divide. Use a related multiplication fact.

9. $20 \div 2 =$ **10**
10. $49 \div 7 =$ **7**
11. $72 \div 9 =$ **8**
12. $56 \div 7 =$ **8**
13. $42 \div 7 =$ **6**
14. $32 \div 8 =$ **4**

Chapter Resources

Grade 4 15 Chapter 4

4 Assess

Formative Assessment

- **How does understanding the Identity Property of Multiplication help with problems such as $3,252 \times 1$?** Sample answer: Any number multiplied by 1 is itself.
- **Explain why understanding the Associative Property of Multiplication is useful when multiplying three factors. Give an example.** Sample answer: You can find the easier product first, such as $7 \times (2 \times 5)$ is easier than $(7 \times 2) \times 5$.

Quick Check **Are students continuing to struggle with properties of multiplication and the division rules?**

If Yes → Strategic Intervention Worksheet (p. 76)

If No → Independent Work Options (p. 150B)
CRM Skills Practice Worksheet (p. 14)
CRM Enrich Worksheet (p. 17)

Ticket Out the Door Use the numbers 1, 2, 3, and 4 to write an example of the Commutative Property of Multiplication, the Associative Property of Multiplication, and the Identity Property of Multiplication on a piece of paper.

TEST Practice

Reviews Lessons 4-1 and 4-2

Assign the Test Practice problems to provide daily reinforcement of test-taking skills.

Spiral Review

Reviews Lessons 3-3, 3-6, and 4-1

Review and assess mastery of skills and concepts from previous chapters.

LESSON 4-3

Multiply and Divide Facts Through 5

Lesson Planner

Objective

Recall multiplication and division facts 0 through 5.

Review Vocabulary

skip count

Resources

Materials: hundred charts

Manipulatives: number lines

Literature Connection: *Math Appeal* by Greg Tang

Alternate Lesson: Use *IMPACT Mathematics*: Unit A to provide practice with multiplication.

Teacher Technology
TeacherWorks • Interactive Classroom • Math Songs Track #8 Lesson Plan

Daily Routine

Use these suggestions before beginning the lesson on p. 154.

5-Minute Check

(Reviews Lesson 4-2)

Identify the property or rule shown by each number sentence.

1. $5 \times 2 = 2 \times 5$ Commutative Property of Multiplication
2. $8 \times 1 = 8$ Identity Property of Multiplication
3. $(6 \times 2) \times 3 = 6 \times (2 \times 3)$ Associative Property of Multiplication
4. $12 \times 0 = 0$ Zero Property
5. $7 \times 9 = 9 \times 7$ Commutative Property of Multiplication

Problem of the Day

Julian washes the dishes every other day. How many days will he wash the dishes in November? 15 days

Focus on Math Background

The Zero Property of Multiplication and Identity Property of Multiplication from the second lesson of this chapter state that $a \times 0 = 0$ and $a \times 1 = a$. These properties help students learn their zeros and ones. Looking for patterns as students skip count by twos, threes, fours, and fives should be emphasized in this lesson. As students skip count by fives, they should notice that the ones digit ends in either 5 or 0.

- Multiplying by two is an extension of "doubling" work in addition, for example,
$$2 \times 6 = 6 + 6 = 12.$$
- Multiplying by four can be thought of as multiplying by two, twice, for example,
$$4 \times 6 = (2 \times 6) \times 2 = 24.$$
- Multiplying by 3 can be thought of as doubling plus the number, for example,
$$3 \times 7 = (2 \times 7) + 7 = 14 + 7 = 21.$$

Review Math Vocabulary

Write the review vocabulary word and its definition on the board.

To get students moving, take them outside or to the gym. They are going to literally skip count. First, have them "skip count" by 1, by simply counting aloud as they skip 12 (or more) steps. Then, have them skip count by 2, counting to themselves as they skip but saying only every other number aloud. Repeat with other numbers as desired.

Differentiated Instruction

Small Group Options

LOGICAL, SPATIAL

Option 1 Gifted and Talented AL

Materials: grid paper, pencil, counters

Have students use the methods they have learned to create arrays for two-digit numbers or three-digit numbers multiplied by 3.

VISUAL, SPATIAL

Option 2 English Language Learners ELL

Materials: copies of multiplication table, counters
Core Vocabulary: up, over, to slide across
Common Use Verb: move

Do Math This strategy introduces the vocabulary for manipulating multiplication tables.

×	0	1	2	3	4	5	6	7	8	9	10
0	0	0	0	0	0	0	0	0	0	0	0
1	0	1	2	3	4	5	6	7	8	9	10
2	0	2	4	6	8	10	12	14	16	18	20
3	0	3	6	9	12	15	18	21	24	27	30
4	0	4	8	12	16	20	24	28	32	36	40
5	0	5	10	15	20	25	30	35	40	45	50
6	0	6	12	18	24	30	36	42	48	54	60
7	0	7	14	21	28	35	42	49	56	63	70
8	0	8	16	24	32	40	48	56	64	72	80
9	0	9	18	27	36	45	54	63	72	81	90
10	0	10	20	30	40	50	60	70	80	90	100

- Give each student a multiplication table and counters.
- Tell students to place the counter on a number, for example, 36.
- Demonstrate to students how to move up and over to find the 9 and 4.
- Demonstrate that 36 divided by 4 is 9.
- Repeat with several numbers.
- Play a game with students by calling out a number, allowing students to say or write the multiplication sentence or division sentence that goes with that number.
- Repeat until students have found all the multiples.

Independent Work Options

LOGICAL, SOCIAL

Option 1 Early Finishers AL OL

Materials: two number cubes with numbers 0 through 5 on each

- In pairs, students take turns rolling the two number cubes. Student 1 rolls the cubes and writes a multiplication problem using the numbers.
- The partner writes the answer.
- Have students take turns doing this several times.

Option 2 Student Technology

Math Online macmillanmh.com

Personal Tutor • Extra Examples

Math Adventures

Math Songs "Multiplication Rap" Track #8

Option 3 Learning Station: Social Studies (p. 142H)

Direct students to the Social Studies Learning Station for opportunities to explore and extend the lesson concept.

Option 4 Problem-Solving Practice

Reinforce problem-solving skills and strategies with the Problem-Solving Practice worksheet.

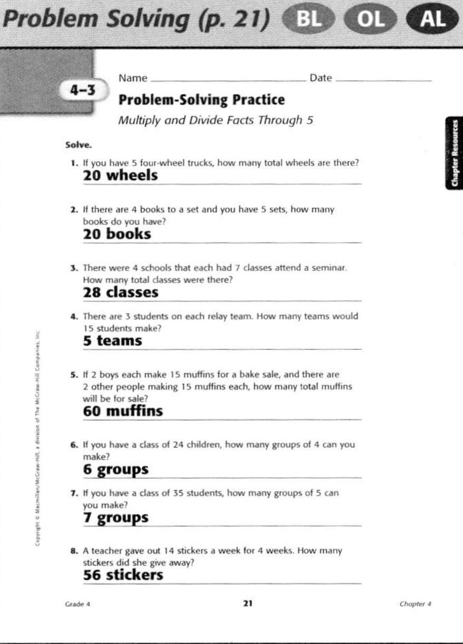

Problem Solving (p. 21) BL OL AL

4–3 Name ______ Date ______

Problem-Solving Practice

Multiply and Divide Facts Through 5

Solve.

1. If you have 5 four-wheel trucks, how many total wheels are there?
   20 wheels
2. If there are 4 books to a set and you have 5 sets, how many books do you have?
   20 books
3. There were 4 schools that each had 7 classes attend a seminar. How many total classes were there?
   28 classes
4. There are 3 students on each relay team. How many teams would 15 students make?
   5 teams
5. If 2 boys each make 15 muffins for a bake sale, and there are 2 other people making 15 muffins each, how many total muffins will be for sale?
   60 muffins
6. If you have a class of 24 children, how many groups of 4 can you make?
   6 groups
7. If you have a class of 35 students, how many groups of 5 can you make?
   7 groups
8. A teacher gave out 14 stickers a week for 4 weeks. How many stickers did she give away?
   56 stickers

Chapter Resources

Grade 4 21 Chapter 4

4-3 Multiply and Divide Facts Through 5

1 Introduce

Activity Choice 1 • Hands-On

- Divide the class into four groups and assign them a number 2 to 5. Each group will stand up and skip count aloud for the rest of the class.
- All students should write down at least one observation about each set of numbers. Once all four groups have counted, discuss and list observations on the board. For example:

  2s: All even numbers; numbers double
  3s: Alternate between even and odd numbers; multiples of 3
  4s: Every other even number; all numbers were also counted by 2s
  5s: All numbers end in 5 or 0; easy to count

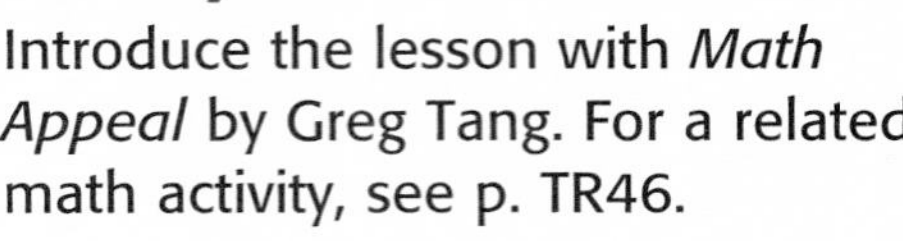

Activity Choice 2 • Literature

Introduce the lesson with *Math Appeal* by Greg Tang. For a related math activity, see p. TR46.

2 Teach

Scaffolding Questions

Give each student a hundreds chart. Have students skip count by 2, shading in the numbers as they count.

- **What pattern do you see?** Sample answers: The numbers are even; the numbers increase by 2s.

Repeat with 3. Students circle the numbers.

- **What pattern do you see?** Sample answer: The numbers alternate between even and odd.

Repeat with 4 and then 5. Have students place an X on the numbers skip counted by 4 and place a square around the numbers skip counted by 5. Again, ask for patterns.

GET READY to Learn

Have students open their books and read the information in **Get Ready to Learn**. Review **skip count**. As a class, work through **Examples 1 and 2**.

4-3 Multiply and Divide Facts Through 5

MAIN IDEA

I will recall multiplication and division facts 0 through 5.

Math Online

macmillanmh.com

- Extra Examples
- Personal Tutor
- Self-Check Quiz

GET READY to Learn

Charlotte is competing in a 3-mile race. Every 4 laps equals 1 mile. How many laps does she need to complete to finish the race?

To find the number of laps that Charlotte needs to complete, multiply. There are different strategies that can be used to multiply.

Real-World EXAMPLE Multiply

1 **RACING** **How many laps does Charlotte need to complete in order to travel 3 miles?**

You need to find 3 × 4.

One Way: Skip Count

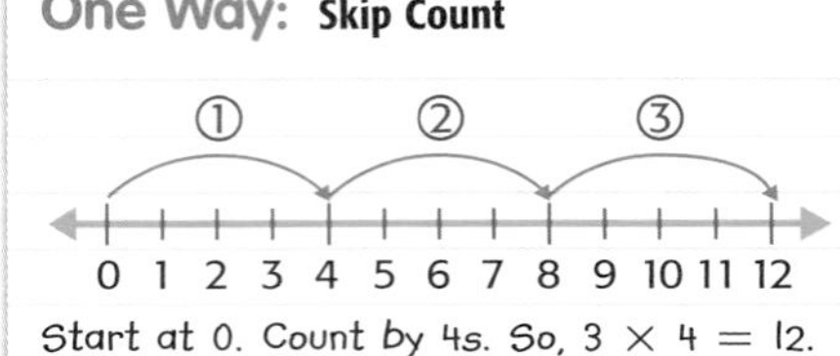

Start at 0. Count by 4s. So, 3 × 4 = 12.

Another Way: Area Model

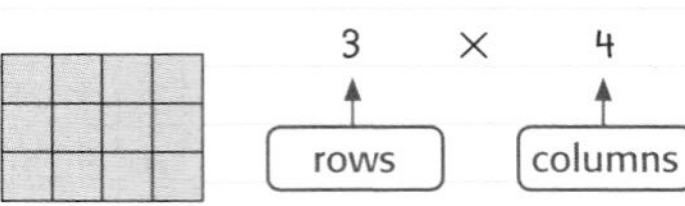

Count the squares. There is a total of 12 squares.

So, Charlotte must complete 12 laps to travel 3 miles.

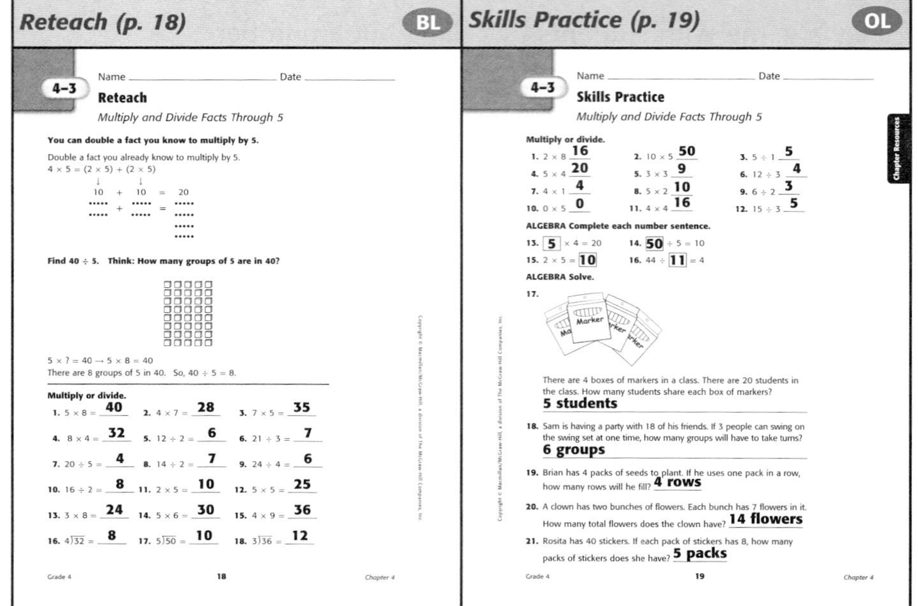

Reteach (p. 18) BL

4-3 Name ______ Date ______

Reteach

Multiply and Divide Facts Through 5

You can double a fact you know to multiply by 5.

Double a fact you already know to multiply by 5.
4 × 5 = (2 × 5) + (2 × 5)
10 + 10 = 20

Find 40 ÷ 5. Think: How many groups of 5 are in 40?

5 × ? = 40 → 5 × 8 = 40
There are 8 groups of 5 in 40. So, 40 ÷ 5 = 8.

Multiply or divide.

1. 5 × 8 = **40**
2. 4 × 7 = **28**
3. 7 × 5 = **35**
4. 8 × 4 = **32**
5. 12 ÷ 2 = **6**
6. 21 ÷ 3 = **7**
7. 20 ÷ 5 = **4**
8. 14 ÷ 2 = **7**
9. 24 ÷ 4 = **6**
10. 16 ÷ 2 = **8**
11. 2 × 5 = **10**
12. 5 × 5 = **25**
13. 3 × 8 = **24**
14. 5 × 6 = **30**
15. 4 × 9 = **36**
16. 4)32 = **8**
17. 5)50 = **10**
18. 3)36 = **12**

Grade 4 18 Chapter 4

Skills Practice (p. 19) OL

4-3 Name ______ Date ______

Skills Practice

Multiply and Divide Facts Through 5

Multiply or divide.

1. 2 × 8 **16**
2. 10 × 5 **50**
3. 5 ÷ 1 **5**
4. 5 × 4 **20**
5. 3 × 3 **9**
6. 12 ÷ 3 **4**
7. 4 × 1 **4**
8. 5 × 2 **10**
9. 6 ÷ 2 **3**
10. 0 × 5 **0**
11. 4 × 4 **16**
12. 15 ÷ 3 **5**

ALGEBRA Complete each number sentence.

13. **5** × 4 = 20
14. **50** ÷ 5 = 10
15. 2 × 5 = **10**
16. 44 ÷ **11** = 4

ALGEBRA Solve.

17. There are 4 boxes of markers in a class. There are 20 students in the class. How many students share each box of markers? **5 students**

18. Sam is having a party with 18 of his friends. If 3 people can swing on the swing set at one time, how many groups will have to take turns? **6 groups**

19. Brian has 4 packs of seeds to plant. If he uses one pack in a row, how many rows will he fill? **4 rows**

20. A clown has two bunches of flowers. Each bunch has 7 flowers in it. How many total flowers does the clown have? **14 flowers**

21. Rosita has 40 stickers. If each pack of stickers has 8, how many packs of stickers does she have? **5 packs**

Grade 4 19 Chapter 4

Chapter Resources

There are different strategies to use when finding division facts.

Real-World EXAMPLE Divide

2 **Omari has football practice 3 days a week. He drinks a sports drink during each practice. Suppose 12 sports drinks come in a package. How many weeks will a package of sports drinks last?**

You need to find 12 ÷ 3.

Remember

You can also draw pictures, use a times table, or use models to help divide.

One Way: Related Facts

12 ÷ 3 = ■ ← THINK 3 × ■ = 12?

12 ÷ 3 = 4

Another Way: Array

Use an array to find 12 ÷ 3. Separate an array of 12 counters into 3 equal groups.

There are 4 counters in each group. So, 12 ÷ 3 = 4.

So, one package of sports drinks will last 4 weeks.

10. Sample answer: 3 × 3 = 9; The factors in a multiplication fact are the divisor and quotient in a related division fact.

CHECK What You Know

Multiply or divide. Use arrays or area models if needed. See Examples 1 and 2 (pp. 154–155)

1. 5 × 3 15
2. 9 × 0 0
3. 1 × 5 5
4. 2 × 8 16

5. 6 ÷ 2 3
6. 24 ÷ 3 8
7. $5\overline{)10}$ 2
8. $4\overline{)28}$ 7

9. Nancy's dog gets 3 treats each day. There are 36 treats in a box. How many days will the treats last? 12 days

10. 

What multiplication fact can help you find 9 ÷ 3? Explain.

Enrich (p. 22) AL

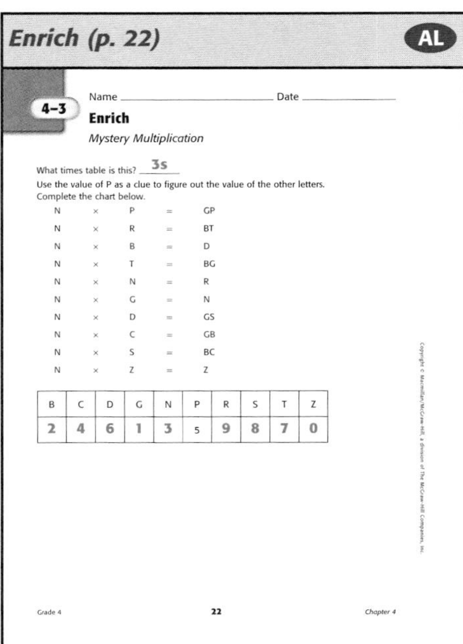

4-3

Name ________ Date ________

Enrich

Mystery Multiplication

What times table is this? 3s

Use the value of P as a clue to figure out the value of the other letters. Complete the chart below.

N × P = GP
N × R = BT
N × B = D
N × T = BG
N × N = R
N × G = N
N × D = GS
N × C = GB
N × S = BC
N × Z = Z

B	C	D	G	N	P	R	S	T	Z
2	4	6	1	3	5	9	8	7	0

Grade 4 22 Chapter 4

Multiply

Example 1 Students can check for reasonableness by remembering that an even number times an odd number results in an even product. Students can also check answers by remembering that an even number times an even number results in an even product. In addition, an odd number times an odd number results in an odd product.

Divide

Example 2 Remind students that the number of rows in an array is the divisor and the number of columns is the quotient.

ADDITIONAL EXAMPLES

1 At the indoor track, eight laps equal one mile. If Tanya runs 3 miles, how many laps did she run? 24 laps

2 Ernesto's family uses two rolls of film each week of their vacation. If they used a pack of six rolls of film, how long was their vacation? 3 wks

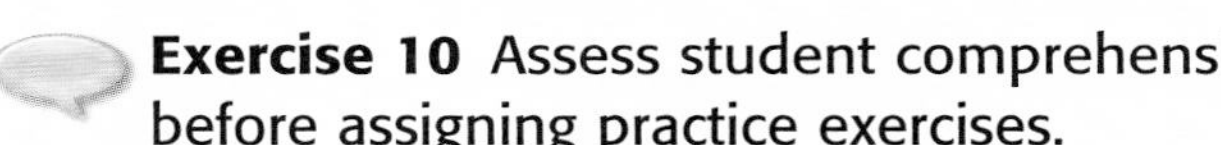

CHECK What You Know

As a class, have students complete Exercises 1–10 in **Check What You Know** as you observe their work.

Exercise 10 Assess student comprehension before assigning practice exercises.

BL Alternate Teaching Strategy

If students have trouble skip counting…

Then use one of these reteach options:

1. CRM **Daily Reteach Worksheet** (p. 18)
2. Provide a number line or hundreds chart for students to use when skip counting.

If students continue to have trouble, provide a number line for each factor, with the multiples of that factor in bold to make skip counting even easier.

3 Practice

Differentiate practice using these leveled assignments for Exercises 11–39.

Level	Assignment
BL Below/Approaching Level	11–16, 19–23, 27, 29, 33, 35
OL On Level	11–31, 33, 35
AL Above/Beyond Level	12–36 even, 37–39

Have students discuss and complete the Higher Order Thinking problems. For Exercise 38, tell students they are considering products and quotients, not operations.

WRITING IN MATH Have students complete Exercise 39 in their Math Journals. You may choose to use this exercise as an optional formative assessment.

COMMON ERROR!

Exercises 31 and 32 may cause some confusion for students. In Exercise 31, some students may answer 3,333,333. Point out that each star has a value of 3 and that the problem models 3 + 3 + 3 + 3 + 3 + 3 + 3. Then remind them that multiplication can be used to solve repeated addition problems.

Practice and Problem Solving

EXTRA PRACTICE See page R10.

Multiply or divide. Use arrays or area models if needed. See Examples 1 and 2 (pp. 154–155)

11. 5×6 30 **12.** 2×3 6 **13.** 9×2 18 **14.** 8×4 32

15. 7×1 7 **16.** 3×7 21 **17.** 9×5 45 **18.** 4×11 44

19. $8 \div 1$ 8 **20.** $10 \div 2$ 5 **21.** $12 \div 3$ 4 **22.** $32 \div 4$ 8

23. $2\overline{)24}$ 12 **24.** $3\overline{)33}$ 11 **25.** $4\overline{)40}$ 10 **26.** $5\overline{)60}$ 12

Algebra Complete each number sentence.

27. $2 \times ■ = 2$ 1 **28.** $■ \times 5 = 35$ 7 **29.** $33 \div ■ = 11$ 3 **30.** $■ \div 5 = 10$ 50

Algebra Solve.

31. If ☆ = 3, then what is ☆ + ☆ + ☆ + ☆ + ☆ + ☆ + ☆? 21

32. If ☺ + ☺ + ☺ + ☺ + ☺ + ☺ + ☺ + ☺ + ☺ = 45, then what is ☺? 5

33. There are 5 sets of paint in an art class. There are 25 students in the art class. How many students share each set of paint? 5 students

34. Jared has 6 packs of baseball cards. There are 5 cards in each pack. How many baseball cards does Jared have? 30 cards

Real-World PROBLEM SOLVING

Technology The number of computers in classrooms is increasing. The results of a recent study are shown to the right.

One computer for every 4 students in a classroom.

Source: *USA Today*

35. There are 5 computers in a fourth grade classroom. The number of students per computer matches the results of the study. How many students are in this classroom? 20 students

36. There are 24 students in Mr. Montoya's class. The number of computers per student matches the results of the study. How many computers are in Mr. Montoya's class? 6 computers

H.O.T. Problems

37. OPEN ENDED Write three 2-digit numbers that are divisible by 2. Sample answer: 10, 12, and 14

38. WHICH ONE DOESN'T BELONG? Identify the expression that does not belong with the other three. Explain. Sample answer: 3 × 4; The other expressions have a product or quotient of 8.

2 × 4	24 ÷ 3	3 × 4	8 ÷ 1

39. WRITING IN MATH Write a real-world problem that can be represented by 55 ÷ 5. Sample answer: There are 55 cars in a parking lot. There are 5 cars in each row. How many rows are there?

TEST Practice

40. George has 3 rows of 5 stamps. Which number sentence shows another way he can arrange the stamps? (Lesson 4-2) D

A 3 + 3 + 3

B 3 + 5

C 5 + 5

D 5 × 3

41. Which number is missing from the number sentence? (Lesson 4-3) J

45 ÷ ■ = 9

F 2

G 3

H 4

J 5

Spiral Review

Algebra **Copy and complete each number sentence. Identify the property or rule used.** (Lesson 4-2)

42. 8 ÷ ■ = 1 — 42. 8; A number divided by itself is 1.

43. ■ × 5 = 5 × 4 — 4; Commutative Property (×)

44. ■ ÷ 12 = 0 — 44. 0; Zero divided by a non-zero number is 0.

Algebra **Copy and complete each fact family.** (Lesson 4-1)

45. 4 × 7 = ■ 7 × ■ = 28 — 28; 4
28 ÷ ■ = 7 28 ÷ 7 = ■ — 4; 4

46. 8 × 9 = ■ ■ × 8 = 72 — 72; 9
72 ÷ ■ = 8 72 ÷ 9 = ■ — 9; 8

47. The number of children who visited a science museum is shown. About how many children visited the museum during the weekend? (Lesson 2-4) 1,000

Museum Visitors

Day	Mon.	Tues.	Wed.	Thur.	Fri.	Sat.	Sun.
Visitors	325	279	312	348	441	519	495

Homework Practice (p. 20) OL

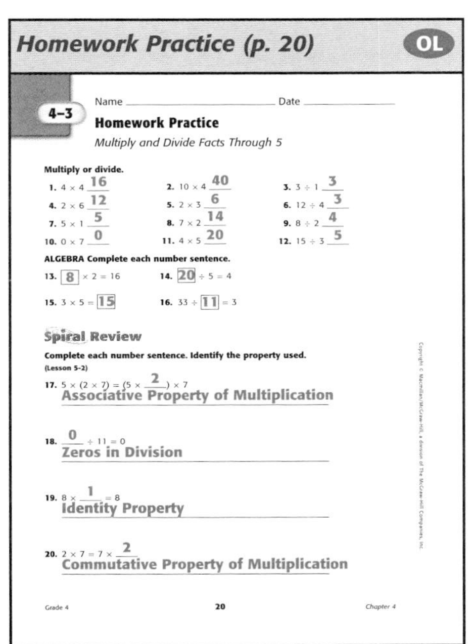
4-3
Name ______ Date ______
Homework Practice
Multiply and Divide Facts Through 5

Multiply or divide.

1. 4 × 4 16 2. 10 × 4 40 3. 3 ÷ 1 3
4. 2 × 6 12 5. 2 × 3 6 6. 12 ÷ 4 3
7. 5 × 1 5 8. 7 × 2 14 9. 8 ÷ 2 4
10. 0 × 7 0 11. 4 × 5 20 12. 15 ÷ 3 5

ALGEBRA Complete each number sentence.

13. 8 × 2 = 16 14. 20 ÷ 5 = 4
15. 3 × 5 = 15 16. 33 ÷ 11 = 3

Spiral Review

Complete each number sentence. Identify the property used. (Lesson 5-2)

17. 5 × (2 × 7) = (5 × 2) × 7 Associative Property of Multiplication
18. 0 ÷ 11 = 0 Zeros in Division
19. 8 × 1 = 8 Identity Property
20. 2 × 7 = 7 × 2 Commutative Property of Multiplication

Grade 4 20 Chapter 4

4 Assess

Formative Assessment

Tell students that using the Commutative Property of Multiplication reduces the number of multiplication facts to learn.

- **Now that you have learned your basic facts through 5, how can you use what you know to find 9 × 5?** It is the same as 5 × 9.
- **What is 11 × 4?** 44
- **What is 12 × 5?** 60

Quick Check **Are students continuing to struggle with multiplication and division facts through 5?**

If Yes → Strategic Intervention Guide (p. 72)

If No → Independent Work Options (p. 154A)
CRM Skills Practice Worksheet (p. 19)
CRM Enrich Worksheet (p. 22)

Name the Math Ask students to describe two different methods that can be used to solve the following problem: *Ginny purchased five 6-packs of fruit drink for her party. How many cans of fruit drink did Ginny buy?*

TEST Practice

Reviews Lessons 4-2 and 4-3

Assign the Test Practice problems to provide daily reinforcement of test-taking skills.

Spiral Review

Reviews Lessons 2-4, 4-1, and 4-2

Review and assess mastery of skills and concepts from previous chapters.

4-4 Problem-Solving Skill
Choose an Operation

Lesson Planner

Objective

Choose an operation to solve a problem.

Resources

Literature Connection: *Amanda Bean's Amazing Dream* by Cindy Neuschwander

Teacher Technology

Interactive Classroom • TeacherWorks

Real-World Problem Solving Library
Math and Social Studies: ***Class Project***
Use these leveled books to reinforce and extend problem-solving skills and strategies.

Leveled for:

- OL On Level
- ELL Sheltered English
- SP Spanish

For additional support, see the Real-World Problem Solving Teacher Guide.

Daily Routine

Use these suggestions before beginning the lesson on p. 158.

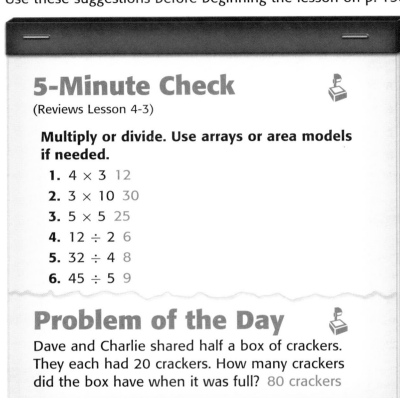

5-Minute Check

(Reviews Lesson 4-3)

Multiply or divide. Use arrays or area models if needed.

1. 4×3 12
2. 3×10 30
3. 5×5 25
4. $12 \div 2$ 6
5. $32 \div 4$ 8
6. $45 \div 5$ 9

Problem of the Day

Dave and Charlie shared half a box of crackers. They each had 20 crackers. How many crackers did the box have when it was full? 80 crackers

Differentiated Instruction

Small Group Options

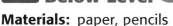

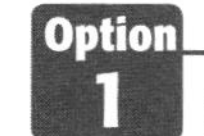

LOGICAL

Option 1 Below Level BL

Materials: paper, pencils

- Review operations. Show students the following examples: 6 + 3 = 9, 6 − 3 = 3, 6 × 3 = 18, 6 ÷ 3 = 2
- Discuss what happens to numbers when each operation is used. For addition and multiplication, answers are larger numbers. For subtraction and division, answers are smaller numbers.
- Read the following problem to students: *Carlos loves to read and has his books arranged on shelves. He has 9 mystery books on each of 5 shelves. How many mystery books does he have?*
- **Will the number of books Carlos has be greater or less than either of the numbers in this problem?** The number of books is greater than the numbers in the problem.
- **Which operation should we use?** While it is not incorrect to use addition, multiplication will be the more efficient operation here.

LOGICAL

Option 2 English Language Learners ELL

Materials: paper, pencil
Core Vocabulary: below, which, of these
Common Use Verb: pick

Hear Math This strategy illustrates that it is important to read a problem carefully when there are several operations to choose from.

- Read the following problem: Paloma had 6 dolls and 2 outfits. Her mom gave her 3 doll outfits for her birthday.
- Ask: "Which of these problems below show how many outfits Paloma has?"

6 + 3
2 + 6
2 + 3
6 − 2

- Allow students to look and then pick the correct problem.
- Scaffold the language for struggling students by allowing students to act out the problem.

Independent Work Options

LOGICAL

Option 1 Early Finishers OL AL

Materials: index cards numbered 1–12, and four index cards, each with a different operation symbol

- Ask each student to choose two number cards and one operation card from the faceup cards on the table (and then replace them). Have students write word problems that use their numbers and operations.
- Once all students have finished writing their problems, have them exchange problems with another student, and solve. Tell them to correct the problems and answers together as time allows.

Option 2 Student Technology

Math Online macmillanmh.com

Personal Tutor • Extra Examples

Option 3 Learning Station: Health (p. 142G)

Direct students to the Health Learning Station for opportunities to explore and extend the lesson concept.

4-4 Problem-Solving Skill

1 Introduce

Activity Choice 1 • Review

- Write the following problem on the board:

  Tia earns $5 per hour when she babysits. Last week she babysat 9 hours. How much money did she make? $45
- **What strategy could you use to solve this problem?** Sample answer: make a table
- On the board, show how a table can be used to solve the problem.

Activity Choice 2 • Literature

Introduce the lesson with *Amanda Bean's Amazing Dream* by Cindy Neuschwander. For a related math activity, see p. TR46.

2 Teach

Have students read the problem on the Twisted Zipper roller coaster. Guide them through the problem-solving steps.

Understand Using the questions, review what students know and need to find.

Plan Have them discuss their strategy.

Solve Guide students to choose multiplication to solve the problem.

- **How many rows of seats are there?** 9 rows
- **How many seats are in each row?** 4 seats
- **What operation can you use to find the total number of seats?** multiplication

Check Have students look back at the problem to make sure that the answer fits the facts given.

- **How else could you check the answer?** Sample answer: repeated addition

COMMON ERROR!

Exercise 8 The word *more* often indicates addition in problem-solving exercises. In this case, asking *how many more* indicates to students that a comparison by subtraction is needed.

4-4 Problem-Solving Skill

MAIN IDEA I will choose an operation to solve a problem.

There are 9 rows on the Twisted Zipper roller coaster. Each row has 4 seats. Choose an operation to find how many people can ride the roller coaster at a time.

Understand	**What facts do you know?** • There are 9 rows. • There are 4 seats per row. **What do you need to find?** • The operation you should use to find how many people can ride the roller coaster at a time.
Plan	There are groups with the same number in each group. So, multiply the number of rows by the number of seats per row.
Solve	Multiply to find the answer. $4 \times 9 = 36$ 4: seats per row; 9: rows So, 36 people can ride the roller coaster at a time.
Check	Look back. Find 4×9 another way to see if you get the same answer. You can use an array. (array of 4 rows of 9 counters; 4, 9) Since $4 \times 9 = 36$, the answer is correct.

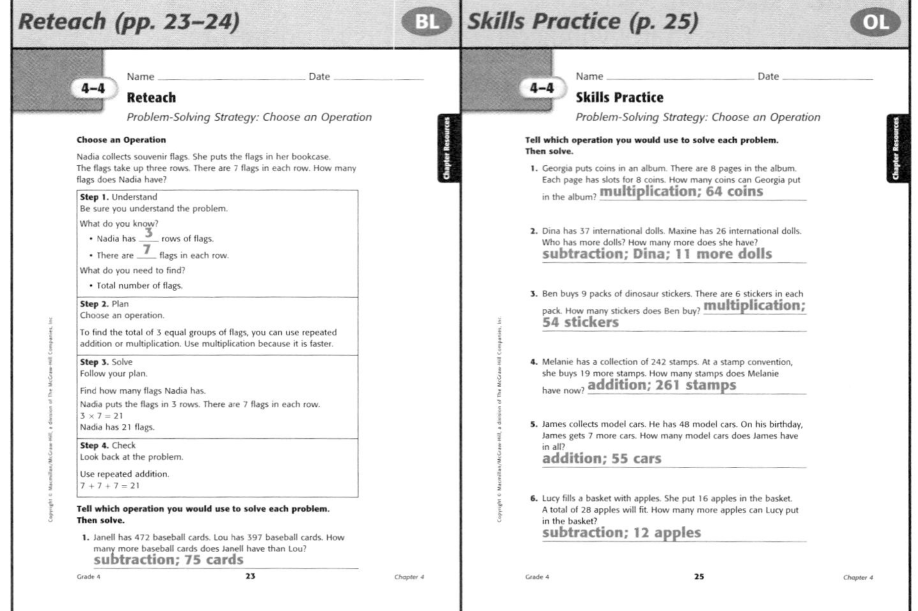

Reteach (pp. 23–24) BL

4-4 Name ______ Date ______

Reteach

Problem-Solving Strategy: Choose an Operation

Choose an Operation

Nadia collects souvenir flags. She puts the flags in her bookcase. The flags take up three rows. There are 7 flags in each row. How many flags does Nadia have?

Step 1. Understand Be sure you understand the problem. What do you know? • Nadia has 3 rows of flags. • There are 7 flags in each row. What do you need to find? • Total number of flags.
Step 2. Plan Choose an operation. To find the total of 3 equal groups of flags, you can use repeated addition or multiplication. Use multiplication because it is faster.
Step 3. Solve Follow your plan. Find how many flags Nadia has. Nadia puts the flags in 3 rows. There are 7 flags in each row. $3 \times 7 = 21$ Nadia has 21 flags.
Step 4. Check Look back at the problem. Use repeated addition. $7 + 7 + 7 = 21$

Tell which operation you would use to solve each problem. Then solve.

1. Janell has 472 baseball cards. Lou has 397 baseball cards. How many more baseball cards does Janell have than Lou? **subtraction; 75 cards**

Grade 4 23 Chapter 4

Skills Practice (p. 25) OL

4-4 Name ______ Date ______

Skills Practice

Problem-Solving Strategy: Choose an Operation

Tell which operation you would use to solve each problem. Then solve.

1. Georgia puts coins in an album. There are 8 pages in the album. Each page has slots for 8 coins. How many coins can Georgia put in the album? **multiplication; 64 coins**
2. Dina has 37 international dolls. Maxine has 26 international dolls. Who has more dolls? How many more does she have? **subtraction; Dina; 11 more dolls**
3. Ben buys 9 packs of dinosaur stickers. There are 6 stickers in each pack. How many stickers does Ben buy? **multiplication; 54 stickers**
4. Melanie has a collection of 242 stamps. At a stamp convention, she buys 19 more stamps. How many stamps does Melanie have now? **addition; 261 stamps**
5. James collects model cars. He has 48 model cars. On his birthday, James gets 7 more cars. How many model cars does James have in all? **addition; 55 cars**
6. Lucy fills a basket with apples. She put 16 apples in the basket. A total of 28 apples will fit. How many more apples can Lucy put in the basket? **subtraction; 12 apples**

Grade 4 25 Chapter 4

ANALYZE the Skill

Refer to the problem on the previous page.

1. Explain why you multiplied 9 and 4 to find the answer. rows times people
2. What operation can be used to check the answer? division
3. If 6 people can sit in each row, how many people could ride in all? 54 people
4. Refer to Exercise 3. How do you know the answer is correct? $54 \div 9 = 6$

PRACTICE the Skill

Tell which operation you would use to solve each problem. Then solve.

5. Jocelyn completed 28 problems for her math homework on Tuesday. She completed 17 more on Thursday than on Tuesday. How many problems did she complete on Thursday? addition; 45 problems
6. There are three jugglers in a circus. Each juggler can juggle 5 balls at a time. How many balls will they need for their act if they all perform at the same time? multiplication; 15 balls
7. A page from Dana's album is shown. Dana puts the same number of stickers on each page. She has 11 pages of stickers. How many stickers does she have in all? multiplication; 132 stickers

8. Park Street School has 98 students who have perfect attendance. West Glenn School has 64 students. How many more students have perfect attendance at Park Street School? subtraction; 34 students
9. **Measurement** The graph shows how long some animals sleep. The koala sleeps 6 hours more than which animal?

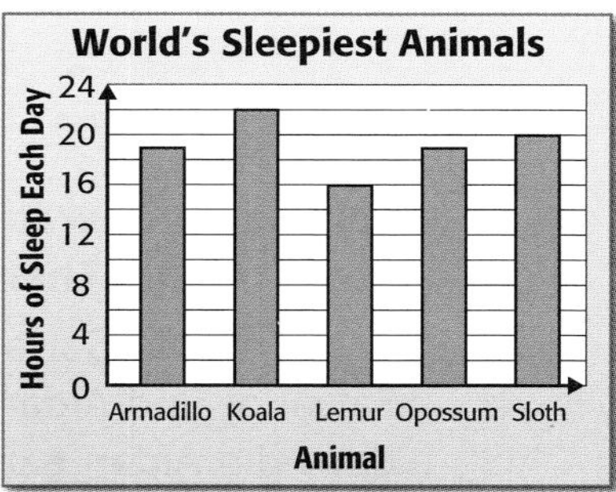

Source: *Scholastic Book of World Records*

subtraction; lemur

10. Use the graph above. How many more hours does a sloth sleep than a lemur? subtraction; 4 hr
11. Corey and his 2 friends earned $12 for doing yard work. How much money will each person get paid if they share the money evenly? division; $4
12. A lizard eats 6 crickets each day. How many crickets does it eat in one week? multiplication; 42 crickets
13. **WRITING IN MATH** Explain how you chose an operation for Exercise 12. Sample answer: The answer could be found by repeated addition. So, multiplication was the best choice.

Lesson 4-4 Problem-Solving Skill: Choose an Operation **159**

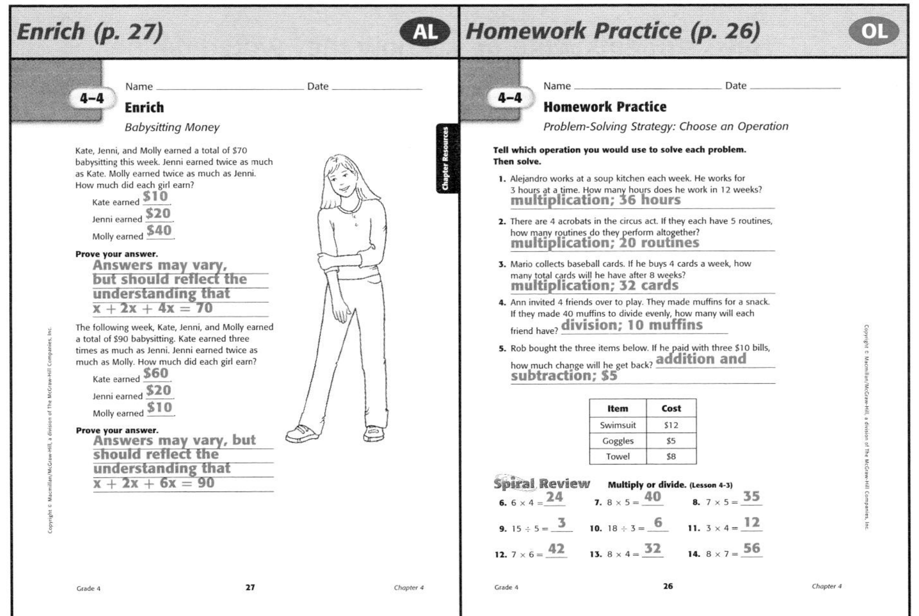

Enrich (p. 27) AL

4–4 Name ________ Date ________

Enrich

Babysitting Money

Kate, Jenni, and Molly earned a total of $70 babysitting this week. Jenni earned twice as much as Kate. Molly earned twice as much as Jenni. How much did each girl earn?

Kate earned $10.
Jenni earned $20.
Molly earned $40.

Prove your answer. Answers may vary, but should reflect the understanding that $x + 2x + 4x = 70$

The following week, Kate, Jenni, and Molly earned a total of $90 babysitting. Kate earned three times as much as Jenni. Jenni earned twice as much as Molly. How much did each girl earn?

Kate earned $60.
Jenni earned $20.
Molly earned $10.

Prove your answer. Answers may vary, but should reflect the understanding that $x + 2x + 6x = 90$

Chapter Resources

Copyright © Macmillan/McGraw-Hill, a division of The McGraw-Hill Companies, Inc.

Grade 4 27 Chapter 4

Homework Practice (p. 26) OL

4–4 Name ________ Date ________

Homework Practice

Problem-Solving Strategy: Choose an Operation

Tell which operation you would use to solve each problem. Then solve.

1. Alejandro works at a soup kitchen each week. He works for 3 hours at a time. How many hours does he work in 12 weeks? multiplication; 36 hours
2. There are 4 acrobats in the circus act. If they each have 5 routines, how many routines do they perform altogether? multiplication; 20 routines
3. Mario collects baseball cards. If he buys 4 cards a week, how many total cards will he have after 8 weeks? multiplication; 32 cards
4. Ann invited 4 friends over to play. They made muffins for a snack. If they made 40 muffins to divide evenly, how many will each friend have? division; 10 muffins
5. Rob bought the three items below. If he paid with three $10 bills, how much change will he get back? addition and subtraction; $5

Item	Cost
Swimsuit	$12
Goggles	$5
Towel	$8

Spiral Review **Multiply or divide.** (Lesson 4-3)

6. $6 \times 4 =$ 24
7. $8 \times 5 =$ 40
8. $7 \times 5 =$ 35
9. $15 \div 5 =$ 3
10. $18 \div 3 =$ 6
11. $3 \times 4 =$ 12
12. $7 \times 6 =$ 42
13. $8 \times 4 =$ 32
14. $8 \times 7 =$ 56

Copyright © Macmillan/McGraw-Hill, a division of The McGraw-Hill Companies, Inc.

Grade 4 26 Chapter 4

Analyze the Strategy Use Exercises 1–4 to analyze and discuss the problem-solving strategy.

BL Alternate Teaching Strategy

If students have trouble choosing which operation to use…

Then use one of these reteach options:

1 CRM **Daily Reteach Worksheet** (pp. 23–24)

2 Help students write examples of problems that use the four operations. Each student should write an example on a piece of construction paper. Then have them write a sentence or two explaining how they would solve the problem and which operation they would use. Make and hang a poster showing students' examples.

3 Practice

Using the Exercises

Exercise 7 shows only one page of the album. Point out that all pages have the same number of stickers.

Exercise 9 Remind students to read the bar graph to answer the question.

4 Assess

Formative Assessment

Present the following problem:

Aisha spends $8 on bus fare every week. How much money does she spend in four weeks?

- **Without solving, describe how you would solve this problem.** Sample answer: Multiply $8 by 4.
- **Solve and check your solution.** $32

Quick Check **Are students continuing to struggle with choosing the correct operation?**

If Yes → Small Group Options (p. 158B)

If No → Independent Work Options (p. 158B)
CRM Skills Practice Worksheet (p. 24)
CRM Enrich Worksheet (p. 27)

LESSON 4-5

Multiply and Divide Facts Through 10

Lesson Planner

Objective

Recall multiplication and division facts through 10.

Review Vocabulary

estimate

Resources

Manipulatives: counters

Literature Connection: *Spaghetti and Meatballs for All!* by Marilyn Burns

Alternate Lesson: Use *IMPACT Mathematics*: Unit A to provide practice with multiplication.

Teacher Technology
TeacherWorks • Interactive Classroom • Math Songs Track #8 Lesson Plan

Daily Routine

Use these suggestions before beginning the lesson on p. 160.

5-Minute Check

(Reviews Lesson 4-4)

Tell which operation you would use to solve the problem. Then solve.

At the picnic, Salvador ate 3 hot dogs. Together, Salvador and Aidan ate 7 hot dogs. How many hot dogs did Aidan eat? subtraction; 4 hot dogs

Problem of the Day

Anne, Lilla, and Eliam like red, yellow, and purple, and daisy, rose, and iris. Anne does not like yellow, purple, or roses. Lilla likes daisies but not yellow. List each person's favorite color and flower. Anne: red, iris; Lilla: purple, daisy; Eliam: yellow, rose.

Focus on Math Background

Although fluency is a goal for multiplication and division facts, intermediate steps are sometimes necessary with larger factors. Modeling the decomposition of products by "cutting" rectangular arrays into two sections can be used to help students decompose products into two partial products that they already know. For example, seven can be decomposed into five and two. This means that 7×8 can be rewritten as 5×8 plus 2×8, which is $40 + 16$ or 56. When used by students frequently, this use of the Distributive Property can become a natural process.

Review Math Vocabulary

Write the review vocabulary word and its definition on the board.

Have students write or say how they would define *estimate* to a friend who had never heard the word before. Ask them to include examples to help their friend understand.

Visual Vocabulary Cards
Use Visual Vocabulary Card 15 to reinforce the vocabulary reviewed in the lesson. (The Define/Example/Ask routine is printed on the back of each card.)

estimate

Differentiated Instruction

Small Group Options

Option 1 LOGICAL

Below Level BL

Materials: paper and pencil

- Ask the first student in each pair to write a "secret number" that the partner cannot see.
- Ask the first student to multiply the secret number by ten and then divide it by two. Then the student gives the paper to his or her partner.
- The partner should multiply the number by two, then divide by ten. The result should be the original secret number.
- Discuss with the students why and how this happens. The topic of inverse operations should be included.
- Repeat this process by asking the partners to take turns entering the secret number.

Option 2 AUDITORY

English Language Learners ELL

Materials: multiplication table, counters
Core Vocabulary: listen carefully, look for, close your eyes
Common Use Verb: cover

Hear Math This strategy sharpens listening skills and students ability to "see" problems in their head.

- Give each student a multiplication chart and counters.
- Say: "Cover the answer that solves this problem." Read a number fact.
- Repeat for more problems, prompting students to close their eyes when you read the problem to see it in their heads.
- Play a game with students by calling out a multiplication or division problem. Tell students to close their eyes, to say, write, or place their marker on the answer.

English Language Learners (p. 43) ELL

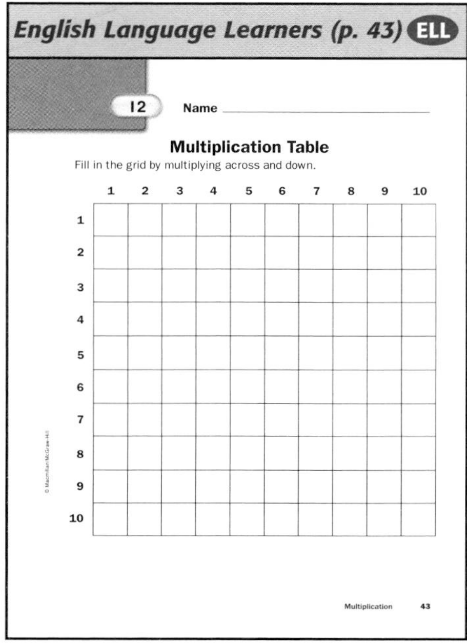

12 Name

Multiplication Table

Fill in the grid by multiplying across and down.

	1	2	3	4	5	6	7	8	9	10
1										
2										
3										
4										
5										
6										
7										
8										
9										
10										

Multiplication 43

Independent Work Options

Option 1 LOGICAL

Early Finishers OL AL

Materials: index cards with various multiplication problems with basic facts through 10 written on them

- This is a card game for two students to play. Each pair of students will need a "deck" of 50 cards.
- Students split the deck of cards evenly, so each player has 25 cards. They both lay down a card, and the player with the larger product collects both cards. In the event of a tie (such as if 9×4 and 6×6 cards are played), each player then plays another card until the tie is broken.
- The winner is the player with more cards at the end of the time period.

Option 2

Student Technology

Math Online macmillanmh.com

Personal Tutor • Extra Examples

Math Adventures

Math Songs, "Multiplication Rap" Track #8

Option 3

Learning Station: Science (p. 142H)

Direct students to the Science Learning Station for opportunities to explore and extend the lesson concept.

Option 4

Problem-Solving Practice

Reinforce problem-solving skills and strategies with the Problem-Solving Practice worksheet.

Problem Solving (p. 31) BL OL AL

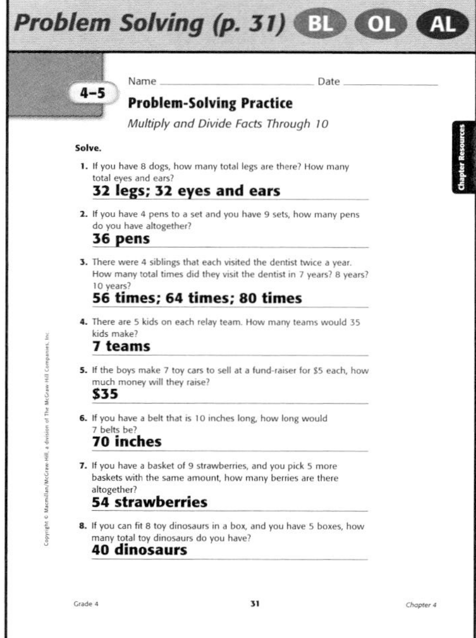

4–5 Name Date

Problem-Solving Practice

Multiply and Divide Facts Through 10

Chapter Resources

Solve.

1. If you have 8 dogs, how many total legs are there? How many total eyes and ears?
32 legs; 32 eyes and ears
2. If you have 4 pens to a set and you have 9 sets, how many pens do you have altogether?
36 pens
3. There were 4 siblings that each visited the dentist twice a year. How many total times did they visit the dentist in 7 years? 8 years? 10 years?
56 times; 64 times; 80 times
4. There are 5 kids on each relay team. How many teams would 35 kids make?
7 teams
5. If the boys make 7 toy cars to sell at a fund-raiser for $5 each, how much money will they raise?
$35
6. If you have a belt that is 10 inches long, how long would 7 belts be?
70 inches
7. If you have a basket of 9 strawberries, and you pick 5 more baskets with the same amount, how many berries are there altogether?
54 strawberries
8. If you can fit 8 toy dinosaurs in a box, and you have 5 boxes, how many total toy dinosaurs do you have?
40 dinosaurs

Grade 4 31 Chapter 4

4-5 Multiply and Divide Facts Through 10

1 Introduce

Activity Choice 1 • Hands-On

- Divide the class into five groups. Assign each group a number between 6 and 10. Tell each group to keep the number a secret. Have each group skip count the first four or five multiples of the number. Then ask the class to identify their numbers.
- Have the group with the number 6 skip count to 30.
- **What are the next seven numbers?** 36, 42, 48, 54, 60, 66, 72
- Have the group with the number 7 skip count to 35.
- **What are the next seven numbers?** 42, 49, 56, 63, 70, 77, 84
- Repeat this for the 8s, 9s, and 10s.

Activity Choice 2 • Literature

Introduce the lesson with *Spaghetti and Meatballs for All!* by Marilyn Burns. For a related math activity, see p. TR47.

2 Teach

Scaffolding Questions

Have students skip count to answer the following questions:

- **What is 7 × 6? What is 7 × 7? What is 7 × 8?** 42; 49; 56
- **What is the difference in the products of 7 × 6 and 7 × 7?** 7
- **Why is the difference between any two consecutive numbers when you skip count by 7 always 7?** Sample answer: Because multiplying by 7 is repeated addition of 7s, so for each consecutive product, you are adding 7 to the previous product.

GET READY to Learn

Have students open their books and read the information in **Get Ready to Learn**. Review fact families. As a class, work through **Examples 1 and 2**.

4-5 Multiply and Divide Facts Through 10

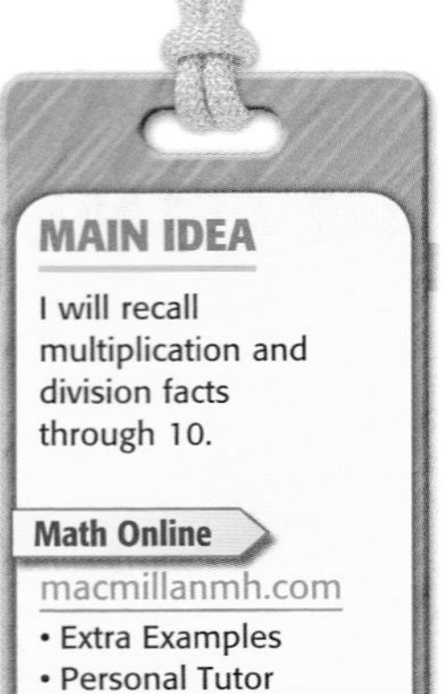

MAIN IDEA
I will recall multiplication and division facts through 10.
Math Online
macmillanmh.com
• Extra Examples
• Personal Tutor
• Self-Check Quiz

GET READY to Learn

Lorenzo is storing his friends' phone numbers in his cell phone. Each number has 7 digits. How many number buttons did Lorenzo press if he has 9 friends?

You can find how many number buttons Lorenzo pressed by multiplying. Two multiplication strategies that you can use are area models and related facts.

Multiply

1 **PHONES Each number has 7 digits. How many number buttons did Lorenzo press if he has 9 friends?**

You need to find 7 × 9.

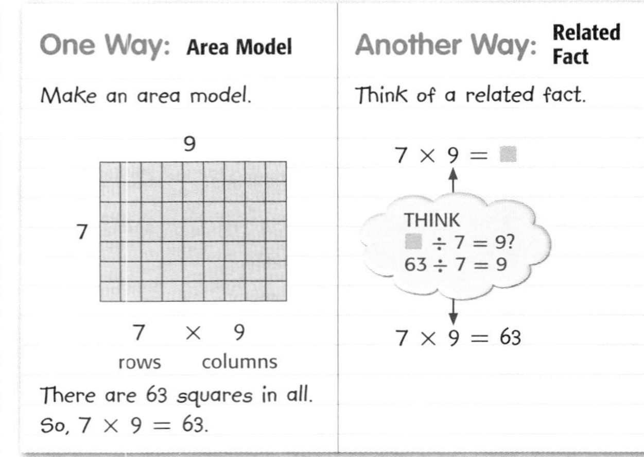

One Way: Area Model
Make an area model.
9
7
7 × 9
rows columns
There are 63 squares in all.
So, 7 × 9 = 63.
Another Way: Related Fact
Think of a related fact.
7 × 9 = ■
THINK
■ ÷ 7 = 9?
63 ÷ 7 = 9
7 × 9 = 63

So, Lorenzo must press 63 number buttons.

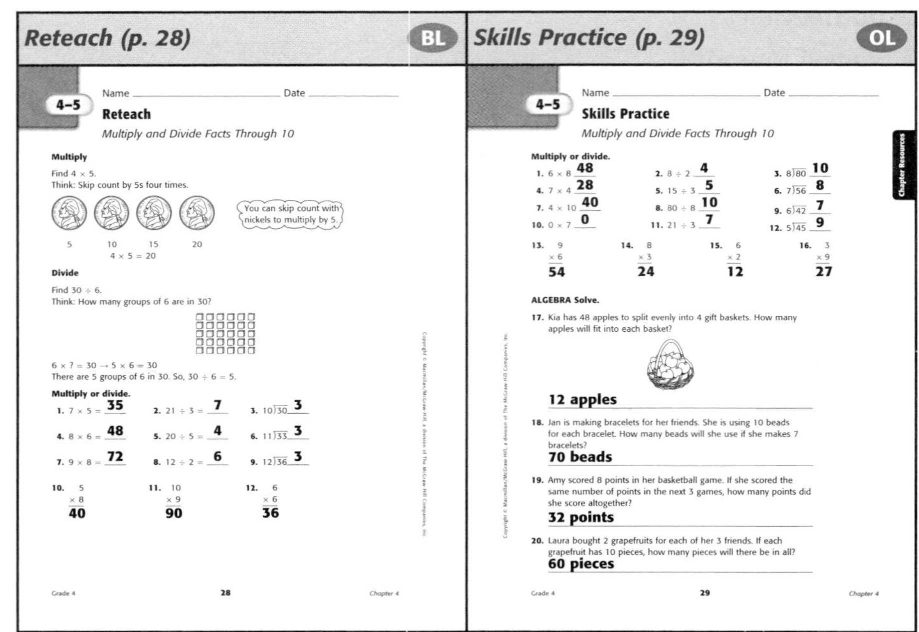

Reteach (p. 28) BL

4-5 Name ______ Date ______

Reteach

Multiply and Divide Facts Through 10

Multiply

Find 4 × 5.
Think: Skip count by 5s four times.

You can skip count with nickels to multiply by 5.

5 10 15 20
4 × 5 = 20

Divide

Find 30 ÷ 6.
Think: How many groups of 6 are in 30?

6 × ? = 30 → 5 × 6 = 30
There are 5 groups of 6 in 30. So, 30 ÷ 6 = 5.

Multiply or divide.

1. 7 × 5 = **35**
2. 21 ÷ 3 = **7**
3. 10)30 **3**
4. 8 × 6 = **48**
5. 20 ÷ 5 = **4**
6. 11)33 **3**
7. 9 × 8 = **72**
8. 12 ÷ 2 = **6**
9. 12)36 **3**
10. 5 × 8 = **40**
11. 10 × 9 = **90**
12. 6 × 6 = **36**

Grade 4 28 Chapter 4

Skills Practice (p. 29) OL

4-5 Name ______ Date ______

Skills Practice

Multiply and Divide Facts Through 10

Chapter Resources

Multiply or divide.

1. 6 × 8 **48**
2. 8 ÷ 2 **4**
3. 8)80 **10**
4. 7 × 4 **28**
5. 15 ÷ 3 **5**
6. 7)56 **8**
7. 4 × 10 **40**
8. 80 ÷ 8 **10**
9. 6)42 **7**
10. 0 × 7 **0**
11. 21 ÷ 3 **7**
12. 5)45 **9**
13. 9 × 6 **54**
14. 8 × 3 **24**
15. 6 × 2 **12**
16. 3 × 9 **27**

ALGEBRA Solve.

17. Kia has 48 apples to split evenly into 4 gift baskets. How many apples will fit into each basket? **12 apples**
18. Jan is making bracelets for her friends. She is using 10 beads for each bracelet. How many beads will she use if she makes 7 bracelets? **70 beads**
19. Amy scored 8 points in her basketball game. If she scored the same number of points in the next 3 games, how many points did she score altogether? **32 points**
20. Laura bought 2 grapefruits for each of her 3 friends. If each grapefruit has 10 pieces, how many pieces will there be in all? **60 pieces**

Grade 4 29 Chapter 4

Real-World EXAMPLE Divide

2 TELEVISION Carolyn noticed that 9 minutes of commercials play during a 30-minute television program. How many 30-minute shows did Carolyn watch during a weekend if she watched 54 minutes of commercials?

Remember

The factors in a multiplication problem become the divisor and quotient in the related division problem.

Each program has 9 minutes of commercials. Divide 54 by 9 to find how many 30-minute shows Carolyn watched.

Separate an array of 54 counters into 9 equal groups.

There are 6 counters in each group.

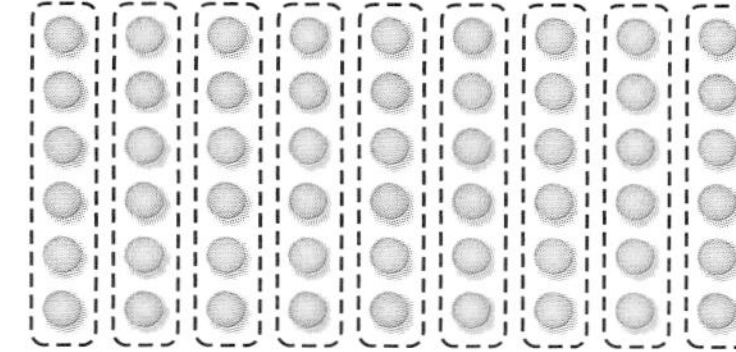

So, Carolyn watched 6 thirty-minute shows.

Check Use a related fact to check your answer. Since $9 \times 6 = 54$, the answer is correct.

So, $54 \div 9 = 6$. ✓

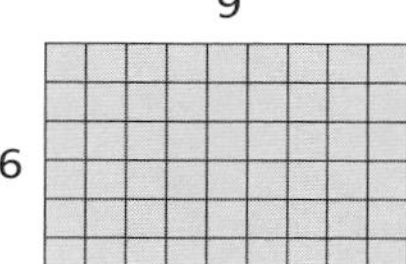

10. Sample answer: The product is the factor that is not 10 with a zero written after it; $5 \times 10 = 50$; To find any product when 10 is a factor, just write a zero after the factor that is not 10.

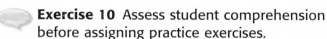

CHECK What You Know

Multiply or divide. Use arrays or area models if needed. See Examples 1 and 2 (pp. 160–161)

1. 9×8 72

2. 10×7 70

3. 6×4 24

4. 8×8 64

5. $49 \div 7$ 7

6. $60 \div 6$ 10

7. $8\overline{)48}$ 6

8. $10\overline{)100}$ 10

9. Linda sold 8 magazine subscriptions to make money for her school. Each magazine subscription costs $9. How much money did Linda collect? $72

10. Talk About It What do you notice when you multiply 10 and a number? Explain an easy method for finding a product when 10 is one of the factors.

Enrich (p. 32) AL

4–5

Name ______________ Date ______________

Enrich

More Mystery Multiplication

Which times table is this **8s**

Use what you have learned about multiplication to figure out the value for each letter. Complete the chart below.

M × M = LY
M × H = M
M × Q = KY
M × J = YW
M × V = FK
M × W = W
M × F = JL
M × L = YM
M × K = HL
M × Y = QK

F	H	J	K	L	M	Q	V	W	Y
7	1	5	2	6	8	3	9	0	4

Grade 4 32 Chapter 4

Divide

Example 2 Remind students that they know the total commercial time Carolyn watched. They also know that each show has 9 minutes of commercials. If they are confused by the number "30" in the problem, suggest that they change "30-minute show" to "half-hour show" or simply "show."

ADDITIONAL EXAMPLES

1. A bus has 8 rows with 6 seats in each row. How many people can be seated in the bus? 48 people
2. Filipa noticed that there are 2 pages of advertisements for every article she reads in a magazine. If she saw a total of 16 pages of advertisements, how many articles did she read? 8

CHECK What You Know

As a class, have students complete Exercises 1–10 in **Check What You Know** as you observe their work.

Exercise 10 Assess student comprehension before assigning practice exercises.

BL Alternate Teaching Strategy

If students have trouble computing multiplication facts through 10…

Then use one of these reteach options:

1. CRM **Daily Reteach Worksheet** (p. 28)
2. Have students use counters to make arrays for each problem. For example, to find 6×8 have them use counters to make an array of 6 rows of 8 counters each.
   - Guide students to see the connection between the written problems and the arrays.
3. Have students use Math Tool Chest to help complete the problem solving exercise.

COMMON ERROR!

Exercise 17 Students often compute 6×8 incorrectly. Address this by providing the rhyme "six times eight is forty-eight," or remind them that 6×8 is 6×4 doubled.

3 Practice

Differentiate practice using these leveled assignments for Exercises 11–34.

Level	Assignment
BL Below/Approaching Level	11, 12, 15, 16, 18, 19, 22–24, 27, 29
OL On Level	11–24, 27, 29–30, 34
AL Above/Beyond Level	11–19 odd, 31–34

Have students discuss and complete the Higher Order Thinking problems. For Exercise 31, point out that there are many correct answers.

WRITING IN MATH Have students complete Exercise 34 in their Math Journals. You may choose to use this exercise as an optional formative assessment.

4 Assess

Formative Assessment

- **Give two examples of patterns that are useful when multiplying through 10.**
  Sample answer: All multiples of 10 end in zero; all multiples of 5 end in 0 or 5.
- **List 6 different facts for each pattern.**
  Answers will vary.

Quick Check **Are students continuing to struggle with multiplication and division facts through 10?**

If Yes → Small Group Options (p. 160B)
Strategic Intervention Guide (p. 74)

If No → Independent Work Options (p. 160B)
CRM Skills Practice Worksheet (p. 29)
CRM Enrich Worksheet (p. 32)

Into the Future Tell students that tomorrow's lesson is on multiplying and dividing by 11 and 12. Ask how they think they can use what they learned in today's lesson to help them with tomorrow's lesson.

Practice and Problem Solving

EXTRA PRACTICE See page R11.

Multiply or divide. Use arrays or area models if needed. See Examples 1 and 2 (pp. 160–161)

11. 6×6 36 **12.** 10×8 80 **13.** 7×7 49 **14.** 6×7 42

15. 9×4 36 **16.** 10×5 50 **17.** 6×8 48 **18.** 10×10 100

19. $30 \div 6$ 5 **20.** $42 \div 7$ 6 **21.** $72 \div 8$ 9 **22.** $90 \div 10$ 9

23. $7\overline{)70}$ 10 **24.** $9\overline{)63}$ 7 **25.** $8\overline{)56}$ 7 **26.** $10\overline{)80}$ 8

27. Juliana played 9 holes of miniature golf. Her total score was 54. Suppose she got the same score on each hole. What was Juliana's score per hole? 6

28. While on vacation, Felipe sent 42 postcards to his friends. How many friends did he send to if he sent 7 postcards to each person? 6

Real-World PROBLEM SOLVING

Fruit Oranges are the fruit of a citrus tree originally from southeast Asia. Oranges grow in different sizes and colors. Most oranges have 10 sections inside.

29. Nadia bought 2 oranges for each member of her family. Nadia has 4 family members. Each orange has 10 sections. How many sections will there be in all? 80 sections

30. Suppose Nadia cuts 6 oranges in half. She finds that there are 54 sections in all. If there are the same number of sections in each orange, how many sections are in each orange? 9 sections

H.O.T. Problems

31. OPEN ENDED Write three number sentences that each contain the number 6 and have a product greater than 40.
Sample answer: $6 \times 7 = 42$, $6 \times 8 = 48$, $6 \times 9 = 54$

32. NUMBER SENSE Explain why the fact family of 7 and 49 has only two number sentences. Sample answer: The factors are the same number.

33. CHALLENGE The product of two numbers is 24. The sum of the numbers is 11. What are the two numbers? 3 and 8

34. WRITING IN MATH Is the quotient of $135 \div 9$ greater than or less than the quotient of $153 \div 9$? Explain how you know without finding the quotients.

34. Sample answer: less than; the division number sentence that has a larger dividend will have a larger quotient.

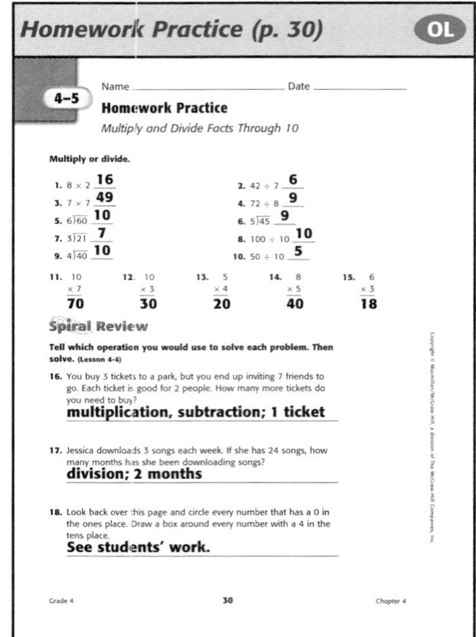

Homework Practice (p. 30) OL

4–5 Name ________ Date ________

Homework Practice

Multiply and Divide Facts Through 10

Multiply or divide.

1. 8×2 **16**
2. $42 \div 7$ **6**
3. 7×7 **49**
4. $72 \div 8$ **9**
5. $6\overline{)60}$ **10**
6. $5\overline{)45}$ **9**
7. $3\overline{)21}$ **7**
8. $100 \div 10$ **10**
9. $4\overline{)40}$ **10**
10. $50 \div 10$ **5**

11. 10×7 **70** 12. 10×3 **30** 13. 5×4 **20** 14. 8×5 **40** 15. 6×3 **18**

Spiral Review

Tell which operation you would use to solve each problem. Then solve. (Lesson 4-4)

16. You buy 3 tickets to a park, but you end up inviting 7 friends to go. Each ticket is good for 2 people. How many more tickets do you need to buy?
multiplication, subtraction; 1 ticket

17. Jessica downloads 3 songs each week. If she has 24 songs, how many months has she been downloading songs?
division; 2 months

18. Look back over this page and circle every number that has a 0 in the ones place. Draw a box around every number with a 4 in the tens place.
See students' work.

Grade 4 30 Chapter 4

Mid-Chapter Check

Lessons 4-1 through 4-5

Write a fact family for each set of numbers. (Lesson 4-1)

1. 7, 28, 4
2. 3, 24, 8

1–2. See Ch. 4 Answer Appendix.

Algebra Divide. Use a related multiplication fact. (Lesson 4-1)

3. $18 \div 2$ 9; $2 \times 9 = 18$
4. $20 \div 5$ 4; $5 \times 4 = 20$
5. $33 \div 3$ 11; $3 \times 11 = 33$
6. $36 \div 4$ 9; $4 \times 9 = 36$

7. **MULTIPLE CHOICE** Which number sentence is in the same fact family as $63 \div 7 = \blacksquare$? (Lesson 4-1) C

   A $7 + \blacksquare = 63$ C $7 \times \blacksquare = 63$

   B $\blacksquare - 7 = 63$ D $63 \times 7 = \blacksquare$

Identify the property or rule shown by each number sentence. (Lesson 4-2)

8. $15 \times 0 = 0$
9. $9 \times 3 = 3 \times 9$

8, 9. See Ch. 4 Answer Appendix.

Algebra Copy and complete each number sentence. Identify the property or rule used. (Lesson 4-2)

10. $5 \div \blacksquare = 1$
11. $7 \times \blacksquare = 0$

10, 11. See Ch. 4 Answer Appendix.

Multiply or divide. (Lesson 4-3)

12. $20 \div 5$ 4
13. 4×3 12

14. Emmett brushes his teeth 3 times a day. How many times does Emmett brush his teeth in one week? (Lesson 4-3) 21

Algebra Complete each number sentence. (Lesson 4-3)

15. $\blacksquare \times 5 = 45$ 9
16. $3 \times \blacksquare = 3$ 1

17. **MULTIPLE CHOICE** Which number is missing from the number sentence? (Lesson 4-3) G

   $27 \div \blacksquare = 9$

   F 2 H 4

   G 3 J 5

Tell which operation you would use to solve each problem. Then solve. (Lesson 4-4)

18. Lance walked 4 dogs on Monday. He walked twice that many on Tuesday. How many dogs did he walk on Tuesday? multiplication; 8 dogs

19. Each row of the stadium can hold 9 people. Diana reserved 3 rows for her family. How many people in Diana's family will be at the stadium? multiplication; 27 people

Multiply or divide. (Lesson 4-5)

20. 10×6 60
21. $56 \div 7$ 8

22. WRITING IN MATH Does the Associative Property work with division? Explain how you know. (Lesson 4-2) See Ch. 4 Answer Appendix.

Formative Assessment 163

Mid-Chapter Check

Lessons 4-1 through 4-5

Formative Assessment

Use the Mid-Chapter Check to assess students' progress in the first half of the chapter.

Customize and create multiple versions of your Mid-Chapter Check and the test answer keys.

FOLDABLES Dinah Zike's Foldables

Use these lesson suggestions to incorporate the Foldables during the chapter.

Lessons 4-1, 4-2 Under the first tab of the Foldable, have students record information and provide definitions about multiplication properties and division rules, and demonstrate their understanding of the relationship between two operations.

Lesson 4-3 Under the second tab of the Foldable, students demonstrate how to multiply and divide facts through 5 and give examples.

Lesson 4-5 Under the third tab of the Foldable, students demonstrate how to multiply and divide facts through 10 and give examples.

Data-Driven Decision Making

Based on the results of the Mid-Chapter Check, use the following resources to review concepts that continue to give students problems.

Exercises	State/Local Standards	What's the Math?	Error Analysis	Resources for Review
1–7 Lesson 4-1		Understand how multiplication and division are related.	Confuses product for a factor. Confuses quotient for divisor.	Strategic Intervention Guide (pp. 70, 72, 74, 76) CRM Chapter 4 Resource Masters (Reteach Worksheets) Math Adventures My Math Zone Chapter 4 Math Online Extra Examples • Concepts in Motion
8–11, 22 Lesson 4-2		Use and interpret properties of multiplication and division rules.	Does not understand Commutative, Identity, or Zero Properties of Multiplication.	
12–17 Lesson 4-3		Recognize multiplication and division facts 0 through 5.	Confuses multiplication and division signs. Does not know multiplication facts.	
18–19 Lesson 4-4		Choose an operation to solve problems.	Does not understand what is being asked. Does not understand "twice."	

Lesson Planner

Objective

Interpret information and data from social studies to solve problems.

National Standard 

Students will understand the folklore and other cultural contributions from various regions of the United States and how they helped to form a national heritage.

Activate Prior Knowledge

Before you turn students' attention to the pages, ask them to discuss soda pop.

- **What makes soda pop fizzy?** carbonated water
- **Who started adding flavors to soda water?** pharmacists

Using the Student Page

Ask students to read the information on pp. 164–165 and answer these questions:

- **If you bought 3 cases of soda in 1894, how many bottles would you have bought?** 72 bottles
- **How many "home-packs" would a case of soda bottles make?** 4

Pop
Culture

Did you know that pop was invented by doctors? Many people thought that the mineral water in natural springs had healing powers. In 1767, a doctor invented the first glass of carbonated water, which came to be known as "soda water."

About 80 years later, pharmacy owners and scientists began to add flavors to soda water. It was renamed "soda pop" in 1861. Soon, Americans could buy soda in bottles from grocery stores and vending machines. These drinks are still very popular.

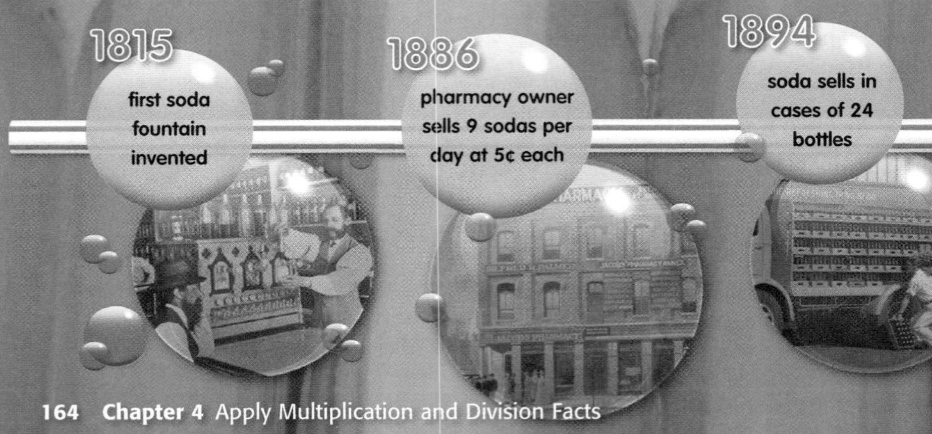
1815
first soda fountain invented
1886
pharmacy owner sells 9 sodas per day at 5¢ each
1894
soda sells in cases of 24 bottles

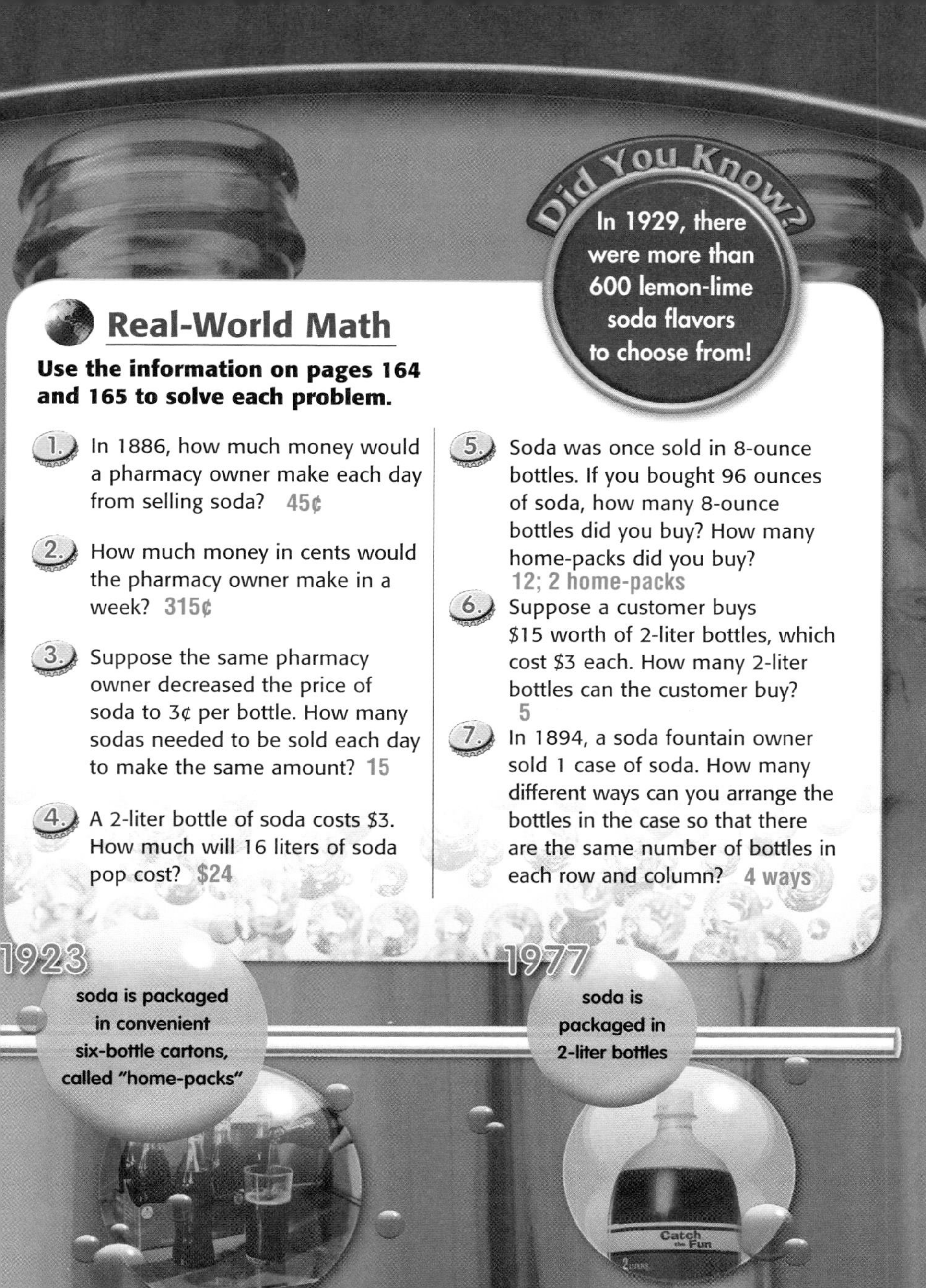

Did You Know?

In 1929, there were more than 600 lemon-lime soda flavors to choose from!

Real-World Math

Use the information on pages 164 and 165 to solve each problem.

1. In 1886, how much money would a pharmacy owner make each day from selling soda? 45¢
2. How much money in cents would the pharmacy owner make in a week? 315¢
3. Suppose the same pharmacy owner decreased the price of soda to 3¢ per bottle. How many sodas needed to be sold each day to make the same amount? 15
4. A 2-liter bottle of soda costs $3. How much will 16 liters of soda pop cost? $24
5. Soda was once sold in 8-ounce bottles. If you bought 96 ounces of soda, how many 8-ounce bottles did you buy? How many home-packs did you buy? 12; 2 home-packs
6. Suppose a customer buys $15 worth of 2-liter bottles, which cost $3 each. How many 2-liter bottles can the customer buy? 5
7. In 1894, a soda fountain owner sold 1 case of soda. How many different ways can you arrange the bottles in the case so that there are the same number of bottles in each row and column? 4 ways

1923 soda is packaged in convenient six-bottle cartons, called "home-packs"

1977 soda is packaged in 2-liter bottles

Real-World Math

Assign the exercises on p. 165. Encourage students to choose a problem-solving strategy before beginning each exercise. If necessary, review the strategies suggested in Lesson 4-7, p. 171.

Exercise 2 Remind students that they need to perform two operations in order to solve this exercise, and they will need to use their answer to Exercise 1.

Exercise 7 Remind students that multiplication facts will be helpful in solving this array exercise.

WRITING IN ▸MATH Have students create a word problem that uses the information found in the text on p. 164.

Extend the Activity

Have students figure out how many ounces are in a case of 24 of today's 12-ounce cans, and how many ounces are in a six-pack.

LESSON 4-6

Multiply with 11 and 12

Lesson Planner

Objective

Recall and apply multiplication facts for 11 and 12.

Vocabulary

Distributive Property of Multiplication

Resources

Materials: hundred charts, crayons or markers

Manipulatives: counters

Literature Connection: *The Grapes of Math* by Greg Tang

Alternate Lesson: Use *IMPACT Mathematics*: Unit A to provide practice with multiplying 11 and 12.

Teacher Technology
TeacherWorks • Interactive Classroom • Math Songs Track #8 Lesson Plan

Daily Routine

Use these suggestions before beginning the lesson on p. 166.

5-Minute Check

(Reviews Lesson 4-5)

Multiply or divide. Use arrays or area models if needed.

1. 8×5 40
2. 9×6 54
3. $64 \div 8$ 8
4. 4×6 24
5. $32 \div 8$ 4

Problem of the Day

Ebo, Bina, and Alejandra bought 2 small and 1 large ice cream cones. Together they paid $7. If a large cone costs $1 more than a small cone, what is the price of each? small cone, $2; large cone, $3.

Focus on Math Background

A student's ability to recall the basic multiplication and division facts is based on his or her ability to understand and use number strategies. Learning to multiply and divide by 11 and 12 depend on being able to "take numbers apart" and "put numbers back together." Appropriate models such as area models, number strategies, and practice form the basis for the development of these basic facts. For example, 8×12 can be thought of as $(8 \times 10) + (8 \times 2) = 80 + 16$ or 96 and 11×12 can be thought of as $(11 \times 10) + (11 \times 2) = 110 + 22$ or 132.

Building Math Vocabulary

Write the lesson vocabulary word and its definition on the board.

Write $3 \times 12 = 36$ on the board. Have students rewrite the multiplication sentence to illustrate the Distributive Property of Multiplication. If necessary, suggest that they start by writing the second factor as the sum of two numbers. Have students share their examples with the class.

Differentiated Instruction

Small Group Options

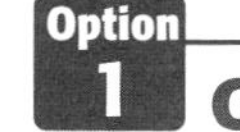

Option 1 Gifted and Talented AL

LOGICAL

Materials: pencils, paper, chart paper

- Review the definition of divisibility. Ask students to share what they already know about the divisibility of 11. They should know that any 2-digit number with the same ones and tens place is divisible by 11.
- Now write 121, 165, 143, 187 on chart paper. Tell students that all these numbers are divisible by 11.
- **What do you notice about all these numbers?** Students should notice that the tens place is always one more than the ones place.
- Write 253, 462, 792, 561 on chart paper. Tell students these are also divisible by 11. Ask the same question. Students should conclude that by adding the ones and hundreds, the sum is the same as the tens digit.
- Ask students to build a number and check to see if it is divisible by 11.

Option 2 English Language Learners ELL

LOGICAL, INTRAPERSONAL

Materials: blank times tables for 11 and 12
Core Vocabulary: act out, clap on, show what you know
Common Use Verb: chant

Do Math This strategy allows students to demonstrate their background knowledge and uses chanting to reinforce and integrate math facts.

- Give each student a blank multiplication table for 11 and 12 and have each student fill it out individually.
- Allow struggling students to find a buddy to complete any unfinished portion of the tables.
- Ask for volunteers to create a kinesthetic pattern to show what they know to their classmates. Have all students clap on the answer as they chant it with the lead student.

Independent Work Options

Option 1 Early Finishers OL AL

VISUAL, SPATIAL

Materials: paper, pencils

- Have students make a fill-in-the-blank puzzle.
- The puzzle they make will have twelve number sentences, with one blank space per sentence. The blank spaces have to be a number 1–12. Each number 1–12 has to be used exactly once.
- Students can exchange and solve each other's puzzles.

Option 2 Student Technology

Math Online macmillanmh.com

Personal Tutor • Extra Examples

 Math Adventures

Math Songs, "Multiplication Rap" Track #8

Option 3 Learning Station: Music (p. 142H)

Direct students to the Music Learning Station for opportunities to explore and extend the lesson concept.

Option 4 Problem-Solving Practice

Reinforce problem-solving skills and strategies with the Problem-Solving Practice worksheet.

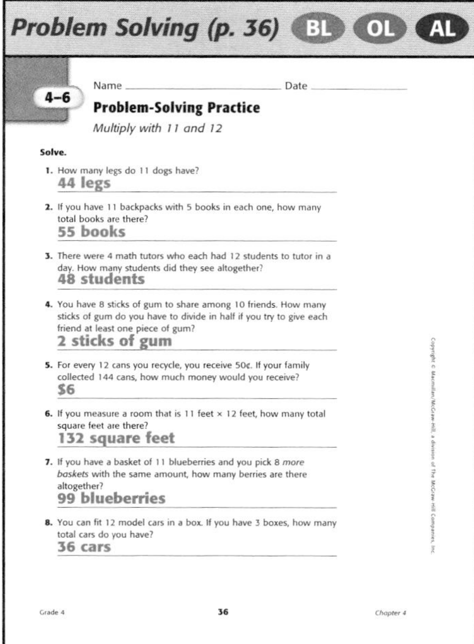

Problem Solving (p. 36) BL OL AL

4–6 Name ______ Date ______

Problem-Solving Practice

Multiply with 11 and 12

Solve.

1. How many legs do 11 dogs have?
   44 legs
2. If you have 11 backpacks with 5 books in each one, how many total books are there?
   55 books
3. There were 4 math tutors who each had 12 students to tutor in a day. How many students did they see altogether?
   48 students
4. You have 8 sticks of gum to share among 10 friends. How many sticks of gum do you have to divide in half if you try to give each friend at least one piece of gum?
   2 sticks of gum
5. For every 12 cans you recycle, you receive 50¢. If your family collected 144 cans, how much money would you receive?
   $6
6. If you measure a room that is 11 feet × 12 feet, how many total square feet are there?
   132 square feet
7. If you have a basket of 11 blueberries and you pick 8 *more baskets* with the same amount, how many berries are there altogether?
   99 blueberries
8. You can fit 12 model cars in a box. If you have 3 boxes, how many total cars do you have?
   36 cars

Grade 4 36 *Chapter 4*

Multiply with 11 and 12

Activity Choice 1 • Hands-On

- Give each pair of students a hundreds chart. Have them color in the 11 facts by skip counting by 11: 11, 22, 33, 44, 55, …
- On the same chart, have them use a different color and color in the 12 facts by skip counting by 12: 12, 24, 36, 48, …
- **What pattern do you see on the chart for the 11 facts?** Sample answer: After coloring 11, you move down one (10) and over one.
- **What pattern do you see on the chart for the 12 facts?** Sample answer: After coloring 12, you move down one (10) and over two.

Activity Choice 2 • Literature

Introduce the lesson with *The Grapes of Math* by Greg Tang. For a related math activity, see p. TR47.

Scaffolding Questions

Have students look at the hundreds chart they colored in Activity Choice 1. Point out that the pattern for the 11 facts is to move down 1 row (over 10) and over 1.

- Explain the pattern. Sample answer: The fact is based on 11, which is equal to 10 + 1. So you move over 10 (which is down one row) and then over one more to add another 11.
- The pattern for the 12 facts is to move down 1 row (over 10) and over 2. Explain the pattern. Sample answer: The fact is based on 12, which is equal to 10 + 2. So you move over 10 (which is down one row) and then over two more to add another 12.

GET READY to Learn

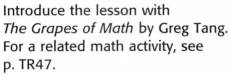

Have students open their books and read the information in **Get Ready to Learn**. Introduce **Distribution Property of Multiplication**. As a class, work through **Examples 1 and 2**.

4-6 Multiply with 11 and 12

MAIN IDEA

I will recall and apply multiplication facts for 11 and 12.

New Vocabulary

Distributive Property of Multiplication

Math Online

macmillanmh.com

- Extra Examples
- Personal Tutor
- Self-Check Quiz

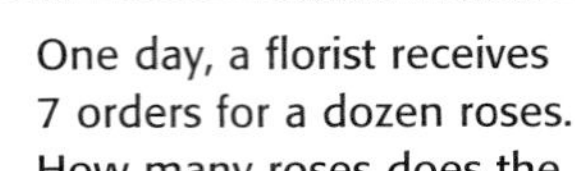

One day, a florist receives 7 orders for a dozen roses. How many roses does the florist need to make the 7 bouquets?

To multiply larger numbers, the Distributive Property of Multiplication is helpful. The **Distributive Property of Multiplication** says that you can multiply the addends of a number and then add the products.

Real-World EXAMPLE Multiply

1 How many roses does the florist need to make 7 bouquets?

There are 12 roses in one dozen. So, you need to find 7×12.

Think of 7×12 as $(7 \times 10) + (7 \times 2)$.

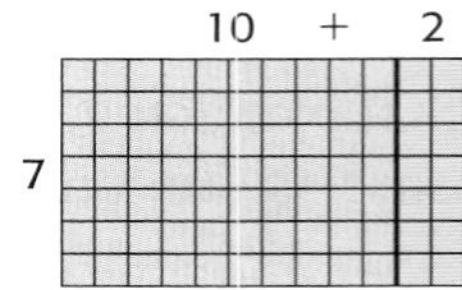

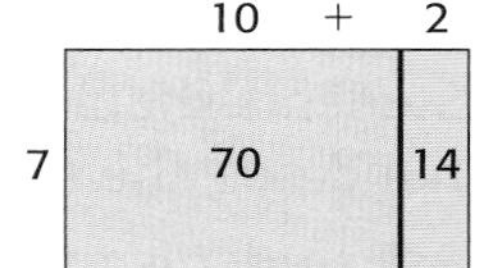

$$\begin{aligned} 7 \times 12 &= (7 \times 10) + (7 \times 2) \\ &= 70 + 14 \\ &= 84 \end{aligned}$$

So, 84 roses are needed to make 7 bouquets.

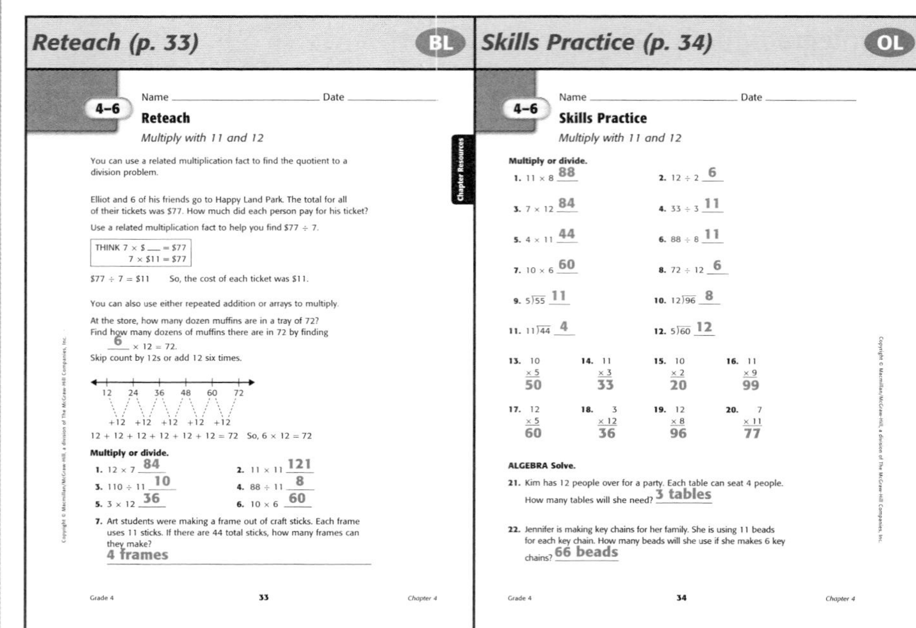

Reteach (p. 33) BL

4-6 Name ______ Date ______

Reteach

Multiply with 11 and 12

Chapter Resources

You can use a related multiplication fact to find the quotient to a division problem.

Elliot and 6 of his friends go to Happy Land Park. The total for all of their tickets was $77. How much did each person pay for his ticket?

Use a related multiplication fact to help you find $77 ÷ 7.

THINK 7 × $___ = $77
7 × $11 = $77

$77 ÷ 7 = $11   So, the cost of each ticket was $11.

You can also use either repeated addition or arrays to multiply.

At the store, how many dozen muffins are in a tray of 72? Find how many dozens of muffins there are in 72 by finding 6 × 12 = 72.

Skip count by 12s or add 12 six times.

12 24 36 48 60 72
+12 +12 +12 +12 +12

12 + 12 + 12 + 12 + 12 + 12 = 72   So, 6 × 12 = 72

Multiply or divide.

1. 12 × 7 84
2. 11 × 11 121
3. 110 ÷ 11 10
4. 88 ÷ 11 8
5. 3 × 12 36
6. 10 × 6 60
7. Art students were making a frame out of craft sticks. Each frame uses 11 sticks. If there are 44 total sticks, how many frames can they make? 4 frames

Grade 4 33 Chapter 4

Skills Practice (p. 34) OL

4-6 Name ______ Date ______

Skills Practice

Multiply with 11 and 12

Multiply or divide.

1. 11 × 8 88
2. 12 ÷ 2 6
3. 7 × 12 84
4. 33 ÷ 3 11
5. 4 × 11 44
6. 88 ÷ 8 11
7. 10 × 6 60
8. 72 ÷ 12 6
9. 5)55 11
10. 12)96 8
11. 11)44 4
12. 5)60 12
13. 10 × 5 = 50
14. 11 × 3 = 33
15. 10 × 2 = 20
16. 11 × 9 = 99
17. 12 × 5 = 60
18. 3 × 12 = 36
19. 12 × 8 = 96
20. 7 × 11 = 77

ALGEBRA Solve.

21. Kim has 12 people over for a party. Each table can seat 4 people. How many tables will she need? 3 tables
22. Jennifer is making key chains for her family. She is using 11 beads for each key chain. How many beads will she use if she makes 6 key chains? 66 beads

Grade 4 34 Chapter 4

You can use a related multiplication fact to find the quotient in a division problem.

Remember

When solving a word problem, think about the facts you know and what you need to find.

Real-World EXAMPLE Divide

2 **MOVIES** **Shaun and 10 of his friends went to a movie. The total cost for the 11 movie tickets was $66. How much did each ticket cost?**

ADMIT ONE 568440

You know that 11 tickets cost $66.
Use a related multiplication fact to help you find $66 ÷ 11.

Shaun + 10 friends

$66 ÷ 11 = ■

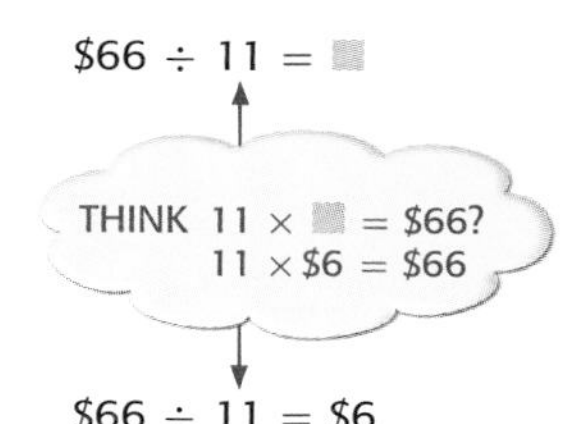

$66 ÷ 11 = $6

So, each ticket cost $6.

Check The area model shows that $6 × 11 = $66.

So, $66 ÷ 11 = $6 is correct. ✓

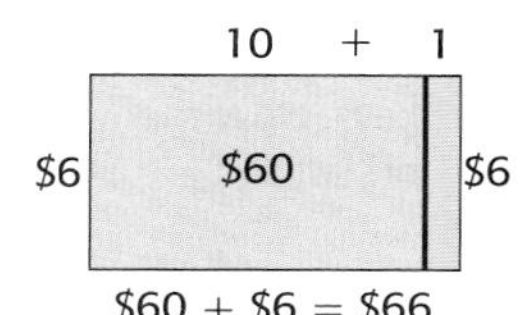

$60 + $6 = $66

10. Sample answer:

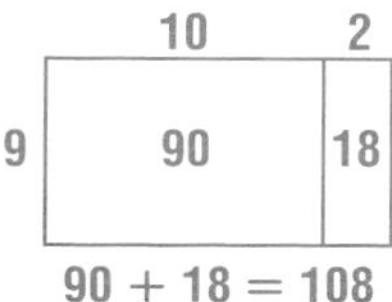

90 + 18 = 108

★ indicates multi-step problem

CHECK What You Know

Multiply or divide. Use arrays or area models if needed.

See Examples 1 and 2 (pp. 166–167)

1. 11×9 99

2. 10×12 120

3. 4 × 11 44

4. 6 × 12 72

5. 88 ÷ 11 8

6. 108 ÷ 9 12

7. 11)121 11

8. 12)132 11

9. There are 8 cartons of eggs on a grocery store shelf. Each carton contains one dozen eggs. How many eggs are on the shelf? 96

10. Talk About It How would you use two smaller area models to find 9 × 12? Draw the area models.

Multiply

Example 1 Have students look at the method used to find the product. What other method could you use? Sample answer: Make an array with counters.

ADDITIONAL EXAMPLES

1 Pang works at a bakery. He received an order for 9 dozen bagels. How many bagels does he need to fill the order? 108 bagels

2 A group of 11 friends went to a minor league baseball game. The total ticket cost was $99. How much did each ticket cost? $9

CHECK What You Know

As a class, have students complete Exercises 1–10 in **Check What You Know** as you observe their work.

Exercise 10 Assess student comprehension before assigning practice exercises.

BL Alternate Teaching Strategy

If students have trouble multiplying by 11 and 12…

Then use one of these reteach options:

1 CRM **Daily Reteach Worksheet** (p. 33)

2 Point out the pattern of numbers when skip counting. For 11s, each digit increases by 1 until 99, then add 11 each time. For 12s, the tens digit increases by 1 while the ones digit increases by 2. So multiplying by 12 is adding 10 and then 2 to the previous product.

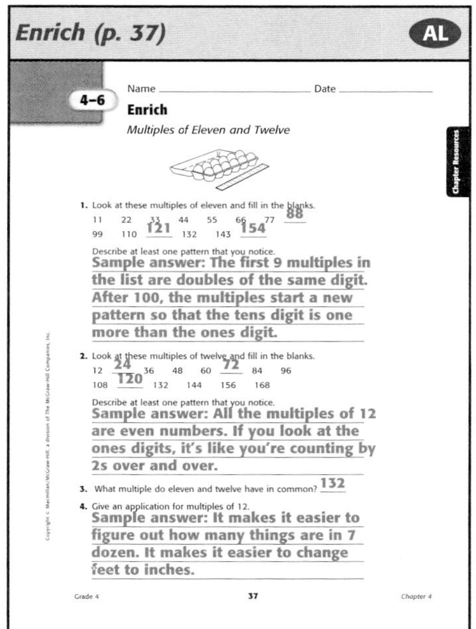

Enrich (p. 37) AL

4–6 Name ______ Date ______

Enrich

Multiples of Eleven and Twelve

Chapter Resources

1. Look at these multiples of eleven and fill in the blanks.
11 22 33 44 55 66 77 88
99 110 121 132 143 154

Describe at least one pattern that you notice.
Sample answer: The first 9 multiples in the list are doubles of the same digit. After 100, the multiples start a new pattern so that the tens digit is one more than the ones digit.

2. Look at these multiples of twelve and fill in the blanks.
12 24 36 48 60 72 84 96
108 120 132 144 156 168

Describe at least one pattern that you notice.
Sample answer: All the multiples of 12 are even numbers. If you look at the ones digits, it's like you're counting by 2s over and over.

3. What multiple do eleven and twelve have in common? 132

4. Give an application for multiples of 12.
Sample answer: It makes it easier to figure out how many things are in 7 dozen. It makes it easier to change feet to inches.

Grade 4 37 Chapter 4

3 Practice

Differentiate practice using these leveled assignments for Exercises 11–43.

Level	Assignment
BL Below/Approaching Level	11–13, 15–17, 21–24, 27, 28, 33, 35, 36
OL On Level	11–29, 33–37, 41
AL Above/Beyond Level	10–38 even, 41–43

Have students discuss and complete the Higher Order Thinking problems. For Exercise 43, encourage students to draw a picture to help explain their real world situation.

WRITING IN MATH Have students complete Exercise 43 in their Math Journals. You may choose to use this exercise as an optional formative assessment.

COMMON ERROR!

Exercises 31–33 Students may struggle with these problems. Remind students what each symbol means. Explain that they need to find the product or quotient of each side and then compare the two.

★ indicates multi-step problem

Practice and Problem Solving

EXTRA PRACTICE See page R11.

Multiply or divide. Use arrays or area models if needed. See Examples 1 and 2 (pp. 166–167)

11. 11×5 55 **12.** 12×5 60 **13.** 11×7 77 **14.** 12×8 96

15. 2×11 22 **16.** 12×7 84 **17.** 11×10 110 **18.** 12×12 144

19. $44 \div 11$ 4 **20.** $72 \div 6$ 12 **21.** $99 \div 11$ 9 **22.** $120 \div 10$ 12

23. $12\overline{)48}$ 4 **24.** $11\overline{)66}$ 6 **25.** $12\overline{)84}$ 7 **26.** $11\overline{)110}$ 10

Algebra Find the value of each number sentence if  **= 12 and**  **= 11.**

27. ♡ × 6 72 **28.** 8 × ☺ 88 **29.** 132 ÷ ☺ 12 **30.** 144 ÷ ♡ 12

Compare. Use >, <, or =.

31. 11×8 ■ 6×12 > **32.** $132 \div 12$ ■ $99 \div 9$ = **33.** 12×10 ■ 11×11 <

34. ★ An octave, or range of notes on a piano, has 7 white keys and 5 black keys. How many keys are in 5 octaves? 60 keys

35. Mrs. Hanson has 12 grandchildren. She gives each grandchild $10. How much money does she give in all? $120

Real-World PROBLEM SOLVING

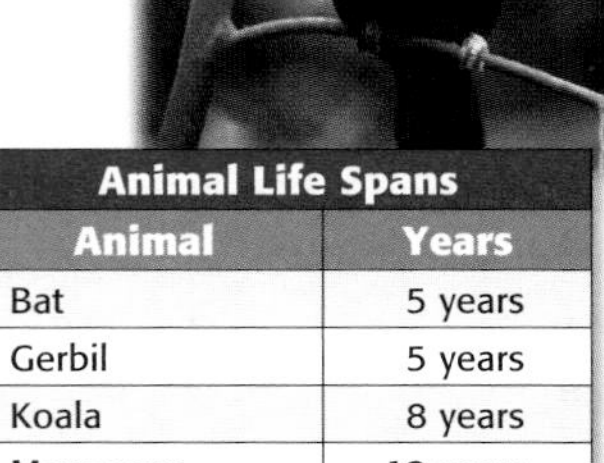

Animals The table gives expected life spans for some animals when they live in the wild.

36. Identify the two animals that have life spans of 60 months. bat and gerbil

37. What is the life span of a Tasmanian devil in months? 96 months

38. ★ How many more months is a platypus expected to live than a koala? 24 months

39. ★ A mongoose is 7 years old. How many months longer is it expected to live? 60 months

40. ★ Find the difference between a mongoose's life span and a toucan's life span in months. 72 months

Animal Life Spans

Animal	Years
Bat	5 years
Gerbil	5 years
Koala	8 years
Mongoose	12 years
Platypus	10 years
Toucan	6 years
Tasmanian devil	8 years

Source: Zoological Society of San Diego

168 Chapter 4 Apply Multiplication and Division Facts

H.O.T. Problems

41. OPEN ENDED Write three number sentences. Each should contain the number 12, a one-digit number as the other factor, and a product less than 60. Sample answer: $12 \times 4 = 48$; $12 \times 3 = 36$; $12 \times 2 = 24$

42. WHICH ONE DOESN'T BELONG? Identify the number sentence that does not belong with the other three. Explain. See margin.

9×11	$99 \div 9$	11×9	$88 \div 11$

43. WRITING IN MATH Write a problem about a real-world situation that involves finding the product of 6 and 12. Sample answer: A baker needed 72 eggs. How many cartons of eggs that contain 12 eggs per carton should the baker buy?

TEST Practice

44. In which number sentence does 8 make the number sentence true? (Lesson 4-5) C

A $36 \div \square = 4$

B $42 \div \square = 6$

C $56 \div \square = 7$

D $81 \div \square = 9$

45. Look at the problem below.

$$\square = \triangle \times 12$$

If $\triangle = 10$, what is $\square$? (Lesson 4-6) F

F 120 **H** 132

G 121 **J** 143

Spiral Review

Multiply or divide. Use arrays or area models if needed. (Lesson 4-5)

46. 7×5 35 **47.** 8×9 72 **48.** $64 \div 8$ 8 **49.** $10\overline{)90}$ 9

Tell which operation you would use to solve each problem. Then solve. (Lesson 4-4) 51. Sample answer: division; 2×12, 3×8, and 4×6

50. There are 108 cotton balls in a bag. Each student needs 9 cotton balls for an art project. How many students will get the cotton balls? division; 12

51. There are 24 rocks in Hatsu's rock collection. She wants to display her rocks in an array. Identify 3 possible ways to display the rocks.

Algebra Complete each number sentence. (Lesson 4-3)

52. $3 \times \square = 3$ 1 **53.** $\square \times 4 = 28$ 7 **54.** $22 \div \square = 11$ 2 **55.** $\square \div 4 = 10$ 40

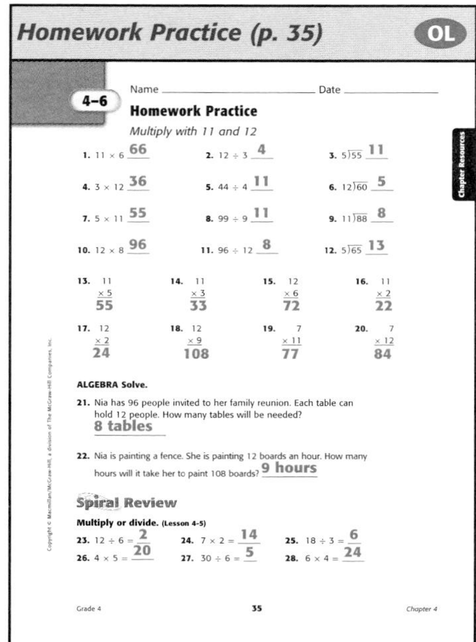

Homework Practice (p. 35) OL

4–6 Name ________ Date ________

Homework Practice

Multiply with 11 and 12

1. 11×6 66
2. $12 \div 3$ 4
3. $5\overline{)55}$ 11
4. 3×12 36
5. $44 \div 4$ 11
6. $12\overline{)60}$ 5
7. 5×11 55
8. $99 \div 9$ 11
9. $11\overline{)88}$ 8
10. 12×8 96
11. $96 \div 12$ 8
12. $5\overline{)65}$ 13
13. 11×5 55
14. 11×3 33
15. 12×6 72
16. 11×2 22
17. 12×2 24
18. 12×9 108
19. 7×11 77
20. 7×12 84

ALGEBRA Solve.

21. Nia has 96 people invited to her family reunion. Each table can hold 12 people. How many tables will be needed? 8 tables

22. Nia is painting a fence. She is painting 12 boards an hour. How many hours will it take her to paint 108 boards? 9 hours

Spiral Review

Multiply or divide. (Lesson 4-5)

23. $12 \div 6 =$ 2
24. $7 \times 2 =$ 14
25. $18 \div 3 =$ 6
26. $4 \times 5 =$ 20
27. $30 \div 6 =$ 5
28. $6 \times 4 =$ 24

Grade 4 35 Chapter 4

Chapter Resources

4 Assess

Formative Assessment

Explain how you could use the Distributive Property of Multiplication to find 4×12.

Sample answer: I could think of 4×12 as $(4 \times 10) + (4 \times 2)$. This gives $40 + 8 = 48$.

Quick Check **Are students continuing to struggle with multiplying with 11 and 12?**

If Yes → Strategic Intervention Guide (p. 82)

If No → Independent Work Options (p. 166B)
CRM Skills Practice Worksheet (p. 34)
CRM Enrich Worksheet (p. 37)

Name the Math Remind students that there are many everyday items that are counted by the dozen. Ask them to list several examples and describe how this relates to today's lesson.

TEST Practice

Reviews Lessons 4-5 and 4-6

Assign the Test Practice problems to provide daily reinforcement of test-taking skills.

Spiral Review

Reviews Lessons 4-3, 4-4, and 4-5

Review and assess mastery of skills and concepts from previous chapters.

Additional Answer

42. Sample answer: $88 \div 11$; The other three number sentences belong to the same fact family, which involves 9 and 11.

4-7 Problem-Solving Investigation
Choose a Strategy

Lesson Planner

Objective

Choose the best strategy to solve a problem.

Resources

Teacher Technology

TeacherWorks • Interactive Classroom

Real-World Problem Solving Library
Math and Social Studies: *Class Project*
Use these leveled books to reinforce and extend problem-solving skills and strategies.

Leveled for:

- OL On Level
- ELL Sheltered English
- SP Spanish

For additional support, see the Real-World Problem Solving Teacher Guide.

Daily Routine

Use these suggestions before beginning the lesson on p. 170.

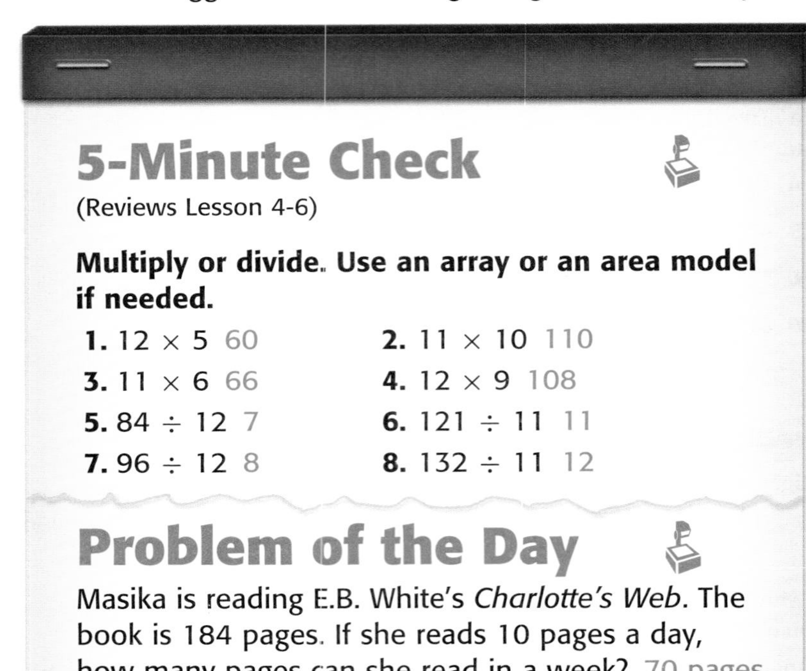

5-Minute Check

(Reviews Lesson 4-6)

Multiply or divide. Use an array or an area model if needed.

1. 12 × 5 60	**2.** 11 × 10 110
3. 11 × 6 66	**4.** 12 × 9 108
5. 84 ÷ 12 7	**6.** 121 ÷ 11 11
7. 96 ÷ 12 8	**8.** 132 ÷ 11 12

Problem of the Day

Masika is reading E.B. White's *Charlotte's Web*. The book is 184 pages. If she reads 10 pages a day, how many pages can she read in a week? 70 pages

Differentiated Instruction

Small Group Options

Option 1 LOGICAL

Gifted and Talented BL

Materials: 1-inch grid paper, paper, pencil

- Hand this problem to students to solve:

  Mrs. Allen wants to plant a small flower garden. She has 24 feet of fence to go around it. How many different ways can she lay out her garden? Use the grid paper to show all the ways that you find. 6 ways; 11 × 1, 10 × 2, 9 × 3, 8 × 4, 7 × 5, 6 × 6
- **Which one do you think would be best?** Answers will vary. However, the 6 × 6 will have the biggest area.

Option 2 LINGUISTIC

English Language Learners ELL

Materials: index cards with factors on one side and answers on the other
Core Vocabulary: to look like, to sound like, reminds me of
Common Use Verb: prompt
See Math This strategy focuses on the ending sounds of numbers while using prompts to reinforce the pronunciation and number word.

- Read "5 × 6 is." Write "thirty" on the board as you wait for students to call it. Prompt "thirty" by holding up 3 fingers up to the /thir/ and make a T shape with your arms for /ty/.
- Repeat "3 × 5 is." Hold up 5 fingers for /fif/ in "fifteen" and squat down, clasping arms around your knees (to look like n) as you say /teen/.
- Have students repeat, allowing them to try various strategies that remind them of how to write and say the number word.

Independent Work Options

Option 1 VISUAL, SPATIAL

Early Finishers OL AL

Materials: paper, markers

- Each student writes a word problem that can be solved using one of the strategies studied.
- Have students exchange papers and solve each others' problems.

Option 2

Student Technology

Math Online macmillanmh.com

Personal Tutor • Extra Examples

Option 3

Learning Station: Writing (p. 142G)

Direct students to the Writing Learning Station for opportunities to explore and extend the lesson concept.

1 Introduce

Activity • Review

- Ask students to list their ideas for solving the following problem:

  Bart and his family are hiking in Eagle Woods. They walk 3 miles every hour. They hike a total of 9 miles. How long did they hike?
  use a four-step plan, make a table, choose an operation, act it out
- **Is one method easier than the others?** Answers will vary.
- **Solve the problem.** 3 hours

2 Teach

Have students read the problem on Kasa's ballet lessons. Guide them through the problem-solving steps.

Understand Using the questions, review what students know and need to find.

Plan Have them discuss their strategy.

Solve Guide students to choose the operations of division and multiplication to solve the problem.

- **How many hours long is each lesson?** 2 hours
- **How many hours does Kasa dance each week?** 6 hours
- **What operations will you use to solve the problem?** division and multiplication

Check Have students look back at the problem to make sure that the answer fits the facts given.

COMMON ERROR!

Exercises 1–7 Students often find a correct solution to a calculation, but they do not answer the question asked. Remind them to check their answers by making sure the solution answers the question asked.

4-7 Problem-Solving Investigation

MAIN IDEA I will choose the best strategy to solve a problem.

P.S.I. TEAM +

KASA: I go to ballet lessons every week. I dance 2 hours during every lesson. I dance a total of 6 hours each week.

YOUR MISSION: Find how many ballet lessons Kasa has in 4 weeks.

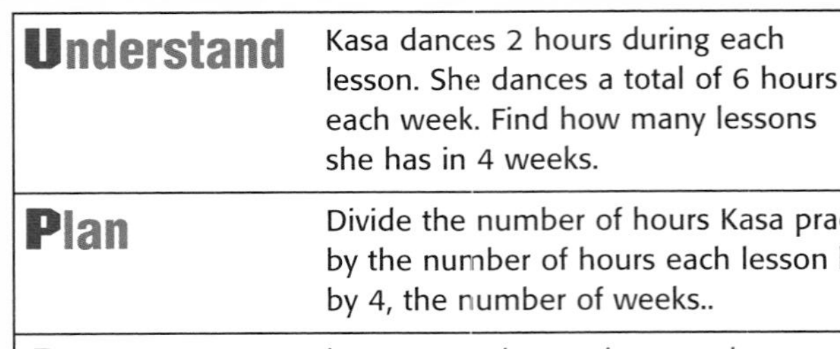

Understand	Kasa dances 2 hours during each lesson. She dances a total of 6 hours each week. Find how many lessons she has in 4 weeks.
Plan	Divide the number of hours Kasa practices each week by the number of hours each lesson lasts. Then multiply by 4, the number of weeks..
Solve	hours per week 6 ÷ hours per lesson 2 = lessons per week 3 So, Kasa has 3 ballet lessons each week. lessons per week 3 × weeks 4 = lessons in 4 weeks 12 So, Kasa has 12 ballet lessons in 4 weeks.
Check	Look back. Check your answer by dividing the number of lessons in 4 weeks by the number of weeks. $12 \div 4 = 3$. Then, multiply the number of hours per lesson by the number of lessons each week. $2 \times 3 = 6$. So, the answer is correct.

170 Chapter 4 Apply Multiplication and Division Facts

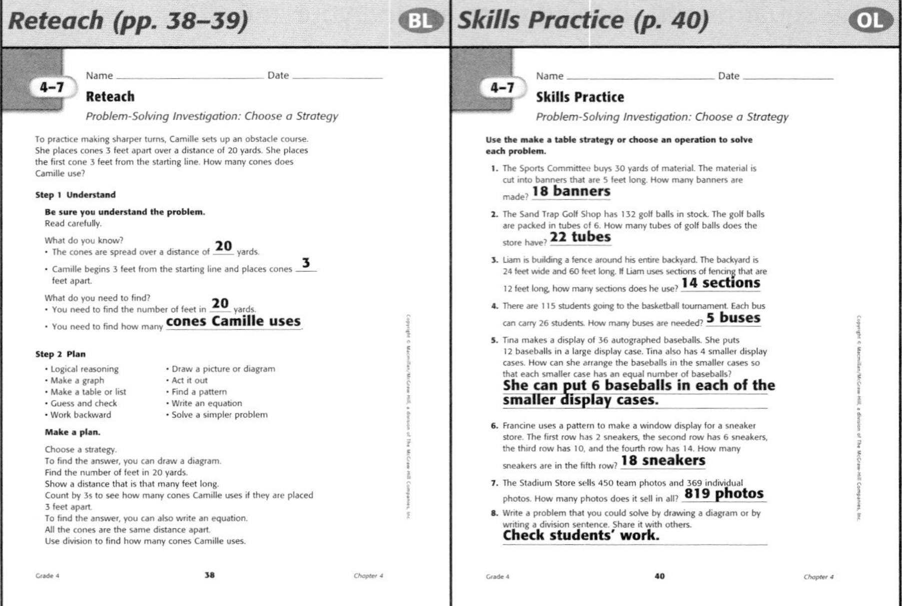

Reteach (pp. 38–39) BL

4-7 Name ______ Date ______

Reteach

Problem-Solving Investigation: Choose a Strategy

To practice making sharper turns, Camille sets up an obstacle course. She places cones 3 feet apart over a distance of 20 yards. She places the first cone 3 feet from the starting line. How many cones does Camille use?

Step 1 Understand

Be sure you understand the problem.
Read carefully.

What do you know?
- The cones are spread over a distance of **20** yards.
- Camille begins 3 feet from the starting line and places cones **3** feet apart.

What do you need to find?
- You need to find the number of feet in **20** yards.
- You need to find how many **cones Camille uses**.

Step 2 Plan

- Logical reasoning
- Make a graph
- Make a table or list
- Guess and check
- Work backward
- Draw a picture or diagram
- Act it out
- Find a pattern
- Write an equation
- Solve a simpler problem

Make a plan.

Choose a strategy.
To find the answer, you can draw a diagram.
Find the number of feet in 20 yards.
Show a distance that is that many feet long.
Count by 3s to see how many cones Camille uses if they are placed 3 feet apart.
To find the answer, you can also write an equation.
All the cones are the same distance apart.
Use division to find how many cones Camille uses.

Grade 4 38 Chapter 4

Skills Practice (p. 40) OL

4-7 Name ______ Date ______

Skills Practice

Problem-Solving Investigation: Choose a Strategy

Use the make a table strategy or choose an operation to solve each problem.

1. The Sports Committee buys 30 yards of material. The material is cut into banners that are 5 feet long. How many banners are made? **18 banners**
2. The Sand Trap Golf Shop has 132 golf balls in stock. The golf balls are packed in tubes of 6. How many tubes of golf balls does the store have? **22 tubes**
3. Liam is building a fence around his entire backyard. The backyard is 24 feet wide and 60 feet long. If Liam uses sections of fencing that are 12 feet long, how many sections does he use? **14 sections**
4. There are 115 students going to the basketball tournament. Each bus can carry 26 students. How many buses are needed? **5 buses**
5. Tina makes a display of 36 autographed baseballs. She puts 12 baseballs in a large display case. Tina also has 4 smaller display cases. How can she arrange the baseballs in the smaller cases so that each smaller case has an equal number of baseballs? **She can put 6 baseballs in each of the smaller display cases.**
6. Francine uses a pattern to make a window display for a sneaker store. The first row has 2 sneakers, the second row has 6 sneakers, the third row has 10, and the fourth row has 14. How many sneakers are in the fifth row? **18 sneakers**
7. The Stadium Store sells 450 team photos and 369 individual photos. How many photos does it sell in all? **819 photos**
8. Write a problem that you could solve by drawing a diagram or by writing a division sentence. Share it with others. **Check students' work.**

Grade 4 40 Chapter 4

★indicates multi-step problem

Mixed Problem Solving

See page R11.

Use the make a table strategy or choose an operation to solve each problem.

PROBLEM-SOLVING STRATEGY
- Make a table.

1. **Geometry** Mr. and Mrs. Lopez are putting square tiles on the floor in their bathroom. They can fit 6 rows of 4 tiles in the bathroom. How many tiles do they need to buy? **24 tiles**

2. **Algebra** A teacher gives quizzes that are each worth 15 points. If the teacher gives 5 quizzes, how many points are all of the quizzes worth? **75 points**

★3. Marisol has 7 books from the library. She gets 5 new books and returns 3 books. How many library books does she have now? **9 books**

4. Raheem is playing a game at a carnival. He needs to earn 400 points to win a large stuffed animal. The dart board below shows the 4 out of 5 darts he has thrown. Is it possible for him to win the large stuffed animal? If so, how many points does he still need? **yes; 100 points**

100
75
50

5. **Measurement** A scout troop went hiking on the trail shown below. They hiked 4 miles an hour. How long did they hike? **3 hr**

6. Wesley needs to finish reading a book before Monday. He started reading the 44-page book on Thursday. How many pages will he need to read each day if he reads an equal number of pages each day? **11 pages**

7. Twenty students want to raise money for new playground equipment. They need $2,200. Copy and complete the table to find out how much money each student needs to raise. **$110**

New Playground Equipment	
Money per Student	**Total Raised**
$90	$1,800
$95	$1,900
$100	$2,000
$105	**$2,100**
$110	**$2,200**

8. **WRITING IN MATH** Tell which problem-solving strategy you used to solve Exercise 7. Explain how you used this strategy when solving Exercise 7. **See Ch. 4 Answer Appendix.**

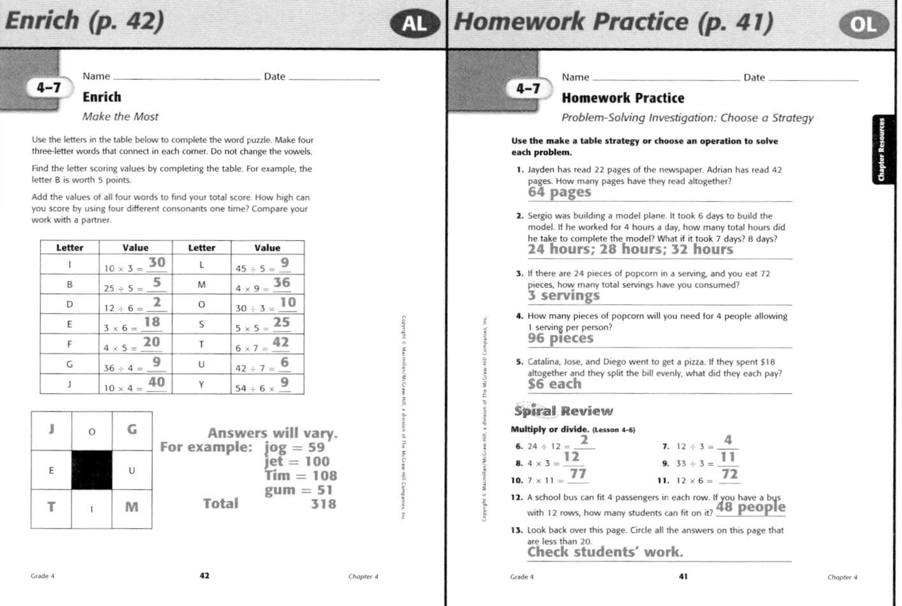

Enrich (p. 42) AL

4-7 Name ________ Date ________

Enrich

Make the Most

Use the letters in the table below to complete the word puzzle. Make four three-letter words that connect in each corner. Do not change the vowels.

Find the letter scoring values by completing the table. For example, the letter B is worth 5 points.

Add the values of all four words to find your total score. How high can you score by using four different consonants one time? Compare your work with a partner.

Letter	Value	Letter	Value
I	10 × 3 = **30**	L	45 ÷ 5 = **9**
B	25 ÷ 5 = **5**	M	4 × 9 = **36**
D	12 ÷ 6 = **2**	O	30 ÷ 3 = **10**
E	3 × 6 = **18**	S	5 × 5 = **25**
F	4 × 5 = **20**	T	6 × 7 = **42**
G	36 ÷ 4 = **9**	U	42 ÷ 7 = **6**
J	10 × 4 = **40**	Y	54 ÷ 6 × **9**

J	O	**G**
E		U
T	I	**M**

Answers will vary.
For example: jog = 59
jet = 100
Tim = 108
gum = 51
Total 318

Grade 4 42 Chapter 4

Homework Practice (p. 41) OL

4-7 Name ________ Date ________

Homework Practice

Problem-Solving Investigation: Choose a Strategy

Chapter Resources

Use the make a table strategy or choose an operation to solve each problem.

1. Jayden has read 22 pages of the newspaper. Adrian has read 42 pages. How many pages have they read altogether? **64 pages**
2. Sergio was building a model plane. It took 6 days to build the model. If he worked for 4 hours a day, how many total hours did he take to complete the model? What if it took 7 days? 8 days? **24 hours; 28 hours; 32 hours**
3. If there are 24 pieces of popcorn in a serving, and you eat 72 pieces, how many total servings have you consumed? **3 servings**
4. How many pieces of popcorn will you need for 4 people allowing 1 serving per person? **96 pieces**
5. Catalina, Jose, and Diego went to get a pizza. If they spent $18 altogether and they split the bill evenly, what did they each pay? **$6 each**

Spiral Review

Multiply or divide. (Lesson 4-6)

6. 24 ÷ 12 = **2**
7. 12 ÷ 3 = **4**
8. 4 × 3 = **12**
9. 33 ÷ 3 = **11**
10. 7 × 11 = **77**
11. 12 × 6 = **72**
12. A school bus can fit 4 passengers in each row. If you have a bus with 12 rows, how many students can fit on it? **48 people**
13. Look back over this page. Circle all the answers on this page that are less than 20. **Check students' work.**

Grade 4 41 Chapter 4

BL Alternate Teaching Strategy

If students have trouble deciding which problem-solving method to use…

Then use one of these reteach options:

1. CRM **Daily Reteach Worksheet** (pp. 38–39)
2. Review the problem-solving strategies that the students have learned. Allow them to make a list and to keep the list handy for reference.

3 Practice

Using the Exercises

Exercises 1–7 provide practice in making a table or choosing an operation to solve a problem.

Exercise 6 is a multi-step problem. Ask students to first determine how many days Wesley has to read the book.

4 Assess

Formative Assessment

Provide the following example for students to solve:

Diego's youth group is organizing a ski trip. If they fill six vans that each hold 6 members, how many members are attending the ski trip?

- **Which strategy would you use to solve this problem?** Sample answer: choose an operation
- **Solve and check your answer.** 36 members

Quick Check **Are students continuing to struggle with choosing a strategy?**

If Yes → Small Group Options (p. 170B)

If No → Independent Work Options (p. 170B)
CRM Skills Practice Worksheet (p. 40)
CRM Enrich Worksheet (p. 42)

LESSON 4-8

Algebra: Multiply Three Numbers

Lesson Planner

Objective

Multiply 3 factors.

Review Vocabulary

Associative Property of Multiplication

Resources

Manipulatives: counters

Literature Connection: *Anno's Mysterious Multiplying Jar* by Masaichiro and Mitsumasa Anno

Teacher Technology

TeacherWorks • Interactive Classroom • Math Songs Track #3 Lesson Plan

Daily Routine

Use these suggestions before beginning the lesson on p. 172.

5-Minute Check

(Reviews Lesson 4-7)

Use the make a table strategy or choose an operation to solve the problem.

1. Leticia is on a swim team that practices 4 days each week. Each practice is 3 hours long. How many hours per week does Leticia have swim practice? 12

Problem of the Day

A dozen golf balls cost $24. Jodi needs only 9 balls. How much will 9 golf balls cost? $18

Focus on Math Background

The Associative Property of Multiplication was introduced in the second lesson of this chapter. This property says that changing the grouping of three factors in a multiplication problem does not change the product. It can be stated as:

$$(a \times b) \times c = a \times (b \times c)$$

Notice that the order of the factors stays the same and that parentheses are used to show which factors are multiplied first. Making good choices, like which factors to multiply first, often helps to simplify a problem.

Review Math Vocabulary

Write the review vocabulary word and its definition on the board.

Ask students to write an example of the Associative Property of Addition and an example of the Associative Property of Multiplication. Have them explain what the parentheses mean in each example.

Differentiated Instruction

Small Group Options

Option 1 LOGICAL

Gifted and Talented AL

Materials: pencils, paper, chart paper

- Review quickly the concept that when multiplying more than 2 numbers, if no parentheses are written, the numbers may be multiplied in any order because of the Commutative Property of Multiplication.
- Explain that this activity uses the work backward strategy. Write the number 40 on chart paper. Ask students if they can think of 3 factors that can be multiplied together to get a product of 40. Possible answers include $2 \times 4 \times 5$ and $10 \times 2 \times 2$.
- Have students do the same with 60, 36, and 48.
- Once answers have been discussed, ask students to write products that can be broken down into 3 or more factors. If students discover that 1 is very convenient, allow them to use it sparingly. Review the Identity Property.

Option 2 LINGUISTIC

English Language Learners ELL

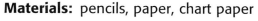

Materials: flow chart labeled first, second, last
Core Vocabulary: from first step to the next step, first, last
Common Use Verb: flow

Write Math This strategy helps students write the steps of solving a multiplication problem with 3 or more numbers using a flow chart.

- Guide students through several problems as a group, prompting for answers that you write in a flow chart. Emphasize first, second or next, and last.
- Give students a flow chart and write a problem with three or more numbers on the board.
- Allow students to write the steps as they solve the problem.
- Once students have completed writing, guide students through the problem, asking them to read their flow chart.

Independent Work Options

Option 1 LOGICAL

Early Finishers OL AL

Materials: dozen index cards, numbered 1–12

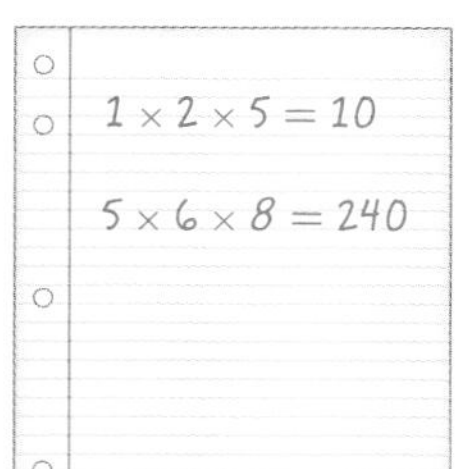

- Play in pairs and take turns. Student 1 places 5 cards face up.
- The partner writes the three factors that will yield the largest product, and the three factors that will yield the smallest product.
- Partners must agree on the factors.

Option 2 Tech Link

Student Technology

macmillanmh.com

Personal Tutor • Extra Examples

Math Adventures

Math Songs, "Multiplication Association" Track #3

Option 3

Learning Station: Art (p. 142G)

Direct students to the Art Learning Station for opportunities to explore and extend the lesson concept.

Option 4

Problem-Solving Practice

Reinforce problem-solving skills and strategies with the Problem-Solving Practice worksheet.

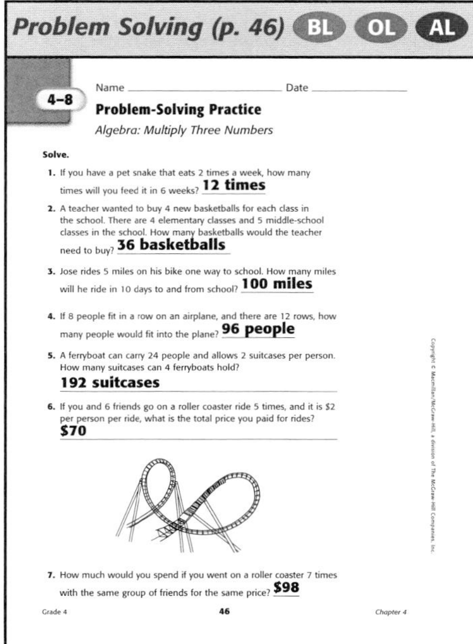

Problem Solving (p. 46) BL OL AL

4–8 Name ________ Date ________

Problem-Solving Practice

Algebra: Multiply Three Numbers

Solve.

1. If you have a pet snake that eats 2 times a week, how many times will you feed it in 6 weeks? **12 times**
2. A teacher wanted to buy 4 new basketballs for each class in the school. There are 4 elementary classes and 5 middle-school classes in the school. How many basketballs would the teacher need to buy? **36 basketballs**
3. Jose rides 5 miles on his bike one way to school. How many miles will he ride in 10 days to and from school? **100 miles**
4. If 8 people fit in a row on an airplane, and there are 12 rows, how many people would fit into the plane? **96 people**
5. A ferryboat can carry 24 people and allows 2 suitcases per person. How many suitcases can 4 ferryboats hold? **192 suitcases**
6. If you and 6 friends go on a roller coaster ride 5 times, and it is $2 per person per ride, what is the total price you paid for rides? **$70**
7. How much would you spend if you went on a roller coaster 7 times with the same group of friends for the same price? **$98**

Grade 4 46 Chapter 4

4-8 Algebra: Multiply Three Numbers

1 Introduce

Activity Choice 1 • Hands-On

- Have a volunteer write 3 factors on the board, such as $5 \times 6 \times 10$.
- Have another volunteer write a sentence using parentheses to show the Associative Property of Multiplication. $5 \times (6 \times 10) = (5 \times 6) \times 10$
- **What does the Associative Property of Multiplication tell you?** When you multiply, the way in which the factors are grouped does not change the product.

Activity Choice 2 • Literature

Introduce the lesson with *Anno's Mysterious Multiplying Jar* by Masaichiro and Mitsumasa Anno. For a related math activity, see p. TR47.

2 Teach

Scaffolding Questions

Write $(2 \times 5) \times 11 = 2 \times (5 \times 11)$ on the board.

- **Identify the property.** Associative Property of Multiplication
- **Are the two sides of the equation equal?** yes
- **What is the product of each side?** 110
- **Which fact is easier to compute? Explain.** Sample answer: $(2 \times 5) \times 11$ is easier because you know the facts of 2×5 and 10×11.

GET READY to Learn

Have students open their books and read the information in **Get Ready to Learn**. Review **Associative Property of Multiplication**. As a class, work through **Example 1**.

Associative Property

Example 1 Provide counters for students to model the multiplication and show that the answer is the same regardless of which factors are multiplied first.

4-8 Algebra: Multiply Three Numbers

MAIN IDEA

I will multiply 3 factors.

Math Online

macmillanmh.com

- Extra Examples
- Personal Tutor
- Self-Check Quiz

GET READY to Learn

There are 2 baseball cards in each pack. There are 6 packs in each box. If Raul buys 3 boxes for his collection, how many cards will he have?

In Lesson 2-1, you learned to use the Associative Property of Addition to add more than two numbers. You can use the Associative Property of Multiplication to multiply more than two numbers.

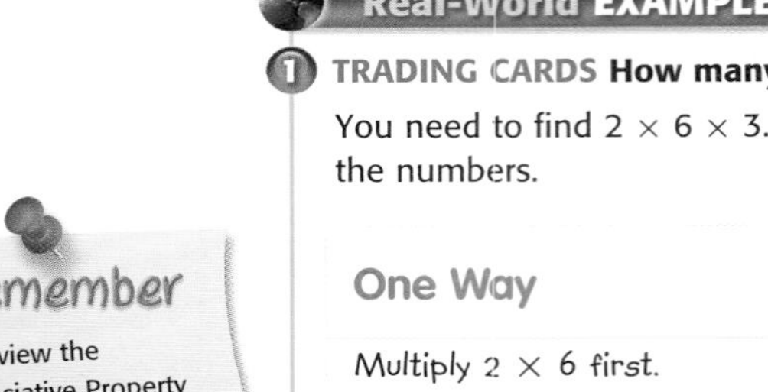

Real-World EXAMPLE — Associative Property

1 TRADING CARDS How many baseball cards will Raul have?

You need to find $2 \times 6 \times 3$. There are two ways to group the numbers.

Remember

To review the Associative Property of Multiplication, see Lesson 4-2 (p. 150).

One Way	Another Way
Multiply 2×6 first.	Multiply 6×3 first.
$2 \times 6 \times 3$	$2 \times 6 \times 3$
$(2 \times 6) \times 3$	$2 \times (6 \times 3)$
12×3	2×18
36	36

So, Raul will have 36 baseball cards.

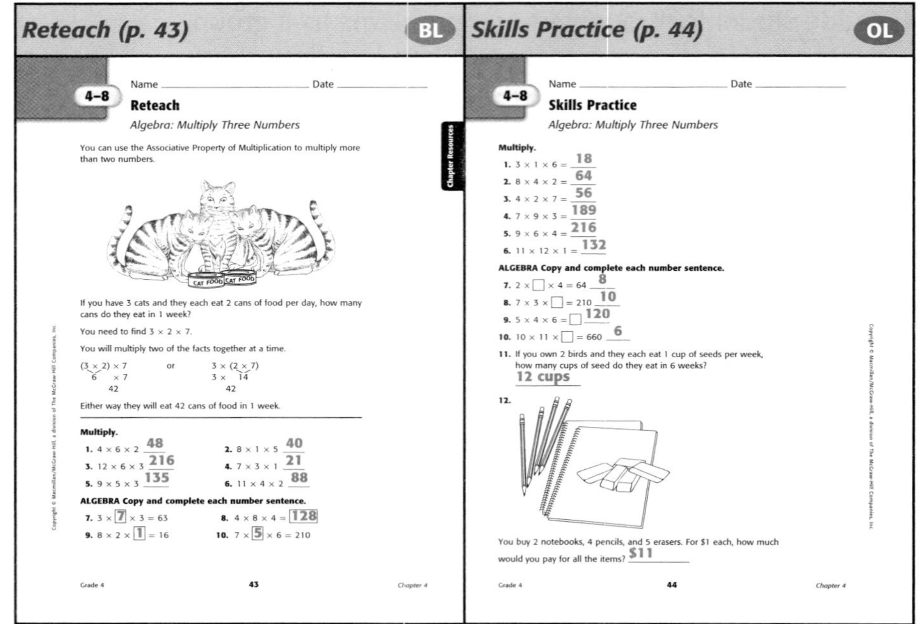

Reteach (p. 43) BL

4-8 Name ______ Date ______

Reteach

Algebra: Multiply Three Numbers

You can use the Associative Property of Multiplication to multiply more than two numbers.

If you have 3 cats and they each eat 2 cans of food per day, how many cans do they eat in 1 week?

You need to find $3 \times 2 \times 7$.

You will multiply two of the facts together at a time.

$(3 \times 2) \times 7$ → 6×7 → 42 or $3 \times (2 \times 7)$ → 3×14 → 42

Either way they will eat 42 cans of food in 1 week.

Multiply.

1. $4 \times 6 \times 2$ **48**
2. $8 \times 1 \times 5$ **40**
3. $12 \times 6 \times 3$ **216**
4. $7 \times 3 \times 1$ **21**
5. $9 \times 5 \times 3$ **135**
6. $11 \times 4 \times 2$ **88**

ALGEBRA Copy and complete each number sentence.

7. $3 \times$ **7** $\times 3 = 63$
8. $4 \times 8 \times 4 =$ **128**
9. $8 \times 2 \times$ **1** $= 16$
10. $7 \times$ **5** $\times 6 = 210$

Grade 4 43 Chapter 4

Skills Practice (p. 44) OL

4-8 Name ______ Date ______

Skills Practice

Algebra: Multiply Three Numbers

Multiply.

1. $3 \times 1 \times 6 =$ **18**
2. $8 \times 4 \times 2 =$ **64**
3. $4 \times 2 \times 7 =$ **56**
4. $7 \times 9 \times 3 =$ **189**
5. $9 \times 6 \times 4 =$ **216**
6. $11 \times 12 \times 1 =$ **132**

ALGEBRA Copy and complete each number sentence.

7. $2 \times \square \times 4 = 64$ **8**
8. $7 \times 3 \times \square = 210$ **10**
9. $5 \times 4 \times 6 = \square$ **120**
10. $10 \times 11 \times \square = 660$ **6**
11. If you own 2 birds and they each eat 1 cup of seeds per week, how many cups of seed do they eat in 6 weeks? **12 cups**
12. You buy 2 notebooks, 4 pencils, and 5 erasers. For $1 each, how much would you pay for all the items? **$11**

Grade 4 44 Chapter 4

★ indicates multi-step problem

CHECK What You Know

Multiply. See Example 1 (p. 172)

1. $3 \times 1 \times 5$ 15 **2.** $2 \times 2 \times 3$ 12 **3.** $3 \times 5 \times 3$ 45

4. $6 \times 2 \times 3$ 36 **5.** $4 \times 2 \times 7$ 56 **6.** $3 \times 4 \times 8$ 96

7. Art supply paint comes in a box that contains 3 sets of 8 bottles of paint. An art teacher ordered 2 boxes. How many bottles of paint were ordered? 48 bottles

8. Talk About It Identify the order that makes it easiest to multiply the factors in the expression $9 \times 6 \times 2$. Explain. See Ch. 4 Answer Appendix.

Practice and Problem Solving

EXTRA PRACTICE See page R12.

Multiply. See Example 1 (p. 172)

9. $6 \times 1 \times 5$ 30 **10.** $2 \times 2 \times 7$ 28 **11.** $5 \times 7 \times 2$ 70

12. $10 \times 2 \times 5$ 100 **13.** $3 \times 9 \times 3$ 81 **14.** $2 \times 6 \times 7$ 84

15. $4 \times 3 \times 7$ 84 **16.** $2 \times 9 \times 4$ 72 **17.** $5 \times 1 \times 12$ 60

Algebra Copy and complete each number sentence.

18. $4 \times ■ \times 1 = 12$ 3 **19.** $2 \times 6 \times ■ = 60$ 5 **20.** $■ \times 3 \times 4 = 24$ 2

Algebra Compare. Use >, <, or =.

21. $4 \times 2 \times 9$ ● $7 \times 4 \times 2$ > **22.** $5 \times 2 \times 8$ ● $6 \times 2 \times 6$ >

Algebra Find the value of each number sentence if ☼ = 2, ☺ = 3, and ☆ = 4.

23. $5 \times 1 \times$ ☆ 20 **24.** $6 \times$ ☼ $\times 9$ 108 **25.** ☺ $\times 12 \times$ ☆ 144

26. **Measurement** Gabriel is training for a race. He jogs 2 miles a day. He jogs this distance 4 days a week. How many miles will he jog in 6 weeks? 48 miles

27. ★ **Measurement** Blanca bikes 2 miles to her grandfather's house and 2 miles back to her house 5 times each month. How many miles does she bike? 20 miles

28. ★ **Measurement** For one week, 4 inches of snow fell every morning, and 3 inches fell every night. Was this enough snow to cover a bench that is 4 feet tall? Explain. yes; 49 in. > 48 in.

29. Helen borrowed 12 books from the library. The books are due in 4 weeks. If she reads 2 books 2 days a week, will she have enough time to read all of the books? Explain. See Ch. 4 Answer Appendix.

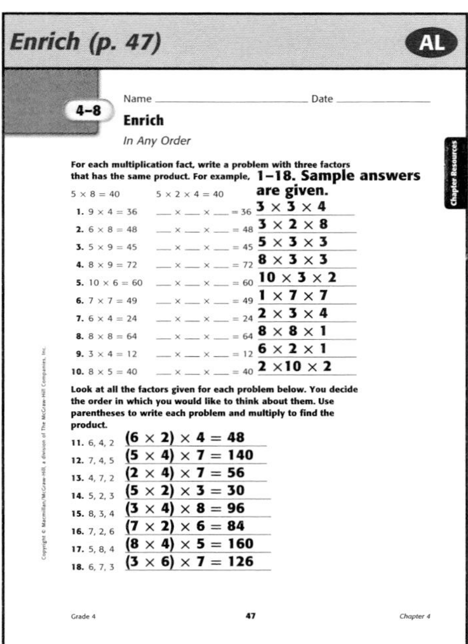
Enrich (p. 47) AL

4-8 Name ______ Date ______

Enrich

In Any Order

For each multiplication fact, write a problem with three factors that has the same product. For example, **1–18. Sample answers are given.**

$5 \times 8 = 40$ $5 \times 2 \times 4 = 40$

1. $9 \times 4 = 36$ ___ × ___ × ___ = 36 **3 × 3 × 4**
2. $6 \times 8 = 48$ ___ × ___ × ___ = 48 **3 × 2 × 8**
3. $5 \times 9 = 45$ ___ × ___ × ___ = 45 **5 × 3 × 3**
4. $8 \times 9 = 72$ ___ × ___ × ___ = 72 **8 × 3 × 3**
5. $10 \times 6 = 60$ ___ × ___ × ___ = 60 **10 × 3 × 2**
6. $7 \times 7 = 49$ ___ × ___ × ___ = 49 **1 × 7 × 7**
7. $6 \times 4 = 24$ ___ × ___ × ___ = 24 **2 × 3 × 4**
8. $8 \times 8 = 64$ ___ × ___ × ___ = 64 **8 × 8 × 1**
9. $3 \times 4 = 12$ ___ × ___ × ___ = 12 **6 × 2 × 1**
10. $8 \times 5 = 40$ ___ × ___ × ___ = 40 **2 × 10 × 2**

Look at all the factors given for each problem below. You decide the order in which you would like to think about them. Use parentheses to write each problem and multiply to find the product.

11. 6, 4, 2 **$(6 \times 2) \times 4 = 48$**
12. 7, 4, 5 **$(5 \times 4) \times 7 = 140$**
13. 4, 7, 2 **$(2 \times 4) \times 7 = 56$**
14. 5, 2, 3 **$(5 \times 2) \times 3 = 30$**
15. 8, 3, 4 **$(3 \times 4) \times 8 = 96$**
16. 7, 2, 6 **$(7 \times 2) \times 6 = 84$**
17. 5, 8, 4 **$(8 \times 4) \times 5 = 160$**
18. 6, 7, 3 **$(3 \times 6) \times 7 = 126$**

Chapter Resources

Grade 4 47 Chapter 4

ADDITIONAL EXAMPLE

1 Mrs. Chu ordered 4 boxes of fruit bars to sell at the baseball concession stand. Each box contains 3 bars, and each bar has 2 pieces. How many pieces did she order? 24 pieces

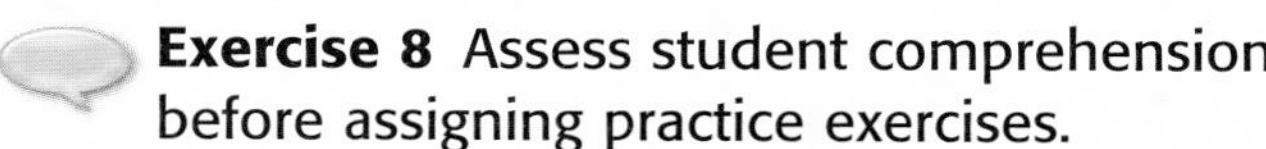

As a class, have students complete Exercises 1–8 in **Check What You Know** as you observe their work.

Exercise 8 Assess student comprehension before assigning practice exercises.

BL Alternate Teaching Strategy

If students have trouble multiplying three numbers…

Then use one of these reteach options:

1 CRM **Daily Reteach Worksheet** (p. 43)

2 Have students use arrays to model the multiplication. For example, to find the product of $(5 \times 3) \times 2$, have students shade a 5×3 grid and name the product. Then have them shade another 5×3 grid and name the product of $(5 \times 3) \times 2$.

3 Practice

Differentiate practice using these leveled assignments for Exercises 9–37.

Level	Assignment
BL Below/Approaching Level	9–13, 18–19, 21, 23–24, 26–27, 30–31
OL On Level	10–17, 19–21, 24–25, 27–29, 31–33, 35
AL Above/Beyond Level	9–32 odd, 34–37

! COMMON ERROR!

Exercises 18–20 Students may find it difficult to fill in the blanks in the equations. Remind them that they should find the product of the two given factors first and then find the missing factor.

Have students discuss and complete the Higher Order Thinking problems. In Exercise 37, there is only one set of 4 factors with a product of 24. Suggest that students find a pair of numbers whose product is 24, and then find a pair of factors for each.

WRITING IN ➤MATH Have students complete Exercise 38 in their Math Journals. You may choose to use this exercise as an optional formative assessment.

4 Assess

Formative Assessment

- **Why do you sometimes regroup factors before multiplying?** Some facts are easier to compute.
- **Explain how you would find the product of $6 \times 4 \times 3$.** Answers will vary; sample answer: Use the Associative Property of Multiplication to first multiply 3×4 to get 12. Then multiply 12×6 to get 72.

Quick Check **Are students continuing to struggle with multiplying three numbers?**

If Yes ➤ Strategic Intervention Guide (p. 78)

If No ➤ Independent Work Options (p. 172B)
CRM Skills Practice Worksheet (p. 44)
CRM Enrich Worksheet (p. 47)

Ticket Out the Door Write $2 \times 9 \times 3$ on the board. Have students write the product on a piece of paper and hand it to you as they leave the room.

Real-World PROBLEM SOLVING

Animals Did you know that pigs are very intelligent animals? They are considered to be smarter than dogs. More information about farm animals is shown to the right.

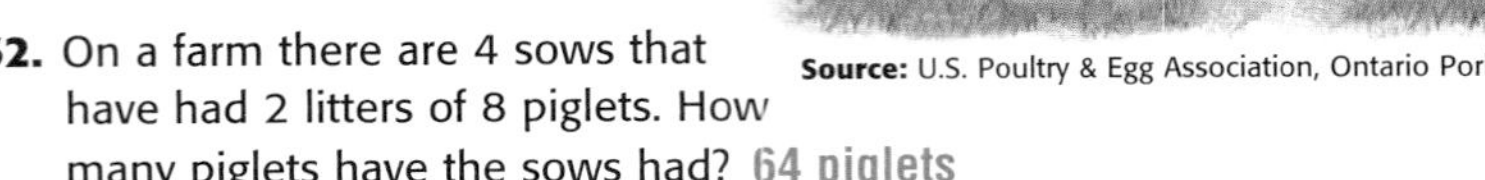

Source: U.S. Poultry & Egg Association, Ontario Pork

30. There are 4 chickens on a farm. How many eggs will they lay in 4 weeks? 80 eggs

31. Use the number sentence $2 \times 5 \times \blacksquare = 30$ to find how many weeks it will take 2 chickens to lay 30 eggs. 3 weeks

32. On a farm there are 4 sows that have had 2 litters of 8 piglets. How many piglets have the sows had? 64 piglets

33. ★ How many weeks would it take 2 chickens to have more eggs than the number of piglets that were mentioned in Exercise 32? 7 weeks

H.O.T. Problems

34. OPEN ENDED Copy and complete $2 \times 11 \times \blacksquare > 4 \times 9 \times 3$ to make a true sentence. Sample answer: 10

35. FIND THE ERROR Lucas and Denise are finding $4 \times \blacksquare \times 7 = 56$. Who is correct? Explain.

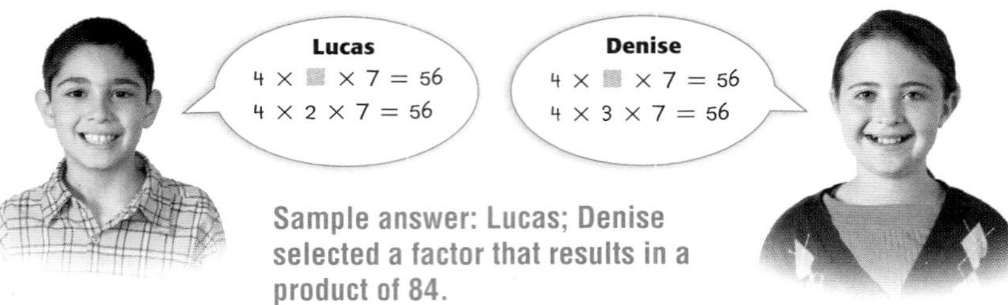

Sample answer: Lucas; Denise selected a factor that results in a product of 84.

36. CHALLENGE Identify four factors that result in a product of 24. 1, 2, 3, and 4

37. WRITING IN ➤MATH Manuel has 24 marbles in his collection. He wants to store his marbles in 2 cases. If the marbles are displayed in even rows and columns, what arrays could the marbles be displayed in? 3×4; 4×3; 2×6; 6×2; 1×12; 12×1

Homework Practice (p. 45) OL

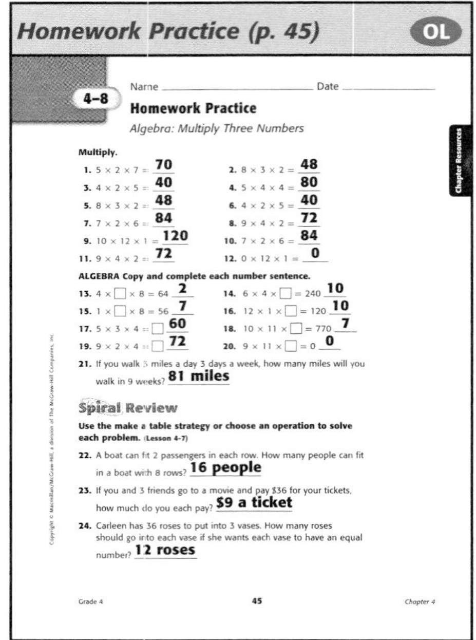

Name ______ Date ______

4–8 **Homework Practice**

Algebra: Multiply Three Numbers

Multiply.

1. $5 \times 2 \times 7 =$ **70**
2. $8 \times 3 \times 2 =$ **48**
3. $4 \times 2 \times 5 =$ **40**
4. $5 \times 4 \times 4 =$ **80**
5. $8 \times 3 \times 2 =$ **48**
6. $4 \times 2 \times 5 =$ **40**
7. $7 \times 2 \times 6 =$ **84**
8. $9 \times 4 \times 2 =$ **72**
9. $10 \times 12 \times 1 =$ **120**
10. $7 \times 2 \times 6 =$ **84**
11. $9 \times 4 \times 2 =$ **72**
12. $0 \times 12 \times 1 =$ **0**

ALGEBRA Copy and complete each number sentence.

13. $4 \times \square \times 8 = 64$ **2**
14. $6 \times 4 \times \square = 240$ **10**
15. $1 \times \square \times 8 = 56$ **7**
16. $12 \times 1 \times \square = 120$ **10**
17. $5 \times 3 \times 4 = \square$ **60**
18. $10 \times 11 \times \square = 770$ **7**
19. $9 \times 2 \times 4 = \square$ **72**
20. $9 \times 11 \times \square = 0$ **0**
21. If you walk 3 miles a day 3 days a week, how many miles will you walk in 9 weeks? **81 miles**

Spiral Review

Use the make a table strategy or choose an operation to solve each problem. (Lesson 4-7)

22. A boat can fit 2 passengers in each row. How many people can fit in a boat with 8 rows? **16 people**
23. If you and 3 friends go to a movie and pay $36 for your tickets, how much do you each pay? **$9 a ticket**
24. Carleen has 36 roses to put into 3 vases. How many roses should go into each vase if she wants each vase to have an equal number? **12 roses**

Chapter Resources

Grade 4 45 Chapter 4

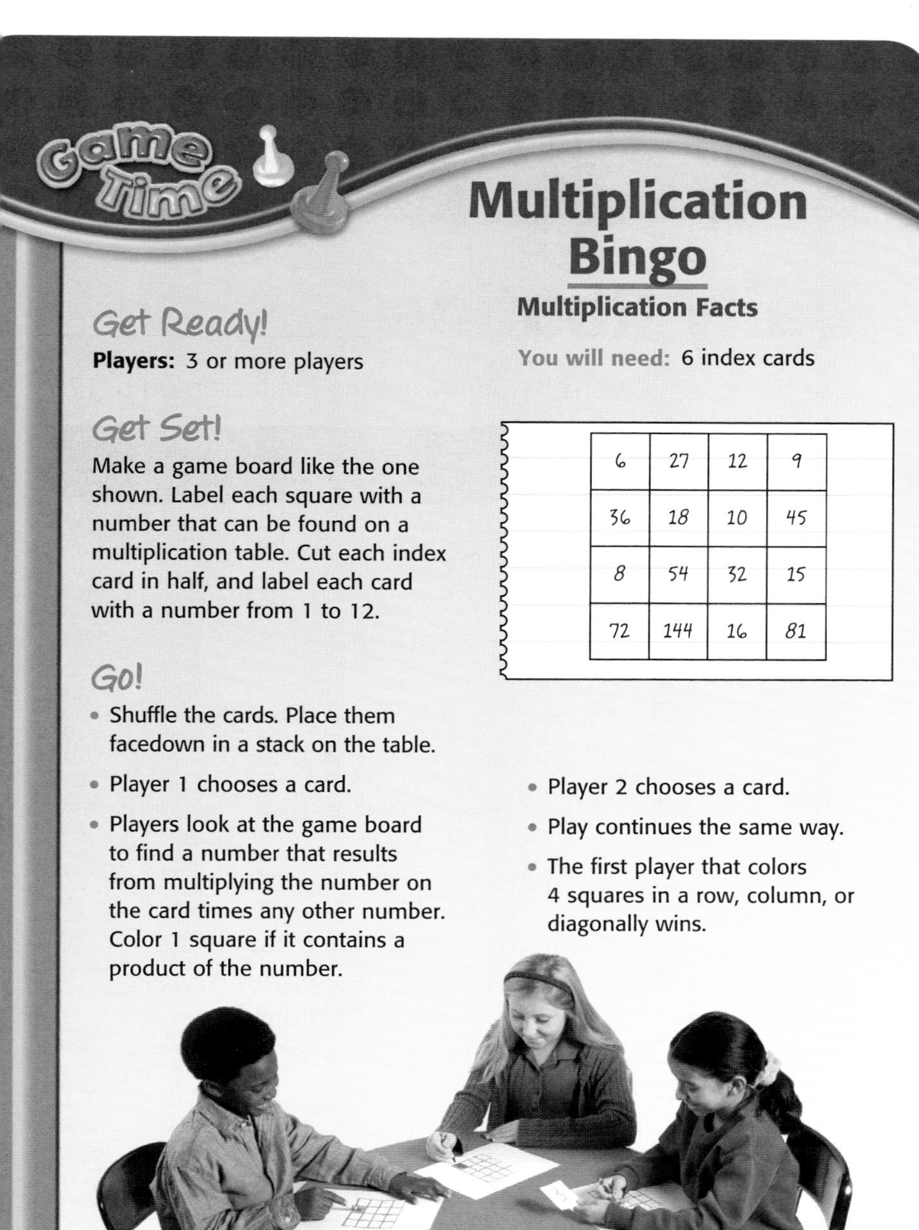

Multiplication Bingo

Multiplication Facts

Get Ready!

Players: 3 or more players

You will need: 6 index cards

Get Set!

Make a game board like the one shown. Label each square with a number that can be found on a multiplication table. Cut each index card in half, and label each card with a number from 1 to 12.

6	27	12	9
36	18	10	45
8	54	32	15
72	144	16	81

Go!

- Shuffle the cards. Place them facedown in a stack on the table.
- Player 1 chooses a card.
- Players look at the game board to find a number that results from multiplying the number on the card times any other number. Color 1 square if it contains a product of the number.
- Player 2 chooses a card.
- Play continues the same way.
- The first player that colors 4 squares in a row, column, or diagonally wins.

Game Time Multiplication Bingo 175

Differentiated Practice

Use these leveled suggestions to differentiate the game for all learners.

Level	Assignment
BL Below/Approaching Level	Students use a multiplication table to help them find multiples of the number chosen.
OL On Level	Have students play the game with the rules as written.
AL Above/Beyond Level	Students make game boards for each other so that they don't know what multiples they have until play begins.

Multiplication Bingo

Math Concept: Multiplication Facts

Materials: 6 index cards, paper, pencils

Introduce the game on p. 175 to your students to play as a class, in small groups, or at a learning workstation to review concepts introduced in this chapter.

Instructions

- Students each create their own 4×4 grid game board on a sheet of paper, labeling each square with a number that can be found on a multiplication table, as shown on p. 175.
- Students cut the index cards in half and label each half with one number, from 1 to 12.
- Students shuffle the cards and place them facedown in a stack on the table. Player 1 chooses a card from the deck, and everyone looks at his or her game board to find a multiple of the number drawn. If so, students color in the square in which the multiple appears.
- Player 2 chooses a card from the deck, and play continues in the same manner until one player colors 4 squares in a row or column. The first player to do so wins.

Extend the Game

Have students make the game using a larger game board, such as the standard 5×5 bingo size, and more cards.

LESSON 4-9

Factors and Multiples

Lesson Planner

Objective

Find factors and multiples of whole numbers.

Vocabulary

factor, **multiple**

Resources

Materials: multiplication tables, grid paper

Manipulatives: counters

Literature Connection: *The Man Who Counted: A Collection of Mathematical Adventures* by Malba Tahan

Alternate Lesson: Use *IMPACT Mathematics*: Unit A to provide practice with factors and multiples.

Teacher Technology
TeacherWorks • Interactive Classroom • Math Songs Track #4 Lesson Plan

Daily Routine

Use these suggestions before beginning the lesson on p. 176.

5-Minute Check

(Reviews Lesson 4-8)

Multiply.

1. $3 \times 4 \times 5$ 60 **2.** $8 \times 4 \times 3$ 96

3. $2 \times 3 \times 9$ 54 **4.** $2 \times 6 \times 4$ 48

5. $8 \times 2 \times 4$ 64 **6.** $7 \times 5 \times 2$ 70

Problem of the Day

National elections in the United States are always held in November. The date of the election is the first Tuesday that follows the first Monday in November. What are the possible dates for national elections? November 2–November 8

Focus on Math Background

Students often get factors and multiples confused even though they have some familiarity with factors, for example, factor $\times$ factor $=$ product.

- To find two factors of a number, you find two numbers whose product is your number. For example, $4 \times 6 = 24$. So, 4 and 6 are two factors of 24.
- To find multiples of a number, you find the product of your number and other factors. For example, $4 \times 6 = 24$. So, 24 is a multiple of 6 because $4 \times 6 = 24$. In fact, 6, 12, 18, 24, and 30 are all multiples of 6 because they can be expressed as 1×6, 2×6, 3×6, 4×6 and 5×6.

Building Math Vocabulary

Write the lesson vocabulary words and their definitions on the board.

Ask students to make a list of numbers as they skip count by 5s. Explain that all the numbers they listed are multiples of 5. Ask them to choose a number on their list and find its factors.

Visual Vocabulary Cards

Use Visual Vocabulary Cards 18 and 27 to reinforce the vocabulary introduced in this lesson. (The Define/Example/Ask routine is printed on the back of each card.)

Differentiated Instruction

Small Group Options

Option 1 Gifted and Talented AL

LINGUISTIC, LOGICAL

Materials: paper, pencil

Challenge students to write a word problem using patterns of multiplication. Have them solve their problems, then exchange them with other students to solve.

Option 2 English Language Learners ELL

LINGUISTIC

Materials: picture of a mountain
Core Vocabulary: bottom, strong, base
Common Use Verb: supports

Write Math This strategy activates background knowledge and helps students visualize factors and multiples of whole numbers.

- Show students the picture. Ask them to tell you about mountains and why mountains are strong.
- Say: "Mountains are **strong** because a **strong bottom *supports*** the top."
- Draw a mountain on the board with a whole number at the top.
- Ask for students to tell you what numbers can be multiplied together to equal the top and write their answers at the base of the mountain.
- Guide students through several examples.

Independent Work Options

Option 1 Early Finishers OL AL

LOGICAL

Materials: paper and pencil

- Assign partners. Student 1 chooses a number but keeps it secret. He or she then writes several factors and several multiples for that number.
- The partner must guess the number by considering the factors and multiples.
- Partners take turns choosing a secret number and guessing their partner's secret number.

Factors 3, 5
Multiples 15, 30
Answer 15

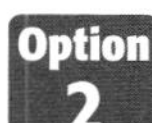

Option 2 Student Technology

Math Online macmillanmh.com

Personal Tutor • Extra Examples

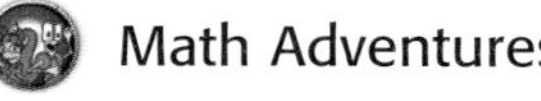

Math Adventures

Math Songs, "Factor Fiction" Track #4

Option 3 Learning Station: Writing (p. 142G)

Direct students to the Writing Learning Station for opportunities to explore and extend the lesson concept.

Option 4 Problem-Solving Practice

Reinforce problem-solving skills and strategies with the Problem-Solving Practice worksheet.

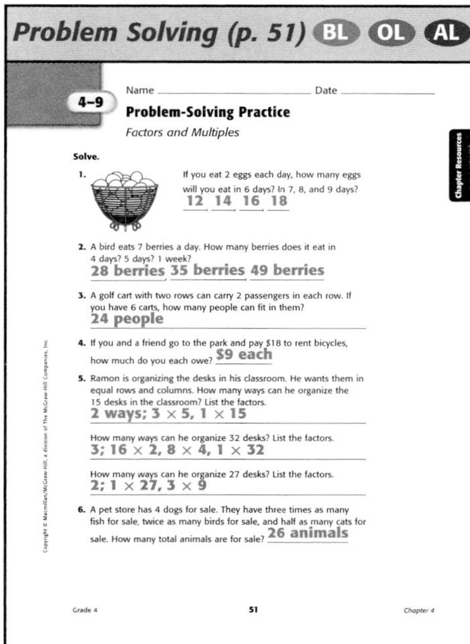

Problem Solving (p. 51) BL OL AL

4–9 Name ______ Date ______

Problem-Solving Practice

Factors and Multiples

Chapter Resources

Solve.

1. If you eat 2 eggs each day, how many eggs will you eat in 6 days? In 7, 8, and 9 days? **12, 14, 16, 18**
2. A bird eats 7 berries a day. How many berries does it eat in 4 days? 5 days? 1 week? **28 berries, 35 berries, 49 berries**
3. A golf cart with two rows can carry 2 passengers in each row. If you have 6 carts, how many people can fit in them? **24 people**
4. If you and a friend go to the park and pay $18 to rent bicycles, how much do you each owe? **$9 each**
5. Ramon is organizing the desks in his classroom. He wants them in equal rows and columns. How many ways can he organize the 15 desks in the classroom? List the factors. **2 ways; 3 × 5, 1 × 15**

   How many ways can he organize 32 desks? List the factors. **3; 16 × 2, 8 × 4, 1 × 32**

   How many ways can he organize 27 desks? List the factors. **2; 1 × 27, 3 × 9**
6. A pet store has 4 dogs for sale. They have three times as many fish for sale, twice as many birds for sale, and half as many cats for sale. How many total animals are for sale? **26 animals**

Grade 4 51 Chapter 4

4-9 Factors and Multiples

1 Introduce

Activity Choice 1 • Hands-On 

Give each student a multiplication table. Also, display one for the group.

- Have students look at the row that starts with 4, and then look at the column that has 4 at the top.
- **Why is skip counting on this table easy?** Sample answer: You can read either across a column or down a row.
- Point out that when you skip count on this table, you are saying the multiples of the number.
- **What are the first five multiples of 4?** 0, 4, 8, 12, 16

Activity Choice 2 • Literature

Introduce the lesson with *The Man Who Counted: A Collection of Mathematical Adventures* by Malba Tahan. For a related math activity, see p. TR47.

2 Teach

Scaffolding Questions

Give each student a piece of grid paper. Ask them draw as many arrays as they can that show 12 squares.

- **What arrays did you draw?** 1 × 12, 2 × 6, 3 × 4, 12 × 1, 6 × 2, 4 × 3 Point out that the numbers 1, 2, 3, 4, 6, and 12 are all factors of 12.
- **Do all numbers have factors?** yes
- **Give an example of a number that has only two factors.** Sample answer: 3; factors are only 3 and 1.
- **Refer to your multiplication table from Activity Choice 1. List the first 5 multiples of 6.** 0, 6, 12, 18, 24

GET READY to Learn

Have students open their books and read the information in **Get Ready to Learn**. Introduce **factor** and **multiple**. As a class, work through **Examples 1 and 2**.

4-9 Factors and Multiples

MAIN IDEA

I will find factors and multiples of whole numbers.

New Vocabulary

factor
multiple

Math Online

macmillanmh.com

- Extra Examples
- Personal Tutor
- Self-Check Quiz

GET READY to Learn

Mrs. Navarro is arranging desks in her classroom. There are 24 desks. How many ways can she arrange the desks so that the number of desks in each row is the same?

Two or more numbers that are multiplied together to form a product are called **factors**. To find the different arrangements of desks, break down or decompose 24 into its factors.

Real-World EXAMPLE Identify Factors

1 SCHOOL How many ways can Mrs. Navarro arrange the desks in her classroom?

Think of number pairs that result in a product of 24.

1 × 24 = 24

2 × 12 = 24

3 × 8 = 24

THINK There are 4 more arrays:
24 × 1 8 × 3
12 × 2 6 × 4

4 × 6 = 24

The factors of 24 are 1, 2, 3, 4, 6, 8, 12, and 24. So, the desks can be arranged in eight ways.

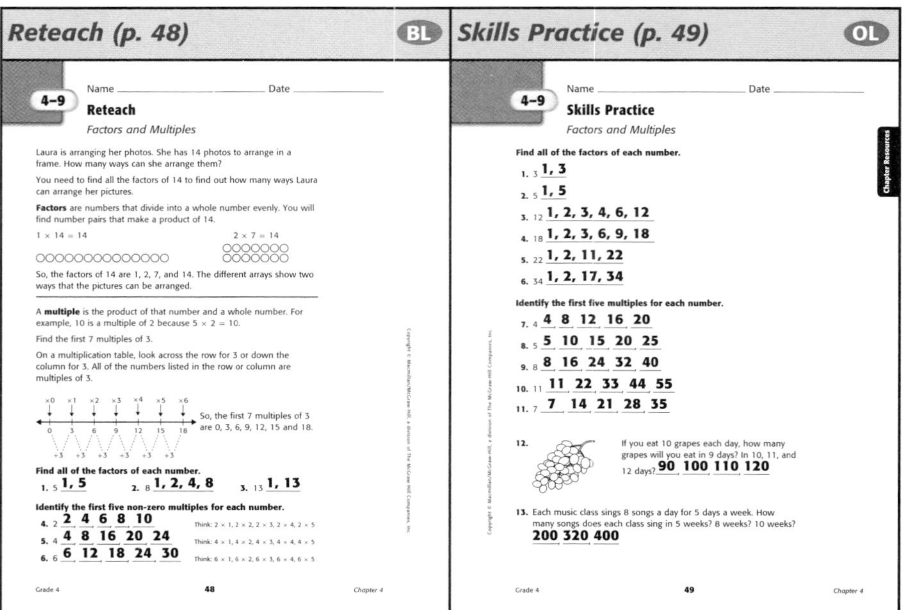

Reteach (p. 48) BL

4-9 Name ____________ Date ____________

Reteach

Factors and Multiples

Laura is arranging her photos. She has 14 photos to arrange in a frame. How many ways can she arrange them?

You need to find all the factors of 14 to find out how many ways Laura can arrange her pictures.

Factors are numbers that divide into a whole number evenly. You will find number pairs that make a product of 14.

1 × 14 = 14 2 × 7 = 14

So, the factors of 14 are 1, 2, 7, and 14. The different arrays show two ways that the pictures can be arranged.

A **multiple** is the product of that number and a whole number. For example, 10 is a multiple of 2 because 5 × 2 = 10.

Find the first 7 multiples of 3.

On a multiplication table, look across the row for 3 or down the column for 3. All of the numbers listed in the row or column are multiples of 3.

×0 ×1 ×2 ×3 ×4 ×5 ×6
0 3 6 9 12 15 18
+3 +3 +3 +3 +3 +3

So, the first 7 multiples of 3 are 0, 3, 6, 9, 12, 15 and 18.

Find all of the factors of each number.

1. 5 **1, 5** 2. 8 **1, 2, 4, 8** 3. 13 **1, 13**

Identify the first five non-zero multiples for each number.

4. 2 **2, 4, 6, 8, 10** Think: 2 × 1, 2 × 2, 2 × 3, 2 × 4, 2 × 5
5. 4 **4, 8, 16, 20, 24** Think: 4 × 1, 4 × 2, 4 × 3, 4 × 4, 4 × 5
6. 6 **6, 12, 18, 24, 30** Think: 6 × 1, 6 × 2, 6 × 3, 6 × 4, 6 × 5

Grade 4 48 Chapter 4

Skills Practice (p. 49) OL

4-9 Name ____________ Date ____________

Skills Practice

Factors and Multiples

Find all of the factors of each number.

1. 3 **1, 3**
2. 5 **1, 5**
3. 12 **1, 2, 3, 4, 6, 12**
4. 18 **1, 2, 3, 6, 9, 18**
5. 22 **1, 2, 11, 22**
6. 34 **1, 2, 17, 34**

Identify the first five multiples for each number.

7. 4 **4, 8, 12, 16, 20**
8. 5 **5, 10, 15, 20, 25**
9. 8 **8, 16, 24, 32, 40**
10. 11 **11, 22, 33, 44, 55**
11. 7 **7, 14, 21, 28, 35**

12. If you eat 10 grapes each day, how many grapes will you eat in 9 days? In 10, 11, and 12 days? **90, 100, 110, 120**

13. Each music class sings 8 songs a day for 5 days a week. How many songs does each class sing in 5 weeks? 8 weeks? 10 weeks? **200, 320, 400**

Grade 4 49 Chapter 4

Chapter Resources

A **multiple** of a number is the product of that number and any whole number. For example, 15 is a multiple of 5 because it is composed or made up of 3 groups of 5.

EXAMPLE Identify Multiples

2 **Identify the first five multiples of 7.**

On a multiplication table, look across the row for 7, or down the column for 7. All of the numbers listed in the row or the column are multiples of 7.

Remember
The first multiple of a number is always zero.

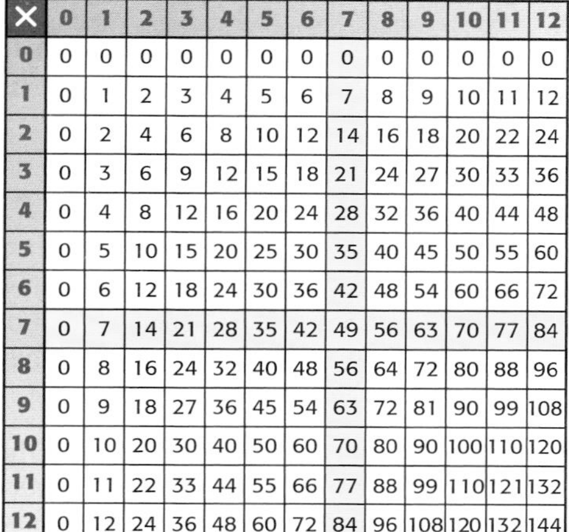

×	0	1	2	3	4	5	6	7	8	9	10	11	12
0	0	0	0	0	0	0	0	0	0	0	0	0	0
1	0	1	2	3	4	5	6	7	8	9	10	11	12
2	0	2	4	6	8	10	12	14	16	18	20	22	24
3	0	3	6	9	12	15	18	21	24	27	30	33	36
4	0	4	8	12	16	20	24	28	32	36	40	44	48
5	0	5	10	15	20	25	30	35	40	45	50	55	60
6	0	6	12	18	24	30	36	42	48	54	60	66	72
7	0	7	14	21	28	35	42	49	56	63	70	77	84
8	0	8	16	24	32	40	48	56	64	72	80	88	96
9	0	9	18	27	36	45	54	63	72	81	90	99	108
10	0	10	20	30	40	50	60	70	80	90	100	110	120
11	0	11	22	33	44	55	66	77	88	99	110	121	132
12	0	12	24	36	48	60	72	84	96	108	120	132	144

So, the first five multiples of 7 are 0, 7, 14, 21, and 28.

10. Sample answer: The result of multiplying two factors together is a multiple.

CHECK What You Know

Find all of the factors of each number. See Example 1 (p. 176) 4. 1, 2, 3, 4, 6, 9, 12, 18, 36

1. 6 1, 2, 3, 6 **2.** 10 1, 2, 5, 10 **3.** 12 1, 2, 3, 4, 6, 12 **4.** 36

Identify the first five multiples for each number. See Example 2 (p. 177)

5. 2 0, 2, 4, 6, 8 **6.** 4 0, 4, 8, 12, 16 **7.** 9 0, 9, 18, 27, 36 **8.** 12 0, 12, 24, 36, 48

9. Elena is baking muffins in the pan shown at the right. How many muffins will Elena make if she uses 1, 2, 3, or 4 pans? 6, 12, 18, or 24

10. Talk About It Explain the relationship between factors and multiples.

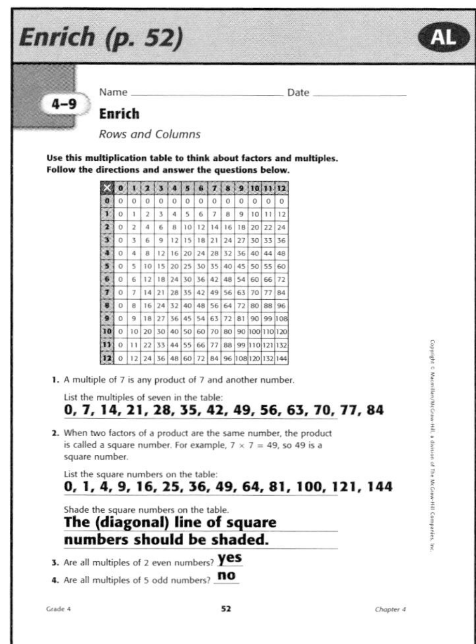

Enrich (p. 52) AL

4–9 Name ______ Date ______

Enrich

Rows and Columns

Use this multiplication table to think about factors and multiples. Follow the directions and answer the questions below.

×	0	1	2	3	4	5	6	7	8	9	10	11	12
0	0	0	0	0	0	0	0	0	0	0	0	0	0
1	0	1	2	3	4	5	6	7	8	9	10	11	12
2	0	2	4	6	8	10	12	14	16	18	20	22	24
3	0	3	6	9	12	15	18	21	24	27	30	33	36
4	0	4	8	12	16	20	24	28	32	36	40	44	48
5	0	5	10	15	20	25	30	35	40	45	50	55	60
6	0	6	12	18	24	30	36	42	48	54	60	66	72
7	0	7	14	21	28	35	42	49	56	63	70	77	84
8	0	8	16	24	32	40	48	56	64	72	80	88	96
9	0	9	18	27	36	45	54	63	72	81	90	99	108
10	0	10	20	30	40	50	60	70	80	90	100	110	120
11	0	11	22	33	44	55	66	77	88	99	110	121	132
12	0	12	24	36	48	60	72	84	96	108	120	132	144

1. A multiple of 7 is any product of 7 and another number.

List the multiples of seven in the table:
0, 7, 14, 21, 28, 35, 42, 49, 56, 63, 70, 77, 84

2. When two factors of a product are the same number, the product is called a square number. For example, $7 \times 7 = 49$, so 49 is a square number.

List the square numbers on the table:
0, 1, 4, 9, 16, 25, 36, 49, 64, 81, 100, 121, 144

Shade the square numbers on the table.
The (diagonal) line of square numbers should be shaded.

3. Are all multiples of 2 even numbers? **yes**

4. Are all multiples of 5 odd numbers? **no**

Grade 4 52 Chapter 4

Identify Multiples

Example 2 Remind students that they can read across a row or down a column to identify multiples of a number. If they do not have a multiplication chart available, skip counting will give them the same result.

ADDITIONAL EXAMPLES

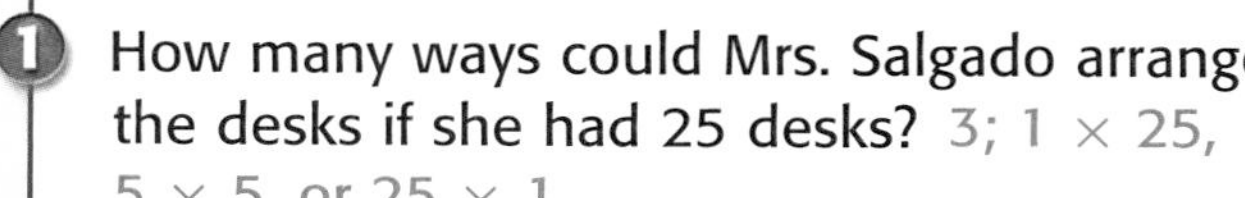

1 How many ways could Mrs. Salgado arrange the desks if she had 25 desks? 3; 1×25, 5×5, or 25×1

2 Identify the first 5 multiples of 9. 0, 9, 18, 27, 36

CHECK What You Know

As a class, have students complete Exercises 1–10 in **Check What You Know** as you observe their work.

Exercise 10 assess student comprehension before assigning practice exercises.

BL Alternate Teaching Strategy

If students have trouble identifying factors of a number…

Then use one of these reteach options:

1 CRM **Daily Reteach Worksheet** (p. 48)

2 Have students use counters and arrange them into an array. For example, to find the factors of 36, give students 36 counters and have them arrange them into as many different arrays as possible. Point out that the number of rows and columns of each array tells them the factors of 36.

3 Practice

Differentiate practice using these leveled assignments for Exercises 11–38.

Level	Assignment
BL Below/Approaching Level	11–15, 19–22, 27–29, 31
OL On Level	11–17, 19–25, 27–29, 31–32, 34, 36
AL Above/Beyond Level	10–34 even, 36–38

Have students discuss and complete the Higher Order Thinking problems. For Exercise 37, suggest students create a list to check possible products.

WRITING IN ▸MATH Have students complete Exercise 38 in their Math Journals. You may choose to use this exercise as an optional formative assessment.

★ indicates multi-step problem

Practice and Problem Solving

EXTRA PRACTICE See page R12.

Find all of the factors of each number. See Example 1 (p. 176) 14. 1, 2, 4, 5, 10, 20

11. 4 1, 2, 4
12. 7 1, 7
13. 14 1, 2, 7, 14
14. 20
15. 28 1, 2, 4, 7, 14, 28
16. 30 1, 2, 3, 5, 6, 10, 15, 30
17. 35 1, 5, 7, 35
18. 42 18. 1, 2, 3, 6, 7, 14, 21, 42

Identify the first five multiples for each number. See Example 2 (p. 177)

19. 1 0, 1, 2, 3, 4
20. 3 0, 3, 6, 9, 12
21. 5 0, 5, 10, 15, 20
22. 6 0, 6, 12, 18, 24
23. 7 0, 7, 14, 21, 28
24. 8 0, 8, 16, 24, 32
25. 9 0, 9, 18, 27, 36
26. 11 0, 11, 22, 33, 44

Identify all of the factors that are related to each array.

27. 1, 2, 4, 8

28. 1, 3, 5, 15

29. A chameleon eats 6 crickets a day. How many crickets does a chameleon eat in one week? in 8, 9, 10, and 11 days? 42; 48, 54, 60, and 66

30. Pedro walks his dog 3 times a day. How many times does Pedro walk his dog in one week? in 10, 11, or 12 days? 21; 30, 33, or 36

31. There are 50 stars on the American flag. One way the stars can be arranged is a 5 × 10 array. Identify two more ways to arrange the stars. Sample answer: 1 × 50 or 2 × 25

32. There are 24 cans of soup on a shelf. One way the cans can be displayed is in a 4 × 6 array. Identify two more ways the cans can be displayed. Sample answer: 2 × 12 and 3 × 8

Science A comet named Kohoutek can be seen every 6 years.

33. How old is a person who has seen the comet 4, 5, 6, or 7 times if they first saw the comet when they were 6 years old? 24, 30, 36, or 42

34. ★ Warren is 10 years old. His dad is 38 years old, and his mom is 36 years old. Find the total number of times Warren and his parents could have seen the comet. 15

35. ★ Suppose the comet can be seen every 4 years. Would your answer to Exercise 34 change? Explain. See margin.

Additional Answer

35. Sample answer: yes; Warren's parents would have seen the comet more times.

COMMON ERROR!

Exercises 27 and 28 Students may identify only the factors shown in the array. Remind them that they need to consider other ways the counters can be arranged in order to find all the factors.

Exercise 34 Using factors, students may assume that Warren has only seen the comet one time. Remind students that if Warren first saw the comet when he was 2 years old, for example, he would have seen it again when he was 8 years old. So, Warren could have potentially seen the comet twice.

H.O.T. Problems

36. **OPEN ENDED** List three numbers that have 2 and 3 as factors.
Sample answer: 6, 12, 18

37. **CHALLENGE** Identify the number less than 144 with the most factors. 120

38. **WRITING IN MATH** A fourth grade class is having a class picture taken for the yearbook. There are 24 students in the class. Explain why standing in 1 row of 24 is not the best way for the students to be arranged for the picture.
Sample answer: It will be harder to get all of the students in the picture than if the students were standing in 2 or more even rows.

TEST Practice

39. In which number sentence does 9 make the equation true? (Lesson 4-8) A

A 3 × ■ × 4 = 108

B 3 × ■ × 7 = 108

C 3 × ■ × 9 = 108

D 4 × ■ × 7 = 108

40. Which number has more than 6 factors? (Lesson 4-9) J

F 6

G 12

H 15

J 360

Spiral Review

Multiply. (Lesson 4-8)

41. 2 × 7 × 3 42

42. 3 × 5 × 4 60

43. 11 × 5 × 2 110

For Exercises 44 and 45, use the picture at the right. Identify the operation you used. (Lesson 4-7)

44. The number of marbles each player gets is shown. There are 5 people who want to play the game. How many marbles do they need in all? 50 marbles; multiplication

45. There are 30 marbles on the game board at the start of a game. How many players are there?
3 players; division

Algebra **Find the value of each if ☆ = 11 and ☼ = 12.** (Lesson 4-6)

46. ☆ × 6 66

47. 132 ÷ ☼ 11

48. ☼ × ☆ 132

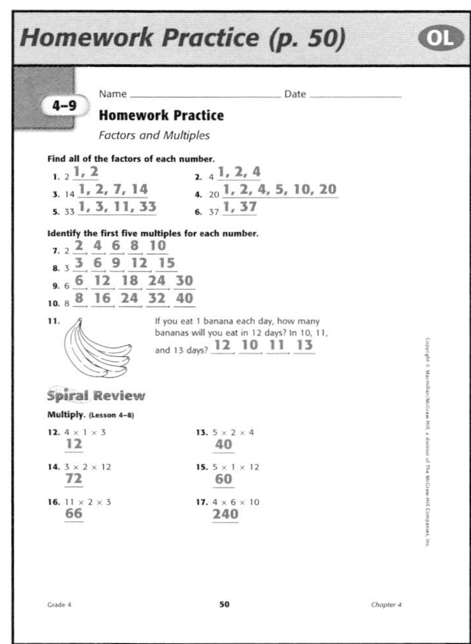

Homework Practice (p. 50) OL

4–9

Name ______________ Date ______________

Homework Practice

Factors and Multiples

Find all of the factors of each number.

1. 2 1, 2
2. 4 1, 2, 4
3. 14 1, 2, 7, 14
4. 20 1, 2, 4, 5, 10, 20
5. 33 1, 3, 11, 33
6. 37 1, 37

Identify the first five multiples for each number.

7. 2 2, 4, 6, 8, 10
8. 3 3, 6, 9, 12, 15
9. 6 6, 12, 18, 24, 30
10. 8 8, 16, 24, 32, 40
11. If you eat 1 banana each day, how many bananas will you eat in 12 days? In 10, 11, and 13 days? 12, 10, 11, 13

Spiral Review

Multiply. (Lesson 4–8)

12. 4 × 1 × 3 12
13. 5 × 2 × 4 40
14. 3 × 2 × 12 72
15. 5 × 1 × 12 60
16. 11 × 2 × 3 66
17. 4 × 6 × 10 240

Copyright © Macmillan/McGraw-Hill, a division of The McGraw-Hill Companies, Inc.

Grade 4 50 Chapter 4

4 Assess

Formative Assessment

- **Why do all numbers have factors?** Sample answer: Because every number is divisible by one and itself.
- **How are skip counting and finding multiples related?** Sample answer: They produce the same result. If you start with the number and skip count, you are finding multiples of that number.

Quick Check **Are students continuing to struggle with factors and multiples?**

If Yes → CRM Reteach Worksheet (p. 48)

If No → Independent Work Options (p. 166B)
CRM Skills Practice Worksheet (p. 49)
CRM Enrich Worksheet (p. 52)

Name the Math Ask students to explain how they would teach the third grade class what a multiple is. Have them provide an example and explain the steps they would take to find several multiples of a number.

TEST Practice

Reviews Lessons 4-8 and 4-9

Assign the Test Practice problems to provide daily reinforcement of test-taking skills.

Spiral Review

Reviews Lessons 4-6, 4-7, and 4-8

Review and assess mastery of skills and concepts from previous chapters.

Chapter 4 Study Guide and Review

FOLDABLES Dinah Zike's Foldables

Use these lesson suggestions to incorporate the Foldable during the chapter. Students can then use their Foldables to review for the test.

Lesson 4-6 Under the fourth tab of the Foldable, students demonstrate how to multiply and divide facts through 12 and give examples.

Lesson 4-8 Under the fifth tab of the Foldable, students demonstrate their ability to multiply three factors, using the Associative Property of Multiplication and parentheses.

Key Vocabulary

The page references after each word denote where that term was first introduced. If students have difficulty answering Exercises 1–4, remind them that they can use these page references to review the vocabulary terms.

Vocabulary Review

Review chapter vocabulary using one of the following options.

- **Visual Vocabulary Cards** (17, 18, 27)
- **eGlossary** at macmillanmh.com

Chapter 4 Study Guide and Review

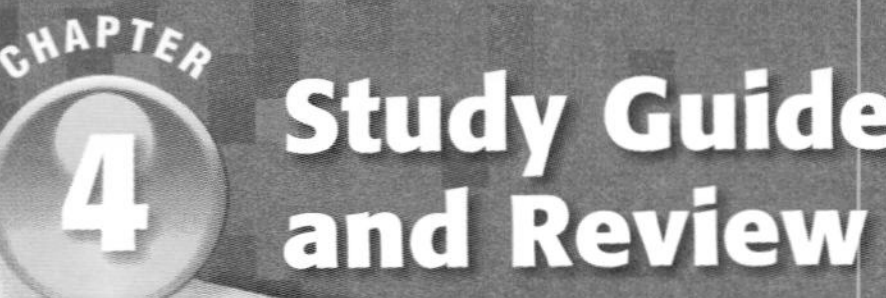

FOLDABLES Study Organizer GET READY to Study

Be sure the following Key Vocabulary words and Key Concepts are written in your Foldable.

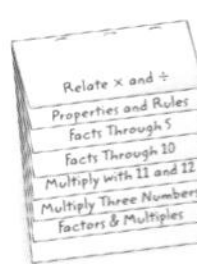

BIG Ideas

Relate Multiplication and Division (p. 147)

- A **fact family** is a set of four related multiplication and division facts.

  $3 \times 4 = 12$ $4 \times 3 = 12$

  $12 \div 4 = 3$ $12 \div 3 = 4$

Multiplication Properties (pp. 150–151)

$3 \times 4 = 4 \times 3$	Commutative Property
$3 \times 0 = 0$	Zero Property
$3 \times 1 = 3$	Identity Property
$3 \times (4 \times 2) = (3 \times 4) \times 2$	Associative Property

Factors and Multiples (pp. 176–177)

- Two or more numbers that are multiplied together to form a product are called **factors**.

  factors of 6: 1, 2, 3, and 6

- A **multiple** of a number is the product of that number and any whole number.

  multiples of 7: 0, 7, 14, 21, …

Key Vocabulary

Associative Property of Multiplication (p. 150)
Commutative Property of Multiplication (p. 150)
Distributive Property of Multiplication (p. 166)
factor (p. 176)
multiple (p. 177)

Vocabulary Check

Complete each sentence with the correct vocabulary word.

1. Two or more numbers that are multiplied together to form a product are called ___?___. factors
2. The ___?___ says that the order of the factors does not change the product when multiplying. Commutative Property of Mult.
3. The ___?___ says that you can multiply the addends of a sum by a number and then add the products. Distributive Property of Mult.
4. A(n) ___?___ of a number is the product of that number and any whole number. multiple

Chapter 4 Project

Daily Multiples Book

Alone, in pairs, or in small groups, have students discuss the results of their completed chapter project with the class. Assess their work using the Chapter Project rubric found in Chapter 4 Resource Masters, p. 63.

Lesson-by-Lesson Review

4-1 Relate Multiplication and Division (pp. 147–149)

Example 1
Write a fact family for the array.

$2 \times 4 = 8$
$4 \times 2 = 8$
$8 \div 4 = 2$
$8 \div 2 = 4$

Example 2
Write a fact family for the numbers 3, 5, and 15.

$3 \times 5 = 15$ $5 \times 3 = 15$
$15 \div 3 = 5$ $15 \div 5 = 3$

Example 3
Stefanie and Eva want to share the shells that they collected on their trip to the beach. They have 18 shells in all. Use related facts and draw an array that will help them decide how they can divide their shells evenly.

$2 \times 9 = 18$
$9 \times 2 = 18$
$18 \div 2 = 9$
$18 \div 9 = 2$

So, each girl will have 9 shells.

Write a fact family for each array or set of numbers. 5–8. See margin.

5. 3, 7, 21 **6.** 9, 5, 45

7.

8.

Algebra **Solve. Use a related multiplication or division fact.**

9. $4 \times 3 = \blacksquare$ 12 **10.** $5 \times 6 = \blacksquare$ 30

11. $36 \div 4 = \blacksquare$ 9 **12.** $40 \div 8 = \blacksquare$ 5

13. Lonzo bought four packs of trading cards. If there are eight cards in each pack, how many trading cards did Lonzo buy? 32 trading cards

14. Andrea needs to read a book with 25 chapters. How many chapters will she need to read each day to finish the book in 5 days? 5 chapters

Lesson-by-Lesson Review

Have students complete the Lesson-by-Lesson Review on pp. 181–186. Then you can use ExamView® Assessment Suite to customize another review worksheet that practices all the objectives of this chapter or only the objectives on which your students need more help.

Intervention If the given examples are not sufficient to review the topics covered by the questions, use the page references next to the exercises to review that topic in the Student Edition.

Additional Answers

5. $3 \times 7 = 21$; $7 \times 3 = 21$; $21 \div 3 = 7$; $21 \div 7 = 3$

6. $5 \times 9 = 45$; $9 \times 5 = 45$; $45 \div 5 = 9$; $45 \div 9 = 5$

7. $2 \times 5 = 10$; $5 \times 2 = 10$; $10 \div 2 = 5$; $10 \div 5 = 2$

8. $8 \times 8 = 64$; $64 \div 8 = 8$

CHAPTER 4 Study Guide and Review

Additional Answers

15. Ones in Division
16. Commutative Property of Multiplication
17. 5; Ones in Division
18. 14; Zeros in Division
19. No; Commutative Property of Multiplication; $3 \times 5 \neq 5 \times 2$

4-2 Algebra: Multiplication Properties and Division Rules (pp. 150–153)

Example 4
Identify the property shown by $9 \times 1 = 9$.

A number is multiplied by 1, and the product is the number. This is the Identity Property of Multiplication.

Example 5
Complete $(5 \times 2) \times 3 = 5 \times (■ \times 3)$. Identify the property used.

$(5 \times 2) \times 3 = 5 \times (2 \times 3)$

The way in which the factors are grouped does not change the product.

This is the Associative Property of Multiplication.

Identify the property or rule shown by each number sentence. 15–19. See margin.

15. $12 \div 12 = 1$ **16.** $3 \times 6 = 6 \times 3$

Algebra **Copy and complete each number sentence. Identify the property or rule used.**

17. $5 \div ■ = 1$ **18.** $■ \div 14 = 0$

19. David has soccer practice for 3 hours each night. Sofia has softball practice for 2 hours each night. Will David and Sofia practice for the same amount of time in 5 nights? Use a multiplication property to justify your answer.

4-3 Multiply and Divide Facts Through 5 (pp. 154–157)

Example 6
Find 4×5.

You can use an area model to find 4×5.

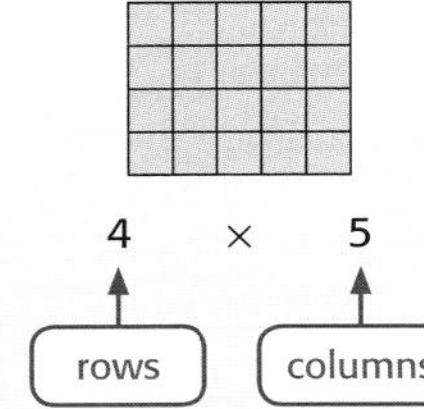

Count the squares. There is a total of 20 squares.

Multiply or divide.

20. 4×4 16 **21.** 5×3 15
22. $6 \div 3$ 2 **23.** $9\overline{)18}$ 2

Algebra **Complete each number sentence.**

24. $■ \times 3 = 6$ 2 **25.** $4 \times ■ = 32$ 8
26. $56 \div ■ = 8$ 7 **27.** $44 \div ■ = 11$ 4

28. **Algebra** If ☆ = 2, then what is ☆ + ☆ + ☆ + ☆ + ☆? 10

4-4 Problem-Solving Skill: Choose an Operation (pp. 158–159)

Example 7
There are 9 rows on the bleachers. Each row holds 10 people. How many people can sit in the bleachers at once?

Understand

What facts do you know?

- There are 9 rows.
- There are 10 seats per row.

What do you need to find?

- The number of people that can sit in the bleachers at a time.

Plan There are groups with the same number in each group. So, multiply the number of rows by the number of seats per row.

Solve Multiply to find the answer.

$9 \times 10 = 90$

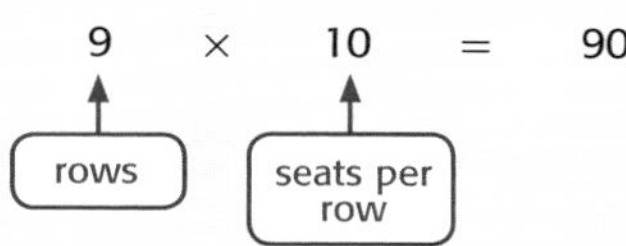

So, 90 people can sit on the bleachers at a time.

Check Look back. Use division to check the answer. Since $90 \div 10 = 9$, the answer is correct.

Tell which operation you would use to solve each problem. Then solve.

29. Lyn spent $80 on 10 concert tickets. Two tickets were for the front row. How many tickets did she buy for each of the other sections? subtraction and division; 2 center and 6 side

Smooth Jazz Concert	
Front row seats	$15
Center section	$10
Side sections	$5

30. **Measurement** Mike's vacation is 2 weeks long. Nina's vacation is 3 weeks longer than Mike's. How long is Nina's vacation? addition; 5 wk

31. Gavin purchased one bus ticket. He paid with a $10 bill. How much change did he get back? subtraction; $5

Bus Tickets
1 for $5
2 for $10
3 for $15

32. There are 5 members in the band who play the drums. Three times as many members play the flute. How many members play the flute? multiplication; 15 members

33. West Elementary has 5 fourth grade classes. Each glass made 12 posters. If 10 posters were destroyed before they could be put up on the wall, how many posters are there in all on the wall? multiplication and subtraction; 50

Chapter 4 Study Guide and Review

4-5 Multiply and Divide Facts Through 10 (pp. 160–162)

Example 8
Find 4 × 7.

Make an area model to represent 4 × 7.

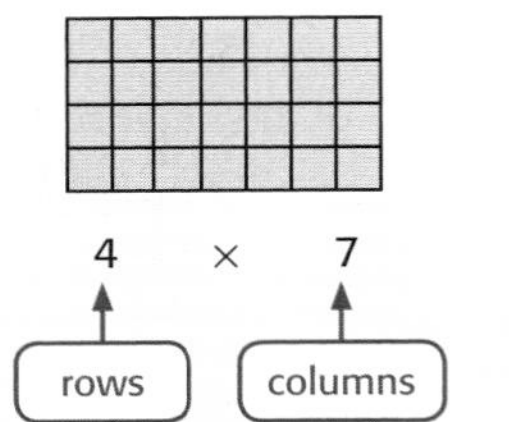

There are 28 squares in all.

So, 4 × 7 = 28.

Multiply or divide.

34. 4 × 8 32 **35.** 9 × 6 54

36. 10 ÷ 2 5 **37.** 90 ÷ 9 10

38. Spencer sold 9 magazine subscriptions to make money for his club. Each magazine subscription costs $7. How much money did Spencer collect? $63

39. Mr. Dunn has 6 rows of desks in his classroom. There are 5 desks in each row. How many desks are in Mr. Dunn's classroom? 30

4-6 Multiply with 11 and 12 (pp. 166–169)

Example 9
Marina has scored 9 points on each of 11 quizzes. How many points has she scored in all?

Think of 9 × 11 as (9 × 10) + (9 × 1).

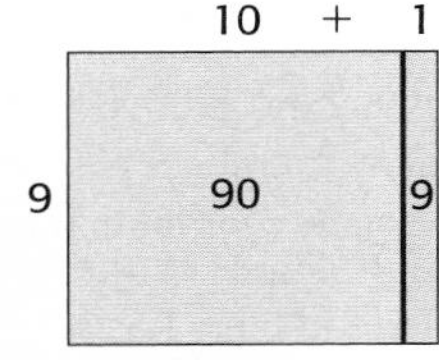

9 × 11 = (9 × 10) + (9 × 1)
= 90 + 9
= 99

So, Marina has scored 99 points.

Multiply or divide.

40. 72 ÷ 8 9 **41.** 12 × 6 72

42. 12)84 7 **43.** 12 × 9 108

Compare. Use >, <, or =.

44. 108 ÷ 12 ■ 88 ÷ 8 <

45. 12 × 6 ■ 8 × 10 <

46. 36 ÷ 3 ■ 6 × 2 =

47. Kirsten's parents go to the grocery store once a week. How many times do they go to the grocery store in one year? 52 times

184 Chapter 4 Apply Multiplication and Division Facts

4-7 Problem-Solving Investigation: Choose a Strategy (pp. 170–171)

Example 10

Carlo wants to buy a frozen yogurt. The flavors of yogurt are vanilla, chocolate, or strawberry. The yogurt comes in a dish or on a cone. How many choices does he have?

Understand

What facts do you know?

- The yogurt flavors are vanilla, chocolate, and strawberry.
- Yogurt comes in a dish or on a cone.

What do you need to find?

- How many yogurt choices Carlo has.

Plan Make a table.

Solve

Flavor	Cone	Dish
Vanilla	X	X
Chocolate	X	X
Strawberry	X	X

Carlo has 6 choices for his yogurt.

Check There are 3 flavors and two choices for each flavor. So, Carlo has 6 choices. The answer is correct.

Use the make a table strategy or choose an operation to solve each problem.

48. Amy wants to buy two dolls. Each doll costs $16. What is the total cost of the dolls? $32

49. Mr. Sullivan bought pizza for the reading club. Each pizza had 10 slices. How many pizzas did he buy if there were 120 slices? 12 pizzas

50. Twyla worked five days in one week. She worked 40 hours during that week. She worked the same number of hours each day. How many hours did she work each day? 8 hr

51. Conchita has 25 math problems for homework each day. Use the table to find how many problems she completes in five days. 125 problems

Day	Problems Completed
1	25
2	50
3	75
4	100
5	125

52. Measurement Bradley has 3 tap dancing lessons each week. Each lesson is 2 hours long. How many hours of lessons will Bradley have completed in 4 weeks? 24 hr

Chapter 4 Study Guide and Review **185**

Chapter 4 Study Guide and Review

Additional Answers

68. 1 × 18, 2 × 9, 3 × 6, 6 × 3, 9 × 2, 18 × 1

4-8 Algebra: Multiply Three Numbers (pp. 172–174)

Example 11
Find 3 × 5 × 4.

There are two ways to group the numbers.

One Way	Another Way
Multiply 3 × 5 first.	Multiply 5 × 4 first.
3 × 5 × 4	3 × 5 × 4
(3 × 5) × 4	3 × (5 × 4)
15 × 4	3 × 20
60	60

So, 3 × 5 × 4 = 60.

Multiply.

53. 6 × 2 × 3 36 **54.** 2 × 4 × 9 72

55. 2 × 8 × 4 64 **56.** 5 × 1 × 11 55

Algebra Copy and complete each number sentence.

57. ■ × 7 × 3 = 42 2

58. 4 × ■ × 3 = 108 9

59. Jason goes to the park for 2 hours a day, 5 days a week. How many hours will he spend in the park in a four-week month? 40 h

4-9 Factors and Multiples (pp. 176–179)

Example 12
Find all of the factors of 6.

Think of number pairs that result in a product of 6.

1 × 6

2 × 3

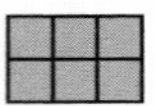

So, the factors of 6 are 1, 2, 3, and 6.

Example 13
Identify the first five multiples of 4.

Multiples of 4: 0, 4, 8, 12, 16, 20, 24, …

The first five multiples of 4 are 0, 4, 8, 12, and 16.

Find all of the factors of each number.

60. 8 1, 2, 4, 8 **61.** 12 1, 2, 3, 4, 6, 12

62. 16 1, 2, 4, 8, 16 **63.** 28 1, 2, 4, 7,14, 28

Identify the first five multiples for each number.

64. 3 0, 3, 6, 9, 12 **65.** 5 0, 5, 10, 15, 20

66. 8 0, 8, 16, 24, 32 **67.** 10 0, 10, 20, 30, 40

68. Lora is arranging her 18 snow globes on a shelf. Write the different ways she can arrange the snow globes. See margin.

69. Glenn reads 11 pages in his book each day. How many pages will he read in one week? in 9, 10, or 11 days? 77; 99, 110, or 121

Chapter Test

For Exercises 1–3, tell whether each statement is *true* or *false*.

1. Two or more numbers that are multiplied together to form a product are called multiples. false
2. Factors are numbers that do not divide into a whole number evenly. false

Algebra Compare. Use >, <, or =.

3. $2 \times 7 \times 3$ ■ $8 \times 3 \times 4$ <
4. $5 \times 3 \times 9$ ■ $4 \times 2 \times 5$ >
5. There are 5 boxes of paints on an art store shelf. Each box contains one dozen colors. How many paint colors are on the shelf? 60 paints

Find all of the factors of each number.

6. 27 1, 3, 9, 27
7. 36 1, 2, 3, 4, 6, 9, 12, 18, 36
8. **MULTIPLE CHOICE** Which of the following numbers will make the number sentence true? C

$4 \times$ ■ $\times 5 = 180$

A 7 **C** 9
B 8 **D** 10

9. Write a fact family for the array.

$4 \times 3 = 12$; $3 \times 4 = 12$; $12 \div 4 = 3$; $12 \div 3 = 4$

Algebra Find the value of each number sentence if ♡ = 5 and ☺ = 10.

10. ♡ × 8 40
11. ☺ ÷ 5 2

Algebra Copy and complete each number sentence. Identify the property or rule used.

12. ■ × 7 = 7 × 4 — 12. 4; Commutative Property (×)
13. ■ ÷ 12 = 0 — 13. 0; Zeros in Division
14. Identify all of the factors related to the array. 1, 2, 4, 5, 10, 20

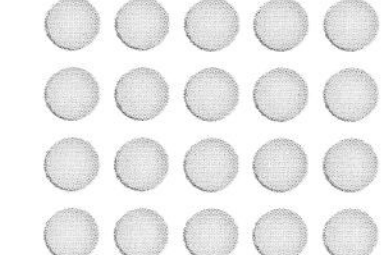

Identify the first five multiples for each number.

15. 7 0, 7, 14, 21, 28
16. 9 0, 9, 18, 27, 36

Multiply.

17. $6 \times 3 \times 12$ 216
18. $4 \times 2 \times 7$ 56

Divide.

19. $33 \div 11$ 3
20. $36 \div 6$ 6
21. **MULTIPLE CHOICE** Which number has more than six factors? J

F 6 **H** 15
G 12 **J** 64

22. **WRITING IN MATH** Explain how multiplication and division are related. Sample answer: They are inverse operations.

Summative Assessment 187

Chapter 4 Chapter Test

Summative Assessment

Use these alternate leveled chapter tests to differentiate assessment for the specific needs of your students.

Leveled Chapter 4 Tests			
Form	Type	Level	CRM Pages
1	Multiple Choice	BL	65–66
2A	Multiple Choice	OL	67–68
2B	Multiple Choice	OL	69–70
2C	Free Response	OL	71–72
2D	Free Response	OL	73–74
3	Free Response	AL	75–76

BL = below/approaching grade level
OL = on grade level
AL = above/beyond grade level

Vocabulary Test

CRM **Chapter 4 Resource Masters** (p. 60)

ExamView Assessment Suite Customize and create multiple versions of your Chapter Test and the test answer keys.

Data-Driven Decision Making

Based on the results of the Chapter Test, use the following to review concepts that continue to present students with problems.

Exercises	State/Local Standards	What's the Math?	Error Analysis	Resources for Review
1–2, 6–7, 14–16, 21		Find factors and multiples for whole numbers.	Does not understand "whole number." Does not know difference between "factor" and "multiple." Does not find all factors.	Strategic Intervention Guide (pp. 70, 72, 74, 76, 78, 82) CRM Chapter 4 Resource Masters (Reteach Worksheets) Math Adventures My Math Zone Chapter 4 Math Online Extra Examples • Personal Tutor • Concepts in Motion
3–4, 8, 17–18		Multiply three factors. Compare two number sentences using "less than", "greater than," or "equal to" signs.	Does not know multiplication facts. Multiplies incorrectly. Confuses comparing signs.	

Test Practice

Formative Assessment

- Use Student Edition pp. 188–189 as practice and cumulative review. The questions are written in the same style as many state tests.
- You can also use these two pages to benchmark student progress, or as an alternate homework assignment.

Additional practice pages can be found in the Chapter 4 Resource Masters.

CRM **Chapter 4 Resource Masters**
Cumulative Test Practice
- Multiple Choice format (pp. 65–70)
- Free Response format (pp. 71–76)

Create practice worksheets or tests that align to your state standards.

Math Online Have students visit macmillanmh.com for additional practice to reinforce your state standards.

Test Practice

Cumulative, Chapters 1–4

PART 1 Multiple Choice

Read each question. Then fill in the correct answer on the answer sheet provided by your teacher or on a sheet of paper.

1. Mrs. Park has 35 students. She puts 7 students in each group. How many groups are there? B

A 4 **C** 6

B 5 **D** 7

2. The table below shows the number of miles Neil biked during June. About how many miles did he bike in all? H

Neil's Biking Distance for June	
Week	**Number of Miles**
1	39
2	52
3	46
4	53

F 150 miles **H** 190 miles

G 175 miles **J** 210 miles

3. Which of the following statements is true? A

A The only factors of 3 are 1 and 3.

B The only factors of 4 are 1 and 4.

C The only factors of 6 are 1 and 6.

D The only factors of 10 are 1 and 10.

4. Which of these is another way to write the number 3,003,013? G

F three million, 3 hundred, thirteen

G three million, 3 thousand, thirteen

H three hundred thousand, thirteen

J thirty million, thirty thousand, thirteen

5. Which of the following has the greatest value? D

A 297,503 **C** 457,650

B 329,450 **D** 479,350

6. A drawer has 6 white, 2 blue, and 4 brown socks. If a sock is picked at random, what is the probability it will be brown? H

F certain **H** unlikely

G likely **J** impossible

7. Which pair of numbers correctly completes this equation? A

○ × 10 = □

A (5) and [50]

B (6) and [9]

C (2) and [200]

D (3) and [15]

Test-Taking Tips

- Make sure students check that they have filled in an oval for each test question.
- Remind students to eliminate unreasonable answers first, and then focus on the remaining answer choices.

Preparing for Standardized Tests

For test-taking strategies and practice, see pages R42–R55.

8. Ajay wants to use one color pencil and one color crayon to make a drawing.

Pencil Colors	Crayon Colors
red	brown
blue	black
green	

Which of the following is possible if Ajay chooses one color pencil and one color crayon? H

F red and green

G blue and purple

H green and brown

J blue and green

9. Which number is 10,000 less than 78,305? A

A 68,305 **C** 78,205

B 77,305 **D** 88,305

10. Which of these is another way to write the product of 12×5? G

F $1 \times 6 \times 5$

G $2 \times 6 \times 5$

H $3 \times 6 \times 5$

J $6 \times 6 \times 5$

PART 2 Short Response

Record your answers on the answer sheet provided by your teacher or on a sheet of paper.

11. Kyra bought 72 eggs at the grocery store for the school breakfast. The eggs come in cartons of 12. How many cartons of eggs did Kyra buy? 6

12. Write a fact family for the array.

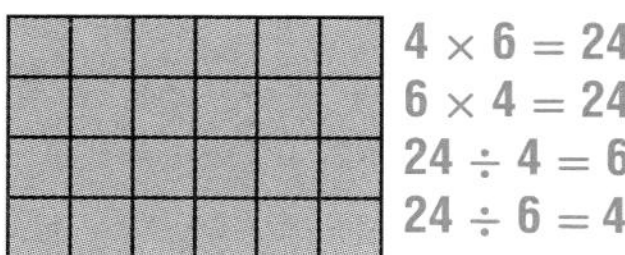

$4 \times 6 = 24$, $6 \times 4 = 24$, $24 \div 4 = 6$, $24 \div 6 = 4$

PART 3 Extended Response

Record your answers on the answer sheet provided by your teacher or on a sheet of paper.

13. How many more students prefer football and baseball than basketball and soccer? Explain your reasoning.

Favorite Sport	
Sport	**Number of Students**
Baseball	9
Basketball	8
Football	12
Soccer	6

See margin.

NEED EXTRA HELP?													
If You Missed Question...	1	2	3	4	5	6	7	8	9	10	11	12	13
Go to Lesson...	4-5	2-2	4-9	1-2	1-4	3-9	4-5	3-8	2-5	4-8	4-6	4-1	2-5

Answer Sheet Practice

Have students simulate taking a state test by recording their answers on a practice recording sheet.

CRM **Chapter 4 Resource Masters**
Student Recording Sheet (p. 81)

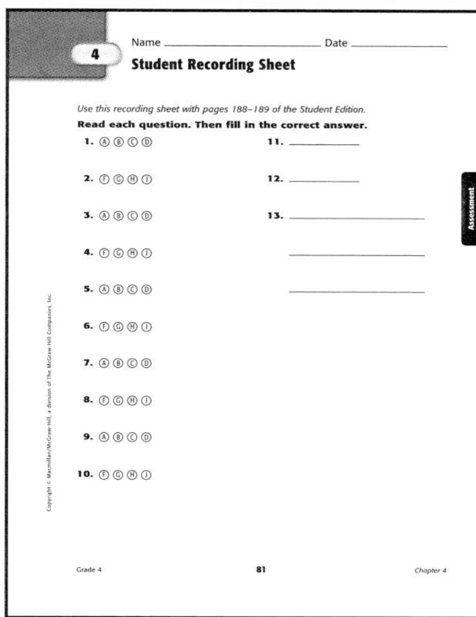
Name ______ Date ______

4 Student Recording Sheet

Use this recording sheet with pages 188–189 of the Student Edition.

Read each question. Then fill in the correct answer.

1. Ⓐ Ⓑ Ⓒ Ⓓ 11. ______
2. Ⓕ Ⓖ Ⓗ Ⓙ 12. ______
3. Ⓐ Ⓑ Ⓒ Ⓓ 13. ______
4. Ⓕ Ⓖ Ⓗ Ⓙ
5. Ⓐ Ⓑ Ⓒ Ⓓ
6. Ⓕ Ⓖ Ⓗ Ⓙ
7. Ⓐ Ⓑ Ⓒ Ⓓ
8. Ⓕ Ⓖ Ⓗ Ⓙ
9. Ⓐ Ⓑ Ⓒ Ⓓ
10. Ⓕ Ⓖ Ⓗ Ⓙ

Grade 4 81 Chapter 4

Additional Answers

13. Sample answer: 7; A total of 12 + 9 or 21 students prefer football and baseball. A total of 8 + 6 or 14 students prefer basketball and soccer. So, 21 − 14 or 7 students prefer football and baseball over basketball and soccer.

Page 149, Lesson 4-1

15. $6 \times 9 = 54, 9 \times 6 = 54, 54 \div 6 = 9, 54 \div 9 = 6$

16. $7 \times 8 = 56, 8 \times 7 = 56, 56 \div 7 = 8, 56 \div 8 = 7$

17. $9 \times 11 = 99, 11 \times 9 = 99, 99 \div 9 = 11, 99 \div 11 = 9$

18. $11 \times 12 = 132, 12 \times 11 = 132, 132 \div 11 = 12, 132 \div 12 = 11$

27. Sample answer: Fact families include 2 multiplication and 2 division facts. So, multiplication facts can be used to solve division problems because the factors in a multiplication problem are the divisor and the quotient in the division problem.

Page 153, Lesson 4-2

24. Sample answer: It is easiest to multiply 2×5 first, because then you multiply 10×9 rather than 18×5.

25. Sample answer: Associative Property of Multiplication; Doubling a larger amount is easier than multiplying 7×12.

Page 163, Mid-Chapter Check

1. $7 \times 4 = 28$; $4 \times 7 = 28$; $28 \div 7 = 4$; $28 \div 4 = 7$

2. $3 \times 8 = 24$; $8 \times 3 = 24$; $24 \div 3 = 8$; $24 \div 8 = 3$

8. Zero Property of Multiplication

9. Commutative Property of Multiplication

10. $5 \div 5 = 1$; Divide by the same number

11. $7 \times 0 = 0$; Zero Property of Multiplication

22. No; The way in which the dividends and divisors are grouped changes the quotient.

Page 171, Lesson 4-7

8. Sample answer: make a table; Making a table is the easiest way to organize and work with the large numbers in this exercise.

Page 173, Lesson 4-8

8. Sample answer: Multiply 6 and 2 first, then you can multiply 12×9.

29. Sample answer: yes; Helen can read up to $2 \times 2 \times 4 = 16$ books in 4 weeks.

NOTES

Chapter Overview

Chapter-at-a-Glance

In Chapter 5, students learn how to write and solve addition and subtraction equations and to write and find the value of addition and subtraction expressions.

Lesson		Math Objective	State/Local Standards
5-1	**Addition and Subtraction Expressions** (pp. 193–195)	Write and find the value of expressions.	
EXPLORE 5-2	**Addition and Subtraction Equations** (pp. 196–197)	Explore addition and subtraction equations.	
5-2	**Solve Equations** (pp. 198–201)	Solve addition and subtraction equations.	
5-3	**Problem-Solving Skill: Extra or Missing Information** (pp. 202–203)	Identify extra or missing information.	
5-4	**Identify, Describe, and Extend Patterns** (pp. 204–206)	Identify, describe, and extend numeric and nonnumeric patterns.	
5-5	**Function Tables: Find a Rule (+, −)** (pp. 208–211)	Find and use rules to write addition and subtraction equations.	
5-6	**Multiplication and Division Expressions** (pp. 214–216)	Write and find the value of multiplication and division expressions.	
5-7	**Problem-Solving Investigation: Choose a Strategy** (pp. 218–219)	Choose the best strategy to solve a problem.	
5-8	**Function Tables: Find a Rule (×, ÷)** (pp. 220–223)	Find and use rules to write multiplication and division equations.	

Describe Algebraic Patterns

BIG Idea Students are introduced to algebraic thinking, beginning with the language of algebra, then building to the evaluation, addition, and subtraction of expressions. Students begin solving simple equations by inspection and later by adding or subtracting the same number on both sides of the equation.

Algebra Students will evaluate expressions and explore patterns to find a rule. This will help prepare them for solving equations algebraically. (Lesson 5-2)

G4-FP4C *Algebra:* Students continue identifying, describing, and extending numeric patterns involving all operations and nonnumeric growing or repeating patterns. Through these experiences, they develop an understanding of the use of a rule to describe a sequence of numbers or objects.

G4-FP1 *Number and Operations* **and** *Algebra:* **Developing quick recall of multiplication facts and related division facts and fluency with whole number multiplication**

Students use understandings of multiplication to develop quick recall of the basic multiplication facts and related division facts. They apply their understanding of models for multiplication (i.e., equal sized groups, arrays, area models, equal intervals on the number line), place value, and properties of operations (in particular, the distributive property) as they develop, discuss, and use efficient, accurate, and generalizable methods to multiply multidigit whole numbers. They select appropriate methods and apply them accurately to estimate products or calculate them mentally, depending on the context and numbers involved. They develop fluency with efficient procedures, including the standard algorithm, for multiplying whole numbers, understand why the procedures work (on the basis of place value and properties of operations), and use them to solve problems.

Skills Trace

Vertical Alignment

Third Grade

In third grade, students learned to:

- Model addition and subtraction expressions using pictures, words, and numbers.
- Use addition, subtraction, multiplication, and division to complete function tables.

Fourth Grade

During this chapter, students learn to:

- Solve addition and subtraction equations.
- Write and find the value of addition, subtraction, multiplication, and division expressions.
- Find and use a rule to write addition, subtraction, multiplication, and division equations.
- Find patterns in sets of numbers.

After this chapter, students learn to:

- Multiply and divide multiples of 10 and 100 using basic facts and patterns. Chapters 6 and 7

Fifth Grade

In fifth grade, students learn to:

- Write and evaluate addition, multiplication, algebraic expressions and number sentences.
- Write and solve addition, subtraction and multiplication equations.

Backmapping and Vertical Alignment **McGraw-Hill's *Math Connects*** program was conceived and developed with the final results in mind: student success in Algebra 1 and beyond. The authors, using the **NCTM Focal Points and Focal Connections** as their guide, developed this brand-new series by backmapping from Algebra 1 concepts, and vertically aligning the topics so that they build upon prior skills and concepts and serve as a foundation for future topics.

Math Vocabulary

The following math vocabulary words for Chapter 5 are listed in the glossary of the ***Student Edition***. You can find interactive definitions in 13 languages in the ***eGlossary*** at macmillanmh.com.

equation A mathematical sentence that contains an equals sign (=) indicating that the left side of the equals sign has the same value as the right side. (p. 198A)

expression A statement with numbers and/or variables, and at least one operation. (p. 193A)

parentheses A pair of symbols used to indicate which operation to perform first. (p. 193A)

pattern A sequence of numbers, figures, or symbols that follows a rule or design. (p. 204)
Example: 2, 4, 6, 8, 10

solve Find the answer to a problem. (p. 198A)

Visual Vocabulary Cards
Use Visual Vocabulary Cards 14 and 16 to reinforce the vocabulary in this lesson. (The Define/Example/Ask routine is printed on the back of each card.)

equation

Chapter Planner

Suggested Pacing		
Instruction	Review & Assessment	TOTAL
9 days	1 day	**10 days**

Diagnostic Assessment
Quick Check (p. 192)

	Lesson 5-1 (Pacing: 1 day)	Explore 5-2 (Pacing: 1 day)	Lesson 5-2 (Pacing: 1 day)
Lesson/ Objective	**Addition and Subtraction Expressions** (pp. 193–195) **Objective:** Write and find the value of expressions.	**Addition and Subtraction Equations** (pp. 196–197) **Objective:** Explore addition and subtraction equations.	**Solve Equations** (pp. 198–201) **Objective:** Solve addition and subtraction equations.
State/Local Standards			
Math Vocabulary	**expression**, **parentheses**		**equation**, **solve**
Lesson Resources	**Materials** paper bag, index cards **Manipulatives** counters **Other Resources** CRM Leveled Worksheets (pp. 8–12) Daily Reteach • 5-Minute Check • Problem of the Day	**Manipulatives** 2-colored counters, plastic cups	**Manipulatives** counters, plastic cups, connecting cubes **Other Resources** CRM Leveled Worksheets (pp. 13–17) Daily Reteach • 5-Minute Check • Problem of the Day
Technology	Math Songs Track #2		Math Adventures Math Songs Track #2
Math Online	Personal Tutor	Concepts in Motion	Personal Tutor
Reaching All Learners	English Learners, p. 193B ELL Gifted and Talented, p. 193B AL Early Finishers, p. 193B AL		English Learners, p. 198B ELL Below Level, p. 198B BL Early Finishers, p. 198B AL
Alternate Lesson	*IMPACT Mathematics:* Unit B		*IMPACT Mathematics:* Unit B

KEY

BL Below/Approaching Level   OL On Level   AL Above/Beyond Level   ELL English Learners
SE Student Edition   TE Teacher Edition   CRM Chapter 5 Resource Masters   CD-Rom
Transparency   Real-World Problem Solving Library

Describe Algebraic Patterns

	Lesson 5-3 (Pacing: 1 day)	Lesson 5-4 (Pacing: 1 day)	Lesson 5-5 (Pacing: 1 day)
Lesson/ Objective	**Problem-Solving Skill** **Extra or Missing Information** (pp. 202–203) **Objective:** Identify extra or missing information.	**Identify, Describe, and Extend Patterns** (pp. 204–206) **Objective:** Identify, describe, and extend numeric and nonnumeric patterns.	**Function Tables: Find a Rule (+, –)** (pp. 208–211) **Objective:** Find and use rules to write addition and subtraction equations.
State/Local Standards			
Math Vocabulary		**pattern**	
Lesson Resources	**Other Resources** CRM Leveled Worksheets (pp. 18–22) Daily Reteach • 5-Minute Check • Problem of the Day *Oceans: Into the Deep*	**Materials** construction paper **Manipulatives** various colored counters or connecting cubes **Other Resources** CRM Leveled Worksheets (pp. 23–27) Daily Reteach • 5-Minute Check • Problem of the Day	**Other Resources** CRM Leveled Worksheets (pp. 28–32) Daily Reteach • 5-Minute Check • Problem of the Day
Technology		Math Adventures	Math Songs Track #2
Math Online	Personal Tutor	Personal Tutor • Concepts in Motion	Personal Tutor
Reaching All Learners	English Learners, p. 202B ELL Gifted and Talented, p. 202B AL Early Finishers, p. 202B OL AL	English Learners, p. 204B ELL Below Level, p. 204B BL Early Finishers, p. 204B AL	English Learners, p. 208B ELL Gifted and Talented, p. 208B AL Early Finishers, p. 208B AL
Alternate Lesson		*IMPACT Mathematics:* Unit B	*IMPACT Mathematics:* Unit B

Formative Assessment
Mid-Chapter Check (p. 207)

Problem Solving in Science
(p. 212)

Chapter Planner

	Lesson 5-6 (Pacing: 1 day)	Lesson 5-7 (Pacing: 1 day)	Lesson 5-8 (Pacing: 1 day)
Lesson/ Objective	**Multiplication and Division Expressions** (pp. 214–216) **Objective:** Write and find the value of multiplication and division expressions.	**Problem-Solving Investigation: Choose a Strategy** (pp. 218–219) **Objective:** Choose the best strategy to solve a problem.	**Function Tables: Find a Rule (×, ÷)** (pp. 220–223) **Objective:** Find and use rules to write multiplication and division equations.
State/Local Standards			
Math Vocabulary			
Lesson Resources	**Materials** index cards, cups **Manipulatives** counters **Other Resources** CRM Leveled Worksheets (pp. 33–37) Daily Reteach • 5-Minute Check • Problem of the Day	**Other Resources** CRM Leveled Worksheets (pp. 38–42) Daily Reteach • 5-Minute Check • Problem of the Day *Oceans: Into the Deep*	**Materials** index cards, chart paper, cardboard box **Manipulatives** counters **Other Resources** CRM Leveled Worksheets (pp. 43–47) Daily Reteach • 5-Minute Check • Problem of the Day
Technology		Math Songs Track #2	Math Songs Track #2
Math Online	Personal Tutor	Personal Tutor	Personal Tutor
Reaching All Learners	English Learners, p. 214B ELL Below Level, p. 214B BL Early Finishers, p. 214B OL AL	English Learners, p. 218B ELL Below Level, p. 218B BL Early Finishers, p. 218B AL	English Learners, p. 220B ELL Gifted and Talented, p. 220B AL Early Finishers, p. 220B OL AL
Alternate Lesson	*IMPACT Mathematics:* Unit B		*IMPACT Mathematics:* Unit B

Game Time
Expression Race (p. 217)

Summative Assessment
- Study Guide/Review (p. 224)
- Chapter Test (p. 231)
- Test Practice (p. 232)

Assessment Options

Diagnostic Assessment

SE *Option 1:* Quick Check (p. 192)
Option 2: Online Quiz macmillanmh.com
CRM *Option 3:* Diagnostic Test (p. 49)
CRM *Option 4:* Chapter Pretest (p. 50)

Formative Assessment

TE Alternate Teaching Strategies (in every lesson)
SE Talk About It (in every lesson)
SE Writing in Math (in every lesson)
SE Check What You Know (in every lesson)
TE Ticket Out the Door (p. 195)
TE Into the Future (p. 211)
TE Name the Math (pp. 201, 206, 216)
SE Mid-Chapter Check (p. 207)
CRM Lesson Quizzes (pp. 51–53)
CRM Mid-Chapter Test (p. 54)

Summative Assessment

SE Chapter Test (p. 231)
SE Test Practice (p. 232)
CRM Vocabulary Test (p. 55)
CRM Leveled Chapter Tests (pp. 60–71)
CRM Cumulative Test Practice (pp. 74–76)
CRM Oral Assessment (pp. 56–57)
ExamView® Assessment Suite
Advance Tracker

Professional Development

Targeted professional development has been articulated throughout **McGraw-Hill's *Math Connects*** program. The **McGraw-Hill Professional Development Video Library** provides short videos that support the **NCTM Focal Points and Focal Connections.** For more information visit macmillanmh.com.

Model Lessons

Instructional Strategies

Assessment Tips

Students will be solving simple addition and subtraction equations by using cups, counters, and the algebra mat.

- Ask students to explain how to solve a given equation.
- Avoid making judgments about the students' work while observing them.
- Jot down observations on small self-sticking notes, including student's name and the date.
- These self-sticking notes can then be filed in the student's portfolio.

Teacher Notes

Learning Stations

Cross-Curricular Links

Writing

individual | LINGUISTIC

Story Time

- A story has a beginning, a middle, and an end. Is this like an equation or an expression? Explain.
- Write a story where the main character starts out with a value, must do something to that value, using either addition or subtraction, and then must solve for the answer. Write an equation to match the action your character must take.

Teacher Note: A story is like an equation because an expression has not been solved yet, so it does not have an ending; stories and equations will vary.

Beginning + Middle = End

Materials:

- paper
- pencil

Health

pair | LOGICAL

Exercise Equations

Balance your exercise equations using the Calorie counts for the exercises listed below.

Yoga: 230 Calories/hour	Tennis: 350 Calories/hour
Light walking: 250 Calories/hour	Football: 460 Calories/hour
Cross-country skiing: 500 Calories/hour	Running: 700 Calories/hour

- Each person writes an amount of exercise on an index card. Hand your card to your partner. Challenge him or her to come up with an equivalent amount of exercise that will balance your equation. Write down your equations.

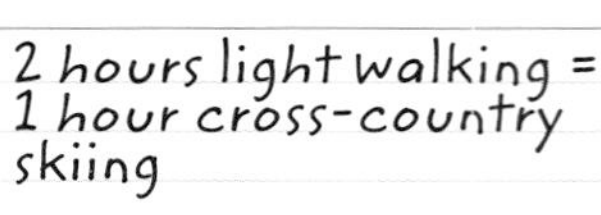

Materials:

- index cards
- markers

Reading

individual | LOGICAL

Measure It

Eratosthenes measured the Earth using camels and a light shining down into a well. You can use things other than rulers, too.

- Read *The Librarian Who Measured The Earth* by Kathryn Lasky by yourself or with a partner.
- How many school buses do you think it would take to measure the length of your school? Use the measurements provided at this Learning Station of a school bus to write and illustrate an equation to show how you would figure this out and solve your equation.

school bus + school bus + school bus = length of school

Materials:

- *The Librarian Who Measured The Earth* by Kathryn Lasky
- measurements of a large school bus
- paper
- pencil

Science

SPATIAL

Balancing Act

- One partner chooses a number of weights and places them on one of the balance scale trays.
- The other partner writes down the weights by denomination on one side of the equation, and then places different weight denominations on the second tray to equal the amount of weight on the first tray.
- The first partner writes down the other side of the equation, using the weight denominations chosen by the second partner.

Materials:
- balance scale
- 1, 5, and 10-gram weights
- paper
- pencils

Music

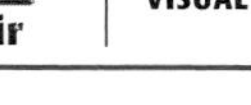
VISUAL

Balanced Tunes

In music, measures are divided into beats. In some songs, quarter notes equal 1 beat, half notes equal 2 beats, and whole notes equal 4 beats in a measure. A half note with a dot next to it equals 3 beats.

- Make a one-measure card using whatever combination of notes you wish, but they must equal 4 beats. Challenge your partner to make a card using different note values, but still equaling 4 beats.
- Combine your two cards to make eight beats on one side of the equation and work together to make a different combination of eight beats to balance the equation.

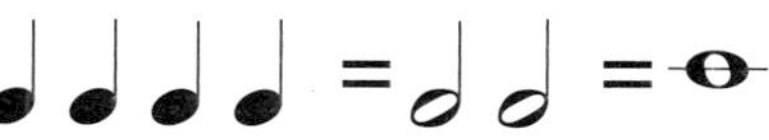

Materials:
- index cards
- markers
- paper
- pencils

Social Studies

VISUAL

Money In, Money Out

State and federal governments try to balance their budgets. This means they try not to spend more money than they take in.

- Each partner starts off with $5 of play money. This is the money that you spend from your budget. Write your amounts in denominations: for example, two $1 bills, 8 quarters, 5 dimes, and 10 nickels. But do not show your partner.
- Exchange your money amounts and write down your new denominations. This is the money you take into your budget. Check your addition to make sure your budget is balanced.

Materials:
- $5 play money per person, different denominations for each partner
- paper
- pencils

Introduce the Chapter

 Real World: How Many Are Here?

Share with students that they are going to learn about variables, expressions, and equations in this chapter. Explain that an equation is a sentence that contains an equals sign and shows that two expressions are equal.

- Present students with the following scenario:

There are two classes for tumblers in a gymnastic school. There are 28 students in one class and 24 students in the other class. How many tumblers are there in all?

You can write an equation to help you find the answer.

- **What operation will you use?** addition
- **What numbers will you add?** 28 + 24 **Write on the board "28 + 24 = ."**
- **What variable can you write to hold the place for the sum?** Accept all reasonable answers.
- Write "*x*" as the variable.
- **What number does the variable *x* represent?** 52
- **How many tumblers are in the two classes?** 52 tumblers

Direct students to Student Edition p. 190. Have students read the paragraph at the top of the page.

- **Which math symbols can you name?** Sample answer: +, −, ×, ÷

WRITING IN MATH

Starting the Chapter
Have students write a short paragraph explaining when they may need an equation to solve a problem.

Key Vocabulary Introduce the key vocabulary in the chapter using the routine below.

Define: An equation is a sentence that contains an equals sign, showing that two expressions are equal.
Example: When I see an equals sign in a number sentence, I know the two sides must be equal.
Ask: How can you check to see if an equation is true?

Read-Aloud Anthology For an optional reading activity to introduce this chapter's math concepts, see the Read-Aloud Anthology on p. TR26.

Describe Algebraic Patterns

BIG Idea What are expressions and equations?

An **expression** is a combination of variables, numbers, and at least one operation. An **equation** is a number sentence that contains an equals sign (=), showing that two expressions are equal.

Example A tiger can live *x* years in the wild and 5 years longer than that in a zoo. The equation below can be used to find how long a tiger could live in the wild if it could live 20 years in a zoo.

x	+	5	=	20
years in wild				years in zoo

What will I learn in this chapter?

- Identify, describe, and extend patterns.
- Write and find the value of expressions.
- Write and solve equations.
- Find and use a rule to write an equation.
- Identify extra or missing information.

Key Vocabulary

expression
parentheses
equation
pattern

Math Online **Student Study Tools at** macmillanmh.com

Chapter 5 Project

Make a Game

Have students create a math game, based on a favorite game or format.

Solve: The game must involve addition or subtraction of whole numbers.

- Students work in groups to decide on the kind of game and the overall design.
- They make the game board, list rules and how to win, and provide computational practice.
- Groups play each other's games and decide on a favorite.

 *Refer to Chapter 5 Resource Masters, p. 58, for a rubric to assess students' progress on this project.*

FOLDABLES Study Organizer

Make this Foldable to help you organize information about describing algebraic patterns. Begin with a piece of 11″ × 17″ paper.

1. **Fold** lengthwise 3″ from the bottom.
2. **Fold** the paper in half.
3. **Open** and staple on either side to form pockets.
4. **Label** as shown. Take notes on index cards.

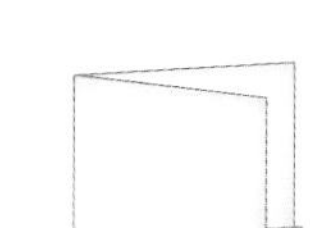

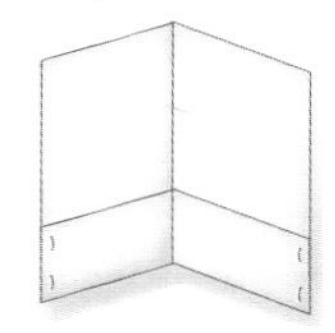

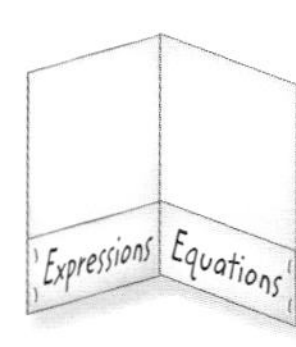

Chapter 5 Describe Algebraic Patterns 191

ELL National ESL Standards Alignment for Chapter 5

Lesson, Page	ESL Standard	Modality	Level
5-1, p. 193B	Goal 2, Standard 2, b	Logical	Intermediate
5-2, p. 198B	Goal 2, Standard 1, a	Logical	Intermediate
5-3, p. 202B	Goal 2, Standard 2, l	Auditory, Social	Advanced
5-4, p. 204B	Goal 2, Standard 2, i	Logical, Visual	Intermediate
5-5, p. 208B	Goal 2, Standard 2, g	Visual, Logical	Intermediate
5-6, p. 214B	Goal 2, Standard 3, h	Logical, Intrapersonal	Intermediate
5-7, p. 218B	Goal 2, Standard 3, g	Logical, Social	Advanced
5-8, p. 220B	Goal 2, Standard 2, a	Kinesthetic	Intermediate

The National ESL Standards can be found in the Teacher Reference Handbook.

FOLDABLES Dinah Zike's Foldables

Guide students through the directions on p. 191 to create their own Foldables graphic organizers for adding and subtracting. Students may also use their Foldables to study and review for chapter assessments.

When to Use It Lessons 5-1, 5-2, 5-4, and 5-6. (Additional instructions for using the Foldable with these lessons are found on pp. 207 and 224.)

Chapter 5 Literature List

Lesson	Book Title
5-1	**The Grapes of Math** Greg Tang
5-2	**Whales** Gail Gibbons
5-3	**Spaghetti and Meatballs for All** Marilyn Burns
5-4	**A Cloak For A Dreamer** Aileen Friedman
5-5	**Two of Everything** Lily Toy Hong
5-6	**Mailing May** Michael O. Tunnel
5-8	**Multiplying Menace: The Revenge of Rumpelstiltskin** Pam Calvert

- Read the Math at Home letter found in the Chapter 5 Resource Masters, p. 4, with the class and have each student sign it. (A Spanish version is found on p. 5.)
- Send home copies of the Math at Home letter with each student.

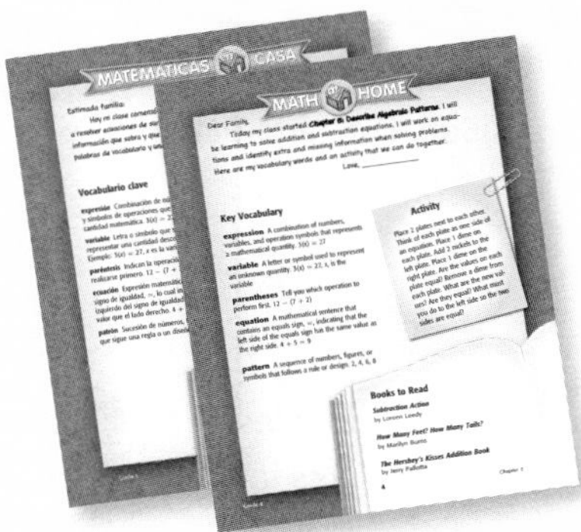

Diagnostic Assessment

Check for students' prerequisite skills before beginning the chapter.

- **Option 1:** ***Quick Check***
  SE Student Edition, p. 192
- **Option 2:** ***Online Assessment***
  Math Online macmillanmh.com
- **Option 3:** ***Diagnostic Tests***
  CRM Chapter 5 Resource Masters, p. 49–50

RTI (Response to Intervention)

Apply the Results Based on the results of the Diagnostic Assessment on Student Edition p. 192, use the chart below to address individual needs before beginning the chapter.

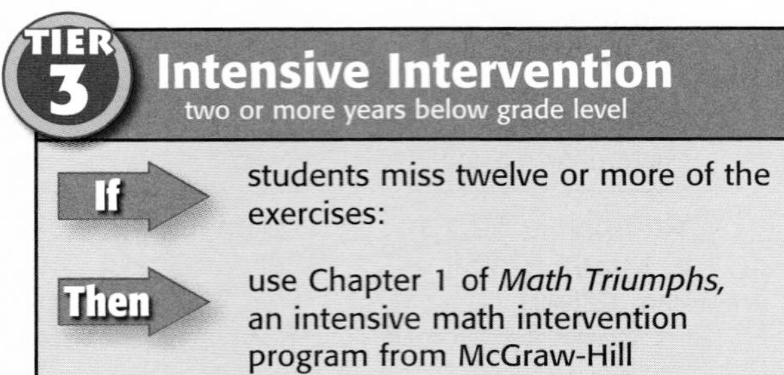
TIER 3 Intensive Intervention
two or more years below grade level

If students miss twelve or more of the exercises:

Then use Chapter 1 of *Math Triumphs,* an intensive math intervention program from McGraw-Hill

ARE YOU READY for Chapter 5?

You have two ways to check prerequisite skills for this chapter.

Option 2

Math Online Take the Chapter Readiness Quiz at macmillanmh.com.

Option 1

Complete the Quick Check below.

QUICK Check

Find the missing number. (Prior Grade) (Used in Lessons 5-1 and 5-2)

1. 8 + ■ = 11 3
2. ■ + 5 = 9 4
3. 6 + ■ = 15 9
4. 13 − ■ = 7 6
5. ■ − 4 = 8 12
6. 18 − ■ = 16 2
7. Use the number sentence 12 + 15 + ■ = 36 to find how many books Tony read in August. 9 books

Summer Reading Club	
Month	Number of Books Read
June	12
July	15
August	■

8. What property is illustrated by 6 + 5 = 5 + 6? Commutative Property of Addition

Find the value of each expression. (Prior Grade) (Used in Lessons 5-1 and 5-2)

9. 8 + 1 + 6 15
10. 7 + 2 − 3 6
11. 2 + 10 − 6 6
12. 11 + 6 − 6 11
13. 12 − 3 + 4 13
14. 16 + 4 − 10 10

Identify each pattern. Then find the next number in the pattern. (Prior Grade) (Used in Lesson 5-4)

15. 3, 6, 9, 12, 15 +3; 18
16. 7, 12, 17, 22, 27 +5; 32
17. 23, 19, 15, 11, 7 −4; 3
18. Each baseball uniform needs 3 buttons. Copy and complete the table to find how many buttons are needed for 12 uniforms.

Uniforms	3	6	9	12
Buttons	9	18	27	■ 36

192 **Chapter 5** Describe Algebraic Patterns

TIER 2 Strategic Intervention
below/approaching grade level

If students miss six to eleven in: **Exercises 1–18**

Then choose a resource:

Strategic Intervention Guide (pp. 30, 32, 34, 132)

TE Start Smart 3: Sun, Fun, and Patterns (p. 6)

Math Online Extra Examples • Personal Tutor • Concepts in Motion

TIER 1 On-Level

If students miss three to five in: **Exercises 1–18**

Then choose a resource:

TE Learning Stations (pp. 190G–190H)

TE Chapter Project (p. 190)

CRM Game: Calculate the Cards

Math Adventures

My Math Zone Chapter 4

Math Online Fact Dash

Above/Beyond Level

If students miss two or less in: **Exercises 1–18**

Then choose a resource:

TE Learning Stations (pp. 190G–190H)

TE Chapter Project (p. 190)

Real-World Problem Solving: *Oceans: Into the Deep*

My Math Zone Chapter 4, 5

Math Online Games

LESSON 5-1

Addition and Subtraction Expressions

Lesson Planner

Objective

Write and find the value of expressions.

Vocabulary

expression, **variable**, **parentheses**

Resources

Materials: paper bag, index cards

Manipulatives: counters

Literature Connection: *The Grapes of Math* by Greg Tang

Alternate Lesson: Use *IMPACT Mathematics: Unit B* to provide practice with expressions.

Teacher Technology
TeacherWorks • Interactive Classroom • Math Songs Track #2 Lesson Plan

Daily Routine

Use these suggestions before beginning the lesson on p. 193.

5-Minute Check

(Reviews Lesson 4-9)

Find all of the factors of each number.

1. 6 1, 2, 3, 6 **2.** 18 1, 2, 3, 6, 9, 18

Identify the first five multiples for each number.

3. 4 0, 4, 8, 12, 16 **4.** 10 0, 10, 20, 30, 40

Problem of the Day

Jake is older than Susana but younger than Gibson. Susana is four years younger than Gibson and two years younger than Jake. Jake is 12. How old are Gibson and Susana? Gibson is 14 and Susana is 10.

Focus on Math Background

It is extremely important for students to understand the algebraic language that is introduced in this lesson. Students should begin to understand the concept of variables that represent numbers and know what expressions are. Knowing what expressions are and aren't will help them in later lessons, as they will need to be able to distinguish between expressions and equations.

$12 + \blacksquare - 3$	$12 + \blacksquare = 3$
expression (no equals sign)	equation (equals sign)

Note that you *evaluate* expressions and you *solve* equations. In this lesson and others in this chapter, encourage students to use precise mathematical language as they talk about expressions and finding the value of them.

Building Math Vocabulary

Write the lesson vocabulary words and their definitions on the board.

Give students mathematical examples of expressions and parentheses. Have students write their own examples for each and put them in their Math Journals.

Visual Vocabulary Cards

Use Visual Vocabulary Card 16 to reinforce the vocabulary introduced in this lesson. (The Define/Example/Ask routine is printed on the back of each card.)

expression

Differentiated Instruction

Small Group Options

LOGICAL, LINGUISTIC

Option 1 Gifted and Talented AL

Materials: paper, pencil

- Challenge students to write an expression for this puzzle.

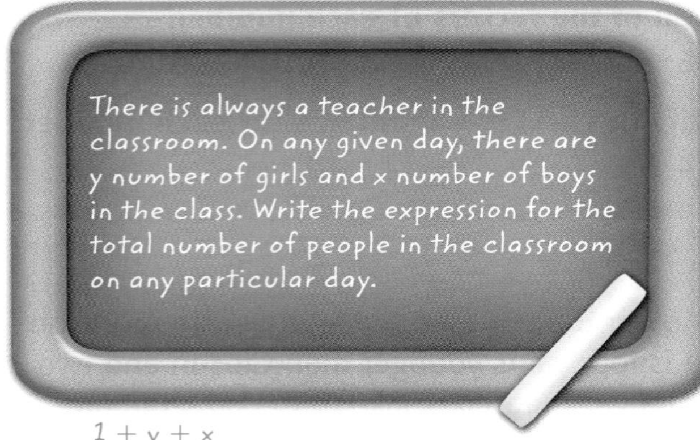

There is always a teacher in the classroom. On any given day, there are y number of girls and x number of boys in the class. Write the expression for the total number of people in the classroom on any particular day.

LOGICAL

Option 2 English Language Learners ELL

Materials: chalk, chalkboard
Core Vocabulary: question mark, symbols, replace
Common Use Verb: is unknown

Hear Math In this strategy, students use symbols to represent a number.

- Post "?" Say: "This is a **question mark**. What is a **question mark** used for?" Accept responses. Say, "A **question mark** is used when something ***is unknown*** or when we have a question about something."
- Write: "5 × ? = ?"
- Work through the problem, filling in 4 into both spaces: 5 × 4 = 4. Say: "Is this true?" Allow students to come up with 5 × 4 = 20.
- Demonstrate replacing each ? with a different symbol.
- Ask students to write a problem replacing two numbers with two symbols. Have their neighbors solve.

Independent Work Options

LINGUISTIC

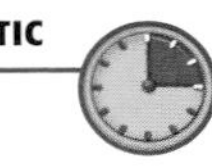

Option 1 Early Finishers AL

Materials: index cards

- Write expressions on several index cards.
- Give each student one card and have him or her write a word problem about the expression. Have students exchange cards with another student to check for accuracy.

Option 2 Student Technology

Math Online macmillanmh.com

Personal Tutor • Extra Examples

Math Songs, "Algebra Rocks" Track #2

Option 3 Learning Station: Writing (p. 190G)

Direct students to the Writing Learning Station for opportunities to explore and extend the lesson concept.

Option 4 Problem-Solving Practice

Reinforce problem-solving skills and strategies with the Problem-Solving Practice worksheet.

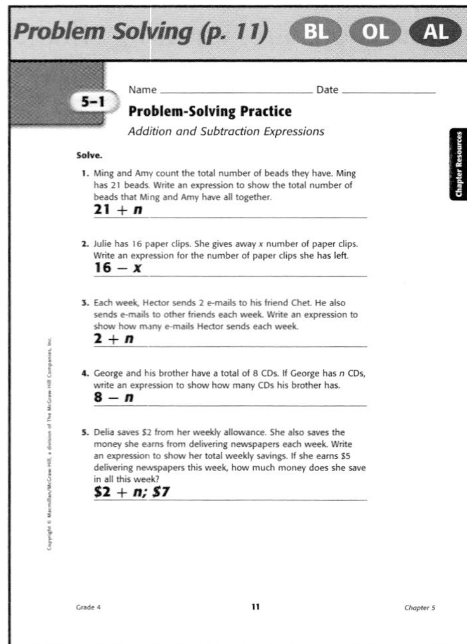

Problem Solving (p. 11) BL OL AL

Name ________ Date ________

5-1 Problem-Solving Practice

Addition and Subtraction Expressions

Chapter Resources

Solve.

1. Ming and Amy count the total number of beads they have. Ming has 21 beads. Write an expression to show the total number of beads that Ming and Amy have all together.
   21 + *n*
2. Julie has 16 paper clips. She gives away *x* number of paper clips. Write an expression for the number of paper clips she has left.
   16 − *x*
3. Each week, Hector sends 2 e-mails to his friend Chet. He also sends e-mails to other friends each week. Write an expression to show how many e-mails Hector sends each week.
   2 + *n*
4. George and his brother have a total of 8 CDs. If George has *n* CDs, write an expression to show how many CDs his brother has.
   8 − *n*
5. Delia saves $2 from her weekly allowance. She also saves the money she earns from delivering newspapers each week. Write an expression to show her total weekly savings. If she earns $5 delivering newspapers this week, how much money does she save in all this week?
   $2 + *n*; $7

Grade 4 11 Chapter 5

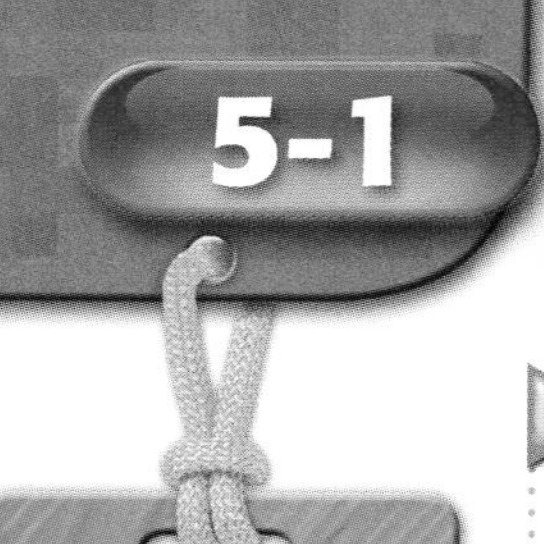

Addition and Subtraction Expressions

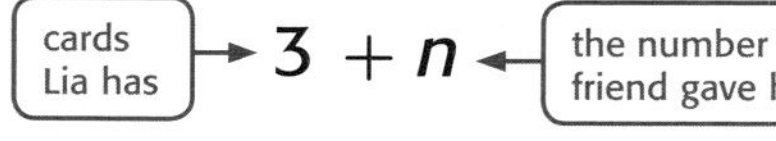

Lia has 3 baseball cards. Her friend gave her some more. You can show the number of cards Lia now has by using the expression below.

cards Lia has → $3 + n$ ← the number her friend gave her

MAIN IDEA

I will write and find the value of expressions.

New Vocabulary

expression
variable
parentheses

Math Online

macmillanmh.com
- Extra Examples
- Personal Tutor
- Self-Check Quiz

An **expression** like $3 + n$ is a statement with numbers and/or variables, and at least one operation. A **variable** can represent the unknown value. You can find the value of an expression if you know the value of the variable.

Real-World EXAMPLE Find Value of an Expression

1 **ALGEBRA If Lia's friend gives her 5 baseball cards, how many cards will she have?**

You need to find the value of $3 + n$ when $n = 5$.

$3 + n$ Write the expression.

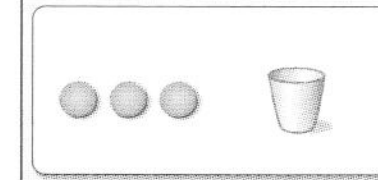

$3 + 5$ Replace n with 5.

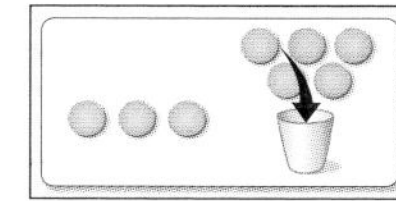

8 Add 3 and 5.

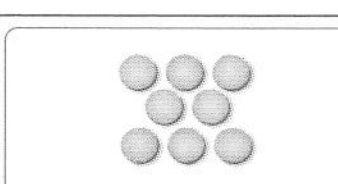

So, the value of $3 + n$ when $n = 5$ is 8.
Lia will have 8 baseball cards.

Addition and Subtraction Expressions

1 Introduce

Activity Choice 1 • Hands-On

- Put several counters in one hand and a closed bag with several counters in it in the other. Tell students that you have counters in the bag.
- **How many counters do I have altogether?** Answers will vary depending on guesses.
- **Does anyone know for sure how many counters I have?** no
- Explain that when you do not know how many or when the number can vary, you can use a variable to stand for the unknown amount.
- Use the actual number of counters that you have in one hand and label the number of counters in the bag as x to write an expression for the number of counters that you have altogether, for example $5 + x$. Write the expression on the board.

Activity Choice 2 • Literature

Introduce the lesson with *The Grapes of Math* by Greg Tang. For a related math activity, see p. TR48.

2 Teach

Scaffolding Questions

On the board, write the expression that you wrote in Activity Choice 1 to represent the total number of counters. To help students see the variability of the variable x, ask the following questions:

- **How many counters do I have if there are 4 counters in the bag?** Answers will vary depending on the expression.
- **How many counters do I have if there are 10 counters in the bag?** Answers will vary depending on the expression.
- **Why is a variable used in an expression?** Sample answer: It stands for an unknown number.

GET READY to Learn

Have students open their books and read the information in **Get Ready to Learn**. Introduce **expression** and **parentheses**. As a class, work through **Examples 1–3**.

Find the Value of an Expression

Example 2 Point out the parentheses in this expression. Call attention to the fact that the operation in the parentheses is performed first.

ADDITIONAL EXAMPLES

1. Mr. and Mrs. Presley and some of their children eat apples in their lunches. Today, 3 of their children are eating apples. What is the value of $2 + c$ when $c = 3$? 5
2. Find the value of $15 + (x - 3)$ if $x = 4$. 16
3. Danielle ran 6 fewer miles than Martha last week. Write an expression for the number of miles Danielle ran. $y - 6$

CHECK What You Know

As a class, have students complete Exercises 1–8 in **Check What You Know** as you observe their work.

Exercise 8 Assess student comprehension before assigning practice exercises.

BL Alternate Teaching Strategy

If students have trouble with addition and subtraction expressions…

Then use one of these reteach options:

1. CRM **Daily Reteach Worksheet** (p. 8)
2. Provide students with an index card on which is written "how many?" Have students use the card (in place of the variable) in problems. Have them read each problem aloud using the card. From Example 1: 3 + "how many?" equals the total number baseball cards Lia will have.

Additional Answer

8. Sample answer: Beth had some pencils. She gave one pencil to each of her six friends. Write an expression for the number of pencils Beth has left.

COMMON ERROR!

Exercises 27 and 28 Students may switch the symbols and numbers when using "subtracted from" and "fewer than." Have students replace the symbol with a simple number like 10 or 50 to think through the correct order of the expression.

Some expressions contain parentheses, ( ). The **parentheses** tell you which operation to perform first.

EXAMPLE Find the Value of an Expression

2 **Find the value of $12 - (r + 2)$ if $r = 7$.**

$12 - (r + 2)$	Write the expression.
$12 - (7 + 2)$	Replace r with 7.
$12 - 9$	Find $(7 + 2)$ first.
3	Next, find $12 - 9$.

Real-World EXAMPLE Write an Expression

3 ALGEBRA **Latisha made 3 fewer baskets than Felisa. Write an expression for the number of baskets Latisha made.**

Words	3 fewer baskets than Felisa
Symbol	Define a variable. Let k represent the baskets Felisa made.
Expression	$k - 3$

So, Latisha made $k - 3$ baskets.

CHECK What You Know

Find the value of each expression if $x = 4$ and $m = 8$. See Examples 1 and 2 (pp. 193–194)

1. $x + 2$ 6
2. $19 - m$ 11
3. $8 - (x + 1)$ 3

Write an expression for each situation. See Example 3 (p. 194)

4. two more than k $k + 2$
5. 44 minus y $44 - y$
6. the sum of 17 and z $17 + z$

Measurement **The length of a condor is 7 inches more than the length of a bald eagle.**

7. If a bald eagle is 12 inches, what is the length of a condor? 19 in.
8. Talk About It Describe a situation that could be represented by $x - 6$. See margin.

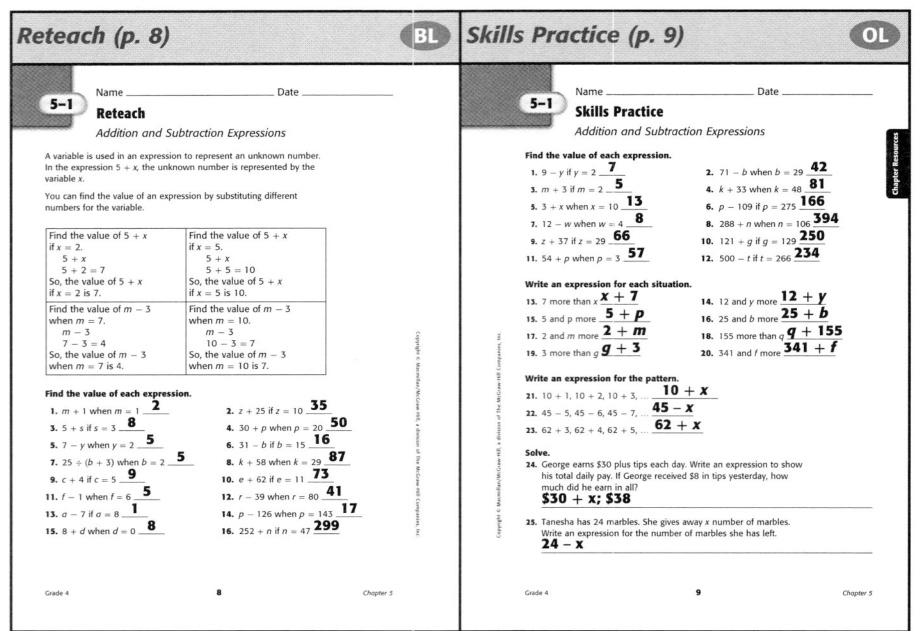

Reteach (p. 8) BL

5-1 Name ______ Date ______

Reteach

Addition and Subtraction Expressions

A variable is used in an expression to represent an unknown number. In the expression $5 + x$, the unknown number is represented by the variable x.

You can find the value of an expression by substituting different numbers for the variable.

Find the value of $5 + x$ if $x = 2$. $5 + x$ $5 + 2 = 7$ So, the value of $5 + x$ if $x = 2$ is 7.	Find the value of $5 + x$ if $x = 5$. $5 + x$ $5 + 5 = 10$ So, the value of $5 + x$ if $x = 5$ is 10.
Find the value of $m - 3$ when $m = 7$. $m - 3$ $7 - 3 = 4$ So, the value of $m - 3$ when $m = 7$ is 4.	Find the value of $m - 3$ when $m = 10$. $m - 3$ $10 - 3 = 7$ So, the value of $m - 3$ when $m = 10$ is 7.

Find the value of each expression.

1. $m + 1$ when $m = 1$ **2**
2. $z + 25$ if $z = 10$ **35**
3. $5 + s$ if $s = 3$ **8**
4. $30 + p$ when $p = 20$ **50**
5. $7 - y$ when $y = 2$ **5**
6. $31 - b$ if $b = 15$ **16**
7. $25 \div (b + 3)$ when $b = 2$ **5**
8. $k + 58$ when $k = 29$ **87**
9. $c + 4$ if $c = 5$ **9**
10. $e + 62$ if $e = 11$ **73**
11. $f - 1$ when $f = 6$ **5**
12. $r - 39$ when $r = 80$ **41**
13. $a - 7$ if $a = 8$ **1**
14. $p - 126$ when $p = 143$ **17**
15. $8 + d$ when $d = 0$ **8**
16. $252 + n$ if $n = 47$ **299**

Grade 4 8 Chapter 5

Skills Practice (p. 9) OL

5-1 Name ______ Date ______

Skills Practice

Addition and Subtraction Expressions

Chapter Resources

Find the value of each expression.

1. $9 - y$ if $y = 2$ **7**
2. $71 - b$ when $b = 29$ **42**
3. $m + 3$ if $m = 2$ **5**
4. $k + 33$ when $k = 48$ **81**
5. $3 + x$ when $x = 10$ **13**
6. $p - 109$ if $p = 275$ **166**
7. $12 - w$ when $w = 4$ **8**
8. $288 + n$ when $n = 106$ **394**
9. $z + 37$ if $z = 29$ **66**
10. $121 + g$ if $g = 129$ **250**
11. $54 + p$ when $p = 3$ **57**
12. $500 - t$ if $t = 266$ **234**

Write an expression for each situation.

13. 7 more than x **$x + 7$**
14. 12 and y more **$12 + y$**
15. 5 and p more **$5 + p$**
16. 25 and b more **$25 + b$**
17. 2 and m more **$2 + m$**
18. 155 more than q **$q + 155$**
19. 3 more than g **$g + 3$**
20. 341 and f more **$341 + f$**

Write an expression for the pattern.

21. $10 + 1, 10 + 2, 10 + 3, \ldots$ **$10 + x$**
22. $45 - 5, 45 - 6, 45 - 7, \ldots$ **$45 - x$**
23. $62 + 3, 62 + 4, 62 + 5, \ldots$ **$62 + x$**

Solve.

24. George earns $30 plus tips each day. Write an expression to show his total daily pay. If George received $8 in tips yesterday, how much did he earn in all?
$30 + x; $38
25. Tanesha has 24 marbles. She gives away x number of marbles. Write an expression for the number of marbles she has left.
24 − x

Grade 4 9 Chapter 5

Practice and Problem Solving

Find the value of each expression if $y = 9$ and $b = 5$. See Examples 1 and 2 (pp. 193–194)

9. $y + 2$ 11 **10.** $b + 9$ 14 **11.** $y - 4$ 5 **12.** $11 - b$ 6

13. $y + 20$ 29 **14.** $14 + b$ 19 **15.** $8 - b$ 3 **16.** $12 - y$ 3

17. $(y - 3) + 7$ 13 **18.** $15 - (b + 1)$ 9 **19.** $(y + 8) - 5$ 12 **20.** $b + (17 - 9)$ 13

21. $(y - 5) + 23$ 27 **22.** $(b - 2) + 8$ 11 **23.** $36 + (y - 1)$ 44 **24.** $(25 - 5) + y$ 29

Write an expression for each situation. See Example 3 (p. 194)

25. three more than t $t + 3$

26. the sum of d and six $d + 6$

27. ten subtracted from m $m - 10$

28. the difference of x and fifty-six $x - 56$

29. the sum of a and seven $a + 7$

30. thirteen more than n $n + 13$

31. the sum of w and 5 subtracted from 16 $16 - (w + 5)$

32. the sum of c and 23 subtracted from 100 $100 - (c + 23)$

Brock had 3 cats. One of the cats had kittens. See Example 3 (p. 194)

33. Define a variable. Then write an expression for the number of cats and kittens Brock has now.
Let k = kittens; $3 + k$

34. Using the expression above, if the one cat has 4 kittens, how many cats will Brock have? 7 cats

Cole has 5 fewer soccer cards than his brother. See Example 3 (p. 194)

35. Define a variable. Then write an expression for the number of cards Cole has.
Let c = brother's cards; $c - 5$

36. Using the expression above, if Cole's brother has 15 cards, how many cards does Cole have? 10 cards

H.O.T. Problems

37. OPEN ENDED Describe a real-world situation for $12 - a$.
Sample answer: Michael had 12 marbles, then lost some.

38. WHICH ONE DOESN'T BELONG? Identify the expression that does not belong with the other three. Explain your reasoning. Sample answer: $2 + 5$; It does not have a variable.

$3 - x$	$2 + 5$	$4 - y$	$z + 1$

39. **WRITING IN ▶MATH** Explain what a variable means in an expression. Sample answer: It means an unknown quantity.

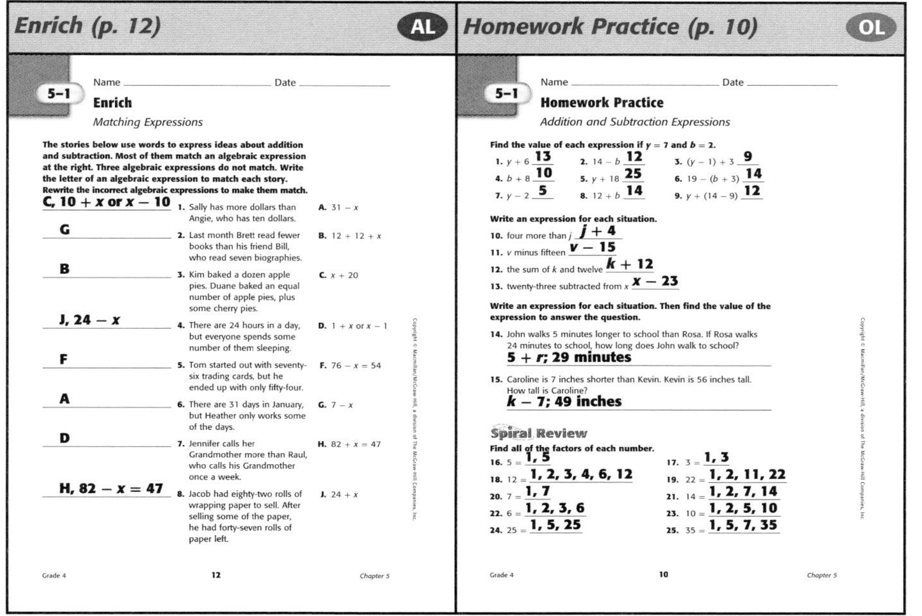

Enrich (p. 12) AL

5-1 Name ______ Date ______

Enrich

Matching Expressions

The stories below use words to express ideas about addition and subtraction. Most of them match an algebraic expression at the right. Three algebraic expressions do not match. Write the letter of an algebraic expression to match each story. Rewrite the incorrect algebraic expressions to make them match.

C, $10 + x$ or $x - 10$ **1.** Sally has more dollars than Angie, who has ten dollars. **A.** $31 - x$

G **2.** Last month Brett read fewer books than his friend Bill, who read seven biographies. **B.** $12 + 12 + x$

B **3.** Kim baked a dozen apple pies. Duane baked an equal number of apple pies, plus some cherry pies. **C.** $x + 20$

J, $24 - x$ **4.** There are 24 hours in a day, but everyone spends some number of them sleeping. **D.** $1 + x$ or $x - 1$

F **5.** Tom started out with seventy-six trading cards, but he ended up with only fifty-four. **F.** $76 - x = 54$

A **6.** There are 31 days in January, but Heather only works some of the days. **G.** $7 - x$

D **7.** Jennifer calls her Grandmother more than Raul, who calls his Grandmother once a week. **H.** $82 + x = 47$

H, $82 - x = 47$ **8.** Jacob had eighty-two rolls of wrapping paper to sell. After selling some of the paper, he had forty-seven rolls of paper left. **J.** $24 + x$

Grade 4 12 Chapter 5

Homework Practice (p. 10) OL

5-1 Name ______ Date ______

Homework Practice

Addition and Subtraction Expressions

Find the value of each expression if $y = 7$ and $b = 2$.

1. $y + 6$ 13 **2.** $14 - b$ 12 **3.** $(y - 1) + 3$ 9

4. $b + 8$ 10 **5.** $y + 18$ 25 **6.** $19 - (b + 3)$ 14

7. $y - 2$ 5 **8.** $12 + b$ 14 **9.** $y + (14 - 9)$ 12

Write an expression for each situation.

10. four more than j $j + 4$

11. v minus fifteen $v - 15$

12. the sum of k and twelve $k + 12$

13. twenty-three subtracted from x $x - 23$

Write an expression for each situation. Then find the value of the expression to answer the question.

14. John walks 5 minutes longer to school than Rosa. If Rosa walks 24 minutes to school, how long does John walk to school?
$5 + r$; 29 minutes

15. Caroline is 7 inches shorter than Kevin. Kevin is 56 inches tall. How tall is Caroline?
$k - 7$; 49 inches

Spiral Review

Find all of the factors of each number.

16. 5 = 1, 5 **17.** 3 = 1, 3

18. 12 = 1, 2, 3, 4, 6, 12 **19.** 22 = 1, 2, 11, 22

20. 7 = 1, 7 **21.** 14 = 1, 2, 7, 14

22. 6 = 1, 2, 3, 6 **23.** 10 = 1, 2, 5, 10

24. 25 = 1, 5, 25 **25.** 35 = 1, 5, 7, 35

Grade 4 10 Chapter 5

3 Practice

Differentiate practice using these leveled assignments for Exercises 9–39.

Level	Assignment
BL Below/Approaching Level	9–16, 25–27, 31–32
OL On Level	13–24, 29–32, 33–34, 38
AL Above/Beyond Level	9–35 odd, 37–39

Have students discuss and complete the Higher Order Thinking problems. For Exercise 37 challenge students to find a real-world situation that would have happened this week.

WRITING IN ▶MATH Have students complete Exercise 39 in their Math Journals. You may choose to use this exercise as an optional formative assessment.

4 Assess

Formative Assessment

- **Write an expression for the total number of people if there are a driver, two assistants, and a number of students on a bus.**
  Sample answer: $3 + y$ or $1 + 2 + y$
- **How would you find the number of people on the bus if there are 35 students?**
  Sample answer: Replace the symbol with 35, then $3 + 35 = 38$.

Quick Check **Are students continuing to struggle with addition and subtraction?**

If Yes → Strategic Intervention Guide (p. 30)

If No → Independent Work Options (p. 183B)
CRM Skills Practice Worksheet (p. 9)
CRM Enrich Worksheet (p. 12)

Ticket Out the Door Give each student on a piece of paper an addition expression with a variable. Have students evaluate the expression when the variable = 20.

Algebra Activity for 5-2

Lesson Planner

Objective

Explore addition and subtraction equations.

Resources

Manipulatives: 2-colored counters, plastic cups

Teacher Technology

macmillanmh.com

Concepts in Motion

1 Introduce

Introduce the Concept

- Begin with 5 counters in your hand and 6 in a cup. Do not let students see what is in the cup. Tell students there are 5 counters in your hand and 11 altogether.
- **How many counters are in the cup?** 6 counters
- **How could we write this situation as an equation?** $5 + x = 11$
- Ask students to use the word "equation" to name the number sentence and give the definition.
- Repeat 2 or 3 times using different amounts.

2 Teach

Activity 1 Students may work individually or in pairs. Check students' work as they model each expression. Each student should place 2 counters in his or her cup.

Algebra Activity for 5-2
Addition and Subtraction Equations

MAIN IDEA

I will explore addition and subtraction equations.

You Will Need
counters
cups

An **equation** is a sentence like $4 + 5 = 9$ that contains an equals sign (=). The equals sign shows that the expressions on each side of it are equal. Equations sometimes have a missing number.

$4 + x = 9$ $\quad$ $10 - m = 6$ $\quad$ $k - 1 = 7$

When you find the value of the missing number that makes the equation true, you **solve** the equation.

1 **Solve $n + 3 = 5$.**

Step 1 **Model the expression on the left side.**

To model $n + 3$, use a cup to show n and 3 counters.

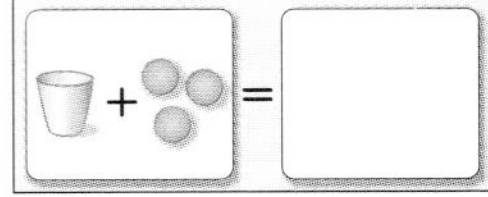

Step 2 **Model the expression on the right side.**

Place 5 counters on the right to show 5. An equals sign shows that both sides are the same.

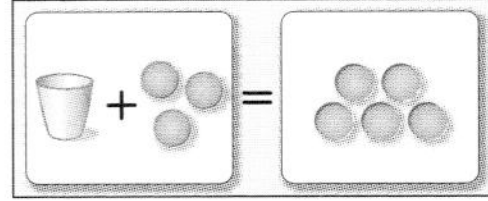

Step 3 **Find the value of n.**

Put enough counters in the cup so that the number of counters on each side of the equals sign is the same.

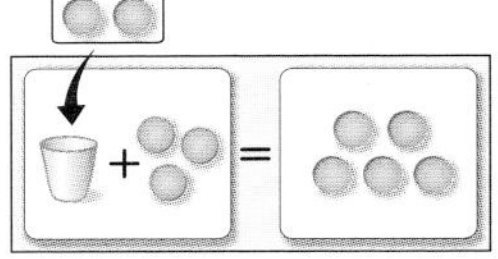

The value of n that makes $n + 3 = 5$ true is 2. So, $n = 2$.

Hands-On Activity

You can also use counters to model equations involving subtraction.

ACTIVITY

2 **Solve $x - 4 = 2$.**

Step 1 **Model $x - 4 = 2$.**

Use a cup and counters to show $x - 4 = 2$.

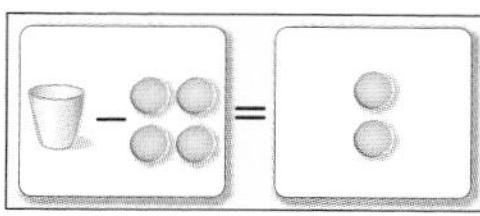

Step 2 **Find the value of x.**

Think how many counters need to be placed in the cup so that when 4 are taken away, 2 will be left.

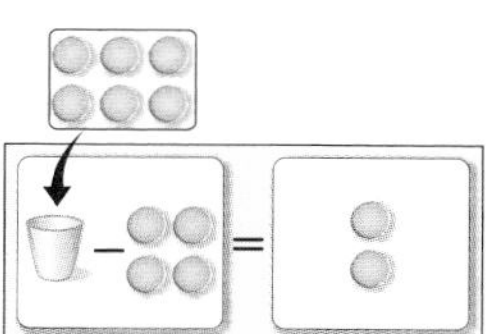

The number of counters in the cup is the missing number. So, the value of x that makes this equation true is 6. So, $x = 6$.

Think About It 1, 3. See margin.

1. How would you model $k + 2 = 9$?
2. What is the value of k in $k + 2 = 9$? 7
3. Explain how to check your answer.

10. Sample answer: An equation has an equals sign, an expression does not. Equation: $k + 2 = 9$; Expression: $h - 2$

CHECK What You Know

Write an equation for each model. Then find the value of n.

4. 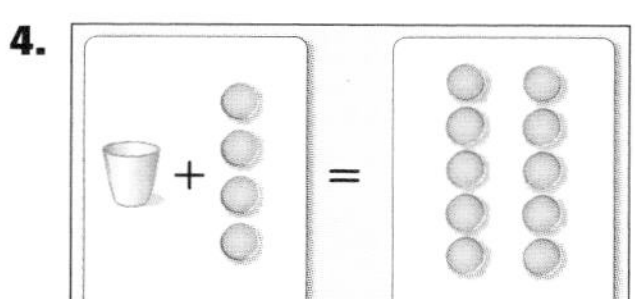 $n + 4 = 10$; 6

5. 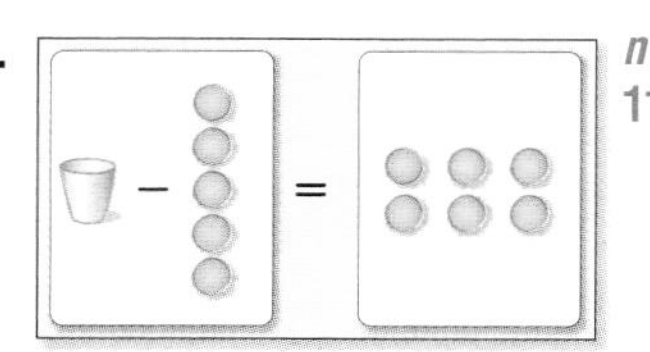 $n - 5 = 6$; 11

Solve each equation. Use models if needed.

6. $b + 3 = 8$ 5
7. $14 - f = 8$ 6
8. $17 - h = 12$ 5
9. $k + 9 = 19$ 10

10. WRITING IN MATH Explain the difference between an expression and an equation. Give an example of each.

Activity 2 After students have each placed two counters in the cup, point out that they must be able to take 4 counters from those in the cup and get 2 counters. Since the cup is to the left of the subtraction sign, you know that the number is greater than 4.

Think About It

Assign Exercises 1–3 to assess student comprehension of the concept presented in the Activities.

3 Assess

Formative Assessment

Use **Check What You Know** Exercises 6 and 7 to assess whether students can use models to solve addition and subtraction equations.

From Concrete to Abstract Use Exercises 6–9 to bridge the gap between using a visual model of an equation and an equation modeled with counters.

Extending the Concept

- **What do you know about the expressions on both sides of the equals sign?** Sample answer: The amounts (or values) on both sides are equal.

Additional Answers

1. Sample answer: Use a cup to show k. Then use 2 counters to show the number 2, and use 9 counters to show the number 9.
3. Sample answer: Place the answer in the equation to make sure it is correct.

LESSON 5-2

Solve Equations

Lesson Planner

Objective

Solve addition and subtraction equations.

Vocabulary

equation, **solve**

Resources

Manipulatives: counters, plastic cups, connecting cubes

Literature Connection: *Whales* by Gail Gibbons

Alternate Lesson: Use *IMPACT Mathematics: Unit B* to provide practice with equations.

Teacher Technology
TeacherWorks • Interactive Classroom • Math Songs Track #2 Lesson Plan

Daily Routine

Use these suggestions before beginning the lesson on p. 198.

5-Minute Check

(Reviews Lesson 5-1)

Find the value of each expression if $x = 3$ and $y = 4$.

1. $(9 - y) + 7$ 12
2. $x + (3 - 2)$ 4
3. $8 + (15 - x)$ 20
4. $4 + (y + 5)$ 13
5. $(y + 4) - 3$ 5

Problem of the Day

Antoine has 125 baseball cards. Jeb has 36 fewer than Antoine. How many baseball cards do they have in all? 214 cards

Focus on Math Background

At this point in the development of algebraic concepts, students are asked to use diagrams of models to solve equations. Diagrams of cups and counters help students move from the concrete activities such as those investigated in the Hands-On Activities for this lesson to more abstract procedures. Note that this lesson stops short of using the properties of equality to solve equations. For example, in the equation $y + 6 = 17$, students are *not* asked to subtract 6 from each side of the equation. Instead, they are told to ask themselves, *What number plus 6 equals 17*? That is, students are asked to use mental math to solve simple one-step addition or subtraction equations.

Building Math Vocabulary

Write the lesson vocabulary words and their definitions on the board.

Have students explain how the words *equation* and *equal* are related. Ask them to write an example of an equation using a variable and addition or subtraction. Have them try to solve their equation.

Visual Vocabulary Cards

Use Visual Vocabulary Cards 14 and 47 to reinforce the vocabulary introduced in this lesson. (The Define/Example/Ask routine is printed on the back of each card.)

Differentiated Instruction

Small Group Options

Option 1 Below Level BL

VISUAL, SPATIAL

Materials: 20 two-colored counters, paper, pencil

- Give students counters and these problems written on paper:
- Have them solve the problems, using the counters to help illustrate their answers.
- Students may need to trace counters on paper to illustrate and solve correctly.

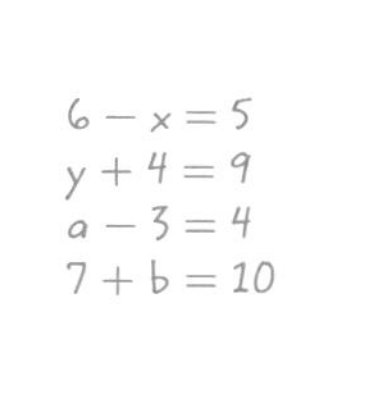

Option 2 English Language Learners ELL

LOGICAL

Materials: small box, pencils
Core Vocabulary: a picture, to picture, mentally
Common Use Verb: imagine

See Math This strategy develops the idea of symbols and expands students' problem-solving vocabulary.

- Model putting their hands interlaced on top of the desk; instruct students to only use their minds to think of the answer; no writing.
- Write or tape a symbol, such as "▲", on a box. Say, "The box will be the symbol."
- Using the tray on the chalkboard, create an equation. For example, place 4 pencils on the tray, hide 6 inside the symbol box, and write "= 10."
- Ask students to imagine how many pencils are in the symbol box.
- Ask students to write or draw how they tried to solve the problem.
- Repeat with different equations (include subtraction problems).

Independent Work Options

Option 1 Early Finishers AL

LOGICAL, LINGUISTIC

Materials: index cards

- Have students write a word problem on one side of an index card and a corresponding expression or equation on the back of the card.
- These cards can be used as part of an exercise series for a learning station or for other activities for early finishers.

Option 2 Student Technology

Math Online macmillanmh.com

Personal Tutor • Extra Examples

 Math Adventures

Math Songs, "Algebra Rocks" Track #2

Option 3 Learning Station: Reading (p. 190G)

Direct students to the Reading Learning Station for opportunities to explore and extend the lesson concept.

Option 4 Problem-Solving Practice

Reinforce problem-solving skills and strategies with the Problem-Solving Practice worksheet.

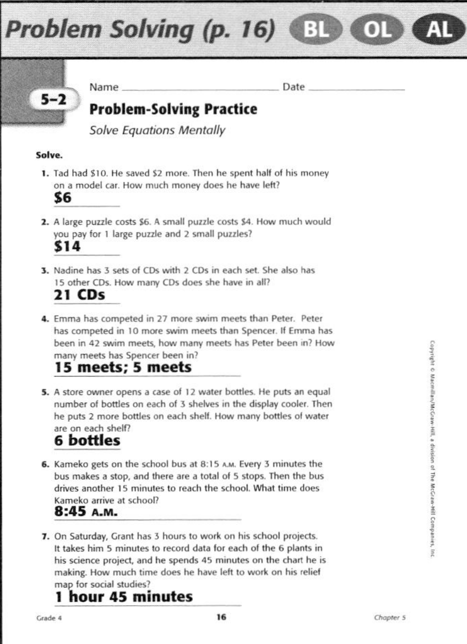

Problem Solving (p. 16) BL OL AL

5–2 Name ______________ Date ________

Problem-Solving Practice

Solve Equations Mentally

Solve.

1. Tad had $10. He saved $2 more. Then he spent half of his money on a model car. How much money does he have left?
$6

2. A large puzzle costs $6. A small puzzle costs $4. How much would you pay for 1 large puzzle and 2 small puzzles?
$14

3. Nadine has 3 sets of CDs with 2 CDs in each set. She also has 15 other CDs. How many CDs does she have in all?
21 CDs

4. Emma has competed in 27 more swim meets than Peter. Peter has competed in 10 more swim meets than Spencer. If Emma has been in 42 swim meets, how many meets has Peter been in? How many meets has Spencer been in?
15 meets; 5 meets

5. A store owner opens a case of 12 water bottles. He puts an equal number of bottles on each of 3 shelves in the display cooler. Then he puts 2 more bottles on each shelf. How many bottles of water are on each shelf?
6 bottles

6. Kameko gets on the school bus at 8:15 A.M. Every 3 minutes the bus makes a stop, and there are a total of 5 stops. Then the bus drives another 15 minutes to reach the school. What time does Kameko arrive at school?
8:45 A.M.

7. On Saturday, Grant has 3 hours to work on his school projects. It takes him 5 minutes to record data for each of the 6 plants in his science project, and he spends 45 minutes on the chart he is making. How much time does he have left to work on his relief map for social studies?
1 hour 45 minutes

Grade 4 16 Chapter 5

5-2 Solve Equations

1 Introduce

Activity Choice 1 • Hands-On 

- Have students use counters and cups to model $x + 4 = 12$. Have students solve the equation with models.
- **How did you model $x + 4$?** an empty cup and 4 counters
- **How did you model 12?** 12 counters
- **What is the value of x?** $x = 8$

Activity Choice 2 • Literature

Introduce the lesson with *Whales* by Gail Gibbons. For a related math activity, see p. TR48.

2 Teach

Scaffolding Questions

- Remind students that they know how to use models to solve equations. Point out that they can also solve equations mentally.
- Write the following equation on the board:
  $$a + 8 = 20$$
- Tell students to think of a number plus 8 that equals 20.
- **What number is that?** 12
- Now show the equation $15 - b = 10$.
- **What question should you ask yourself?** Fifteen minus what number equals 10?
- **Solve the equation.** $b = 5$

GET READY to Learn

Have students open their books and read the information in **Get Ready to Learn**. Introduce **equation**, and **solve**. As a class, work through **Examples 1–3**.

COMMON ERROR!

In subtraction exercises, students may reverse the order of subtraction. To help them avoid this error, remind them to always check their solutions with addition.

5-2 Solve Equations

MAIN IDEA

I will solve addition and subtraction equations.

New Vocabulary

equation
solve

Math Online

macmillanmh.com

- Extra Examples
- Personal Tutor
- Self-Check Quiz

GET READY to Learn

Wendy downloaded 4 songs on Monday. After she downloaded some more songs on Tuesday, she had a total of 9 songs. How many songs did she download on Tuesday?

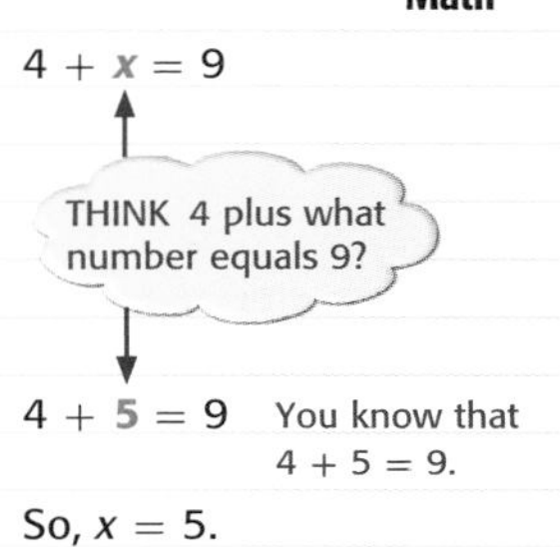

In the previous Explore Activity, you **solved equations** using models. Equations can also be solved mentally.

Solve Addition Equations

1 **MUSIC** **How many songs did Wendy download on Tuesday?**

One Way: Use Models

Step 1 Model the equation.

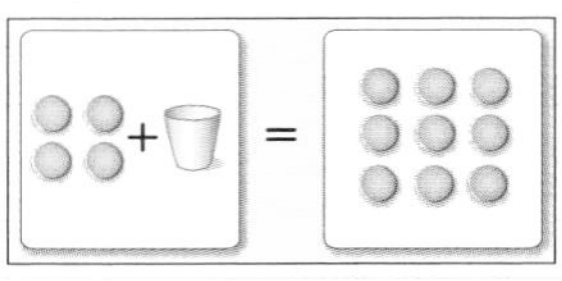

$4 + x = 9$

Step 2 Find the value of x.

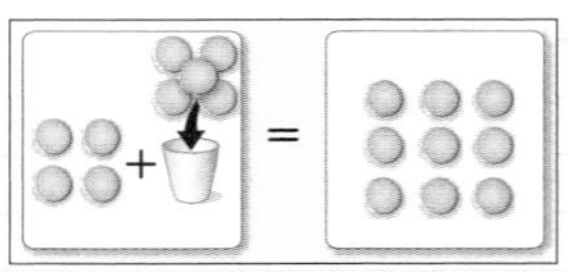

Another Way: Mental Math

$4 + x = 9$

THINK 4 plus what number equals 9?

$4 + 5 = 9$ You know that $4 + 5 = 9$.

So, $x = 5$.

So, $x = 5$. Wendy downloaded 5 songs on Tuesday.

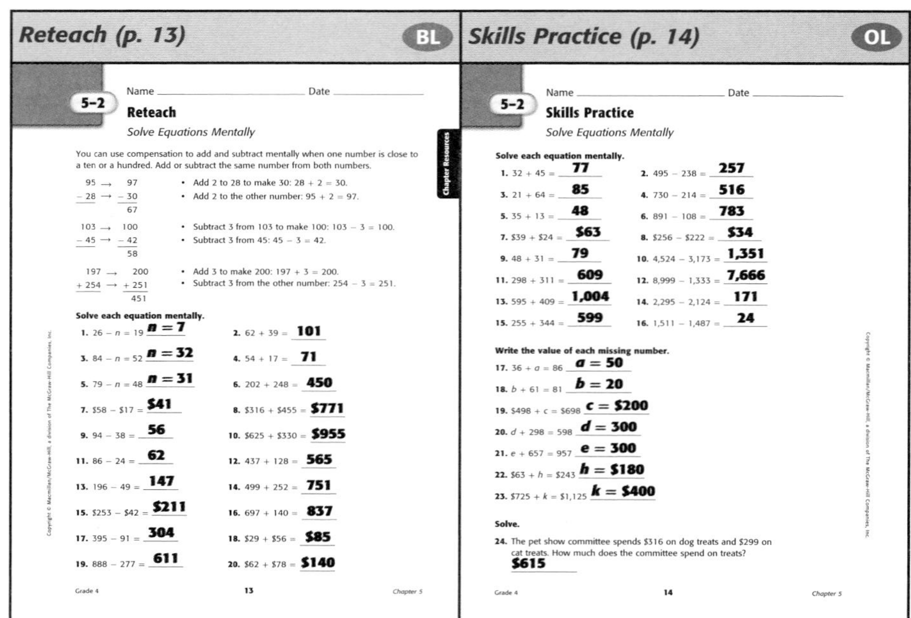

Reteach (p. 13) BL

5-2 Name ______ Date ______

Reteach

Solve Equations Mentally

You can use compensation to add and subtract mentally when one number is close to a ten or a hundred. Add or subtract the same number from both numbers.

95 → 97; − 28 → − 30; 67
- Add 2 to 28 to make 30: $28 + 2 = 30$.
- Add 2 to the other number: $95 + 2 = 97$.

103 → 100; − 45 → − 42; 58
- Subtract 3 from 103 to make 100: $103 - 3 = 100$.
- Subtract 3 from 45: $45 - 3 = 42$.

197 → 200; + 254 → + 251; 451
- Add 3 to make 200: $197 + 3 = 200$.
- Subtract 3 from the other number: $254 - 3 = 251$.

Solve each equation mentally.

1. $26 - n = 19$ **$n = 7$**
2. $62 + 39 =$ **101**
3. $84 - n = 52$ **$n = 32$**
4. $54 + 17 =$ **71**
5. $79 - n = 48$ **$n = 31$**
6. $202 + 248 =$ **450**
7. $\$58 - \$17 =$ **$\$41$**
8. $\$316 + \$455 =$ **$\$771$**
9. $94 - 38 =$ **56**
10. $\$625 + \$330 =$ **$\$955$**
11. $86 - 24 =$ **62**
12. $437 + 128 =$ **565**
13. $196 - 49 =$ **147**
14. $499 + 252 =$ **751**
15. $\$253 - \$42 =$ **$\$211$**
16. $697 + 140 =$ **837**
17. $395 - 91 =$ **304**
18. $\$29 + \$56 =$ **$\$85$**
19. $888 - 277 =$ **611**
20. $\$62 + \$78 =$ **$\$140$**

Grade 4 13 Chapter 5

Chapter Resources

Skills Practice (p. 14) OL

5-2 Name ______ Date ______

Skills Practice

Solve Equations Mentally

Solve each equation mentally.

1. $32 + 45 =$ **77**
2. $495 - 238 =$ **257**
3. $21 + 64 =$ **85**
4. $730 - 214 =$ **516**
5. $35 + 13 =$ **48**
6. $891 - 108 =$ **783**
7. $\$39 + \$24 =$ **$\$63$**
8. $\$256 - \$222 =$ **$\$34$**
9. $48 + 31 =$ **79**
10. $4{,}524 - 3{,}173 =$ **1,351**
11. $298 + 311 =$ **609**
12. $8{,}999 - 1{,}333 =$ **7,666**
13. $595 + 409 =$ **1,004**
14. $2{,}295 - 2{,}124 =$ **171**
15. $255 + 344 =$ **599**
16. $1{,}511 - 1{,}487 =$ **24**

Write the value of each missing number.

17. $36 + a = 86$ **$a = 50$**
18. $b + 61 = 81$ **$b = 20$**
19. $\$498 + c = \$698$ **$c = \$200$**
20. $d + 298 = 598$ **$d = 300$**
21. $e + 657 = 957$ **$e = 300$**
22. $\$63 + h = \$243$ **$h = \$180$**
23. $\$725 + k = \$1{,}125$ **$k = \$400$**

Solve.

24. The pet show committee spends \$316 on dog treats and \$299 on cat treats. How much does the committee spend on treats? **$\$615$**

Grade 4 14 Chapter 5

 Solve Subtraction Equations

2 **Solve $18 - y = 13$.**

$18 - y = 13$ — 18 minus what number equals 13?

$18 - 5 = 13$ — You know that $18 - 5 = 13$.

$y = 5$

So, the value of y is 5.

 **Real-World EXAMPLE** Write and Solve Equations

3 ALGEBRA **Garcia had 9 video games. He bought some more video games and now has a total of 12. How many video games did he buy?**

Write and solve an equation.

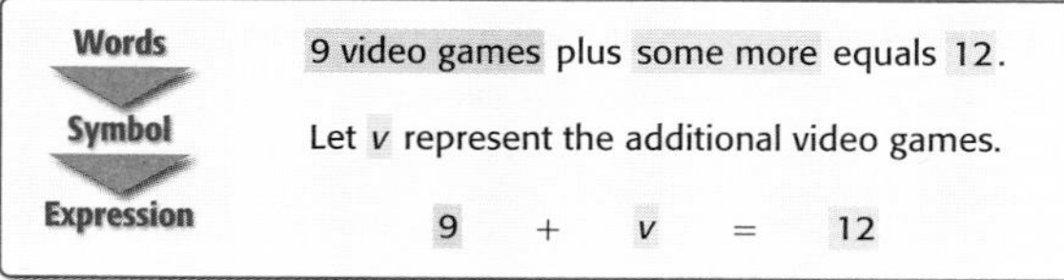

Words	9 video games plus some more equals 12.
Symbol	Let v represent the additional video games.
Expression	$9 \quad + \quad v \quad = \quad 12$

$9 + v = 12$ — 9 plus what number equals 12?

$9 + 3 = 12$ — You know that $9 + 3 = 12$.

$v = 3$

So, $v = 3$. Garcia bought 3 more video games.

8. Sample answer: Think: what number can 3 be subtracted from to get 12? $15 - 3 = 12$; so $k = 15$.

CHECK What You Know

Solve each equation. See Examples 1 and 2 (pp. 198–199)

1. $5 + c = 11$ 6 **2.** $k + 9 = 17$ 8 **3.** $13 + n = 20$ 7

4. $8 - h = 4$ 4 **5.** $14 - f = 9$ 5 **6.** $m - 12 = 12$ 24

7. Keisha scored 14 points in the first half of a basketball game. At the end of the game, she had a total of 36 points. Write and solve an equation to find how many points she scored in the second half of the game. See Example 3 (p. 199) $14 + n = 36; 22$

8. Talk About It Explain how to solve $k - 3 = 12$.

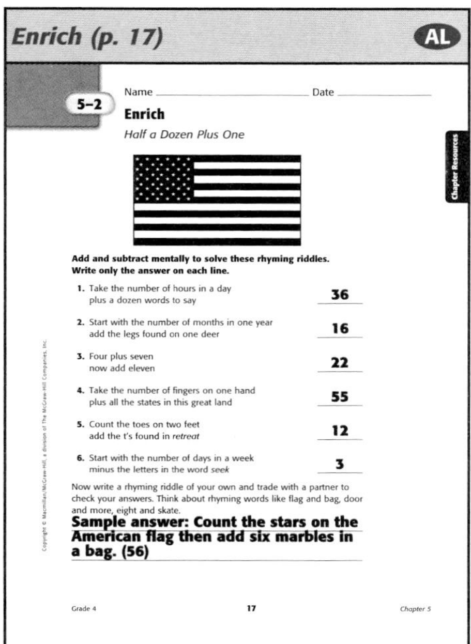

Enrich (p. 17) AL

5-2 Name ______ Date ______

Enrich

Half a Dozen Plus One

Add and subtract mentally to solve these rhyming riddles. Write only the answer on each line.

1. Take the number of hours in a day plus a dozen words to say **36**
2. Start with the number of months in one year add the legs found on one deer **16**
3. Four plus seven now add eleven **22**
4. Take the number of fingers on one hand plus all the states in this great land **55**
5. Count the toes on two feet add the t's found in *retreat* **12**
6. Start with the number of days in a week minus the letters in the word *seek* **3**

Now write a rhyming riddle of your own and trade with a partner to check your answers. Think about rhyming words like flag and bag, door and more, eight and skate.

Sample answer: Count the stars on the American flag then add six marbles in a bag. (56)

Chapter Resources

Grade 4 17 Chapter 5

Solve Addition Equations

Example 1 Encourage students to use mental math to check their answers.

ADDITIONAL EXAMPLES

1. Ming baby sat for 6 hours in 2 days. For how many hours did Ming baby sit on the second day if she baby sat 2 hours on the first day? Solve this equation: $2 + n = 6$ $n = 4$
2. Solve $19 - n = 12$. $n = 7$
3. Big Red had 7 puppies last spring. This spring she had some more puppies and now has a total of 13 puppies. How many puppies did she have this spring? Write and solve an equation. $7 + n = 13; n = 6$

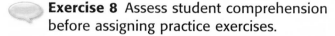

CHECK What You Know

As a class, have students complete Exercises 1–8 in **Check What You Know** as you observe their work.

Exercise 8 Assess student comprehension before assigning practice exercises.

BL Alternate Teaching Strategy

If students have trouble solving equations…

Then use one of these reteach options:

1. CRM **Daily Reteach Worksheet** (p. 13)
2. Have students use cubes to model $7 + a = 12$. Have students draw an equals sign in the middle of a sheet of paper. On the right side, they place a cube train of 12 cubes vertically and trace around them. (Make sure students trace around each individual cube.) Then have students remove the cubes.

   On the left side of the equals sign they trace a cube train of 7 cubes, aligned at the bottom with the train on the right. Have students decide how many cubes must be added to the top of the train at the left to equal the number at the right.

3 Practice

Differentiate practice using these leveled assignments for Exercises 9–28.

Level	Assignment
BL Below/Approaching Level	9–16, 21–24, 25
OL On Level	9–19, 22–25, 27
AL Above/Beyond Level	10–26 even, 27–28

Have students discuss and complete the Higher Order Thinking problems. For Exercise 27, suggest that students find the value of n for each equation to determine whether Caleb and Adriana are correct.

WRITING IN MATH Have students complete Exercise 28 in their Math Journals. You may choose to use this exercise as an optional formative assessment.

Practice and Problem Solving

See page R13.

Solve each equation. See Examples 1 and 2 (pp. 198–199)

9. $1 + a = 4$ 3
10. $d + 4 = 6$ 2
11. $6 + f = 10$ 4
12. $h + 8 = 15$ 7
13. $k + 10 = 17$ 7
14. $9 + n = 20$ 11
15. $4 - b = 2$ 2
16. $m - 5 = 6$ 11
17. $7 - r = 2$ 5
18. $w - 8 = 12$ 20
19. $9 = 15 - y$ 6
20. $11 = z - 12$ 23

Write and solve an equation for each situation. See Example 3 (p. 199)

21. A number plus 8 equals 19. $n + 8 = 19$; 11

22. The sum of 11 and a number is 35. $11 + n = 35$; 24

23. Nine subtracted from a number equals 12. $n - 9 = 12$; 21

24. Fifteen less than a number is 15. $n - 15 = 15$; 30

Real-World PROBLEM SOLVING

Science Some mammals live as long as humans. The table shows the average number of years some mammals can live.

Mammals with Longest Lives	
Mammal	**Years Lived**
Killer whale	90
Blue whale	80
Human	76
African elephant	70
Gorilla	35

Source: *Scholastic Book of World Records*

25. Write an equation to represent a killer whale's life span minus x years equals the African elephant's life span. Find x. $90 - x = 70$; 20

26. Write an equation to represent a human's life span plus another mammal's life span (y) equals 111. What is the value of y? Which animal's life span does the y stand for? $76 + y = 111$; 35; gorilla

H.O.T. Problems

27. FIND THE ERROR Caleb and Adriana say that the two equations have the same solution for n. Are they correct? Explain. 27, 28. See Ch. 5 Answer Appendix.

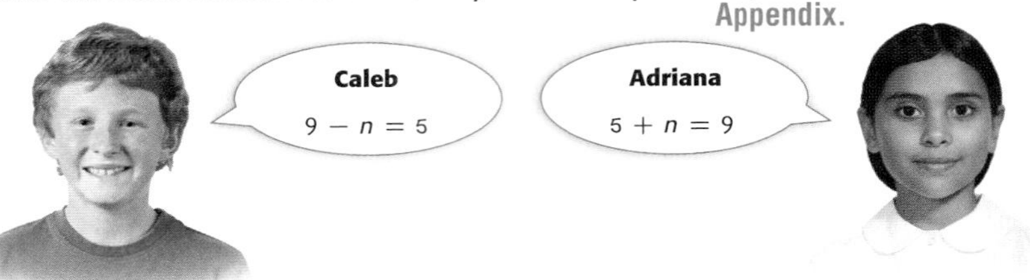

28. **WRITING IN MATH** Write one or two sentences explaining how to solve an equation.

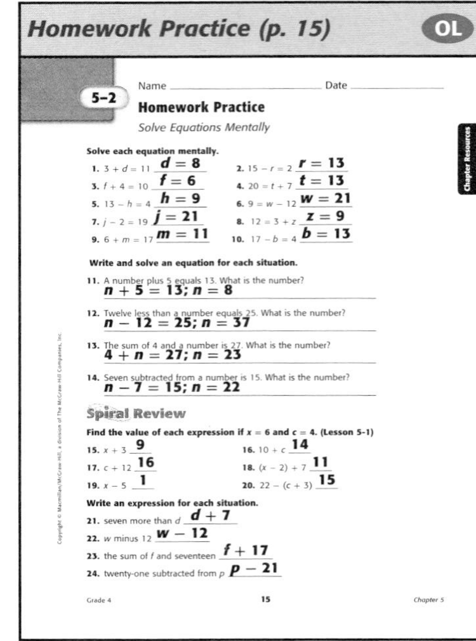

Homework Practice (p. 15) OL

5-2

Name ______ Date ______

Homework Practice

Solve Equations Mentally

Solve each equation mentally.

1. $3 + d = 11$ $d = 8$
2. $15 - r = 2$ $r = 13$
3. $f + 4 = 10$ $f = 6$
4. $20 = t + 7$ $t = 13$
5. $13 - h = 4$ $h = 9$
6. $9 = w - 12$ $w = 21$
7. $j - 2 = 19$ $j = 21$
8. $12 = 3 + z$ $z = 9$
9. $6 + m = 17$ $m = 11$
10. $17 - b = 4$ $b = 13$

Write and solve an equation for each situation.

11. A number plus 5 equals 13. What is the number? $n + 5 = 13; n = 8$
12. Twelve less than a number equals 25. What is the number? $n - 12 = 25; n = 37$
13. The sum of 4 and a number is 27. What is the number? $4 + n = 27; n = 23$
14. Seven subtracted from a number is 15. What is the number? $n - 7 = 15; n = 22$

Spiral Review

Find the value of each expression if $x = 6$ and $c = 4$. (Lesson 5-1)

15. $x + 3$ 9
16. $10 + c$ 14
17. $c + 12$ 16
18. $(x - 2) + 7$ 11
19. $x - 5$ 1
20. $22 - (c + 3)$ 15

Write an expression for each situation.

21. seven more than d $d + 7$
22. w minus 12 $w - 12$
23. the sum of f and seventeen $f + 17$
24. twenty-one subtracted from p $p - 21$

Chapter Resources

Grade 4 15 Chapter 5

29. What is the value of the expression $16 - (8 + x)$ if $x = 2$? (Lesson 5-1) A

A 6

B 10

C 20

D 22

30. What is the value of the expression below if $y = 5$? (Lesson 5-2) F

$$y + (22 - 7)$$

F 20

G 21

H 22

J 24

31. Ann sweeps the floor every third day. If she sweeps the floor on September 10, on which of the following days will she NOT have to sweep the floor? (Lesson 5-2) C

September

Sunday	Monday	Tuesday	Wednesday	Thursday	Friday	Saturday
	1	2	3	4	5	6
7	8	9	10	11	12	13
14	15	16	17	18	19	20
21	22	23	24	25	26	27
28	29	30				

A September 13

B September 19

C September 23

D September 28

Spiral Review

32. Write an expression for *three less than n*. (Lesson 5-1) $n - 3$

Find all the factors of each number. (Lesson 4-9)

33. 36 1,2,3,4,6,9,12,18,36 34. 45 1,3,5,9,15,45 35. 100 1,2,4,5,10,20,25,50,100

36. A giant panda bear eats 84 pounds of bamboo a day. Copy and complete the table to find out the total amount of bamboo the bear will eat in a week. (Lesson 3-3)

Day	1	2	■3	4	5	■6	7
Bamboo	84	■ 168	252	336	■ 420	504	■ 588

37. **Measurement** The longest airport runway in the world is 5,000 meters. The shortest airport runway is 533 meters. What is the difference in the lengths of these two runways? (Lesson 2-5) 4,467

Compare. Use >, <, or = . (Lesson 1-4)

38. 4,714 ● 4,741 <

39. 64,962 ● 64,926 >

4 Assess

Formative Assessment

Present the following problem:

During the frost yesterday, 7 trees lost their fruit. During the frost this morning, more trees lost their fruit. The total number of trees that lost fruit is 11. How many trees lost fruit today?

- **Write an equation to represent this situation.** $7 + n = 11$
- **How would you solve the equation? Explain.** Sample answer: Think 7 plus what number equals 11. $4 + 7 = 11$, so, $n = 4$.

Quick Check **Are students continuing to struggle with writing and solving equations mentally?**

If Yes → Small Group Options (p. 188B)
Strategic Intervention Guide (p.132)

If No → Independent Work Options (p. 88B)
CRM Skills Practice Worksheet (p. 14)
CRM Enrich Worksheet (p. 17)

Name the Math Have students explain how to solve the equation $x - 7 = 21$.

Reviews Lessons 5-1 and 5-2

Assign the Test Practice problems to provide daily reinforcement of test-taking skills.

Reviews Lessons 1-4, 2-5, 3-3, 4-9, and 5-1

Review and assess mastery of skills and concepts from previous chapters.

5-3 Problem-Solving Skill
Extra or Missing Information

Lesson Planner

Objective

Identify extra or missing information.

Resources

Literature Connection: *Spaghetti and Meatballs for All* by Marilyn Burns

Teacher Technology
TeacherWorks • Interactive Classroom

Real-World Problem Solving Library
Math and Science: *Oceans: Into the Deep*
Use these leveled books to reinforce and extend problem-solving skills and strategies.

Leveled for:

- OL On Level
- ELL Sheltered English
- SP Spanish

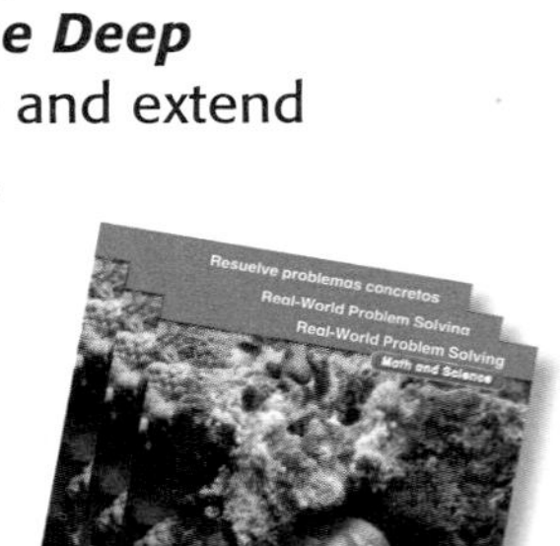

For additional support, see the Real-World Problem Solving Teacher Guide.

Daily Routine

Use these suggestions before beginning the lesson on p. 202.

5-Minute Check

(Reviews Lesson 5-2)

Solve each equation.

1. $6 + x = 13$ $x = 7$
2. $y - 2 = 7$ $y = 9$
3. $8 - a = 3$ $a = 5$
4. $n + 4 = 15$ $n = 11$

Problem of the Day

Tye and three friends bought CDs for $14, $15, $16, and $17. Lisa did not buy the most expensive CD. Janey spent a dollar more than Donovan and 2 dollars less than Tye. How much did each person spend? Donovan spent $14, Janey spent $15, Lisa $16, and Tye $17

Differentiated Instruction

Small Group Options

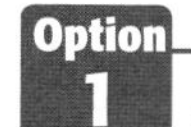

LOGICAL

Option 1 Gifted and Talented AL

Materials: paper and pencil

- Share this problem with students:
- Sandy wants to fix hot dogs for a picnic for her whole class. She buys hot dogs in packs of 8 and buns in packs of 6. Will 3 packs of buns be enough? Explain your answer. Not enough information—Students will need to know how many classmates will attend the picnic. However, 3 packs of buns = 18 buns, and 2 packs of hot dogs = 16 hot dogs. Thus, 3 packs of buns will be enough for every 2 packs of hot dogs.

SOCIAL, AUDITORY

Option 2 English Language Learners ELL

Materials: counters, classroom materials (book, paper, pencils)
Core Vocabulary: missing, lowest score, correct answers
Common Use Verb: win
Talk Math This strategy introduces extra and missing vocabulary.

- Tell students you are going to play a game. Divide the group into 2 teams.
- Call out simple addition or subtraction problems. Give the team with the correct (or fastest) answer a small number of points. Give the team with the wrong answer twice as many points. Confirm the answers are correct or incorrect.
- Repeat until the groups complain that the scoring is unfair.
- Say: "Some information is missing. Can you guess what it is?"
- Discuss why correct answers got fewer points. Reveal the winning group has the *lowest* score. Discuss how the missing information made understanding the game difficult.

Independent Work Options

LOGICAL, LINGUISTIC

Option 1 Early Finishers OL AL

Materials: paper and pencil

- Have students write two word problems: one with extra information and one with missing information. Be sure they solve the problems themselves before presenting them to another student.
- Have each student exchange problems with another student. Have the second student decide which problem is missing information and which has extra information. Ask students to solve the problems that have solutions.

Option 2 Student Technology

Math Online macmillanmh.com

Personal Tutor • Extra Examples

Option 3 Learning Station: Writing (p. 190G)

Direct students to the Writing Learning Station for opportunities to explore and extend the lesson concept.

Problem-Solving Skill: Extra or Missing Information

1 Introduce

Activity Choice 1 • Review

- Present the following problem:
  Maria has 116 gems in her rock collection and 205 quartz crystals. What is the total number of rocks in her collection?
- **Will the solution be an estimate or exact?** exact
- **Solve the problem.** 321 rocks

Activity Choice 2 • Literature

Introduce the lesson with *Spaghetti and Meatballs for All* by Marilyn Burns. For a related math activity, see p. TR48.

2 Teach

Have students read the problem on friendship bracelets. Guide them through the problem-solving steps.

Understand Using the questions, review what students know and need to find.

Plan Have them discuss their strategy.

Solve Guide students to use the identifying extra or missing information strategy to solve the problem.

- **Which numbers are needed to solve the problem?** 21 bracelets and 63 bracelets
- **What information is not needed to solve the problem?** the $2 price of each bracelet

Check Have students look back at the problem to make sure that the answer fits the facts given.

- **Do you use the $2 price of each bracelet when you check? Explain.** no; Sample answer: The $2 is extra information. It is not used in the check.

COMMON ERROR!

Exercise 8 Students may not understand that Zoe trains and rides *each* horse for a total of 50 minutes. Suggest that these students reread the problem carefully.

Problem-Solving Skill

MAIN IDEA I will identify extra or missing information.

Trina is making friendship bracelets to sell for $2 each. Last week, she sold 63 bracelets. Two weeks ago, she sold 21 bracelets. How many more bracelets did Trina sell last week than two weeks ago?

Understand

What facts do you know?

- Trina sells friendship bracelets for $2 each.
- She sold 63 bracelets last week.
- She sold 21 bracelets two weeks ago.

What do you need to find?

- Find how many more bracelets Trina sold last week than two weeks ago.

Plan

Once you identify the information needed to solve the problem, you can write an equation. Look for any extra information.

Solve

Subtract 21 from 63. You do not need to know how much the bracelets cost. This is extra information.

last week		two weeks ago		
63	−	21	=	n
	42		=	n

So, Trina sold 42 more bracelets last week than the week before.

Check

Look back. Check the subtraction with addition. Since $21 + 42 = 63$, the answer is correct.

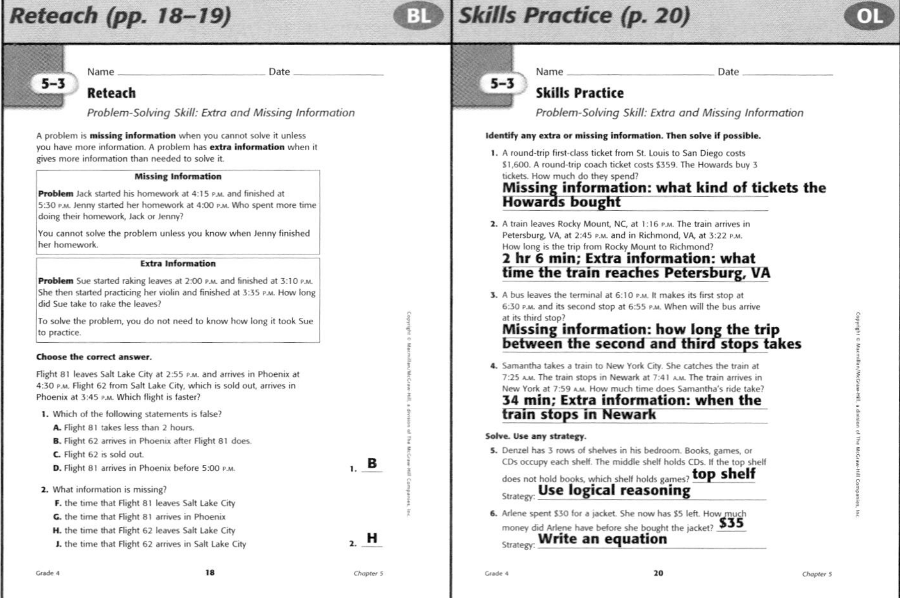

Reteach (pp. 18–19) BL

5-3 Name ________ Date ________

Reteach

Problem-Solving Skill: Extra and Missing Information

A problem is **missing information** when you cannot solve it unless you have more information. A problem has **extra information** when it gives more information than needed to solve it.

Missing Information

Problem Jack started his homework at 4:15 P.M. and finished at 5:30 P.M. Jenny started her homework at 4:00 P.M. Who spent more time doing their homework, Jack or Jenny?

You cannot solve the problem unless you know when Jenny finished her homework.

Extra Information

Problem Sue started raking leaves at 2:00 P.M. and finished at 3:10 P.M. She then started practicing her violin and finished at 3:35 P.M. How long did Sue take to rake the leaves?

To solve the problem, you do not need to know how long it took Sue to practice.

Choose the correct answer.

Flight 81 leaves Salt Lake City at 2:55 P.M. and arrives in Phoenix at 4:30 P.M. Flight 62 from Salt Lake City, which is sold out, arrives in Phoenix at 3:45 P.M. Which flight is faster?

1. Which of the following statements is false?
   A. Flight 81 takes less than 2 hours.
   B. Flight 62 arrives in Phoenix after Flight 81 does.
   C. Flight 62 is sold out.
   D. Flight 81 arrives in Phoenix before 5:00 P.M.

   1. **B**

2. What information is missing?
   F. the time that Flight 81 leaves Salt Lake City
   G. the time that Flight 81 arrives in Phoenix
   H. the time that Flight 62 leaves Salt Lake City
   J. the time that Flight 62 arrives in Salt Lake City

   2. **H**

Grade 4 18 Chapter 5

Skills Practice (p. 20) OL

5-3 Name ________ Date ________

Skills Practice

Problem-Solving Skill: Extra and Missing Information

Identify any extra or missing information. Then solve if possible.

1. A round-trip first-class ticket from St. Louis to San Diego costs $1,600. A round-trip coach ticket costs $359. The Howards buy 3 tickets. How much do they spend?
   Missing information: what kind of tickets the Howards bought
2. A train leaves Rocky Mount, NC, at 1:16 P.M. The train arrives in Petersburg, VA, at 2:45 P.M. and in Richmond, VA, at 3:22 P.M. How long is the trip from Rocky Mount to Richmond?
   2 hr 6 min; Extra information: what time the train reaches Petersburg, VA
3. A bus leaves the terminal at 6:10 P.M. It makes its first stop at 6:30 P.M. and its second stop at 6:55 P.M. When will the bus arrive at its third stop?
   Missing information: how long the trip between the second and third stops takes
4. Samantha takes a train to New York City. She catches the train at 7:25 A.M. The train stops in Newark at 7:41 A.M. The train arrives in New York at 7:59 A.M. How much time does Samantha's ride take?
   34 min; Extra information: when the train stops in Newark

Solve. Use any strategy.

5. Denzel has 3 rows of shelves in his bedroom. Books, games, or CDs occupy each shelf. The middle shelf holds CDs. If the top shelf does not hold books, which shelf holds games? **top shelf**
   Strategy: **Use logical reasoning**
6. Arlene spent $30 for a jacket. She now has $5 left. How much money did Arlene have before she bought the jacket? **$35**
   Strategy: **Write an equation**

Grade 4 20 Chapter 5

ANALYZE the Skill

Refer to the problem on the previous page. 1, 2. See Ch. 5 Answer Appendix.

1. Explain why you do not need to know the cost of the bracelets.
2. Suppose the problem did not include how many bracelets were sold last week. Could you solve it? Explain.
3. If you need to find the difference in profit between the two weeks, is there enough information to solve the problem? yes
4. Find the difference in profit between the two weeks. $84

★ indicates multi-step problem

PRACTICE the Skill

EXTRA PRACTICE
See page R13.

Identify any missing or extra information. Then solve if possible.

★5. Chango the monkey eats 4 apples and 3 bananas every day at 12:30 P.M. How much fruit does he eat in a week? extra: eats at 12:30 P.M.; 49 pieces of fruit

6. Nidia asked her classmates to name their favorite flavor of ice cream. Chocolate received 14 votes, which is 5 more votes than vanilla. How many students liked vanilla? no extra or missing information; 9 students

7. Sheri and two friends want to go to a movie. The movie starts at 2 P.M. How much will it cost for these 3 students to go to the movie?

MOVIE THEATER
Adult Ticket $6
Student Ticket $4
Movie Times 10A.M., 12P.M., 2P.M.

See Ch. 5 Answer Appendix.

8. **Measurement** Each day, Zoe trains each of her horses for 30 minutes and then rides them for 20 minutes. How much time does Zoe spend with her horses in one day? missing: the number of horses Zoe has

9. Candace wants to buy the fish aquarium supplies shown. How much change will she get back?

missing: the amount of money Candace has to buy the supplies

10. Three fourth-grade classes are going on a field trip. How many students are going on a field trip? missing: the number of students in each class

11. James and Donna have $18. Each pack of baseball cards costs $3. There are 8 cards in each pack. How many packs can they buy? extra: There are 8 cards in each pack; 6 packs

12. The Video Depot is having a sale on DVDs. The cost is $27 for 3. How many DVDs can Edgar buy? missing: the amount of money Edgar has

13. **WRITING IN MATH** Explain how you identified any extra or missing information in Exercise 12. See Ch. 5 Answer Appendix.

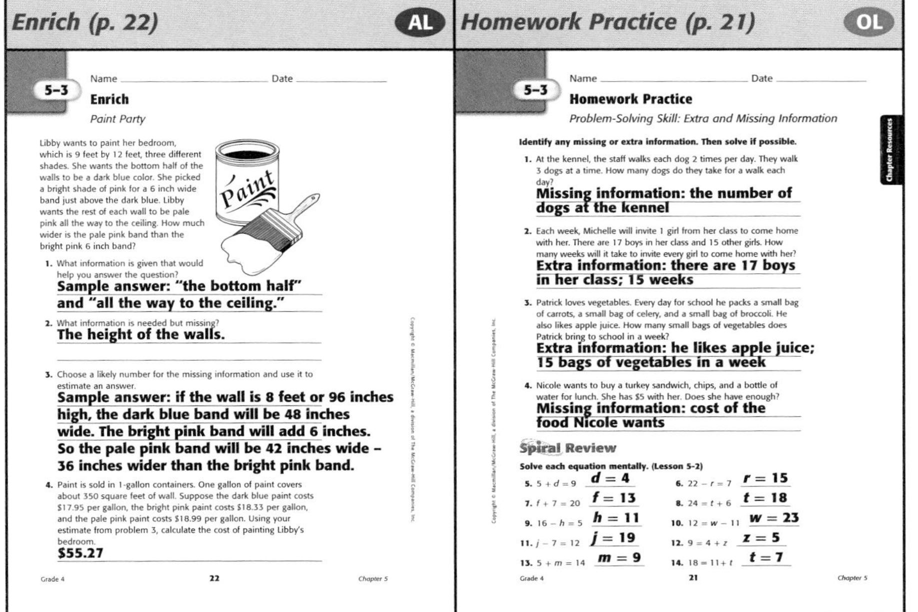

Enrich (p. 22) AL

5-3 Name ______ Date ______

Enrich

Paint Party

Libby wants to paint her bedroom, which is 9 feet by 12 feet, three different shades. She wants the bottom half of the walls to be a dark blue color. She picked a bright shade of pink for a 6 inch wide band just above the dark blue. Libby wants the rest of each wall to be pale pink all the way to the ceiling. How much wider is the pale pink band than the bright pink 6 inch band?

1. What information is given that would help you answer the question? **Sample answer: "the bottom half" and "all the way to the ceiling."**
2. What information is needed but missing? **The height of the walls.**
3. Choose a likely number for the missing information and use it to estimate an answer. **Sample answer: if the wall is 8 feet or 96 inches high, the dark blue band will be 48 inches wide. The bright pink band will add 6 inches. So the pale pink band will be 42 inches wide – 36 inches wider than the bright pink band.**
4. Paint is sold in 1-gallon containers. One gallon of paint covers about 350 square feet of wall. Suppose the dark blue paint costs $17.95 per gallon, the bright pink paint costs $18.33 per gallon, and the pale pink paint costs $18.99 per gallon. Using your estimate from problem 3, calculate the cost of painting Libby's bedroom. **$55.27**

Grade 4 22 Chapter 5

Homework Practice (p. 21) OL

5-3 Name ______ Date ______

Homework Practice

Problem-Solving Skill: Extra and Missing Information

Chapter Resources

Identify any missing or extra information. Then solve if possible.

1. At the kennel, the staff walks each dog 2 times per day. They walk 3 dogs at a time. How many dogs do they take for a walk each day? **Missing information: the number of dogs at the kennel**
2. Each week, Michelle will invite 1 girl from her class to come home with her. There are 17 boys in her class and 15 other girls. How many weeks will it take to invite every girl to come home with her? **Extra information: there are 17 boys in her class; 15 weeks**
3. Patrick loves vegetables. Every day for school he packs a small bag of carrots, a small bag of celery, and a small bag of broccoli. He also likes apple juice. How many small bags of vegetables does Patrick bring to school in a week? **Extra information: he likes apple juice; 15 bags of vegetables in a week**
4. Nicole wants to buy a turkey sandwich, chips, and a bottle of water for lunch. She has $5 with her. Does she have enough? **Missing information: cost of the food Nicole wants**

Spiral Review

Solve each equation mentally. (Lesson 5-2)

5. $5 + d = 9$ **$d = 4$**
6. $22 - r = 7$ **$r = 15$**
7. $f + 7 = 20$ **$f = 13$**
8. $24 = t + 6$ **$t = 18$**
9. $16 - h = 5$ **$h = 11$**
10. $12 = w - 11$ **$w = 23$**
11. $j - 7 = 12$ **$j = 19$**
12. $9 = 4 + z$ **$z = 5$**
13. $5 + m = 14$ **$m = 9$**
14. $18 = 11 + t$ **$t = 7$**

Grade 4 21 Chapter 5

Analyze the Strategy Use Exercises 1–4 to analyze and discuss the problem-solving strategy.

BL Alternate Teaching Strategy

If students have trouble identifying missing or extra information...

Then use one of these reteach options:

1. CRM **Daily Reteach Worksheet** (pp. 18–19)
2. Make a copy of the practice problems. Have students cross out the extra information and underline the information needed to solve the problem. For missing information, have them identify the needed information.

3 Practice

Using the Exercises

Exercises 5–12 provide students with an opportunity to solve problems that may not have enough information or have extra information.

Exercise 5 Students may not read the problem carefully. Point out that the problem asks for the amount eaten in one week.

4 Assess

Formative Assessment

Present the following problem:

The school vans leave at 7:00 A.M. for the zoo. There are 4 vans that hold 10 students each. Half of the students are boys. What is the total number of students that can go in the vans?

- **What information do you need to solve the problem?** the number of vans and the number of students in each van
- **What information is not needed?** the time the vans leave and the fact that half the students are boys

Quick Check **Are students continuing to struggle with identifying extra or missing information?**

If Yes → CRM Reteach Worksheet (pp. 18–19)

If No → Independent Work Options (p. 192B)
CRM Skills Practice Worksheet (p. 20)
CRM Enrich Worksheet (p. 22)

LESSON 5-4

Identify, Describe, and Extend Patterns

Lesson Planner

Objective

Identify, describe, and extend numeric and nonnumeric patterns.

Vocabulary

pattern

Resources

Materials: construction paper

Manipulatives: various colored counters or connecting cubes

Literature Connection: *A Cloak For A Dreamer* by Aileen Friedman

Alternate Lesson: Use *IMPACT Mathematics: Unit B* to provide practice with patterns.

Teacher Technology

TeacherWorks • Interactive Classroom • Concepts in Motion

Daily Routine

Use these suggestions before beginning the lesson on p. 204.

5-Minute Check

(Reviews Lessons 5-3)

Identify any missing or extra information. Then solve if possible.

Marcellio bought 3 boxes of pens. There are 12 pens in each box. If each box costs $4, how much change will Marcellio get back if he gives the cashier a $20 bill? extra: There are 12 pens in each box; $8

Problem of the Day

Chandler's mother is shopping for new pillows. At the first store, they cost $19 each. The second store has a sale, 2 for $30. How much will she save by buying 4 pillows at the second store? $16

Focus on Math Background

The concept of patterns is basic to all of mathematics. Students come to you with experience looking at patterns and writing rules. This begins early as students look at patterns made of objects such as

ball, pencil, pencil, ball, pencil, pencil, ball, …

At this point they learned to use words to describe and extend repeating or iterative patterns.

Later, students write rules such as "add 4" to describe geometric and arithmetic patterns such as 3, 7, 11, 15, …. Once a rule is found for a pattern, the rule is used to extend the pattern. In this lesson, students use this background and examine more complicated patterns. Once again, they are asked to find a rule and use that rule to extend a given pattern.

Building Math Vocabulary

Write the lesson vocabulary word and its definition on the board.

Ask students to copy the word and its definition into their Math Journals. Then have them write or draw an example of a pattern on a piece of construction paper. Display these patterns around the room or in the hall.

Differentiated Instruction

Small Group Options

LOGICAL

Option 1 Below Level BL

Materials: chart paper, markers, paper, pencils

- Draw from left to right a triangle, square, pentagon, triangle, square, pentagon.
- Ask the students to study the pattern formed by those shapes. Have the students use a sound with each shape, such as snap with the triangles.
- Students should extend the pattern noticing how the sound and shapes are making the pattern together.
- Discuss this pattern and ask the students to make up a pattern of their own using polygons and sounds.

LOGICAL, VISUAL

Option 2 English Language Learners ELL

Materials: per group: 100s chart, light crayon or highlighter
Core Vocabulary: What's (what is), next, every _____ number
Common Use Verb: am going + infinitive (to count, to color)

Do Math This strategy allows students to practice and visualize skip counting patterns.

- Say, "I **am going to count** using a pattern 10, 20, 30, ... **What's next?**" (up to 100).
- Say, "Count using this pattern: 5, 10, 15, ... What is next?" (up to 100).
- Model coloring a chart. Say: "I **am going to color** every other number."
- Distribute 100s charts. Assign each group to color every third, fourth, fifth, seventh, or eleventh number.
- After students finish, show all papers. Discuss patterns using target vocabulary.

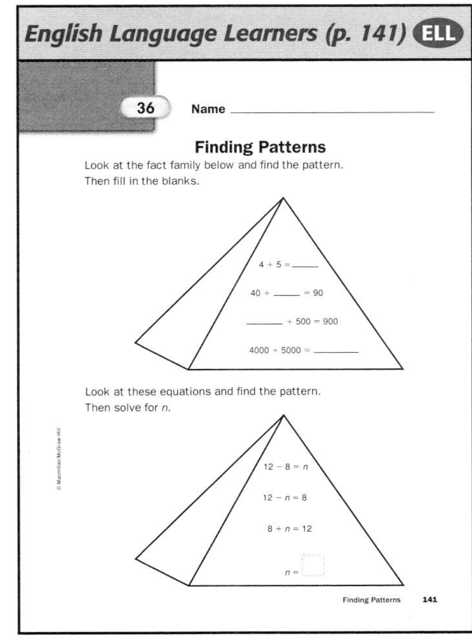

English Language Learners (p. 141) ELL

36 Name _____

Finding Patterns

Look at the fact family below and find the pattern. Then fill in the blanks.

4 + 5 = _____
40 + _____ = 90
_____ + 500 = 900
4000 + 5000 = _____

Look at these equations and find the pattern. Then solve for *n*.

$12 - 8 = n$
$12 - n = 8$
$8 + n = 12$
$n =$ ☐

© Macmillan/McGraw-Hill

Finding Patterns 141

Use this worksheet to provide additional support for English Language Learners.

Independent Work Options

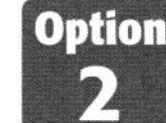

KINESTHIETIC

Option 1 Early Finishers AL

Materials: pairs of number cubes, paper, pencil

- Have students roll two number cubes to generate 2 numbers. Have them use the two numbers as the first two numbers in a pattern and then extend the pattern to 5 numbers. For example, if the rolls were 2 and 4, one pattern might be: 2, 4, 3, 5, 4. (rule: add 2 then subtract 1; next number: 6)
- Have students exchange patterns with a partner. Have the partner find a rule and the next number for the pattern.

Option 2 Student Technology

Math Online macmillanmh.com

Personal Tutor • Extra Examples

Option 3 Learning Station: Reading (p. 190G)

Direct students to the Reading Learning Station for opportunities to explore and extend the lesson concept.

Option 4 Problem-Solving Practice

Reinforce problem-solving skills and strategies with the Problem-Solving Practice worksheet.

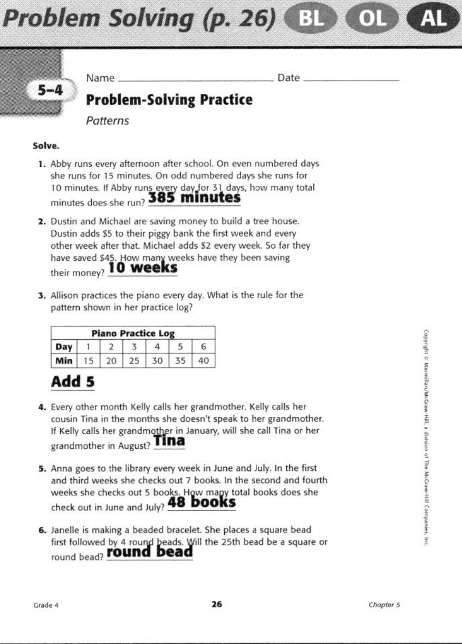

Problem Solving (p. 26) BL OL AL

Name _____ Date _____

5–4 **Problem-Solving Practice**

Patterns

Solve.

1. Abby runs every afternoon after school. On even numbered days she runs for 15 minutes. On odd numbered days she runs for 10 minutes. If Abby runs every day for 31 days, how many total minutes does she run? **385 minutes**
2. Dustin and Michael are saving money to build a tree house. Dustin adds $5 to their piggy bank the first week and every other week after that. Michael adds $2 every week. So far they have saved $45. How many weeks have they been saving their money? **10 weeks**
3. Allison practices the piano every day. What is the rule for the pattern shown in her practice log?

Piano Practice Log						
Day	1	2	3	4	5	6
Min	15	20	25	30	35	40

Add 5

4. Every other month Kelly calls her grandmother. Kelly calls her cousin Tina in the months she doesn't speak to her grandmother. If Kelly calls her grandmother in January, will she call Tina or her grandmother in August? **Tina**
5. Anna goes to the library every week in June and July. In the first and third weeks she checks out 7 books. In the second and fourth weeks she checks out 5 books. How many total books does she check out in June and July? **48 books**
6. Janelle is making a beaded bracelet. She places a square bead first followed by 4 round beads. Will the 25th bead be a square or round bead? **round bead**

Grade 4 26 *Chapter 5*

Identify, Describe and Extend Patterns

1 Introduce

Activity Choice 1 • Hands-On

- Use connecting cubes to create the following pattern: 3 red, 2 blue, 4 yellow, 3 red, 2 blue, 4 yellow. Then show the pattern to the students. **What is the rule for my pattern?** 3 red, 2 blue, 4 yellow **What comes next in my pattern?** 3 red
- Divide the students into pairs. Provide each pair with about 50 counters or connecting cubes in two or three different colors.
- Ask partners to make a pattern with the colored counters or cubes. Have volunteers share their patterns with the class. Then have the class find a rule for the pattern and tell how to extend the pattern.

Activity Choice 2 • Literature

Introduce the lesson with *A Cloak For A Dreamer* by Aileen Friedman. For a related math activity, see p. TR48.

2 Teach

Scaffolding Questions

- Write the following patterns on the board:
  A) 6, 12, 18, 24, 30 B) 0, 3, 2, 5, 4, 7
- **Look at Pattern A. What number comes next? How do you know?** 36; To get from one number to the next, add 6.
- **Look at Pattern B. What number comes next? How do you know?** 6; This is an "add 3, subtract 1" pattern.
- **Can a pattern have more than one step? Explain.** Yes, as in Pattern B.
- Explain that patterns do not have to have numbers in them. Show students a set of examples and nonexamples by drawing two sets of four polygons, one with an even number of sides, and the other with an odd number of sides.
- **Draw a shape to fit into each group.** See students' work.

GET READY to Learn

Have students open their books and read the information in **Get Ready** to Learn. Introduce **pattern**. As a class, work through Examples 1–3.

5-4 Identify, Describe, and Extend Patterns

MAIN IDEA

I will identify, describe, and extend numeric and nonnumeric patterns.

New Vocabulary

pattern
rule

Math Online

macmillanmh.com
- Extra Examples
- Personal Tutor
- Self-Check Quiz

GET READY to Learn

Carla sells 3 picture frames for $15 and 4 picture frames for $20. If the pattern for the price of the frames remains the same, how much will Carla make if she sells 6 frames?

In this situation, there is a pattern in the cost of the frames. A **pattern** is a sequence of numbers, figures, or symbols that follow a **rule**. You can find and extend a pattern.

Real-World EXAMPLE Complete a Pattern

1 **MONEY How much will Carla make if she sells 6 frames?**

Identify and describe the pattern by dividing the total cost by the number of frames.

Carla sells 3 picture frames for $15, and 4 picture frames for $20.

$\$15 \div 3 = \$5$
$\$20 \div 4 = \$5$

So, one picture frame costs $5. The rule is to multiply the number of frames by $5.

Use the rule to extend the pattern.

Number of Frames	1	2	3	4	5	6
Cost	$5	$10	$15	$20	$25	$30

+$5 +$5 +$5 +$5 +$5

So, Carla will make $5 × 6 or $30 if she sells 6 picture frames.

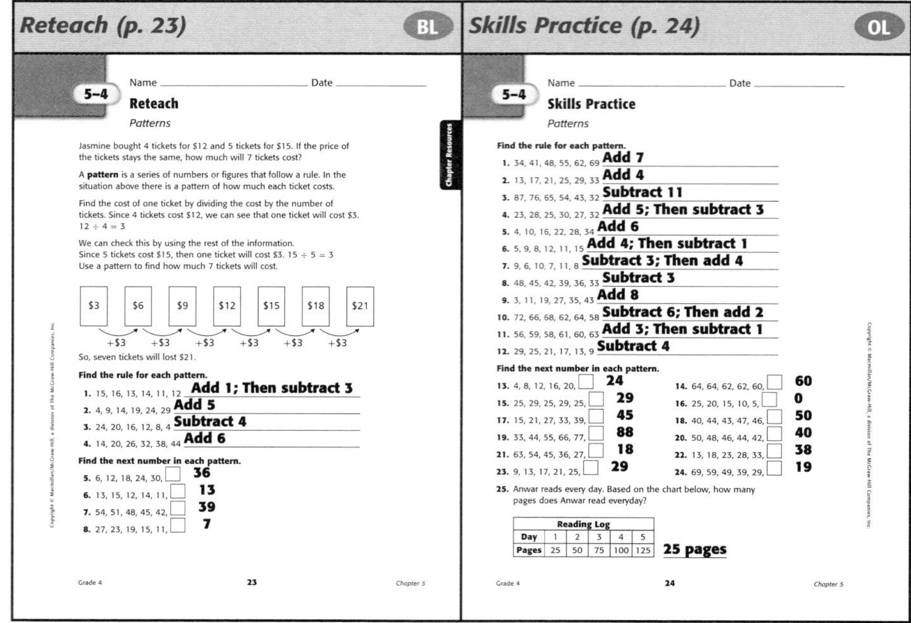

Reteach (p. 23) BL

5-4 Name ______ Date ______

Reteach

Patterns

Jasmine bought 4 tickets for $12 and 5 tickets for $15. If the price of the tickets stays the same, how much will 7 tickets cost?

A **pattern** is a series of numbers or figures that follow a rule. In the situation above there is a pattern of how much each ticket costs.

Find the cost of one ticket by dividing the cost by the number of tickets. Since 4 tickets cost $12, we can see that one ticket will cost $3.
$12 \div 4 = 3$

We can check this by using the rest of the information.
Since 5 tickets cost $15, then one ticket will cost $3. $15 \div 5 = 3$
Use a pattern to find how much 7 tickets will cost.

$3 $6 $9 $12 $15 $18 $21
+$3 +$3 +$3 +$3 +$3 +$3

So, seven tickets will lost $21.

Find the rule for each pattern.

1. 15, 16, 13, 14, 11, 12 **Add 1; Then subtract 3**
2. 4, 9, 14, 19, 24, 29 **Add 5**
3. 24, 20, 16, 12, 8, 4 **Subtract 4**
4. 14, 20, 26, 32, 38, 44 **Add 6**

Find the next number in each pattern.

5. 6, 12, 18, 24, 30, ☐ **36**
6. 13, 15, 12, 14, 11, ☐ **13**
7. 54, 51, 48, 45, 42, ☐ **39**
8. 27, 23, 19, 15, 11, ☐ **7**

Grade 4 23 Chapter 5

Chapter Resources

Skills Practice (p. 24) OL

5-4 Name ______ Date ______

Skills Practice

Patterns

Find the rule for each pattern.

1. 34, 41, 48, 55, 62, 69 **Add 7**
2. 13, 17, 21, 25, 29, 33 **Add 4**
3. 87, 76, 65, 54, 43, 32 **Subtract 11**
4. 23, 28, 25, 30, 27, 32 **Add 5; Then subtract 3**
5. 4, 10, 16, 22, 28, 34 **Add 6**
6. 5, 9, 8, 12, 11, 15 **Add 4; Then subtract 1**
7. 9, 6, 10, 7, 11, 8 **Subtract 3; Then add 4**
8. 48, 45, 42, 39, 36, 33 **Subtract 3**
9. 3, 11, 19, 27, 35, 43 **Add 8**
10. 72, 66, 68, 62, 64, 58 **Subtract 6; Then add 2**
11. 56, 59, 58, 61, 60, 63 **Add 3; Then subtract 1**
12. 29, 25, 21, 17, 13, 9 **Subtract 4**

Find the next number in each pattern.

13. 4, 8, 12, 16, 20, ☐ **24**
14. 64, 64, 62, 62, 60, ☐ **60**
15. 25, 29, 25, 29, 25, ☐ **29**
16. 25, 20, 15, 10, 5, ☐ **0**
17. 15, 21, 27, 33, 39, ☐ **45**
18. 40, 44, 43, 47, 46, ☐ **50**
19. 33, 44, 55, 66, 77, ☐ **88**
20. 50, 48, 46, 44, 42, ☐ **40**
21. 63, 54, 45, 36, 27, ☐ **18**
22. 13, 18, 23, 28, 33, ☐ **38**
23. 9, 13, 17, 21, 25, ☐ **29**
24. 69, 59, 49, 39, 29, ☐ **19**
25. Anwar reads every day. Based on the chart below, how many pages does Anwar read everyday?

Reading Log					
Day	1	2	3	4	5
Pages	25	50	75	100	125

25 pages

Grade 4 24 Chapter 5

Sometimes, patterns are not easily identified.

Real-World EXAMPLES Find the Rule

2 **READING** **The chapters in Daniel's book follow a pattern. Identify, describe, and extend the pattern to find how many pages are in the sixth chapter.**

> **Remember**
> A pattern can be identified by looking at the relationship among the numbers in the pattern.

Look at the table to identify and describe the pattern.

The table shows that the odd numbered chapters have 16 pages and the even numbered chapters have 12 pages.

Daniel's Book		
Chapter	**Ending Page**	
1	16	
2	28	+12
3	44	+16
4	56	+12
5	72	+16
6		+12

3 **What is the page number of the last page in chapter 6?**

Extend the pattern to find the page number of the last page in chapter 6.

The sixth chapter will have 12 pages. So, the last page is 72 + 12, or 84.

Real-World EXAMPLE Examples and Non-examples

4 **ART** **Alyssa is drawing the figures to the right. If the pattern continues, which of the figures shown below will she draw next?**

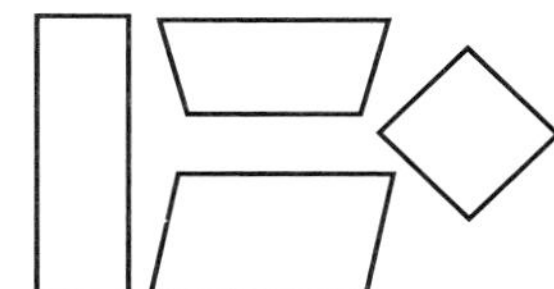

figure A

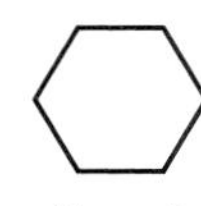
figure B

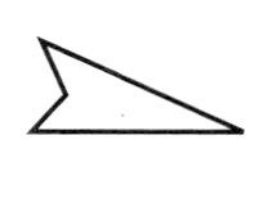
figure C

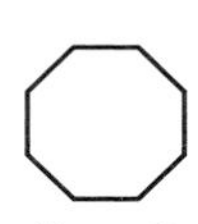
figure D

Identify and describe what the figures Alyssa is drawing have in common.

The figures Alyssa is drawing all have 4 sides. So, she will draw figure C next.

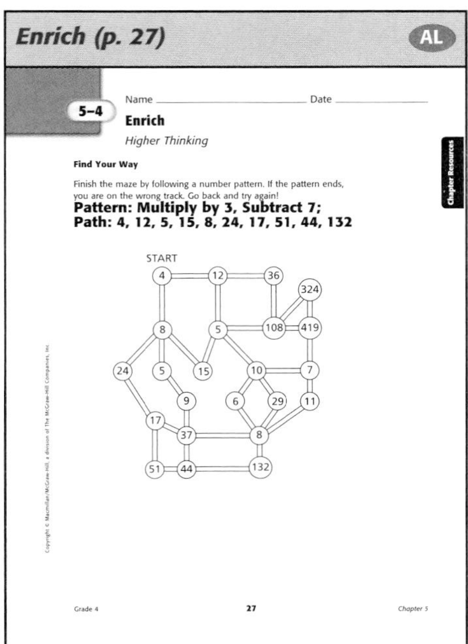

Enrich (p. 27) AL

5–4 Name ________ Date ________

Enrich

Higher Thinking

Find Your Way

Finish the maze by following a number pattern. If the pattern ends, you are on the wrong track. Go back and try again!

Pattern: Multiply by 3, Subtract 7;
Path: 4, 12, 5, 15, 8, 24, 17, 51, 44, 132

Grade 4 27 Chapter 5

Find the Rule for Each Pattern

Example 2 Point out that the rule for a pattern can have more than one step. In this example, there are 2 distinct steps: add 16, add 12, add 16, add 12, etc.

ADDITIONAL EXAMPLES

1 Four plants cost \$16 and 5 cost \$20. How much will 7 plants cost if the price of the plants remains the same? \$28

2 The rows of desks in Mr. Ho's classroom are arranged in a pattern. How many desks are in row 5? How many desks are in the whole classroom? 5; 23

Row	Number of Desks
1	5
2	4
3	5
4	4
5	

3 Jeanne selects letters like A, L, M, T, and X, while Joyce selects letters like B, D, O, S, and U. Which of the following letters would Jeanne select? C, G, J, or H H

CHECK What You Know

As a class, have students complete Exercises 1–5 in **Check What You Know** as you observe their work.

Exercise 5 Assess student comprehension before assigning practice exercises.

BL Alternate Teaching Strategy

If students have trouble finding patterns in sets of numbers…

Then use one of these reteach options:

1. CRM **Daily Reteach Worksheet** (p. 23)
2. Have students use counters to model the pattern. Seeing the pattern the counters create rather than looking at a list of numbers may help them recognize what changes each time. **Model the pattern: 3, 6, 9, 12, 15. What comes next?** 18

COMMON ERROR!

Exercise 5 Students may give up without trying this problem if they think they are supposed to know what Inexes are. Explain that it this a made-up name given to a group of shapes that have something in common. Their challenge is to discover what the figures have in common.

3 Practice

Differentiate practice using these leveled assignments for Exercises 6–16.

Level	Assignment
BL Below/Approaching Level	6–7, 9–10, 12
OL On Level	8–11, 12–13, 14
AL Above/Beyond Level	6–14 even, 15–16

Have students discuss and complete the Higher Order Thinking problems. Suggest students make a table to solve Exercise 15.

Have students complete Exercise 16 in their Math Journals. You may choose to use this exercise as an optional formative assessment.

4 Assess

Formative Assessment

- **Using at least one example, explain how to find the next number in a pattern.** Answers will vary depending on student examples. Sample answer: Determine the change in the previous numbers, and apply that rule to the last number in the pattern.

Quick Check **Are students continuing to struggle with finding patterns in sets of numbers?**

If Yes → Small Group Options (p. 194B)

If No → Independent Work Options (p. 194B)
CRM Skills Practice Worksheet (p. 24)
CRM Enrich Worksheet (p. 27)

Name the Math Write the pattern 12, 10, 14, 12, 16, 14 on the board. Have students write about how they would find a rule for the pattern and then find the next number in the pattern.

CHECK What You Know

Identify, describe, and extend each pattern. See Examples 1–3 (pp. 204–205)

1. 9, 12, 15, 18, 21, ■ Add 3; 24
2. 5, 6, 4, 5, 3, ■ Add 1 then subtract 2; 4
3. 3, 5, 7, 9, 11, ■ Add 2; 13

4. Marcos reads each day. What is the rule for the pattern shown in his reading log? See Example 3 (p. 205) Add 30.

Reading Log					
Day	1	2	3	4	5
Time (min)	30	60	90	120	150

5. Talk About It These are Inexes.

Explain why these are not Inexes. See Example 4 (p. 205) because they do not have rounded sides

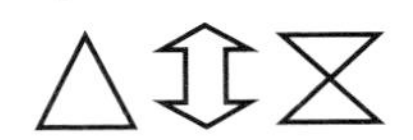

Practice and Problem Solving

EXTRA PRACTICE See page R13.

Identify, describe, and extend each pattern. See Examples 1–3 (pp. 204–205)

6. 26, 30, 34, 38, 42, ■ Add 4; 46
7. 13, 18, 23, 28, 33, ■ Add 5; 38
8. 8, 8, 6, 6, 4, ■ Subtract 0. Then subtract 2; 4
9. 10, 20, 30, 40, 50, ■ Add 10; 60
10. 28, 24, 28, 24, 28, ■ Repeat 28 and 24; 24
11. 3, 6, 12, 15, 21, ■ Add 3. Then add 6; 24

12. Explain why 75 is not an example of a number that would be in the number pattern in Exercise 9. Sample answer: The pattern is add 10 and all the numbers are tens

13. Bob swims 10 laps on even numbered dates. He swims 15 laps on odd numbered dates. How many laps has he swum during a month by the sixth? 65 laps

14. It is recommended to drink 64 fluid ounces of water each day. Below is a pattern to show how many days it would take to drink 448 fluid ounces. Explain how another pattern could be used to find the same answer. Second pattern: —64 from 448

Recommended Water in a Week							
Day	1	2	3	4	5	6	7
Amount (fl oz)	64	128	192	256	320	384	448

+64 +64 +64 +64 +64 +64

H.O.T. Problems

15. OPEN ENDED Create a number pattern involving two operations. Explain your pattern. Sample answer: 6, 12, 9, 15, 12, 18, 15; The pattern is add six and then subtract 3.

16. WRITING IN MATH Describe the pattern. What figure comes next?

△ ▷ ▽ ◁ △ ▷ ▽ ◁

See Ch. 5 Answer Appendix.

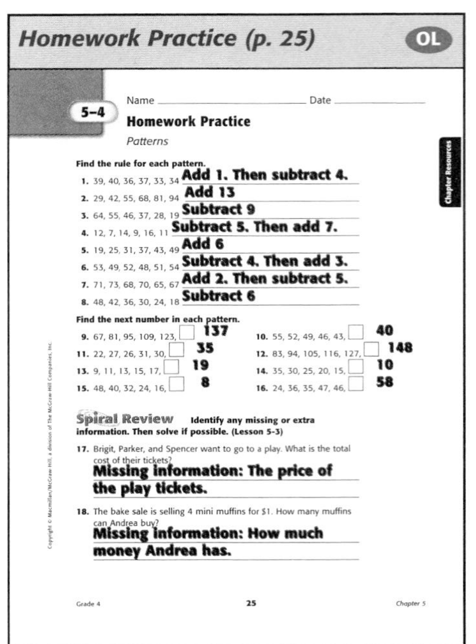

Homework Practice (p. 25) OL

Name ____________ Date ____________

5-4 **Homework Practice**
Patterns

Find the rule for each pattern.
1. 39, 40, 36, 37, 33, 34 **Add 1. Then subtract 4.**
2. 29, 42, 55, 68, 81, 94 **Add 13**
3. 64, 55, 46, 37, 28, 19 **Subtract 9**
4. 12, 7, 14, 9, 16, 11 **Subtract 5. Then add 7.**
5. 19, 25, 31, 37, 43, 49 **Add 6**
6. 53, 49, 52, 48, 51, 54 **Subtract 4. Then add 3.**
7. 71, 73, 68, 70, 65, 67 **Add 2. Then subtract 5.**
8. 48, 42, 36, 30, 24, 18 **Subtract 6**

Find the next number in each pattern.
9. 67, 81, 95, 109, 123, **137**
10. 55, 52, 49, 46, 43, **40**
11. 22, 27, 26, 31, 30, **35**
12. 83, 94, 105, 116, 127, **148**
13. 9, 11, 13, 15, 17, **19**
14. 35, 30, 25, 20, 15, **10**
15. 48, 40, 32, 24, 16, **8**
16. 24, 36, 35, 47, 46, **58**

Spiral Review Identify any missing or extra information. Then solve if possible. (Lesson 5-3)

17. Brigit, Parker, and Spencer want to go to a play. What is the total cost of their tickets?
Missing information: The price of the play tickets.

18. The bake sale is selling 4 mini muffins for $1. How many muffins can Andrea buy?
Missing information: How much money Andrea has.

Grade 4 25 Chapter 5

Mid-Chapter Check

CHAPTER 5

Lessons 5-1 through 5-4

Find the value of each expression if $x = 2$ and $m = 8$. (Lesson 5-1)

1. $x + 3$ 5
2. $18 - m$ 10
3. $m - (1 + 4)$ 3
4. $(m - 2) + x$ 8

Write an expression for each situation. (Lesson 5-1)

5. three more than k $k + 3$
6. the sum of 27 and z $27 + z$

Amado has 13 more books than Sara. (Lesson 5-1)

7. Define a variable. Then write an expression for the number of books Amado has. Let b = Sara's books; $b + 13$
8. If Sara has 8 books, how many does Amado have? 21 books

Solve each equation. (Lesson 5-2)

9. $7 + a = 11$ 4
10. $m - 4 = 12$ 16

11. **MULTIPLE CHOICE** Which number makes the equation true? (Lesson 5-2) A

$$67 + y = 121$$

A 54 **C** 64

B 56 **D** 68

Write and solve the equation for the situation. (Lesson 5-2)

12. A number plus 7 equals 19. What is the number? $y + 7 = 19$; $y = 12$

Identify any missing or extra information. Then solve. (Lesson 5-3)

13. Raekwon bought his lunch every day this week. How much did he spend on lunches this week?
13–14. See Ch. 5 Answer Appendix.
14. Dakota is buying a basketball for $12 and an air pump for $5. She wants to buy a baseball for $6. After purchasing the basketball and pump the cashier gives Dakota $3. How much money did Dakota give the cashier?

15. **MULTIPLE CHOICE** Extend the pattern in the table. (Lesson 5-4) H

Party Supplies						
Tables	2	4	6	8	10	12
Chairs	12	24	36	48	60	■

F 68 **H** 72

G 70 **J** 74

Identify, describe, and extend each pattern. (Lesson 5-4)

16. 4, 9, 14, 19, 24, ■ add 5; 29
17. 41, 34, 27, 20, 13, ■ subtract 7; 6
18. 12, 10, 13, 11, 14, ■ subtract 2, add 3; 12
19. **WRITING IN MATH** Explain how to extend the pattern below. (Lesson 5-4)

6, 10, 14, 18, 22, ■

See Ch. 5 Answer Appendix.

Formative Assessment 207

Mid-Chapter Check

CHAPTER 5

Lessons 5-1 through 5-4

Formative Assessment

Use the Mid-Chapter Check to assess students' progress in the first half of the chapter.

Based on the results of the Mid-Chapter Check, use the following resources to review concepts that continue to give students problems.

ExamView Assessment Suite

Customize and create multiple versions of your Mid-Chapter Check and the test answer keys.

Dinah Zike's Foldables

Use these lesson suggestions for incorporating the Foldables during the chapter.

Lesson 5-1 Students use the left column of the pocket chart Foldable to define mathematical symbols and properties used to simplify addition and subtraction expressions. Examples of student work are provided on quarter sheets of paper or index cards and stored in the left side pocket.

Lessons 5-2 and 5-4 Students use the right column and right pocket of the Foldable to define mathematical symbols and properties.

Data-Driven Decision Making

Based on the results of the Mid-Chapter Check, use the following resources to review concepts that continue to give students problems.

Exercises	State/Local Standards	What's the Math?	Error Analysis	Resources for Review
1–8 Lesson 5-1		Demonstrate understanding of mathematical symbols and properties.	Does not understand word "value," "expression." Does not add or subtract correctly. Does not know what to do with parentheses.	Strategic Intervention Guide (pp. 30, 32, 34, 132) CRM Chapter 5 Resource Masters (Reteach Worksheets) Math Adventures My Math Zone Chapter 5 Math Online Extra Examples • Concepts in Motion
9–12 Lesson 5-2		Write and simplify expressions and sentences.	Does not add/subtract accurately. Does not understand word "situation."	
15–19 Lesson 5-4		Understand that an equation is a prescription for determining a second number when a first number is given.	Does not discover equation for chart. Does not accurately fill in chart. Does not understand "input" and "output."	

LESSON 5-5

Function Tables: Find a Rule (+, −)

Lesson Planner

Objective

Find and use rules to write addition and subtraction equations.

Review Vocabulary

equation, pattern

Resources

Literature Connection: *Two of Everything* by Lily Toy Hong

Alternate Lesson: Use *IMPACT Mathematics: Unit B* to provide practice with functions.

Teacher Technology
TeacherWorks • Interactive Classroom • Math Songs Track #2 Lesson Plan

Daily Routine

Use these suggestions before beginning the lesson on p. 208.

5-Minute Check

(Reviews Lesson 5-4)

Find the rule for each pattern.

1. 12, 17, 22, 27, 32, 37 Add 5.

2. 2, 5, 4, 7, 6, 9, 8 Add 3. Then subtract 1.

Find the next number in each pattern.

3. 12, 14, 13 ,15, 14, 16, ■ 15

4. 12, 17, 12, 17, 12, 17, ■ 12

Problem of the Day

The first digit in Taylor's 7-digit phone number is 5. The sum of the first three digits is 15. The sum of the last four digits is 13. None of the digits are even. What is a possible phone number for Taylor? Sample answer: 555-5017

Focus on Math Background

Now that students have acquired a basic background with expressions and equations, they are ready to write equations to describe the patterns found in input/output tables. When using equations to describe simple addition or subtraction patterns, the equations are usually written in one of these forms:

output = input ± some number

input ± some number = output

Notice that in this lesson, the latter form is used.

Review Math Vocabulary

Write the review vocabulary words and their definitions on the board.

Have students discuss how they would explain *pattern* and *equation* to a new student in the class.

Visual Vocabulary Cards

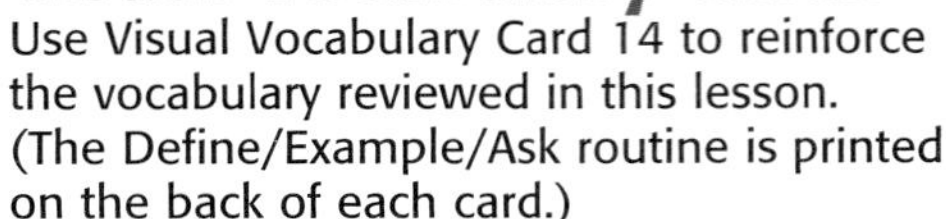

Use Visual Vocabulary Card 14 to reinforce the vocabulary reviewed in this lesson. (The Define/Example/Ask routine is printed on the back of each card.)

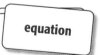

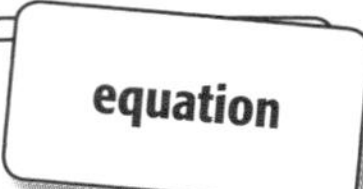

Differentiated Instruction

Small Group Options

Option 1 Gifted and Talented AL

LOGICAL

Materials: unlined paper, pencil, crayons or markers

- Have students create an input/output table that displays the following data:

  Hector babysits for several families. He charges $4 per hour. Help Hector make a table to show his baby-sitting fees to his customers.

Hector's Babysitting Fees

Input	hours	1	2	3	4	5
Output	cost	$4	$8	$12	$16	$20

- Have students extend the chart to five places and add colorful graphics to increase interest in his business.

Option 2 English Language Learners ELL

VISUAL, SPATIAL, LOGICAL

Materials: number cube, paper
Core Vocabulary: rules, instead of, riddle
Common Use Verb: switch

See Math This strategy helps students understand symbols and function rules.

- Say: "We can use symbols to represent numbers. This is a **riddle**. I have written **symbols instead of** some of the numbers. See if you can figure out the rule the **symbol** represents." Write: 10 ∩ = 17
  - Ask students to find the riddle's rule. +7
  - Model: "____ ∩ = ?" using a rolled number in the blank to complete the number sentence.
- Have students repeat and switch the rule.
- Have students write several number sentences with rules and switch with partners who solve for the rule.

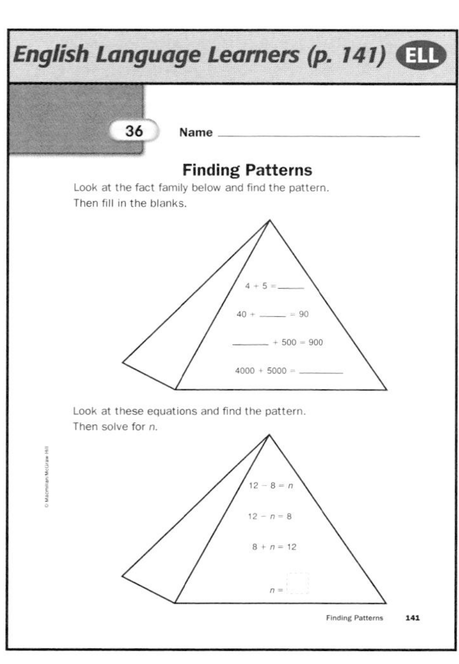

English Language Learners (p. 141) ELL

36 Name __________

Finding Patterns

Look at the fact family below and find the pattern. Then fill in the blanks.

4 + 5 = ____
40 + ____ = 90
____ + 500 = 900
4000 + 5000 = ____

Look at these equations and find the pattern. Then solve for *n*.

$12 - 8 = n$
$12 - n = 8$
$8 + n = 12$
$n =$ ____

© Macmillan/McGraw-Hill

Finding Patterns 141

Use this worksheet to provide additional support for English Language Learners.

Independent Work Options

Option 1 Early Finishers AL

LINGUISTIC

Materials: paper and pencil

- Have students play "What's My Rule?" with a partner. (Instructions are found in Activity Choice 1 on p. 198.) Remind students to only use rules that involve addition and subtraction.

Option 2 Student Technology

Math Online macmillanmh.com

Personal Tutor • Extra Examples

Math Songs, "Algebra Rocks" Track #2

Option 3 Learning Station: Social Studies (p. 190H)

Direct students to the Social Studies Learning Station for opportunities to explore and extend the lesson concept.

Option 4 Problem-Solving Practice

Reinforce problem-solving skills and strategies with the Problem-Solving Practice worksheet.

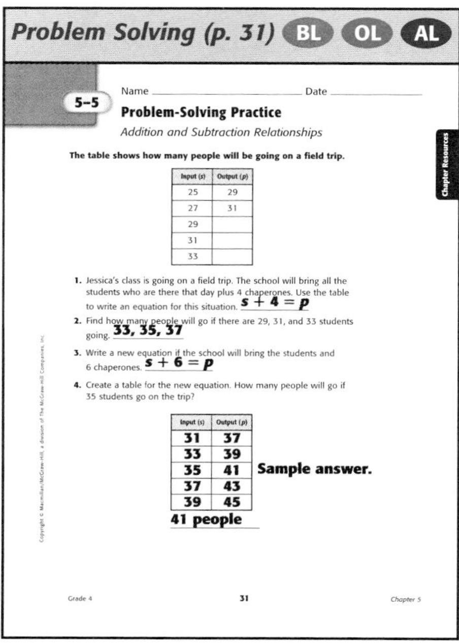

Problem Solving (p. 31) BL OL AL

5–5 Name ________ Date ________

Problem-Solving Practice

Addition and Subtraction Relationships

Chapter Resources

The table shows how many people will be going on a field trip.

Input (s)	Output (p)
25	29
27	31
29	
31	
33	

1. Jessica's class is going on a field trip. The school will bring all the students who are there that day plus 4 chaperones. Use the table to write an equation for this situation. $s + 4 = p$
2. Find how many people will go if there are 29, 31, and 33 students going. **33, 35, 37**
3. Write a new equation if the school will bring the students and 6 chaperones. $s + 6 = p$
4. Create a table for the new equation. How many people will go if 35 students go on the trip?

Input (s)	Output (p)
31	37
33	39
35	41
37	43
39	45

Sample answer.

41 people

Grade 4 31 Chapter 5

5-5 Function Tables: Find a Rule (+, −)

1 Introduce

Activity Choice 1 • Hands-On

- Begin the lesson with a "What's My Rule" activity. Start easy. Use something like $x + 2 = y$.
- Ask for a number and give a response. For example, if a student gives the number 6 and the rule is $x + 2 = y$, the response should be 8.
- Ask for another number and give a response.
- After repeating several times, ask for another number. This time, ask the students if they can give you the response. Continue until it appears that everyone can give the answer. Then ask them for the rule.
- Write the rule on the board.

Activity Choice 2 • Literature

Introduce the lesson with *Two of Everything* by Lily Toy Hong. For a related math activity, see p. TR49.

2 Teach

Scaffolding Questions

Repeat the "What's My Rule" activity from Activity Choice 1. This time, use $x - 4 = y$, and ask students for a number greater than 4. Then make a 2-column input/output table to record the student numbers, x, and the teacher responses, y. Fill in 4 numbers and responses.

- Have students look at the table.
- **What do you have to do to the number in the first column to get the number in the second column?** Subtract 4.
- **How can you write the rule as an equation?** $x - 4 = y$

GET READY to Learn

Have students open their books and read the information in **Get Ready to Learn**. Review **equation** and **pattern**. As a class, work through **Examples 1–3**.

5-5 Function Tables: Find a Rule (+, −)

MAIN IDEA

I will find and use rules to write addition and subtraction equations.

New Vocabulary

function

Math Online

macmillanmh.com

- Extra Examples
- Personal Tutor
- Self-Check Quiz

GET READY to Learn

Mr. Mathis put an input number into his *function* machine. The function machine took the input number and performed one or more operations on it to get an output number.

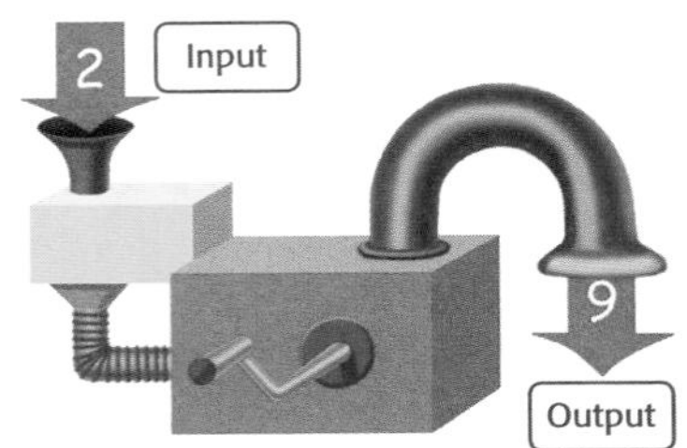

A relationship where one quantity depends upon another quantity is called a **function**. You can use a rule to write an equation that describes a pattern between input and output numbers.

EXAMPLES Find an Addition Rule

1 Write an equation that describes the pattern in the table.

Input (x)	Output (y)
2	9
4	11
6	13
8	■
10	■
12	■

Pattern: $2 + 7 = 9$
$4 + 7 = 11$
$6 + 7 = 13$

Rule: Add 7.

Equation: $x + 7 = y$ (input ↑ x, output ↑ y)

2 Use the equation to find the next three numbers.

Find the next three numbers when the input (x) is 8, 10, and 12.

$x + 7 = y$	$x + 7 = y$	$x + 7 = y$
$8 + 7 = 15$	$10 + 7 = 17$	$12 + 7 = 19$

So, the next three numbers in the pattern are 15, 17, and 19.

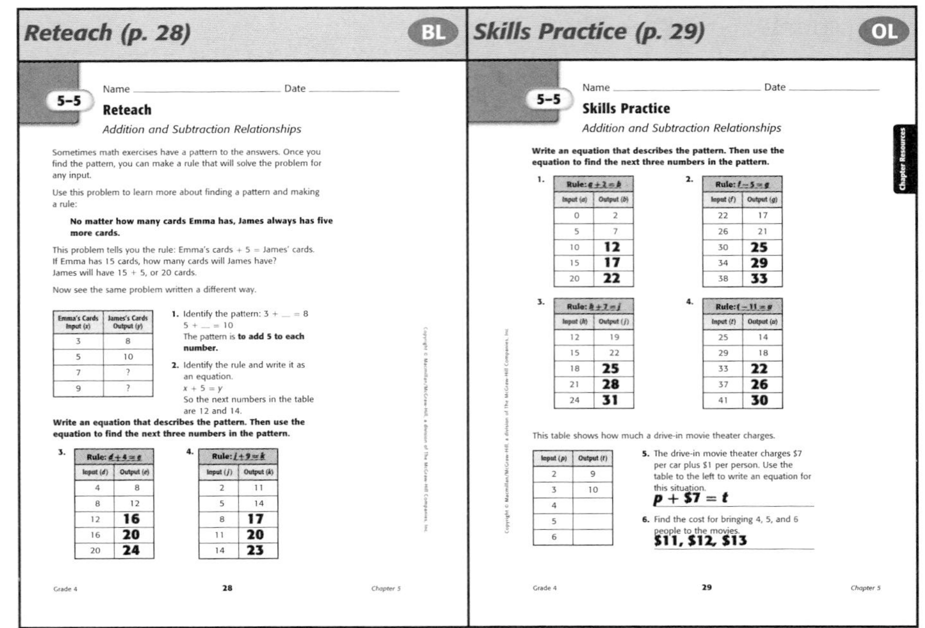

Reteach (p. 28) BL

5-5 Name ______ Date ______

Reteach

Addition and Subtraction Relationships

Sometimes math exercises have a pattern to the answers. Once you find the pattern, you can make a rule that will solve the problem for any input.

Use this problem to learn more about finding a pattern and making a rule:

No matter how many cards Emma has, James always has five more cards.

This problem tells you the rule: Emma's cards + 5 = James' cards. If Emma has 15 cards, how many cards will James have? James will have 15 + 5, or 20 cards.

Now see the same problem written a different way.

Emma's Cards Input (x)	James's Cards Output (y)
3	8
5	10
7	?
9	?

1. Identify the pattern: 3 + __ = 8
   5 + __ = 10
   The pattern is **to add 5 to each number.**
2. Identify the rule and write it as an equation.
   $x + 5 = y$
   So the next numbers in the table are 12 and 14.

Write an equation that describes the pattern. Then use the equation to find the next three numbers in the pattern.

3.

Rule: $d + 4 = e$	
Input (d)	Output (e)
4	8
8	12
12	**16**
16	**20**
20	**24**

4.

Rule: $j + 9 = k$	
Input (j)	Output (k)
2	11
5	14
8	**17**
11	**20**
14	**23**

Grade 4 28 Chapter 5

Skills Practice (p. 29) OL

5-5 Name ______ Date ______

Skills Practice

Addition and Subtraction Relationships

Write an equation that describes the pattern. Then use the equation to find the next three numbers in the pattern.

1.

Rule: $a + 2 = b$	
Input (a)	Output (b)
0	2
5	7
10	**12**
15	**17**
20	**22**

2.

Rule: $f - 5 = g$	
Input (f)	Output (g)
22	17
26	21
30	**25**
34	**29**
38	**33**

3.

Rule: $h + 7 = j$	
Input (h)	Output (j)
12	19
15	22
18	**25**
21	**28**
24	**31**

4.

Rule: $t - 11 = u$	
Input (t)	Output (u)
25	14
29	18
33	**22**
37	**26**
41	**30**

This table shows how much a drive-in movie theater charges.

Input (p)	Output (t)
2	9
3	10
4	
5	
6	

5. The drive-in movie theater charges $7 per car plus $1 per person. Use the table to the left to write an equation for this situation.
   $p + \$7 = t$
6. Find the cost for bringing 4, 5, and 6 people to the movies.
   $11, $12, $13

Chapter Resources

Grade 4 29 Chapter 5

208 **Chapter 5** Describe Algebraic Patterns

Real-World EXAMPLE Find a Subtraction Rule

Remember

Always check to make sure the equation works for each pair of numbers in the table.

3 **ALGEBRA A pizza shop offers $3 off any order over $10. Write an equation that describes the pattern. Then use the equation to find the next three costs.**

Input (c)	Output (d)
$11	$8
$12	$9
$14	$11
$16	■
$18	■
$20	■

Identify the rule and write it as an equation.

Rule: Subtract 3.

Equation: $c - \$3 = d$

(input: c; output: d)

Find the next three numbers when the input (c) is $16, $18, and $20.

$c - \$3 = d$	$c - \$3 = d$	$c - \$3 = d$
$\$16 - \$3 = \$13$	$\$18 - \$3 = \$15$	$\$20 - \$3 = \$17$

So, the next three amounts are $13, $15, and $17.

4. Sample answer: Return to step one to figure out the equation, which is *find the pattern.*

CHECK What You Know

Write an equation that describes each pattern. Then use the equation to find the next three numbers.

See Examples 1–3 (pp. 208–209)

1.

Input (a)	5	9	13	17	21	25
Output (b)	9	13	17	■	■	■

$a + 4 = b$; 21, 25, 29

2.

Input (m)	11	16	21	26	31	36
Output (n)	2	7	12	■	■	■

$m - 9 = n$; 17, 22, 27

3. The amounts a bus company charges to take students on a field trip are shown at the right. How much would it cost for 30, 40, and 50 students to go on a field trip? $s + \$50 = c$; $80, $90, $100

Students	Cost ($)
10	$60
20	$70
30	■
40	■
50	■

4. 

Explain what you should do if you test a number in an equation and it does not work.

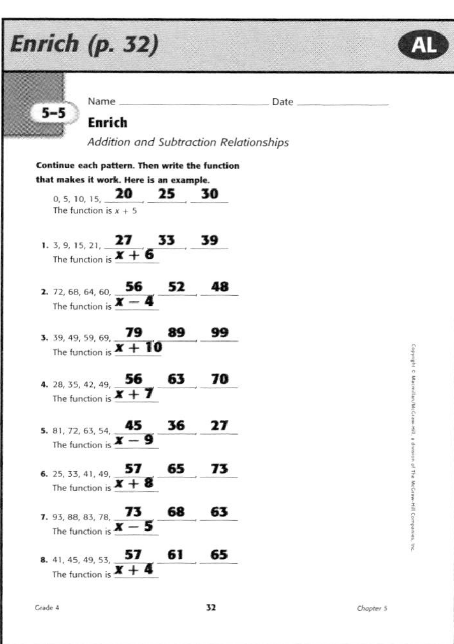

Enrich (p. 32) AL

5–5 Name ______ Date ______

Enrich

Addition and Subtraction Relationships

Continue each pattern. Then write the function that makes it work. Here is an example.

0, 5, 10, 15, **20**, **25**, **30**
The function is $x + 5$

1. 3, 9, 15, 21, **27**, **33**, **39**
The function is **$x + 6$**

2. 72, 68, 64, 60, **56**, **52**, **48**
The function is **$x - 4$**

3. 39, 49, 59, 69, **79**, **89**, **99**
The function is **$x + 10$**

4. 28, 35, 42, 49, **56**, **63**, **70**
The function is **$x + 7$**

5. 81, 72, 63, 54, **45**, **36**, **27**
The function is **$x - 9$**

6. 25, 33, 41, 49, **57**, **65**, **73**
The function is **$x + 8$**

7. 93, 88, 83, 78, **73**, **68**, **63**
The function is **$x - 5$**

8. 41, 45, 49, 53, **57**, **61**, **65**
The function is **$x + 4$**

Grade 4 32 Chapter 5

Find a Subtraction Rule

Example 3 If students are having trouble seeing why the table begins at $11, remind them to read the facts again. Point out which information is important.

ADDITIONAL EXAMPLES

1 Write an equation that describes the pattern in the table.

Input (x)	1	3	5	7	9
Output (y)	5	7	■	■	■

$x + 4 = y$

2 Use the equation to find the next three numbers. 9, 11, 13

3 The uniform store is offering a $5 discount for any purchase of $20 or more. Use a rule to write an equation to describe the pattern. Then use the equation to find the next three prices.

Input (x)	20	21	22	23	24
Output (y)	15	16	■	■	■

$x - 5 = y$; 17, 18, 19

CHECK What You Know

As a class, have students complete Exercises 1–4 in **Check What You Know** as you observe their work.

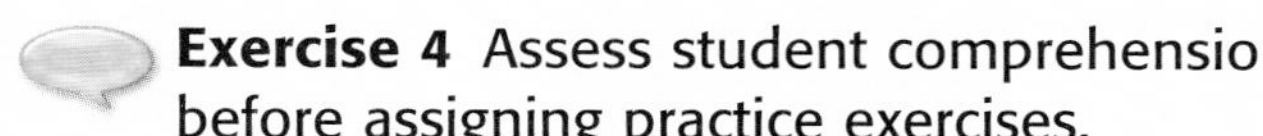

Exercise 4 Assess student comprehension before assigning practice exercises.

BL Alternate Teaching Strategy

If students struggle with addition and subtraction relationships…

Then use one of these reteach options:

1 CRM **Daily Reteach Worksheet** (p. 28)

2 Have them draw an input/output machine. A number goes in the top, the machine works on it, and the output number comes out the bottom. For example, if the machine is a $y + 2$ machine, a 3 goes in and comes out a 5. Otherwise, it works exactly as the "What's My Rule" activity.

3 Practice

Differentiate practice using these leveled assignments for Exercises 5–19.

Level	Assignment
BL Below/Approaching Level	5–10, 13
OL On Level	5–7, 9–11, 13–16, 18
AL Above/Beyond Level	5–17 odd, 18–19

Have students discuss and complete the Higher Order Thinking problems. For Exercise 18, encourage students to think about how the input and output numbers are related.

WRITING IN MATH Have students complete Exercise 19 in their Math Journals. You may choose to use this exercise as an optional formative assessment.

Practice and Problem Solving

See page R14.

Write an equation that describes each pattern. Then use the equation to find the next three numbers. See Examples 1–3 (pp. 208–209)

5.

Input (f)	3	6	9	12	15	18
Output (h)	6	9	12	■	■	■

6.

Input (s)	2	6	10	14	18	22
Output (t)	15	19	23	■	■	■

7.

Input (v)	16	22	28	34	40	46
Output (w)	5	11	17	■	■	■

8.

Input (g)	14	19	24	29	34	39
Output (h)	9	14	19	■	■	■

5–12. See Ch. 5 Answer Appendix.

Create an input/output table for each equation.

9. $y + 4 = z$ **10.** $t + 11 = v$ **11.** $a - 7 = c$ **12.** $g - 10 = h$

Real-World PROBLEM SOLVING

Money The table shows what a taxi company charges c for every m miles traveled.

Taxi Rates	
Input (m)	Output (c)
10	$12
15	$17
20	■
25	■
30	■

13. Use the table to write an equation for this situation. $c = m + \$2$

14. Find the costs of a 20-mile, 25-mile, and 30-mile trip. $22, $27, $32

15. Use the equation you wrote for Exercise 13 to find the cost of a 60-mile trip. $\$62 = 60 + \$2$

16. Write an equation for the number of miles traveled and $4 charged for each trip. $c = m + \$4$

17. How much would a 40-mile trip cost? See Ch. 5 Answer Appendix.

H.O.T. Problems

18. **OPEN ENDED** Write a real-world situation that can be represented by the table. 18, 19. See Ch. 5 Answer Appendix.

Input (h)	1	2	3	4	5
Output (m)	$10	$20	■	■	■

19. **WRITING IN MATH** Explain how the pattern of the input numbers is related to the pattern of the output numbers.

TEST Practice

20. Which of the following describes the rule for this pattern? (Lesson 5-4) B

Input (a)	Output (b)
16	15
18	17
20	19
22	21
24	23
26	25

A Add 4, subtract 3.
B Subtract 4, add 3.
C Subtract 3, add 4.
D Add 3, subtract 5.

21. Each number in Set R is paired with a number in Set S. (Lesson 5-5) H

Set R	Set S
2	10
5	13
6	14

The relationship for each pair of numbers is the same. If the number in Set R is 12, how will you find its paired number in Set S?

F Add 8 to 8.
G Subtract 8 from 12.
H Add 8 to 12.
J Subtract 12 from 12.

Spiral Review

Identify, describe, and extend each pattern. (Lesson 5-4)

22. 28, 25, 22, 19, 16, 13 −3; 10

23. 9, 12, 15, 18, 21, 24 +3; 27

Identify any missing or extra information. Then solve if possible. (Lesson 5-3)

24. Callie the cat is two years old. Callie eats treats twice a day. If there are 365 days in a year, how many days old is Callie?
extra: Callie eats twice a day; 730

25. Camille scored 12 points in the first half of a basketball game. She scored a total of 26 points at the end of the game. How many points did she score during the second half of the game? 14

Solve each equation. (Lesson 5-2)

26. $a + 15 = 25$ 10

27. $b - 36 = 4$ 40

28. $12 + c = 26$ 14

Round each number to the given place value. (Lesson 1-6)

29. 16,543; hundreds 16,500

30. 2,345; tens 2,350

31. 67,343; thousands 67,000

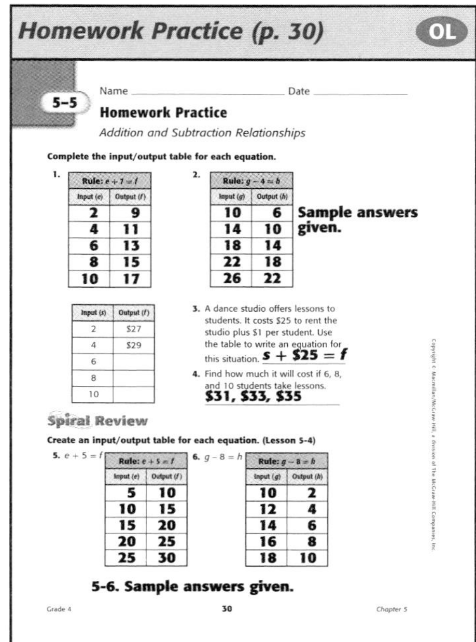

Homework Practice (p. 30) OL

5-5

Name ______ Date ______

Homework Practice

Addition and Subtraction Relationships

Complete the input/output table for each equation.

1.

Rule: $e + 7 = f$	
Input (e)	Output (f)
2	9
4	11
6	13
8	15
10	17

2.

Rule: $g - 4 = h$	
Input (g)	Output (h)
10	6
14	10
18	14
22	18
26	22

Sample answers given.

Input (s)	Output (f)
2	$27
4	$29
6	
8	
10	

3. A dance studio offers lessons to students. It costs $25 to rent the studio plus $1 per student. Use the table to write an equation for this situation. $s + \$25 = f$

4. Find how much it will cost if 6, 8, and 10 students take lessons. $31, $33, $35

Spiral Review

Create an input/output table for each equation. (Lesson 5-4)

5. $e + 5 = f$

Rule: $e + 5 = f$	
Input (e)	Output (f)
5	10
10	15
15	20
20	25
25	30

6. $g - 8 = h$

Rule: $g - 8 = h$	
Input (g)	Output (h)
10	2
12	4
14	6
16	8
18	10

5-6. Sample answers given.

Grade 4 30 Chapter 5

4 Assess

Formative Assessment

- **Why is it important for you to test your rule?** The rule needs to work for all the pairs of numbers, not just one pair.

Quick Check **Are students continuing to struggle with addition and subtraction relationships?**

If Yes → CRM Reteach Worksheet (p. 28)

If No → Independent Work Options (p. 198B)
CRM Skills Practice Worksheet (p. 29)
CRM Enrich Worksheet (p. 32)

Into the Future Tell students that the next lesson is a lesson on multiplication and division expressions. Ask them to write how they think today's lesson will help them with tomorrow's lesson.

TEST Practice

Reviews Lessons 5-4 and 5-5

Assign the Test Practice problems to provide daily reinforcement of test-taking skills.

Spiral Review

Reviews Lessons 1-6, 5-2, 5-3, and 5-4

Review and assess mastery of skills and concepts from previous chapters.

COMMON ERROR!

Exercises 7 and 8 Students may tend to reverse the variable for the unknown when writing the equation. Point out that after they write the equation, all pairs must make the equation true.

Lesson Planner

Objective

Interpret information and data from science to solve problems.

Science Standard 

Students should develop an understanding of the characteristics of organisms.

Vocabulary

expression, **rule**

Activate Prior Knowledge

Before you turn students' attention to the pages, ask them to discuss flying squirrels.

- **Do flying squirrels actually fly? How do they get from tree to tree?** No, they do not fly; they glide.
- **Remind students that squirrels have flaps of skin under their arms that help them glide.**
- **Where do flying squirrels live? What do they eat?** They live in nests in trees; they eat nuts and berries.

Using the Student Page

Ask students to read the information on p. 212 and answer these questions:

- **A southern squirrel lives to be 4 years old. How many years less than its average life span did it live to be? Write and find the value of an expression.** 5 − 4 = 1; 1 year
- **If a squirrel jumps from a tree that is 30 feet tall, how far will the squirrel glide?** 36 feet

Do Flying Squirrels Really Fly?

There are 36 types of flying squirrels. Southern flying squirrels and northern flying squirrels are found in the United States. These squirrels do not actually fly. They glide from tree to tree. These animals climb as high as 30 feet into trees. Then they use their hind legs to push off from branches.

Flying squirrels build their nests in trees, where they collect nuts and berries. They store up to 15,000 nuts in a season. What an appetite.

Southern Flying Squirrel Facts

Length of Body, including Tail . . . . .14 inches
Length of Tail . . . . .6 inches
Weight of Adult. . . . . .3 ounces
Life Span . . . . .5 years

How Far Flying Squirrels Glide

Height of Squirrel in Tree (ft)	5	10	15	20
Distance of Glide (ft)	11	16	21	26

Did You Know?
Some flying squirrels can glide as far as 1,500 feet!

Real-World Math

Use the information on page 212 to solve each problem.

1. What is the length of a southern flying squirrel's body? Write and find the value of an expression.
   14 − 6; 8 in.
2. The length of a northern squirrel's body, including the tail, is 16 inches. Its tail is the same length as a southern squirrel's tail. Write and find the value of an equation to find the length of the northern squirrel's body.
   $16 - 6 = x$; 10 in.
3. A southern flying squirrel lives to be 8 years old. How many years did this squirrel live beyond its average life span?
   $8 - 5 = x$; 3 yrs
4. Write a rule that describes how far a flying squirrel will glide when it jumps from a given height.
   rule: height of squirrel in tree + 6
5. Suppose a squirrel jumps from a tree that is 25 feet tall. How far will the squirrel glide? 31 ft
6. A squirrel jumps from a tree that is 30 feet tall. Will it glide farther than 40 feet? Explain.
   no; 36 ft < 40 ft
7. What is the difference in gliding distances of a squirrel that jumps from a 40-foot tree and a squirrel that jumps from a 50-foot tree?
   10 ft

Real-World Math

Assign the exercises on p. 213. Encourage students to choose a problem-solving strategy before beginning each exercise.

Exercise 2 Remind students that they will use the same operation they used in Exercise 1, only with a different beginning value.

Exercise 4 Tell students that they need to look for a pattern in the glide distance for each 5 feet of tree height.

Exercise 5 Remind students that they can use the rule they wrote in Exercise 4 to solve this problem.

WRITING IN MATH Have students create a word problem that uses the information found in the text and in the picture on p. 212.

Extend the Activity

Have students make a rule chart for the squirrel's glide distance, using the data on p. 212, and try different values in it.

LESSON 5-6

Multiplication and Division Expressions

Lesson Planner

Objective

Write and find the value of multiplication and division expressions.

Review Vocabulary

expression

Resources

Materials: index cards, cups

Manipulatives: counters

Literature Connection: *Mailing May* by Michael O. Tunnel

Alternate Lesson: Use *IMPACT Mathematics: Unit B* to provide practice with expressions.

Teacher Technology
TeacherWorks • Interactive Classroom • Math Songs Track #2 Lesson Plan

Focus on Math Background

In earlier lessons in this chapter, students were introduced to the concept of a variable and algebraic expressions using addition and subtraction. In this lesson, students will continue their work with these topics. The expressions introduced here are multiplication and division expressions. Three examples follow:

$(6 \div x) \times 2$ $6 \div (x \times 2)$ $6 \div x \times 2$

In order to evaluate these expressions for $x = 3$, you must pay attention to the order in which you multiply and divide. The first two expressions contain parentheses, so the operations inside the parentheses are performed first. In the last expression, you multiply and divide in order from left to right.

$(6 \div x) \times 2$	$6 \div (x \times 2)$	$6 \div x \times 2$
$(6 \div 3) \times 2$	$6 \div (3 \times 2)$	$6 \div 3 \times 2$
2×2 or 4	$6 \div 6$ or 1	2×2 or 4

Daily Routine

Use these suggestions before beginning the lesson on p. 214.

5-Minute Check

(Reviews Lesson 5-5)

Write an equation that describes the pattern. Then use the equation to find the next three numbers in the pattern.

1.

Input (x)	5	7	9	11	13	15
Output (y)	7	9	11	■	■	■

$x + 2 = y$; 13, 15, 17

2.

Input (x)	10	15	20	25	30	35
Output (y)	7	12	17	■	■	■

$x - 3 = y$; 22, 27, 32

Problem of the Day

How many ways can you write a two-digit number using the digit 3 exactly once in each number?
17 ways

Review Math Vocabulary

Write the review vocabulary word and its definitions on the board.

Have students review the word in their Math Journals or notebooks. Discuss and compare the math meaning of the word to everyday English usage.

Visual Vocabulary Cards

Use Visual Vocabulary Card 16 to reinforce the vocabulary reviewed in this lesson. (The Define/Example/Ask routine is printed on the back of each card.)

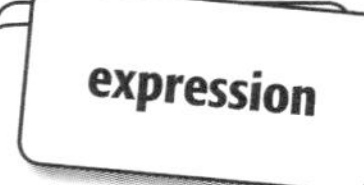

Differentiated Instruction

Small Group Options

LOGICAL

Option 1 Below Level BL

Materials: pencils, paper, chart paper

- Write the following expression on the chart paper and ask the students to find the value: $12 - 5 + 6$. 13
- Now write the expression as follows and ask the students to find its value: $12 - (5 + 6)$. 1
- Ask the students to identify what is the same and what is different about these two expressions. Typical answers should include the numbers and the operation signs are the same, but the parentheses are included only in the second expression.
- Conclude the lesson by writing the following examples on chart paper for the students to solve: $13 - (6 + 3)$; $13 - 6 + 3$; $7 + 6 - 2$; $7 + (6 - 2)$. 4, 10, 11, 11

LOGICAL, INTRAPERSONAL

Option 2 English Language Learners ELL

Materials: empty boxes, pencils

Core Vocabulary: alphabet, letters, take the place of

Common Use Verb: do/don't

See Math This strategy connects student knowledge of the alphabet with previous lessons on "what's missing."

- Ask students to tell you a symbol.
- Say: "Symbols are used in math when we do not know what a number is."
- Before the lesson, put 2 pencils in three boxes.
- Say: "We **don't know** how many pencils are in each box, but we can write an expression: 3 × ▒. ▒ stands for the number of pencils in each box."
- Show students the pencils in the box and find the value of the expression.
- Repeat several times with different numbers of pencils and symbols.

Independent Work Options

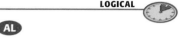

LOGICAL

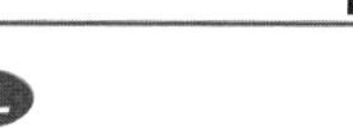

Option 1 Early Finishers OL AL

Materials: paper and pencil

- Have each student write three expressions on one side of a piece of paper.
- On the other side, have the student write each expression in words.
- Students can challenge classmates to write the expression in words and then check the answers by turning over the paper.

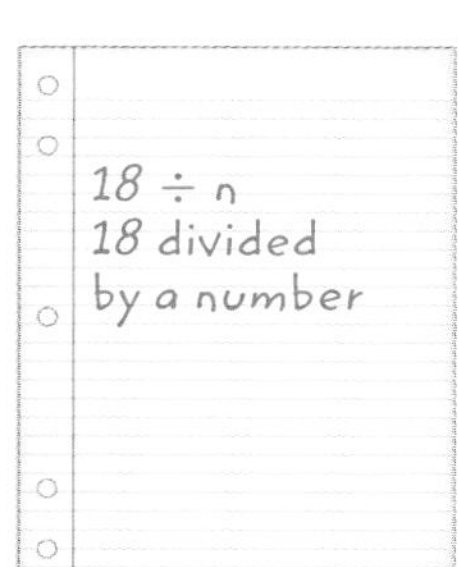

Option 2 Student Technology

Math Online macmillanmh.com

Personal Tutor • Extra Examples

Math Songs, "Algebra Rocks" Track #2

Option 3 Learning Station: Art (p. 190G)

Direct students to the Art Learning Station for opportunities to explore and extend the lesson concept.

Option 4 Problem-Solving Practice

Reinforce problem-solving skills and strategies with the Problem-Solving Practice worksheet.

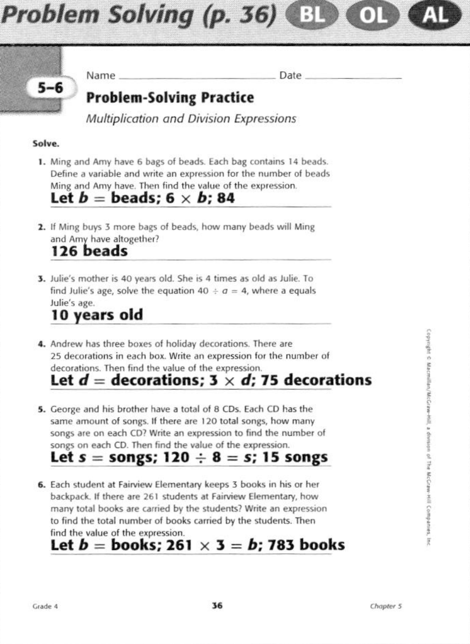

Problem Solving (p. 36) BL OL AL

5–6 Name ________ Date ________

Problem-Solving Practice

Multiplication and Division Expressions

Solve.

1. Ming and Amy have 6 bags of beads. Each bag contains 14 beads. Define a variable and write an expression for the number of beads Ming and Amy have. Then find the value of the expression.
   Let b = beads; $6 \times b$; 84
2. If Ming buys 3 more bags of beads, how many beads will Ming and Amy have altogether?
   126 beads
3. Julie's mother is 40 years old. She is 4 times as old as Julie. To find Julie's age, solve the equation $40 \div a = 4$, where a equals Julie's age.
   10 years old
4. Andrew has three boxes of holiday decorations. There are 25 decorations in each box. Write an expression for the number of decorations. Then find the value of the expression.
   Let d = decorations; $3 \times d$; 75 decorations
5. George and his brother have a total of 8 CDs. Each CD has the same amount of songs. If there are 120 total songs, how many songs are on each CD? Write an expression to find the number of songs on each CD. Then find the value of the expression.
   Let s = songs; $120 \div 8 = s$; 15 songs
6. Each student at Fairview Elementary keeps 3 books in his or her backpack. If there are 261 students at Fairview Elementary, how many total books are carried by the students? Write an expression to find the total number of books carried by the students. Then find the value of the expression.
   Let b = books; $261 \times 3 = b$; 783 books

Grade 4 36 Chapter 5

Multiplication and Division Expressions

Introduce

Activity Choice 1 • Hands-On

- Students, working in pairs, make a matching game with expressions. Give each pair 24 index cards. Ask them to write an expression on one card and the value of the expression on another card. For example: card 1: $2 + (5 \times 3)$; card 2: 17. Continue this until all 24 cards are completed.
- Now have the students play a matching game. To play, students shuffle the cards and place them facedown. Player 1 turns up 2 cards. If they are a pair, that player keeps the cards and plays again. If Player 1 does not turn a pair, then the cards are replaced and it is Player 2's turn. Students play until all the cards have been matched. The player with the most pairs wins.

Activity Choice 2 • Literature

Introduce the lesson with *Mailing May* by Michael O. Tunnel. For a related math activity, see p. TR49.

Teach

Scaffolding Questions

Show students five empty cups. Place two counters in the first cup.

- Put two counters each in the second and the third cup. **How many counters have I put into cups now? How do you know?** 6 counters; Sample answer: $3 \times 2 = 6$
- Repeat with the fourth and fifth cups, asking the same questions each time. Then use ten cups, putting two counters in each of the new cups. Ask the same questions.
- Suppose you did not know how many cups there were. **Could you write an expression that could help you find the number of counters?** yes; Sample answer: $n \times 2$ where n is the number of cups

GET READY to Learn

Have students open their books and read the information in **Get Ready to Learn**. Review **expression**. As a class, work through **Examples 1–3**.

Multiplication and Division Expressions

MAIN IDEA

I will write and find the value of multiplication and division expressions.

Math Online

macmillanmh.com

- Extra Examples
- Personal Tutor
- Self-Check Quiz

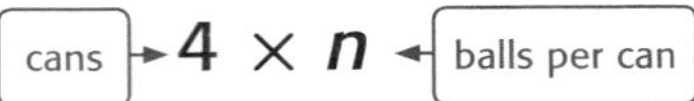

Liza has 4 cans of tennis balls. The total number of balls can be represented by the expression below.

cans → $4 \times n$ ← balls per can

Finding the value of multiplication and division expressions is similar to finding the value of addition and subtraction expressions.

Real-World EXAMPLE Find Value of an Expression

1. **TENNIS BALLS If there are 3 balls in each can, what is the total number of tennis balls? Find the value of $4 \times n$ if $n = 3$.**

$4 \times n$	Write the expression.
4×3	Replace n with 3.
12	Multiply 4 and 3.

The value of the expression is 12. Liza has 12 tennis balls.

Recall that you perform the operations inside parentheses first.

EXAMPLE Find the Value of an Expression

2. **Find the value of $2 \times (15 \div x)$ if $x = 5$.**

$2 \times (15 \div x)$	Write the expression.
$2 \times (15 \div 5)$	Replace x with 5.
2×3	Find $(15 \div 5)$ first.
6	Next, find 2×3.

You can write expressions for real-world situations.

Write an Expression

3 MONEY Jorge has d dollars to buy airplane models. Write an expression for the number of models Jorge can buy with his money.

Write an expression. You know that Jorge has d dollars and that the cost of one model plane is $7.

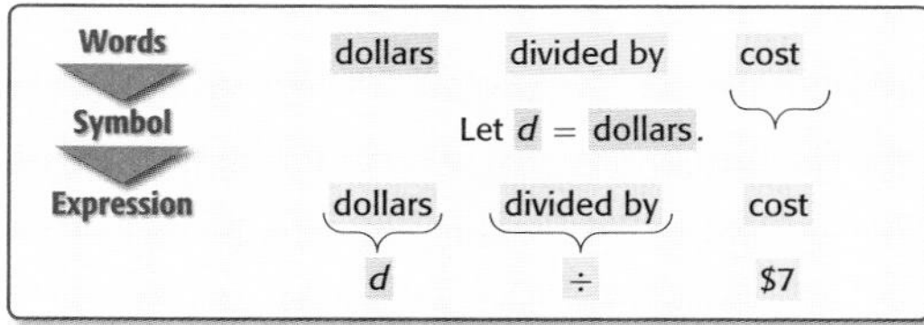

Words
Symbol
Expression
dollars
divided by
cost
Let d = dollars.
dollars
divided by
cost
d
÷
$7

So, the number of airplane models Jorge can buy is $d \div \$7$.

CHECK What You Know

Find the value of each expression if $a = 3$ and $c = 6$. See Examples 1 and 2 (p. 214)

1. $2 \times a$ 6 **2.** $c \div a$ 2 **3.** $(15 \div a) \times 6$ 30

Write an expression for each situation. See Example 3 (p. 215)

4. 9 times n $9 \times n$

5. n multiplied by 12 $n \times 12$

6. a number divided by 8 $n \div 8$

7. 24 divided by a number $24 \div n$

For Exercises 8 and 9, use the following information. See Example 3 (p. 215)
Luis has four times as much money as Kyle.

8. Define a variable. Then write an expression for the amount of money Luis has. Let k = Kyle's money; $4 \times k$

9. If Kyle has $8, how much money does Luis have? $\$8 \times 4 = \$32$

10. Talk About It How do you find the value of $9 \times (y \div 4)$ when $y = 20$?
Sample answer: Replace y with 20. Then find $20 \div 4$ and multiply the result by 9.

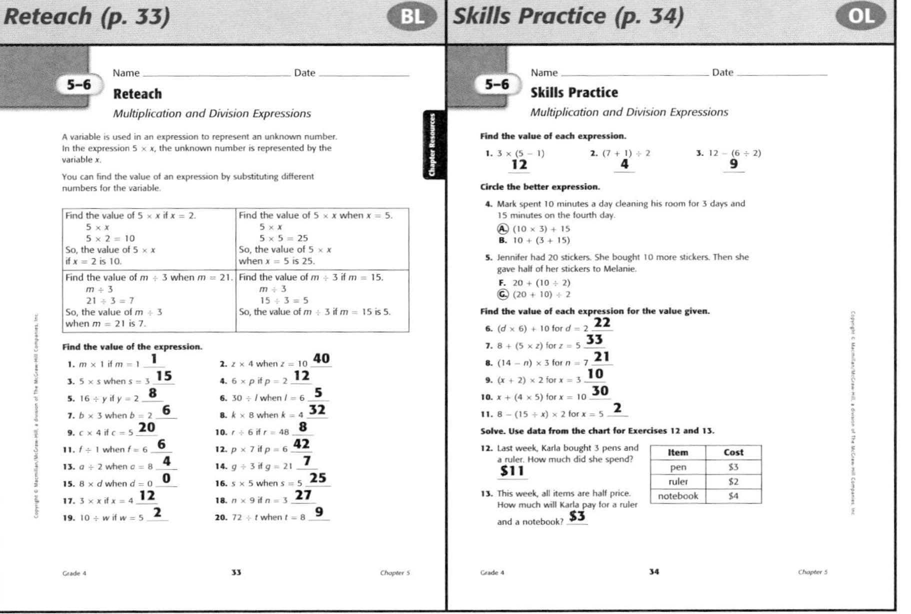

Reteach (p. 33) BL

5-6 Name ______ Date ______

Reteach

Multiplication and Division Expressions

A variable is used in an expression to represent an unknown number. In the expression $5 \times x$, the unknown number is represented by the variable x.

You can find the value of an expression by substituting different numbers for the variable.

Find the value of $5 \times x$ if $x = 2$. $5 \times x$ $5 \times 2 = 10$ So, the value of $5 \times x$ if $x = 2$ is 10.	Find the value of $5 \times x$ when $x = 5$. $5 \times x$ $5 \times 5 = 25$ So, the value of $5 \times x$ when $x = 5$ is 25.
Find the value of $m \div 3$ when $m = 21$. $m \div 3$ $21 \div 3 = 7$ So, the value of $m \div 3$ when $m = 21$ is 7.	Find the value of $m \div 3$ if $m = 15$. $m \div 3$ $15 \div 3 = 5$ So, the value of $m \div 3$ if $m = 15$ is 5.

Find the value of the expression.

1. $m \times 1$ if $m = 1$ **1**
2. $z \times 4$ when $z = 10$ **40**
3. $5 \times s$ when $s = 3$ **15**
4. $6 \times p$ if $p = 2$ **12**
5. $16 \div y$ if $y = 2$ **8**
6. $30 \div l$ when $l = 6$ **5**
7. $b \times 3$ when $b = 2$ **6**
8. $k \times 8$ when $k = 4$ **32**
9. $c \times 4$ if $c = 5$ **20**
10. $r \div 6$ if $r = 48$ **8**
11. $f \div 1$ when $f = 6$ **6**
12. $p \times 7$ if $p = 6$ **42**
13. $a \div 2$ when $a = 8$ **4**
14. $g \div 3$ if $g = 21$ **7**
15. $8 \times d$ when $d = 0$ **0**
16. $s \times 5$ when $s = 5$ **25**
17. $3 \times x$ if $x = 4$ **12**
18. $n \times 9$ if $n = 3$ **27**
19. $10 \div w$ if $w = 5$ **2**
20. $72 \div t$ when $t = 8$ **9**

Grade 4 33 Chapter 5

Chapter Resources

Skills Practice (p. 34) OL

5-6 Name ______ Date ______

Skills Practice

Multiplication and Division Expressions

Find the value of each expression.

1. $3 \times (5 - 1)$ **12**
2. $(7 + 1) \div 2$ **4**
3. $12 - (6 \div 2)$ **9**

Circle the better expression.

4. Mark spent 10 minutes a day cleaning his room for 3 days and 15 minutes on the fourth day.
   (A.) $(10 \times 3) + 15$
   B. $10 + (3 + 15)$
5. Jennifer had 20 stickers. She bought 10 more stickers. Then she gave half of her stickers to Melanie.
   F. $20 + (10 \div 2)$
   (G.) $(20 + 10) \div 2$

Find the value of each expression for the value given.

6. $(d \times 6) + 10$ for $d = 2$ **22**
7. $8 + (5 \times z)$ for $z = 5$ **33**
8. $(14 - n) \times 3$ for $n = 7$ **21**
9. $(x + 2) \times 2$ for $x = 3$ **10**
10. $x + (4 \times 5)$ for $x = 10$ **30**
11. $8 - (15 \div x) \times 2$ for $x = 5$ **2**

Solve. Use data from the chart for Exercises 12 and 13.

12. Last week, Karla bought 3 pens and a ruler. How much did she spend? **$11**
13. This week, all items are half price. How much will Karla pay for a ruler and a notebook? **$3**

Item	Cost
pen	$3
ruler	$2
notebook	$4

Grade 4 34 Chapter 5

Write an Expression

Example 3 Encourage students to show all of their work. Suggest that they write out the words and define the variable for the unknown before they write the expression.

ADDITIONAL EXAMPLES

1. Jake had 4 boxes of apples. There are 6 apples in each box. Find the value of $4 \times a$ if $a = 6$. 24
2. Find the value of $b \div (3 \times 2)$ if $b = 30$. 5
3. Judy has d dollars to buy bottles of water that cost $2 each. Write an expression for the number of bottles of water she can buy. $d \div 2$

CHECK What You Know

As a class, have students complete Exercises 1–10 in **Check What You Know** as you observe their work.

Exercise 10 Assess student comprehension before assigning practice exercises.

BL Alternate Teaching Strategy

If students have trouble with multiplication and division expressions…

Then use one of these reteach options:

1 CRM **Daily Reteach Worksheet** (p. 33)

2 Have students write out the steps for writing an expression, as shown in Example 3.

Have students review the basic facts for multiplication and division.

3 Practice

Differentiate practice using these leveled assignments for Exercises 11–31.

Level	Assignment
BL Below/Approaching Level	11–16, 20–21, 26–28
OL On Level	14–19, 21–22, 24–25, 28–30
AL Above/Beyond Level	11–29 odd, 30–31

Have students discuss and complete the Higher Order Thinking problems. For Exercise 31, have students think of a division fact whose quotient is 3.

WRITING IN MATH Have students complete Exercise 31 in their Math Journals. You may choose to use this exercise as an optional formative assessment.

4 Assess

Formative Assessment

Find the value of each expression if $x = 3$ and $y = 6$.

- $x \times y$ 18
- $18 \div x$ 6
- $(x \times y) \div 2$ 9

Quick Check **Are students continuing to struggle with finding the value of an expression?**

If Yes → Small Group Options (p. 204B)

If No → Independent Work Options (p. 204B)
CRM Skills Practice Worksheet (p. 34)
CRM Enrich Worksheet (p. 37)

Name the Math Write $(12 \div x) \times 5$ on the board. Ask students to write the steps they would take to find the value if $x = 3$.

COMMON ERROR!

Exercises 22 and 23 Students may write the number and variable in the wrong order. Remind students that division is not commutative. Review *dividend* and *divisor*.

Practice and Problem Solving

See page R14.

Find the value of each expression if $f = 10$ and $g = 5$. See Examples 1 and 2 (p. 214)

11. $6 \times g$ 30 **12.** $f \times 7$ 70 **13.** $f \div 5$ 2

14. $g \div 5$ 1 **15.** $g \times f$ 50 **16.** $f \div g$ 2

17. $4 \times (f \div 2)$ 20 **18.** $(f \div g) \times 9$ 18 **19.** $(f \times g) \div 5$ 10

Write an expression for each situation. See Example 3 (p. 215)

20. n multiplied by 5 $n \times 5$

21. the product of 2 and a number $2 \times n$ or $n \times 2$

22. 8 divided by n $8 \div n$

23. 18 divided by a number $18 \div n$

A teacher has some boxes of pens. Each box contains 8 pens. See Example 3 (p. 215)

24. Define a variable. Then write an expression for the number of pens the teacher has. Let b = boxes; $b \times 8$

25. If the teacher has 9 boxes of pens, how many pens will the teacher have? 72 pens

Eduardo has some CDs with 9 songs on each of them. See Example 3 (p. 215)

26. Define a variable. Then write an expression for the number of songs that are on the CDs. Let c = CDs; $c \times 9$

27. Eduardo has 5 CDs and lets a friend borrow 2 of his CDs. How many songs will be on the CDs he has left? 27 songs

Data File

The state reptile of Illinois is the painted turtle. This turtle gets its name from the bottom of its shell that looks like it is painted.

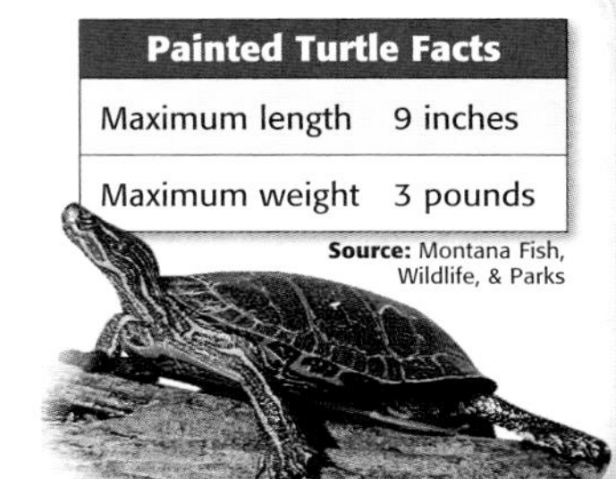

Painted Turtle Facts	
Maximum length	9 inches
Maximum weight	3 pounds

Source: Montana Fish, Wildlife, & Parks

28. Write an expression for the total weight of n turtles. $3 \times n$

29. Measurement Find the total length of 4 turtles that are laid head to tail. 36 in.

H.O.T. Problems

30. Sample answer: $21 \div n$

30. OPEN ENDED Write a division expression that has a value of 3 if $n = 7$.

31. WRITING IN MATH Write a problem that uses the expression $(4 \times n) \div 7$. See Ch. 5 Answer Appendix.

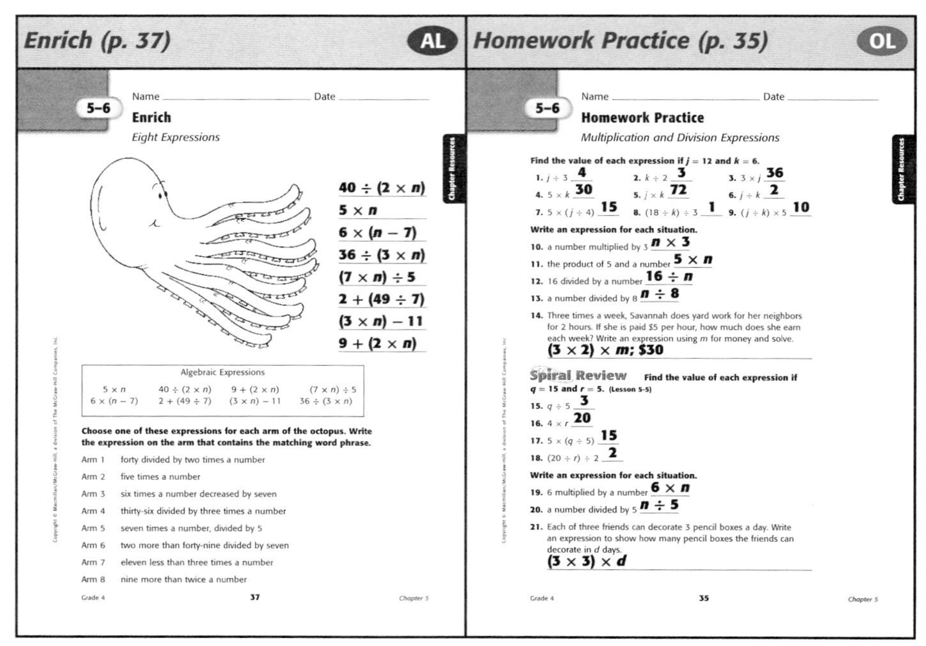

Enrich (p. 37) AL

5-6 Name ______ Date ______

Enrich

Eight Expressions

$40 \div (2 \times n)$
$5 \times n$
$6 \times (n - 7)$
$36 \div (3 \times n)$
$(7 \times n) \div 5$
$2 + (49 \div 7)$
$(3 \times n) - 11$
$9 + (2 \times n)$

Algebraic Expressions			
$5 \times n$	$40 \div (2 \times n)$	$9 + (2 \times n)$	$(7 \times n) \div 5$
$6 \times (n - 7)$	$2 + (49 \div 7)$	$(3 \times n) - 11$	$36 \div (3 \times n)$

Choose one of these expressions for each arm of the octopus. Write the expression on the arm that contains the matching word phrase.

Arm 1 forty divided by two times a number
Arm 2 five times a number
Arm 3 six times a number decreased by seven
Arm 4 thirty-six divided by three times a number
Arm 5 seven times a number, divided by 5
Arm 6 two more than forty-nine divided by seven
Arm 7 eleven less than three times a number
Arm 8 nine more than twice a number

Grade 4 37 Chapter 5

Homework Practice (p. 35) OL

5-6 Name ______ Date ______

Homework Practice

Multiplication and Division Expressions

Find the value of each expression if $j = 12$ and $k = 6$.

1. $j \div 3$ **4** 2. $k \div 2$ **3** 3. $3 \times j$ **36**
4. $5 \times k$ **30** 5. $j \times k$ **72** 6. $j \div k$ **2**
7. $5 \times (j \div 4)$ **15** 8. $(18 \div k) \div 3$ **1** 9. $(j \div k) \times 5$ **10**

Write an expression for each situation.

10. a number multiplied by 3 $n \times 3$
11. the product of 5 and a number $5 \times n$
12. 16 divided by a number $16 \div n$
13. a number divided by 8 $n \div 8$
14. Three times a week, Savannah does yard work for her neighbors for 2 hours. If she is paid $5 per hour, how much does she earn each week? Write an expression using m for money and solve. $(3 \times 2) \times m$; $30

Spiral Review **Find the value of each expression if $q = 15$ and $r = 5$. (Lesson 5-5)**

15. $q \div 5$ **3**
16. $4 \times r$ **20**
17. $5 \times (q \div 5)$ **15**
18. $(20 \div r) \div 2$ **2**

Write an expression for each situation.

19. 6 multiplied by a number $6 \times n$
20. a number divided by 5 $n \div 5$
21. Each of three friends can decorate 3 pencil boxes a day. Write an expression to show how many pencil boxes the friends can decorate in d days. $(3 \times 3) \times d$

Grade 4 35 Chapter 5

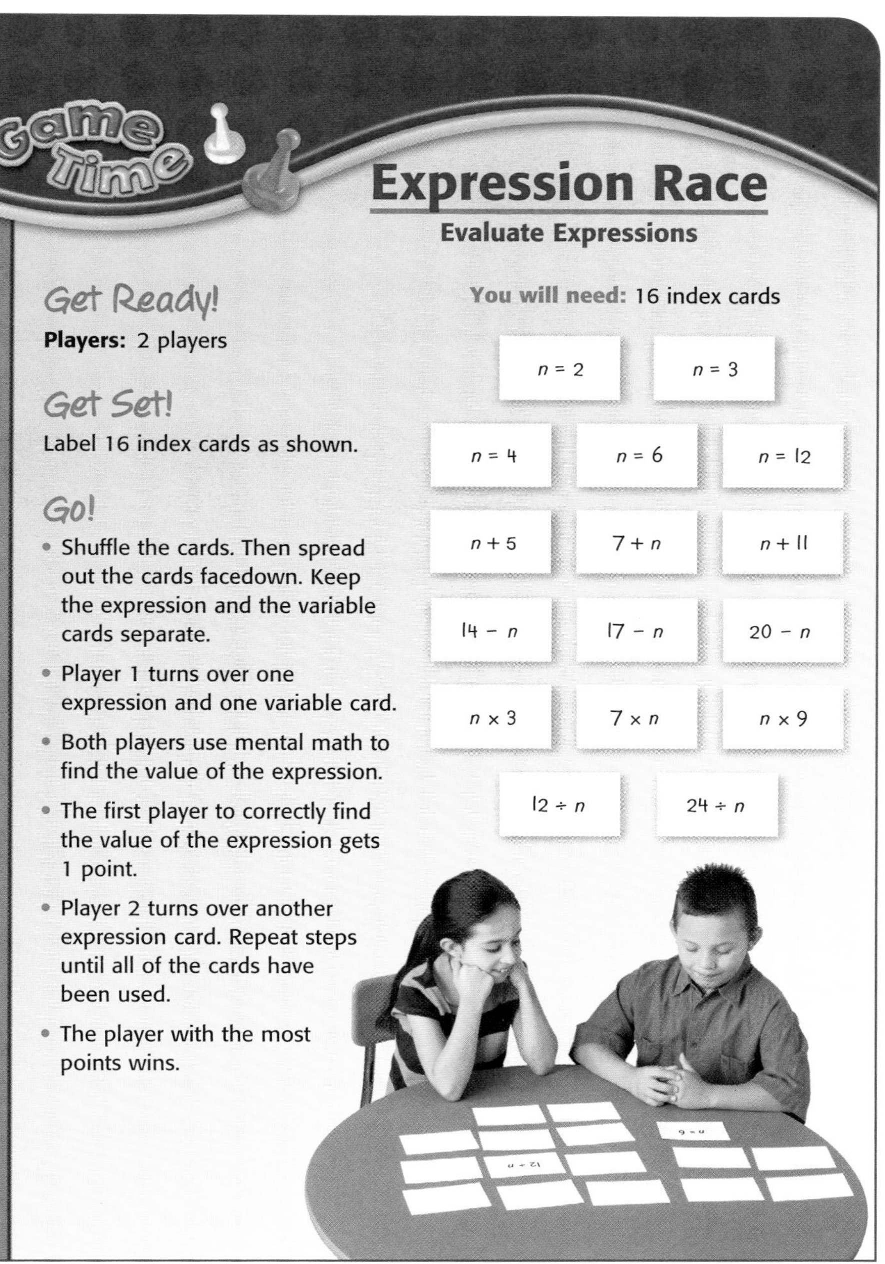

Expression Race

Evaluate Expressions

Get Ready!

Players: 2 players

Get Set!

Label 16 index cards as shown.

Go!

- Shuffle the cards. Then spread out the cards facedown. Keep the expression and the variable cards separate.
- Player 1 turns over one expression and one variable card.
- Both players use mental math to find the value of the expression.
- The first player to correctly find the value of the expression gets 1 point.
- Player 2 turns over another expression card. Repeat steps until all of the cards have been used.
- The player with the most points wins.

You will need: 16 index cards

$n = 2$, $n = 3$

$n = 4$, $n = 6$, $n = 12$

$n + 5$, $7 + n$, $n + 11$

$14 - n$, $17 - n$, $20 - n$

$n \times 3$, $7 \times n$, $n \times 9$

$12 \div n$, $24 \div n$

Game Time Expression Race **217**

Differentiated Practice

Use these leveled suggestions to differentiate the game for all learners.

Level	Assignment
BL Below/Approaching Level	Students take turns trying to find the solution, rather than racing.
OL On Level	Have students play the game with the rules as written.
AL Above/Beyond Level	Students make new cards and play the game again.

Expression Race

Math Concept: Evaluate Expressions

Materials: 16 index cards

Introduce the game on p. 217 to your students to play as a class, in small groups, or at a learning station to review concepts introduced in this chapter.

Instructions

- Label 16 index cards as shown on page 217.
- Students shuffle the cards and place them in a pile facedown on the table. Keep the expression cards and the variable cards separate. Player 1 picks an expression card and one variable card. Both players use mental math to find the value of the expression.
- The first player to correctly find the value of the expression gets 1 point.
- Player 2 selects an expression card, and play continues in the same manner.
- Play continues until all cards have been used. The player with the most points wins.

Extend the Game

Have students make the game using expressions they come up with themselves.

5-7 Problem-Solving Investigation
Choose a Strategy

Lesson Planner

Objective

Choose the best strategy to solve a problem.

Resources

Teacher Technology

TeacherWorks • Interactive Classroom

Real-World Problem Solving Library
Math and Science: *Oceans: Into the Deep*
Use these leveled books to reinforce and extend problem-solving skills and strategies.

Leveled for:

- OL On Level
- ELL Sheltered English
- SP Spanish

For additional support, see the Real-World Problem Solving Teacher Guide.

Daily Routine

Use these suggestions before beginning the lesson on p. 218.

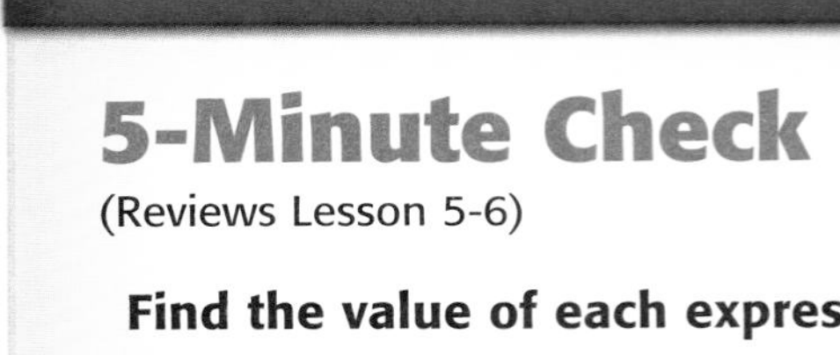

5-Minute Check

(Reviews Lesson 5-6)

Find the value of each expression if $x = 8$ and $y = 12$.

1. $3x$ 24
2. $5 \times x$ 40
3. $y \div 6$ 2
4. $56 \div x$ 7
5. $3 \times (y \div 3)$ 12
6. $(x \times y) \div 2$ 48

Problem of the Day

What do all of these numbers have in common?

14 23 113 320 401 500

Find a 1-digit number that belongs to this group.
The sum of the digits is always 5; 5

Differentiated Instruction

Small Group Options

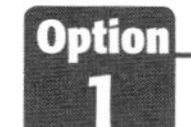

Option 1 Below Level BL

VISUAL, SPATIAL

Materials: posterboard, markers

- Ask students to read the following problem together.
- *Carmen and Jin were collecting rocks. Carmen found 4 smooth rocks, 3 crystals, and 5 jagged rocks. Jin found 7 smooth rocks, 6 crystals, and 8 jagged rocks. How many rocks were found in all? Draw a picture to solve this problem.* See students' work.
- As a group, the students will create a poster to represent this problem and solve for the correct number of rocks.

Option 2 English Language Learners ELL

LOGICAL, SOCIAL

Materials: classroom objects
Core Vocabulary: gift, add, side
Common Use Verb: balance

See Math This strategy activates background knowledge by asking students to think of their brothers and sisters at home to extend the idea of balancing equations.

- Say: "Do you feel sad when your brother or sister gets a gift and you do not?"
- Ask for student volunteers to be brothers or sisters.
- Give one brother two gifts (anything from around classroom) and the other brother two gifts. Then give one brother 2 more gifts.
- Say: "How many **gifts** does the other brother need to be the same as his brother?"
- Write an equation on the board.
- Instruct students that if you add a number to one side of an equation, you must add the same to the other side so they are equal.

Independent Work Options

Option 1 Early Finishers AL

KINESTHETIC, SOCIAL

Materials: pattern blocks

- Have students make a pattern using sets of blocks or counters. Then have the student add the next three sets of blocks or counters to the pattern.

- Ask students to record their patterns on paper.

Option 2 Student Technology

Math Online macmillanmh.com

Personal Tutor • Extra Examples

Option 3 Learning Station: Health (p. 190G)

Direct students to the Health Learning Station for opportunities to explore and extend the lesson concept.

1 Introduce

Activity • Review

- Have students consider the following:

  Mikalah wants to buy a rare stone that costs $150. She can sell her gems for $82, and her crystals for $50. Will she have enough to buy the rare stone if she sells her gems and crystals?
- Brainstorm with students the problem-solving strategies that they have learned. Have a volunteer record the responses on the board.
- **What strategy could you use to solve the problem?** Answers may vary.
- **How should you begin?** four-step plan
- **Solve the problem.** No, she does not have enough money.

2 Teach

Have students read the problem about the car wash. Guide them through the problem-solving steps.

Understand Using the questions, review what students know and need to find.

Plan Have them discuss their strategy.

Solve Guide students to use the make a table strategy to solve the problem.

- **Why is the make a table strategy a good choice?** Sample answer: It helps you organize the information.
- **Why does the number $72 belong with 2 hours?** Sample answer: 36 dollars in each hour, so 2 hours means $36 + $36 = $72.
- **How can you use this addition pattern to solve the problem?** Sample answer: Continue adding 36 dollars for each hour until you reach 5 hours.

Check Have students look back at the problem to make sure that the answer fits the facts given.

COMMON ERROR!

Exercise 3 Students will seek a pattern going from term to term. Encourage them to also look at alternating terms to find the pattern.

5-7 Problem-Solving Investigation

MAIN IDEA I will choose the best strategy to solve a problem.

P.S.I. TEAM +

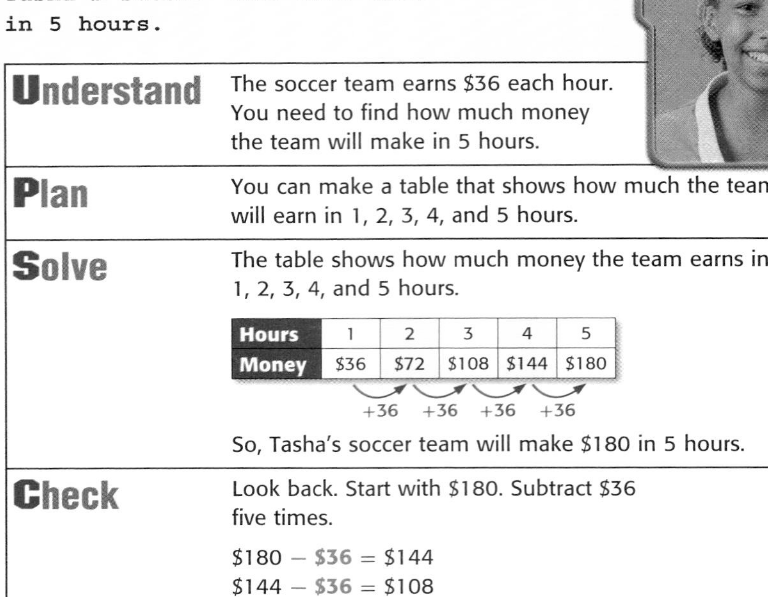

TASHA: My soccer team is raising money by having a car wash. We earn $36 each hour of washing cars.

YOUR MISSION: Find how much money Tasha's soccer team will make in 5 hours.

Understand The soccer team earns $36 each hour. You need to find how much money the team will make in 5 hours.

Plan You can make a table that shows how much the team will earn in 1, 2, 3, 4, and 5 hours.

Solve The table shows how much money the team earns in 1, 2, 3, 4, and 5 hours.

Hours	1	2	3	4	5
Money	$36	$72	$108	$144	$180

+36 +36 +36 +36

So, Tasha's soccer team will make $180 in 5 hours.

Check Look back. Start with $180. Subtract $36 five times.

$180 − $36 = $144
$144 − $36 = $108
$108 − $36 = $72
$72 − $36 = $36
$36 − $36 = $0

So, you know the answer is correct.

218 **Chapter 5** Describe Algebraic Patterns

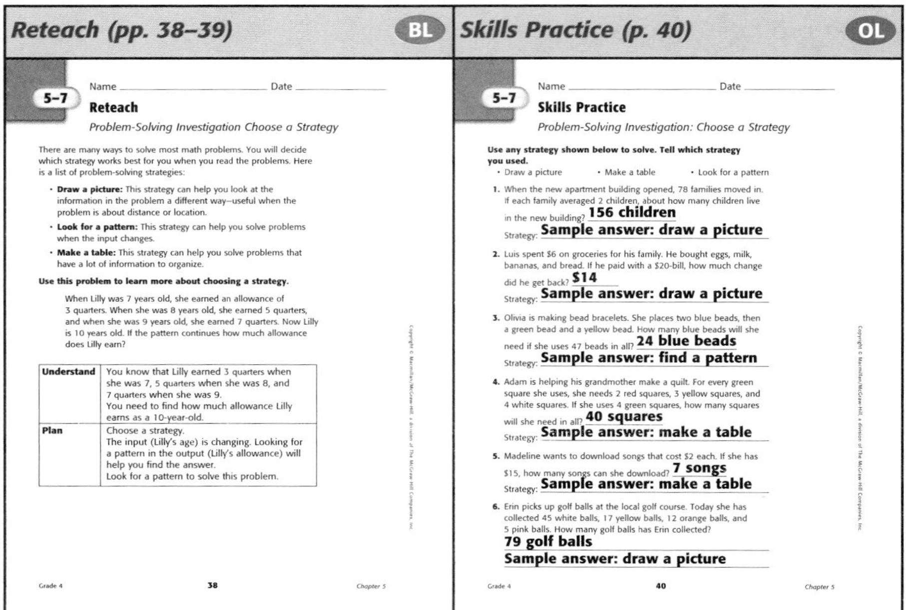

Reteach (pp. 38–39) BL

5-7 Name ______ Date ______

Reteach

Problem-Solving Investigation Choose a Strategy

There are many ways to solve most math problems. You will decide which strategy works best for you when you read the problems. Here is a list of problem-solving strategies:

- **Draw a picture:** This strategy can help you look at the information in the problem a different way–useful when the problem is about distance or location.
- **Look for a pattern:** This strategy can help you solve problems when the input changes.
- **Make a table:** This strategy can help you solve problems that have a lot of information to organize.

Use this problem to learn more about choosing a strategy.

When Lilly was 7 years old, she earned an allowance of 3 quarters. When she was 8 years old, she earned 5 quarters, and when she was 9 years old, she earned 7 quarters. Now Lilly is 10 years old. If the pattern continues how much allowance does Lilly earn?

Understand	You know that Lilly earned 3 quarters when she was 7, 5 quarters when she was 8, and 7 quarters when she was 9. You need to find how much allowance Lilly earns as a 10-year-old.
Plan	Choose a strategy. The input (Lilly's age) is changing. Looking for a pattern in the output (Lilly's allowance) will help you find the answer. Look for a pattern to solve this problem.

Grade 4 **38** *Chapter 5*

Skills Practice (p. 40) OL

5-7 Name ______ Date ______

Skills Practice

Problem-Solving Investigation: Choose a Strategy

Use any strategy shown below to solve. Tell which strategy you used.

- Draw a picture • Make a table • Look for a pattern

1. When the new apartment building opened, 78 families moved in. If each family averaged 2 children, about how many children live in the new building? **156 children**
   Strategy: **Sample answer: draw a picture**
2. Luis spent $6 on groceries for his family. He bought eggs, milk, bananas, and bread. If he paid with a $20-bill, how much change did he get back? **$14**
   Strategy: **Sample answer: draw a picture**
3. Olivia is making bead bracelets. She places two blue beads, then a green bead and a yellow bead. How many blue beads will she need if she uses 47 beads in all? **24 blue beads**
   Strategy: **Sample answer: find a pattern**
4. Adam is helping his grandmother make a quilt. For every green square she uses, she needs 2 red squares, 3 yellow squares, and 4 white squares. If she uses 4 green squares, how many squares will she need in all? **40 squares**
   Strategy: **Sample answer: make a table**
5. Madeline wants to download songs that cost $2 each. If she has $15, how many songs can she download? **7 songs**
   Strategy: **Sample answer: make a table**
6. Erin picks up golf balls at the local golf course. Today she has collected 45 white balls, 17 yellow balls, 12 orange balls, and 5 pink balls. How many golf balls has Erin collected?
   79 golf balls
   Sample answer: draw a picture

Grade 4 **40** *Chapter 5*

★ indicates multi-step problem

Mixed Problem Solving

See page R14.

Use any strategy shown below to solve. Tell what strategy you used.

1. **Algebra** Gigi is planting flowers in her garden in the pattern shown. How many daisies will she have if she plants 24 flowers in one row? 16

2. Julio is setting up square tables for a party. One person can sit at each side of a table. He connects the tables together to form one long table. He invited 9 friends. How many tables does he need for everyone, including himself? 4 tables

3. Victor wants to buy CDs that cost \$12 each. He has \$40. How many CDs can he buy? 3 CDs

★4. Russell wants to buy juice, a fruit cup, and a salad for lunch. He has \$5. How much change will he get back? 150¢

LUNCH MENU
Juice....... $1
Milk .... 50¢
Fruit cup.. 50¢
Salad........ $2
Spaghetti.. $2

5. **Measurement** Kirk rode his bike to school, which is 2 miles away. After school, he rode to his friend's house, which is 1 mile from school. Then he rode home. If he rode a total of 4 miles, how far does he live from his friend? 1 mile

★6. Della made 2 bowls of fruit punch for a family reunion. Each bowl fills 24 glasses. There are 12 family members at the reunion. How many glasses of punch can each person get? 4 glasses

7. **Algebra** What are the next two figures in the pattern?

See Ch. 5 Answer Appendix.

8. Polly is making a scrapbook. She is making the pattern shown as a border for one of the pages. How many bones will she need to glue to the page if she uses 36 shapes in all? 12 bones

9. Darnell has baseball practice four days a week. Practice lasts for two hours each day. How many hours does he practice in four weeks? 32 hrs

10. WRITING IN MATH Niles's bedtime was 8:00 P.M. in first grade. It was 8:30 P.M. in second grade and 9:00 P.M. in third grade. The answer is 10:00 P.M. What is the question? See Ch. 5 Answer Appendix.

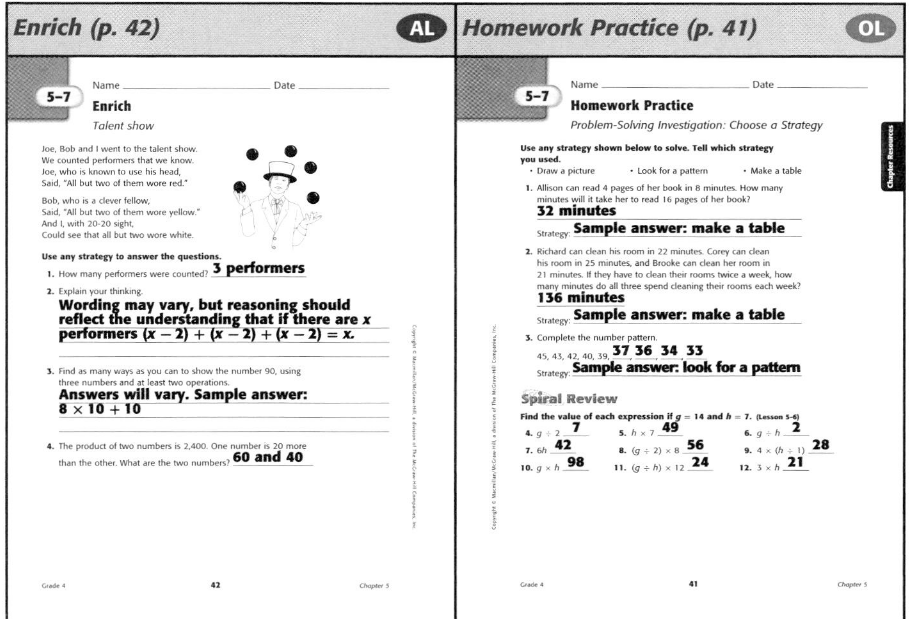

Enrich (p. 42) AL

5–7 Name ______ Date ______

Enrich

Talent show

Joe, Bob and I went to the talent show.
We counted performers that we know.
Joe, who is known to use his head,
Said, "All but two of them wore red."

Bob, who is a clever fellow,
Said, "All but two of them wore yellow."
And I, with 20-20 sight,
Could see that all but two wore white.

Use any strategy to answer the questions.

1. How many performers were counted? **3 performers**
2. Explain your thinking. **Wording may vary, but reasoning should reflect the understanding that if there are x performers $(x - 2) + (x - 2) + (x - 2) = x$.**
3. Find as many ways as you can to show the number 90, using three numbers and at least two operations. **Answers will vary. Sample answer: $8 \times 10 + 10$**
4. The product of two numbers is 2,400. One number is 20 more than the other. What are the two numbers? **60 and 40**

Grade 4 42 Chapter 5

Homework Practice (p. 41) OL

5–7 Name ______ Date ______

Homework Practice

Problem-Solving Investigation: Choose a Strategy

Use any strategy shown below to solve. Tell which strategy you used.

• Draw a picture • Look for a pattern • Make a table

1. Allison can read 4 pages of her book in 8 minutes. How many minutes will it take her to read 16 pages of her book? **32 minutes**
   Strategy: **Sample answer: make a table**
2. Richard can clean his room in 22 minutes. Corey can clean his room in 25 minutes, and Brooke can clean her room in 21 minutes. If they have to clean their rooms twice a week, how many minutes do all three spend cleaning their rooms each week? **136 minutes**
   Strategy: **Sample answer: make a table**
3. Complete the number pattern.
   45, 43, 42, 40, 39, **37**, **36**, **34**, **33**
   Strategy: **Sample answer: look for a pattern**

Spiral Review

Find the value of each expression if $g = 14$ and $h = 7$. (Lesson 5-6)

4. $g \div 2$ **7**
5. $h \times 7$ **49**
6. $g \div h$ **2**
7. $6h$ **42**
8. $(g \div 2) \times 8$ **56**
9. $4 \times (h \div 1)$ **28**
10. $g \times h$ **98**
11. $(g \div h) \times 12$ **24**
12. $3 \times h$ **21**

Grade 4 41 Chapter 5

Chapter Resources

BL Alternate Teaching Strategy

If students have trouble deciding on the best strategy…

Then use one of these reteach options:

1 CRM **Daily Reteach Worksheet** (pp. 38–39)

2 Have students use the strategy list as a guide. Refer them back to it often.

Ask which strategies can be used to solve the problem. Then ask which of those would work the best.

Consider displaying the list of all the strategies, with an example for each, as a class resource.

3 Practice

Using the Exercises

Exercises 2 and 5 The draw a picture strategy will help students visualize and understand these exercises.

Exercises 6–7 Ask students to show all of their work to demonstrate their mathematical reasoning.

4 Assess

Formative Assessment

Have students look over their work and answer the following questions.

- **How do you know the look for a pattern strategy is a good strategy for Exercises 1, 7, and 8?** Sample answer: The word "pattern" is in the problem.

Quick Check **Are students continuing to struggle with choosing the best strategy to solve a problem?**

If Yes → Small Group Options (p. 218B)

If No → Independent Work Options (p. 218B)
CRM Skills Practice Worksheet (p. 40)
CRM Enrich Worksheet (p. 42)

LESSON 5-8

Function Tables: Find a Rule (×, ÷)

Lesson Planner

Objective

Find and use rules to write multiplication and division equations.

Review Vocabulary

equation

Resources

Materials: index cards, chart paper, cardboard box

Manipulatives: counters

Literature Connection: *Multiplying Menace: The Revenge of Rumpelstiltskin* by Pam Calvert

Alternate Lesson: Use *IMPACT Mathematics: Unit B* to provide practice with functions.

Teacher Technology
TeacherWorks • Interactive Classroom • Math Songs Track #2 Lesson Plan

Focus on Math Background

In Lesson 5-5, students were introduced to input/output tables and wrote equations to describe the patterns they found. They used the following forms to describe the "add some number" or "subtract some number" patterns found in the tables:

input + some number = output
input − some number = output

In this lesson students examine tables that exhibit "multiply by some number" or "divide by some number" patterns. The equations that describe the patterns are usually written in one of the following forms:

input × some number = output
input ÷ some number = output

Daily Routine

Use these suggestions before beginning the lesson on p. 220.

5-Minute Check

(Reviews Lesson 5-7)

Use any strategy to solve. Tell which strategy you used.
Mario is 6 years old and his brother is 2 years old. How old will each of them be when Mario is twice his brother's age? Mario will be 8 and his brother will be 4.

Problem of the Day

Find the sum of the first 5 even numbers and the sum of the first 5 odd numbers. Which is greater? How much greater? 30; 25; the sum of the first 5 even numbers; 5

Review Math Vocabulary

Write the review vocabulary word and its definition on the board.

Have students write how they would explain the word *equation* to a new student in the class.

Visual Vocabulary Cards
Use Visual Vocabulary Card 14 to reinforce the vocabulary reviewed in this lesson. (The Define/Example/Ask routine is printed on the back of each card.)

Differentiated Instruction

Small Group Options

Option 1 Gifted and Talented AL

LOGICAL, SOCIAL

Materials: pencils, paper, chart paper

- Review the concept by using the relatively easy rule of multiply by 3, so $x \times 3 = y$.
- Write the following table on chart paper:

x	1	2	3	8
y	3	5	7	17

- Ask students to work with a partner to find another rule. The rule is multiply by 2 and add 1, or $2 \times x + 1 = y$.

x	3	4	5	9
y	11	15	19	35

- Write the chart shown above on chart paper.
- Ask students to work with a partner to find the rule. multiply by 4 and subtract 1, or $4 \times x - 1 = y$.
- To complete the activity, ask students to make up a chart and rule system and try it out on a partner.

Option 2 English Language Learners ELL

KINESTHETIC

Materials: masking tape, note cards

Core Vocabulary: invisible rule, this/that end, here/there

Common Use Verb: spin

See Math This strategy uses kinesthetic action to help students figure out the guiding invisible rule.

- Make three 2-feet-long parallel lines on the floor with masking tape.
- Ask 2 students to stand on one end and 6 students on the other end.
- What number do we need to multiply to go from the 2 to the 6? 3
- Demonstrate to students that the 3 is repeated and this becomes a rule for these three problems.
- Repeat with 4–12 and 6–18.
- Repeat with different numbers and division.

Independent Work Options

Option 1 Early Finishers OL AL

LOGICAL

Materials: paper and pencil

- Have the students use each rule below to fill in the table.
- $x \times 5 = y$

Input (x)	Output (y)
1	5
2	10
3	15
4	20

- $x \div 3 = y$

Input (x)	Output (y)
15	5
12	4
9	3
6	2

Option 2 Student Technology

Math Online macmillanmh.com

Personal Tutor • Extra Examples

Math Songs, "Algebra Rocks" Track #2

Option 3 Learning Station: Music (p. 190H)

Direct students to the Music Learning Station for opportunities to explore and extend the lesson concept.

Option 4 Problem-Solving Practice

Reinforce problem-solving skills and strategies with the Problem-Solving Practice worksheet.

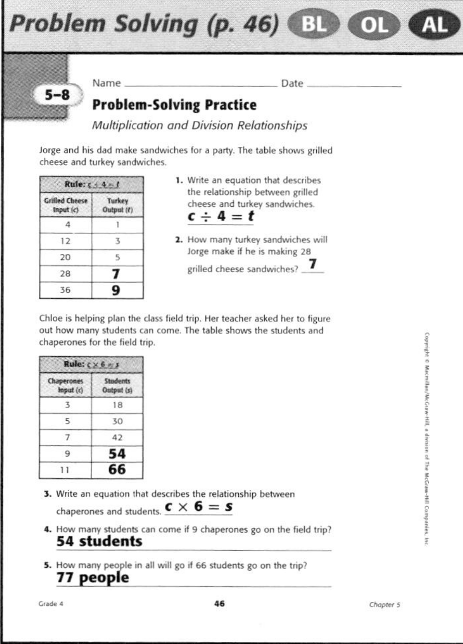

Problem Solving (p. 46) BL OL AL

5-8 Name ______ Date ______

Problem-Solving Practice

Multiplication and Division Relationships

Jorge and his dad make sandwiches for a party. The table shows grilled cheese and turkey sandwiches.

Rule: $c \div 4 = t$	
Grilled Cheese Input (c)	Turkey Output (t)
4	1
12	3
20	5
28	**7**
36	**9**

1. Write an equation that describes the relationship between grilled cheese and turkey sandwiches. $c \div 4 = t$
2. How many turkey sandwiches will Jorge make if he is making 28 grilled cheese sandwiches? **7**

Chloe is helping plan the class field trip. Her teacher asked her to figure out how many students can come. The table shows the students and chaperones for the field trip.

Rule: $c \times 6 = s$	
Chaperones Input (c)	Students Output (s)
3	18
5	30
7	42
9	**54**
11	**66**

3. Write an equation that describes the relationship between chaperones and students. $c \times 6 = s$
4. How many students can come if 9 chaperones go on the field trip? **54 students**
5. How many people in all will go if 66 students go on the trip? **77 people**

Grade 4 46 Chapter 5

5-8 Function Tables: Find a Rule (×, ÷)

1 Introduce

Activity Choice 1 • Hands-On

- Make an input/output machine by wrapping a box in paper and cutting out opposite ends of the box.
- On 1 index card write a 1 and on another write a 2. Have a volunteer slide the 1 card into one end of the box and pull the 2 card out the other side of the box. Explain to the students that the machine performs an operation to the number you put in and gives you another number.
- This time have a volunteer put in an index card labeled 2 and pull out a card labeled 4. Ask the students if they can guess the rule. The rule is multiply by 2. If they cannot guess the rule, put in a 3 card and pull out a 6 card. Continue until the rule is found.

Activity Choice 2 • Literature

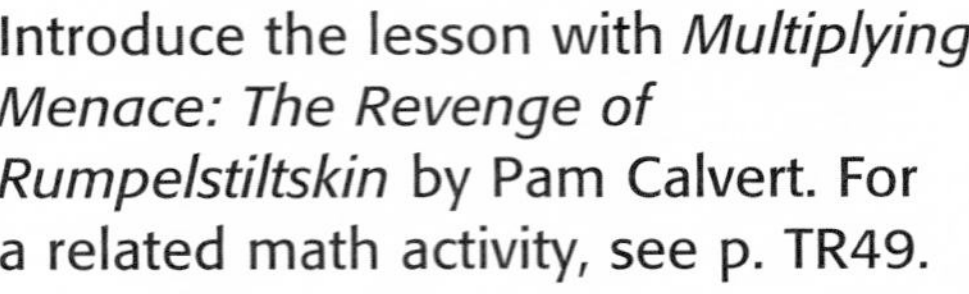

Introduce the lesson with *Multiplying Menace: The Revenge of Rumpelstiltskin* by Pam Calvert. For a related math activity, see p. TR49.

2 Teach

Scaffolding Questions

- Play "What's My Rule" for $x + 5 = y$. Display a two-column input (x) output (y) table.
- Have a volunteer write a number in the input column. Write 5 times the input number in the output column.
- Have another volunteer write another number for x in the input column.
- Write 5 times the input number in the output column. Repeat two more times.
- **What do you have to do to the input number in the first column to get the output number in the second column?** Multiply by 5.
- **How can you write the rule as an equation?** $x \times 5 = y$

GET READY to Learn

Have students open their books and read the information in **Get Ready to Learn**. Review **equation**. As a class, work through **Examples 1–4**.

5-8 Function Tables: Find a Rule (×, ÷)

MAIN IDEA

I will find and use rules to write multiplication and division equations.

Math Online

macmillanmh.com

- Extra Examples
- Personal Tutor
- Self-Check Quiz

GET READY to Learn

Tracy rakes yards to earn money. If she rakes 2 yards a day, she earns \$12. If she rakes 4 yards, she earns \$24. If she rakes 6 yards, she earns \$36. How much money will she earn if she rakes 8, 10, or 12 yards?

You can write an equation to describe and extend a pattern.

Real-World EXAMPLES — Find a Multiplication Rule

1 MONEY Write an equation that describes the amount of money Tracy earns.

Show the information in a table. Then look for the pattern that describes the rule.

Yards Raked	Amount Earned (\$)
Input (a)	Output (b)
2	12
4	24
6	36
8	■
10	■
12	■

Pattern: $2 \times 6 = 12$
$4 \times 6 = 24$
$6 \times 6 = 36$

Rule: Multiply by 6.

Equation: $a \times 6 = b$ (input a, output b)

2 Use the equation to find how much money Tracy will earn if she rakes 8, 10, and 12 yards.

$a \times \$6 = b$, $8 \times \$6 = \$48$

$a \times \$6 = b$, $10 \times \$6 = \$60$

$a \times \$6 = b$, $12 \times \$6 = \$72$

So, Tracy will earn \$48, \$60, and \$72.

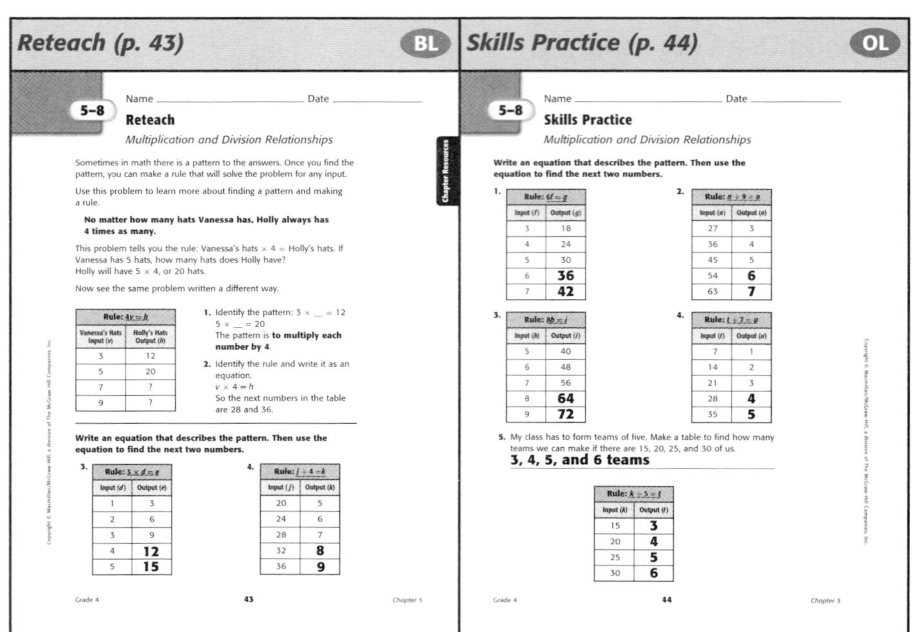

Reteach (p. 43) BL

Name ________ Date ________

5–8 **Reteach**

Multiplication and Division Relationships

Sometimes in math there is a pattern to the answers. Once you find the pattern, you can make a rule that will solve the problem for any input.

Use this problem to learn more about finding a pattern and making a rule.

No matter how many hats Vanessa has, Holly always has 4 times as many.

This problem tells you the rule: Vanessa's hats × 4 = Holly's hats. If Vanessa has 5 hats, how many hats does Holly have?
Holly will have 5 × 4, or 20 hats.

Now see the same problem written a different way.

Rule: $4v = h$	
Vanessa's Hats Input (v)	Holly's Hats Output (h)
3	12
5	20
7	?
9	?

1. Identify the pattern: 3 × __ = 12
5 × __ = 20
The pattern is **to multiply each number by 4**.
2. Identify the rule and write it as an equation.
$v \times 4 = h$
So the next numbers in the table are 28 and 36.

Write an equation that describes the pattern. Then use the equation to find the next two numbers.

3.

Rule: $3 \times d = e$	
Input (d)	Output (e)
1	3
2	6
3	9
4	**12**
5	**15**

4.

Rule: $j \div 4 = k$	
Input (j)	Output (k)
20	5
24	6
28	7
32	**8**
36	**9**

Grade 4 43 Chapter 5

Skills Practice (p. 44) OL

Name ________ Date ________

5–8 **Skills Practice**

Multiplication and Division Relationships

Write an equation that describes the pattern. Then use the equation to find the next two numbers.

1.

Rule: $6f = g$	
Input (f)	Output (g)
3	18
4	24
5	30
6	**36**
7	**42**

2.

Rule: $n \div 9 = o$	
Input (n)	Output (o)
27	3
36	4
45	5
54	**6**
63	**7**

3.

Rule: $8h = i$	
Input (h)	Output (i)
5	40
6	48
7	56
8	**64**
9	**72**

4.

Rule: $t \div 7 = u$	
Input (t)	Output (u)
7	1
14	2
21	3
28	**4**
35	**5**

5. My class has to form teams of five. Make a table to find how many teams we can make if there are 15, 20, 25, and 30 of us.
3, 4, 5, and 6 teams

Rule: $k \div 5 = t$	
Input (k)	Output (t)
15	**3**
20	**4**
25	**5**
30	**6**

Grade 4 44 Chapter 5

Real-World EXAMPLES Find a Division Rule

3 MONEY The cost of crackers is shown. Write an equation that describes the pattern.

Total Cost ($)	Boxes of Crackers
Input (g)	Output (h)
4	1
8	2
12	3
16	■
20	■
24	■

Look for the pattern that describes the rule.

Pattern: $4 \div 4 = 1$
$8 \div 4 = 2$
$12 \div 4 = 3$

Rule: Divide by 4.

Equation: $g \div 4 = h$

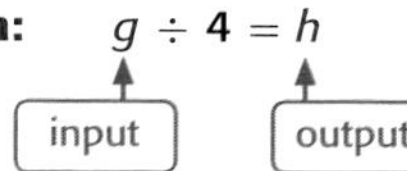

> **Remember**
> Always check to make sure the rule works for each number in the table.

4 Use the equation to find how many boxes you get for $16, $20, or $24.

$g \div 4 = h$	$g \div 4 = h$	$g \div 4 = h$
$\$16 \div 4 = 4$	$\$20 \div 4 = 5$	$\$24 \div 4 = 6$

So, $16, $20, or $24 will buy 4, 5, or 6 boxes of crackers.

CHECK What You Know

Write an equation that describes each pattern. Then use the equation to find the next three numbers. See Examples 1–4 (pp. 220–221)

1.

Input (w)	2	4	6	8	10	12
Output (v)	12	24	36	■	■	■

$w \times 6 = v$; 48, 60, 72

2.

Input (x)	16	24	32	40	48	56
Output (y)	2	3	4	■	■	■

$x \div 8 = y$; 5, 6, 7

3. The table shows the cost of movie tickets. How many tickets will you get for $72? See Examples 1–4 (pp. 220–221) $c \div 6 = t$; 12

Total Cost	Input (c)	$12	$24	$36	$48	$60	$72
Tickets	Output (t)	2	4	6	■	■	■

4. **Talk About It** How are a rule and an equation alike? How are they different? See Ch. 5 Answer Appendix.

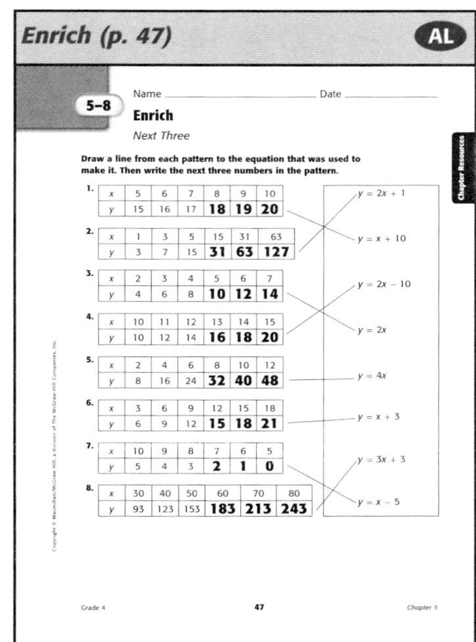

Enrich (p. 47) **AL**

5-8 Name ____________ Date ____________

Enrich

Next Three

Draw a line from each pattern to the equation that was used to make it. Then write the next three numbers in the pattern.

1.

x	5	6	7	8	9	10
y	15	16	17	**18**	**19**	**20**

2.

x	1	3	5	15	31	63
y	3	7	15	**31**	**63**	**127**

3.

x	2	3	4	5	6	7
y	4	6	8	**10**	**12**	**14**

4.

x	10	11	12	13	14	15
y	10	12	14	**16**	**18**	**20**

5.

x	2	4	6	8	10	12
y	8	16	24	**32**	**40**	**48**

6.

x	3	6	9	12	15	18
y	6	9	12	**15**	**18**	**21**

7.

x	10	9	8	7	6	5
y	5	4	3	**2**	**1**	**0**

8.

x	30	40	50	60	70	80
y	93	123	153	**183**	**213**	**243**

$y = 2x + 1$
$y = x + 10$
$y = 2x - 10$
$y = 2x$
$y = 4x$
$y = x + 3$
$y = 3x + 3$
$y = x - 5$

Chapter Resources

Find a Multiplication Rule

Example 1 Emphasize that the rule must apply to each input number in the table equally.

ADDITIONAL EXAMPLES

1. Mike earns $10 when he babysits for 2 hours. He earns $20 for 4 hours. He earns $30 for 6 hours. Write a rule that describes the money Mike earns. Then use the rule to write an equation.
   Multiply by $5; $x \times \$5 = y$

2. The cost of admission into a water park is shown in the table below. Find a rule that describes the number pattern. Then use the rule to write an equation.

Total Cost	Number of People
Input (x)	**Output (y)**
$6	1
$12	2
$18	3

   Divide by 6; $x \div 6 = y$

3. Use the equation from Example 2 to find how many people will be admitted to the park for $24, $30, and $36.
   4 people, 5 people, 6 people

CHECK What You Know

As a class, have students complete Exercises 1–4 in **Check What You Know** as you observe their work.

Exercise 4 Assess student comprehension before assigning practice exercises.

BL Alternate Teaching Strategy

If students have trouble finding a rule…

Then use one of these reteach options:

1. CRM **Daily Reteach Worksheet** (p. 43)
2. Students use counters to find the rule.
3. Have students list the factors of the numbers. Remember that a prime number is a number with exactly two factors, 1 and itself. Knowing if the numbers in the function table are prime or composite numbers may help them find the rule.

3 Practice

Differentiate practice using these leveled assignments for Exercises 5–16.

Level	Assignment
BL Below/Approaching Level	5–7, 9–14
OL On Level	5–12, 14–16
AL Above/Beyond Level	6–12 even, 14–16

Have students discuss and complete the Higher Order Thinking problems. Have students verbalize the patterns they find in the tables.

WRITING IN ▸MATH Have students complete Exercise 16 in their Math Journals. You may choose to use this exercise as an optional formative assessment.

Practice and Problem Solving

See page R15.

Write an equation that describes each pattern. Then use the equation to find the next three numbers. See Examples 1–4 (pp. 220–221)

5.

Input (m)	1	3	5	7	9	11
Output (n)	5	15	25			

$m \times 5 = n$; 35, 45, 55

6.

Input (b)	2	4	6	8	10	12
Output (c)	14	28	42			

$b \times 7 = c$; 56, 70, 84

7.

Input (j)	4	8	12	16	20	24
Output (k)	1	2	3			

$j \div 4 = k$; 4, 5, 6

8.

Input (e)	10	20	30	40	50	60
Output (f)	2	4	6			

$e \div 5 = f$; 8, 10, 12

9. A local sports team sells $6 tickets for $3, $8 tickets for $4, and $10 tickets for $5. Write a rule and equation to find the cost of a $20 ticket.
divide by 2; $c \div 2 = d$; $10

10. The admission for an art museum costs $5 per person. Make a table to find how much it would cost for 2, 3, 4, 5, and 6 people to attend the exhibit.
See Ch. 5 Answer Appendix.

Real-World PROBLEM SOLVING

Art Sari makes bead necklaces. The table shows the number of blue beads and green beads Sari uses.

Blue Beads	Green Beads
Input (j)	Output (k)
3	1
9	3
15	5
21	
27	
33	

11. Write an equation that describes the relationship between green beads and blue beads. $j \div 3 = k$

12. How many green beads does Sari need if she is using 36 blue beads? 12 green beads

13. How many beads does Sari have in all if she has 9 green beads? 36 beads

H.O.T. Problems

14–16. See Ch. 5 Answer Appendix.

14. **OPEN ENDED** Create a table that shows inputs and outputs. Choose a multiplication or division rule for the table. Then choose six input numbers and find the output numbers.

15. **CHALLENGE** Can both an addition equation and a multiplication equation be written for the number pattern in the table to the right? Explain.

Input (m)	Output (n)
1	2
2	4
3	6

16. **WRITING IN ▸MATH** Write a real-world problem that involves a pattern. What equation describes the pattern?

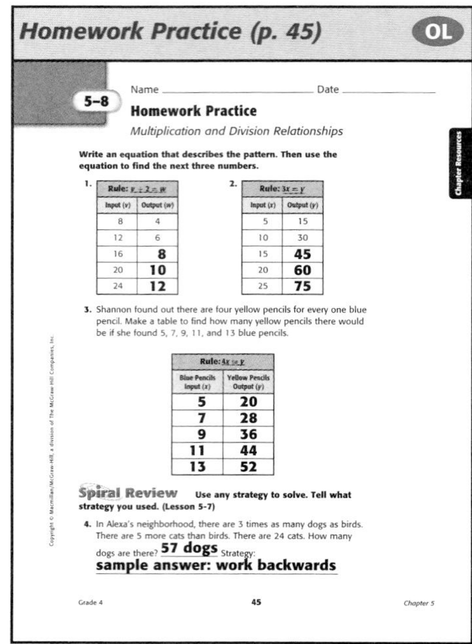
Homework Practice (p. 45) OL

5–8 Name ______ Date ______

Homework Practice

Multiplication and Division Relationships

Chapter Resources

Write an equation that describes the pattern. Then use the equation to find the next three numbers.

1.

Rule: $v \div 2 = w$	
Input (v)	Output (w)
8	4
12	6
16	8
20	10
24	12

2.

Rule: $3x = y$	
Input (x)	Output (y)
5	15
10	30
15	45
20	60
25	75

3. Shannon found out there are four yellow pencils for every one blue pencil. Make a table to find how many yellow pencils there would be if she found 5, 7, 9, 11, and 13 blue pencils.

Rule: $4x = y$	
Blue Pencils Input (x)	Yellow Pencils Output (y)
5	20
7	28
9	36
11	44
13	52

Spiral Review **Use any strategy to solve. Tell what strategy you used. (Lesson 5-7)**

4. In Alexa's neighborhood, there are 3 times as many dogs as birds. There are 5 more cats than birds. There are 24 cats. How many dogs are there? **57 dogs** Strategy: **sample answer: work backwards**

Grade 4 45 Chapter 5

17. What is the value of the expression below if $n = 6$? (Lesson 5-6) C

$9 \times n + 3$

A 18

B 27

C 57

D 81

18. What is the value of the expression below? (Lesson 5-6) G

$8 \times (9 - 6)$

F 11

G 24

H 48

J 66

19. Which equation can be used to describe the pattern in the table? (Lesson 5-8) C

Input (a)	Output (b)
1	■
3	9
5	15
7	21
9	27

A $a + 3 = b$

B $a + 6 = b$

C $a \times 3 = b$

D $b \times 3 = a$

Spiral Review

For Exercises 20 and 21, copy and complete each number pattern. (Lesson 5-7)

20. 2, 4, 8, 16, ■, ■, ■ 32, 64, 128

21. 5, 17, 29, 41, ■, ■, ■ 53, 65, 77

Find the value of each expression if $a = 12$ and $b = 3$. (Lesson 5-6)

22. $b \times 6$ 18

23. $a \div 4$ 3

24. $a \div b$ 4

Write an equation that describes each pattern. Then use the equation to find the next two numbers. (Lesson 5-5)

25. $a - 10 = b$

Input (a)	Output (b)
30	20
24	14
18	8
15	■ 5
16	■ 6

26. $m + 12 = n$

Input (m)	Output (n)
3	15
5	17
7	19
9	■ 21
11	■ 23

4 Assess

Formative Assessment

Mercedes is selling granola bars. She sells the bars for $3 each.

- **Explain why the equation $y \times \$3 = x$ to find the total cost of a number of granola bars can be used.** You would multiply the number of bars by $3 to get the total cost.

Quick Check

Are students continuing to struggle with finding a rule and writing an equation?

If Yes → Reteach Worksheet (p. 43)

If No → Independent Work Options (p. 210B)
CRM Skills Practice Worksheet (p. 44)
CRM Enrich Worksheet (p. 47)

Yesterday's News Ask students to write how they think the lesson on Multiplication and Division Expressions helped them with today's lesson.

Reviews Lessons 5-6 and 5-8

Assign the Test Practice problems to provide daily reinforcement of test-taking skills.

Spiral Review

Reviews Lesson 5-5, 5-6, and 5-7

Review and assess mastery of skills and concepts from previous chapters.

COMMON ERROR!

Exercise 9 Some students may be confused by the dollar signs. Make sure they understand that the tickets are on sale.

CHAPTER 5 Study Guide and Review

FOLDABLES Dinah Zike's Foldables

Use these lesson suggestions for incorporating the Foldables during the chapter. Students can then use their Foldables to review for the test.

Lesson 5-6 Students use the right column of the pocket chart Foldable to define mathematical variables and properties used in the multiplication and division of equations. Examples of student work are provided on quarter sheets of paper or index cards and stored in the right side pocket.

Key Vocabulary

The page references after each word denote where that term was first introduced. If students have difficulty answering Exercises 1–6, remind them they can use the page references to review the vocabulary terms.

Vocabulary Review

Review chapter vocabulary using one of the following options.

- **Visual Vocabulary Cards** (14, 16, and 47)
- **eGlossary** at macmillanmh.com

CHAPTER 5 Study Guide and Review

FOLDABLES Study Organizer GET READY to Study

Be sure the following Key Vocabulary words and Key Concepts are written in your Foldable.

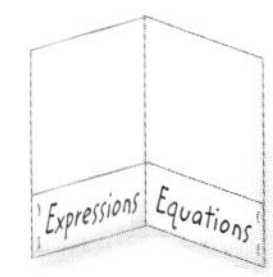

Key Concepts

Expressions

- An **expression** is a combination of variables, numbers, and at least one operation. (p. 193)

$n - 3$

Equations

- An **equation** is a number sentence with an equals sign (=), showing that two expressions are equal. (p. 198)

$n + 8 = 17$

- An equation can be used to describe the pattern in a table. (p. 208)

Input (a)	8	10	15	26	28
Output (b)	12	14	19		

Rule: Add 4.

Equation: $a + 4 = b$

Key Vocabulary

equation (p. 198)
expression (p. 193)
parentheses (p. 194)
pattern (p. 204)
variable (p. 193)

Vocabulary Check

Choose the vocabulary word that completes each sentence.

1. A(n) ___?___ is a statement with numbers and/or variables and at least one operation. expression
2. $9 + n = 19$ is a(n) ___?___. equation
3. In an expression or an equation, the operation in the ___?___ should be performed first. parentheses
4. A(n) ___?___ is a sequence of numbers, figures, or symbols that follow a rule. pattern
5. $6 - 2 = 4$ is a(n) ___?___. equation
6. In the expression $2 + (7 - 3)$ you should do what is in the ___?___ first. parentheses
7. $n + 18$ is a(n) ___?___. expression

Chapter 5 Project

Make a Game

Alone, in pairs, or in small groups, have students discuss the results of their completed chapter project with the class. Assess their work using the Chapter Project rubric found in Chapter 5 Resource Masters, p. 58.

Lesson-by-Lesson Review

5-1 Addition and Subtraction Expressions (pp. 193–195)

Example 1
What is the value of $5 + n$ if $n = 2$?

$5 + n$ Write the expression.

$5 + 2$ Replace n with 2.

7 Add 5 and 2.

Example 2
Find the value of $13 - (x + 3)$ if $x = 8$.

$13 - (x + 3)$ Write the expression.

$13 - (8 + 3)$ Replace x with 8.

$13 - 11$ Add $(8 + 3)$ first.

2 Subtract $13 - 11$.

Find the value of each expression if $f = 9$ and $g = 5$.

8. $f + 3$ 12
9. $12 + g$ 17
10. $(f - 2) + 6$ 13
11. $14 - (g + 2)$ 7

Write an expression for each situation.

12. five more than n $n + 5$
13. the sum of n and four $n + 4$
14. seven subtracted from n $n - 7$

Hayden's score was 15 more than Mario's.

15. Define a variable. Then write an expression for Hayden's score. m = Mario's score; $m + 15$
16. If Mario's score was 60, what was Hayden's score? 75

5-2 Solve Equations (pp. 198–201)

Example 3
Solve $4 + x = 10$.

$4 + x = 10$ 4 plus what equals 10?

$4 + 6 = 10$ $4 + 6 = 10$

$x = 6$

Example 4
Solve $18 - n = 12$.

$18 - n = 12$ 18 minus what equals 12?

$18 - 6 = 12$ $18 - 6 = 12$

$n = 6$

Solve each equation.

17. $k + 10 = 18$ 8
18. $c - 8 = 11$ 19
19. $7 - z = 3$ 4
20. $m + 9 = 15$ 6

Write and solve an equation for each situation.

21. A number plus 7 equals 19. What is the number? $n + 7 = 19$; 12
22. Five subtracted from a number equals 12. What is the number? $n - 5 = 12$; 17

Lesson-by-Lesson Review

Have students complete the Lesson-by-Lesson Review on pp. 225–230. Then you can use ExamView® Assessment Suite to customize another review worksheet that practices all the objectives of this chapter or only the objectives on which your students need more help.

Intervention If the given examples are not sufficient to review the topics covered by the questions, use the page references next to the exercises to review that topic in the Student Edition.

CHAPTER 5

Study Guide and Review

Additional Answer

26. extra; the distance Kendra's aunt flew to Seattle; 538 miles

5-3 Problem-Solving Skill: Extra or Missing Information

(pp. 202–203)

Example 5
Troy's family went to the zoo. Admission to the local zoo is $12 for adults and $5 for children. How much did it cost for Troy's family to go to the zoo?

Understand

What facts do you know?

Troy's family went to the zoo.

Zoo admission is $12 for adults and $5 for children.

What do you need to find?

Find the cost for Troy's family to go to the zoo.

Plan Identify the information needed to solve the problem. Look for any extra or missing information.

Solve To find the cost of admission, add the cost of each family member.

This information is missing, so the problem can not be solved.

Check Since no answer was found, there is no answer to check.

Identify any missing or extra information. Then solve if possible.

23. The table shows the points Yoshi scored in a basketball game. How many points did she score in the second half of the game?

Points Yoshi Scored		
first half	second half	total
12 points	■	26 points

no extra or missing information; 14

24. The Cougars scored 36 points and defeated the Falcons by 12 points. How many points did the Falcons score? no extra or missing information; 24

25. A pet frog is two years old. It eats four times a week. If there are 365 days in a year, how many days old is the frog? extra: The frog eats four times a day; 730 days

26. Kendra's parents drove 269 miles to Seattle. Kendra's aunt flew 457 miles to Seattle. What is the round-trip distance Kendra's parents will drive to Seattle and back? See margin.

27. **Measurement** Malia bikes one mile in five minutes. How many miles did Malia bike? missing; the number of minutes biked

226 Chapter 5 Describe Algebraic Patterns

5-4 Identify, Describe, and Extend Patterns (pp. 204–206)

Example 6

Harry plays ball with his friends. The table shows how long he plays each day. Identify, describe, and extend the pattern to find how many minutes he will play ball on Friday.

Day	Time
Monday	15 minutes
Tuesday	30 minutes
Wednesday	45 minutes
Thursday	60 minutes
Friday	■ minutes

+15 +15 +15 +15

Look at the table to identify and describe the pattern.

The table shows that Harry played ball for 15 minutes on Monday, and that he plays 15 minutes more each day than the previous day.

Extending the pattern, you find that Harry will play ball for 60 + 15, or 75 minutes on Friday.

Example 7

Genni drew these figures.

Which of the following is like the figures she drew? Explain.

Since she has drawn triangles, the triangle is most like the others.

Identify, describe, and extend each pattern.

28. 26, 23, 20, 17, ■, ■ subtract 3; 14, 11

29. 200, 175, 150, ■, ■ subtract 25; 125, 100

30. Tomás is making a pattern with shells from his family vacation. In the first row, there are 4 shells. In the second row, there are 10 shells, and in the third row, there are 16 shells. How many shells will be in the fourth and fifth rows? 22, 28

31. Cynthia sold oatmeal bars at 4 for \$1. How much would 10 oatmeal bars cost? 250¢

32. The table shows the cost of admission to an outdoor theater. How much will it cost for 5 people to go to the theater? \$40

People	Cost (\$)
1	8
2	16
3	24
4	32
5	■

33. Look at the figures below.

Which of the following would not belong in this group of figures? Explain. See margin.

Additional Answer

33. circle; because it is round and the others have flat sides.

Chapter 5 Study Guide and Review **227**

CHAPTER 5 Study Guide and Review

5-5 Function Tables: Find a Rule (+, −) (pp. 208–211)

Example 8
Write an equation that describes the pattern in the table. Then use the equation to find the next two numbers in the pattern.

Input (a)	Output (b)
12	2
17	7
22	12
27	■
32	■
37	■

First, write an equation.

Pattern: $12 - \mathbf{10} = 2$
$17 - \mathbf{10} = 7$
$22 - \mathbf{10} = 12$

Rule: Subtract 10.

Equation: $a - 10 = b$

Then use the equation to find the next three numbers.

Find the next three numbers when the input (a) is 27, 32, and 37.

$a - 10 = b$

$27 - 10 = 17$

$32 - 10 = 22$

$37 - 10 = 27$

So, the next three numbers in the pattern are 17, 22, and 27.

Write an equation to describe the pattern. Then use the equation to find the next two numbers.

34.

Input (x)	Output (y)
14	5
21	12
27	18
33	■
39	■
45	■

$x - 9 = y$; 24, 30, 36

35.

Input (a)	Output (b)
15	21
20	26
25	31
30	■
35	■
40	■

$a + 6 = b$; 36, 41, 46

36.

Input (m)	Output (n)
11	7
13	9
15	11
17	■
19	■
21	■

$m - 4 = n$; 13, 15, 17

228 **Chapter 5** Describe Algebraic Patterns

5-6 Multiplication and Division Expressions (pp. 214–216)

Example 9
Find the value of $5 \times n$ if $n = 3$.

$5 \times n$ Write the expression.

5×3 Replace n with 3.

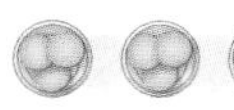
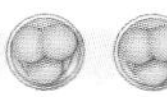

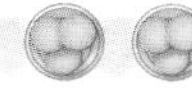

15 Multiply 5 and 3.

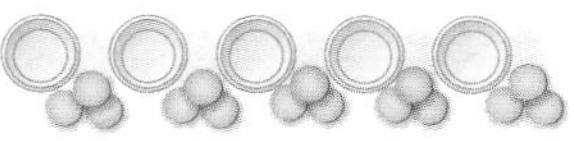

So, the value of the expression is 15.

Example 10
Maggie has some money to buy kites for her club. Write an expression for the number of kites Maggie can buy with her money.

$5

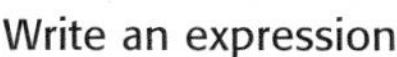

Write an expression.

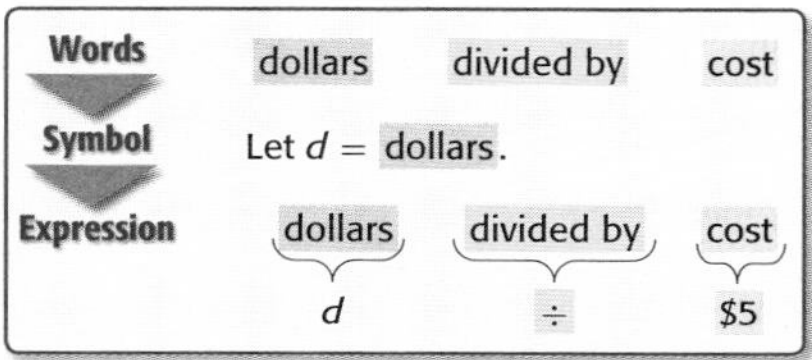

Words	dollars	divided by	cost
Symbol	Let d = dollars.		
Expression	dollars	divided by	cost
	d	$\div$	$5

So, the number of kites Maggie can buy is $d \div \$5$.

Find the value of each expression if $a = 4$ and $b = 6$.

37. $a \times 3$ 12

38. $b \div 2$ 3

39. $24 \div (b \times 2)$ 2

40. $(16 \div a) \times b$ 24

Write an expression for each situation.

41. a number divided by 7 $n \div 7$

42. 32 divided by a number $32 \div n$

43. Terri has 4 times as many coins as Kuni. Write an expression for the number of coins Terri has. $4 \times k$

44. Jason wants to buy five toy cars. Write an expression to show how much he will pay for the cars. $5 \times d$

45. Brenden has 3 times as much paper as Clark. If Clark has 10 sheets of paper, how many sheets does Brenden have? Write an expression. Then solve. $3 \times n$; $3 \times 10 = 30$

Chapter 5 Study Guide and Review **229**

Chapter 5 Study Guide and Review

5-7 Problem-Solving Investigation: Choose a Strategy (pp. 218–219)

Example 11

Sonia's bank account increases with each paycheck. Use the table to find how much her account increased after her fourth and fifth paychecks.

Number of Paychecks	Account Total
1	\$25
2	\$75
3	\$125
4	■
5	■

Use the table to find a pattern. Each paycheck shows a rule of +\$50. So, the missing outputs are \$175 and \$225.

Use any strategy to solve.

46. Lucas is collecting coupons to raise funds for his school. The first week he collects 525. The second week he collects 600. He collects 675 in the third week. If this pattern continues, how many should he collect the 7th week? 975 coupons

47. Karina has \$27 and Jessica has \$48. Do they have enough money to buy the \$82 concert tickets they want? Explain. no; \$27 + \$48 = \$75 and \$75 < \$82

5-8 Function Tables: Find a Rule (×, ÷) (pp. 220–223)

Example 12
Write an equation that describes the pattern in the table.

Input (a)	Output (b)
5	1
10	2
15	3

Each input is divided by 5 to result in each output.

So, $a \div 5 = b$ is the equation.

(input: a; output: b)

Write an equation that describes the pattern. Then use the equation to find the next number.

48.

Input (x)	Output (y)
1	7
3	21
5	35
7	■ 49

$x \times 7 = y$

49.

Input (m)	Output (n)
9	3
18	6
27	9
36	■ 12

$m \div 3 = n$

Chapter Test

Math Online macmillanmh.com
• Chapter Test

For Exercises 1–3, tell whether each statement is *true* or *false*.

1. The parentheses tell you which operation to perform first. true
2. An expression is a math statement without numbers and symbols. false
3. A pattern is a series of numbers or figures that follow a rule. true

Write an expression for each situation.

4. thirty subtracted from a $a - 30$
5. the difference of m and twenty-six $m - 26$
6. the sum of x and 13 $x + 13$
7. eight more than c $c + 8$

Solve each equation.

8. $13 + b = 25$ 12
9. $n - 12 = 22$ 34
10. Justice rode his bike for 35 minutes on Monday, 20 minutes on Tuesday, and 44 minutes on Saturday. Did he spend more than an hour riding his bike on Monday and Tuesday? Identify any missing or extra information. See Ch. 5 Answer Appendix.
11. **MULTIPLE CHOICE** Which number would make the equation true? B

$$17 + x = 20$$

A 2 **C** 37
B 3 **D** 33

Solve each equation.

12. $f \div 10 = 12$ 120
13. $6 \times z = 54$ 9
14. The product of a number and 12 is 84. Write an equation to find the number. $n \times 12 = 84$; 7
15. **MULTIPLE CHOICE** Which equation describes the pattern? H

Input (a)	Output (b)
8	1
24	3
40	5
56	7
72	9

F $a - 7 = b$ **H** $a \div 8 = b$
G $a \div 7 = b$ **J** $b + 7 = b$

16. The ski club is having a car wash. They make $5 for each car they wash. Write a rule and an equation to find how much money they will make if they wash 4 cars. multiply by 5; $c \times 5 = p$; $20

Find the value of each expression if $a = 2$ and $b = 6$.

17. $b \times 4$ 24
18. $16 \div a$ 8
19. WRITING IN MATH Explain how to find the missing number in the equation $(9 \times 4) \div n = 60 \div 10$. See Ch. 5 Answer Appendix.

Formative Assessment 231

Chapter 5 Chapter Test

Summative Assessment

Use these alternate leveled chapter tests to differentiate assessment for the specific needs of your students.

Leveled Chapter 5 Tests			
Form	Type	Level	CRM Pages
1	Multiple Choice	BL	60–61
2A	Multiple Choice	OL	62–63
2B	Multiple Choice	OL	64–65
2C	Free Response	OL	66–67
2D	Free Response	OL	68–69
3	Free Response	AL	70–71

BL = below/approaching grade level
OL = on grade level
AL = above/beyond grade level

Vocabulary Test

CRM **Chapter 5 Resource Masters** (p. 55)

ExamView Assessment Suite Customize and create multiple versions of your Chapter Test and the test answer keys.

Data-Driven Decision Making

Based on the results of the Chapter Test, use the following to review concepts that continue to present students with problems.

Exercises	State/Local Standards	What's the Math?	Error Analysis	Resources for Review
1–7, 11 Lesson 5-1		Understand expressions, parentheses, symbols.	Does not understand words "parentheses," "expression," "operation," "symbols," "value."	Strategic Intervention Guide (pp. 30, 32, 34, 132) CRM Chapter 5 Resource Masters (Reteach) Math Adventures My Math Zone Chapter 5 Math Online Extra Examples • Concepts in Motion
8–10 Lesson 5-2		Demonstrate understanding of mathematical symbols, and properties.	Does not understand "expression," "difference," "solve." Does not read problem correctly.	
15–16 Lesson 5-6		Understand that an equation is a prescription for determining a second number when a first number is given.	Does not understand how to make "input/output" chart. Does not accurately fill in chart.	

Test Practice

Formative Assessment

- Use Student Edition pp. 232–233 as practice and cumulative review. The questions are written in the same style as many state tests.
- You can also use these two pages to benchmark student progress, or as an alternate homework assignment.

Additional practice pages can be found in the Chapter 5 Resource Masters.

Chapter 5 Resource Masters
Cumulative Test Practice
- Multiple Choice format (pp. 60–65)
- Free Response format (pp. 66–71)

Create practice worksheets or tests that align to your state standards.

Math Online Have students visit macmillanmh.com for additional practice to reinforce your state standards.

Math Online macmillanmh.com
- Test Practice

Test Practice

Cumulative, Chapters 1–5

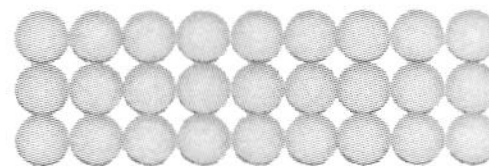

Read each question. Then fill in the correct answer on the answer sheet provided by your teacher or on a sheet of paper.

1. What expression is shown? D

A 2×9 **C** 3×10
B 3×8 **D** 3×9

2. Find $24 + (n - 8)$ if $n = 12$. H

F 4 **H** 28
G 12 **J** 44

3. Find the value of y in the equation. B

$$y + 27 = 48$$

A 20 **C** 32
B 21 **D** 75

4. Which equation can be used to describe the pattern in the table? G

Input (x)	1	2	3	4	5	6
Output (y)	5	10	15	20	25	30

F $y = 3x$ **H** $y = x \div 3$
G $y = 5x$ **J** $y = x \div 5$

5. There are 48 students traveling on a field trip. Each van holds 8 students. How many vans are needed in all? A

A 6 **C** 8
B 7 **D** 9

6. The graph shows the number of points scored by Mark and Kim during the first 4 games of the basketball season. G

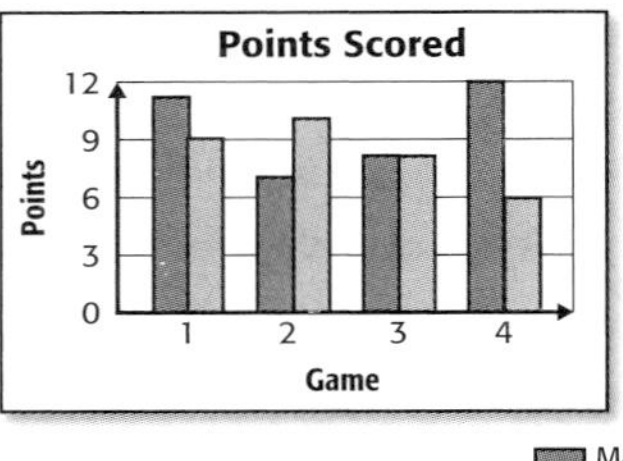

How many more points did Kim score than Mark in Game 2?

F 2 points **H** 4 points
G 3 points **J** 5 points

7. Tonisha's family has 2 newspapers delivered to their house each day. When they came back from a trip, there were 14 newspapers. Which equation can be used to find the number of days they were gone? A

A $14 \div 2 = d$ **C** $14 - d = 2$
B $14 + d = 2$ **D** $14 \times 2 = d$

Test-Taking Tip

- Remind students to eliminate unreasonable answers first, and then focus on the remaining answer choices.

Preparing for Standardized Tests

For test-taking strategies and practice, see pages R42–R55.

8. Which rule describes the pattern? G

Input (c)	Output (d)
12	19
19	26
28	35
37	44

F Add 5.
H Add 8.
G Add 7.
J Add 9.

9. Darin bought four books. Each book cost \$6. Darin has \$16 left. Which equation can be used to find how much money he had before he went shopping? Let m = money. A

A $m - (4 \times \$6) = \$16$
B $(4 \times \$6) - m = \$16$
C $(4 \times \$6) - \$16 = m$
D $\$16 - (4 \times m) = \$6$

10. What number goes in the box to make this number sentence true? J

$(8 - 5) \times 9 = 3 \times \square$

F 3
H 8
G 5
J 9

PART 2 Short Response

Record your answers on the answer sheet provided by your teacher or on a sheet of paper.

11. Write an equation to describe the pattern below. $x + 5 = y$

Input (x)	Output (y)
2	7
4	9
6	11
8	13

12. Steve added 5 coins to his collection. Now he has 62 coins. Write an equation to show how many coins he had before. $62 - 5 = c$

PART 3 Extended Response

Record your answers on the answer sheet provided by your teacher or on a sheet of paper.

13. Which rule describes the pattern in the table below? Explain. See margin.

Input (x)	Output (y)
1	4
2	8
3	12
4	16

NEED EXTRA HELP?													
If You Missed Question...	1	2	3	4	5	6	7	8	9	10	11	12	13
Go to Lesson...	4-3	5-1	5-2	5-8	4-5	3-6	5-8	5-5	5-8	4-2	5-5	5-8	5-8

Answer Sheet Practice

Have students simulate taking a state test by recording their answers on a practice recording sheet.

CRM **Chapter 5 Resource Masters**
Student Recording Sheet (p. 76)

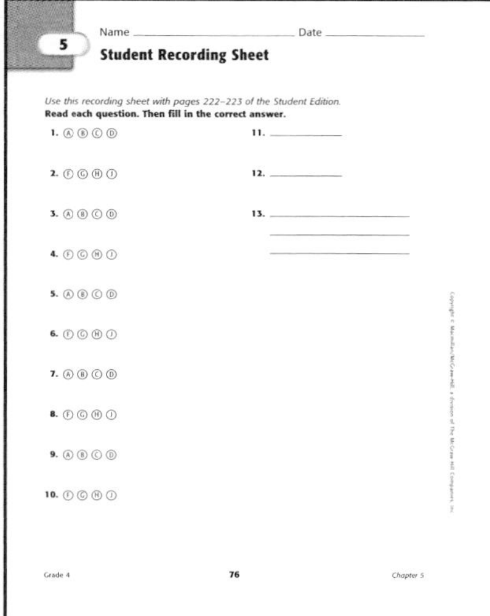

Additional Answer

13. Sample answer: Multiply by 4; Determine the relationship between the input and output numbers. Since $1 \times 4 = 4$ and $2 \times 4 = 8$, etc., the rule is multiply by 4.

Page 200, Lesson 5-2

27. Sample answer: yes; The value of n that makes both equations true is 4. In Caleb's equation, $9 - n = 5$, $n = 4$. In Adriana's equation, $5 + n = 9$, $n = 4$.

28. Sample answer: Think about what number when added to or subtracted from a given number equals a specified result.

Page 203, Lesson 5-3

1. Sample answer: The problem did not ask any questions involving cost.

2. Sample answer: no; you need to find the difference of two numbers and only one number would be given

7. extra; The movie starts at 2 P.M.; $12.

13. Sample answer: In order to solve Exercise 11, the amount of money Edgar has is necessary information. This information is missing.

Page 206, Lesson 5-4

16. Sample answer: The pattern is to rotate the triangle one quarter turn clockwise. △

Page 207, Mid-Chapter Check

13. Missing: The price of a lunch for one day as well as how many days are in the week.

14. $20; The information about the baseball is not needed.

19. Sample answer: Add 4; 26

Page 210, Lesson 5-5

5. $f + 3 = h$; 15, 18, 21

6. $s + 13 = t$; 27, 31, 35

7. $v - 11 = w$; 23, 29, 35

8. $g - 5 = h$; 24, 29, 34

9. Sample answer:

Input (y)	Output (z)
1	5
2	6
3	7
4	8
5	9

10. Sample answer:

Input (t)	Output (v)
3	14
5	16
7	18
9	20
11	22

11. Sample answer:

Input (a)	Output (c)
12	5
15	8
18	11
21	14
24	17

12. Sample answer:

Input (g)	Output (h)
25	15
30	20
35	25
40	30
45	35

17. Sample answer:

Input (m)	Output (c)
20	$24
25	$29
30	$34
35	$39
40	$44

18. Sample answer: Steve mows lawns on weekends for $10 an hour. How much money will he earn for 3, 4, and 5 hours?

19. Sample answer: The rate of increase or decrease is the same for both patterns.

Page 216, Lesson 5-6

31. Sample answer: Robert has 4 bags of rocks. There are n rocks in each bag. The rocks must be divided equally among 7 people. How many rocks will each person get?

Page 219, Lesson 5-7

7. 

10. Sample answer: If this pattern continues, what time will Niles have to go to bed in fifth grade?

Page 221, Lesson 5-8

4. A rule and an equation describe what is taking place in a number pattern.

A rule describes what happens to an input number to get an output number.

An equation is a number sentence that shows that two expressions have the same value.

10. Sample answer:

Visitors	Total Cost ($)
Input (*j*)	**Output (*k*)**
2	10
3	15
4	20
5	25
6	30

14. Sample answer:

Input (*a*)	2	4	6	8	10	12
Output (*b*)	10	20	30	40	50	60

15. Sample answer: yes; you can write the multiplication equation $m \times 2 = n$ and the addition equation $m + m = n$.

16. Sample answer: Marquez bought some books on sale. A $10 book was $5, a $12 book was $6, and a $14 book was $7. Write a rule and equation to find the cost of a $20 book; $b \div 2 = c$.

Page 231, Chapter Test

10. no; extra information; amount of time Justice spent riding the bike on Saturday.

19. Sample answer: The expression on the right side of the equals sign equals 6. The number that is missing will result in the equation on the left side to equal 6. So, the missing number is 6.

Chapter Overview

Chapter-at-a-Glance

In Chapter 6, the emphasis is on finding and estimating products by multiplying multi-digit numbers by one-digit numbers.

Lesson		Math Objective	State/Local Standards
6-1	**Multiples of 10, 100, and 1,000** (pp. 237–239)	Multiply multiples of 10, 100, and 1,000 using basic facts and patterns.	
6-2	**Problem-Solving Skill: Reasonable Answers** (pp. 240–241)	Decide whether an answer to a problem is reasonable.	
6-3	**Use Rounding to Estimate Products** (pp. 242–245)	Estimate answers by rounding.	
6-4	**Multiply Two-Digit Numbers** (pp. 246–248)	Multiply a two-digit number by a one-digit number.	
6-5	**Problem-Solving Investigation: Choose a Strategy** (pp. 250–251)	Choose the best strategy to solve a problem.	
6-6	**Multiply Multi-digit Numbers** (pp. 252–255)	Multiply a multi-digit number by a one-digit number.	
6-7	**Multiply Across Zeros** (pp. 258–261)	Multiply multi-digit numbers with zeros by a one-digit number.	

Multiply By One-Digit Numbers

BIG Idea In third grade, students continued work on number sense by learning multiplication facts from zero to ten. In this chapter, students build upon this prior knowledge by multiplying one-digit numbers with larger numbers. It is important for students to have a firm grasp of the concepts taught in this chapter because they serve as the basis for the concept of multiplying multi-digit numbers presented in the next chapter.

Algebra Students multiply numbers by multiples of 10, 100, and 1,000. This concept will help prepare them for algebra concepts, such as exponents and scientific notation. (Lesson 6-1)

G4-FP1 *Number and Operations* **and** *Algebra:* **Developing quick recall of multiplication facts and related division facts and fluency with whole number multiplication**

Students use understandings of multiplication to develop quick recall of the basic multiplication facts and related division facts. They apply their understanding of models for multiplication (i.e., equal sized groups, arrays, area models, equal intervals on the number line), place value, and properties of operations (in particular, the distributive property) as they develop, discuss, and use efficient, accurate, and generalizable methods to multiply multidigit whole numbers. They select appropriate methods and apply them accurately to estimate products or calculate them mentally, depending on the context and numbers involved. They develop fluency with efficient procedures, including the standard algorithm, for multiplying whole numbers, understand why the procedures work (on the basis of place value and properties of operations), and use them to solve problems.

Skills Trace

Vertical Alignment

Third Grade

In third grade, students learned to:

- Multiply mutli-digit numbers by a one-digit number and estimate products to check for reasonableness.
- Multiply amounts of money.

Fourth Grade

During this chapter, students learn to:

- Multiply multi-digit numbers by one-digit numbers and check answers for reasonableness.
- Estimate to verify the reasonableness of calculated results.

After this chapter, students learn to:

- Multiply by two-digit numbers.

Fifth Grade

In fifth grade, students learn to:

- Multiply up to a three-digit number by one- and two-digit numbers.
- Multiply whole numbers by a decimal and estimate products by rounding and the clustering strategy.

Backmapping and Vertical Alignment **McGraw-Hill's *Math Connects*** program was conceived and developed with the final results in mind: student success in Algebra 1 and beyond. The authors, using the **NCTM Focal Points and Focal Connections** as their guide, developed this brand-new series by backmapping from Algebra 1 concepts, and vertically aligning the topics so that they build upon prior skills and concepts and serve as a foundation for future topics.

Math Vocabulary

The following math vocabulary words for Chapter 6 are listed in the glossary of the ***Student Edition***. You can find interactive definitions in 13 languages in the ***eGlossary*** at macmillanmh.com.

estimate A number close to an exact value; an estimate indicates about how much. (p. 242A)
Example: 47 + 22 (estimate 50 + 20) is about 70.

factor A number that divides into a whole number evenly. Also a number that is multiplied by another number. (p. 246A)

multiple A multiple of a number is the product of that number and any whole number. (p. 237A)
Example: 15 is a multiple of 5 because $3 \times 5 = 15$.

product The answer to a multiplication problem. It also refers to expressing a number as product of its factors. (p. 246A)

regroup To use place value to exchange equal amounts when renaming a number. (p. 246A)

round To change the value of a number to one that is easier to work with. To find the nearest value of a number based on a given place value. (p. 242A)

Visual Vocabulary Cards
Use Visual Vocabulary Cards 15, 18, 27, and 42 to reinforce the vocabulary in this lesson. (The Define/Example/Ask routine is printed on the back of each card.)

regroup

Chapter Planner

Suggested Pacing		
Instruction	Review & Assessment	TOTAL
7 days	1 day	**8 days**

Diagnostic Assessment
Quick Check (p. 236)

	Lesson 6-1 (Pacing: 1 day)	Lesson 6-2 (Pacing: 1 day)	Lesson 6-3 (Pacing: 1 day)
Lesson/ Objective	**Multiples of 10, 100, and 1,000** (pp. 237–239) **Objective:** Multiply multiples of 10, 100, and 1,000 using basic facts and patterns.	**Problem-Solving Skill Reasonable Answers** (pp. 240–241) **Objective:** Decide whether an answer to a problem is reasonable.	**Use Rounding to Estimate Products** (pp. 242–245) **Objective:** Estimate products by rounding.
State/Local Standards			
Math Vocabulary	**multiple**		**estimate**, **round**
Lesson Resources	**Other Resources** CRM Leveled Worksheets (pp. 8–12) Daily Reteach • 5-Minute Check • Problem of the Day	**Other Resources** CRM Leveled Worksheets (pp. 13–17) Daily Reteach • 5-Minute Check • Problem of the Day *Expanding the United States*	**Other Resources** CRM Leveled Worksheets (pp. 18–22) Daily Reteach • 5-Minute Check • Problem of the Day
Technology	Math Adventures Math Songs Track #8		Math Adventures
Math Online	Personal Tutor		Personal Tutor
Reaching All Learners	English Learners, p. 237B ELL Gifted and Talented, p. 237B AL Early Finishers, p. 237B OL AL	English Learners, p. 240B ELL Below Level, p. 240B BL Early Finishers, p. 240B OL AL	English Learners, p. 242B ELL Below Level, p. 242B BL Early Finishers, p. 242B AL
Alternate Lesson			*IMPACT Mathematics:* Unit C

Game Time
Estimation Station (p. 245)

KEY

BL Below/Approaching Level
OL On Level
AL Above/Beyond Level
ELL English Learners
SE Student Edition
TE Teacher Edition
CRM Chapter 6 Resource Masters
CD-Rom
Transparency
Real-World Problem Solving Library

	Lesson 6-4 (Pacing: 1 day)	Lesson 6-5 (Pacing: 1 day)	Lesson 6-6 (Pacing: 1 day)
Lesson/ Objective	**Multiply Two-Digit Numbers** (pp. 246–248) **Objective:** Multiply a two-digit number by a one-digit number.	**Problem-Solving Investigation** **Choose a Strategy** (pp. 250–251) **Objective:** Choose the best strategy to solve a problem.	**Multiply Multi-digit Numbers** (pp. 252–255) **Objective:** Multiply a multi-digit number by a one-digit number.
State/Local Standards			
Math Vocabulary	**factor**, **product**, **regroup**		
Lesson Resources	**Materials** rectangle cut-outs, grid paper **Manipulatives** base-ten blocks **Other Resources** CRM Leveled Worksheets (pp. 23–27) Daily Reteach • 5-Minute Check • Problem of the Day	**Other Resources** CRM Leveled Worksheets (pp. 28–32) Daily Reteach • 5-Minute Check • Problem of the Day *Expanding the United States*	**Materials** rectangle cut-outs **Other Resources** CRM Leveled Worksheets (pp. 33–37) Daily Reteach • 5-Minute Check • Problem of the Day
Technology	Math Adventures Math Songs Track #6		Math Adventures Math Songs Track #6
Math Online	Personal Tutor • Concepts in Motion		Personal Tutor
Reaching All Learners	English Learners, p. 246B ELL Gifted and Talented, p. 246B AL Early Finishers, p. 246B AL	English Learners, p. 250B ELL Gifted and Talented, p. 250B AL Early Finishers, p. 250B OL AL	English Learners, p. 252B ELL Gifted and Talented, p. 252B AL Early Finishers, p. 252B AL
Alternate Lesson			

Formative Assessment
Mid-Chapter Check (p. 249)

Problem Solving in Science
Emperors of the Ice (p. 256)

Chapter Planner

Lesson 6-7

Pacing: 1 day

Lesson/ Objective	**Multiply Across Zeros** (pp. 258–261) **Objective:** Multiply multi-digit numbers with zeros by a one-digit number.
State/Local Standards	
Math Vocabulary	
Lesson Resources	**Materials** grid paper **Manipulatives** base-ten blocks **Other Resources** CRM Leveled Worksheets (pp. 38–42) Daily Reteach • 5-Minute Check • Problem of the Day
Technology	
Math Online	Personal Tutor
Reaching All Learners	English Learners, p. 258B ELL Gifted and Talented, p. 258B AL Early Finishers, p. 258B AL
Alternate Lesson	

Summative Assessment

- Study Guide/Review (p. 262)
- Chapter Test (p. 267)
- Test Practice (p. 268)

Assessment Options

Diagnostic Assessment

- SE *Option 1:* Quick Check (p. 238)
- *Option 2:* Online Quiz macmillanmh.com
- CRM *Option 3:* Diagnostic Test (p. 44)
- CRM *Option 4:* Chapter Pretest (p. 45)

Formative Assessment

- TE Alternate Teaching Strategy (every lesson)
- SE Talk About It (every lesson)
- SE Writing in Math (every lesson)
- SE Check What You Know (every lesson)
- TE Ticket Out the Door (pp. 239, 255)
- TE Into the Future (p. 244)
- TE Yesterday's News (p. 248)
- SE Mid-Chapter Check (p. 275)
- CRM Lesson Quizzes (pp. 46–48)
- CRM Mid-Chapter Test (p. 49)

Summative Assessment

- SE Chapter Test (p. 267)
- SE Test Practice (p. 268)
- CRM Vocabulary Test (p. 50)
- CRM Leveled Chapter Tests (pp. 55–66)
- CRM Cumulative Test Practice (pp. 69–71)
- CRM Oral Assessment (p. 51)
- ExamView® Assessment Suite
- Advance Tracker

McGraw Hill Professional Development

Targeted professional development has been articulated throughout **McGraw-Hill's *Math Connects*** program. The **McGraw-Hill Professional Development Video Library** provides short videos that support the **NCTM Focal Points and Focal Connections.** For more information visit macmillanmh.com.

Model Lessons

Instructional Strategies

Teacher Notes

Learning Stations

Cross-Curricular Links

Writing

individual | LOGICAL

Low or High Roller?

- Roll the number cube five times. Use the first four numbers to create a four-digit number, and then use the fifth roll as your multiplier. Estimate the product of your four-digit number and your single-digit number by rounding.
- How do you know if your estimate is going to be greater than or less than the exact amount? Write a paragraph to explain.

I rounded up and estimated my product to be 32,000. This was a high estimate...

Materials:
- number cube
- paper
- pencil

Art

individual | VISUAL

Font Artist

- On a computer, you can display the letters of the alphabet in many different ways, using fonts. Graphic artists use different fonts to enhance their images.
- Think of a word with less than ten letters. Type the word into a word processing document on your school's computer. Then type it again on the next line, using a different font. If you kept typing and displayed that word in 20 different fonts, how many letters have you displayed on the screen? Try it and count to check your multiplication.

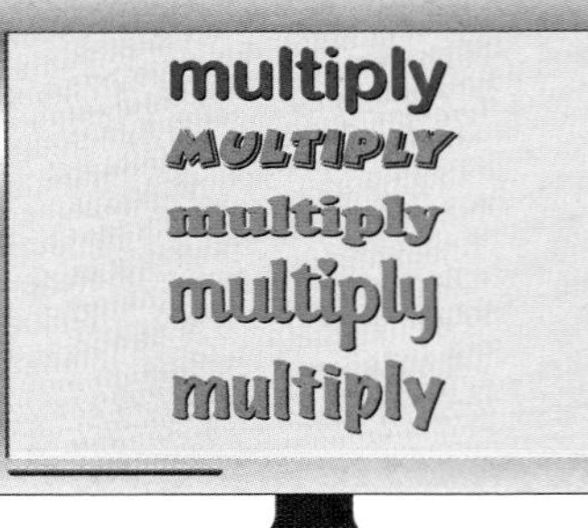

Materials:
- computer workstation with word processing program document open
- paper
- pencil

Health

individual | LOGICAL

Super-Size Me

How do serving sizes make a difference?

- A 6.75-ounce box of juice has about 100 Calories. A 16-ounce bottle of juice has 240 Calories.
- Line up the number of bottles of juice you would drink in one week. Multiply that amount by the number of Calories in a bottle of juice. Then model the same number of boxes and multiply that amount by the number of Calories in a box of juice.
- If you are drinking bottles of juice, how many more Calories per week are you drinking?

Materials:
- 6.75-ounce juice boxes and 16-ounce juice bottles
- paper
- pencil

Science

pair | SPATIAL

Wildfires

Wildfires are extremely hard to stop, and in southern California, they can burn through 40 miles of land a day. Roll to see how far your fire goes before you can put it out!

- Take turns rolling the number cube. The score you roll is how many days it takes your firefighters to set up a firebreak. Multiply to find out how many miles the fire traveled, and model it with base-ten blocks lined up end to end. Allow each partner to have five turns to roll and set up another firebreak.
- The partner whose fire traveled the least distance wins!

Materials:
- number cubes
- base-ten blocks
- paper
- pencils

Music

individual | LOGICAL

Musical Minutes

Music CDs can have up to 74 minutes of music on them, but not all artists fill up their CDs completely. If you want to know how much music you have, you need to estimate.

- Use the music CDs as counters. Model a multiplication expression using the CDs, showing how many minutes of music you could have in total on the CDs if the full amount of time were used.
- Use rounding to estimate your product. Then add up the actual number of minutes of music listed for each CD on its label. How close did your estimate come? Was your estimate high or low?

× 74 = 444 min

Materials:
- 9 music CDs
- paper
- pencil

Social Studies

pair | LOGICAL

Conservation City

Most Americans use almost 38 gallons of gasoline a month per person. How much could a whole city or town conserve if each person used only two gallons less per month?

- Each person rolls the number cube twice. The first roll is the first digit in your city's population. The second roll is the number of zeros in the population. How many people are in your city or town?
- Write an expression that shows how much gasoline your city or town can save by using two gallons less per person. Solve it, and see which of you saved the most energy.

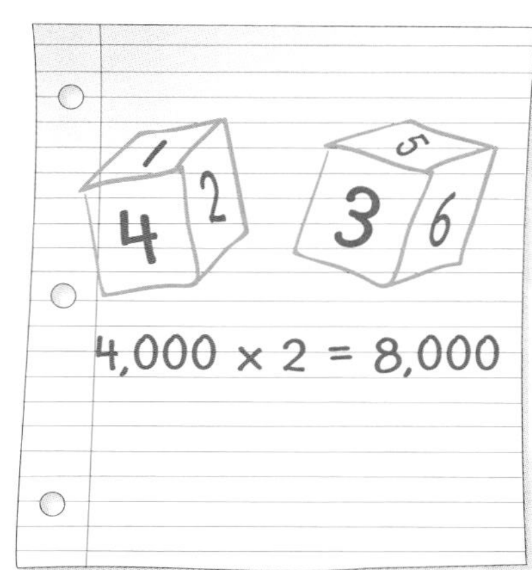

Materials:
- 1–5 number cube
- paper
- pencils

Introduce the Chapter

Real World: The Soccer Tournament

Materials: connecting cubes or small counters to make multiple groups of the same color in a variety of colors, grid paper, colored pencils

Explain to students that they will be extending their knowledge of multiplication in this chapter. Remind them that multiplication is an operation on equal groups to find a total.

Tell students that they are in charge of ordering uniforms for the 4 teams that will attend a soccer tournament. Each team will bring 15 players.

- Divide students into small groups.
- Ask the class what multiplication sentence they could write to show the total number of uniforms that will be needed.
- Have them use the materials to model the problem.
- **How many uniforms will be needed for 4 teams?** 60 uniforms for 4 teams
- Repeat the process for other numbers of teams.

Direct students to Student Edition p. 234. Have students read the paragraph at the top of the page.

- **What are some other times that you use multiplication in your life?** Sample answers: using a recipe, figuring money totals

WRITING IN MATH

Starting the Chapter
Ask students to write about ways they modeled the multiplication sentence 4×15. Have them give examples.

Key Vocabulary Introduce the key vocabulary in the chapter using the routine below.

Define: When you estimate a number, you are finding a number close to the exact value.
Example: At the movies popcorn costs $3.75 and a drink costs $2. I estimate that it will cost $6 to buy both items.
Ask: Can you name a time when it would be useful to find an estimate?

Read-Aloud Anthology For an optional reading activity to introduce this chapter's math concepts, see the Read-Aloud Anthology (p. TR30).

Chapter 6 Multiply by One-Digit Numbers

BIG Idea How do you multiply by one-digit numbers?

Multiply each digit by the one-digit number, starting with the ones place. Regroup when necessary.

Example A great white shark can swim 2,900 miles on a single meal. If a great white shark eats 3 meals a day, it could swim $2,900 \times 3$ or 8,700 miles.

2,900	
× 3	
6,000	Multiply $3 \times 2,000$.
+ 2,700	Multiply 3×900.
8,700	Add the partial products.

What will I learn in this chapter?

- Multiply multiples of 10, 100, and 1,000.
- Estimate products using rounding.
- Multiply a multi-digit number by a one-digit number.
- Determine reasonable answers.

Key Vocabulary

multiply
estimate
product
Distributive Property of Multiplication

Math Online Student Study Tools at macmillanmh.com

Chapter 6 Project

Healthy Foods Party

Students look at portion sizes and then estimate how much they will need for a healthy foods party.

- Students use the Internet or other nutritional resources to come up with serving sizes for healthy foods, such as cut vegetables, pita bread, whole-grain crackers, hummus, and all-natural fruit juices.
- Students use serving sizes and the number of students in the room as factors. They estimate how much of each food they will need in order to plan a healthy foods party for their class.
- Challenge students to find Calorie counts for one serving of each food. How many Calories would servings for the whole class contain?

Refer to Chapter 6 Resource Masters, p. 53, for a rubric to assess students' progress on this project.

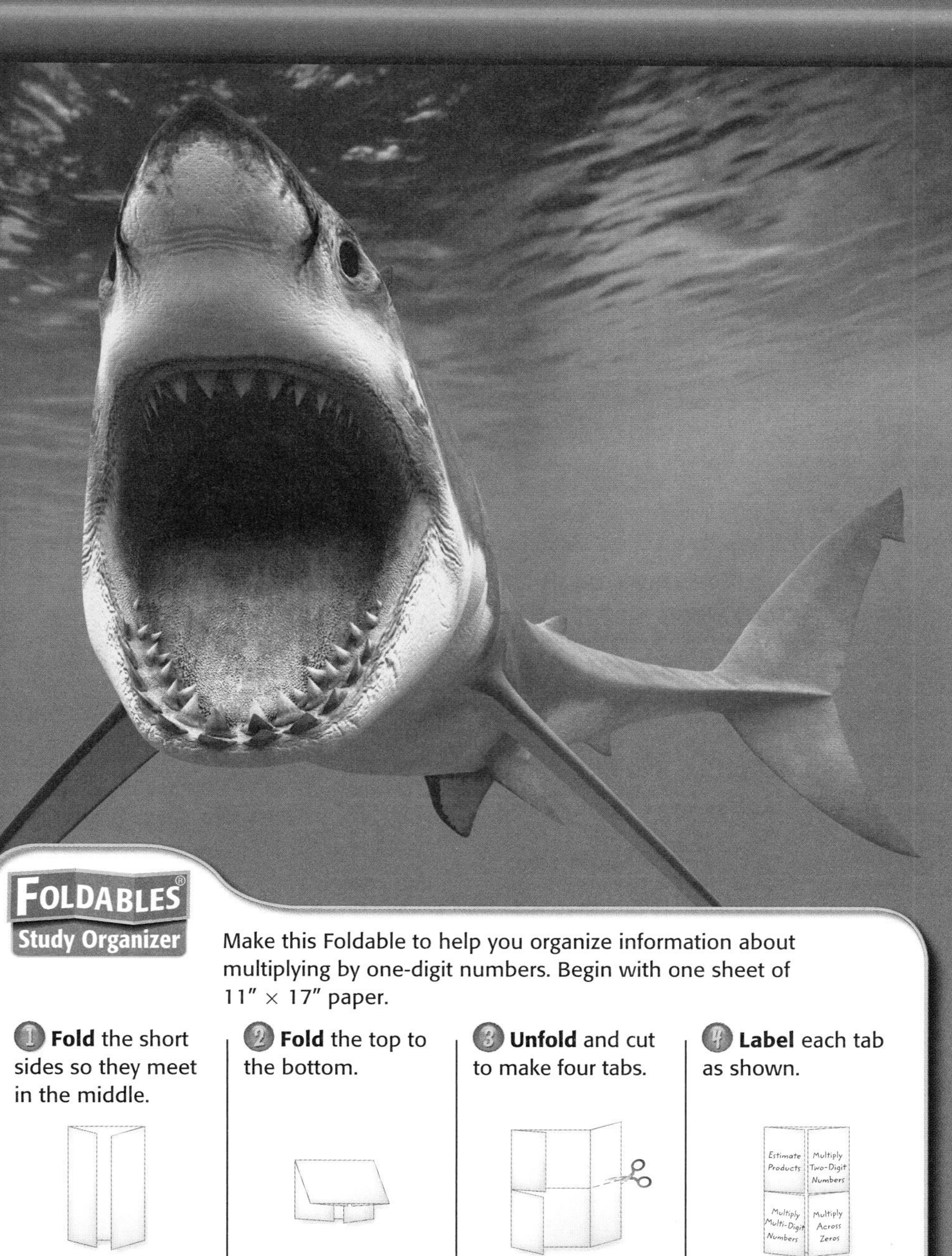

FOLDABLES Study Organizer

Make this Foldable to help you organize information about multiplying by one-digit numbers. Begin with one sheet of 11″ × 17″ paper.

1. **Fold** the short sides so they meet in the middle.
2. **Fold** the top to the bottom.
3. **Unfold** and cut to make four tabs.
4. **Label** each tab as shown.

ELL National ESL Standards Alignment for Chapter 6

Lesson, Page	ESL Standard	Modality	Level
6-1, p. 237B	Goal 1, Standard 3, k	Auditory, Visual	Beginning
6-2, p. 240B	Goal 2, Standard 2, j	Auditory, Logical	Advanced
6-3, p. 242B	Goal 1, Standard 3, c	Linguistic	Beginning
6-4, p. 246B	Goal 2, Standard 2, e	Auditory, Social	Beginning
6-5, p. 250B	Goal 2, Standard 3, e	Linguistic	Advanced
6-6, p. 252B	Goal 2, Standard 1, c	Social, Linguistic	Advanced
6-7, p. 258B	Goal 2, Standard 2, g	Social, Kinesthetic	Intermediate

The National ESL Standards can be found in the Teacher Reference Handbook.

FOLDABLES Dinah Zike's Foldables

Guide students through the directions on p. 235 to create their own Foldable graphic organizers for multiplying one-digit numbers. Students may also use their Foldables to study and review for chapter assessments.

When to Use It Lessons 6-2, 6-4, 6-5, and 6-6. (Additional instructions for using the Foldables with these lessons are found on pp. 249 and 262.)

Chapter 6 Literature List

Lesson	Book Title
6-1	**Is a Blue Whale the Biggest Thing There Is?** Robert E. Wells
6-2	**Minnie's Diner: A Multiplying Menu** Dayle Ann Dodds and John Manders
6-3	**Betcha!** Stuart J. Murphy
6-4	**The 12 Circus Rings** Seymour Chwast
6-6	**Bats on Parade** Kathi Appelt
6-7	**Each Orange Had 8 Slices** Paul Giganti, Jr.
Any	**Math Man** Teri Daniels

- Read the Math at Home letter found in the Chapter 6 Resource Masters, p. 4, with the class and have each student sign it. (A Spanish version is found on p. 5.)
- Send home copies of the Math at Home letter with each student.

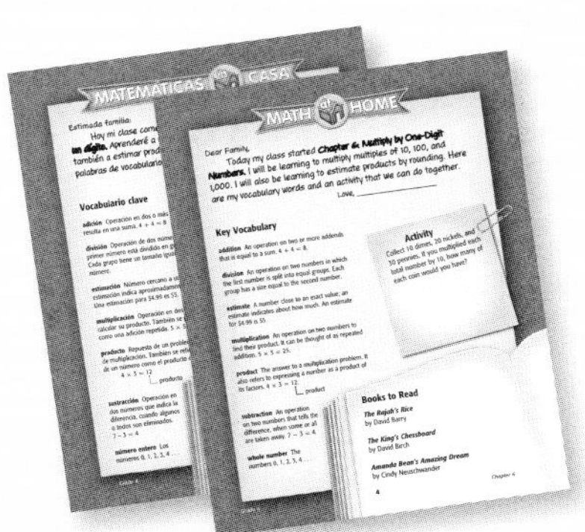

Diagnostic Assessment

Check for students' prerequisite skills before beginning the chapter.

- **Option 1:** ***Quick Check***

  SE Student Edition, p. 236

- **Option 2:** ***Online Assessment***

  Math Online macmillanmh.com

- **Option 3:** ***Diagnostic Tests***

  CRM Chapter 6 Resource Masters, p. 44–45

RTI (Response to Intervention)

Apply the Results Based on the results of the diagnostic assessment on Student Edition p. 236, address individual needs before beginning the chapter.

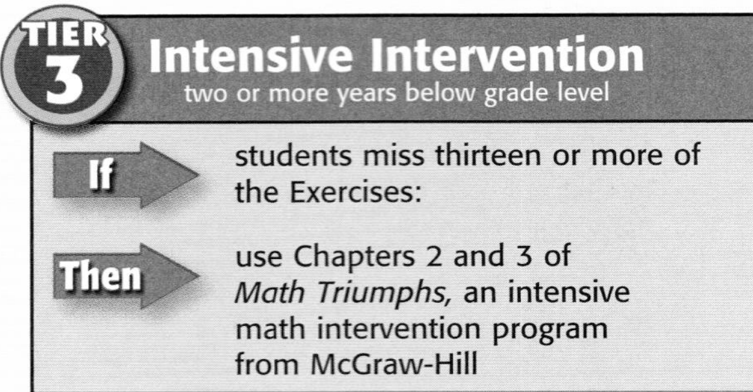

TIER 3 Intensive Intervention
two or more years below grade level

If students miss thirteen or more of the Exercises:

Then use Chapters 2 and 3 of *Math Triumphs,* an intensive math intervention program from McGraw-Hill

ARE YOU READY for Chapter 6?

You have two ways to check prerequisite skills for this chapter.

Option 2

Math Online Take the Chapter Readiness Quiz at macmillanmh.com.

Option 1

Complete the Quick Check below.

QUICK Check

Multiply. Use models if needed. (Lessons 4-3 and 4-5) (Used in Lessons 6-1, 6-3, and 6-4)

1. 2×3 6 **2.** $4 \times \$4$ \$16 **3.** 5×6 30 **4.** $7 \times \$8$ \$56

5. 9×4 36 **6.** 8×3 24 **7.** $\$7 \times 5$ \$35 **8.** 9×9 81

9. Evan's photo album has 8 pages of pictures. How many photos are in Evan's album if the same number of photos are on each page? 32

Identify the place value of the underlined digit. (Lesson 1-1) (Used in Lessons 6-1, 6-3, and 6-6)

10. 1,630 hundreds **11.** \$5,367 thousands **12.** 20,495 tens **13.** \$89,196 ten thousands

14. **Measurement** Mount Everest's tallest peak is 29,035 feet. It is the highest point on Earth. Identify the place value of each digit in 29,035. 2: ten thousands; 9: thousands; 0: hundreds; 3: tens; 5: ones

Round each number to its greatest place value. (Lesson 1-6) (Used in Lesson 6-3)

15. 26 30 **16.** \$251 \$300 **17.** 4,499 4,000 **18.** \$33,103 \$30,000

19. There are 1,366 students at Sunrise Elementary School. Approximately how many students attend the school? Sample answer: 1,000

236 **Chapter 6** Multiply by One-Digit Numbers

TIER 2 Strategic Intervention below/approaching grade level	TIER 1 On-Level	Above/Beyond Level
If students miss six to twelve in: **Exercises 1–19**	**If** students miss three to five in: **Exercises 1–19**	**If** students miss two or less in: **Exercises 1–19**
Then choose a resource:	**Then** choose a resource:	**Then** choose a resource:
Strategic Intervention Guide (pp. 16, 70, 108, 110) CRM Chapter 6 Resource Masters Reteach Worksheets Math Online Extra Examples • Personal Tutor • Concepts in Motion	TE Learning Stations (pp. 234G–234H) TE Chapter Project (p. 234) CRM Game: Product Plus Math Adventures My Math Zone Chapter 5 Math Online Fact Dash	TE Learning Stations (pp. 234G–234H) TE Chapter Project (p. 234) Real-World Problem Solving: *Expanding the United States* My Math Zone Chapters 5 and 6 Math Online Games

LESSON 6-1

Multiples of 10, 100, and 1,000

Lesson Planner

Objective

Multiply multiples of 10, 100, and 1,000 using basic facts and patterns.

Review Vocabulary

multiple

Resources

Literature Connection: *Is a Blue Whale the Biggest Thing There Is?* by Robert E. Wells

Teacher Technology

TeacherWorks • Interactive Classroom • Math Songs Track #8 Lesson Plan

Daily Routine

Use these suggestions before beginning the lesson on p. 237.

5-Minute Check

(Reviews Lesson 5-8)

Write an equation that describes the pattern. Then use the equation to find the next three numbers. multiply by 4; $d \times 4 = e$; 28, 36, 44

Input *d*	1	3	5	7	9	11
Input e	4	12	20	■	■	■

Problem of the Day

Jon is filling his digital audio player with songs. He started by saving 5 rock songs and then another 8 popular songs. By the end of the day, the player held 20 songs. Use *s* as the variable and write an equation for the situation. What is the value of *s*? Sample answer: $s + 5 + 8 = 20$; $s = 7$

Focus on Math Background

This lesson brings together some big ideas and concepts that are taught in the elementary grades, namely:

- Place value is multiplicative in nature. Each place has a value that is ten times greater than the place to its immediate right.
- The Commutative and Associative Properties of Multiplication can be used to manipulate expressions so that they can be evaluated mentally.

On the surface, it appears that students in this lesson are learning to multiply some types of larger numbers mentally. More importantly, they are learning to recognize and use patterns—patterns made possible by the Commutative and Associative Properties of Multiplication:

$6 \times 4 = 24$, so

$6 \times 40 \rightarrow 6 \times (4 \times 10) \rightarrow (6 \times 4) \times 10 \rightarrow 24 \times 10 = 240$

Review Math Vocabulary

Write the review vocabulary word and its definition on the board.

Review this term with students. Ask students to provide examples of multiples. Remind them that skip counting on a number line can help them find multiples. Tell students to copy these examples of multiples of 4 into their Math Journals: $4 \times 1 = \mathbf{4}$, $4 \times 2 = \mathbf{8}$, $4 \times 3 = \mathbf{12}$, etc. Ask them to continue through 4×12.

Visual Vocabulary Cards

Use Visual Vocabulary Card 27 to reinforce the vocabulary reviewed in this lesson. (The Define/Example/Ask routine is printed on the back of each card.)

Differentiated Instruction

Small Group Options

LOGICAL, SPATIAL

Option 1 Gifted and Talented AL

Materials: paper and pencil

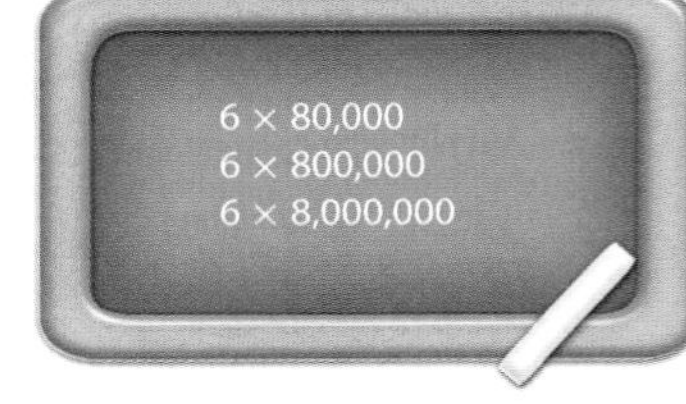

- What if this lesson were called Multiples of 10,000, 100,000, and 1,000,000?
- Solve Exercises 1–3, but substitute in the new numbers.

  Ex. 2: 6 × 80,000
  6 × 800,000
  6 × 8,000,000
- Introduce students to other symbols for multiplication such as (), or •. Encourage them to use these symbols while practicing multiples. 6(8 × 10,000) or 6 • 800,000

AUDITORY, VISUAL

Option 2 English Language Learners ELL

Materials: chalkboard
Core Vocabulary: zeros, sing, remember
Common Use Verb: listen

Hear Math This strategy uses music to teach how to line up multiples of 10.

- Model writing a problem vertically, writing each place value in a different color.
- Guide students through the problem as you sing the following song to the tune of "Three Blind Mice."

Line them up, move to regroup (repeat) If you have ten ones, then regroup again. If you have 10 tens, then regroup again, and line them up.

- Repeat for other problems with multiples of 10.

English Language Learners (p. 55) ELL

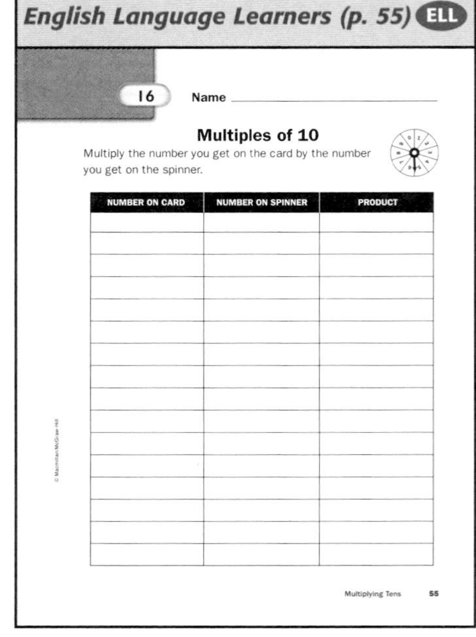

16 Name ____________

Multiples of 10

Multiply the number you get on the card by the number you get on the spinner.

NUMBER ON CARD	NUMBER ON SPINNER	PRODUCT

Multiplying Tens 55

Use this worksheet to provide additional support for English Language Learners.

Independent Work Options

VISUAL, SPATIAL

Option 1 Early Finishers OL AL

Materials: two decks of index cards numbered 1–9, set of index cards labeled × 10, × 100, and × 1,000.

- Pair students. Each should begin with a pile of number cards facedown. Set the pile of "10" multiple cards in the center of the table, also facedown.

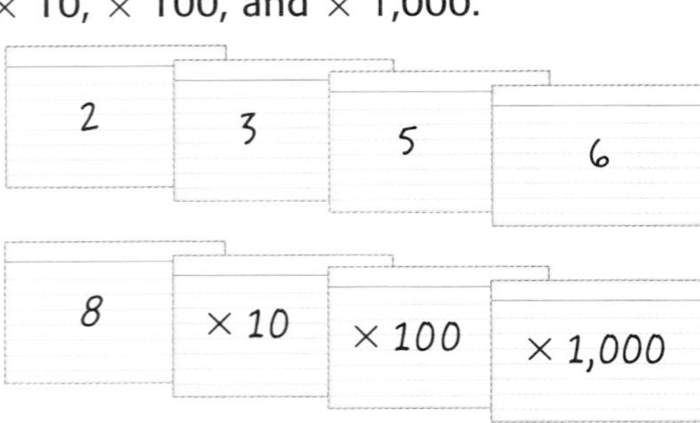

Option 2 Student Technology

Math Online macmillanmh.com

Personal Tutor • Extra Examples

Math Adventures

Math Songs, "Multiplication Rap" Track #8

Option 3 Learning Station: Health (p. 234G)

Direct students to the Health Learning Station for opportunities to explore and extend the lesson concept.

Option 4 Problem-Solving Practice

Reinforce problem-solving skills and strategies with the Problem-Solving Practice worksheet.

Problem Solving (p. 11) BL OL AL

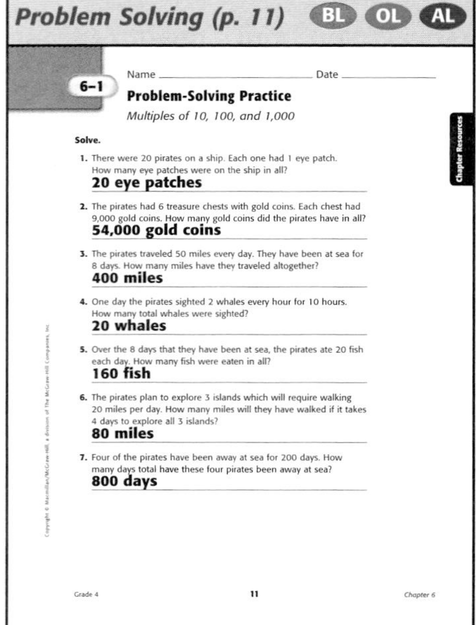

6–1 Name ____________ Date ____________

Problem-Solving Practice

Multiples of 10, 100, and 1,000

Solve.

1. There were 20 pirates on a ship. Each one had 1 eye patch. How many eye patches were on the ship in all? **20 eye patches**
2. The pirates had 6 treasure chests with gold coins. Each chest had 9,000 gold coins. How many gold coins did the pirates have in all? **54,000 gold coins**
3. The pirates traveled 50 miles every day. They have been at sea for 8 days. How many miles have they traveled altogether? **400 miles**
4. One day the pirates sighted 2 whales every hour for 10 hours. How many total whales were sighted? **20 whales**
5. Over the 8 days that they have been at sea, the pirates ate 20 fish each day. How many fish were eaten in all? **160 fish**
6. The pirates plan to explore 3 islands which will require walking 20 miles per day. How many miles will they have walked if it takes 4 days to explore all 3 islands? **80 miles**
7. Four of the pirates have been away at sea for 200 days. How many days total have these four pirates been away at sea? **800 days**

Grade 4 11 Chapter 6

6-1 Multiples of 10, 100, and 1,000

GET READY to Learn

The whale shark is the world's largest fish. Its mouth is 5 feet long, and each foot contains 600 teeth. How many teeth does a whale shark have?

MAIN IDEA

I will multiply multiples of 10, 100, and 1,000 using basic facts and patterns.

Math Online

macmillanmh.com
- Extra Examples
- Personal Tutor
- Self-Check Quiz

You can use basic facts and number patterns to multiply.

Real-World EXAMPLE — Multiples of 100

1. **ANIMALS How many teeth does a whale shark have?**

You need to find 5×600. Use basic facts and patterns.

$5 \times 6 = 30$	5×6 ones $= 30$ ones $= 30$
$5 \times 60 = 300$	5×6 tens $= 30$ tens $= 300$
$5 \times 600 = 3{,}000$	5×6 hundreds $= 30$ hundreds $= 3{,}000$

So, a whale shark has 3,000 teeth. Notice that this answer is 5×6 with two zeros at the end.

EXAMPLE — Multiples of 1,000

2. **Find $3 \times 7{,}000$.**

$3 \times 7 = 21$	3×7 ones $= 21$ ones $= 21$
$3 \times 70 = 210$	3×7 tens $= 21$ tens $= 210$
$3 \times 700 = 2{,}100$	3×7 hundreds $= 21$ hundreds $= 2{,}100$
$3 \times 7{,}000 = 21{,}000$	3×7 thousands $= 21$ thousands $= 21{,}000$

So, $3 \times 7{,}000$ is 21,000. Notice that this answer is 3×7 with three zeros at the end.

6-1 Multiples of 10, 100, and 1,000

1 Introduce

Activity Choice 1 • Hands-On 

Complete the following. Have students follow along:

- Fold a sheet of lined paper to make 3 columns. Label the top of the first column "Basic Fact: 2×4" and write these equations down the column:

$$2 \times 4 = 8$$
$$2 \times 40 = 80$$
$$2 \times 400 = 800$$

- Now label the top of the second column "Basic Fact: 3×6" and write:

$$3 \times 6 = 18$$
$$3 \times 60 = 180$$
$$3 \times 600 = 1{,}800$$

- **What pattern do you see?** Sample answer: When you multiply by a multiple of 10, the product has one zero after the product of the basic fact. When you multiply by a multiple of 100, the product has two zeros after the product of the basic fact.

Activity Choice 2 • Literature

Introduce the lesson with *Is A Blue Whale the Biggest Thing There Is?* by Robert E. Wells. For a related math activity, see p. TR50.

2 Teach

Scaffolding Questions

Continue Activity Choice 1 by labeling the top of the third column "Basic Fact: 5×4" and write these equations down the column.

$5 \times 4 = ?$ $\quad 5 \times 40 = ?$ $\quad 5 \times 400 = ?$

- **What are the products for each number sentence?** 20, 200, 2,000
- **Compare this pattern to the pattern you found for the first two columns. What do you notice?** Sample answer: There appears to be an extra zero in each product.
- **Explain the extra zero.** Sample answer: The product of 5×4 has a zero in it.

GET READY to Learn

Have students open their books and read the information in **Get Ready to Learn**. Review **multiple**. As a class, work through **Examples 1–3**.

Multiples of 100

Example 1 Point out that the basic fact 5 × 6 has a zero in the product. So when you multiply 5 by 600, there will be 3 zeros in the product.

ADDITIONAL EXAMPLES

1. A leopard shark gives birth to 8 pups in 1 litter. How many pups would be in 300 litters of that size? 2,400
2. Find 8 × 7,000. 56,000
3. Orca whales live in pods and can weigh up to 8,000 pounds. What is the total weight of a pod of 6 orca whales? 48,000 pounds

CHECK What You Know

As a class, have students complete Exercises 1–8 in **Check What You Know** as you observe their work.

Exercise 8 Assess student comprehension before assigning practice exercises.

BL Alternate Teaching Strategy

If students are confused about the number of zeros to use…

Then use one of these reteach options:

1 CRM **Daily Reteach Worksheet** (p. 8)

2 Have students highlight the factors of the basic fact in one color, and highlight the zeros in the multiple of 10, 100, or 1,000 in a different color.

- When they find the product, have them check to make sure that the product of their basic fact is correct and that the correct number of zeros are there.
- Encourage students to use estimation to decide if their products are correct.

COMMON ERROR!

Exercises 7, 8, 14, and 18 Students may have trouble with numbers whose basic fact results in an ending zero. Suggest that they identify the basic fact by underlining it and then draw a circle around the zeros in the multiple of 10, 100, or 1,000. For example, 5 × 4(00) = 2,0(00)

When you know basic facts and number patterns, you can multiply mentally.

Remember

As the number of zeros in a factor increases, the number of zeros in the product increases.

Real-World EXAMPLE Multiply Mentally

3 **MEASUREMENT** **The weight of a fire truck is 8 × 4,000 pounds. What is its weight in pounds?**

To find its weight, you need to find 8 × 4,000.

8 × 4,000

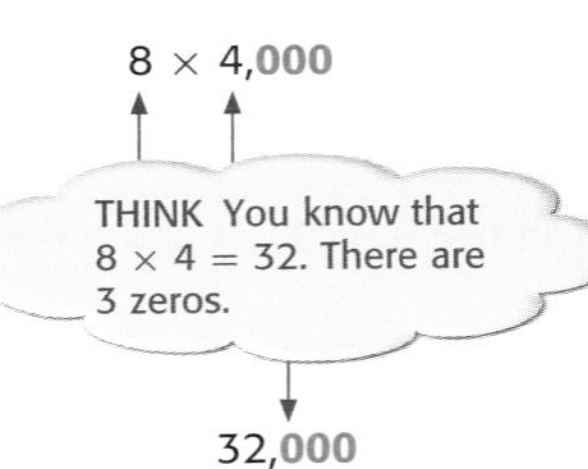

THINK You know that 8 × 4 = 32. There are 3 zeros.

32,000

Since 8 × 4,000 = 32,000, the weight of the fire truck is 32,000 pounds.

CHECK What You Know

Multiply. Use basic facts and patterns. See Examples 1 and 2 (p. 237)

1. 2 × 1 2; 20; 200; 2,000
   2 × 10
   2 × 100
   2 × 1,000
2. 6 × 8
   6 × 80
   6 × 800
   6 × 8,000
   48; 480; 4,800, 48,000
3. 7 × 9
   7 × 90
   7 × 900
   7 × 9,000
   63; 630; 6,300; 63,000

Multiply. Use mental math. See Example 3 (p. 238)

4. 3 × 20 60
5. 8 × 600 4,800
6. 9 × 9,000 81,000
7. A zookeeper is in charge of feeding an anteater. Each day the anteater eats 5 × 6,000 ants. How many ants must the zookeeper give the anteater each day? 30,000
8. **Talk About It** What is the product of 4 and 5,000? Explain why there are more zeros in the product than in the factors in the problem. Sample answer: 20,000; 4 × 5 = 20, which produces an extra zero.

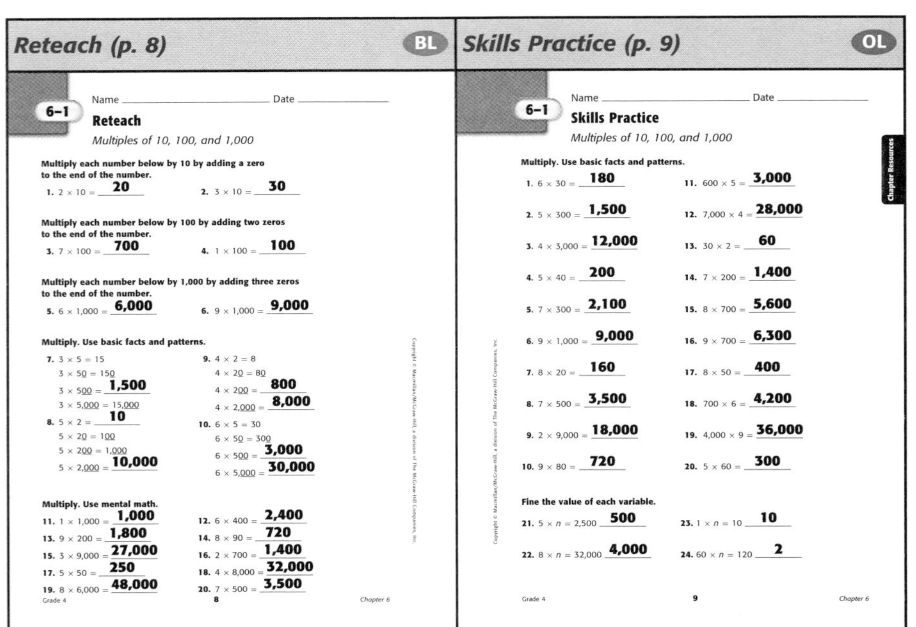

Reteach (p. 8) BL

6-1 Name ______ Date ______

Reteach

Multiples of 10, 100, and 1,000

Multiply each number below by 10 by adding a zero to the end of the number.

1. 2 × 10 = **20**
2. 3 × 10 = **30**

Multiply each number below by 100 by adding two zeros to the end of the number.

3. 7 × 100 = **700**
4. 1 × 100 = **100**

Multiply each number below by 1,000 by adding three zeros to the end of the number.

5. 6 × 1,000 = **6,000**
6. 9 × 1,000 = **9,000**

Multiply. Use basic facts and patterns.

7. 3 × 5 = 15
   3 × 50 = 150
   3 × 500 = **1,500**
   3 × 5,000 = 15,000
8. 5 × 2 = **10**
   5 × 20 = 100
   5 × 200 = 1,000
   5 × 2,000 = **10,000**
9. 4 × 2 = 8
   4 × 20 = 80
   4 × 200 = **800**
   4 × 2,000 = **8,000**
10. 6 × 5 = 30
    6 × 50 = 300
    6 × 500 = **3,000**
    6 × 5,000 = **30,000**

Multiply. Use mental math.

11. 1 × 1,000 = **1,000**
12. 6 × 400 = **2,400**
13. 9 × 200 = **1,800**
14. 8 × 90 = **720**
15. 3 × 9,000 = **27,000**
16. 2 × 700 = **1,400**
17. 5 × 50 = **250**
18. 4 × 8,000 = **32,000**
19. 8 × 6,000 = **48,000**
20. 7 × 500 = **3,500**

Skills Practice (p. 9) OL

6-1 Name ______ Date ______

Skills Practice

Multiples of 10, 100, and 1,000

Chapter Resources

Multiply. Use basic facts and patterns.

1. 6 × 30 = **180**
2. 5 × 300 = **1,500**
3. 4 × 3,000 = **12,000**
4. 5 × 40 = **200**
5. 7 × 300 = **2,100**
6. 9 × 1,000 = **9,000**
7. 8 × 20 = **160**
8. 7 × 500 = **3,500**
9. 2 × 9,000 = **18,000**
10. 9 × 80 = **720**
11. 600 × 5 = **3,000**
12. 7,000 × 4 = **28,000**
13. 30 × 2 = **60**
14. 7 × 200 = **1,400**
15. 8 × 700 = **5,600**
16. 9 × 700 = **6,300**
17. 8 × 50 = **400**
18. 700 × 6 = **4,200**
19. 4,000 × 9 = **36,000**
20. 5 × 60 = **300**

Fine the value of each variable.

21. 5 × n = 2,500 **500**
22. 8 × n = 32,000 **4,000**
23. 1 × n = 10 **10**
24. 60 × n = 120 **2**

Practice and Problem Solving

See page R15.

Multiply. Use basic facts and patterns. See Examples 1 and 2 (p. 237)

9. 5×3
5×30
5×300
$5 \times 3{,}000$
15; 150; 1,500; 15,000

10. 3×4
3×40
3×400
$3 \times 4{,}000$
12; 120; 1,200, 12,000

11. 2×9
2×90
2×900
$2 \times 9{,}000$
18; 180; 1,800; 18,000

12. 6×7
6×70
6×700
$6 \times 7{,}000$
42; 420; 4,200; 42,000

13. 9×1
9×10
9×100
$9 \times 1{,}000$
9; 90; 900, 9,000

14. 8×5
8×50
8×500
$8 \times 5{,}000$
40; 400; 4,000; 40,000

Multiply. Use mental math. See Example 3 (p. 238)

15. 4×30 120
16. 6×40 240
17. 7×200 1,400
18. 4×500 2,000
19. $3 \times 9{,}000$ 27,000
20. $9 \times 6{,}000$ 54,000

Algebra **Copy and complete.**

21. If $6 \times \blacksquare = 42$,
then $60 \times \blacksquare = 4{,}200$. 7; 70

22. If $5 \times 7 = \blacksquare$,
then $50 \times \blacksquare = 3{,}500$. 35; 70

23. Mr. Singh's car payments are $300 a month. How much money will he pay in 6 months? $1,800

24. Mia's cell phone plan includes 2,000 monthly minutes. How many minutes does she get over 6 months? 12,000 min

Real-World PROBLEM SOLVING

Travel The Williams family is going to a theme park.

25. Admission tickets cost $30 for each person. What is the total cost for the 5 family members for one day? $150

26. The cost for each person to eat for one week is $100. Find the total cost for the family to eat for one week. $500

27. Suppose each family member goes on 70 rides during the week. How many rides will they go on altogether? 350 rides

H.O.T. Problems

28. OPEN ENDED Write two multiplication expressions that have a product of 20,000. Sample answer: $4 \times 5{,}000$ and $2 \times 10{,}000$

29. WRITING IN ▶MATH How would you find $1 \times 10{,}000$? What is $1 \times 10{,}000$? Use the Identity Property of Multiplication; $1 \times 10{,}000 = 10{,}000$.

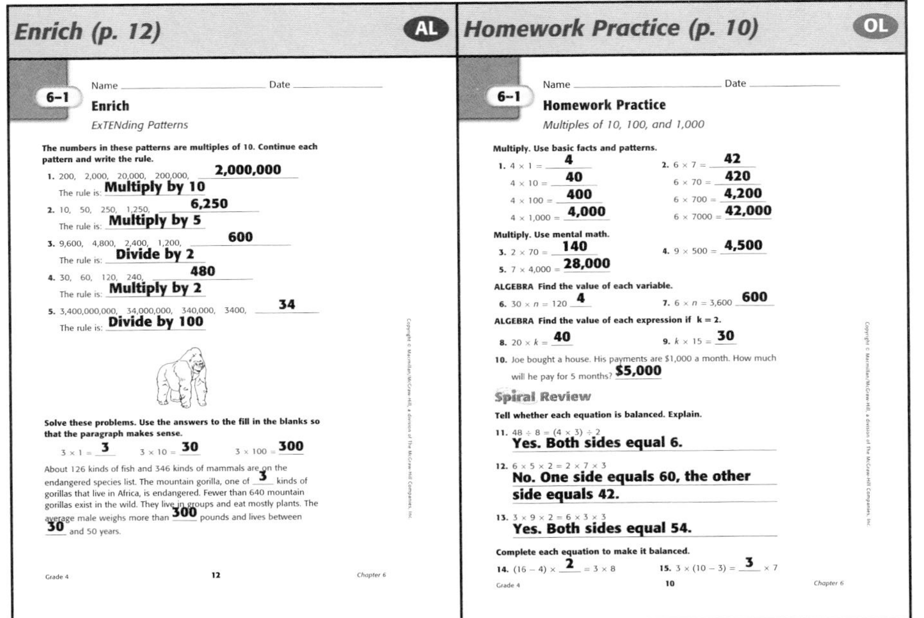

Enrich (p. 12) AL

6–1
Name ____________ Date ____________
Enrich
ExTENding Patterns

The numbers in these patterns are multiples of 10. Continue each pattern and write the rule.

1. 200, 2,000, 20,000, 200,000, **2,000,000**
The rule is: **Multiply by 10**
2. 10, 50, 250, 1,250, **6,250**
The rule is: **Multiply by 5**
3. 9,600, 4,800, 2,400, 1,200, **600**
The rule is: **Divide by 2**
4. 30, 60, 120, 240, **480**
The rule is: **Multiply by 2**
5. 3,400,000,000, 34,000,000, 340,000, 3400, **34**
The rule is: **Divide by 100**

Solve these problems. Use the answers to the fill in the blanks so that the paragraph makes sense.

$3 \times 1 =$ **3** $3 \times 10 =$ **30** $3 \times 100 =$ **300**

About 126 kinds of fish and 346 kinds of mammals are on the endangered species list. The mountain gorilla, one of **3** kinds of gorillas that live in Africa, is endangered. Fewer than 640 mountain gorillas exist in the wild. They live in groups and eat mostly plants. The average male weighs more than **300** pounds and lives between **30** and 50 years.

Grade 4 12 Chapter 6

Homework Practice (p. 10) OL

6–1
Name ____________ Date ____________
Homework Practice
Multiples of 10, 100, and 1,000

Multiply. Use basic facts and patterns.

1. $4 \times 1 =$ **4**
$4 \times 10 =$ **40**
$4 \times 100 =$ **400**
$4 \times 1{,}000 =$ **4,000**

2. $6 \times 7 =$ **42**
$6 \times 70 =$ **420**
$6 \times 700 =$ **4,200**
$6 \times 7000 =$ **42,000**

Multiply. Use mental math.

3. $2 \times 70 =$ **140**
4. $9 \times 500 =$ **4,500**
5. $7 \times 4{,}000 =$ **28,000**

ALGEBRA Find the value of each variable.

6. $30 \times n = 120$ **4**
7. $6 \times n = 3{,}600$ **600**

ALGEBRA Find the value of each expression if $k = 2$.

8. $20 \times k =$ **40**
9. $k \times 15 =$ **30**

10. Joe bought a house. His payments are $1,000 a month. How much will he pay for 5 months? **$5,000**

Spiral Review

Tell whether each equation is balanced. Explain.

11. $48 \div 8 = (4 \times 3) \div 2$
Yes. Both sides equal 6.
12. $6 \times 5 \times 2 = 2 \times 7 \times 3$
No. One side equals 60, the other side equals 42.
13. $3 \times 9 \times 2 = 6 \times 3 \times 3$
Yes. Both sides equal 54.

Complete each equation to make it balanced.

14. $(16 - 4) \times$ **2** $= 3 \times 8$
15. $3 \times (10 - 3) =$ **3** $\times 7$

Grade 4 10 Chapter 6

3 Practice

Differentiate practice using these leveled assignments for Exercises 9–29.

Level	Assignment
BL Below/Approaching Level	9–11, 15–17, 21, 23, 25–26
OL On Level	9–11, 15–26, 28
AL Above/Beyond Level	9–27 odd, 28–29

Have students discuss and complete the Higher Order Thinking problems. Remind students to look for the basic fact first and then count the zeros in the multiple(s) of 10, 100, 1,000, etc.

WRITING IN ▶MATH Have students complete Exercise 29 in their Math Journals. You may choose to use this exercise as an optional formative assessment.

4 Assess

Formative Assessment

Write 1,500 on the board.

- **What two factors could result in this product if one factor must be a multiple of 100?** 3×500, 5×300

Quick Check **Are students continuing to struggle with multiples of 10, 100, and 1,000?**

If Yes → Strategic Intervention Guide (p. 12)

If No → Independent Work Options (p. 237B)
CRM Skills Practice Worksheet (p. 9)
CRM Enrich Worksheet (p. 12)

Ticket Out the Door Write $5 \times 6{,}000$ on the board. Have students write the product on a small piece of paper. Also, ask them to write the basic fact that they used to solve the sentence. Have them hand their papers to you as they leave the room.

6-2 Problem-Solving Skill
Reasonable Answers

Lesson Planner

Objective

Decide if an answer to a problem is reasonable.

Resources

Materials: pencil, paper

Literature Connection: *Minnie's Diner: A Multiplying Menu* by Dayle Ann Dodds and John Manders

Teacher Technology
TeacherWorks • Interactive Classroom

Real-World Problem Solving Library
Math and Social Studies: *Expanding the United States*
Use these leveled books to reinforce and extend problem-solving skills and strategies.

Leveled for:

- OL On Level
- ELL Sheltered English
- SP Spanish

For additional support, see the Real-World Problem Solving Teacher Guide.

Daily Routine

Use these suggestions before beginning the lesson on p. 240.

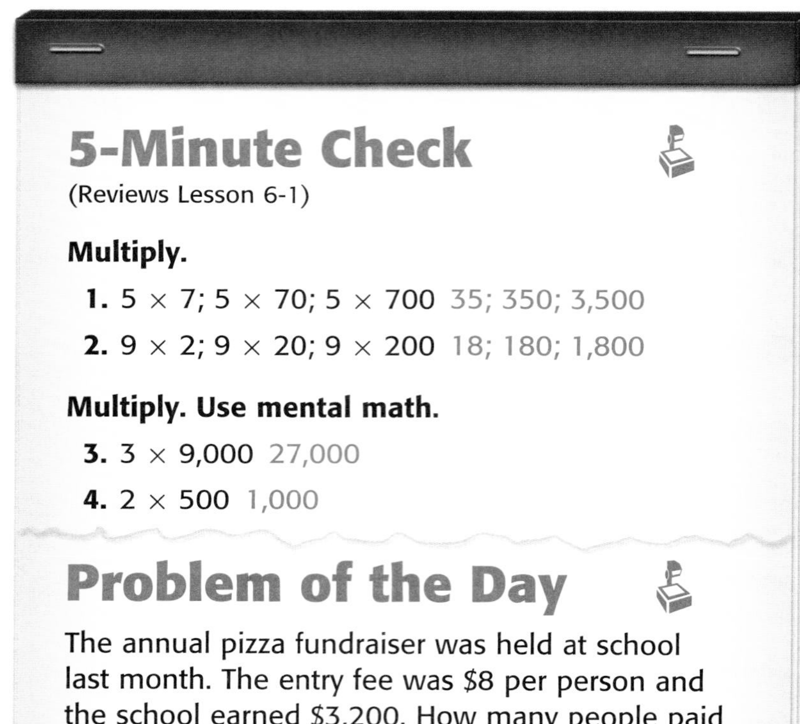

5-Minute Check

(Reviews Lesson 6-1)

Multiply.

1. 5×7; 5×70; 5×700 35; 350; 3,500

2. 9×2; 9×20; 9×200 18; 180; 1,800

Multiply. Use mental math.

3. $3 \times 9{,}000$ 27,000

4. 2×500 1,000

Problem of the Day

The annual pizza fundraiser was held at school last month. The entry fee was $8 per person and the school earned $3,200. How many people paid to eat pizza? How many more people would have had to eat pizza for the school to raise $4,000?
400 people; 100 more people

Differentiated Instruction

Small Group Options

LOGICAL

Option 1 Below Level BL

Materials: pencils, paper

- Review with the students the meaning of the word "reasonable." Tell them you are going to do a little exercise to practice this concept.
- Ask them to number from 1 to 5 on their paper, and read the following statements to them. Students will write *yes* or *no* for each exercise.
- Discuss the answers to these exercises.

1. It is reasonable to expect $50 a week for allowance.
2. It is reasonable to expect to go home after school.
3. It is reasonable to expect to have math homework every school day.
4. 150°F is a reasonable temperature in January.
5. 25–23 is a reasonable score for a soccer game.

AUDITORY, LOGICAL

Option 2 English Language Learners ELL

Materials: note cards
Core Vocabulary: near, guess, line up under
Common Use Verb: have enough
Do Math This strategy teaches reasonable answers and vocabulary.

- Write several problems on the board involving zeros (e.g., 2 × 1,000).
- Give each student a note card with an answer that will match one of the problems on the board.
- Inform students that *enough* means that their answers are reasonable because they are correct or close to correct.
- Allow students to work out problems as a group on the board. Prompt students to ***guess*** the answer by lining up under the most reasonable problem.
- Ask: "Who **has enough**?" As you visually check answers, ask students if their number is **enough**.
- Repeat with several problems.

Independent Work Options

VISUAL, LINGUISTIC

Option 1 Early Finishers OL AL

Materials: index cards, scissors, glue, construction paper

- Have students write a word problem on an index card. The problems should be similar to those that students solved in Analyze the Skill on p. 267. Place all the index cards in a shoe box with a slot cut in the top.
- Have students select a problem from the shoebox. Cut or copy the problem onto a piece of construction paper.
- Students should analyze and solve their chosen problem. Once they are finished solving, they should write a few sentences describing why they thought the solution was reasonable or not.

Option 2 Student Technology

Math Online macmillanmh.com

Personal Tutor • Extra Examples

Option 3 Learning Station: Art (p. 234G)

Direct students to the Art Learning Station for opportunities to explore and extend the lesson concept.

6-2 Problem-Solving Skill

1 Introduce

Activity Choice 1 • Review

- Give students the following problem:

  There are now 35 students riding on the bus. At the first stop, 12 students got off. At the second stop, 9 students got off. How many students were originally on the bus?
- **What strategy could you use to solve this problem?** work backward
- Have students solve. Check the solution. 56 students were originally on the bus.

Activity Choice 2 • Literature

Introduce the lesson with *Minnie's Diner: A Multiplying Menu* by Dayle Ann Dodds and John Manders. For a related math activity, see p. TR51.

2 Teach

Have students read the problem on dog treats. Guide them through the problem-solving steps.

Understand Using the questions, review what students know and need to find.

Plan Have them discuss their strategy.

Solve Guide students to use the reasonable answer strategy to solve the problem.

- **How many cases of treats were donated?** 3
- **How many treats are in each case?** 900
- **How do you find out how many treats are in 3 cases?** multiply
- **Then what do you have to do?** Compare the number of treats donated to the number that are needed.

Check Have students look back at the problem to make sure that the answer fits the facts given.

COMMON ERROR!

Exercise 8 Students may not remember the customary units of length. Take this opportunity to review these relationships by writing the following on the board:

12 inches = 1 foot
3 feet = 1 yard

6-2 Problem-Solving Skill

MAIN IDEA I will decide whether an answer to a problem is reasonable.

Odell donated 3 cases of dog treats to a dog shelter. Each case has 900 treats. The dogs eat 2,500 treats each month. Odell says he has donated enough treats for more than one month. Is his claim reasonable?

Understand

What facts do you know?

- 3 cases of treats were donated.
- Each case has 900 treats.
- The animals eat 2,500 treats each month.

What do you need to find?

- Is it reasonable to say that the 3 cases of treats will last longer than one month?

Plan Find 3×900. Then determine if the amount is reasonable.

Solve

3×900

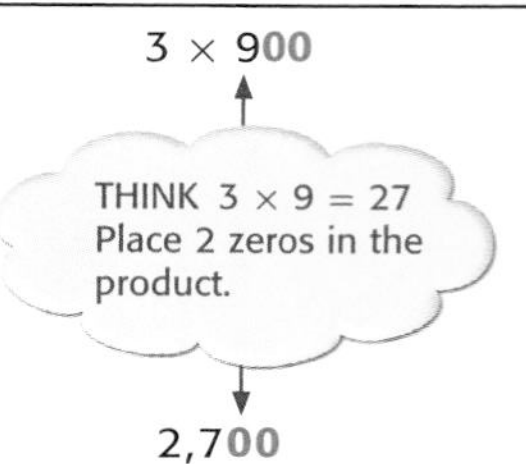

2,700

Since $2{,}700 > 2{,}500$, it is reasonable to say that the three cases will last longer than one month.

Check You can add to check the multiplication.

$900 + 900 + 900 = 2{,}700$

So, the answer is correct.

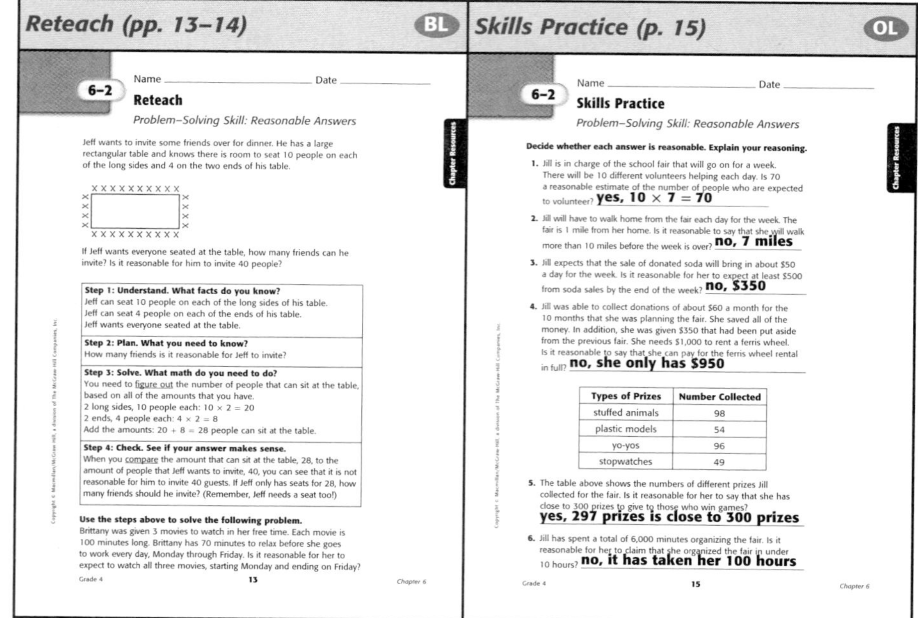

Reteach (pp. 13–14) BL

6–2 Name ______ Date ______

Reteach

Problem–Solving Skill: Reasonable Answers

Jeff wants to invite some friends over for dinner. He has a large rectangular table and knows there is room to seat 10 people on each of the long sides and 4 on the two ends of his table.

If Jeff wants everyone seated at the table, how many friends can he invite? Is it reasonable for him to invite 40 people?

Step 1: Understand. What facts do you know?
Jeff can seat 10 people on each of the long sides of his table.
Jeff can seat 4 people on each of the ends of his table.
Jeff wants everyone seated at the table.

Step 2: Plan. What you need to know?
How many friends is it reasonable for Jeff to invite?

Step 3: Solve. What math do you need to do?
You need to figure out the number of people that can sit at the table, based on all of the amounts that you have.
2 long sides, 10 people each: $10 \times 2 = 20$
2 ends, 4 people each: $4 \times 2 = 8$
Add the amounts: $20 + 8 = 28$ people can sit at the table.

Step 4: Check. See if your answer makes sense.
When you compare the amount that can sit at the table, 28, to the amount of people that Jeff wants to invite, 40, you can see that it is not reasonable for him to invite 40 guests. If Jeff only has seats for 28, how many friends should he invite? (Remember, Jeff needs a seat too!)

Use the steps above to solve the following problem.

Brittany was given 3 movies to watch in her free time. Each movie is 100 minutes long. Brittany has 70 minutes to relax before she goes to work every day, Monday through Friday. Is it reasonable for her to expect to watch all three movies, starting Monday and ending on Friday?

Grade 4 13 Chapter 6

Skills Practice (p. 15) OL

6–2 Name ______ Date ______

Skills Practice

Problem–Solving Skill: Reasonable Answers

Decide whether each answer is reasonable. Explain your reasoning.

1. Jill is in charge of the school fair that will go on for a week. There will be 10 different volunteers helping each day. Is 70 a reasonable estimate of the number of people who are expected to volunteer? **yes, $10 \times 7 = 70$**
2. Jill will have to walk home from the fair each day for the week. The fair is 1 mile from her home. Is it reasonable to say that she will walk more than 10 miles before the week is over? **no, 7 miles**
3. Jill expects that the sale of donated soda will bring in about \$50 a day for the week. Is it reasonable for her to expect at least \$500 from soda sales by the end of the week? **no, \$350**
4. Jill was able to collect donations of about \$60 a month for the 10 months that she was planning the fair. She saved all of the money. In addition, she was given \$350 that had been put aside from the previous fair. She needs \$1,000 to rent a ferris wheel. Is it reasonable to say that she can pay for the ferris wheel rental in full? **no, she only has \$950**

Types of Prizes	Number Collected
stuffed animals	98
plastic models	54
yo-yos	96
stopwatches	49

5. The table above shows the numbers of different prizes Jill collected for the fair. Is it reasonable for her to say that she has close to 300 prizes to give to those who win games? **yes, 297 prizes is close to 300 prizes**
6. Jill has spent a total of 6,000 minutes organizing the fair. Is it reasonable for her to claim that she organized the fair in under 10 hours? **no, it has taken her 100 hours**

Grade 4 15 Chapter 6

ANALYZE the Skill

Refer to the problem on the previous page. 1–4. See Ch. 6 Answer Appendix.

1. Explain why 3 is multiplied by 900 to decide if Odell's claim was reasonable.
2. Explain why there are 2 zeros at the end of the product of 3 and 900.
3. Look back at the example. What would make Odell's claim *not* reasonable?
4. Suppose Odell donates 5 cases of treats. Is it reasonable to believe the treats will last 2 months? Explain.

★ indicates multi-step problem

PRACTICE the Skill

EXTRA PRACTICE See page R15.

Decide whether each answer is reasonable. Explain your reasoning.

★**5. Measurement** The calendar shows the number of days each month Olivia rides her bike.

September						
Sun	Mon	Tues	Wed	Thurs	Fri	Sat
					1	2 B
3 B	4	5	6	7	8 B	9
10 B	11	12	13 B	14	15	16 B
17	18	19	20	21	22 B	23
24 B	25	26	27	28 B	29	30 B

Each time she rides her bike, she travels 10 miles. Is it reasonable to say that Olivia will bike more than 500 miles in 6 months? yes; $6 \times 100 = 600$

6. Ben delivers 40 newspapers each day. Is 400 a reasonable estimate for the number of newspapers Ben delivers each week? no; $7 \times 40 = 280$

★**7.** Jay makes $40 a week doing yard work. He is saving his money to buy a computer that costs $400. He has already saved $120. Is it reasonable to say that Jay will save enough money to buy the computer in 6 weeks? See Ch. 6 Answer Appendix.

8. Measurement The distance from Ian's home to the museum is 2,640 yards. Is it reasonable to say that Ian's home is more than 9,000 feet away from the museum? (3 feet = 1 yard) no; $3 \times 2,640 = 7,920$

9. Kiri spends 60 minutes a week walking to school. Is it reasonable to say that she spends 240 minutes walking to school in four weeks? yes; $4 \times 60 = 240$

10. The table below shows the number of pennies collected by four children.

Pennies Collected	
Child	Number of Pennies
Myron	48
Teresa	52
Veronica	47
Warren	53

Is it reasonable to say that the children collected about 200 pennies in all? yes; $4 \times 50 = 200$

11. WRITING IN MATH Write a problem where $180 would be a reasonable answer. See Ch. 6 Answer Appendix.

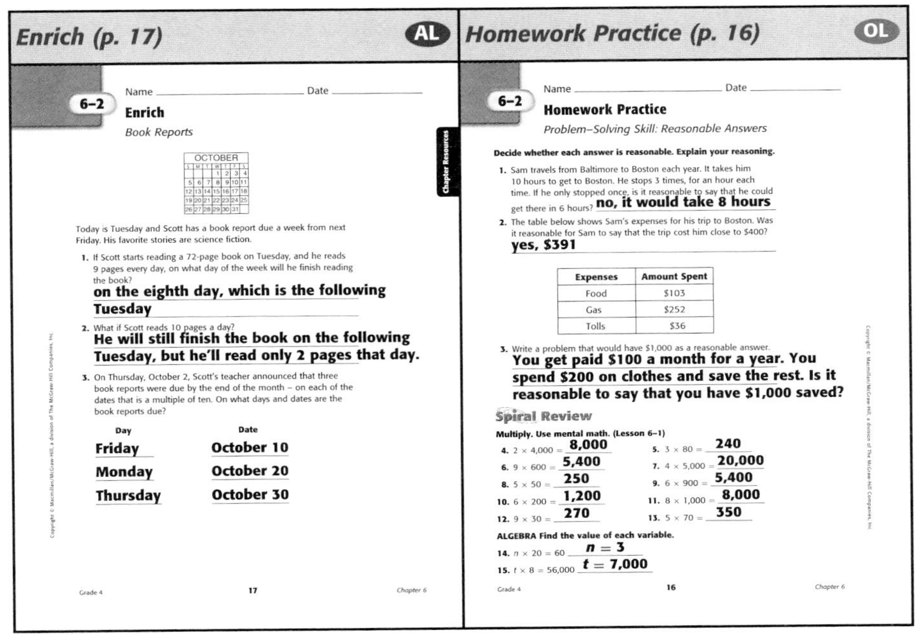

Enrich (p. 17) AL

6–2 Name ________ Date ________

Enrich

Book Reports

OCTOBER						
S	M	T	W	T	F	S
			1	2	3	4
5	6	7	8	9	10	11
12	13	14	15	16	17	18
19	20	21	22	23	24	25
26	27	28	29	30	31	

Today is Tuesday and Scott has a book report due a week from next Friday. His favorite stories are science fiction.

1. If Scott starts reading a 72-page book on Tuesday, and he reads 9 pages every day, on what day of the week will he finish reading the book? **on the eighth day, which is the following Tuesday**
2. What if Scott reads 10 pages a day? **He will still finish the book on the following Tuesday, but he'll read only 2 pages that day.**
3. On Thursday, October 2, Scott's teacher announced that three book reports were due by the end of the month – on each of the dates that is a multiple of ten. On what days and dates are the book reports due?

Day	Date
Friday	**October 10**
Monday	**October 20**
Thursday	**October 30**

Grade 4 17 Chapter 6

Chapter Resources

Homework Practice (p. 16) OL

6–2 Name ________ Date ________

Homework Practice

Problem–Solving Skill: Reasonable Answers

Decide whether each answer is reasonable. Explain your reasoning.

1. Sam travels from Baltimore to Boston each year. It takes him 10 hours to get to Boston. He stops 3 times, for an hour each time. If he only stopped once, is it reasonable to say that he could get there in 6 hours? **no, it would take 8 hours**
2. The table below shows Sam's expenses for his trip to Boston. Was it reasonable for Sam to say that the trip cost him close to $400? **yes, $391**

Expenses	Amount Spent
Food	$103
Gas	$252
Tolls	$36

3. Write a problem that would have $1,000 as a reasonable answer. **You get paid $100 a month for a year. You spend $200 on clothes and save the rest. Is it reasonable to say that you have $1,000 saved?**

Spiral Review

Multiply. Use mental math. (Lesson 6–1)

4. $2 \times 4,000 =$ **8,000**
5. $3 \times 80 =$ **240**
6. $9 \times 600 =$ **5,400**
7. $4 \times 5,000 =$ **20,000**
8. $5 \times 50 =$ **250**
9. $6 \times 900 =$ **5,400**
10. $6 \times 200 =$ **1,200**
11. $8 \times 1,000 =$ **8,000**
12. $9 \times 30 =$ **270**
13. $5 \times 70 =$ **350**

ALGEBRA Find the value of each variable.

14. $n \times 20 = 60$ **$n = 3$**
15. $t \times 8 = 56,000$ **$t = 7,000$**

Grade 4 16 Chapter 6

Analyze the Skill Use Exercises 1–4 to analyze and discuss the problem-solving skill.

BL Alternate Teaching Strategy

If students have trouble finding the important information when reading problems…

Then use one of these reteach options:

1. CRM **Daily Reteach Worksheet** (pp. 13–14)
2. Working with a partner, each student is to read and write down the information given. Have them compare their information and decide how to solve the problem. Together they can check answers for reasonableness.

3 Practice

Using the Exercises

Exercises 1–10 provide opportunities for students to decide if their answers are reasonable by going back over the information given.

Exercises 6, 8, and 9 require students to recall several units of measure. Exercise 5 requires knowing that there are 7 days in a week; Exercise 8 that there are 12 months in a year; and Exercise 9 that there are 3 feet in a yard.

4 Assess

Formative Assessment

- **How can you determine whether a solution is reasonable?** Show the computation. Compare the answer from the worked-out solution to the data in the problem. Look to see if the solution is greater than, less than, or equal to the data in the problem.

Quick Check **Are students continuing to struggle with deciding whether an answer is reasonable?**

If Yes → Small Group Options (p. 240B)

If No → Independent Work Options (p. 240B)
CRM Skills Practice Worksheet (p. 15)
CRM Enrich Worksheet (p. 17)

LESSON 6-3

Use Rounding to Estimate Products

Lesson Planner

Objective

Estimate products by rounding.

Vocabulary

estimate, **round**

Resources

Literature Connection: *Betcha!* by Stuart J. Murphy

Alternate Lesson: Use *IMPACT Mathematics:* Unit C to provide practice with estimation.

Teacher Technology

TeacherWorks • Interactive Classroom • Math Tool Chest

Daily Routine

Use these suggestions before beginning the lesson on p. 242.

5-Minute Check

(Reviews Lesson 6-2)

Decide whether the answer is reasonable. Explain your reasoning.

Kyle delivers 50 papers a day in his neighborhood. Is it reasonable to expect that he will deliver 320 by the end of 1 week? Yes, 7 days in one week × 50 papers per day is 350 papers. He will deliver at least 320.

Problem of the Day

The first day of a book drive, a school earned \$1. Each day after that, the amount tripled from the day before. How much did the school earn if the book drive lasted for five days?

\$1 + \$3 + \$9 + \$27 + \$81 = \$121

Focus on Math Background

This lesson brings together what students learned about multiplying by multiples of 10, 100, and 1,000 in the previous lesson and what they learned about rounding numbers in Chapter 1. Students will draw on these previous skills as they use rounding of one factor to its greatest place to estimate products. As students make these estimates, it is often helpful to ask them if their estimates are greater than or less than the exact answers.

$7 \times 487 \approx 3{,}500$	$4 \times 621 \approx 2{,}400$
factor rounded up estimate greater than the exact product	factor rounded down estimate less than the exact product

Building Math Vocabulary

Write the vocabulary words and their definitions on the board.

Have students discuss their experiences with estimating and rounding. Have students come to the board and model how to round numbers such as 1,276 and 35,755 to the nearest hundred. Remind students to keep the rules of rounding in mind throughout the lesson.

Visual Vocabulary Cards

Use Visual Vocabulary Cards 15 and 42 to reinforce the vocabulary introduced in this lesson. (The Define/Example/Ask routine is printed on the back of each card.)

Differentiated Instruction

Small Group Options

Option 1 Below Level BL

LOGICAL, SOCIAL

Materials: pencils, paper, chart paper

- Draw a number line from 0 to 100. Each ten is broken into a hill and a valley. Each hill has a multiple of 5 at the peak, leaning to the right. This is to remind students that numbers 5 and more round up and those 4 and less round down. This same number line can be drawn for hundreds using multiples of 50.
- Try rounding a few numbers to the nearest 10, then the nearest 100, then to the nearest 1,000.
- Apply the skill to this problem: 6×729. 729 rounded to the nearest hundred is 700, so the estimated product can be found by multiplying 6×700; 4,200.

Option 2 English Language Learners ELL

LINGUISTIC

Materials: notebook paper

Core Vocabulary: meaning, definition, near

Common Use Verb: round

See Math This strategy activates background knowledge by using students' native language to clarify vocabulary.

- Ask students to draw two circles.
- Ask: "How do you say ***round*** in your native language?"
- Ask students to write their native word in one circle.
- Tell students that *round* in the English language has two meanings.
- When used in math, *round* means to find a number **near** another number.
- Tell students to write in the other circle "355 ***rounds*** to 400."

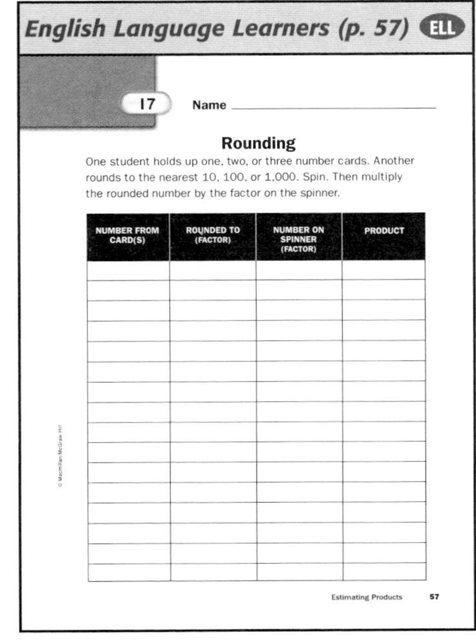

English Language Learners (p. 57) ELL

17 Name ____________

Rounding

One student holds up one, two, or three number cards. Another rounds to the nearest 10, 100, or 1,000. Spin. Then multiply the rounded number by the factor on the spinner.

NUMBER FROM CARD(S)	ROUNDED TO (FACTOR)	NUMBER ON SPINNER (FACTOR)	PRODUCT

Estimating Products 57

Use this worksheet to provide additional support for English Language Learners.

Independent Work Options

Option 1 Early Finishers AL

VISUAL, SPATIAL

Materials: colored cubes or counters in at least 4 different colors

- Spill a random number of colored cubes or counters out and group them according to these rules: red = 1,000, yellow = 100, blue = 10, and green = 1.
- Compute the number represented by the cubes and round the number to the greatest place.
- Record the numbers created by the cubes and the rounded numbers. Explain the rounding rule used for each number.

Option 2 Student Technology

Math Online macmillanmh.com

Math Tool Chest Place Value Level #2

Personal Tutor • Extra Examples

Math Adventures

Option 3 Learning Station: Writing (p. 234G)

Direct students to the Writing Learning Station for opportunities to explore and extend the lesson concept.

Option 4 Problem-Solving Practice

Reinforce problem-solving skills and strategies with the Problem-Solving Practice worksheet.

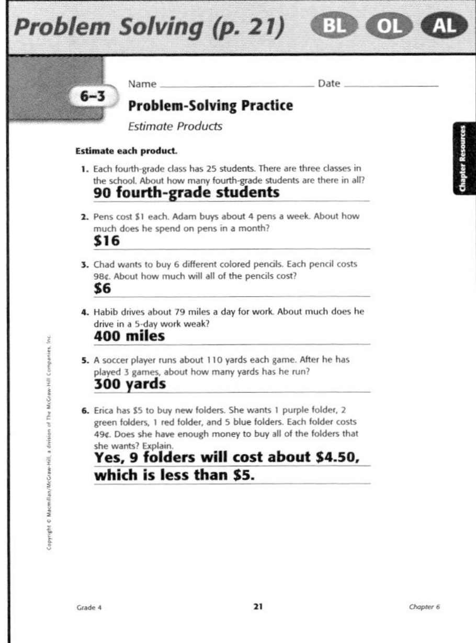

Problem Solving (p. 21) BL OL AL

6–3 Name ____________ Date ____________

Problem-Solving Practice

Estimate Products

Chapter Resources

Estimate each product.

1. Each fourth-grade class has 25 students. There are three classes in the school. About how many fourth-grade students are there in all?
   90 fourth-grade students
2. Pens cost $1 each. Adam buys about 4 pens a week. About how much does he spend on pens in a month?
   $16
3. Chad wants to buy 6 different colored pencils. Each pencil costs 98¢. About how much will all of the pencils cost?
   $6
4. Habib drives about 79 miles a day for work. About much does he drive in a 5-day work weak?
   400 miles
5. A soccer player runs about 110 yards each game. After he has played 3 games, about how many yards has he run?
   300 yards
6. Erica has $5 to buy new folders. She wants 1 purple folder, 2 green folders, 1 red folder, and 5 blue folders. Each folder costs 49¢. Does she have enough money to buy all of the folders that she wants? Explain.
   Yes, 9 folders will cost about $4.50, which is less than $5.

Grade 4 21 Chapter 6

6-3 Use Rounding to Estimate Products

1 Introduce

Activity Choice 1 • Hands-On

- Remind students that they learned to round numbers in Chapter 1. Write the number 4,857 on the board and tell students to round it to its greatest place.
- **What digit is in its greatest place?** 4
- **How can you use rounding rules to round this number to the nearest thousand?** Sample answer: Look at the digit to the right of the 4. If it is 4 or less, round to 4,000. If it is 5 or greater, round to 5,000. Since the digit to the right of the 4 is an 8, you round the number to 5,000.
- Tell students that in this lesson, they will use rounding to estimate answers.

Activity Choice 2 • Literature

Introduce the lesson with *Betcha!* by Stuart J. Murphy. For a related math activity, see p. TR51.

2 Teach

Scaffolding Questions

Tell students that one way to estimate a product is to round the greater factor to its greatest place. Write 5 × 4,857 on the board.

- **Why do you round 4,857 up to 5,000?** Sample answer: You round up when the digit to the right of the digit to which you are rounding is 5 or greater.
- **What is 5 × 5,000?** 25,000
- **Will your estimated product of 25,000 be greater than or less than the exact answer? Explain.** It will be greater than the exact answer because you rounded up.

GET READY to Learn

Have students open their books and read the information in **Get Ready to Learn**. Introduce **estimate** and **round**. As a class, work through **Examples 1–3**.

6-3 Use Rounding to Estimate Products

MAIN IDEA

I will estimate products by rounding.

New Vocabulary

estimate

Math Online

macmillanmh.com

- Extra Examples
- Personal Tutor
- Self-Check Quiz

GET READY to Learn

The fastest passenger train in the world actually floats above its track. This train in China can travel up to 267 miles per hour. About how far can the train travel in 3 hours?

To **estimate** products, round factors to their greatest place.

Real-World EXAMPLE — Estimate Products

1 TRAVEL About how far can the train travel in 3 hours?

Estimate 3 × 267. Round the larger factor to its greatest place. Then use basic facts and patterns to multiply.

3 × 267
↓

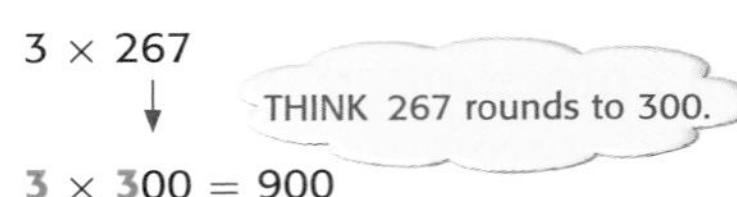

3 × 300 = 900

So, the train can travel about 900 miles in 3 hours. Since 267 was rounded up, the estimated product is greater than the actual product.

EXAMPLE — Estimate Greater Products

2 Estimate 8 × 2,496.

First round, then multiply using basic facts and patterns.

8 × 2,496
↓

8 × 2,000 = 16,000

So, 8 × 2,496 is about 16,000.
Since 2,496 was rounded down, the estimated product is less than the actual product.

242 Chapter 6 Multiply by One-Digit Numbers

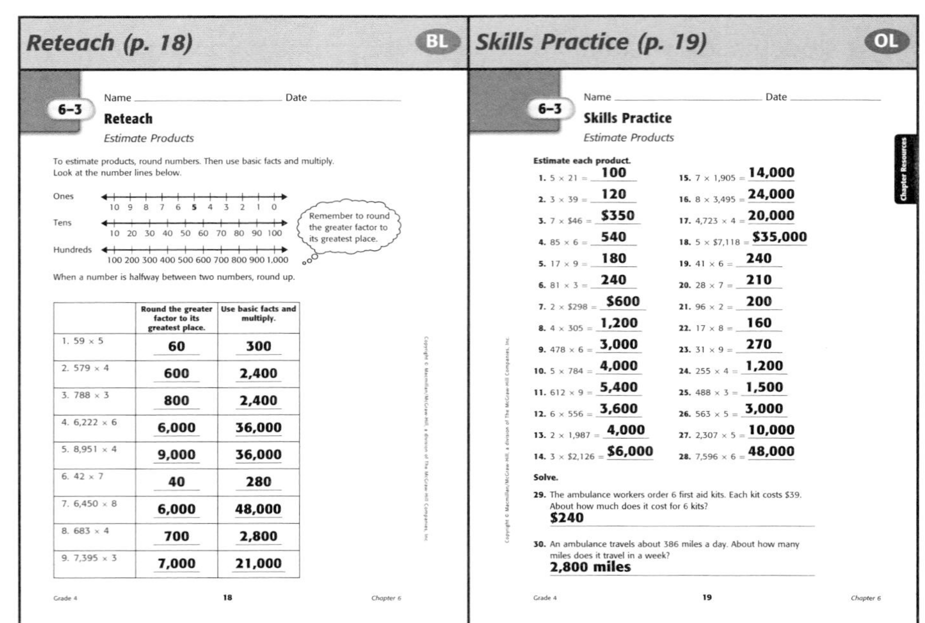

Reteach (p. 18) BL

6–3 Name ______ Date ______

Reteach

Estimate Products

To estimate products, round numbers. Then use basic facts and multiply. Look at the number lines below.

When a number is halfway between two numbers, round up.

	Round the greater factor to its greatest place.	Use basic facts and multiply.
1. 59 × 5	**60**	**300**
2. 579 × 4	**600**	**2,400**
3. 788 × 3	**800**	**2,400**
4. 6,222 × 6	**6,000**	**36,000**
5. 8,951 × 4	**9,000**	**36,000**
6. 42 × 7	**40**	**280**
7. 6,450 × 8	**6,000**	**48,000**
8. 683 × 4	**700**	**2,800**
9. 7,395 × 3	**7,000**	**21,000**

Grade 4 18 Chapter 6

Skills Practice (p. 19) OL

6–3 Name ______ Date ______

Skills Practice

Estimate Products

Chapter Resources

Estimate each product.

1. 5 × 21 = **100**
2. 3 × 39 = **120**
3. 7 × $46 = **$350**
4. 85 × 6 = **540**
5. 17 × 9 = **180**
6. 81 × 3 = **240**
7. 2 × $298 = **$600**
8. 4 × 305 = **1,200**
9. 478 × 6 = **3,000**
10. 5 × 784 = **4,000**
11. 612 × 9 = **5,400**
12. 6 × 556 = **3,600**
13. 2 × 1,987 = **4,000**
14. 3 × $2,126 = **$6,000**
15. 7 × 1,905 = **14,000**
16. 8 × 3,495 = **24,000**
17. 4,723 × 4 = **20,000**
18. 5 × $7,118 = **$35,000**
19. 41 × 6 = **240**
20. 28 × 7 = **210**
21. 96 × 2 = **200**
22. 17 × 8 = **160**
23. 31 × 9 = **270**
24. 255 × 4 = **1,200**
25. 488 × 3 = **1,500**
26. 563 × 5 = **3,000**
27. 2,307 × 5 = **10,000**
28. 7,596 × 6 = **48,000**

Solve.

29. The ambulance workers order 6 first aid kits. Each kit costs $39. About how much does it cost for 6 kits? **$240**

30. An ambulance travels about 386 miles a day. About how many miles does it travel in a week? **2,800 miles**

Grade 4 19 Chapter 6

You can also estimate products involving money.

Remember

- When you round up, the estimated product is greater than the actual product.
- When you round down, the estimated product is less than the actual product.

Real-World EXAMPLE Estimate Money

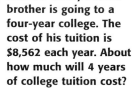

3 **MONEY Lacey's older brother is going to a four-year college. The cost of his tuition is $8,562 each year. About how much will 4 years of college tuition cost?**

You need to estimate $4 \times \$8,562$.

First round, then multiply.

$4 \times \$8,562$

↓

THINK 8,562 rounds to 9,000.

$4 \times \$9,000 = \$36,000$

So, tuition will cost about $36,000.

4. $\$1,000 \times 7 = \$7,000$; less than

5. $6,000 \times 6 = 36,000$; greater than

6. $\$7,000 \times 9 = \$63,000$; less than

CHECK What You Know

Estimate each product. Then tell if the estimate is *greater than* or *less than* the actual product. See Examples 1–3 (pp. 242–243)

3. $3,000 \times 3 = 9,000$; less than

1. 449×5 $400 \times 5 = 2,000$; less than

2. $\$870 \times 9$ $\$900 \times 9 = \$8,100$; greater than

3. $3,293 \times 3$

4. $7 \times \$1,395$

5. $6 \times 5,500$

6. $9 \times \$7,420$

For Exercises 7 and 8, use the data at the right.

7. Mr. and Mrs. Rivera are planning to go on an African safari. They have saved $1,125 a year for 8 years. If the trip costs $9,830, do they have enough money saved for the trip? Explain.

7, 8. See Ch. 6 Answer Appendix.

8. Talk About It Suppose Mr. and Mrs. Rivera saved $1,499 a year for 8 years. Why would an estimated answer be misleading for the amount saved?

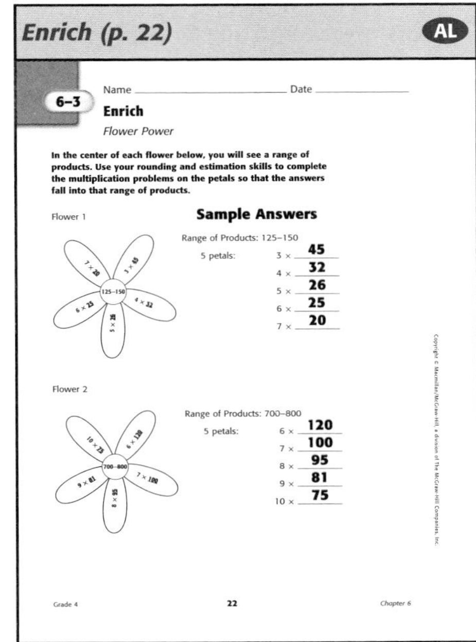

Enrich (p. 22) AL

6–3 Name ______ Date ______

Enrich

Flower Power

In the center of each flower below, you will see a range of products. Use your rounding and estimation skills to complete the multiplication problems on the petals so that the answers fall into that range of products.

Sample Answers

Flower 1

Range of Products: 125–150

5 petals: 3 × **45**, 4 × **32**, 5 × **26**, 6 × **25**, 7 × **20**

Flower 2

Range of Products: 700–800

5 petals: 6 × **120**, 7 × **100**, 8 × **95**, 9 × **81**, 10 × **75**

Grade 4 22 Chapter 6

Estimate Products

Example 1 Be sure that students understand that exact answers are not required. Rounded factors will result in a reasonable, estimated product.

ADDITIONAL EXAMPLES

1 The distance from Sydney, Australia, southwest to Wagga Wagga, Australia, is 470 km. About how many km will be traveled in a round trip? 470 rounds to 500; $500 \times 2 = 1,000$ km

2 Estimate $8 \times 3,252$. $8 \times 3,000 = 24,000$

3 A trip to the Grand Canyon will cost $2,804 per person. About how much will it cost for a group of 5 friends to travel there? 2,804 rounds to 3,000; $3,000 \times 5 = \$15,000$

CHECK What You Know

As a class, have students complete Exercises 1–8 in **Check What You Know** as you observe their work.

Exercise 8 Assess student comprehension before assigning practice exercises.

BL Alternate Teaching Strategy

If students have trouble estimating products…

Then use one of these reteach options:

1 CRM **Daily Reteach Worksheet** (p. 18)

2 First, show them how to use a number line to round the larger factor. For example, if you want to estimate 4×547, draw a number line from 500 to 600 and place a dot at 547.

- **How does a number line help you round 547?** Sample answer: You can see that 547 is closer to 500 than 600.
- **How would you estimate 4×547?** Sample answer: Multiply 4×500.

3 Tech Link Have students use Math Tool Chest to help complete the problem-solving exercises.

3 Practice

Differentiate practice using these leveled assignments for Exercises 9–31.

Level	Assignment
BL Below/Approaching Level	9–10, 13–18, 25, 27–28
OL On Level	9–20, 25, 27–29, 30
AL Above/Beyond Level	10–28 even, 30–31

Have students discuss and complete the Higher Order Thinking problems. Remind them to look at the factors for both the estimated and exact products when they are asked to compare estimated and exact answers.

WRITING IN MATH Have students complete Exercise 31 in their Math Journals. You may choose to use this exercise as an optional formative assessment.

Assess

Formative Assessment

- **Why do you round the greater factor when estimating a product?** Sample answer: You can use patterns to find the product mentally.

Quick Check **Are students continuing to struggle with estimating products?**

If Yes → Small Group Options (p. 42B)
Strategic Intervention Guide (p. 16)

If No → Independent Work Options (p. 42B)
CRM Skills Practice Worksheet (p. 19)
CRM Enrich Worksheet (p. 22)

Into the Future Tell students that the next lesson involves multiplying two-digit numbers by a one-digit number. Ask them to write how the skills practiced today will be useful tomorrow.

! COMMON ERROR!

Exercises 9–24 Students may attempt to use multiplication facts to find the exact products. Remind them to round the greatest factor to the greatest value and then to estimate the product using multiplication facts.

Practice and Problem Solving

See page R16.

Estimate each product. Then tell if the estimate is *greater than* or *less than* the actual product. See Examples 1–3 (pp. 242–243) 9–24. See Ch. 6 Answer Appendix.

9. 562×6 **10.** 896×2 **11.** 729×8 **12.** 949×4

13. 2 × $438 **14.** 8 × $647 **15.** 5 × $355 **16.** 7 × $450

17. 7 × 1,125 **18.** 3 × 5,489 **19.** 9 × 3,500 **20.** 6 × 8,816

21. 4 × $6,502 **22.** 7 × $8,856 **23.** 9 × $9,498 **24.** 7 × $9,310

25. There are 24 students in each class at Watson Elementary School. About how many students are there if there are 8 classes? 20 × 8 = 160 students

26. The round-trip distance from Woodward to Oklahoma City is 139 miles. Ms. Hodges travels this distance 6 days a week. About how many miles does she travel each week? 600 miles

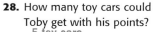

Real-World PROBLEM SOLVING

Entertainment Toby and Lena like to go to the arcade. They earn points toward prizes.

27. Toby went to the arcade 2 times. He earned 5,150 points each time. What is the biggest prize Toby can get? small stuffed animal

28. How many toy cars could Toby get with his points? 5 toy cars

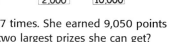

29. Lena went to the arcade 7 times. She earned 9,050 points each time. What are the two largest prizes she can get? large and small stuffed animal

H.O.T. Problems

30. **NUMBER SENSE** Explain how you can tell if your estimated answer is more or less than the exact answer to a multiplication problem.

30, 31. See Ch. 6 Answer Appendix.

31. **WRITING IN MATH** Suppose you need to find the exact answer to 4 × $189. How can you use estimation to check the reasonableness of your answer?

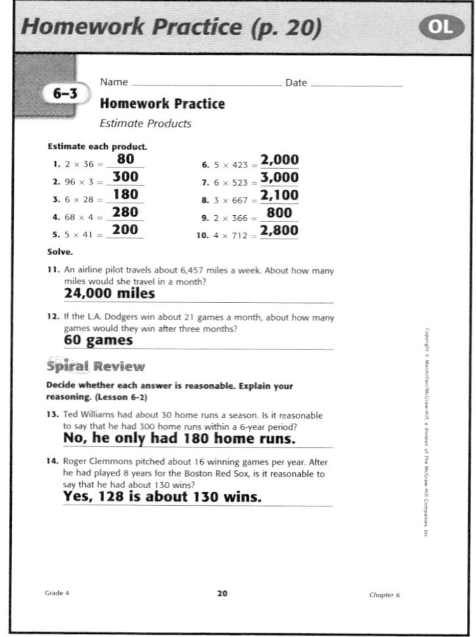

Homework Practice (p. 20) OL

6–3 Name ____________ Date ____________

Homework Practice

Estimate Products

Estimate each product.

1. 2 × 36 = **80**
2. 96 × 3 = **300**
3. 6 × 28 = **180**
4. 68 × 4 = **280**
5. 5 × 41 = **200**
6. 5 × 423 = **2,000**
7. 6 × 523 = **3,000**
8. 3 × 667 = **2,100**
9. 2 × 366 = **800**
10. 4 × 712 = **2,800**

Solve.

11. An airline pilot travels about 6,457 miles a week. About how many miles would she travel in a month? **24,000 miles**

12. If the L.A. Dodgers win about 21 games a month, about how many games would they win after three months? **60 games**

Spiral Review

Decide whether each answer is reasonable. Explain your reasoning. (Lesson 6-2)

13. Ted Williams had about 30 home runs a season. Is it reasonable to say that he had 300 home runs within a 6-year period? **No, he only had 180 home runs.**

14. Roger Clemmons pitched about 16 winning games per year. After he had played 8 years for the Boston Red Sox, is it reasonable to say that he had about 130 wins? **Yes, 128 is about 130 wins.**

Grade 4 20 Chapter 6

Estimation Station

Math Concept: Estimate Products

Materials: spinner, 1 number cube, 2 whiteboards

Introduce the game on p. 245 to your students to play as a class, in small groups, or at a learning workstation to review concepts introduced in this chapter.

Instructions

- Students create a game board on the whiteboard, as shown on p. 245.
- Students spin the spinner to see who will go first. The greatest number goes first.
- Player 1 rolls the number cube to find a one-digit factor, and records it on the whiteboard. Then Player 1 spins to find how many digits will be in the larger factor. Player 1 rolls the number cube to determine each digit in the second factor, recording the digits on the whiteboard.
- Player 1 estimates the product of the two factors and gets 1 point if the estimate is correct.
- Player 2 takes a turn, following the same procedure. Play continues until one player reaches 10 points. The first player to do so wins.

Extend the Game

Have students roll and spin to select numbers for each other instead of for themselves.

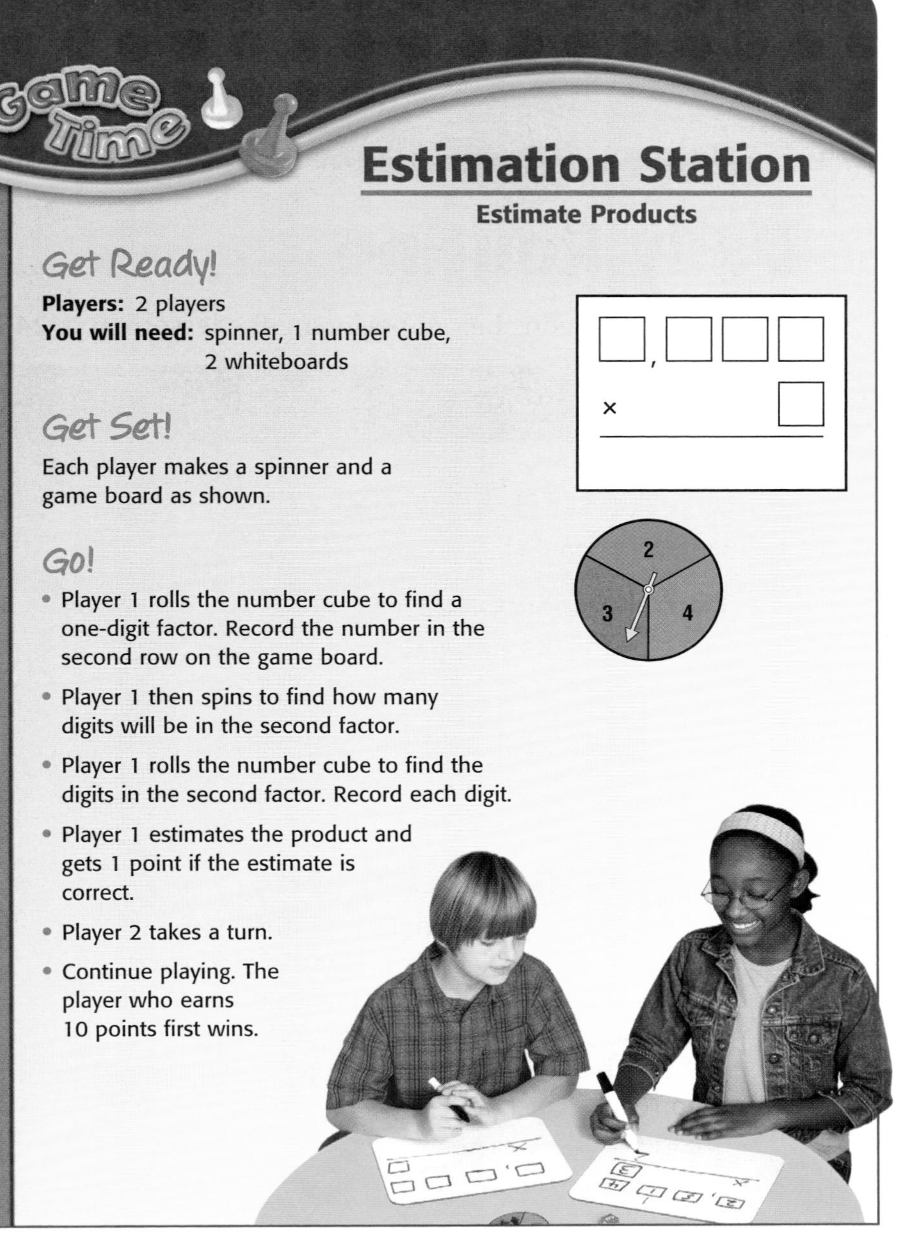
Game Time

Estimation Station

Estimate Products

Get Ready!

Players: 2 players

You will need: spinner, 1 number cube, 2 whiteboards

Get Set!

Each player makes a spinner and a game board as shown.

Go!

- Player 1 rolls the number cube to find a one-digit factor. Record the number in the second row on the game board.
- Player 1 then spins to find how many digits will be in the second factor.
- Player 1 rolls the number cube to find the digits in the second factor. Record each digit.
- Player 1 estimates the product and gets 1 point if the estimate is correct.
- Player 2 takes a turn.
- Continue playing. The player who earns 10 points first wins.

Game Time Estimation Station **245**

Differentiated Practice

Use these leveled suggestions to differentiate the game for all learners.

Level	Assignment
BL Below/Approaching Level	Students use base-ten blocks to model products of the rounded factors used in their estimation.
OL On Level	Have students play the game with the rules as written.
AL Above/Beyond Level	Students make a spinner with four equal sections, labeling the sections 2, 3, 4, and 5.

Multiply Two-Digit Numbers

Lesson Planner

Objective

Multiply a two-digit number by a one-digit number.

Review Vocabulary

factor, **product**, **regroup**

Resources

Materials: rectangle cut-outs, grid paper

Manipulatives: base-ten blocks

Literature Connection: *The 12 Circus Rings* by Seymour Chwast

Teacher Technology
TeacherWorks • Interactive Classroom • Concepts in Motion • Math Songs Track #6 Lesson Plan

Daily Routine

Use these suggestions before beginning the lesson on p. 246.

5-Minute Check

(Reviews Lesson 6-3)

Estimate products.

1. 3 × 439 439 rounds to 400 × 3 = 1,200
2. 6 × 912 912 rounds to 900 × 6 = 5,400
3. 7 × 291 291 rounds to 300 × 7 = 2,100
4. 4 × 68 68 rounds to 70 × 4 = 280

Problem of the Day

An author was signing books at a store. She promised not to stop until she had signed each book sold. If she signed 135 books an hour, is it reasonable to expect that she signed all of the 1,000 books sold that day in a 6-hour signing session? No, 125 rounds down to 100 × 6 hours, or about 600 books signed.

Focus on Math Background

Students know how to multiply two numbers if both factors are one-digit numbers. They also know how to multiply by multiples of the powers of ten (multiples of 10, 100, and 1,000). Putting those two ideas together, along with visual presentations using base-ten blocks, allows students to begin to multiply one-digit times two-digit numbers. After students have worked with pictorial models, but before they move to the standard algorithm for multiplying, it is helpful to show them how to multiply using expanded notation or partial products. For example,

$$\begin{array}{r} 43 \\ \times\ 2 \\ \hline \end{array} \Big\} \rightarrow \begin{array}{r} 40 + 3 \\ \times \quad 2 \\ \hline 80 + 6 = 86 \end{array}$$

Expanded notation

$$\begin{array}{r} 43 \\ \times\ 2 \\ \hline \end{array} \Big\} \rightarrow \begin{array}{r} 43 \\ \times\ 2 \\ \hline 6 \\ 80 \\ \hline \end{array} \Big\} \rightarrow \begin{array}{r} 43 \\ \times\ 2 \\ \hline 6 \\ 80 \\ \hline 86 \end{array}$$

Partial products

Review Math Vocabulary

Write the review vocabulary words and their definitions on the board.

Review **factor, product,** and **regroup** by having students silently write definitions for the terms. Share definitions only to see if others in the group can guess the term being defined.

Visual Vocabulary Cards

Use Visual Vocabulary Card 18 to reinforce the vocabulary reviewed in this lesson. The Define/Example/Ask routine is printed on the back of each card.

factor

Differentiated Instruction

Small Group Options

LOGICAL

Option 1 Gifted and Talented AL

Materials: pencils, paper, chart paper

- Review the concept of expanded form with a two-digit and a three-digit number. Tell students that they can use this concept to multiply a two-digit number.
- Write 3 × 56 on the chart paper.
- Introduce the concept of the Distributive Property by saying that this property uses expanded form.
- Write 3 × (50 + 6).
- Now tell students that this expression can be rewritten according to the Distributive Property.
- Write (3 × 50) + (3 × 6). Ask students to solve.

3×56
$3 \times (50 + 6)$
$(3 \times 50) + (3 \times 6)$
$150 + 18 = 168$

KINESTHETIC, AUDITORY, SOCIAL

Option 2 English Language Learners ELL

Core Vocabulary: write what you hear, chunks, pieces
Common Use Verb: dictate

Hear Math This strategy allows students to practice responding to dictated numbers and introduces grouping as a comprehension strategy.

- Have a student write a two-digit number on the board and read it. If the student has correctly read the number, other students should put thumbs up to agree. If they put thumbs down, the student has to restate the number correctly.
- Repeat building a two-digit multiplication problem. Continue to have students vocalize the steps as they solve it, with remaining students checking for auditory correctness.
- Repeat with other problems.

Use this worksheet to provide additional support for English Language Learners.

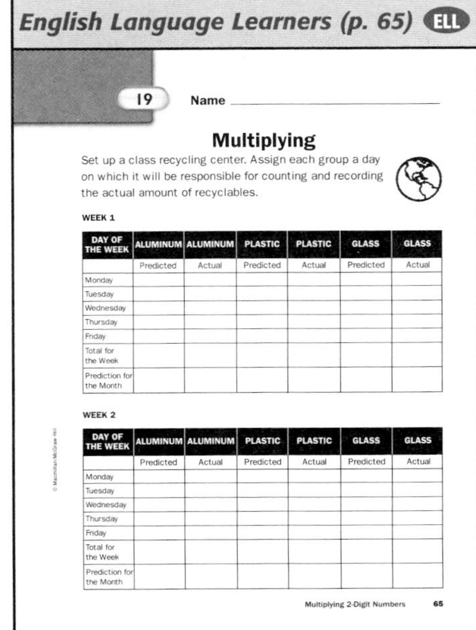

English Language Learners (p. 65) ELL

19 Name ____________

Multiplying

Set up a class recycling center. Assign each group a day on which it will be responsible for counting and recording the actual amount of recyclables.

WEEK 1

DAY OF THE WEEK	ALUMINUM	ALUMINUM	PLASTIC	PLASTIC	GLASS	GLASS
	Predicted	Actual	Predicted	Actual	Predicted	Actual
Monday						
Tuesday						
Wednesday						
Thursday						
Friday						
Total for the Week						
Prediction for the Month						

WEEK 2

DAY OF THE WEEK	ALUMINUM	ALUMINUM	PLASTIC	PLASTIC	GLASS	GLASS
	Predicted	Actual	Predicted	Actual	Predicted	Actual
Monday						
Tuesday						
Wednesday						
Thursday						
Friday						
Total for the Week						
Prediction for the Month						

Multiplying 2-Digit Numbers 65

Independent Work Options

LOGICAL, SOCIAL

Option 1 Early Finishers AL

Materials: two number cubes, spinner labeled 1–6

- Have students roll the cubes to build a two-digit factor. Then have them spin to find a one-digit factor.
- Multiply using any method. Have students pair up and check one another's work.

Option 2 Student Technology

Math Online macmillanmh.com

Personal Tutor • Extra Examples

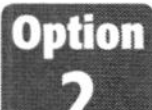 Math Adventures

 Math Songs, "Bring it On!" Track #6

Option 3 Learning Station: Science (p. 260H)

Direct students to the Science Learning Station for opportunities to explore and extend the lesson concept.

Option 4 Problem-Solving Practice

Reinforce problem-solving skills and strategies with the Problem-Solving Practice worksheet.

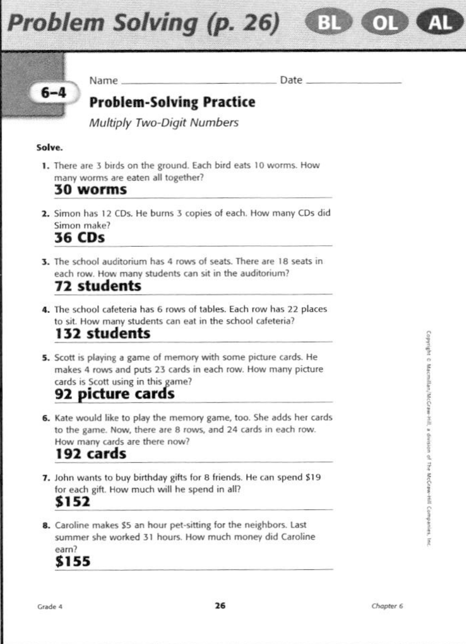

Problem Solving (p. 26) BL OL AL

6–4 Name ____________ Date ____________

Problem-Solving Practice

Multiply Two-Digit Numbers

Solve.

1. There are 3 birds on the ground. Each bird eats 10 worms. How many worms are eaten all together?
   30 worms
2. Simon has 12 CDs. He burns 3 copies of each. How many CDs did Simon make?
   36 CDs
3. The school auditorium has 4 rows of seats. There are 18 seats in each row. How many students can sit in the auditorium?
   72 students
4. The school cafeteria has 6 rows of tables. Each row has 22 places to sit. How many students can eat in the school cafeteria?
   132 students
5. Scott is playing a game of memory with some picture cards. He makes 4 rows and puts 23 cards in each row. How many picture cards is Scott using in this game?
   92 picture cards
6. Kate would like to play the memory game, too. She adds her cards to the game. Now, there are 8 rows, and 24 cards in each row. How many cards are there now?
   192 cards
7. John wants to buy birthday gifts for 8 friends. He can spend $19 for each gift. How much will he spend in all?
   $152
8. Caroline makes $5 an hour pet-sitting for the neighbors. Last summer she worked 31 hours. How much money did Caroline earn?
   $155

Grade 4 26 Chapter 6

6-4 Multiply Two-Digit Numbers

1 Introduce

Activity Choice 1 • Hands-On

Cut out two rectangles and label them to show 3 × 20 and 3 × 4. It is important that the rectangles are the same height, and the lengths proportional to the second factor.

- Have a volunteer tape the 3 × 20 rectangle on the chalkboard. **What is the product?** 60
- Then ask for a student to tape the 3 × 4 rectangle next to the first rectangle. **What is the product?** 12
- **What is the sum of the products of the rectangles?** 60 + 12 = 72

Activity Choice 2 • Literature

Introduce the lesson with *The 12 Circus Rings* by Seymour Chwast. For a related math activity, see p. TR51.

2 Teach

Scaffolding Questions

Write the following problem on the board:

$$\begin{array}{r} 24 \\ \times\ 3 \\ \hline \end{array}$$

- **How many ones are in 24?** 4
- Multiply the ones by 3. **What is the product?** 12
- Multiply the tens by 3. **What is the product?** 60
- Add the two products together. **What is the sum?** 72
- Tell students to look at the rectangles on the board. **What do you notice?** Sample answer. The rectangles show the product of 3 × 24.

GET READY to Learn

Hands-On Mini-Activity Distribute base-ten blocks for the Hands-On Mini-Activity. In Step 2, make sure students understand that they can regroup 12 ones by trading them for 1 ten and 2 ones.

6-4 Multiply Two-Digit Numbers

MAIN IDEA

I will multiply a two-digit number by a one-digit number.

Math Online

macmillanmh.com

- Extra Examples
- Personal Tutor
- Self-Check Quiz
- Concepts in Motion

GET READY to Learn

Hands-On Mini Activity

Materials: base-ten blocks

Base-ten blocks can be used to explore multiplying two-digit numbers. In this activity, you will find 4 × 13.

Step 1 Model 4 groups of 13.

Step 2 Combine the tens and ones. Regroup 12 ones as 1 ten and 2 ones.

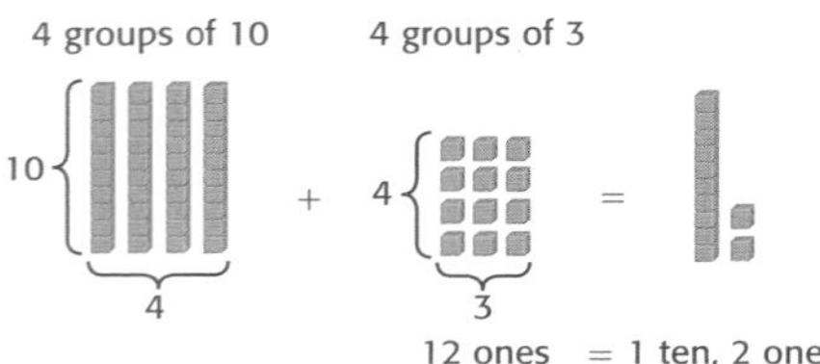

Step 3 Add the partial products.

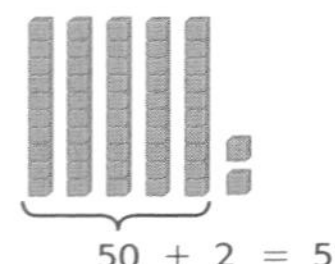

So, 4 × 13 = 52.

Find each product. Use base-ten blocks.

1. 3 × 18 54 **2.** 4 × 19 76 **3.** 3 × 21 63

4. Multiplication can be a shortcut for which operation? addition

5. When is it necessary to regroup in a multiplication problem? When is regrouping not needed?

5. See Ch. 6 Answer Appendix.

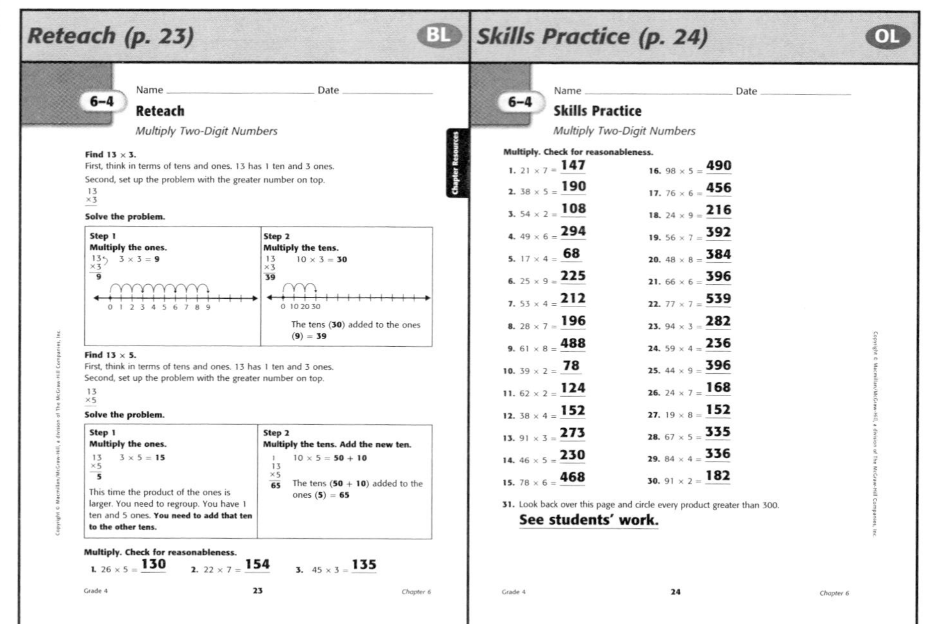

Reteach (p. 23) BL

6-4 Name ______ Date ______

Reteach

Multiply Two-Digit Numbers

Find 13 × 3.

First, think in terms of tens and ones. 13 has 1 ten and 3 ones.

Second, set up the problem with the greater number on top.

$$\begin{array}{r} 13 \\ \times 3 \\ \hline \end{array}$$

Solve the problem.

Step 1 **Multiply the ones.**	**Step 2** **Multiply the tens.**
13 × 3 = 9; 3 × 3 = **9** (0 1 2 3 4 5 6 7 8 9)	13 × 3 = 39; 10 × 3 = **30** (0 10 20 30) The tens (**30**) added to the ones (**9**) = **39**

Find 13 × 5.

First, think in terms of tens and ones. 13 has 1 ten and 3 ones.

Second, set up the problem with the greater number on top.

$$\begin{array}{r} 13 \\ \times 5 \\ \hline \end{array}$$

Solve the problem.

Step 1 **Multiply the ones.**	**Step 2** **Multiply the tens. Add the new ten.**
13 × 5 = 5; 3 × 5 = **15** This time the product of the ones is larger. You need to regroup. You have 1 ten and 5 ones. **You need to add that ten to the other tens.**	13 × 5 = 65; 10 × 5 = **50 + 10** The tens (**50 + 10**) added to the ones (**5**) = **65**

Multiply. Check for reasonableness.

1. 26 × 5 = **130** 2. 22 × 7 = **154** 3. 45 × 3 = **135**

Grade 4 23 Chapter 6

Chapter Resources

Skills Practice (p. 24) OL

6-4 Name ______ Date ______

Skills Practice

Multiply Two-Digit Numbers

Multiply. Check for reasonableness.

1. 21 × 7 = **147**
2. 38 × 5 = **190**
3. 54 × 2 = **108**
4. 49 × 6 = **294**
5. 17 × 4 = **68**
6. 25 × 9 = **225**
7. 53 × 4 = **212**
8. 28 × 7 = **196**
9. 61 × 8 = **488**
10. 39 × 2 = **78**
11. 62 × 2 = **124**
12. 38 × 4 = **152**
13. 91 × 3 = **273**
14. 46 × 5 = **230**
15. 78 × 6 = **468**
16. 98 × 5 = **490**
17. 76 × 6 = **456**
18. 24 × 9 = **216**
19. 56 × 7 = **392**
20. 48 × 8 = **384**
21. 66 × 6 = **396**
22. 77 × 7 = **539**
23. 94 × 3 = **282**
24. 59 × 4 = **236**
25. 44 × 9 = **396**
26. 24 × 7 = **168**
27. 19 × 8 = **152**
28. 67 × 5 = **335**
29. 84 × 4 = **336**
30. 91 × 2 = **182**
31. Look back over this page and circle every product greater than 300. **See students' work.**

Grade 4 24 Chapter 6

Using place-value models is not the only way to multiply a two-digit number by a one-digit number.

Remember

To review the Distributive Property of Multiplication, see Lesson 4-6 (p. 166).

EXAMPLE Multiply with Regrouping

1 **Find 6 × 38.** **Estimate** $6 \times 38 \longrightarrow 6 \times 40 = 240$

One Way: Distributive Property

$$6 \times 38 = (6 \times 30) + (6 \times 8)$$
$$= 180 + 48$$
$$= 228$$

Another Way: Partial Products

```
   38
 ×  6
   48   Multiply 6 × 8.
+ 180   Multiply 6 × 30.
  228   Add the partial products.
```

	30	8
6	180	48

180 + 48 = 228

Another Way: Paper and Pencil

Step 1 Multiply the ones.

```
  4
  38   6 × 8 = 48
×  6   Regroup 48 ones
   8   as 4 tens and
       8 ones.
```

Step 2 Multiply the tens.

```
  4
  38   6 × 3 = 18
×  6   Add the
 228   regrouped
       tens, 4.
```

Check for Reasonableness

The product, 228, is close to the estimate, 240. ✓

5. Sample answer: Multiply the ones first, 6 × 7 = 42, regroup. Multiply the tens next. 6 × 30 = 180. The product is 42 + 180, or 222.

★ indicates multi-step problem

CHECK What You Know

Multiply. Check for reasonableness. See Example 1 (p. 247)

1. 23 × 2 46; 2 × 20 = 40

2. 42 × 2 84; 2 × 40 = 80

3. 8 × $98 $784; 8 × $100 = $800

4. Haley can fit 25 books on each of 5 shelves. How many books will fit in all? 125 books

5. Talk About It Explain how to find 6 × 37.

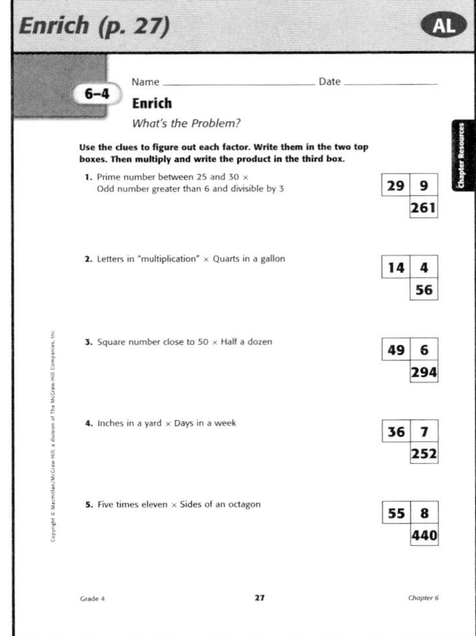

Enrich (p. 27) AL

6–4 Name ________ Date ________

Enrich

What's the Problem?

Use the clues to figure out each factor. Write them in the two top boxes. Then multiply and write the product in the third box.

1. Prime number between 25 and 30 × Odd number greater than 6 and divisible by 3 — 29, 9, 261
2. Letters in "multiplication" × Quarts in a gallon — 14, 4, 56
3. Square number close to 50 × Half a dozen — 49, 6, 294
4. Inches in a yard × Days in a week — 36, 7, 252
5. Five times eleven × Sides of an octagon — 55, 8, 440

Chapter Resources

Grade 4 27 Chapter 6

Multiply with Regrouping

Example 1 Students may need to write problems on grid paper to emphasize the place value of the factors being multiplied. Use the partial product method to reinforce place value.

ADDITIONAL EXAMPLES

1 Find 3 × 56. 168

2 Jeremiah and four friends each have 15 pencils. How many pencils are there in all? 75 pencils

CHECK What You Know

As a class, have students complete Exercises 1–5 in **Check What You Know** as you observe their work.

Exercise 5 Assess student comprehension before assigning practice exercises.

BL Alternate Teaching Strategy

If students have trouble multiplying a two-digit numbers by a one digit number…

Then use one of these reteach options:

1 CRM **Daily Reteach Worksheet** (p. 23)

2 Have students use base-ten blocks to model the problem.

- Students should build equal groups of the two-digit number to match the problem. For example, to model 3 × 72, have students show 3 groups of 7 tens and 2 ones.
- Once the model is complete, have students count the ones and regroup if necessary.
- Then have students count the tens and regroup 10 tens for a hundred if necessary. Once the regrouping is complete, have them use their model to identify the product.

COMMON ERROR!

Students often forget to regroup. Remind them of the importance of regrouping and point out that an easy way to remember to regroup is to write the place-value digit of the regrouped number over the corresponding place value in the factor.

3 Practice

Differentiate practice using these leveled assignments for Exercises 6–25.

Level	Assignment
BL Below/Approaching Level	6–7, 10–13, 18, 20–22
OL On Level	7–16, 18–22, 24
AL Above/Beyond Level	7–21 odd, 23–25

Have students discuss and complete the Higher Order Thinking problems. For Exercise 24, encourage students to work each multiplication problem and examine the products.

WRITING IN MATH Have students complete Exercise 25 in their Math Journals. You may choose to use this exercise as an optional formative assessment.

4 Assess

Formative Assessment

Draw a place-value chart on the board.

- **How does knowing place value help you find the product when multiplying two-digit numbers?** Place value helps you know if you are multiplying ones or tens. The same digit will have a different value depending upon which place it is in the product.

Quick Check **Are students continuing to struggle with two-digit multiplication?**

If Yes → CRM Reteach Worksheet (p. 23)

If No → Independent Work Options (p. 246B)
CRM Skills Practice Worksheet (p. 24)
CRM Enrich Worksheet (p. 27)

Yesterday's News Have students write a brief explanation of how the last lesson on estimating products helped with today's two-digit multiplication. Tell them to include an example.

Practice and Problem Solving

See page R16.

Multiply. Check for reasonableness. See Example 1 (p. 247)

6. 33×2 66; $2 \times 30 = 60$
7. $\$24 \times 2$ \$48; $2 \times 20 = 40$
8. 11×7 77; $7 \times 10 = 70$
9. 13×3 39; $3 \times 10 = 30$
10. $2 \times \$27$ \$54; $20 \times \$30 = \$60$
11. 4×29 116; $4 \times 30 = 120$
12. 5×18 90; $5 \times 20 = 100$
13. $7 \times \$36$ \$252; $7 \times \$40 = \$280$
14. 6×52 312; $6 \times 50 = 300$
15. 8×75 600; $8 \times 80 = 640$
16. $4 \times \$83$ \$332; $4 \times \$80 = \$320$
17. 9×99 891; $9 \times 90 = 900$
18. Will makes \$4 an hour shampooing dogs at a pet shop. Last month he worked 26 hours. How much money did Will earn? \$104
19. Suppose the sales tax is 7 cents for each dollar that is spent on any item. How much sales tax is charged for a badminton set that costs \$35? 245 cents or \$2.45

Data File

Crystal Cave Park is located in Kutztown, Pennsylvania.

20. ★ The Diaz family has 2 adults and 3 children. How much would it cost for the family to go on a walking tour? \$81
21. Can the Diaz family pan for gemstones for \$75? Explain.
22. ★ Find the total cost for the Diaz family to take the walking tour and pan for gemstones. \$141

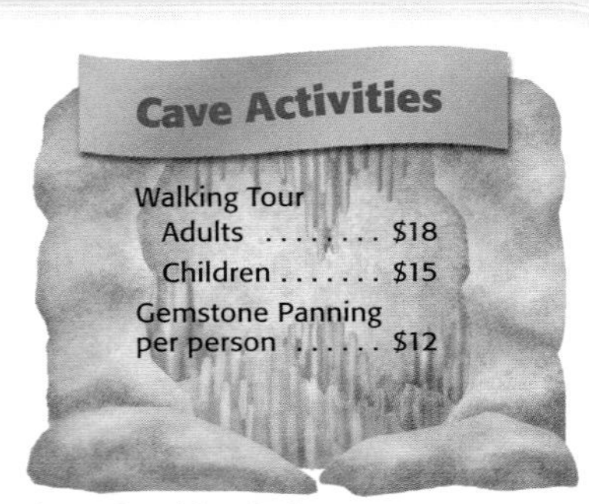

Source: Crystal Cave Co., Inc.

21. Sample answer: yes; For 5 people gemstone panning would cost $5 \times \$12$ or \$60.

H.O.T. Problems

23. **OPEN ENDED** Write two problems that result in a product of 120. Sample answer: 3×40 and 6×20
24. **WHICH ONE DOESN'T BELONG?** Which multiplication problem does not belong with the other three? Explain.

12×8 | 22×4 | 52×2 | 33×3

25. **WRITING IN MATH** How do you use partial products to find 6×42? 24, 25. See Ch. 6 Answer Appendix.

248 **Chapter 6** Multiply by One-Digit Numbers

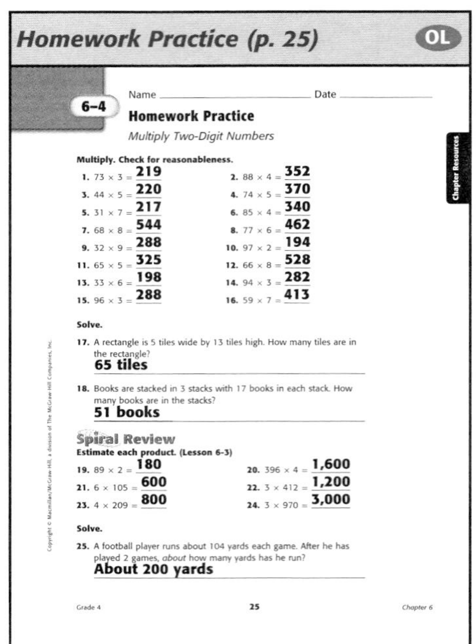

Homework Practice (p. 25) OL

Name ________ Date ________

6–4 **Homework Practice**
Multiply Two-Digit Numbers

Multiply. Check for reasonableness.

1. $73 \times 3 =$ **219**
2. $88 \times 4 =$ **352**
3. $44 \times 5 =$ **220**
4. $74 \times 5 =$ **370**
5. $31 \times 7 =$ **217**
6. $85 \times 4 =$ **340**
7. $68 \times 8 =$ **544**
8. $77 \times 6 =$ **462**
9. $32 \times 9 =$ **288**
10. $97 \times 2 =$ **194**
11. $65 \times 5 =$ **325**
12. $66 \times 8 =$ **528**
13. $33 \times 6 =$ **198**
14. $94 \times 3 =$ **282**
15. $96 \times 3 =$ **288**
16. $59 \times 7 =$ **413**

Solve.

17. A rectangle is 5 tiles wide by 13 tiles high. How many tiles are in the rectangle? **65 tiles**
18. Books are stacked in 3 stacks with 17 books in each stack. How many books are in the stacks? **51 books**

Spiral Review

Estimate each product. (Lesson 6-3)

19. $89 \times 2 =$ **180**
20. $396 \times 4 =$ **1,600**
21. $6 \times 105 =$ **600**
22. $3 \times 412 =$ **1,200**
23. $4 \times 209 =$ **800**
24. $3 \times 970 =$ **3,000**

Solve.

25. A football player runs about 104 yards each game. After he has played 2 games, *about* how many yards has he run? **About 200 yards**

Chapter Resources

Grade 4 25 Chapter 6

Mid-Chapter Check

Chapter 6

Lessons 6-1 through 6-4

Multiply. Use basic facts and patterns. (Lesson 6-1) 1. 12; 120; 1,200; 12,000

1. 3×4
3×40
3×400
$3 \times 4{,}000$

2. 12×5
12×50
12×500
$12 \times 5{,}000$

2. 60; 600; 6,000; 60,000

3. A Triceratops weighs $2 \times 7{,}000$ pounds. How much does a Triceratops weigh? 14,000 lb

4. Kyra needs 292 toothpicks for a project. A box holds 150 toothpicks. Is it reasonable to buy 2 boxes? Explain. (Lesson 6-2) 4, 5. See margin.

5. Mara and Billy have 6 bags of 12 balloons. Is it reasonable to say they have more than 75 balloons? (Lesson 6-2)

Estimate each product. (Lesson 6-3)

6. 3×252 900

7. $5 \times 7{,}493$ 35,000

8. MULTIPLE CHOICE Jada pays $1,875 a year in car payments. About how much money will she pay in 5 years? (Lesson 6-3) D

A $5,000 **C** $9,375

B $7,500 **D** $10,000

9. Juan plans to read 264 pages a month to complete his book in 6 months. About how many pages are in his book? (Lesson 6-3) 1,800 pages

10. Measurement Each gallon of paint covers about 350 square feet. Ann estimated that 3 gallons of paint would be enough to cover 1,400 square feet. Will Ann have enough paint? Explain. (Lesson 6-3) no; She underestimated. She needs another gallon.

Multiply. Check for reasonableness. (Lesson 6-4)

11. 43×2 86

12. $\$51 \times 3$ $153

13. 9×62 558

14. 8×47 376

15. MULTIPLE CHOICE There are 27 boxes of markers in the art room. If each box holds 8 markers, how many markers are in the art room? (Lesson 6-4) H

F 106 **H** 216

G 166 **J** 226

16. WRITING IN MATH Cassie got the following problem wrong on her math test. Explain what she did wrong. (Lesson 6-4) See margin.

$$\begin{array}{r} {}^{5} \\ 47 \\ \times\ 8 \\ \hline 326 \end{array}$$

Chapter 6 Mid-Chapter Check

Lessons 6-1 through 6-4

Formative Assessment

Use the Mid-Chapter Check to assess students' progress in the first half of the chapter.

Customize and create multiple versions of your Mid-Chapter Check and the test answer keys.

FOLDABLES Dinah Zike's Foldables

Use these lesson suggestions to incorporate the Foldable during the chapter.

Lesson 6-2 Under the top left flap of the Foldable, students provide examples of estimating products by rounding factors.

Lesson 6-4 Under the top right flap of the Foldable, students demonstrate their ability to multiply a two-digit number by a one-digit number with regrouping.

Additional Answers

4. Sample answer: yes; Two boxes of toothpicks contains 150×2 or 300 toothpicks. $300 > 292$ so, it is reasonable to buy 2 boxes.
5. Sample answer: no, Six bags of 12 balloons is 72, which is less than 75.
16. Sample answer: She did not add the 5 into the product of the 10 place.

Data-Driven Decision Making

Based on the results of the Mid-Chapter Check, use the following resources to review concepts that continue to present students with problems.

Exercises	State/Local Standard	What's the Mathematics?	Error Analysis	Resources for Review
1–2 Lesson 6-1		Multiply multiples of 10, 100, and 1,000 using basic facts and patterns.	Does not know basic facts. Does not understand or use the pattern.	Strategic Intervention Guide (pp. 70, 72, 80) CRM Chapter 6 Resource Masters (Reteach) Math Adventures My Math Zone Chapter 6 Math Online Extra Examples • Concepts in Motion
5–13 Lesson 6-3		Estimate by rounding. Evaluate the reasonableness of a solution in the context of a situation.	Does not understand term "reasonable." Cannot apply estimation to real-world situation. Gives exact answers.	
14–16 Lesson 6-4		Multiply a two-digit number by a one-digit number.	Does not know multiplication facts. Adds two numbers instead of multiplying them. Did not add tens after multiplying by ones.	

6-5 Problem-Solving Investigation
Choose a Strategy

Lesson Planner

Objective

Choose the best strategy to solve a problem.

Resources

Teacher Technology

TeacherWorks • Interactive Classroom

Real-World Problem Solving Library
Math and Social Studies: *Expanding the United States*
Use these leveled books to reinforce and extend problem-solving skills and strategies.

Leveled for:

- OL On Level
- ELL Sheltered English
- SP Spanish

For additional support, see the Real-World Problem Solving Teacher Guide.

Daily Routine

Use these suggestions before beginning the lesson on p. 250.

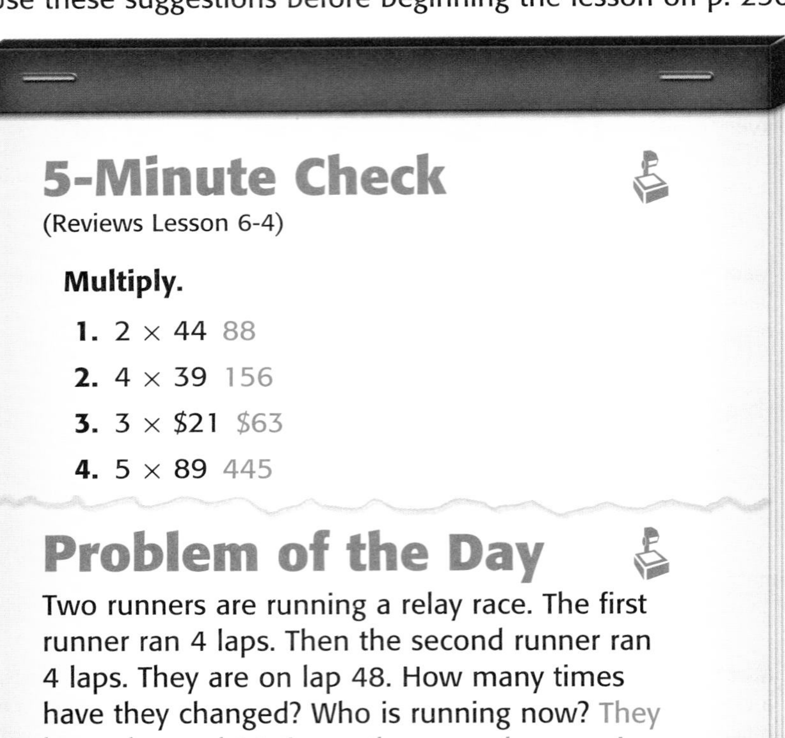

5-Minute Check

(Reviews Lesson 6-4)

Multiply.

1. 2 × 44 88

2. 4 × 39 156

3. 3 × $21 $63

4. 5 × 89 445

Problem of the Day

Two runners are running a relay race. The first runner ran 4 laps. Then the second runner ran 4 laps. They are on lap 48. How many times have they changed? Who is running now? They have changed 11 times; the second runner is running now.

Differentiated Instruction

Small Group Options

LOGICAL 

Option 1 Gifted and Talented AL

Materials: paper, pencils, chart paper, markers

- Write the following problem on chart paper: *Carlos has a rectangular garden that has an area of 50 square feet. One side measures 5 feet long. If he adds a border of one foot around the garden, what will the area of the garden be then?*
- **What is the best strategy to use for this problem?** Accept any reasonable answer, but encourage the students to use a drawing to solve it.
- **What is the measurement of the other side?** 10 feet, Check the students' drawings. The answer is 84 square feet.

LINGUISTIC 

Option 2 English Language Learners ELL

Materials: paper and pencil
Core Vocabulary: after, before, next
Common Use Verb: use

Write Math This strategy allows students to choose strategies to solve a real-world problem mathematically.

- Ask students to make a list of their normal daily activities and assign the times for each activity.
- Have students label the amount of time each activity takes.
- Using this information, ask students to write a mathematical problem.
- Have students share their problem with a classmate to solve.
- Allow students to present their solution. With the class, discuss and evaluate the strategies chosen.

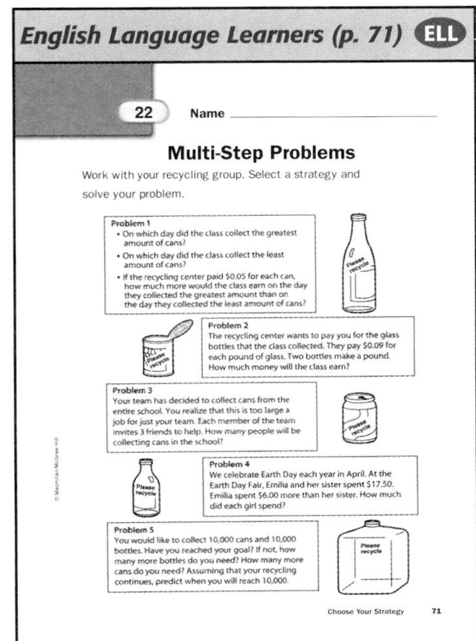

English Language Learners (p. 71) ELL

22 Name ____________

Multi-Step Problems

Work with your recycling group. Select a strategy and solve your problem.

Problem 1
- On which day did the class collect the greatest amount of cans?
- On which day did the class collect the least amount of cans?
- If the recycling center paid $0.05 for each can, how much more would the class earn on the day they collected the greatest amount than on the day they collected the least amount of cans?

Problem 2
The recycling center wants to pay you for the glass bottles that the class collected. They pay $0.09 for each pound of glass. Two bottles make a pound. How much money will the class earn?

Problem 3
Your team has decided to collect cans from the entire school. You realize that this is too large a job for just your team. Each member of the team invites 3 friends to help. How many people will be collecting cans in the school?

Problem 4
We celebrate Earth Day each year in April. At the Earth Day Fair, Emilia and her sister spent $17.50. Emilia spent $6.00 more than her sister. How much did each girl spend?

Problem 5
You would like to collect 10,000 cans and 10,000 bottles. Have you reached your goal? If not, how many more bottles do you need? How many more cans do you need? Assuming that your recycling continues, predict when you will reach 10,000.

Choose Your Strategy 71

Use this worksheet to provide additional support for English Language Learners.

Independent Work Options

LOGICAL 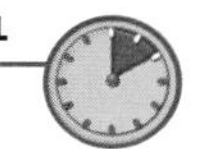

Option 1 Early Finishers OL AL

Materials: index cards, shoebox with a hole in the top

- Have students write multiplication problems on index cards.
- Students place their cards in the shoebox or other receptacle. Shake the box to mix up the cards.
- Have students draw cards from the box and solve the problem on the card that they drew. Exchange with a partner to check solutions.

Option 2 Student Technology

Math Online macmillanmh.com

Personal Tutor • Extra Examples

Option 3 Learning Station: Music (p. 234H)

Direct students to the Music Learning Station for opportunities to explore and extend the lesson concept.

1 Introduce

Activity • Review

- Give students the following problem:

  Robin is taking a karate class at school. Her parents have budgeted $1,000 to pay for the class for six months. The monthly fee is $195. They say that they have budgeted enough money. Is their claim reasonable?
- Remind students of the problem-solving strategies they have learned this year. **What strategy could you use to solve this problem?** choose an operation
- Solve the problem. **Was the amount budgeted reasonable?** Round $195 to $200; $200 × 6 = $1,200; $1,200 > $1,000. They have not budgeted enough, so their claim is not reasonable.

2 Teach

Have students read the problem on making punch. Guide them through the problem-solving steps.

Understand Using the questions, review what students know and need to find.

Plan Have them discuss their strategy.

Solve Guide students to use the four-step plan to solve the problem.

- **What are the four steps of the four-step plan?** understand, plan, solve, and check
- **How many people does one bowl of punch serve?** 35
- **How do you find how many people four bowls will serve?** Multiply 4 × 35.

Check Have students look back at the problem to make sure that the answer fits the facts given.

- **What other method could you use to check your answer?** estimation

COMMON ERROR!

Although each strategy is different, a typical error made by students is to use the wrong information. Careful reading and rereading of the problem may help students avoid this error.

6-5 Problem-Solving Investigation

MAIN IDEA I will choose the best strategy to solve a problem.

P.S.I. TEAM +

ISABEL: I am making punch for a party. One bowl of punch serves 35 guests. I am going to make four bowls of punch.

YOUR MISSION: Find how many guests four bowls of punch serve.

Understand One bowl of punch serves 35 guests. Isabel is making four bowls of punch. Find how many guests will be served by four bowls of punch.

Plan Use the four-step plan and write a number sentence. Multiply the number of guests served by one bowl of punch by the number of bowls being made.

Solve You need to find 35 × 4 = ■.

```
   35
 ×  4
   20   Multiply 4 × 5.
 +120   Multiply 4 × 30.
  140   Add.
```

	30	5
4	120	20

120 + 20 = 140

So, four bowls of punch will serve 140 guests.

Check Look back. You can use repeated addition to check your answer.

35 + 35 + 35 + 35 = 140.

So, the answer is correct.

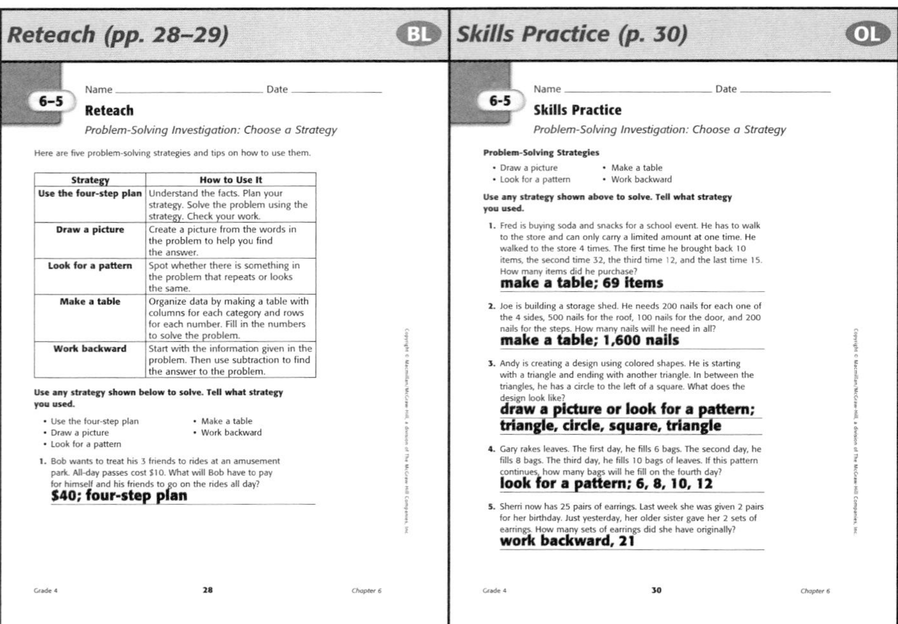

Reteach (pp. 28–29) BL

6–5 Name ______ Date ______

Reteach

Problem-Solving Investigation: Choose a Strategy

Here are five problem-solving strategies and tips on how to use them.

Strategy	How to Use It
Use the four-step plan	Understand the facts. Plan your strategy. Solve the problem using the strategy. Check your work.
Draw a picture	Create a picture from the words in the problem to help you find the answer.
Look for a pattern	Spot whether there is something in the problem that repeats or looks the same.
Make a table	Organize data by making a table with columns for each category and rows for each number. Fill in the numbers to solve the problem.
Work backward	Start with the information given in the problem. Then use subtraction to find the answer to the problem.

Use any strategy shown below to solve. Tell what strategy you used.

- Use the four-step plan
- Draw a picture
- Look for a pattern
- Make a table
- Work backward

1. Bob wants to treat his 3 friends to rides at an amusement park. All-day passes cost $10. What will Bob have to pay for himself and his friends to go on the rides all day?
   $40; four-step plan

Grade 4 28 Chapter 6

Skills Practice (p. 30) OL

6-5 Name ______ Date ______

Skills Practice

Problem-Solving Investigation: Choose a Strategy

Problem-Solving Strategies

- Draw a picture
- Look for a pattern
- Make a table
- Work backward

Use any strategy shown above to solve. Tell what strategy you used.

1. Fred is buying soda and snacks for a school event. He has to walk to the store and can only carry a limited amount at one time. He walked to the store 4 times. The first time he brought back 10 items, the second time 32, the third time 12, and the last time 15. How many items did he purchase?
   make a table; 69 items
2. Joe is building a storage shed. He needs 200 nails for each one of the 4 sides, 500 nails for the roof, 100 nails for the door, and 200 nails for the steps. How many nails will he need in all?
   make a table; 1,600 nails
3. Andy is creating a design using colored shapes. He is starting with a triangle and ending with another triangle. In between the triangles, he has a circle to the left of a square. What does the design look like?
   draw a picture or look for a pattern; triangle, circle, square, triangle
4. Gary rakes leaves. The first day, he fills 6 bags. The second day, he fills 8 bags. The third day, he fills 10 bags of leaves. If this pattern continues, how many bags will he fill on the fourth day?
   look for a pattern; 6, 8, 10, 12
5. Sherri now has 25 pairs of earrings. Last week she was given 2 pairs for her birthday. Just yesterday, her older sister gave her 2 sets of earrings. How many sets of earrings did she have originally?
   work backward, 21

Grade 4 30 Chapter 6

★ indicates multi-step problem

Mixed Problem Solving

Use any strategy shown below to solve. Tell what strategy you used.

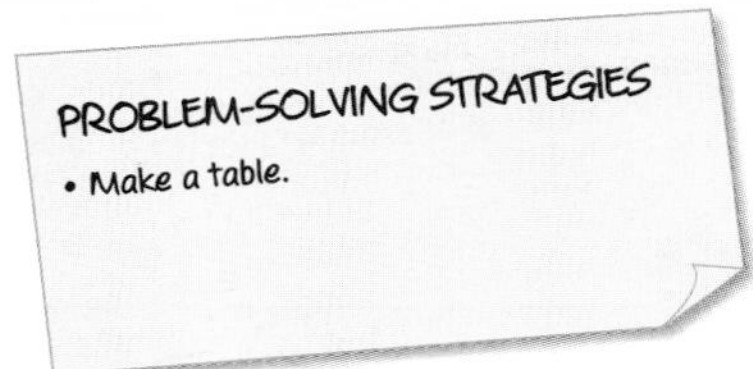

1. **Algebra** There are 12 members in each scout troop. Make a table to find out how many members will attend a meeting if there are 10, 11, 12, or 13 scout troops attending.
   1, 2. See Ch. 6 Answer Appendix.

2. Nate is trying to choose 3 items from the menu below. What are 3 possible combinations Nate could choose?

3. Kishi is choosing an outfit to wear to school. She has 3 shirts, 2 pairs of pants, and 3 pairs of shoes to choose from. How many different outfits does she have to choose from? **18 outfits**

★4. While on a class field trip, Hally learned that four bears eat 2,000 ants per day. How many ants will 2 bears eat in one day? **1,000 ants**

5. There are 18 stickers on each sheet. There are five sheets in one pack. How many stickers are in one pack?
   90 stickers

6. **Algebra** Copy and complete the pattern below. Describe the pattern.
   800; 3,200; Multiply by 2.
   100, 200, 400, ■, 1,600, ■, 6,400

7. **Geometry** If this pattern is repeated, identify the 18th shape in the pattern.

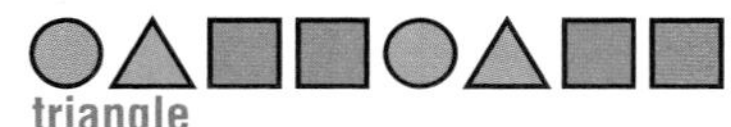

   triangle

8. A wall has an animal poster to the right of a car poster. A space poster is last. A music poster is to the left of the space poster. What is the order of the 4 posters? **car, animal, music, space**

★9. Emma now has $32. She earned $12 babysitting and she received $5 for her allowance. How much money did she have originally? **$15**

★10. The Turner family played miniature golf. What is the total cost if 2 adults and 3 children played 18 holes of golf?
   $29

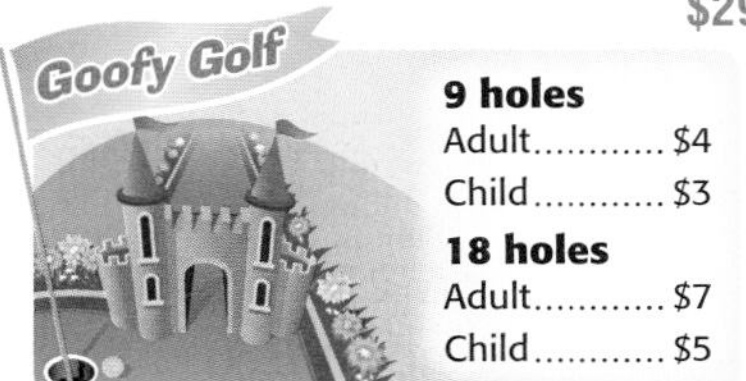

Goofy Golf
9 holes
Adult........... $4
Child........... $3
18 holes
Adult........... $7
Child........... $5

11. **WRITING IN MATH** Look at Exercise 9. Identify the strategy you used. Explain how you used this strategy to solve the problem.
   See Ch. 6 Answer Appendix.

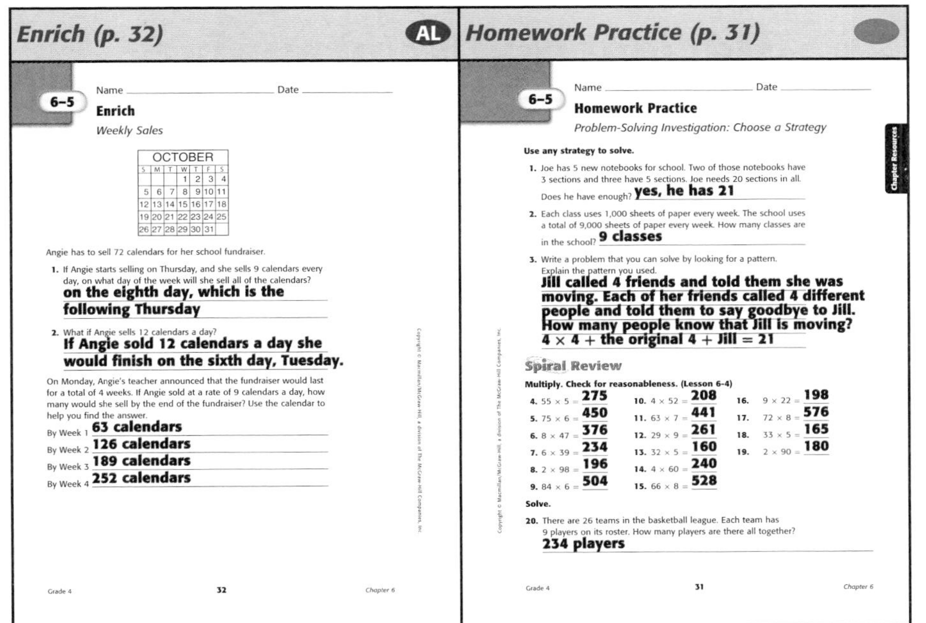

Enrich (p. 32) AL

6–5

Name ______________ Date ______________

Enrich

Weekly Sales

OCTOBER						
S	M	T	W	T	F	S
			1	2	3	4
5	6	7	8	9	10	11
12	13	14	15	16	17	18
19	20	21	22	23	24	25
26	27	28	29	30	31	

Angie has to sell 72 calendars for her school fundraiser.

1. If Angie starts selling on Thursday, and she sells 9 calendars every day, on what day of the week will she sell all of the calendars?
   on the eighth day, which is the following Thursday

2. What if Angie sells 12 calendars a day?
   If Angie sold 12 calendars a day she would finish on the sixth day, Tuesday.

On Monday, Angie's teacher announced that the fundraiser would last for a total of 4 weeks. If Angie sold at a rate of 9 calendars a day, how many would she sell by the end of the fundraiser? Use the calendar to help you find the answer.

By Week 1 **63 calendars**
By Week 2 **126 calendars**
By Week 3 **189 calendars**
By Week 4 **252 calendars**

Grade 4 32 Chapter 6

Homework Practice (p. 31)

6–5

Name ______________ Date ______________

Homework Practice

Problem-Solving Investigation: Choose a Strategy

Chapter Resources

Use any strategy to solve.

1. Joe has 5 new notebooks for school. Two of those notebooks have 3 sections and three have 5 sections. Joe needs 20 sections in all. Does he have enough? **yes, he has 21**

2. Each class uses 1,000 sheets of paper every week. The school uses a total of 9,000 sheets of paper every week. How many classes are in the school? **9 classes**

3. Write a problem that you can solve by looking for a pattern. Explain the pattern you used.
   Jill called 4 friends and told them she was moving. Each of her friends called 4 different people and told them to say goodbye to Jill. How many people know that Jill is moving? 4 × 4 + the original 4 + Jill = 21

Spiral Review

Multiply. Check for reasonableness. (Lesson 6-4)

4. 55 × 5 = **275**
5. 75 × 6 = **450**
6. 8 × 47 = **376**
7. 6 × 39 = **234**
8. 2 × 98 = **196**
9. 84 × 6 = **504**
10. 4 × 52 = **208**
11. 63 × 7 = **441**
12. 29 × 9 = **261**
13. 32 × 5 = **160**
14. 4 × 60 = **240**
15. 66 × 8 = **528**
16. 9 × 22 = **198**
17. 72 × 8 = **576**
18. 33 × 5 = **165**
19. 2 × 90 = **180**

Solve.

20. There are 26 teams in the basketball league. Each team has 9 players on its roster. How many players are there all together?
   234 players

Grade 4 31 Chapter 6

BL Alternate Teaching Strategy

If students have trouble choosing a strategy…

Then use one of these reteach options:

1. CRM **Daily Reteach Worksheet** (pp. 28–29)
2. Have them design bookmark reminders listing the four-step plan, draw a picture, look for a pattern, make a table, and work backward strategies. These could be hand-designed or computer generated. Laminate the bookmarks.

3 Practice

Using the Exercises

Exercises 1–11 provide practice using a variety of strategies. Remind students that there is often more than one way to solve a problem.

Exercises 1 and 4 provide practice using the make a table strategy.

4 Assess

Formative Assessment

- **How do you decide whether a problem can be solve using patterns?** Sample answer: Look for changes in numbers or geometric figures to see if they form a pattern.
- **How can you use tables to solve problems?** Sample answer: Tables can help you organize data, and once the data are organized, you can sometimes find a rule for the table.

Quick Check **Are students continuing to struggle with choosing a strategy?**

If Yes → CRM Reteach Worksheet (p. 28–29)

If No → Independent Work Options (p. 250B)
CRM Skills Practice Worksheet (p. 30)
CRM Enrich Worksheet (p. 32)

LESSON 6-6

Multiply Multi-Digit Numbers

Lesson Planner

Objective

Multiply a multi-digit number by a one-digit number.

Review Vocabulary

product, **regroup**

Resources

Materials: rectangle cut-outs

Literature Connection: *Bats on Parade* by Kathi Appelt

Teacher Technology
TeacherWorks • Interactive Classroom • Math Songs Track #6 Lesson Plan

Daily Routine

Use these suggestions before beginning the lesson on p. 252.

5-Minute Check

(Reviews Lesson 6-5)

Use any strategy to solve. Tell what strategy you used.

Adriana went to an amusement park on a camp trip during summer vacation. She spent $24 on an admission ticket, $3 on a drink, and bought 4 souvenir postcards for $1 each. If she had $12 left, how much money did she start with? $43, work backward

Problem of the Day

A 220-pound female panda can eat up to 84 pounds of bamboo a day. Is 600 pounds of bamboo enough food for the panda for one week? Explain. Yes; $7 \times 84 = 588$ pounds a week.

Focus on Math Background

After students have learned the basic ideas behind multiplying a two-digit number by a one-digit number, multiplying a multi-digit number by a one-digit number is not a big leap. As in the previous lesson, this lesson does not begin by showing pictorial models. Instead, students begin with an expanded algorithm of partial products and then move to the standard (shorter) algorithm. They also learn to multiply money (in decimal form) in this lesson. Estimation of the product *before* multiplying is particularly important when multiplying a decimal number by a whole number, as errors are often made in the placement of the decimal point in the product.

Review Math Vocabulary

Write the review vocabulary words and their definitions on the board.

Discuss students' understandings of the terms in the context of this lesson.

Differentiated Instruction

Small Group Options

Option 1 Gifted and Talented 

LOGICAL, SPATIAL

Materials: paper, pencil

Ask students to find two factors that are multiplied to get a product of 25,626. Tell them one factor is a 1-digit number.

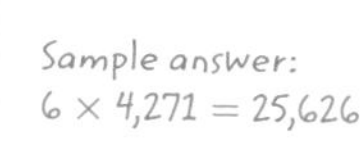

Option 2 English Language Learners ELL

SOCIAL, LINGUISTIC

Materials: note cards, sentence strips

Core Vocabulary: ordinal numbers (first, second, third, ...), multiply by

Common Use Verb: sequence

Write Math This strategy scaffolds multiplying and teaches ordinal numbers.

- Allow students to work in groups to create a collaborative writing piece.
- Guide students through a problem on the board (365 × 9).
- Divide the class into groups for each step. Write the ordinal words on note cards and give each student within the group a different note card and sentence strip.
- Review ordinal numbers with students.
- Write the problem vertically. Read it as you point to each number.
- Have groups write the problem-solving step according to the card.
- When the first group finishes, call them to the board to write out the answer. Have them post "first" to the left and "multiply 9 by 5" sentence strip to the right of "45."
- Re-read the problem, pointing out ordinal numbers and steps. Discuss as time permits.

Independent Work Options

Option 1 Early Finishers AL

LOGICAL

Materials: pencil, paper

Put this information on the board:

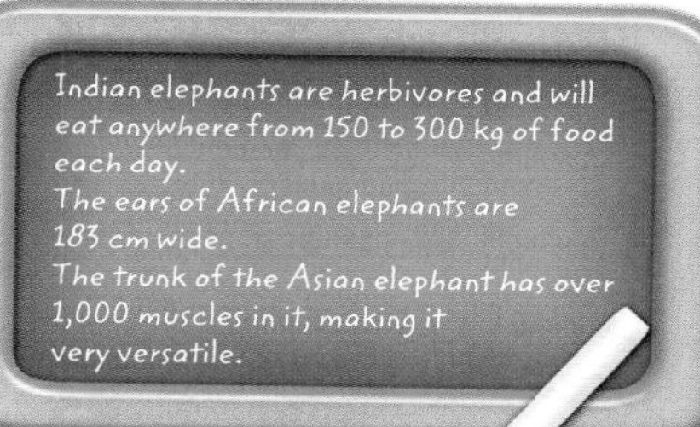

Indian elephants are herbivores and will eat anywhere from 150 to 300 kg of food each day.
The ears of African elephants are 183 cm wide.
The trunk of the Asian elephant has over 1,000 muscles in it, making it very versatile.

- Direct students to use this information about elephants to create multi-digit multiplication problems.
- Challenge students to arrange problems in order of complexity.

Option 2 Student Technology

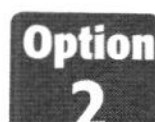

Math Online macmillanmh.com

Personal Tutor • Extra Examples

Math Adventures

Math Songs, "Bring it on!" Track #6

Option 3 Learning Station: Social Studies (p. 234H)

Direct students to the Social Studies Learning Station for opportunities to explore and extend the lesson concept.

Option 4 Problem-Solving Practice

Reinforce problem-solving skills and strategies with the Problem-Solving Practice worksheet.

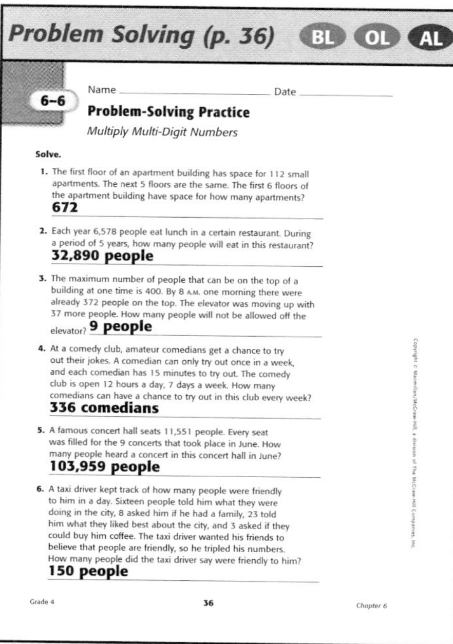

Problem Solving (p. 36) BL OL AL

6–6 Name ____________ Date ________

Problem-Solving Practice

Multiply Multi-Digit Numbers

Solve.

1. The first floor of an apartment building has space for 112 small apartments. The next 5 floors are the same. The first 6 floors of the apartment building have space for how many apartments? **672**
2. Each year 6,578 people eat lunch in a certain restaurant. During a period of 5 years, how many people will eat in this restaurant? **32,890 people**
3. The maximum number of people that can be on the top of a building at one time is 400. By 8 A.M. one morning there were already 372 people on the top. The elevator was moving up with 37 more people. How many people will not be allowed off the elevator? **9 people**
4. At a comedy club, amateur comedians get a chance to try out their jokes. A comedian can only try out once in a week, and each comedian has 15 minutes to try out. The comedy club is open 12 hours a day, 7 days a week. How many comedians can have a chance to try out in this club every week? **336 comedians**
5. A famous concert hall seats 11,551 people. Every seat was filled for the 9 concerts that took place in June. How many people heard a concert in this concert hall in June? **103,959 people**
6. A taxi driver kept track of how many people were friendly to him in a day. Sixteen people told him what they were doing in the city, 8 asked him if he had a family, 23 told him what they liked best about the city, and 3 asked if they could buy him coffee. The taxi driver wanted his friends to believe that people are friendly, so he tripled his numbers. How many people did the taxi driver say were friendly to him? **150 people**

Grade 4 36 *Chapter 6*

6-6 Multiply Multidigit Numbers

1 Introduce

Activity Choice 1 • Hands-On

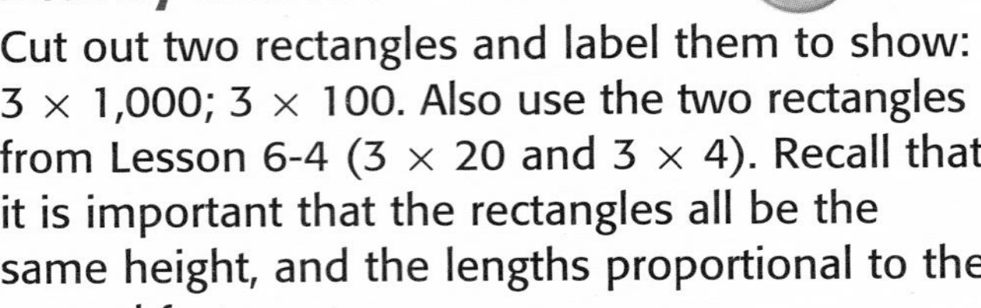

Cut out two rectangles and label them to show: 3 × 1,000; 3 × 100. Also use the two rectangles from Lesson 6-4 (3 × 20 and 3 × 4). Recall that it is important that the rectangles all be the same height, and the lengths proportional to the second factors.

- Using a bulletin board or chalkboard, have a volunteer tape the 3 × 1,000 rectangle to the board. **What is the product?** 3,000
- Then have volunteers tape in order the 3 × 100, the 3 × 20, and the 3 × 4 rectangles to the board. **What are the products?** 300, 60 and 12
- **What is the sum of the products of the four rectangles?** 3,000 + 300 + 60 + 12 = 3,372

Activity Choice 2 • Literature

Introduce the lesson with *Bats on Parade* by Kathi Appelt. For a related math activity, see p. TR51.

2 Teach

Scaffolding Questions

Write the following on the board:

$$\begin{array}{r} 1{,}124 \\ \times \quad 3 \\ \hline \end{array}$$

- **How many ones are in 1,124?** 4 Multiply the ones by 3. **What is the product?** 12
- Multiply the tens. **What is the product?** 60
- Multiply the hundreds. **What is the product?** 300
- Multiply the thousands. **What is the product?** 3,000
- Add the three products together. **What is the sum?** 3,372
- Tell students to look at the rectangles on the board. **What do you notice?** Sample answer. The rectangles show the product of 3 × 1,124.

GET READY to Learn

Have students open their books and read the information in **Get Ready to Learn**. Review **regroup** and **product**. As a class, work through **Examples 1 and 2**.

6-6 Multiply Multi-Digit Numbers

MAIN IDEA

I will multiply a multi-digit number by a one-digit number.

Math Online

macmillanmh.com
- Extra Examples
- Personal Tutor
- Self-Check Quiz

GET READY to Learn

Today is Laura's birthday, and she is nine years old. Except for leap years, there are 365 days in one year. How many days old is Laura?

You multiply multi-digit numbers the same way you multiply a two-digit number by a one-digit number.

Real-World EXAMPLE — Partial Products

1 TIME How many days old is Laura?

To find how old Laura is in days, multiply the number of days in a year by the number of years. That is, find 365 × 9. You can use partial products.

Estimate 9 × 365 ⟶ 9 × 400 = 3,600

365	
× 9	
45	Multiply 9 × 5.
540	Multiply 9 × 60.
+ 2,700	Multiply 9 × 300.
3,285	Add the partial products.

	300	+ 60	+ 5
9	2,700	540	45

2,700
540
+ 45
3,285

So, Laura is 3,285 days old.

Check for Reasonableness

The product, 3,285, is close to the estimate, 3,600. ✓

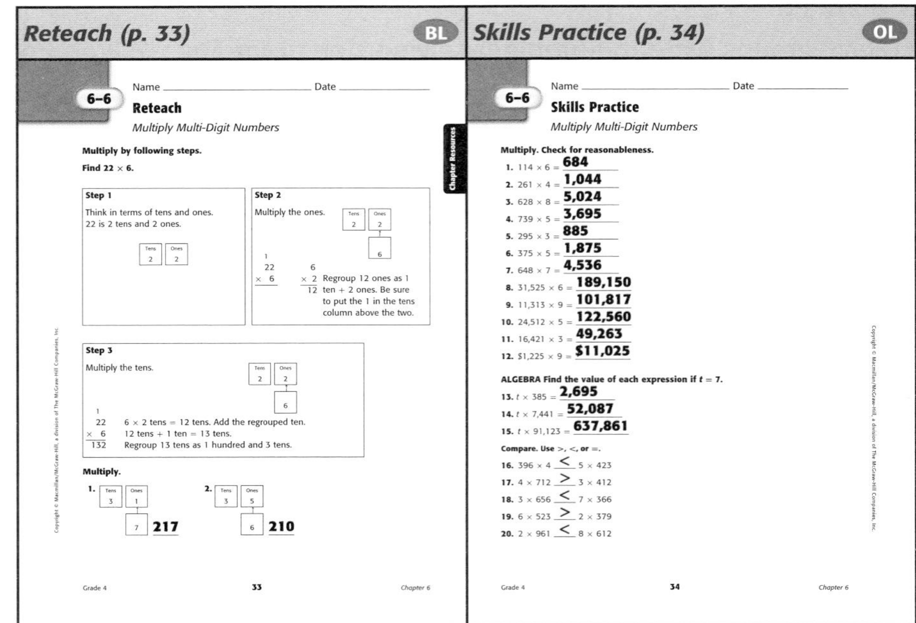

Reteach (p. 33) BL

6–6 Name ________ Date ________

Reteach

Multiply Multi-Digit Numbers

Multiply by following steps.

Find 22 × 6.

Step 1
Think in terms of tens and ones.
22 is 2 tens and 2 ones.
Tens 2 | Ones 2

Step 2
Multiply the ones.
Tens 2 | Ones 2 → 6
22 × 6; 6 × 2 = 12. Regroup 12 ones as 1 ten + 2 ones. Be sure to put the 1 in the tens column above the two.

Step 3
Multiply the tens.
Tens 2 | Ones 2 → 6
22 × 6 = 132
6 × 2 tens = 12 tens. Add the regrouped ten.
12 tens + 1 ten = 13 tens.
Regroup 13 tens as 1 hundred and 3 tens.

Multiply.

1. Tens 3 | Ones 1 → 7 **217**
2. Tens 3 | Ones 5 → 6 **210**

Grade 4 33 Chapter 6

Skills Practice (p. 34) OL

6–6 Name ________ Date ________

Skills Practice

Multiply Multi-Digit Numbers

Multiply. Check for reasonableness.

1. 114 × 6 = **684**
2. 261 × 4 = **1,044**
3. 628 × 8 = **5,024**
4. 739 × 5 = **3,695**
5. 295 × 3 = **885**
6. 375 × 5 = **1,875**
7. 648 × 7 = **4,536**
8. 31,525 × 6 = **189,150**
9. 11,313 × 9 = **101,817**
10. 24,512 × 5 = **122,560**
11. 16,421 × 3 = **49,263**
12. $1,225 × 9 = **$11,025**

ALGEBRA Find the value of each expression if $t = 7$.

13. t × 385 = **2,695**
14. t × 7,441 = **52,087**
15. t × 91,123 = **637,861**

Compare. Use >, <, or =.

16. 396 × 4 **<** 5 × 423
17. 4 × 712 **>** 3 × 412
18. 3 × 656 **<** 7 × 366
19. 6 × 523 **>** 2 × 379
20. 2 × 961 **<** 8 × 612

Grade 4 34 Chapter 6

You can also use paper and pencil to multiply.

Remember

Always check for reasonableness.

3 × $1,175
↓
3 × $1,000 = $3,000

Since $3,525 is close to $3,000, the answer is reasonable.

EXAMPLE Multiply Money

2 **Find 3 × $1,175.**

Step 1 Multiply the ones.

```
     1
$1,175    3 × 5 ones = 15
×    3    Regroup 15 ones as 1 ten and 5 ones.
     5
```

Step 2 Multiply the tens.

```
    21    3 × 7 tens = 21 tens
$1,175    Add the regrouped tens.
×    3    21 tens + 1 ten = 22 tens
    25    Regroup 22 tens as 2 hundreds and 2 tens.
```

Step 3 Multiply the hundreds.

```
    21
$1,175    3 × 1 hundred = 3 hundreds
×    3    Add the regrouped hundreds.
   525    3 hundreds + 2 hundreds = 5 hundreds
```

Step 4 Multiply the thousands.

```
    21
$1,175
×    3
$3,525    3 × 1 thousand = 3 thousands
```

	$1,000 +	$100 +	$70 +	$5
3	$3,000	$300	$210	$15

```
  $3,000
    $300
    $210
+    $15
  $3,525
```

6. Sample answer: This helps to check that the answer is reasonable.

★ indicates multi-step problem

CHECK What You Know

Multiply. Check for reasonableness. See Examples 1 and 2 (pp. 252–253)

1. 135 × 2 270; 2 × 100 = 200

2. 532 × 6 3,192; 6 × 500 = 3,000

3. 2 × $2,957 $5,914; 2 × $3,000 = $6,000

4. 7 × 7,832 54,824; 7 × 8,000 = 56,000

5. A vacation costs $1,389 for one person. What is the total cost of this vacation for a family of four? $5,556

6. Talk About It Explain why it is a good idea to estimate answers to multiplication problems.

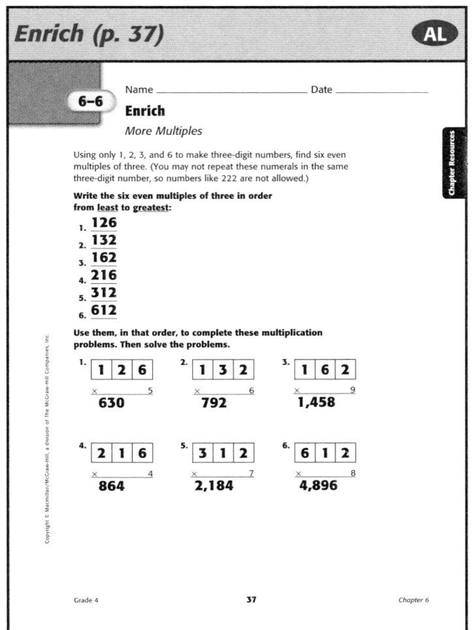

Enrich (p. 37) AL

6–6 Name ______ Date ______

Enrich

More Multiples

Using only 1, 2, 3, and 6 to make three-digit numbers, find six even multiples of three. (You may not repeat these numerals in the same three-digit number, so numbers like 222 are not allowed.)

Write the six even multiples of three in order from least to greatest:

1. 126
2. 132
3. 162
4. 216
5. 312
6. 612

Use them, in that order, to complete these multiplication problems. Then solve the problems.

1. 126 × 5 = 630
2. 132 × 6 = 792
3. 162 × 9 = 1,458
4. 216 × 4 = 864
5. 312 × 7 = 2,184
6. 612 × 8 = 4,896

Chapter Resources

Grade 4 37 Chapter 6

Partial Products

Example 1 Multiplying using partial products can be confusing with larger numbers if the products are not aligned properly. Check to see that students align all products at the right side.

ADDITIONAL EXAMPLES

1 Aisha's teacher bought 5 bags of rubber bands. If each bag has 185 bands in it, how many bands did she buy? 925

2 Find 2 × $4,387 $8,774

CHECK What You Know

As a class, have students complete Exercises 1–6 in **Check What You Know** as you observe their work.

Exercise 6 Assess student comprehension before assigning practice exercises.

BL Alternate Teaching Strategy

If students have trouble with multi-digit multiplication…

Then use one of these reteach options:

1. CRM **Daily Reteach Worksheet** (p. 33)
2. Use base-ten blocks to model a sample problem. Show students the multiplication sentences modeled by the hundreds, tens, and ones models. Then find the sum of the products. This can then be repeated for other numbers. **Note: Some problems might require regrouping 10 hundreds and trading them for one thousand.**

! COMMON ERROR!

Some students add the regrouped number before multiplying. Remind them that they must always multiply first, then add. Show them how to first multiply, then "look up" to the regrouped number and add it.

3 Practice

Differentiate practice using these leveled assignments for Exercises 7–35.

Level	Assignment
BL Below/Approaching Level	7–10, 15–18, 23–24, 27, 29, 31
OL On Level	8–13, 16–21, 24–28, 30–32, 34
AL Above/Beyond Level	7–31, odd, 33–35

Have students discuss and complete the Higher Order Thinking problems. Students may not be comfortable working backward from the product to name the factors. Remind them to think of fact families and patterns.

WRITING IN MATH Have students complete Exercise 35 in their Math Journals. You may choose to use this exercise as an optional formative assessment.

Additional Answers

7. \$336; 2 × \$200 = \$400
8. 939; 3 × 300 = 900
9. 504; 2 × 300 = 600
10. \$1,014; 3 × \$300 = \$900
11. 952; 4 × 200 = 800
12. 4,095; 5 × 800 = 4,000
13. \$3,905; 5 × \$800 = \$4,000
14. 2,040; 6 × 300 = 1,800
15. \$29,120; 7 × \$4,000 = \$28,000
16. 39,277; 7 × 6,000 = 42,000
17. 50,624; 8 × 6,000 = 48,000
18. \$51,111; 9 × \$6,000 = \$54,000
19. 58,704; 8 × 7 = 56,000
20. 59,283; 7 × 8,000 = 56,000
21. \$89,343; 9 × \$10,000 = \$90,000
22. 77,274; 9 × 9,000 = 81,000

Practice and Problem Solving

Multiply. Check for reasonableness. See Examples 1 and 2 (pp. 252–253)

7. \$168 × 2 **8.** 313 × 3 **9.** 252 × 2 **10.** \$338 × 3

11. 238 × 4 **12.** 819 × 5 **13.** \$781 × 5 **14.** 340 × 6

15. 7 × \$4,160 **16.** 7 × 5,611 **17.** 8 × 6,328 **18.** 9 × \$5,679

19. 8 × 7,338 **20.** 7 × 8,469 **21.** 9 × \$9,927 **22.** 9 × 8,586

7–22. See margin.

Algebra Find the value of each expression if n = 8.

23. n × 295 2,360 **24.** 737 × n 5,896 **25.** n × \$2,735 \$21,880 **26.** 7,372 × n 58,976

Compare. Replace each ● with >, <, or =.

27. 4 × 198 ● 3 × 248 >

28. 7 × 385 ● 6 × 457 <

29. Ms. Gibbons buys 8 cases of seeds at the school plant sale. If there are 144 packages of seeds in each case, how many packages of seeds has she bought? 1,152 packages

30. Measurement On average 1,668 gallons of water are used by each person in the United States daily. How much water is used by one person in a week? 11,676 gallons

Real-World PROBLEM SOLVING

Science The rainforests are the richest, oldest, and most productive ecosystems on Earth. Animals such as anacondas, iguanas, monkeys, and parrots live in rainforests.

31. A four-square-mile section of rainforest has 125 mammals. How many mammals would live in an area 3 times that size? 375 mammals

32. ★ Rainforest land that is used to raise cattle is worth \$60 an acre. Rainforest land that is used for its plants is worth \$2,400 an acre. Find the difference in the worth of 5 acres used to raise cattle compared to 5 acres used for plants. \$11,700

H.O.T. Problems

33. OPEN ENDED Write a four-digit number and a one-digit number whose product is greater than 6,000 and less than 6,200. Sample answer: 1,225 × 5

34. FIND THE ERROR Roberta and Camden are finding 362 × 2. Who is correct? Explain. 34, 35. See margin.

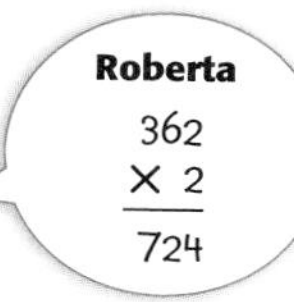

35. WRITING IN ▸MATH Write a real-world problem that involves multiplying a three-digit by a one-digit number, and regrouping.

TEST Practice

36. How long would 6 train cars be? (Lesson 6-4) B

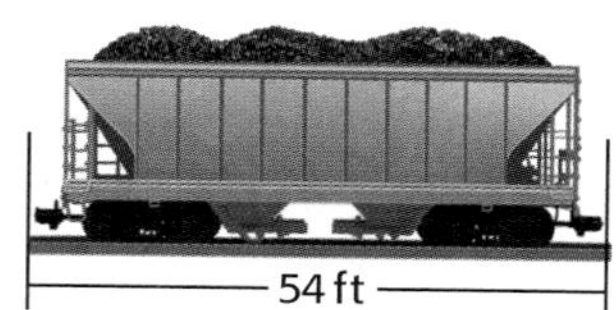

A 300 ft **C** 330 ft

B 324 ft **D** 360 ft

37. There are 1,440 minutes in a day. How many minutes are in 7 days? (Lesson 6-6) H

F 7,880 minutes

G 9,880 minutes

H 10,080 minutes

J 11,080 minutes

Spiral Review

Multiply. Check for reasonableness. (Lesson 6-4)

38. 3 × 21 63; 3 × 20 = 60 **39.** 5 × 34 170; 5 × 30 = 150 **40.** 8 × $72 $576; 8 × $70 = $560

Estimate each product. (Lesson 6-3)

41. 2 × 265 600 **42.** 3 × 849 2,400 **43.** 7 × 5,513 42,000

★**44.** One teacher, 24 students, and 7 parents are going on a field trip. Each car can hold 4 people. Is it reasonable to say that 7 cars will allow every person to go on the field trip? Explain. (Lesson 6-2) See margin.

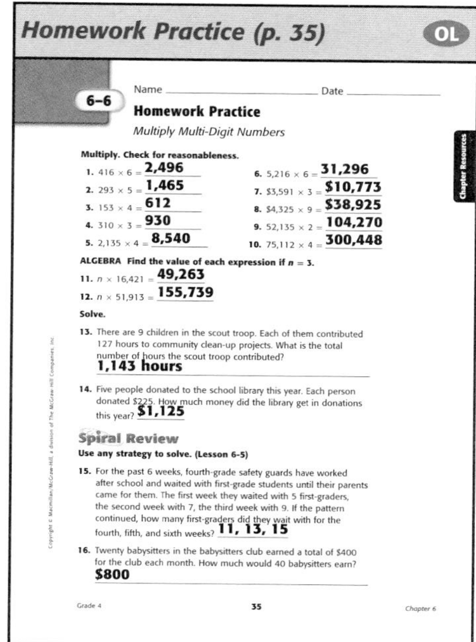

Homework Practice (p. 35) OL

6–6 Name ________ Date ________

Homework Practice

Multiply Multi-Digit Numbers

Multiply. Check for reasonableness.

1. 416 × 6 = **2,496**
2. 293 × 5 = **1,465**
3. 153 × 4 = **612**
4. 310 × 3 = **930**
5. 2,135 × 4 = **8,540**
6. 5,216 × 6 = **31,296**
7. $3,591 × 3 = **$10,773**
8. $4,325 × 9 = **$38,925**
9. 52,135 × 2 = **104,270**
10. 75,112 × 4 = **300,448**

ALGEBRA Find the value of each expression if $n = 3$.

11. n × 16,421 = **49,263**
12. n × 51,913 = **155,739**

Solve.

13. There are 9 children in the scout troop. Each of them contributed 127 hours to community clean-up projects. What is the total number of hours the scout troop contributed? **1,143 hours**

14. Five people donated to the school library this year. Each person donated $225. How much money did the library get in donations this year? **$1,125**

Spiral Review

Use any strategy to solve. (Lesson 6-5)

15. For the past 6 weeks, fourth-grade safety guards have worked after school and waited with first-grade students until their parents came for them. The first week they waited with 5 first-graders, the second week with 7, the third week with 9. If the pattern continued, how many first-graders did they wait with for the fourth, fifth, and sixth weeks? **11, 13, 15**

16. Twenty babysitters in the babysitters club earned a total of $400 for the club each month. How much would 40 babysitters earn? **$800**

Chapter Resources

Grade 4 35 Chapter 6

4 Assess

Formative Assessment

- **What steps would you use to multiply 3 × 2,741?** Sample answer: Multiply the ones, then continue multiplying through the thousands. Regroup if necessary.
- **Find the product.** 8,223

Quick Check **Are students continuing to struggle with multiplying multi-digit numbers?**

If Yes → Strategic Intervention Guide (p. 70)

If No → Independent Work Options (p. 252B)
CRM Skills Practice Worksheet (p. 34)
CRM Enrich Worksheet (p. 37)

Ticket Out the Door Have students solve 215 × 7 on a small piece of paper and hand it to you as they leave class for the day.

TEST Practice

Reviews Lessons 6-4 and 6-6

Assign the Test Practice problems to provide daily reinforcement of test-taking skills.

Spiral Review

Reviews Lessons 6-2, 6-3, and 6-4

Review and assess mastery of skills and concepts from previous chapters.

Additional Answers

34. Sample answer: Roberta; Camden forget to regroup.

35. Sample answer: Jed's cat is 3 years old. If there are 365 days in one year, how many days old is Jed's cat?

44. Sample answer: no; 7 cars is not reasonable because 7 cars will transport 28 people, and there are 31 people.

Lesson Planner

Objective

Interpret information and data from science to solve problems.

National Standard 

Students should develop an understanding of organisms and environments.

Activate Prior Knowledge

Before you turn students' attention to the pages, ask them to discuss penguins.

- **What types of penguins can you name?** Emperor penguins
- **Where do these penguins usually live?** in cold environments; Antarctica

Using the Student Page

Ask students to read the information on pp. 256–257 and answer these questions:

- **About how many individual emperor penguins live in Antarctica?** 400,000
- **If a penguin took 3 minutes to return to the surface, how many times would its heart beat during that time?** 600 times

Problem Solving in Science
EMPERORS OF THE ICE
There are 17 different types of penguins. Emperor penguins are the tallest and heaviest penguins. An Emperor penguin is over 3 feet tall and can weigh from 42 to 101 pounds. The average Emperor penguin weighs 66 pounds and can swim 15 miles per hour.
About 200,000 pairs of Emperor penguins live in 40 different groups in Antarctica. Penguins huddle together to share their body heat during the cold winter temperatures and bitter winds.
Did You Know?
Emperor penguins usually dive 60 to 70 feet. An average dive lasts 3 to 6 minutes.
256 Chapter 6 Multiply by One-Digit Numbers

Real-World Math

Use the information on pages 256 and 257 to solve each problem.

1. Suppose that eight average-sized Emperor penguins are standing together. What is their total weight? 528 lb
2. Six Emperor penguins of varying weights are standing together. What is the least they can weigh? the most? 252 lb; 606 lb
3. Suppose an Emperor penguin's dive lasts 4 minutes. How many times did its heart beat during the dive? 80 times
4. How many miles can an Emperor penguin swim in 3 hours? 45 miles
5. Suppose it takes a penguin 3 minutes to walk from its resting place to the place where it dives. What is a reasonable number of times its heart beats in these three minutes before it dives? 540–600 times
6. Based on the following table, estimate how many times a penguin's heart beats after completing all of the activities listed for two minutes each. 1,130–1,170 times

Penguin Heartbeat

Activity	Heartbeat (beats per minute)
Resting	65
Before a dive	180–200
Hitting the water	100
Diving	20
Returning to surface	200

Real-World Math

Assign the exercises on p. 257. Encourage students to choose a problem-solving strategy before beginning each exercise. If necessary, review the strategies suggested in Lesson 6-5, p. 250.

Exercise 2 Remind students that there is a lowest weight and a highest weight given for the Emperor penguin.

Exercise 5 Remind students that they need to know the lowest number of times and the highest number of times the penguin's heart could beat in order to know what would be reasonable.

Exercise 6 Tell students that they can calculate both how many times the penguin's heart beats for each activity and how many times it beats in total for all of the activities listed on the chart.

WRITING IN MATH Have students create a word problem that uses the information found in the text and in the chart on pp. 256–257.

Extend the Activity

Have students figure out the range of number of heartbeats a penguin could have during an average dive, using the 3-to-6-minute time range.

LESSON

6-7 Multiply Across Zeros

Lesson Planner

Objective

Multiply multidigit numbers with zeros by a one-digit number.

Review Vocabulary

multiple, **estimate**, **round**, **factor**, **product**, **regroup**

Resources

Materials: grid paper

Manipulatives: base-ten blocks

Literature Connection: *Each Orange Had 8 Slices* by Paul Giganti, Jr.

Teacher Technology
TeacherWorks • Interactive Classroom

Daily Routine

Use these suggestions before beginning the lesson on p. 258.

5-Minute Check

(Reviews Lesson 6-6)

Multiply. Check for reasonableness.

1. 2 × 596 1,192
2. 4 × 623 2,492
3. 3 × 5,188 15,564
4. 5 × 1,923 9,615

Problem of the Day

Find a 3-digit number using the following clues:

- the sum of the digits is 16;
- the sum of the ones digit and the hundreds digit equals the tens digit;
- the tens digit is two more than the ones. 286

Focus on Math Background

In this lesson, students extend what they have learned about multiplying with multi-digit numbers to working with multi-digit numbers with zeros. Although to adults, the zero does not seem as if it would be confusing (because it makes adding the regrouping numbers easier), to some students it is a stumbling block. Once again, beginning with an expanded algorithm of partial products might be helpful. For example:

```
 406  }→  406  }→  406
× 2  }   × 2  }   × 2
           12        12
           00        00
          800       800
                    812
```

Review Math Vocabulary

Write the review vocabulary words and their definitions on the board.

Have students write one sentence for each review vocabulary word used in this chapter and leave a blank for each word in the sentence. Exchange papers with a partner and fill in the blanks. Have pairs correct each others papers and discuss their answers.

Visual Vocabulary Cards

Use Visual Vocabulary Cards 27, 15, 42, 18, 44, and 47 to reinforce the vocabulary reviewed in this lesson. (The Define/Example/Ask routine is printed on the back of each card.)

Differentiated Instruction

Small Group Options

Option 1 Gifted and Talented AL

LOGICAL, LINGUISTIC, SOCIAL

Materials: paper, pencils, chart paper, markers

- Write the following on the chart paper:

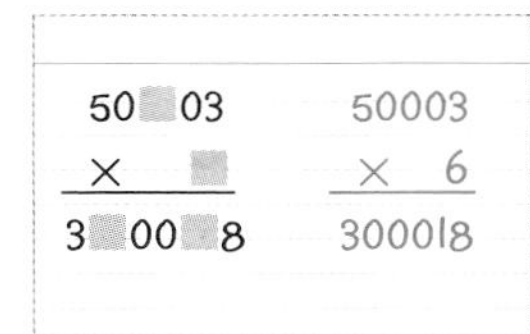

- Ask students to copy the problem and fill in the boxes with digits to make this a correct problem.
- Discuss possible strategies for solving this problem. As students finish, have them turn to a partner to check answers.

Option 2 English Language Learners ELL

SOCIAL, KINESTHETIC

Materials: 3 chairs, white boards
Core Vocabulary: speak, pass
Common Use Verb: to pass

Do Math This strategy scaffolds multiplying across zeros.

- Give each group white boards labeled ones, tens, or hundreds. Place chairs side by side in front of room. Write 305 × 3 on the board.
- Have the ones group solve 3 × 5 and sit with the answer written on their board in front on the far right chair.
- Repeat for 0 × 5 sitting in the middle chair and 3 × 3 sitting behind the left chair.
- Discuss problems with writing numbers as is (9,015) Ask "Is 9,015 the answer to 305 × 3?"
- Prompt students to explain why the answer is 915.
- Repeat with other zero problems as time permits.

Independent Work Options

Option 1 Early Finishers AL

LOGICAL

Materials: index cards, markers

- Have students create problems where 0 is a digit in the tens or hundreds place of the multi-digit factor and the product can be found mentally. Use this example to begin. 2,103 × 3.
- Have them record the problems on the front of index cards and write the answers on the back. Challenge classmates to solve the equations.

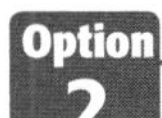

Option 2 Student Technology

Math Online macmillanmh.com

Personal Tutor • Extra Examples

Option 3 Learning Station: Health (p. 234G)

Direct students to the Health Learning Station for opportunities to explore and extend the lesson concept.

Option 4 Problem-Solving Practice

Reinforce problem-solving skills and strategies with the Problem-Solving Practice worksheet.

Problem Solving (p. 41) BL OL AL

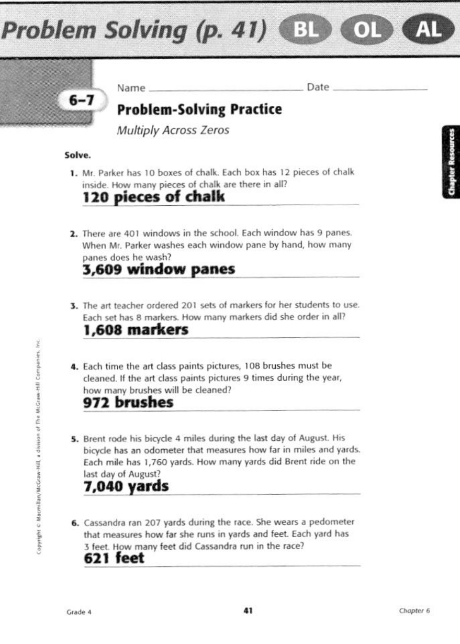

Name ________ Date ________

6-7 **Problem-Solving Practice**
Multiply Across Zeros

Solve.

1. Mr. Parker has 10 boxes of chalk. Each box has 12 pieces of chalk inside. How many pieces of chalk are there in all?
120 pieces of chalk
2. There are 401 windows in the school. Each window has 9 panes. When Mr. Parker washes each window pane by hand, how many panes does he wash?
3,609 window panes
3. The art teacher ordered 201 sets of markers for her students to use. Each set has 8 markers. How many markers did she order in all?
1,608 markers
4. Each time the art class paints pictures, 108 brushes must be cleaned. If the art class paints pictures 9 times during the year, how many brushes will be cleaned?
972 brushes
5. Brent rode his bicycle 4 miles during the last day of August. His bicycle has an odometer that measures how far in miles and yards. Each mile has 1,760 yards. How many yards did Brent ride on the last day of August?
7,040 yards
6. Cassandra ran 207 yards during the race. She wears a pedometer that measures how far she runs in yards and feet. Each yard has 3 feet. How many feet did Cassandra run in the race?
621 feet

Grade 4 41 Chapter 6

6-7 Multiply Across Zeros

1 Introduce

Activity Choice 1 • Hands-On 

- Use the four rectangles from Lessons 6-4 and 6-6 (3 × 1,000, 3 × 100, 3 × 20, and 3 × 4).
- Using a bulletin board or chalkboard, have a volunteer tape the 3 × 1,000 rectangle to the board. **What is the product?** 3,000
- Then leave out a rectangle that represents a factor times a multiple of ten. For example, have volunteers tape the 3 × 100 rectangle next to the one on the board and the 3 × 4 rectangle next to the second one. **What are these products?** 300 and 12
- **What is the sum of the products of the three rectangles?** 3,000 + 300 + 12 or 3,312

Activity Choice 2 • Literature

Introduce the lesson with *Each Orange Had 8 Slices* by Paul Giganti, Jr. For a related math activity, see p. TR52.

2 Teach

Scaffolding Questions

Write the following on the board:

$$\begin{array}{r} 1{,}104 \\ \times \quad 3 \\ \hline \end{array}$$

- **How many ones are in 1,104?** 4 Multiply the ones by 3. **What is the product?** 12
- **How many tens are in 1,104?** 0 **What is the product of any number and 0?** 0
- Multiply the hundreds. **What is the product?** 300
- Multiply the thousands. **What is the product?** 3,000
- Add the three products together. **What is the sum?** 3,312
- Tell students to look at the rectangles on the board. **What do you notice?** Sample answer: The rectangles show the product of 3 × 1,104.

GET READY to Learn

Have students open their books and read the information in **Get Ready to Learn**. Review the vocabulary. As a class, work through **Examples 1 and 2**.

6-7 Multiply Across Zeros

MAIN IDEA

I will multiply multi-digit numbers with zeros by a one-digit number.

Math Online

macmillanmh.com

- Extra Examples
- Personal Tutor
- Self-Check Quiz

GET READY to Learn

The cost of Iván's braces is about $108 each month for 4 years. How much money will his parents pay in 6 months?

You can use partial products or the Distributive Property to multiply across zeros.

Real-World EXAMPLE — Multiply Across Zeros

1 MONEY How much will Iván's parents pay in 6 months for his braces?

Multiply the cost of each month by 6. That is, find 6 × $108.

Estimate 6 × $108 ⟶ 6 × $100 = $600

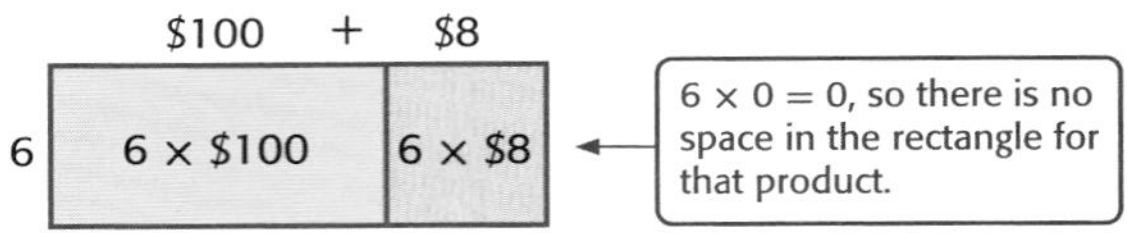

$100 + $8
6
6 × $100
6 × $8
6 × 0 = 0, so there is no space in the rectangle for that product.

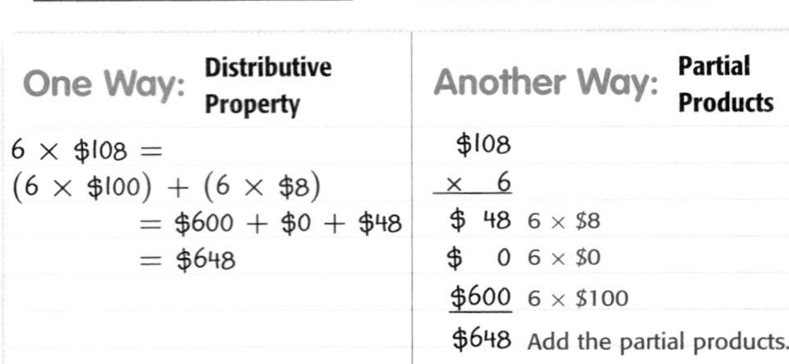

One Way: Distributive Property

6 × $108 =
(6 × $100) + (6 × $8)
= $600 + $0 + $48
= $648

Another Way: Partial Products

$108	
× 6	
$ 48	6 × $8
$ 0	6 × $0
$600	6 × $100
$648	Add the partial products.

So, Iván's parents will pay $648 in 6 months.

Check for Reasonableness

The answer, $648, is close to the estimate, $600. ✓

258 Chapter 6 Multiply by One-Digit Numbers

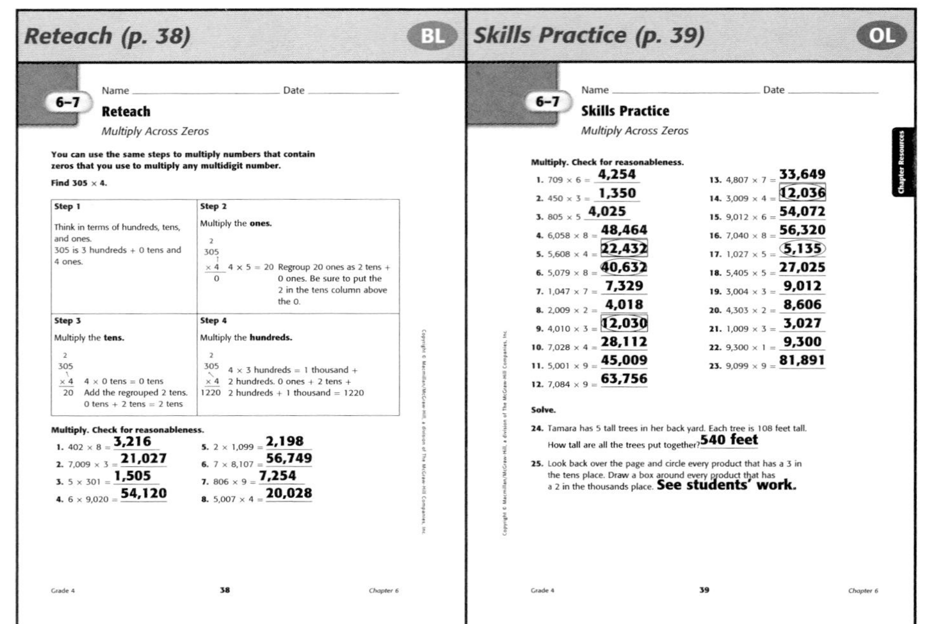

Reteach (p. 38) BL

6–7 Name ______ Date ______

Reteach

Multiply Across Zeros

You can use the same steps to multiply numbers that contain zeros that you use to multiply any multidigit number.

Find 305 × 4.

Step 1	**Step 2**
Think in terms of hundreds, tens, and ones. 305 is 3 hundreds + 0 tens and 4 ones.	Multiply the **ones.** 305 × 4 = 0 (regrouped 2); 4 × 5 = 20 Regroup 20 ones as 2 tens + 0 ones. Be sure to put the 2 in the tens column above the 0.
Step 3	**Step 4**
Multiply the **tens.** 305 × 4 = 20; 4 × 0 tens = 0 tens Add the regrouped 2 tens. 0 tens + 2 tens = 2 tens	Multiply the **hundreds.** 305 × 4 = 1220; 4 × 3 hundreds = 1 thousand + 2 hundreds. 0 ones + 2 tens + 2 hundreds + 1 thousand = 1220

Multiply. Check for reasonableness.

1. 402 × 8 = **3,216**
2. 7,009 × 3 = **21,027**
3. 5 × 301 = **1,505**
4. 6 × 9,020 = **54,120**
5. 2 × 1,099 = **2,198**
6. 7 × 8,107 = **56,749**
7. 806 × 9 = **7,254**
8. 5,007 × 4 = **20,028**

Grade 4 38 Chapter 6

Skills Practice (p. 39) OL

6–7 Name ______ Date ______

Skills Practice

Multiply Across Zeros

Chapter Resources

Multiply. Check for reasonableness.

1. 709 × 6 = **4,254**
2. 450 × 3 = **1,350**
3. 805 × 5 **4,025**
4. 6,058 × 8 = **48,464**
5. 5,608 × 4 = **22,432**
6. 5,079 × 8 = **40,632**
7. 1,047 × 7 = **7,329**
8. 2,009 × 2 = **4,018**
9. 4,010 × 3 = **12,030**
10. 7,028 × 4 = **28,112**
11. 5,001 × 9 = **45,009**
12. 7,084 × 9 = **63,756**
13. 4,807 × 7 = **33,649**
14. 3,009 × 4 = **12,036**
15. 9,012 × 6 = **54,072**
16. 7,040 × 8 = **56,320**
17. 1,027 × 5 = **5,135**
18. 5,405 × 5 = **27,025**
19. 3,004 × 3 = **9,012**
20. 4,303 × 2 = **8,606**
21. 1,009 × 3 = **3,027**
22. 9,300 × 1 = **9,300**
23. 9,099 × 9 = **81,891**

Solve.

24. Tamara has 5 tall trees in her back yard. Each tree is 108 feet tall. How tall are all the trees put together? **540 feet**
25. Look back over the page and circle every product that has a 3 in the tens place. Draw a box around every product that has a 2 in the thousands place. **See students' work.**

Grade 4 39 Chapter 6

You can also use an algorithm to multiply.

Real-World EXAMPLE Multiply Across Zeros

2 **TREES** **If three trees are each 2,025 years old, what is the total age of the trees?**

Estimate $3 \times 2{,}025 \longrightarrow 3 \times 2{,}000 = 6{,}000$

Step 1 Multiply the ones.

$$\begin{array}{r} \scriptstyle 1 \\ 2{,}025 \\ \times \quad 3 \\ \hline 5 \end{array}$$

3 × 5 ones = 15 ones
Regroup 15 ones as 1 ten and 5 ones.

Step 2 Multiply the tens.

$$\begin{array}{r} \scriptstyle 1 \\ 2{,}025 \\ \times \quad 3 \\ \hline 75 \end{array}$$

3 × 2 tens = 6 tens
Add the regrouped tens.
6 tens + 1 ten = 7 tens

Step 3 Multiply the hundreds.

$$\begin{array}{r} \scriptstyle 1 \\ 2{,}025 \\ \times \quad 3 \\ \hline 075 \end{array}$$

3 × 0 hundreds = 0 hundreds

Step 4 Multiply the thousands.

$$\begin{array}{r} \scriptstyle 1 \\ 2{,}025 \\ \times \quad 3 \\ \hline 6{,}075 \end{array}$$

3 × 2 thousands = 6 thousands

So, the total age of the trees is 6,075 years.

Check for Reasonableness

The answer, 6,075, is close to the estimate, 6,000. ✓

8. Sample answer: Multiply the ones, regroup 32 ones as 3 tens, 2 ones. Multiply the tens and add the regrouped tens. Multiply the hundreds. Multiply the thousands. So, the product is 8,032.

CHECK What You Know

Multiply. Check for reasonableness. See Examples 1 and 2 (pp. 258–259)

1. 303 × 3 — 909; 3 × 300 = 900
2. \$507 × 6 — \$3,042; 6 × \$500 = \$3,000
3. 908 × 8 — 7,264; 8 × 900 = 7,200
4. 2 × 1,073 — 2,146; 2 × 1,000 = 2,000
5. 7 × \$3,102 — \$21,714; 7 × \$3,000 = \$21,000
6. 9 × 7,004 — 63,036; 9 × 7,000 = 63,000
7. Valerie jogs 3 miles every day. If there are 5,280 feet in a mile, how many feet does she run in one day? 15,840 ft
8. **Talk About It** Explain how to find the product of 4 and 2,008.

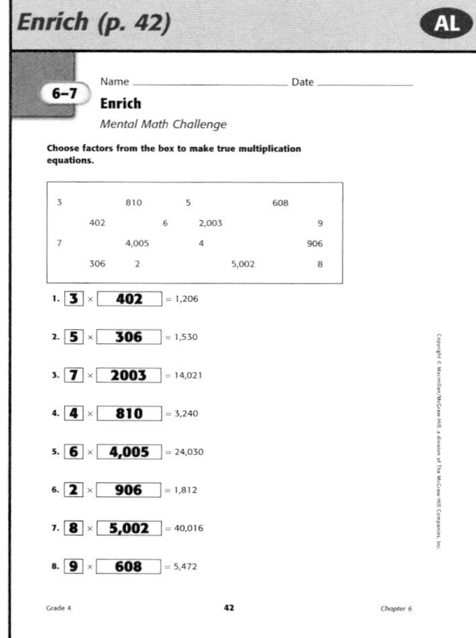

Enrich (p. 42) AL

6–7 Name ______ Date ______

Enrich

Mental Math Challenge

Choose factors from the box to make true multiplication equations.

3 810 5 608
402 6 2,003 9
7 4,005 4 906
306 2 5,002 8

1. **3** × **402** = 1,206
2. **5** × **306** = 1,530
3. **7** × **2003** = 14,021
4. **4** × **810** = 3,240
5. **6** × **4,005** = 24,030
6. **2** × **906** = 1,812
7. **8** × **5,002** = 40,016
8. **9** × **608** = 5,472

Grade 4 42 Chapter 6

Multiply Across Zeros

Example 2 Be sure that students remember to add a regrouped number after multiplying, even when the regrouped number is above a zero.

ADDITIONAL EXAMPLES

1. The lease payment for the school's video equipment is \$704 a month. How much can the school expect to pay for the first 5 months of school? 5 × 704 = \$3,520
2. A record-breaking pumpkin weighed 1,061 pounds. What would be the total weight of 4 of these pumpkins? 4 × 1,061 = 4,244 lb

CHECK What You Know

As a class, have students complete Exercises 1–8 in **Check What You Know** as you observe their work.

Exercise 8 Assess student comprehension before assigning practice exercises.

BL Alternate Teaching Strategy

If students have trouble multiplying across zeros…

Then use one of these reteach options:

1. CRM **Daily Reteach Worksheet** (p. 38)
2. Have students record partial products and add to find the final product. Have them use grid paper to keep the digits of the problem aligned as they work.

   Calculating partial products using grid paper is often the visual cue students need to transition to regrouping mentally.

3 Practice

Differentiate practice using these leveled assignments for Exercises 9–30.

Level	Assignment
BL Below/Approaching Level	9–12, 13–16, 21, 23, 25
OL On Level	9–20, 22, 24, 25–27, 29
AL Above/Beyond Level	10–26 even, 28–30

Have students discuss and complete the Higher Order Thinking problems. Guide students to use related facts to solve these problems. Knowing the product and one factor often makes the missing factor obvious as in 5 × ■ = 5.

WRITING IN ▶MATH Have students complete Exercise 30 in their Math Journals. You may choose to use this exercise as an optional formative assessment.

Additional Answers

9. 402; 2 × 200 = 400
10. $1,206; 3 × $400 = $1,200
11. 3,545; 5 × 700 = 3,500
12. 8,136; 9 × 900 = 8,100
13. $2,216; 2 × $1,000 = $2,000
14. 24,148; 4 × 6,000 = 24,000
15. 25,512; 3 × 9,000 = 27,000
16. $45,410; 5 × $9,000 = $45,000
17. 24,030; 6 × 4,000 = 24,000
18. 36,042; 6 × 6,000 = 36,000
19. $56,063; 7 × $8,000 = $56,000
20. 81,018; 9 × 9 = 81,000

COMMON ERROR!

Some students may be insecure in knowing what to do when regrouping is required in problems that have zeros in the multi-digit factor. In some cases, it may be helpful to use place-value models such as base-ten blocks to model the problem and visually show the regrouping to the students.

Practice and Problem Solving

See page R17.

Multiply. Check for reasonableness. See Examples 1 and 2 (pp. 258–259) 9–20. See margin.

9. 201 × 2
10. $402 × 3
11. 709 × 5
12. 904 × 9
13. 2 × $1,108
14. 4 × 6,037
15. 3 × 8,504
16. 5 × $9,082
17. 6 × 4,005
18. 6 × 6,007
19. 7 × $8,009
20. 9 × 9,002

Algebra **Copy and complete each table.**

21. Rule: Multiply by 4.

Input	Output
607	■ 2,428
1,085	■ 4,340
3,009	■ 12,036
5,104	■ 20,416
8,006	■ 32,024

22. Rule: Multiply by 6,008.

Input	Output
2	■ 12,016
3	■ 18,024
5	■ 30,040
7	■ 42,056
8	■ 48,064

23. **Measurement** A city in Africa is one of the wettest places in the world. It receives 405 inches of rain each year. How many inches of rain would it receive in 5 years? 2,025 in.

24. Diller Elementary is collecting money to donate to the Special Olympics. About $103 is collected each month. How much money is collected over the 9 months of the school year? $927

Health The bar graph shows the time people spend on certain activities in one year.

25. How many times will a person laugh in 3 years? 15,120

26. How many dreams does a person have in five years? 7,300

27. How many telephone calls does a family of 4 make in one year? 4,560

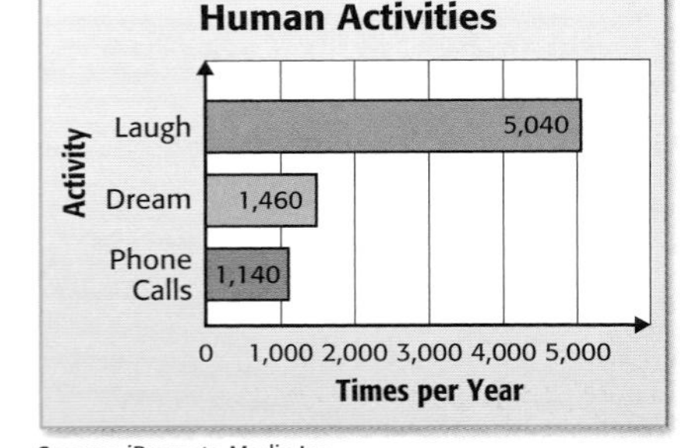

Source: iPromote Media Inc.

H.O.T. Problems

28. OPEN ENDED Copy and complete ▒,005 × ▒ = ▒,0 ▒5. Sample answer: $5,005 \times 5 = 25,025$

29. FIND THE ERROR Silvia and Dexter are finding $3 \times 6,005$. Who is correct? Explain. Sample answer: Dexter; Silvia did not add the regrouped tens.

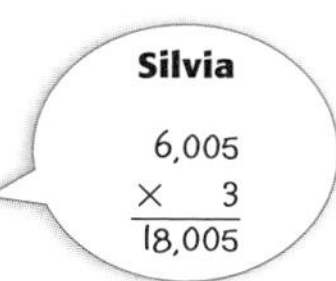

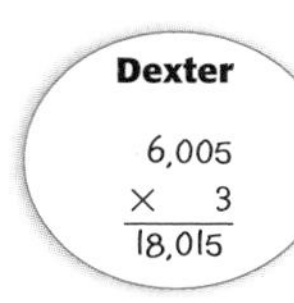

30. WRITING IN ➤MATH Write a real-world problem that involves multiplying a 4-digit number with a zero in the hundreds place by a 1-digit number. Sample answer: Otto wants to buy a car. He will have to pay $2,025 a year for 5 years. What is the total amount he will have to pay?

TEST Practice

31. There are 245 boxes of canned juice in a warehouse. If there are 6 cans of juice in each box, how many cans of juice are in the warehouse? (Lesson 6-6) C

A 1,240

B 1,440

C 1,470

D 1,480

32. The weights of animals are shown. What is the total weight of 6 bison? (Lesson 6-7) J

Animals' Weights

Animal	Weight (lb)
African elephant	14,432
White rhinoceros	7,937
Hippopotamus	5,512
Giraffe	3,527
American bison	2,205

Source: *Scholastic Book of World Records*

F 12,200 lb **H** 13,200 lb

G 12,230 lb **J** 13,230 lb

Spiral Review

Multiply. Check for reasonableness. (Lessons 6-6 and 6-4)

33. 4×65 260; $4 \times 70 = 280$

34. $7 \times \$327$ \$2,289; $7 \times \$300 = \$2,100$

35. $9 \times 1,948$ 17,532; $9 \times 2,000 = 18,000$

36. Suppose the pattern 7, 12, 17, 22, 27, ... continues until there is a total of 12 numbers. Find the sum of the last two numbers. (Lesson 6-5) 119

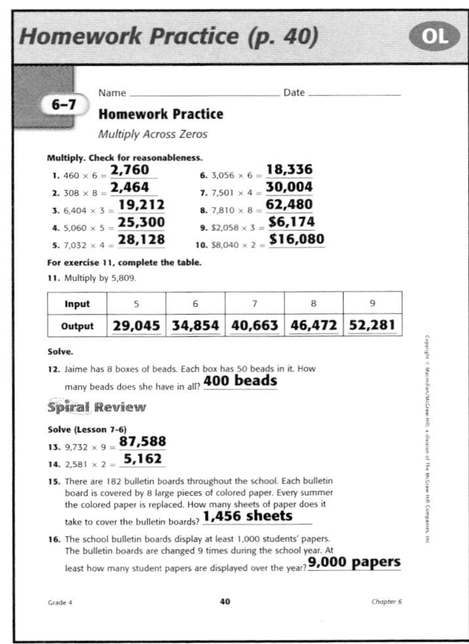

Homework Practice (p. 40) OL

6-7 Name ________ Date ________

Homework Practice

Multiply Across Zeros

Multiply. Check for reasonableness.

1. 460 × 6 = **2,760**
2. 308 × 8 = **2,464**
3. 6,404 × 3 = **19,212**
4. 5,060 × 5 = **25,300**
5. 7,032 × 4 = **28,128**
6. 3,056 × 6 = **18,336**
7. 7,501 × 4 = **30,004**
8. 7,810 × 8 = **62,480**
9. $2,058 × 3 = **$6,174**
10. $8,040 × 2 = **$16,080**

For exercise 11, complete the table.

11. Multiply by 5,809.

Input	5	6	7	8	9
Output	**29,045**	**34,854**	**40,663**	**46,472**	**52,281**

Solve.

12. Jaime has 8 boxes of beads. Each box has 50 beads in it. How many beads does she have in all? **400 beads**

Spiral Review

Solve (Lesson 7-6)

13. 9,732 × 9 = **87,588**
14. 2,581 × 2 = **5,162**
15. There are 182 bulletin boards throughout the school. Each bulletin board is covered by 8 large pieces of colored paper. Every summer the colored paper is replaced. How many sheets of paper does it take to cover the bulletin boards? **1,456 sheets**
16. The school bulletin boards display at least 1,000 students' papers. The bulletin boards are changed 9 times during the school year. At least how many student papers are displayed over the year? **9,000 papers**

Grade 4 40 Chapter 6

Assess

Formative Assessment

Ask students to multiply 3×809 and explain how they found the product. 2,427; Sample answer: Multiply the ones first and get 27, multiply the tens and get 0, multiply the hundreds and get 2400; Add $2,400 + 0 + 27$ to get the product 2,427.

Quick Check **Are students continuing to struggle with multiplying across zeros?**

If Yes → Strategic Intervention Guide (p. 70)

If No → Independent Work Options (p. 258B)

CRM Skills Practice Worksheet (p. 39)

CRM Enrich Worksheet (p. 42)

Name the Math Ask students to multiply $4 \times 2,061$. Tell them to show all their work and explain the steps they used.

Reviews Lessons 6-6 and 6-7

Assign the Test Practice problems to provide daily reinforcement of test-taking skills.

Spiral Review

Reviews Lessons 6-4, 6-5, and 6-6

Review and assess mastery of skills and concepts from previous chapters.

Chapter 6 Study Guide and Review

FOLDABLES Dinah Zike's Foldables

Use these lesson suggestions for incorporating the Foldables during the chapter. Students can then use their Foldables to review for the test.

Lesson 6-5 Students demonstrate their ability to multiply a multi-digit number by a one-digit number in the space provided beneath the bottom left flap of the Foldable.

Lesson 6-6 Under the bottom right flap of the Foldable, students demonstrate their ability to multiply multi-digit numbers with zeros by a one-digit number.

Key Vocabulary

The page references after each word denote where that term was first introduced. If students have difficulty answering Exercise 1, remind them that they can use the page references to review the vocabulary terms.

Vocabulary Review

Review chapter vocabulary using one of the following options.

- **Visual Vocabulary Cards** (15, 18, 27, 42, 47)
- **eGlossary** at macmillanmh.com

Chapter 6 Study Guide and Review

FOLDABLES Study Organizer GET READY to Study

Be sure the following Key Vocabulary words and Key Concepts are written in your Foldable.

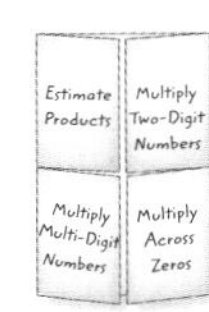

Key Concepts

Multiply Multiples of 10, 100, and 1,000

Use basic facts and patterns. (p. 237)

3 × 7 = 21	3 × 7 ones
3 × 70 = 210	3 × 7 tens
3 × 700 = 2,100	3 × 7 hundreds
3 × 7,000 = 21,000	3 × 7 thousands

Estimate Products (p. 242)

4 × 192 → 4 × 200 = 800

Multiply by Multi-Digit Numbers (p. 252)

There are many ways you can multiply.

	3,000 +	500 +	0 +	2
6	18,000	3,000	0	12

18,000
3,000
0
+ 12
21,012

$$\begin{array}{r} {}^{3}\ {}^{1}\ \ \\ 3{,}502 \\ \times\quad 6 \\ \hline 21{,}012 \end{array}$$

Multiply the ones, tens, hundreds, and thousands. Regroup as needed.

Key Vocabulary

Distributive Property of Multiplication (pp. 166, 247)
estimate (pp. 58, 242)
multiply (pp. 142, 237)
product (p. 242)

Vocabulary Check

Choose the vocabulary word that completes the sentence.

1. When you do not need an exact answer, you can ___?___. estimate
2. Finding the product means you need to ___?___. multiply
3. The ___?___ says that you can multiply the addends of a number and then add the products. Distributive Property of Multiplication
4. To ___?___ products, round factors to their greatest place. estimate
5. When two factors are multiplied together, the result is a(n) ___?___. product
6. You need to ___?___ to find the total of equal groups. multiply

Chapter 6 Project

Healthy Foods Party

Alone, in pairs, or in small groups, have students discuss the results of their completed chapter project with the class. Assess their work using the Chapter Project rubric found in Chapter 6 Resource Masters, p. 53.

Lesson-by-Lesson Review

6-1 Multiples of 10, 100, and 1,000 (pp. 237–239)

Example 1
Find 7 × 6,000.

Use basic facts and patterns to find 7 × 6,000.

7 × 6 = 42	7 × 6 ones
7 × 60 = 420	7 × 6 tens
7 × 600 = 4,200	7 × 6 hundreds
7 × 6,000 = 42,000	7 × 6 thousands

So, 7 × 6,000 = 42,000.
Notice that this answer is 7 × 6 with three zeros added to the end.

Multiply. Use basic facts and patterns.

7. 2 × 50 100
8. 4 × 90 360
9. 5 × 400 2,000
10. 8 × 600 4,800
11. 6 × 3,000 18,000
12. 9 × 7,000 63,000
13. Measurement One ton is equal to 2,000 pounds. How many pounds are equal to 7 tons? 14,000

6-2 Problem-Solving Skill: Reasonable Answers (pp. 240–241)

Example 2
Andrés walks 40 miles each month. Is it reasonable to say that he will walk more than 300 miles in 6 months? Explain.

Andrés walks 40 miles each month. Find if it is reasonable to say he will walk more than 300 miles in 6 months. Find 6 × 40 and then compare.

6 × 4 = 24

6 × 40 = 240

240 < 300. So, it is not reasonable to say Andrés will walk more than 300 miles in 6 months.

14. Edmund's family eats 12 fruit cups each week. Is 200 a reasonable number of fruit cups they will eat in four weeks? Explain.

14–16. See margin.

15. There are 8 party bags. Each bag contains the items shown. Is it reasonable to say that the bags will have 75 items in all? Explain.

16. Ahmik donates $200 each month to the local homeless shelter. Is it reasonable to say that he will give more than $3,000 a year? Explain.

Lesson-by-Lesson Review

Have students complete the Lesson-by-Lesson Review on pp. 263–266. Then you can use ExamView® Assessment Suite to customize another review worksheet that practices all the objectives of this chapter or only the objectives on which your students need more help.

Intervention If the given examples are not sufficient to review the topics covered by the questions, use the page references next to the exercises to review that topic in the Student Edition.

Additional Answers

14. Sample answer: no; 12 × 4 rounds to 10 × 4 and 40 is much less than 200.

15. Sample answer: yes; 8 bags × 12 items = 96 items, so it is reasonable to say that more than 75 items will be placed in the bags.

16. Sample answer: no; 12 × $200 = $2,400 donated, which is less than $3,000.

CHAPTER 6 Study Guide and Review

Additional Answers

17. 1,000; less than
18. 4,200; greater than
19. 4,000; less than
20. 72,000; less than
25. 105; $3 \times 40 = 120$
26. 440; $5 \times 90 = 450$

6-3 Use Rounding to Estimate Products (pp. 242–244)

Example 3
Estimate 4 × 8,596.

First round. Then use basic facts and patterns to multiply.

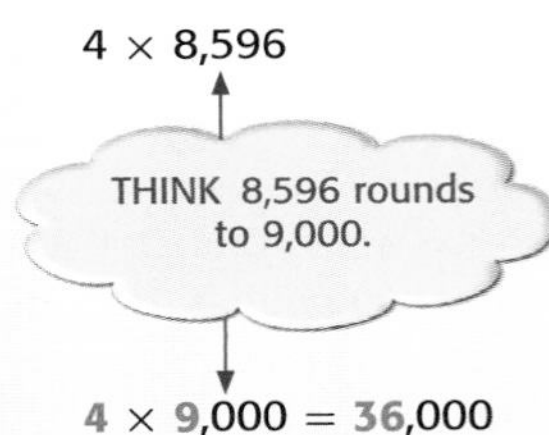
4 × 8,596
THINK 8,596 rounds to 9,000.
4 × 9,000 = 36,000

So, 4 × 8,596 is about 36,000.

Estimate each product. Then tell if the estimate is *greater than* or *less than* the actual product.

17. 5 × 248 **18.** 7 × 584

19. 1,478 × 4 **20.** 9,385 × 8

17–20. See margin.

21. About how many children play football if there are 9 teams of 18 children? 180 children

22. Rob can read a 240-page book in a week. About how many pages can he read in 6 weeks? 1,200 pages

6-4 Multiply Two-Digit Numbers (pp. 246–248)

Example 4
Tania has four decks of 52 cards. How many cards does Tania have?

Find 4 × 52.

Step 1 Multiply the ones.

52 × 4 = 8 $4 \times 2 = 8$

Step 2 Multiply the tens.

52 × 4 = 208 $4 \times 5 = 20$

	50	+ 2
4	200	8

200 + 8 = 208

So, Tania has 208 cards.

Multiply. Check for resonableness.

23. 62 × 7 434; $7 \times 60 = 420$ **24.** 77 × 9 693; $9 \times 80 = 720$

25. 35 × 3 **26.** 88 × 5

25–26. See margin.

27. **Measurement** A kangaroo can jump as far as 44 feet in a single jump. What distance would three jumps of this size cover?
132 ft; $3 \times 40 = 120$

28. Paulo watched 7 movies in one month. Each movie was 120 minutes long. How many minutes did Paulo watch movies during this month?
840 min; $7 \times 100 = 700$

6-5 Problem-Solving Investigation: Choose a Strategy (pp. 250–251)

Example 5
Dominic is making dinner. Setting the table and preparing a salad will take 15 minutes each. Making the entree will take 1 hour. If dinner is to be served at 6:00 P.M., what time does he need to start preparing dinner?

Use the work backward strategy.

6 P.M.	end result
− 1 hour	entree
5 P.M.	
−15 minutes	salad
4:45 P.M.	
−15 minutes	set table
4:30 P.M.	

So, Dominic needs to start at 4:30 P.M.

Use any strategy to solve.

29. There are 11 fish in an aquarium. Three of the fish are yellow. There are twice as many blue fish as yellow fish. The rest of the fish are red. How many red fish are there? 2 red fish

30. Adelina earns $35 a day for babysitting. She earns a total of $315 for babysitting. How many days did she babysit? 9 days

31. Katelyn is going to rent a movie last. She is going to the post office second. She is going to the pet store before the post office. She is going to the library before she rents a movie. In what order is she completing her errands? pet store, post office, library, rent a movie

6-6 Multiply Multi-Digit Numbers (pp. 252–255)

Example 6
Find $1,276 × 4.

Step 1
Multiply ones.

```
     2
$1,276
×    4
     4
```

Step 2
Multiply tens.

```
    32
$1,276
×    4
    04
```

Step 3
Multiply hundreds.

```
   1 32
 $1,276
 ×    4
    104
```

Step 4
Multiply thousands.

```
   1 32
 $1,276
 ×    4
 $5,104
```

Multiply. Check for reasonableness.

32. 6×109 654; $6 \times 100 = 600$

33. 8×854 6832; $8 \times 900 = 7,200$

34. 4,355 × 3

35. 5,820 × 7

34–37. See margin.

36. A hen lays an average of 228 eggs in one year. How many eggs does a hen lay in four years?

37. **Measurement** Except for leap years, there are 365 days in one year. Kevin is 8 years old. How many days old is Kevin?

Additional Answers

34. 13,065; $3 \times 4,000 = 12,000$

35. 40,740; $7 \times 6,000 = 42,000$

36. 912; $4 \times 200 = 800$

37. 2,920; $8 \times 400 = 3,200$

CHAPTER 6 Study Guide and Review

Additional Answers

40. 2,454; $6 \times 400 = 2,400$

41. 4,221; $7 \times 600 = 4,200$

42. 7,248; $8 \times 900 = 7,200$

43. 30,045; $5 \times 6,000 = 30,200$

6-7 Multiply Across Zeros (pp. 258–261)

Example 7

The cost for one person to go skiing for two days is $109. What is the cost for a family of five to go skiing for two days?

You need to find the product of $109 × 5.

Step 1 Multiply the ones.

$$\begin{array}{r} {\scriptstyle 4} \\ \$109 \\ \times \quad 5 \\ \hline 5 \end{array}$$

5 × 9 ones = 45 ones
Regroup 45 ones as 4 tens and 5 ones.

Step 2 Multiply the tens.

$$\begin{array}{r} {\scriptstyle 4} \\ \$109 \\ \times \quad 5 \\ \hline 45 \end{array}$$

5 × 0 tens = 0 tens
Add the regrouped tens.
0 tens + 4 tens = 4 tens

Step 3 Multiply the hundreds.

$$\begin{array}{r} {\scriptstyle 4} \\ \$109 \\ \times \quad 5 \\ \hline \$545 \end{array}$$

5 × 1 hundred = 5 hundreds

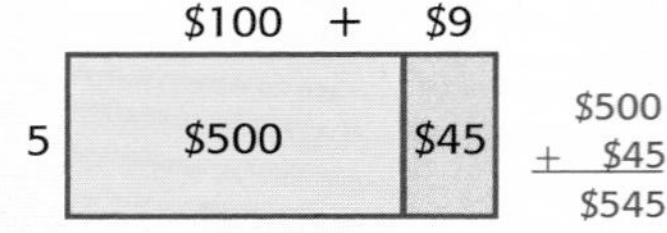

$$\begin{array}{r} \$500 \\ + \ \$45 \\ \hline \$545 \end{array}$$

So, the cost is $545.

Multiply. Check for reasonableness.

214; $2 \times 100 = 200$ 820; $4 \times 200 = 800$

38. $\begin{array}{r} 107 \\ \times \ 2 \\ \hline \end{array}$ **39.** $\begin{array}{r} 205 \\ \times \ 4 \\ \hline \end{array}$

40–43. See margin.

40. $\begin{array}{r} 409 \\ \times \ 6 \\ \hline \end{array}$ **41.** $\begin{array}{r} 603 \\ \times \ 7 \\ \hline \end{array}$

42. 8 × 906 **43.** 5 × 6,009

Algebra **Find the value of *y*.**

44. $3 \times 207 = y$ 621 **45.** $y = 7 \times 4,081$ 28,567

46. Copy and complete the table.

Rule: Multiply by 6.		
Input	Output	
307	■	1,842
1,009	■	6,054
4,708	■	28,248
6,003	■	36,018
9,002	■	54,012

47. Measurement A truck driver covered the distance shown in the table below. How many miles did he cover in 5 weeks? 14,431 miles

Distance Covered	
Week	Distance (miles)
1	3,008
2	3,008
3	2,805
4	2,805
5	2,805

Chapter Test

Multiply. Use basic facts and patterns.

1. 5 × 4 20
   5 × 40 200
   5 × 400 2,000
   5 × 4,000 20,000
2. 9 × 6 54
   9 × 60 540
   9 × 600 5,400
   9 × 6,000 54,000

Multiply. Use mental math.

3. 2 × 60 120
4. 4 × 50 200
5. 6 × 800 4,800
6. 8 × 9,000 72,000
7. School supplies cost $30. Is it reasonable for 9 students to purchase supplies with $300? Explain. See Ch. 6 Answer Appendix.
8. **MULTIPLE CHOICE** Which pair of numbers best completes the equation? B

   ☐ × 100 = ⬭

   A 65 and 650

   B 65 and 6,500

   C 605 and 6,500

   D 650 and 6,500
9. Fiona makes $25 a day babysitting. Is it reasonable to say she will have more than $200 at the end of a week? Explain. See Ch. 6 Answer Appendix.

Estimate each product.

10. 4 × 657 2,800
11. 7 × 9,431 63,000

Multiply.

12. 5 × 604 3,020
13. 9 × 7,005 63,045
14. Hakeem takes 60-minute tennis lessons twice a week. How many minutes of tennis lessons does Hakeem take in four weeks? 480 min

Algebra Find the value of each expression if $n = 6$.

15. $n \times 827$ 4,962
16. $3,285 × n $19,710

Multiply.

17. 4 × 226 904
18. 8 × 591 4,728

Algebra Copy and complete.

19. If 3 × ■ = 21, then 30 × ■ = 2,100. 7; 70
20. If 8 × ■ = 48, then 80 × ■ = 4,800. 6; 60
21. **MULTIPLE CHOICE** A plane carries 234 passengers. If the plane makes 4 trips a day, how many passengers does the plane transport a day? H

   F 826 **H** 936

   G 926 **J** 981
22. **WRITING IN MATH** Joshua does not understand why 4,200 is not a reasonable estimate for 681 × 7. Explain. See Ch. 6 Answer Appendix.

Chapter 6 Chapter Test

Summative Assessment

Use these alternate leveled Chapter Tests to differentiate assessment for the specific needs of your students.

Leveled Chapter 6 Tests			
Form	**Type**	**Level**	**CRM Pages**
1	Multiple Choice	BL	55–56
2A	Multiple Choice	OL	57–58
2B	Multiple Choice	OL	59–60
2C	Free Response	OL	61–62
2D	Free Response	OL	63–64
3	Free Response	AL	65–66

BL = below/approaching grade level
OL = on grade level
AL = above/beyond grade level

Vocabulary Test

CRM **Chapter 6 Resource Masters** (p. 50)

ExamView Assessment Suite Customize and create multiple versions of your Chapter Test and the test answer keys.

Data-Driven Decision Making

Based on the results of the Chapter Test, use the following to review concepts that continue to present students with problems.

Exercises	State/Local Standard	What's the Math?	Error Analysis	Resources for Review
1–6		Multiply multiples of 10, 100, and 1,000 using basic facts and patterns. Solve problems involving multiples of 10.	Does not know basic facts. Does not understand or use the pattern. Does not know basic multiplication facts.	Strategic Intervention Guide (pp. 70, 72, 80) CRM Chapter 6 Resource Masters (Reteach Worksheets) Math Adventures My Math Zone Chapter 6 Math Online Extra Examples • Concepts in Motion
10–11, 22		Estimate by rounding. Evaluate the reasonableness of a solution in the context of a situation.	Does not understand terms "reasonable," "estimate." Gives exact answers.	
12–14		Multiply two-digit by one-digit numbers.	Does not know multiplication facts. Does not add tens to tens value after multiplying units.	

Test Practice

Formative Assessment

- Use Student Edition pp. 268–269 as practice and cumulative review. The questions are written in the same style as many state tests.
- You can also use these two pages to benchmark student progress, or as an alternate homework assignment.

Additional practice pages can be found in the Chapter 6 Resource Masters.

CRM **Chapter 6 Resource Masters**
Cumulative Test Practice
- Multiple Choice format (pp. 55–60)
- Free Response format (pp. 61–66)

Create practice worksheets or tests that align to your state standards.

Math Online Have students visit macmillanmh.com for additional practice to reinforce your state standards.

Test Practice

Cumulative, Chapters 1–6

PART I Multiple Choice

Read each question. Then fill in the correct answer on the answer sheet provided by your teacher or on a sheet of paper.

1. Cora has 9 rolls of pennies. Suppose 50 pennies are in each roll. How many pennies does she have? C

A 360 **C** 450
B 400 **D** 500

2. Find *n* if $38 + n = 107$. G

F 68 **H** 79
G 69 **J** 145

3. The bar graph shows Connor's savings for the month of April.

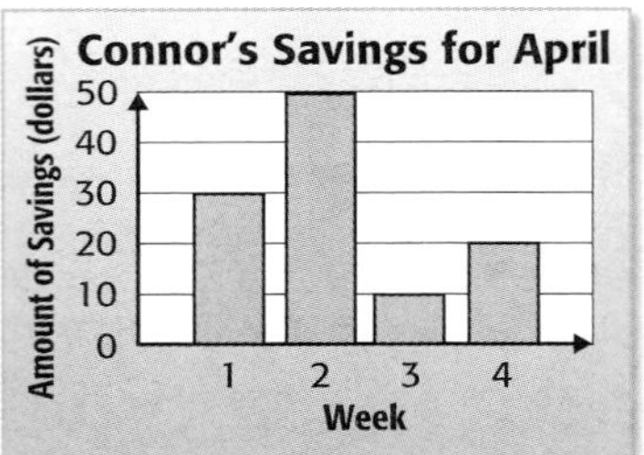

Which week did Connor save more than $30? B

A Week 1 **C** Week 3
B Week 2 **D** Week 4

4. How many sheets of paper are there in 6 packages? F

F 3,000 **H** 3,500
G 3,200 **J** 4,000

5. Which is the value of the digit 3 in 564,327? B

A 30 **C** 3,000
B 300 **D** 30,000

6. Hugh practices the piano 30 minutes per day 6 days per week. Which expression shows how many minutes he practices in 10 weeks? H

F $6 \times 10 + 30$ **H** $6 \times 10 \times 30$
G $6 + 10 + 30$ **J** $30 \div 10 \times 6$

7. Joel is going on a three-day biking trip. The daily cost is $46. How much will the trip cost? C

A $92 **C** $138
B $128 **D** $460

Test-Taking Tip

Exercise 10 Tell students to look back at their estimate to determine if their answer is reasonable.

Preparing for Standardized Tests
For test-taking strategies and practice, see pages R42–R55.

8. Shandra has 3 red crayons, 2 blue crayons, and 4 green crayons. Suppose a crayon is selected at random. Describe the probability that it will be blue. H

F certain **H** unlikely
G likely **J** impossible

9. Samir earns $22 each week mowing lawns. How much will he earn in 4 weeks? C

A $75 **C** $88
B $80 **D** $125

10. The table shows the number of miles the Lin family drove over three days.

Day	Miles
Tuesday	176
Wednesday	228
Thursday	132

Approximately how many miles did the Lin family drive in the three days? H

F 300 miles
G 400 miles
H 500 miles
J 600 miles

PART 2 Short Response

Record your answers on the answer sheet provided by your teacher or on a sheet of paper.

11. How many CDs are there in 8 packages? 400

12. Adult admission to the aquarium is $9. On Tuesday, 345 adults visited the aquarium. How much money did the aquarium collect on Tuesday? $3,105

PART 3 Extended Response

Record your answers on the answer sheet provided by your teacher or on a sheet of paper.

13. The Marshall School has 8 classrooms. Each classroom has 22 desks. How many desks does the school have? Explain. 13, 14. See margin.

14. A male tortoise can weigh up to 573 pounds. What is the greatest amount seven male tortoises can weigh? Explain.

NEED EXTRA HELP?														
If You Missed Question...	1	2	3	4	5	6	7	8	9	10	11	12	13	14
Go to Lesson...	6-1	5-2	3-5	6-1	1-1	5-6	6-4	3-9	6-4	2-2	6-1	6-6	6-4	6-6

Answer Sheet Practice

Have students simulate taking a state test by recording their answers on a practice recording sheet.

CRM Chapter 6 Resource Masters
Student Recording Sheet (p. 71)

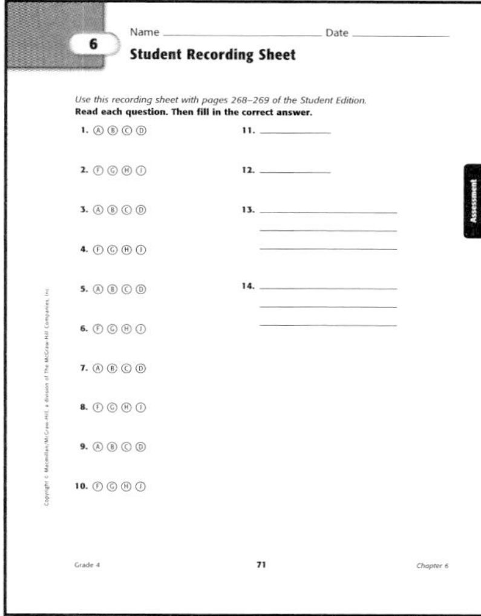
6 Name ____ Date ____
Student Recording Sheet

Use this recording sheet with pages 268–269 of the Student Edition.
Read each question. Then fill in the correct answer.

1. Ⓐ Ⓑ Ⓒ Ⓓ 11. ____
2. Ⓕ Ⓖ Ⓗ Ⓙ 12. ____
3. Ⓐ Ⓑ Ⓒ Ⓓ 13. ____
4. Ⓕ Ⓖ Ⓗ Ⓙ
5. Ⓐ Ⓑ Ⓒ Ⓓ 14. ____
6. Ⓕ Ⓖ Ⓗ Ⓙ
7. Ⓐ Ⓑ Ⓒ Ⓓ
8. Ⓕ Ⓖ Ⓗ Ⓙ
9. Ⓐ Ⓑ Ⓒ Ⓓ
10. Ⓕ Ⓖ Ⓗ Ⓙ

Grade 4 71 Chapter 6

Additional Answers

13. Sample answer: 176; $8 \times 22 = 176$

14. Sample answer: 4,011 pounds; $573 \times 7 = 4{,}011$

Page 241, Lesson 6-2

1. Sample answer: 3 represents 3 cases of treats, and 900 represents the number of treats per case.
2. Sample answer: There are 2 zeros in one of the factors.
3. Sample answer: If Odell had donated 2 cases of treats, his claim would not be reasonable.
4. Sample answer: 5 cases of treats = 4,500 treats; this is not enough treats to last 2 months because 5,000 treats are needed for 2 months.
7. no; $120 + (6 × $40) = $360 and $360 < $400
11. Sample answer: Myra is buying video games that cost $30 a piece. Is it reasonable to say that Myra will spend $180 on 6 video games?

Pages 243–244, Lesson 6-3

7. Sample answer: Mr. and Mrs. Rivera have not saved enough money; an estimate of how much they have saved is $8,000.
8. Sample answer: The estimate would be $8,000, which is misleading because they actually saved $11,992. This would be enough money for the vacation.
9. 600 × 6 = 3,600; greater than
10. 900 × 2 = 1,800; greater than
11. 700 × 8 = 5,600; less than
12. 900 × 4 = 3,600; less than
13. 2 × $400 = $800; less than
14. 8 × $600 = $4,800; less than
15. 5 × $400 = $2,000; greater than
16. 7 × $500 = $3,500; greater than
17. 7 × 1,000 = 7,000; less than
18. 3 × 5,000 = 15,000; less than
19. 9 × 4,000 = 36,000; greater than
20. 6 × 9,000 = 54,000; greater than
21. 4 × $7,000 = $28,000; greater than
22. 7 × $9,000 = $63,000; greater than
23. 9 × $9,000 = $81,000; less than
24. 7 × $9,000 = $63,000; less than
30. Sample answer: The estimated answer is more than the exact answer if you rounded a factor up. The estimated answer is less than the exact answer if you rounded a factor down.
31. Sample answer: Find 4 × $189. Then find the estimate. Compare the two products. The exact answer is reasonable if it is close to the estimate.

Page 246, Hands-On Mini Activity

5. Sample answer: Regouping is necessary when a product of two digits is greater than 9, and it is not necessary when the product of two digits is 9 or less.

Page 246, Lesson 6-4

21. Sample answer: yes; for 5 people gemstone panning would cost 5 × $12 or $60.
24. Sample answer: 52 × 2; this multiplication problem results in the only 3-digit product.
25. Multiply the ones. Then multiply the tens. Last, add the products,
    6 × 2 = 12 and
    6 × 40 = 240, then 12 + 240 = 252.

Page 251, Lesson 6-5

1. Make a table

Troops	10	11	12	13
Scouts	120	132	144	156

2. Sample answer: steak, potatoes, milk; spaghetti, salad, water; chicken, vegetables, juice
11. Sample answer: Start with the end result and work backward one step at a time. $32 – $12 = $20. Then $20 – $5 = $15

Page 267, Chapter Test

7. Sample answer: yes; 9 × $30 = $270, which is less than $300
9. Sample answer: no; 7 × $25 = $175, which is less than $200
22. Sample answer: Joshua rounded 681 down, when he should have rounded up.

NOTES

Chapter Overview

Chapter-at-a-Glance

In Chapter 7, the emphasis is on finding and estimating products by multiplying multi-digit numbers by two-digit numbers.

Lesson		Math Objective	State/Local Standards
7-1	**Multiply by Tens** (pp. 273–275)	Multiply a whole number by a multiple of ten.	
7-2	**Estimate Products** (pp. 276–279)	Estimate products by rounding.	
7-3	**Problem-Solving Strategy: Act It Out** (pp. 280–281)	Solve problems by using the act it out strategy.	
EXPLORE 7-4	**Multiply Two-Digit Numbers** (pp. 282–283)	Explore multiplying by two-digit numbers.	
7-4	**Multiply Two-Digit Numbers** (pp. 284–286)	Multiply two-digit numbers.	
7-5	**Multiply Three-Digit Numbers by Two-Digit Numbers** (pp. 288–291)	Multiply a three-digit number by a two-digit number.	
7-6	**Problem Solving Investigation: Choose a Strategy** (pp. 294–295)	Choose the best strategy to solve a problem.	
7-7	**Multiply Greater Numbers** (pp. 296–299)	Multiply four- and five-digit numbers by a two-digit number.	

Multiply by Two-Digit Numbers

BIG Idea In this chapter, students extend the multiplication concepts they learned in the previous chapter. Students apply skills in one-digit multiplication to multiplying by two-digit numbers. As a transition, this chapter has students working first on multiplying by multiples of ten, and then estimating to find products. The remaining lessons focus on multiplying by two-digit numbers.

Algebra Students multiply numbers by multiples of ten. This concept will help prepare them for algebra concepts, such as exponents and scientific notation. (Lesson 7-1)

G4-FP1 *Number and Operations* **and** *Algebra:* **Developing quick recall of multiplication facts and related division facts and fluency with whole number multiplication**

Students use understandings of multiplication to develop quick recall of the basic multiplication facts and related division facts. They apply their understanding of models for multiplication (i.e., equal sized groups, arrays, area models, equal intervals on the number line), place value, and properties of operations (in particular, the distributive property) as they develop, discuss, and use efficient, accurate, and generalizable methods to multiply multidigit whole numbers. They select appropriate methods and apply them accurately to estimate products or calculate them mentally, depending on the context and numbers involved. They develop fluency with efficient procedures, including the standard algorithm, for multiplying whole numbers, understand why the procedures work (on the basis of place value and properties of operations), and use them to solve problems.

Skills Trace

Vertical Alignment

Third Grade

In third grade, students learned to:

- Multiply multi-digit numbers by a one-digit number and estimate the sums to check for reasonableness.
- Multiply amounts of money.

Fourth Grade

During this chapter, students learn to:

- Multiply two-digit numbers and estimate products by rounding.
- Multiply multi-digit numbers by a two-digit number.

After this chapter, students learn to:

- Divide by a one-digit number.

Fifth Grade

In fifth grade, students learn to:

- Multiply up to a three-digit number by one- and two-digit numbers.
- Multiply a whole number by a decimal and estimate products by rounding and the clustering strategy.

Backmapping and Vertical Alignment **McGraw-Hill's *Math Connects*** program was conceived and developed with the final results in mind: student success in Algebra 1 and beyond. The authors, using the **NCTM Focal Points and Focal Connections** as their guide, developed this brand-new series by backmapping from Algebra 1 concepts, and vertically aligning the topics so that they build upon prior skills and concepts and serve as a foundation for future topics.

Math Vocabulary

The following math vocabulary words for Chapter 7 are listed in the glossary of the ***Student Edition***. You can find interactive definitions in 13 languages in the ***eGlossary*** at macmillanmh.com.

Distributive Property of Multiplication To multiply a sum by a number, you can multiply each addend by the same number and add the products. (p. 282)
Example: $4 \times (1 + 3) = (4 \times 1) + (4 \times 3) = 16$

estimate A number close to an exact value; an estimate indicates about how much. (p. 276)
Example: 47 + 22 (estimate 50 + 20) about 70.

factor A number that divides into a whole number evenly. Also a number that is multiplied by another number. (p. 273A)

multiple A multiple of a number is the product of that number and any whole number. (p. 273A)
Example: 15 is a multiple of 5 because $3 \times 5 = 15$.

product The answer to a multiplication problem. It also refers to expressing a number as product of its factors. (p. 273A)

regroup To use place value to exchange equal amounts when renaming a number. (p. 288A)

round To change the value of a number to one that is easier to work with. To find the nearest value of a number based on a given place value. (p. 276A)

Visual Vocabulary Cards
Use Visual Vocabulary Card 42 to reinforce the vocabulary in this lesson. (The Define/Example/Ask routine is printed on the back of each card.)

round

Chapter Planner

Suggested Pacing		
Instruction	Review & Assessment	TOTAL
8 days	1 day	**9 days**

Diagnostic Assessment
Quick Check (p. 272)

	Lesson 7-1 (Pacing: 1 day)	Lesson 7-2 (Pacing: 1 day)	Lesson 7-3 (Pacing: 1 day)
Lesson/ Objective	**Multiply by Tens** (pp. 273–271) **Objective:** Multiply a whole number by a multiple of ten.	**Estimate Products** (pp. 276–279) **Objective:** Estimate products by rounding.	**Problem-Solving Strategy Act It Out** (pp. 280–281) **Objective:** Solve problems by using the act it out strategy.
State/Local Standards			
Math Vocabulary		**estimate**, **round**	
Lesson Resources	**Materials** grid paper **Other Resources** CRM Leveled Worksheets (pp. 8–12) Daily Reteach • 5-Minute Check • Problem of the Day	**Materials** masking tape, index cards **Other Resources** CRM Leveled Worksheets (pp. 13–17) Daily Reteach • 5-Minute Check • Problem of the Day	**Materials** index cards, transparent tape **Manipulatives** money, square pattern blocks **Other Resources** CRM Leveled Worksheets (pp. 18–22) Daily Reteach • 5-Minute Check • Problem of the Day *What is Recycling?*
Technology	Math Adventures	Math Adventures	
Math Online	Personal Tutor	Personal Tutor	
Reaching All Learners	English Learners, p. 273B ELL Below Level, p. 273B BL Early Finishers, p. 273B OL AL	English Learners, p. 276B ELL Below Level, p. 276B BL Early Finishers, p. 276B OL AL	English Learners, p. 280B ELL Below Level, p. 280B BL Early Finishers, p. 280B OL AL
Alternate Lesson	*IMPACT Mathematics:* Unit A	*IMPACT Mathematics:* Unit A	

KEY

- BL Below/Approaching Level
- OL On Level
- AL Above/Beyond Level
- ELL English Learners
- SE Student Edition
- TE Teacher Edition
- CRM Chapter 7 Resource Masters
- CD-Rom
- Transparency
- Real-World Problem Solving Library

	Explore 7-4 (Pacing: 1 day)	Lesson 7-4 (Pacing: 1 day)	Lesson 7-5 (Pacing: 1 day)
Lesson/ Objective	**Multiply Two-Digit Numbers** (pp. 282–283) **Objective:** Explore multiplying by two-digit numbers.	**Multiply Two-Digit Numbers** (pp. 284–286) **Objective:** Multiply two-digit numbers.	**Multiply Three-Digit Numbers by Two-Digit Numbers** (pp. 288–291) **Objective:** Multiply a three-digit number by a two-digit number.
State/Local Standards			
Math Vocabulary	**Distributive Property of Multiplication**		**regroup**
Lesson Resources	**Materials** grid paper, red, blue, orange, and green colored pencils **Manipulatives** two-colored counters	**Materials** grid paper **Manipulatives** base-ten blocks **Other Resources** CRM Leveled Worksheets (pp. 23–27) Daily Reteach • 5-Minute Check • Problem of the Day	**Other Resources** CRM Leveled Worksheets (pp. 28–32) Daily Reteach • 5-Minute Check • Problem of the Day
Technology Math Online		Math Adventures Personal Tutor	Math Adventures Personal Tutor
Reaching All Learners		English Learners, p. 284B ELL Gifted and Talented, p. 284B AL Early Finishers, p. 284B OL AL	English Learners, p. 288B ELL Below Level, p. 288B BL Early Finishers, p. 288B OL AL
Alternate Lesson		*IMPACT Mathematics:* Unit A	

Formative Assessment
Mid-Chapter Check (p. 287)

Problem Solving in History
Walls With History (p. 292)

Chapter Planner

	Lesson 7-6 (Pacing: 1 day)	Lesson 7-7 (Pacing: 1 day)
Lesson/ Objective	**Problem-Solving Investigation** **Choose a Strategy** (pp. 294–295) **Objective:** Choose the best strategy to solve a problem.	**Multiply Greater Numbers** (pp. 296–299) **Objective:** Multiply four- and five-digit numbers by a two-digit number.
State/Local Standards		
Math Vocabulary		
Lesson Resources	**Manipulatives** money, clock **Other Resources** CRM Leveled Worksheets (pp. 33–37) Daily Reteach • 5-Minute Check • Problem of the Day *What Is Recycling?*	**Materials** colored pencils **Other Resources** CRM Leveled Worksheets (pp. 38–42) Daily Reteach • 5-Minute Check • Problem of the Day
Technology		Math Adventures
Math Online		Personal Tutor
Reaching All Learners	English Learners, p. 294B ELL Gifted and Talented, p. 294B AL Early Finishers, p. 294B OL	English Learners, p. 296B ELL Gifted and Talented, p. 296B AL Early Finishers, p. 296B OL AL
Alternate Lesson		

Game Time (p. 299)

Summative Assessment
- Study Guide/Review (p. 300)
- Chapter Test (p. 305)
- Test Practice (p. 306)

Assessment Options

Diagnostic Assessment

- SE *Option 1:* Quick Check (p. 272)
- *Option 2:* Online Quiz macmillanmh.com
- CRM *Option 3:* Diagnostic Test (p. 44)
- CRM *Option 4:* Chapter Pretest (p. 45)

Formative Assessment

- TE Alternate Teaching Strategy (every lesson)
- SE Talk About It (every lesson)
- SE Writing in Math (every lesson)
- SE Check What You Know (every lesson)
- TE Ticket Out the Door (p. 291)
- TE Into the Future (pp. 275, 298)
- TE Yesterday's News (p. 279)
- SE Mid-Chapter Check (p. 287)
- CRM Lesson Quizzes (pp. 46–48)
- CRM Mid-Chapter Test (p. 49)

Summative Assessment

- SE Chapter Test (p. 305)
- SE Test Practice (p. 306)
- CRM Vocabulary Test (p. 50)
- CRM Leveled Chapter Tests (pp. 55–66)
- CRM Cumulative Test Practice (pp. 69–71)
- CRM Oral Assessment (p. 51–52)
- ExamView® Assessment Suite
- Advance Tracker

Mc Graw Hill Professional Development

Targeted professional development has been articulated throughout **McGraw-Hill's *Math Connects*** program. The **McGraw-Hill Professional Development Video Library** provides short videos that support the **NCTM Focal Points and Focal Connections.** For more information visit macmillanmh.com.

Model Lessons

Instructional Strategies

Teacher Notes

Learning Stations

Cross-Curricular Links

Writing

pair | LOGICAL

Which Way?

There are five multiplication properties. They are the Associative Property, Commutative Property, Distributive Property, Identity Property, and Zero Property.

- Write a paragraph describing your chosen multiplication strategy for multiplying two-digit numbers. Why did you pick this strategy?
- Now, write a paragraph describing why you did *not* pick another strategy.
- Discuss your strategy paragraphs with your partner. Did you both pick the same property? Are your reasons for your choices similar or different?

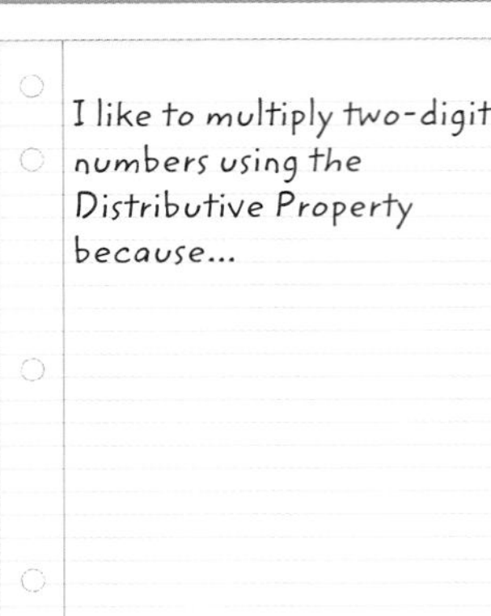

I like to multiply two-digit numbers using the Distributive Property because...

Materials:
- paper
- pencils

Art

pair | LOGICAL

Museum Multiplication

- Each partner starts out with ten rooms in his or her art museum. Without allowing your partner to see, roll one number cube each to find out the number of rooms you get to add to your museum. Write it down, but do not show your partner! Draw models of your rooms on your paper.
- Now, take turns rolling both number cubes at the same time. Use the numbers you rolled to make a two-digit number. This is the number of paintings you have to put in each room of your museum. The partner with the most paintings in his or her museum wins.

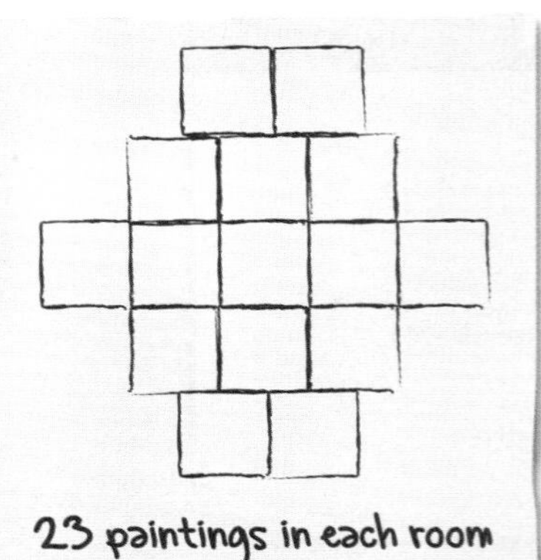

Materials:
- number cubes
- paper
- pencils

Reading

group | LOGICAL

Multiplication Opportunities

- Read *Math Man* by Teri Daniels by yourself or with a group.
- What do you have to pay for one of each of the food items shown?
- What if every person in your class decided to buy one of each of the same food items? What strategy would you use to figure out how much your class's total bill would be?
- Start by counting the number of people in your class. Then, take one item per person, and calculate the cost of getting one for each class member. Draw rectangular models to separate factors. Get back together as a group and add it all up.

Materials:
- *Math Man* by Teri Daniels
- food containers with prices marked on them
- paper
- pencils

Science

pair
SPATIAL

Feed the Sharks

In an aquarium, white sharks are fed about 180 pounds of food every day. Play a game to see who has to make the most food for the sharks.

- Take turns rolling two number cubes. Make the lowest two-digit number you can from the numbers you roll. This number represents the number of sharks you have to feed today.
- Write expressions showing how much food you have to make for your sharks. Model the shark food using base-ten blocks. The player with the smallest pile of shark food wins.

Materials:
- base-ten blocks
- number cubes
- paper
- pencils

Health

group
LOGICAL

Solve it Fast

- During recess, measure out a 50-yard dash course. Make a chart on a posterboard, with space to record each student's time for running the dash.
- Choose one student to time everyone's dash and record it on the chart, in seconds.
- At the bottom of the poster board, write an expression to figure out how much time your group would run if everyone ran as fast as the fastest runner. Do the same for the slowest time. Then write an expression for how many yards your group ran as a whole.

Materials:
- meter stick
- posterboard
- markers
- stopwatch

Social Studies

pair
LOGICAL

Population Estimates

Did you know that population figures for cities are actually estimates? Try to estimate your school's population.

- Use two methods of estimation. One partner rounds the number of students in your class. Model the number with unit blocks. Count the number of classrooms in your school and model the same number of students for each classroom. What is your total?
- The other partner uses the exact number of students in your class and models it using the unit blocks. Make models for each classroom in the school, and calculate your total. Which estimate was greater? Which is more accurate?

Estimated number of students per class: 20.
Number of classrooms: 30.

Materials:
- card displaying school's total population
- unit blocks
- paper
- pencils

CHAPTER 7

Introduce the Chapter

 Real World: How Many Chairs?

Materials: construction paper, markers

Remind students that they learned how to multiply by one-digit numbers in the last chapter. Tell them that they will now learn how to multiply by two-digit numbers.

Pose the following problem:

There are 15 tables in the cafeteria. Each table has 12 chairs around it. How many chairs are there?

Have partners work together to draw a picture that models the problem. They should draw 15 tables with 12 chairs at each table.

- **How many groups of 12 chairs are there?** 15
- **What are two ways to solve this problem?** Add 12 fifteen times; multiply 15 by 12

Write 12 + 12 + 12 + 12 + 12 + 12 + 12 + 12 + 12 + 12 + 12 + 12 + 12 + 12 + 12 = 15 × 12 on the board.

Direct students to Student Edition p. 270. Have students read the paragraph at the top of the page.

- **How could you use the Distributive Property of Multiplication to make 15 × 12 easier to solve?** Sample answer: (15 × 10) + (15 × 2) = 150 + 30 = 180

WRITING IN MATH

Starting the Chapter
Have students write about the steps they take when they multiply a two-digit number by a one-digit number. Then have them predict how multiplying a two-digit number by a two-digit number will be similar or different.

Key Vocabulary Introduce the key vocabulary in the chapter using the routine below.

Define: The Distributive Property of Multiplication is a property that states when two addends are multiplied by a number, the product is the same as when each addend is multiplied by the same number and the products are added together.
Example: $4 \times (1 + 3) = (4 \times 1) + (4 \times 3) = 16$
Ask: When might you use the Distributive Property of Multiplication?

Read-Aloud Anthology For an optional reading activity to introduce this chapter's math concepts, see the Read-Aloud Anthology on p. TR31.

CHAPTER 7

Multiply by Two-Digit Numbers

BIG Idea **How do you multiply by a two-digit number?**

You can use area models and partial products.

Example During recycling week, 15 students collected 12 pounds of recyclable items each. The model shows that 15 × 12 or 180 pounds of recyclable items were collected.

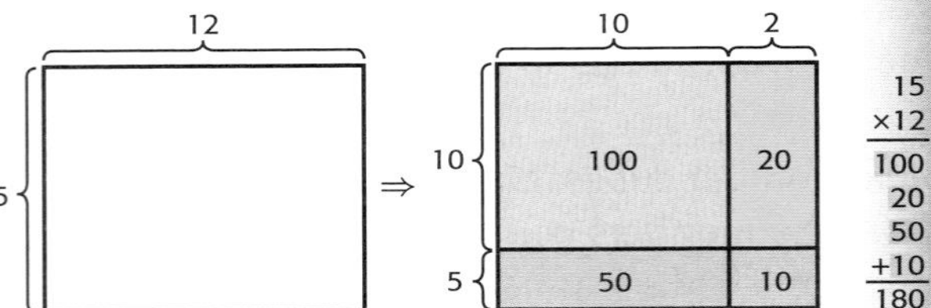

What will I learn in this chapter?

- Multiply by multiples of ten.
- Estimate products by rounding.
- Multiply by two-digit numbers.
- Determine when to estimate or find an exact answer.

Key Vocabulary

Distributive Property of Multiplication
estimate
factor
multiple
product

Math Online Student Study Tools at macmillanmh.com

 Chapter 7 Project

Name That Digit

Students create a game show where the object is to name missing digits in multiplication problems.

- Choose a game show host. Each student writes a multiplication problem and its answer on an index card and gives it to the host. The host shuffles the cards and the game begins.
- The host puts one problem on the board, but leaves out one digit. The digit can be from one of the factors or from the product.
- Divide into teams of 3. Each team has 30 seconds to figure out what the missing digit is, and write it on a sheet of paper. The host goes from team to team and asks them to show their answer to the audience. If the team gets the answer right, they get a point. It is possible that all teams will get a point in the round. Play until one team reaches 20 points.

CRM *Refer to Chapter 7 Resource Masters, p. 53, for a rubric to assess students' progress on this project.*

FOLDABLES® Study Organizer

Make this Foldable to help you organize information about multiplying by two-digit numbers. Begin with 3 sheets of $8\frac{1}{2}" \times 11"$ paper.

1. **Stack** the paper so that the sheets are $\frac{3}{4}$ inch apart.

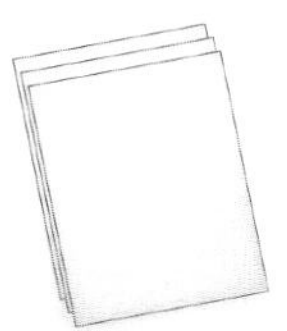

2. **Roll** up the edges so tabs are the same size.

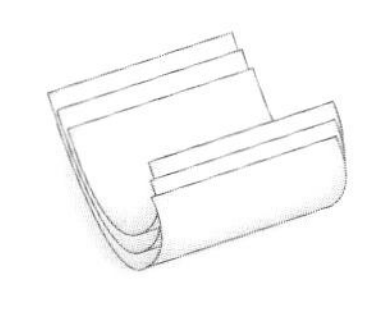

3. **Crease** and staple along the fold as shown.

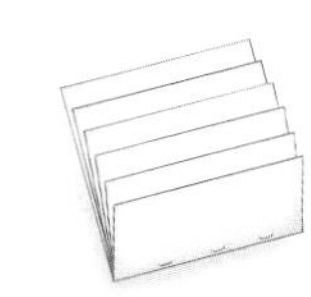

4. **Label** the tabs as shown.

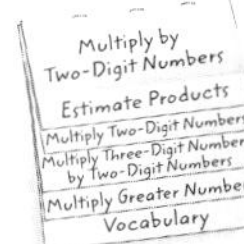

FOLDABLES® Dinah Zike's Foldables

Guide students through the directions on p. 271 to create their own Foldable graphic organizers for multiplying by two-digit numbers. Students may also use their Foldables to study and review chapter assignments.

When to Use It Lessons 7-2, 7-3, 7-4, and 7-6. (Additional instructions for using the Foldables with these lessons are found on pp. 287 and 300.)

Chapter 7 Literature List

Lesson	Book Title
7-1	**Melisande** E. Nesbit
7-2	**Moira's Birthday** Robert Munsch
7-3	**Ten Mile Day: And the Building of the Transcontinental Railroad** Mary Ann Fraser
7-4	**Sea Squares** Joy N. Hulme
7-5	**Snakes: Long Longer Longest** Jerry Pallotta
7-7	**$882\frac{1}{2}$ Amazing Answers To Your Questions About The Titanic** Hugh Brewster and Laurie Coulter
Any	**The Twelve Circus Rings** Seymour Chwast

ELL National ESL Standards Alignment for Chapter 7

Lesson, Page	ESL Standard	Modality	Level
7-1, p. 273B	Goal 1, Standard 2, d	Auditory, Visual	Beginning
7-2, p. 276B	Goal 2, Standard 2, d	Auditory	Intermediate
7-3, p. 280B	Goal 2, Standard 2, i	Kinesthetic, Social	Advanced
7-4, p. 284B	Goal 2, Standard 1, d	Linguistic, Intrapersonal	Intermediate
7-5, p. 288B	Goal 2, Standard 2, h	Social	Advanced
7-6, p. 294B	Goal 2, Standard 1, c	Intrapersonal, Linguistic	Advanced
7-7, p. 296B	Goal 1, Standard 3, f	Social, Linguistic	Beginning

The National ESL Standards can be found in the Teacher Reference Handbook.

- Read the Math at Home letter found in the Chapter 7 Resource Masters, p. 4, with the class and have each student sign it. (A Spanish version is found on p. 5.)
- Send home copies of the Math at Home letter with each student.

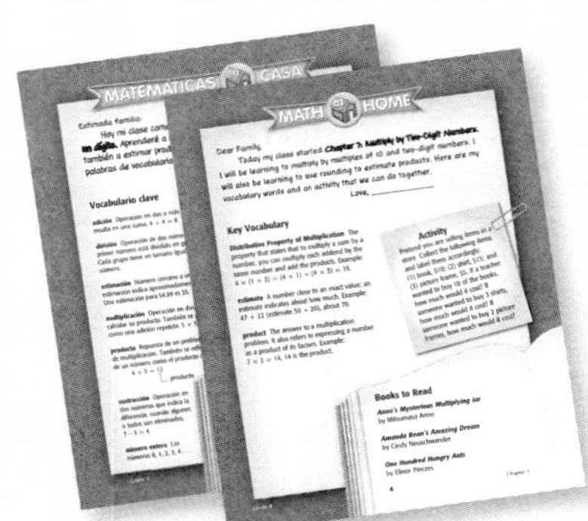

Diagnostic Assessment

Check for students' prerequisite skills before beginning the chapter.

- **Option 1:** ***Quick Check***

  SE Student Edition, p. 272

- **Option 2:** ***Online Assessment***

  Math Online macmillanmh.com

- **Option 3:** ***Diagnostic Tests***

  CRM Chapter 7 Resource Masters, pp. 44–45

RTI (Response to Intervention)

Apply the Results Based on the results of the diagnostic assessment on Student Edition p. 272, use the chart below to address individual needs before beginning the chapter.

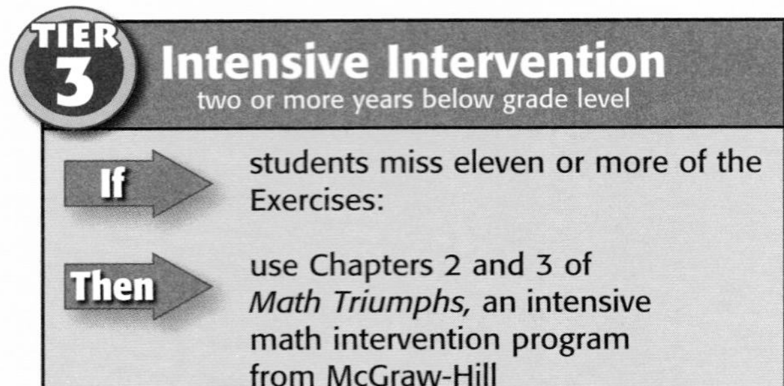

TIER 3
Intensive Intervention
two or more years below grade level
If
students miss eleven or more of the Exercises:
Then
use Chapters 2 and 3 of *Math Triumphs,* an intensive math intervention program from McGraw-Hill

ARE YOU READY for Chapter 7?

You have two ways to check prerequisite skills for this chapter.

Option 2

Math Online Take the Chapter Readiness Quiz at macmillanmh.com.

Option 1

Complete the Quick Check below.

QUICK Check

Round to the given place. (Lesson 1-6) (Used in Lessons 7-2, 7-4, 7-5, and 7-7)

1. 604; nearest hundred 600

2. 2,188; nearest thousand 2,000

3. 85,888; nearest ten-thousand 90,000

4. 681,002; nearest hundred thousand 700,000

5. The students raised $6,784 for a new playground. To the nearest thousand, about how much money did the students raise? $7,000

Add. (Lesson 2-4) (Used in Lessons 7-4, 7-5, and 7-7)

6. 759 + 307 1,066

7. 5,138 + 507 5,645

8. 9,290 + 812 10,102

9. 6,005 + 8,204 14,209

10. 34,068 + 6,055 40,123

11. 242,607 + 480,196 722,803

Write the multiplication expression for each model. Then multiply. (Lesson 6-4) (Used in Lesson Explore 7-4)

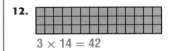

12. $3 \times 14 = 42$

13. 13. $5 \times 11 = 55$

Multiply. (Used in Lessons 7-1, 7-4, 7-5, and 7-7)

14. 36×7 252

15. 40×9 360

16. 86×5 430

272 **Chapter 7** Multiply by Two-Digit Numbers

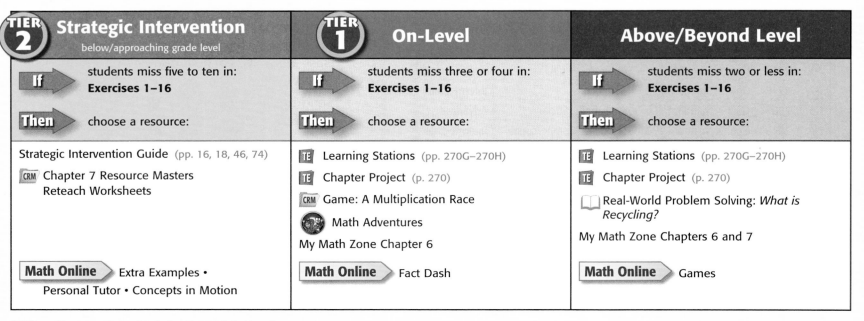

TIER 2 Strategic Intervention (below/approaching grade level)	TIER 1 On-Level	Above/Beyond Level
If students miss five to ten in: **Exercises 1–16**	**If** students miss three or four in: **Exercises 1–16**	**If** students miss two or less in: **Exercises 1–16**
Then choose a resource:	**Then** choose a resource:	**Then** choose a resource:
Strategic Intervention Guide (pp. 16, 18, 46, 74) CRM Chapter 7 Resource Masters Reteach Worksheets **Math Online** Extra Examples • Personal Tutor • Concepts in Motion	TE Learning Stations (pp. 270G–270H) TE Chapter Project (p. 270) CRM Game: A Multiplication Race Math Adventures My Math Zone Chapter 6 **Math Online** Fact Dash	TE Learning Stations (pp. 270G–270H) TE Chapter Project (p. 270) Real-World Problem Solving: *What is Recycling?* My Math Zone Chapters 6 and 7 **Math Online** Games

7-1 Multiply by Tens

Lesson Planner

Objective

Multiply a whole number by a multiple of ten.

Review Vocabulary

product, **multiple**, **factor**

Resources

Materials: grid paper

Literature Connection: *Melisande* by E. Nesbit

Teacher Technology
TeacherWorks • Interactive Classroom

Alternate Lesson: Use *IMPACT Mathematics: Unit A* to provide practice with multiplication.

Daily Routine

Use these suggestions before beginning the lesson on p. 273.

5-Minute Check

(Reviews Lesson 6-7)

Multiply. Check for reasonableness.

1. 203 × 2 = 406

2. 506 × 7 = 3,542

3. 3 × 7,035 21,105

4. 8 × $4,209 $33,672

5. 6 × 5,008 30,048

Problem of the Day

What one number can you write in the box to make each of the following equations true? 2

■ × ■ = 4 4 ÷ ■ = ■

■ + ■ = 4 4 − ■ = ■

Focus on Math Background

In previous lessons, students focused on the patterns that one can use to multiply by multiples of ten. This is a powerful tool for mental math. In this first lesson of the chapter, the Commutative and Associative properties take a starring role. Using the properties as tools to manipulate expressions to make them easier to deal with is a concept that is very useful for students now and will be even more useful in subsequent algebraic experiences. For example, to multiply 73 by 20, you can think of 20 as 2 × 10 and use the Associative Property of Multiplication. So,

$$73 \times 20 \rightarrow 73 \times (2 \times 10) \rightarrow (73 \times 2) \times 10 \rightarrow 146 \times 10 = 1{,}460$$

Review Math Vocabulary

Write the review vocabulary words and their definitions on the board.

Have students write a multiplication sentence in their notebooks. They should label each part as the product, multiple, and factor.

Differentiated Instruction

Small Group Options

Option 1 Below Level BL

SOCIAL, LOGICAL

Materials: paper, pencils, chart paper, markers

- Write the problem 54 × 30 on the chart paper. Ask students to copy and solve it.
- Write the same problem, but exchange 40 for 30.
- **How are these products the same and how are they different?** The ones place has a 0 both times. The other digits are different.
- From here, lead a discussion regarding the ones place when you multiply by a multiple of 10. Allow students to come to the conclusion that they will always have a 0 in the ones place when multiplying by a multiple of 10.

Option 2 English Language Learners ELL

AUDITORY, VISUAL

Materials: chalkboard
Core Vocabulary: easier, at the end, down
Common Use Verb: slide

Hear Math This strategy helps students vocalize and remember how to multiply zeros.

- Sing the following song to the tune of "Old MacDonald":

  When you have to multiply, zeros can slide down.
  Make the problem easier, zeros can slide down.
  With a multiple of ten, take the zero at the end,
  See the zero, slide the zero, you can slide the zero
  Make the problem easier, zeros can slide down.

- Note: You can use an overhead and number manipulatives to illustrate sliding the zeros down. Repeat as time permits.

Independent Work Options

Option 1 Early Finishers OL AL

LOGICAL, LINGUISTIC

Materials: list of the following five statements of equality:

- Have students look at each statement, decide if it is true or false, and tell or write how they know.
- Ask each student to write a true or false statement to exchange with a partner. Partners will decide if the statement is true or false and explain how they know.

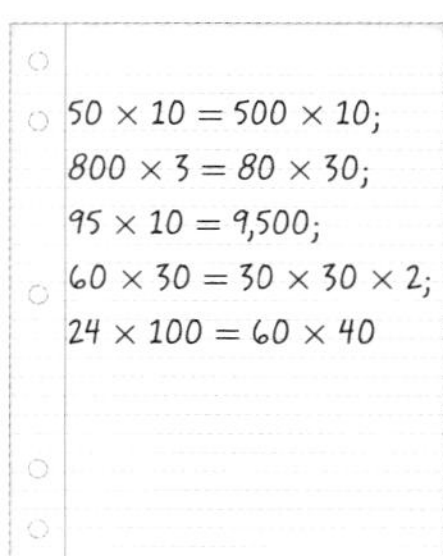

$50 \times 10 = 500 \times 10$;
$800 \times 3 = 80 \times 30$;
$95 \times 10 = 9{,}500$;
$60 \times 30 = 30 \times 30 \times 2$;
$24 \times 100 = 60 \times 40$

Option 2 Student Technology

Math Online macmillanmh.com

Personal Tutor • Extra Examples

 Math Adventures

Option 3 Learning Station: Art (p. 270G)

Direct students to the Art Learning Station for opportunities to explore and extend the lesson concept.

Option 4 Problem-Solving Practice

Reinforce problem-solving skills and strategies with the Problem-Solving Practice worksheet.

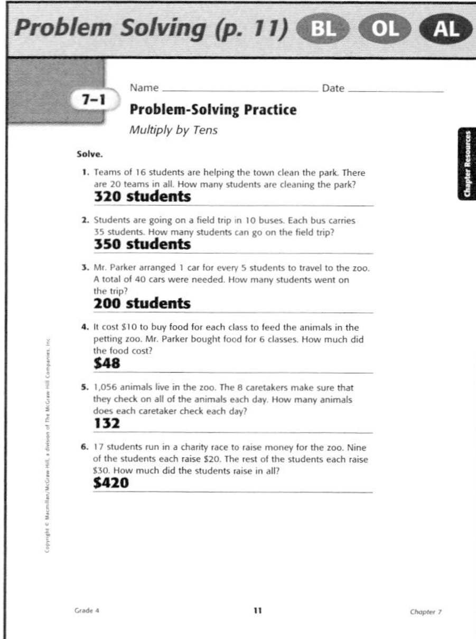

Problem Solving (p. 11) BL OL AL

7–1 Name ________ Date ________

Problem-Solving Practice

Multiply by Tens

Solve.

1. Teams of 16 students are helping the town clean the park. There are 20 teams in all. How many students are cleaning the park?
   320 students
2. Students are going on a field trip in 10 buses. Each bus carries 35 students. How many students can go on the field trip?
   350 students
3. Mr. Parker arranged 1 car for every 5 students to travel to the zoo. A total of 40 cars were needed. How many students went on the trip?
   200 students
4. It cost $10 to buy food for each class to feed the animals in the petting zoo. Mr. Parker bought food for 6 classes. How much did the food cost?
   $48
5. 1,056 animals live in the zoo. The 8 caretakers make sure that they check on all of the animals each day. How many animals does each caretaker check each day?
   132
6. 17 students run in a charity race to raise money for the zoo. Nine of the students each raise $20. The rest of the students each raise $30. How much did the students raise in all?
   $420

Chapter Resources

Grade 4 11 Chapter 7

7-1 Multiply by Tens

GET READY to Learn

Rita took 20 pictures at her family reunion. She printed the pictures so that each of her 25 family members could have them. How many pictures did Rita print?

MAIN IDEA

I will multiply a whole number by a multiple of ten.

Math Online

macmillanmh.com

- Extra Examples
- Personal Tutor
- Self-Check Quiz

When you multiply a two-digit number by a multiple of ten such as 20, 30, 40, ..., the digit in the ones place is always a zero.

Real-World EXAMPLE Multiply by Tens

1 **PHOTOGRAPHS** **How many pictures did Rita print?**

You need to find 25×20.

One Way: **Use Properties**

25×20	Write the problem.
$25 \times (10 \times 2)$	Think of 20 as 10×2.
$25 \times (2 \times 10)$	Commutative Property of Multiplication
$(25 \times 2) \times 10$	Associative Property of Multiplication
50×10	Multiply. $25 \times 2 = 50$
500	Mental Math

Another Way: **Use Paper and Pencil**

Step 1 Multiply the ones.

$$\begin{array}{r} 25 \\ \times\ 20 \\ \hline 0 \end{array} \quad \leftarrow 0 \text{ ones} \times 25 = 0$$

Step 2 Multiply the tens.

$$\begin{array}{r} 25 \\ \times\ 20 \\ \hline 500 \end{array} \quad \leftarrow 2 \text{ tens} \times 25 = 50 \text{ tens}$$

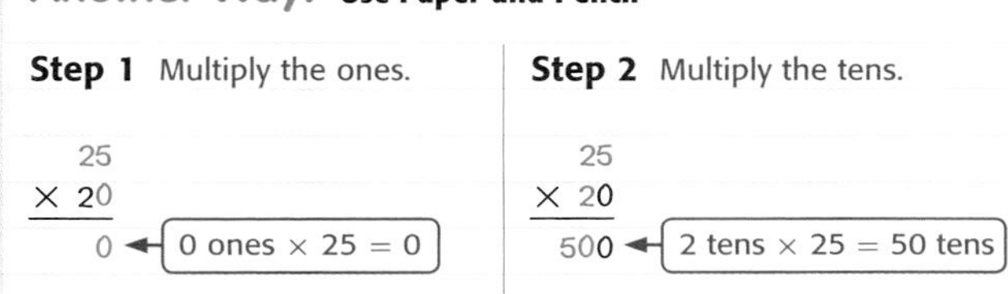

So, Rita printed 500 pictures.

7-1 Multiply by Tens

1 Introduce

Activity Choice 1 • Hands-On

- Review multiples of 10, 100, and 1,000.
- **What are the multiples of ten from 0 to 99?** 0, 10, 20, 30, 40, 50, 60, 70, 80, 90
- Ask a volunteer to name a basic multiplication fact and write the multiplication sentence on the board. For example, $4 \times 7 = 28$.
- To create patterns, have different students write new sentences, one below the other on the board, in which they change the second factor to a multiple of 10, 100, or 1,000. For example, $4 \times 70 = 280$, $4 \times 700 = 2{,}800$, or $4 \times 7{,}000 = 28{,}000$.
- Repeat several times with various basic facts.
- Have students examine the multiplication sentences and describe the patterns they see.

Activity Choice 2 • Literature

Introduce the lesson with *Melisande* by E. Nesbit. For a related math activity, see p. TR52.

2 Teach

Scaffolding Questions

Have students choose a number from 11–99 and a multiple of ten from 10–90. Have them use patterns to find the product of the two numbers.

- **What number will be in the ones place when you multiply by a multiple of ten?** 0
- **If you know the product of 14×3, how can you find 14×30?** Write the product of 14×3 and put one 0 at the end.
- **Explain to a classmate how to multiply any number by 20.** Sample answer: Write 0 in the ones place. Multiply the number by 2 tens and write the product to the left of the 0.

GET READY to Learn

Have students open their books and read the information in **Get Ready to Learn**. Review **product**, **multiple**, and **factor**. As a class, work through **Examples 1 and 2**.

Multiply by Tens

Example 1 Remind students that any multiple of ten can be rewritten as two factors: a whole number multiplied by 10. In this example, 20 is rewritten as 2×10. The Associative Property of Multiplication is then used to group the factors so that the product can be found with mental math.

ADDITIONAL EXAMPLES

1. There are 35 packs of markers in an art classroom. Each pack contains 50 markers. How many markers are there in all? 1,750
2. A store has 20 children's bicycles in stock that cost $159 each. How much do all of the bicycles cost altogether? $3,180

CHECK What You Know

As a class, have students complete Exercises 1–8 in **Check What Your Know** as you observe their work.

Exercise 8 Assess student comprehension before assigning practice exercises.

BL Alternate Teaching Strategy

If students have trouble multiplying a whole number by a multiple of ten…

Then use one of these reteach options:

1 CRM **Daily Reteach Worksheet** (p. 8)

2 Have students make grid paper diagrams of arrays to model each exercise. For Exercise 2, have them create an array with 30 rows and 53 columns broken apart to show 50 + 3. Have students multiply each part by 30 and add to find the product.

COMMON ERROR!

Exercises 4, 9 and 13 Students may omit the 0 in the ones place when the product of the tens ends with 0. Remind students to always multiply by ones first and write 0, then multiply the tens. Have them use estimation to check the reasonableness of their answers.

Real-World EXAMPLE Multiply by Tens

2 MUSIC An electronics store has 30 digital music players in stock that cost $125 each. How much do the digital music players cost altogether?

Step 1 Multiply the ones.

$$\begin{array}{r} \$125 \\ \times\ 30 \\ \hline 0 \end{array} \leftarrow \boxed{0 \text{ ones} \times 125 = 0}$$

Remember
When you multiply a number by a multiple of ten, the digit in the ones place is always zero.

Step 2 Multiply the tens.

$$\begin{array}{r} \$125 \\ \times\ 30 \\ \hline \$3{,}750 \end{array} \leftarrow \boxed{3 \text{ tens} \times 125 = 375 \text{ tens}}$$

So, the music players cost a total of $3,750.

Check
Think of 30×125 as $3 \times 10 \times 125$.

$30 \times \$125$	Write the problem.
$(3 \times 10) \times \$125$	Think of 30 as 3×10.
$(10 \times 3) \times \$125$	Commutative Property
$10 \times (3 \times \$125)$	Associative Property
$10 \times \$375$	Multiply. $3 \times \$125 = \$375$
$\$3{,}750$	Mental Math

So, the answer is correct. ✓

8. Sample answer: $4 \times 10 = 40$, so 40 can be replaced by its factors.

CHECK What You Know

Multiply. See Examples 1 and 2 (pp. 273–274)

1. 36×10 360
2. 53×30 1,590
3. 79×80 6,320
4. $255× 20 $5,100
5. $\$389 \times 40$ $15,560
6. $\$518 \times 70$ $36,260
7. **Measurement** Latasha bikes 20 miles every week. There are 52 weeks in a year. How many miles does she bike in a year? 1,040 miles
8. Talk About It Joey is finding 40×67. Explain why he can think of 40×67 as $4 \times 10 \times 67$.

274 **Chapter 7** Multiply by Two-Digit Numbers

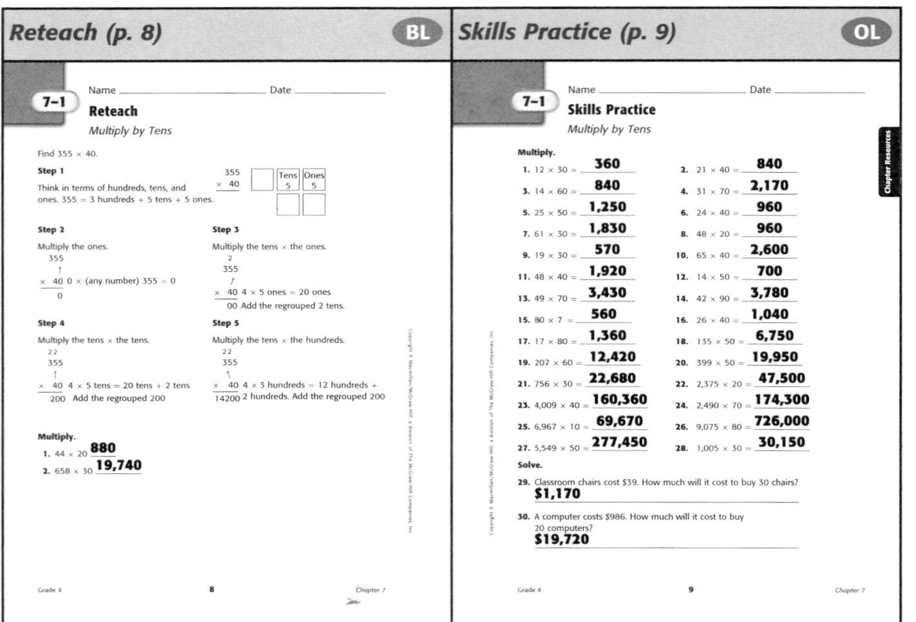

Reteach (p. 8) BL

7-1 Name ______ Date ______
Reteach
Multiply by Tens

Find 355×40.

Step 1
Think in terms of hundreds, tens, and ones. 355 = 3 hundreds + 5 tens + 5 ones.

355 × 40 | Tens 5 | Ones 5

Step 2
Multiply the ones.
355 × 40 — 0 × (any number) 355 = 0 — 0

Step 3
Multiply the tens × the ones.
355 × 40 — 4 × 5 ones = 20 ones — 00 Add the regrouped 2 tens.

Step 4
Multiply the tens × the tens.
355 × 40 — 4 × 5 tens = 20 tens + 2 tens — 200 Add the regrouped 200

Step 5
Multiply the tens × the hundreds.
355 × 40 — 4 × 3 hundreds = 12 hundreds + 2 hundreds. Add the regrouped 200 — 14200

Multiply.
1. 44 × 20 **880**
2. 658 × 30 **19,740**

Grade 4 8 Chapter 7

Skills Practice (p. 9) OL

7-1 Name ______ Date ______
Skills Practice
Multiply by Tens

Multiply.

1. 12 × 30 = **360**
2. 21 × 40 = **840**
3. 14 × 60 = **840**
4. 31 × 70 = **2,170**
5. 25 × 50 = **1,250**
6. 24 × 40 = **960**
7. 61 × 30 = **1,830**
8. 48 × 20 = **960**
9. 19 × 30 = **570**
10. 65 × 40 = **2,600**
11. 48 × 40 = **1,920**
12. 14 × 50 = **700**
13. 49 × 70 = **3,430**
14. 42 × 90 = **3,780**
15. 80 × 7 = **560**
16. 26 × 40 = **1,040**
17. 17 × 80 = **1,360**
18. 135 × 50 = **6,750**
19. 207 × 60 = **12,420**
20. 399 × 50 = **19,950**
21. 756 × 30 = **22,680**
22. 2,375 × 20 = **47,500**
23. 4,009 × 40 = **160,360**
24. 2,490 × 70 = **174,300**
25. 6,967 × 10 = **69,670**
26. 9,075 × 80 = **726,000**
27. 5,549 × 50 = **277,450**
28. 1,005 × 30 = **30,150**

Solve.

29. Classroom chairs cost $39. How much will it cost to buy 30 chairs? **$1,170**
30. A computer costs $986. How much will it cost to buy 20 computers? **$19,720**

Grade 4 9 Chapter 7

Practice and Problem Solving

EXTRA PRACTICE See page R17.

Multiply. See Examples 1 and 2 (pp. 273–274)

9. 15×20 300
10. 27×30 810
11. 46×40 1,840
12. 53×60 3,180

13. 80×80 6,400
14. 94×90 8,460
15. $275 × 10 $2,750
16. $312 × 30 $9,360

17. $381 × 50 $19,050
18. $457 × 50 $22,850
19. $564 × 70 $39,480
20. $698 × 80 $55,840

21. If $7 \times 29 = 203$, then what is 70×29? 2,030

22. If $3 \times 52 = 156$, then what is 30×52? 1,560

23. Baby robins eat 14 feet of earthworms each day. How many feet of worms does a baby robin eat in 20 days? 280 ft

24. Mozart could learn a piece of music in 30 minutes. How long would it take him to learn 15 pieces of music? 450 min

Real-World PROBLEM SOLVING

Birds Hummingbirds feed every 10 minutes. They fly about 25 miles per hour and flap their wings 60 to 80 times each second.

25. What is the least number of times a hummingbird will flap its wings in 15 seconds? 900

26. What is the greatest number of times it will flap its wing in 15 seconds? 1,200

27. How many minutes have passed if a hummingbird has eaten 45 times? 450 min

28. If a hummingbird flies a total of 20 hours, how far did it fly? 500 miles

H.O.T. Problems

29. OPEN ENDED Create a number sentence with two 2-digit factors whose product has 3 zeros. Sample answer: $80 \times 50 = 4,000$

30. WHICH ONE DOESN'T BELONG? Identify the multiplication problem that does not belong with the other three. Explain.

15×30 28×20 41×21 67×40

30, 31. See Ch. 7 Answer Appendix.

31. WRITING IN ▸MATH How many zeros would be in the product of 50 and 60? Explain.

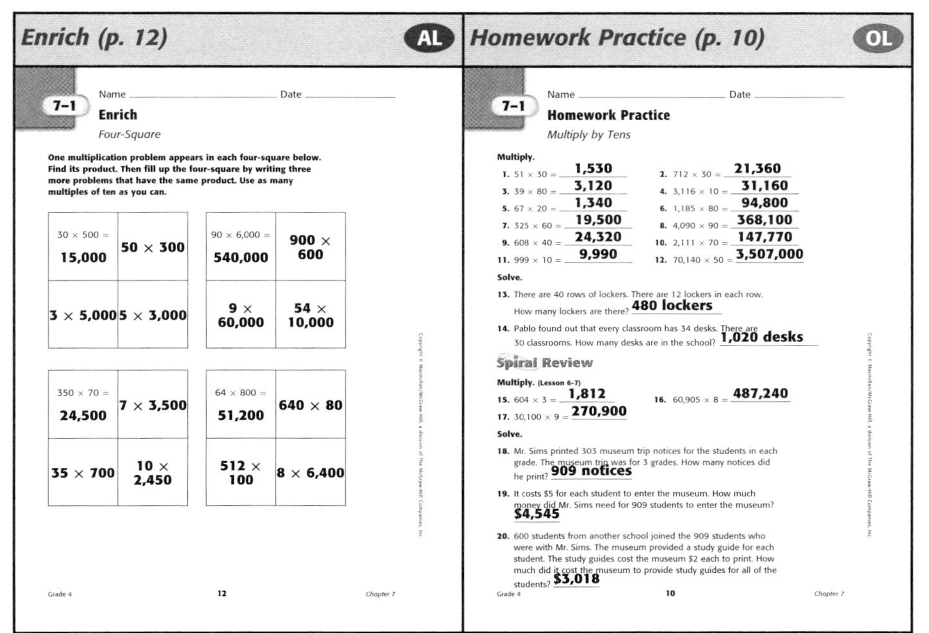

Enrich (p. 12) AL

7-1 Name ______ Date ______

Enrich

Four-Square

One multiplication problem appears in each four-square below. Find its product. Then fill up the four-square by writing three more problems that have the same product. Use as many multiples of ten as you can.

$30 \times 500 =$ **15,000**	**50 × 300**
3 × 5,000	**5 × 3,000**

$90 \times 6,000 =$ **540,000**	**900 × 600**
9 × 60,000	**54 × 10,000**

$350 \times 70 =$ **24,500**	**7 × 3,500**
35 × 700	**10 × 2,450**

$64 \times 800 =$ **51,200**	**640 × 80**
512 × 100	**8 × 6,400**

Grade 4 12 Chapter 7

Homework Practice (p. 10) OL

7-1 Name ______ Date ______

Homework Practice

Multiply by Tens

Multiply.

1. $51 \times 30 =$ **1,530**
2. $712 \times 30 =$ **21,360**
3. $39 \times 80 =$ **3,120**
4. $3,116 \times 10 =$ **31,160**
5. $67 \times 20 =$ **1,340**
6. $1,185 \times 80 =$ **94,800**
7. $325 \times 60 =$ **19,500**
8. $4,090 \times 90 =$ **368,100**
9. $608 \times 40 =$ **24,320**
10. $2,111 \times 70 =$ **147,770**
11. $999 \times 10 =$ **9,990**
12. $70,140 \times 50 =$ **3,507,000**

Solve.

13. There are 40 rows of lockers. There are 12 lockers in each row. How many lockers are there? **480 lockers**
14. Pablo found out that every classroom has 34 desks. There are 30 classrooms. How many desks are in the school? **1,020 desks**

Spiral Review

Multiply. (Lesson 6-7)

15. $604 \times 3 =$ **1,812**
16. $60,905 \times 8 =$ **487,240**
17. $30,100 \times 9 =$ **270,900**

Solve.

18. Mr. Sims printed 303 museum trip notices for the students in each grade. The museum trip was for 3 grades. How many notices did he print? **909 notices**
19. It costs $5 for each student to enter the museum. How much money did Mr. Sims need for 909 students to enter the museum? **$4,545**
20. 600 students from another school joined the 909 students who were with Mr. Sims. The museum provided a study guide for each student. The study guides cost the museum $2 each to print. How much did it cost the museum to provide study guides for all of the students? **$3,018**

Grade 4 10 Chapter 7

3 Practice

Differentiate practice using these leveled assignments for Exercises 9–31.

Level	Assignment
BL Below/Approaching Level	9–11, 15–18, 23–26
OL On Level	9–18, 21–24, 27–28, 29
AL Above/Beyond Level	9–27 odd, 29–31

Have students discuss and complete the Higher Order Thinking problems. For Exercise 29, encourage children to write a product with 3 zeros first and work backward to find the two 2-digit factors.

WRITING IN ▸MATH Have students complete Exercise 31 in their Math Journals. You may choose to use this exercise as an optional formative assessment.

4 Assess

Formative Assessment

Write 49×60 on the board.

- **Describe one way to find the product.** Sample answer: Multiply the ones and write 0 in the ones place. Then multiply the tens and write the product to the left of 0.
- **How could you check your work?** Sample answer: Use the Associative Property of Multiplication and mental math.
- **What is the product?** 2,940

Quick Check **Are students continuing to struggle with multiplying a whole number by a multiple of ten?**

If Yes → Small Group Options (p. 273B)
Strategic Intervention Guide (p. 80)

If No → Independent Work Options (p. 273B)
CRM Skills Practice Worksheet (p. 9)
CRM Enrich Worksheet (p. 12)

Into the Future Have students predict what they will learn next about multiplying by two-digit numbers. Have them write or say a sample problem they may be asked to solve.

LESSON **7-2**

Estimate Products

Lesson Planner

Objective

Estimate products by rounding.

Review Vocabulary

estimate, **round**

Resources

Materials: masking tape, index cards

Literature Connection: *Moira's Birthday* by Robert Munsch

Teacher Technology
TeacherWorks • Interactive Classroom

Alternate Lesson: Use *IMPACT Mathematics: Unit C* to provide practice with estimating products.

Daily Routine

Use these suggestions before beginning the lesson on p. 302.

5-Minute Check

(Reviews Lesson 7-1)

Multiply.

1. 87×10 870

2. 34×30 1,020

3. 65×80 5,200

4. $\$23 \times 50$ \$1,150

5. $\$79 \times 90$ \$7,110

6. $\$57 \times 60$ \$3,420

Problem of the Day

Marie draws a triangle of circles. She draws 1 circle in the top row, 3 in the second row, 5 in the third row, and 7 in the fourth row. How many circles will Marie draw in the seventh row? If Marie has ten rows, how many circles will she draw in all? 13; 100

Focus on Math Background

Estimation is an important skill, not only in the mathematics classroom, but in the real world as well. So often, an exact answer is less necessary than a reasonable estimate. In the previous chapter, students rounded one factor to the greatest place and used mental math to find an estimate. In this chapter, students round both factors to estimate the product. Once again, it is important to stress the need to know when your estimate is high and when it is low.

- When both factors are rounded up, the estimate will be high.
- When both factors are rounded up, the estimate will be low.
- When one factor is rounded up and one is rounded down, it may not be immediately apparent as to whether the estimate is high or low.

Review Math Vocabulary

Write the review vocabulary words and their definitions on the board.

Point out that the term *round* has more than one meaning. Have students locate a round object in the classroom. Then have them write a sentence using *round* (as defined on the board) and *estimate* to show that they understand their meanings and relationship. Have students share their sentences.

Visual Vocabulary Cards

Use Visual Vocabulary Cards 15 and 42 to reinforce the vocabulary reviewed in this lesson. (The Define/Example/Ask routine is printed on the back of each card.)

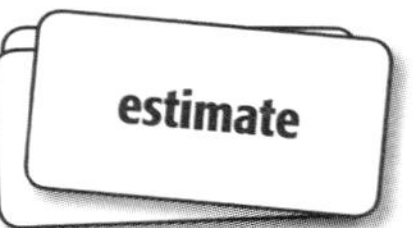

Differentiated Instruction

Small Group Options

Option 1 Below Level BL

LOGICAL

Materials: paper, pencils, chart paper

- Review the concept of rounding 2 two-digit numbers in order to estimate their product. For example, 33×48 rounds to 30×50.
- Using the zero strategy, the product will have at least 2 zeroes in it. The product of 3 and 5 is 15, so the product of 30 and 50 is 1,500.
- Simply put, the zero strategy is to count the zeroes at the end of the factors and add them to the product of the rest of the factors.
- Practice this with some numbers already rounded but containing no zeroes naturally in the product.
- When the students are ready, introduce 40×50.
- The product—2,000—contains one more zero than already in the problem because the product of 4 and 5 is 20.

Option 2 English Language Learners ELL

AUDITORY

Core Vocabulary: less than, penny, a nickel or better
Common Use Verb: rounds up
See Math This strategy helps students visualize the concept of rounding.

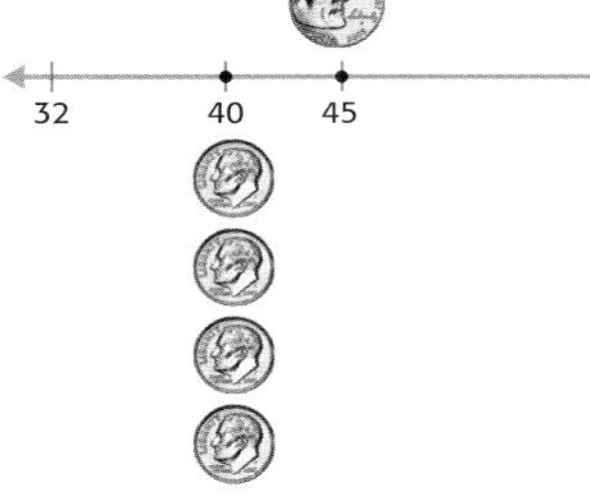

- Demonstrate how 45 is midway between 40 and 50.
- Say, "**a nickel or better *rounds up*, less than a nickel rounds down**" as you roll the nickel and your voice up and down accordingly.
- Say: "Is 46 **a nickel or better**?"
- Add a penny to the nickel. Say: "46 is **a nickel or better** so it ***rounds up***."
- Repeat for other numbers.

Independent Work Options

Option 1 Early Finishers OL AL

VISUAL, LINGUISTIC

Materials: 20–30 index cards

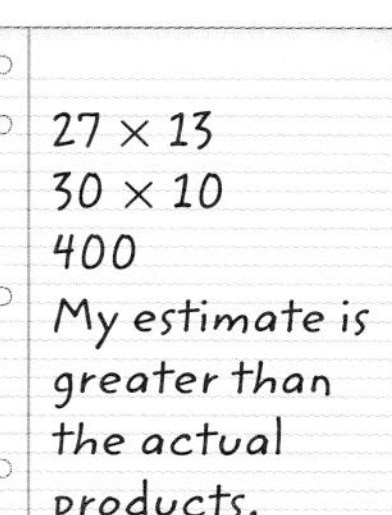

27 × 13
30 × 10
400
My estimate is greater than the actual products.

- Have students write 10 numbers from 11–99, one per index card. Combine and place facedown in a pile.
- Students choose two cards and estimate the product of the numbers. Students decide whether their estimate is greater or less than the actual product.
- Finally, students find the product.

Option 2 Student Technology

Math Online macmillanmh.com

Personal Tutor • Extra Examples

 Math Adventures

Option 3 Learning Station: Social Studies (p. 270H)

Direct students to the Social Studies Learning Station for opportunities to explore and extend the lesson concept.

Option 4 Problem-Solving Practice

Reinforce problem-solving skills and strategies with the Problem-Solving Practice worksheet.

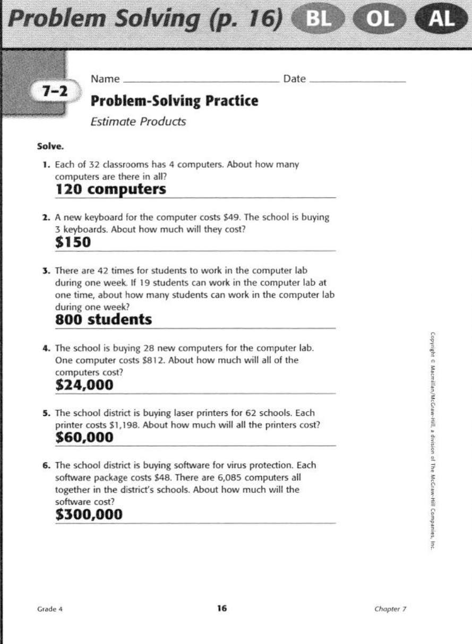

Problem Solving (p. 16) BL OL AL

7–2 Name ______ Date ______

Problem-Solving Practice

Estimate Products

Solve.

1. Each of 32 classrooms has 4 computers. About how many computers are there in all?
120 computers
2. A new keyboard for the computer costs $49. The school is buying 3 keyboards. About how much will they cost?
$150
3. There are 42 times for students to work in the computer lab during one week. If 19 students can work in the computer lab at one time, about how many students can work in the computer lab during one week?
800 students
4. The school is buying 28 new computers for the computer lab. One computer costs $812. About how much will all of the computers cost?
$24,000
5. The school district is buying laser printers for 62 schools. Each printer costs $1,198. About how much will all the printers cost?
$60,000
6. The school district is buying software for virus protection. Each software package costs $48. There are 6,085 computers all together in the district's schools. About how much will the software cost?
$300,000

Grade 4 16 Chapter 7

7-2 Estimate Products

1 Introduce

Activity Choice 1 • Hands-On 

- Use masking tape and index cards to create two class number lines on the floor: one showing multiples of ten from 0 to 100 and the other showing multiples of 100 from 0 to 1,000.
- Have several volunteers name a two-digit number to round to the nearest ten. Have them write their number on an index card and place the card in its approximate position on the number line from 0 to 100.
- **Which ten comes before your number? Which ten comes after? Which ten is your number closer to? How do you know?** Answers will vary.
- Repeat for each number.
- Repeat the activity, this time rounding three-digit numbers to the nearest hundred.

Activity Choice 2 • Literature

Introduce the lesson with *Moira's Birthday* by Robert Munsch. For a related math activity, see p. TR52.

2 Teach

Scaffolding Questions

- **Does 45 round up to 50 or round down to 40? Explain.** Up to 50; if the number in the ones place is 5 or greater, I round up to the next ten.
- **How is rounding to the nearest ten different from rounding to the nearest hundred?** I look at the ones digit when I round to the nearest ten. I look at the tens digit when I round to the nearest hundred.
- **Choose 2 two-digit numbers from the first number line to multiply. How could you use rounding to estimate the product?** Round each number to the nearest ten and then multiply.

GET READY to Learn

Have students open their books and read the informaton in **Get Ready to Learn**. Review **estimate** and **round**. As a class, work through **Examples 1 and 2**.

7-2 Estimate Products

MAIN IDEA

I will estimate products by rounding.

Math Online

macmillanmh.com
- Extra Examples
- Personal Tutor
- Self-Check Quiz

GET READY to Learn

Did you know that a hamster sleeps more than half the day? It sleeps about 14 hours each day. About how many hours does it sleep in 3 weeks?

The word *about* tells you to estimate. When you estimate the product of two two-digit factors, it is helpful to round them both.

Real-World EXAMPLE Estimate Products

1 **ANIMALS A hamster sleeps 14 hours each day. About how many hours does a hamster sleep in 3 weeks?**

There are 21 days in 3 weeks. So, estimate 21×14.

Step 1 Round each factor to the nearest ten.

$$\begin{array}{r} 21 \\ \times\ 14 \end{array} \rightarrow \begin{array}{r} 20 \\ \times\ 10 \end{array}$$

21 rounds to 20.
14 rounds to 10.

Step 2 Multiply.

$$\begin{array}{r} 20 \\ \times\ 10 \\ \hline 200 \end{array}$$

0 ones × 20 = 0
1 ten × 20 = 20 tens

So, a hamster sleeps about 200 hours in 21 days or 3 weeks. Since both factors were rounded down, the estimate is less than the actual product.

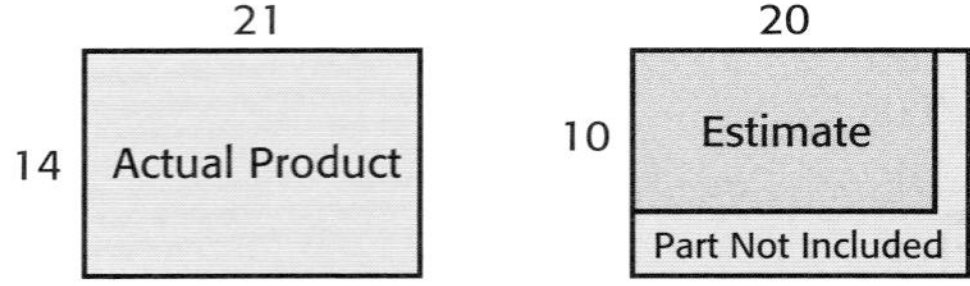

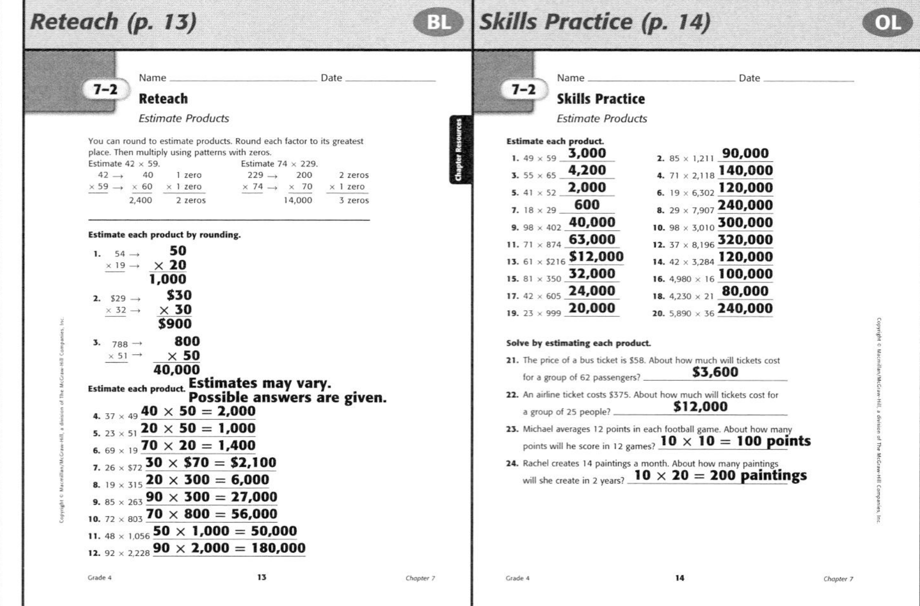

Reteach (p. 13) BL

7-2 Name ________ Date ________

Reteach

Estimate Products

You can round to estimate products. Round each factor to its greatest place. Then multiply using patterns with zeros.

Estimate 42 × 59.

$42 \rightarrow 40$, $\times 59 \rightarrow \times 60$, $= 2{,}400$ (1 zero × 1 zero = 2 zeros)

Estimate 74 × 229.

$229 \rightarrow 200$, $\times 74 \rightarrow \times 70$, $= 14{,}000$ (2 zeros × 1 zero = 3 zeros)

Estimate each product by rounding.

1. 54 × 19 → 50 × 20 = **1,000**
2. \$29 × 32 → \$30 × 30 = **\$900**
3. 788 × 51 → 800 × 50 = **40,000**

Estimate each product. **Estimates may vary. Possible answers are given.**

4. 37 × 49 **40 × 50 = 2,000**
5. 23 × 51 **20 × 50 = 1,000**
6. 69 × 19 **70 × 20 = 1,400**
7. 26 × \$72 **30 × \$70 = \$2,100**
8. 19 × 315 **20 × 300 = 6,000**
9. 85 × 263 **90 × 300 = 27,000**
10. 72 × 803 **70 × 800 = 56,000**
11. 48 × 1,056 **50 × 1,000 = 50,000**
12. 92 × 2,228 **90 × 2,000 = 180,000**

Grade 4 13 Chapter 7

Skills Practice (p. 14) OL

7-2 Name ________ Date ________

Skills Practice

Estimate Products

Estimate each product.

1. 49 × 59 **3,000**
2. 85 × 1,211 **90,000**
3. 55 × 65 **4,200**
4. 71 × 2,118 **140,000**
5. 41 × 52 **2,000**
6. 19 × 6,302 **120,000**
7. 18 × 29 **600**
8. 29 × 7,907 **240,000**
9. 98 × 402 **40,000**
10. 98 × 3,010 **300,000**
11. 71 × 874 **63,000**
12. 37 × 8,196 **320,000**
13. 61 × \$216 **\$12,000**
14. 42 × 3,284 **120,000**
15. 81 × 350 **32,000**
16. 4,980 × 16 **100,000**
17. 42 × 605 **24,000**
18. 4,230 × 21 **80,000**
19. 23 × 999 **20,000**
20. 5,890 × 36 **240,000**

Solve by estimating each product.

21. The price of a bus ticket is \$58. About how much will tickets cost for a group of 62 passengers? **\$3,600**
22. An airline ticket costs \$375. About how much will tickets cost for a group of 25 people? **\$12,000**
23. Michael averages 12 points in each football game. About how many points will he score in 12 games? **10 × 10 = 100 points**
24. Rachel creates 14 paintings a month. About how many paintings will she create in 2 years? **10 × 20 = 200 paintings**

Grade 4 14 Chapter 7

Estimate Products

2 **MEASUREMENT Tonya spends 35 minutes playing at the park each day. About how many minutes does she play at the park in a year?**

There are approximately 365 days in a year. So, you need to estimate 365×35.

Step 1 Round each factor to its greatest place.

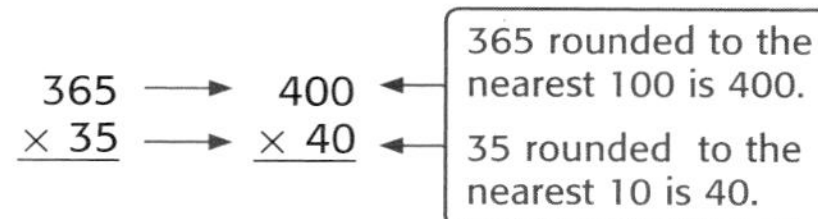

365 → 400
× 35 → × 40
365 rounded to the nearest 100 is 400.
35 rounded to the nearest 10 is 40.

Remember

If one factor is rounded up and one factor is rounded down, it will not be obvious whether the estimate is greater or less than the actual product.

Step 2 Multiply.

$$\begin{array}{r} 400 \\ \times\ 40 \\ \hline 16{,}000 \end{array}$$

So, Tonya spends about 16,000 minutes playing at the park in a year. Since both factors were rounded up, the estimate is greater than the actual product.

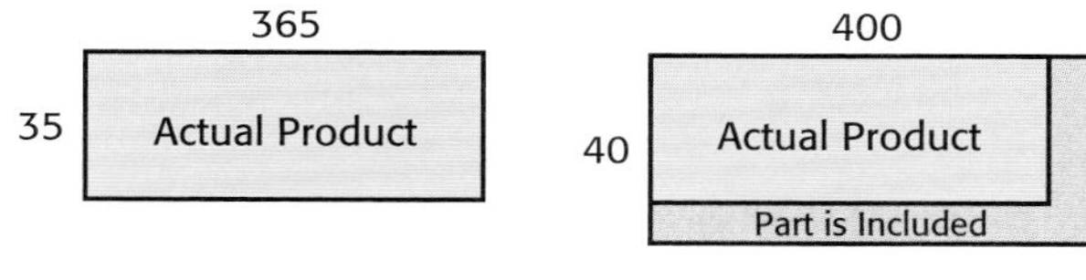

6. If both factors are rounded down, the estimate is less than the actual product. If both factors are rounded up, the estimate is greater than the actual product.

CHECK What You Know

Estimate. Tell whether the estimate is *greater than* or *less than* the actual product. See Examples 1 and 2 (pp. 276–277)

1. 34×12 — $30 \times 10 = 300$; less

2. 57×25 — $60 \times 30 = 1{,}800$; greater

3. $\$376 \times 17$ — $\$400 \times 20 = \$8{,}000$; greater

4. 525×43 — $500 \times 40 = 20{,}000$; less

5. The average person makes about 22 phone calls each week. About how many phone calls is this each year? $50 \times 20 = 1{,}000$

6. Talk About It Explain how you know if an estimated product is more or less than the actual product.

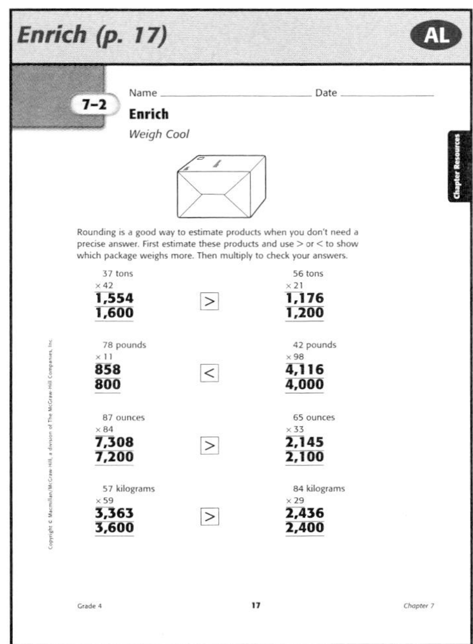

Enrich (p. 17) AL

7–2 Name ____ Date ____

Enrich

Weigh Cool

Rounding is a good way to estimate products when you don't need a precise answer. First estimate these products and use > or < to show which package weighs more. Then multiply to check your answers.

37 tons × 42 = **1,554**; **1,600**	>	56 tons × 21 = **1,176**; **1,200**
78 pounds × 11 = **858**; **800**	<	42 pounds × 98 = **4,116**; **4,000**
87 ounces × 84 = **7,308**; **7,200**	>	65 ounces × 33 = **2,145**; **2,100**
57 kilograms × 59 = **3,363**; **3,600**	>	84 kilograms × 29 = **2,436**; **2,400**

Chapter Resources

Grade 4 17 Chapter 7

Estimate Products

Example 2 Remind students that there are about 365 days in one year. Explain that we can estimate the total minutes Tonya plays in a year by rounding 365 days and 35 minutes and multiplying the rounded factors. Point out that, in this lesson, we will round three-digit numbers to the nearest hundred and two-digit numbers to the nearest ten.

ADDITIONAL EXAMPLES

1. Kaylee is awake for about 16 hours each day. About how many hours is she awake in 4 weeks? about 600 hours
2. A company bought 53 computers for \$909 each. About how much did they spend in all? about \$45,000

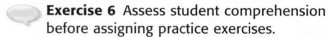

As a class, have students complete Exercises 1–6 in **Check What Your Know** as you observe their work.

Exercise 6 Assess student comprehension before assigning practice exercises.

BL Alternate Teaching Strategy

If students have trouble deciding whether the estimate is more or less than the actual product…

Then use one of these reteach options:

1 CRM **Daily Reteach Worksheet** (p. 13)

2 Draw and label a rectangle on the board that represents 24 by 62. Ask students to visualize a 20-by-60 rectangle and compare it to the one drawn on the board.

- **Is the rectangle you are thinking of larger or smaller than the one on the board?** smaller
- **How do you know?** because each side of the new rectangle is smaller

Repeat the activity and questions with a 38-by-46 rectangle and a 29-by-41 rectangle. Have students discuss why it is difficult to make a comparison in the last example.

3 Practice

Differentiate practice using these leveled

Level	Assignment
BL Below/Approaching Level	7–9, 15–16, 23–24, 27–28
OL On Level	8–13, 16–25, 27–28, 30
AL Above/Beyond Level	8–28 even, 29–31

Have students discuss and complete the Higher Order Thinking problems. For Exercise 29, encourage students to start by thinking of two factors with a product of 20.

WRITING IN ▸MATH Have students complete Exercise 31 in their Math Journals. You may choose to use this exercise as an optional formative assessment.

Additional Answers

7. $30 \times 30 = 900$; greater than
8. $40 \times 10 = 400$; less than
9. $\$60 \times 40 = \$2,400$; greater than
10. $60 \times 30 = 1,800$; greater than
11. $60 \times 40 = 2,400$; less than
12. $80 \times 60 = 4,800$; greater than
13. $\$90 \times 60 = 5,400$; less than
14. $90 \times 80 = 7,200$; less than
15. $\$200 \times 10 = \$2,000$; less than
16. $400 \times 40 = 16,000$; greater than
17. $500 \times 90 = 45,000$; greater than
18. $500 \times 40 = 20,000$; less than
19. $700 \times 60 = 42,000$; greater than
20. $700 \times 80 = 56,000$; less than
21. $900 \times 80 = 72,000$; greater than
22. $900 \times 90 = 81,000$; less than

COMMON ERROR!

Exercises 4 and 15–17 Students may use the number in the ones place to round three-digit numbers. Remind students to look at the value of the tens when rounding to the nearest hundred. Have students write each factor and circle the number that tells them how to round.

Practice and Problem Solving

See page R18.

Estimate. Tell whether the estimate is *greater than* or *less than* the actual product. See Examples 1 and 2 (pp. 276–277) 7–22. See margin.

7. 28×25 **8.** 43×14 **9.** $\$56 \times 37$ **10.** 58×29

11. 64×41 **12.** 79×55 **13.** $\$91 \times 64$ **14.** 94×82

15. $\$234 \times 11$ **16.** 352×37 **17.** 489×86 **18.** 535×42

19. 678×56 **20.** 739×84 **21.** 891×78 **22.** 919×92

23. An antelope can run 55 miles per hour. About how many miles would it travel if it ran a total of 12 hours? $60 \times 10 = 600$ miles

24. Gabe averages 16 points in each basketball game. About how many points will he score in 14 games? $20 \times 10 = 200$ points

25. A certain type of millipede has 750 legs. About how many legs would 12 of these millipedes have? $800 \times 10 = 8,000$ legs

26. **Measurement** About how many pounds of fruit would the average American eat in 11 years? $10 \times 100 = 1,000$ lb

Food Eaten Each Year

Type of Food	Amount (lb)
Fresh fruit	127
Fresh vegetables	148
Milk and cream	205

Source: *The Top 100 of Everything*

Data File

People rushed to California in search of gold in 1849. This is called the California Gold Rush.

27. About how many miles would the wind wagon travel over 7 days traveling 8 hours each day? $20 \times 10 \times 10 = 2,000$ miles

28. People paid up to \$100 for a glass of water on the trail to California. If it cost \$93 for 1 glass, about how much would 12 glasses of water cost? $\$90 \times 10 = \$900$

- A wind wagon was used by some people as transportation to California.
- It could travel 15 miles per hour.

H.O.T. Problems

29. OPEN ENDED Identify two factors that have an estimated product of 2,000. Sample answer: $38 \times 52 \rightarrow 40 \times 50 = 2{,}000$

30. NUMBER SENSE Estimate 51×39 and 84×45. Which is closer to its actual product? Explain your reasoning. 30, 31. See margin.

31. WRITING IN MATH Write a real-world problem that involves estimating the product of two 2-digit numbers.

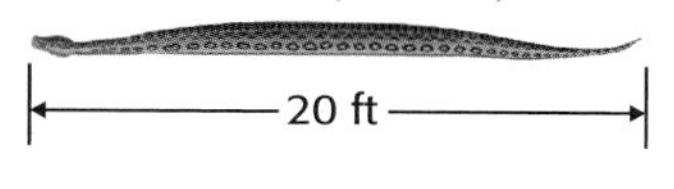

32. What is the total length of 35 anacondas? (Lesson 7-1) B

20 ft

A 600 feet **C** 800 feet

B 700 feet **D** 900 feet

33. There are 365 days in a year. Which is the best estimate of the number of days in 12 years? (Lesson 7-2) J

F 7,000

G 6,000

H 5,000

J 4,000

Spiral Review

Multiply. (Lesson 7-1)

34. 27×10 = 270

35. 43×50 = 2,150

36. $\$96 \times 70$ = \$6,720

Multiply. Check for reasonableness. (Lesson 6-7) 39. $63{,}360;\ 9 \times 7{,}000 = 63{,}000$

37. $1{,}006 \times 3$ $3{,}018;\ 3 \times 1000 = 3{,}000$

38. $4{,}065 \times 6$ $24{,}390;\ 6 \times 4{,}000 = 24{,}000$

39. $7{,}040 \times 9$

40. Write an equation that describes the pattern in the table. Then use the equation to find the next three numbers. (Lesson 5-8)

Input (*w*)	1	3	5	7	9	11
Output (*v*)	4	12	20	■	■	■

40, 41. See Ch. 7 Answer Appendix.

41. Arthur earns \$20 for every lawn he mows. He mows 12 lawns twice a month. He has been mowing for 3 months. How much money does he make in 1 month? Identify any extra or missing information. Then solve. (Lesson 5-3)

Write the value of the underlined digit. (Lesson 1-2)

42. 189,3<u>9</u>7 90

43. <u>2</u>,670,830 2,000,000

44. 34,7<u>9</u>1,028 90,000

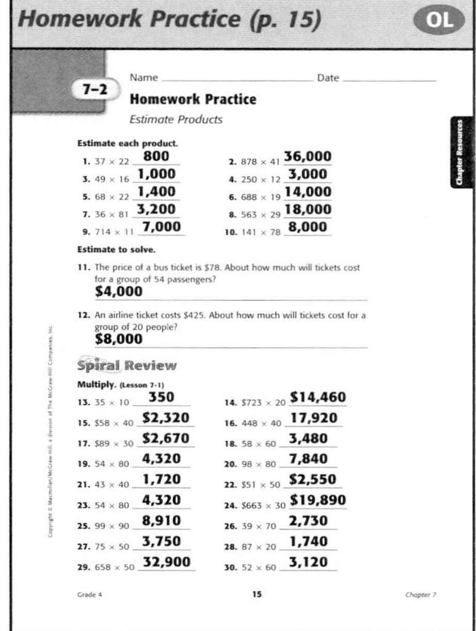

Homework Practice (p. 15) OL

Name ________ Date ________

7–2 **Homework Practice**

Estimate Products

Estimate each product.

1. 37 × 22 **800**
2. 878 × 41 **36,000**
3. 49 × 16 **1,000**
4. 250 × 12 **3,000**
5. 68 × 22 **1,400**
6. 688 × 19 **14,000**
7. 36 × 81 **3,200**
8. 563 × 29 **18,000**
9. 714 × 11 **7,000**
10. 141 × 78 **8,000**

Estimate to solve.

11. The price of a bus ticket is \$78. About how much will tickets cost for a group of 54 passengers? **\$4,000**

12. An airline ticket costs \$425. About how much will tickets cost for a group of 20 people? **\$8,000**

Spiral Review

Multiply. (Lesson 7-1)

13. 35 × 10 **350**
14. \$723 × 20 **\$14,460**
15. \$58 × 40 **\$2,320**
16. 448 × 40 **17,920**
17. \$89 × 30 **\$2,670**
18. 58 × 60 **3,480**
19. 54 × 80 **4,320**
20. 98 × 80 **7,840**
21. 43 × 40 **1,720**
22. \$51 × 50 **\$2,550**
23. 54 × 80 **4,320**
24. \$663 × 30 **\$19,890**
25. 99 × 90 **8,910**
26. 39 × 70 **2,730**
27. 75 × 50 **3,750**
28. 87 × 20 **1,740**
29. 658 × 50 **32,900**
30. 52 × 60 **3,120**

Chapter Resources

Grade 4 15 Chapter 7

4 Assess

Formative Assessment

Write 339×44 on the board.

- **How would you estimate 339×44? What is the estimated product?** Round 339 down to 300 and 44 down to 40. Multiply 300×40. The estimated product is 12,000.
- **Is the estimated product more or less than the actual product? How do you know?** Less; I rounded both factors down.

Quick Check **Are students continuing to struggle with rounding to estimate products?**

If Yes → Small Group Options (p. 276B)
Strategic Intervention Guide (p. 72)

If No → Independent Work Options (p. 276B)
CRM Skills Practice Worksheet (p. 14)
CRM Enrich Worksheet (p. 17)

Yesterday's News Have students write a paragraph describing how rounding and multiplying by tens helped them estimate products in this lesson.

Reviews Lessons 7-1 and 7-2

Assign the Test Practice problems to provide daily reinforcement of test-taking skills.

Spiral Review

Reviews Lessons 1-2, 5-3, 5-8, 6-7, and 7-1

Review and assess mastery of skills and concepts from previous chapters.

Additional Answers

30. Sample answer: 51×39; Its actual factors are closer to the estimated factors.

31. Sample answer: George walks 45 minutes for 16 days each month. How many minutes does he walk a month?

Act It Out

Lesson Planner

Objective

Solve problems by using the act it out strategy.

Resources

Materials: index cards, transparent tape

Manipulatives: money, square pattern blocks

Literature Connection: *Ten Mile Day: And the Building of the Transcontinental Railroad* by Mary Ann Fraser

Teacher Technology
TeacherWorks • Interactive Classroom

Real-World Problem Solving Library
Math and Science: ***What Is Recycling?***
Use these leveled books to reinforce and extend problem-solving skills and strategies.

Leveled for:

- OL On Level
- ELL Sheltered English
- SP Spanish

For additional support, see the Real-World Problem Solving Teacher Guide.

Daily Routine

Use these suggestions before beginning the lesson on p. 306.

5-Minute Check

(Reviews Lesson 7-2)

Estimate. Tell whether the estimate is greater than or less than the actual product.

1. 39×35
1,600; greater

2. 63×44
2,400; less

3. $\$54 \times 81$
$4,000; less

4. $274 × 16
$6,000; greater

5. 719 × 94
63,000; less

Problem of the Day

A flag has 14 stripes. There is a blue stripe only at each end of the flag. The pattern of colors after the first stripe is green, red, and white. What is the color of the tenth stripe? How many stripes of that color are on the flag? white; 4 stripes

Differentiated Instruction

Small Group Options

LOGICAL

1 Below Level BL

Materials: paper, pencils, chart paper

- Write the following problem on the chart paper:

$$\begin{array}{r} 48 \\ \times\ 30 \\ \hline \end{array}$$

- Tell the students that this problem can be written differently to make it easier to solve.

$$\begin{array}{r} 48 \\ \times\ 30 \\ \hline \end{array}$$

- To solve, bring down the zero first, then multiply as if it were a one-digit times a two-digit problem.
- The answer will look like this:

$$\begin{array}{r} 48 \\ \times\ 30 \\ \hline 1440 \end{array}$$

- Practice other problems with a zero in the bottom factor.

Option

KINESTHETIC, SOCIAL

2 English Language Learners ELL

Materials: see art

Core Vocabulary: act out, problem, solution

Common Use Verb: get/got

Do Math This strategy scaffolds creating and writing number sentences.

- Act out the story problem using students as characters: Students A, B, and C got 3 books each. Students D and E got 5 books each. The remaining students got 1 book each. How many books did they get altogether?
- Scaffold writing the number sentence as the group solves.
- Give groups a set of manipulatives and have them create a math problem.
- Groups will act out their problem as you write it in the number sentence.

Independent Work Options

SOCIAL, KINESTHETIC

1 Early Finishers OL AL

Materials: play money (optional)

- Have small groups of students examine the example and exercises in Lesson 7-3. Have them work together to write 2–3 problems that can be solved using the act it out strategy.
- Have groups trade the problems they have written. Groups will use the act it out strategy to solve the problem.

2 Student Technology

Math Online macmillanmh.com

Personal Tutor • Extra Examples

Option

3 Learning Station: Health (p. 270H)

Direct students to the Health Learning Station for opportunities to explore and extend the lesson concept.

7-3 Problem-Solving Strategy

1 Introduce

Activity Choice 1 • Review

- Present students with the following problem:
  Andy had $14 more yesterday than he does today. Yesterday, he had $33. How much does Andy have today? $19
- **What problem-solving strategy could you use to solve the problem?** work backward
- Go over how to work backward to solve the problem: subtract $14 from $33.

Activity Choice 2 • Literature

Introduce the lesson with *Ten Mile Day: The Building of the Transcontinental Railroad* by Mary Ann Fraser. For a related math activity, see p. TR52.

2 Teach

Have students read the problem on coins. Guide them through the problem-solving steps.

Understand Using the questions, review what students know and need to find.

Plan Have them discuss their strategy.

Solve Guide students to use the act it out strategy to solve the problem.

- **How can you use play money to help you solve the problem?** Put together coins that have a value of 65¢.
- **If the first combination uses less than 6 coins, what should you do next?** Try again with different coins; exchange one coin for more coins with the same value.

Check Have students look back at the problem to make sure that the answer fits the facts given.

! COMMON ERROR!

Exercise 1 Students may think that the least amount of coins means coins with the least value. Tell students to find the smallest number of coins that makes 55¢ by using coins with the greatest values.

7-3 Problem-Solving Strategy

MAIN IDEA I will solve a problem by acting it out.

Sonoda has 6 coins in his bank. The coins equal 65¢. What combination of coins does he have in his bank?

Understand

What facts do you know?

- Sonoda has 6 coins.
- The value of the 6 coins is 65¢.

What do you need to find?

- Find the coins Sonoda has in his bank.

Plan

You can use play money to act out different combinations of 65¢.

Solve

One way to make 65¢ is with 2 quarters, 1 dime, and 1 nickel. But, that is only 4 coins. You need 2 more coins.

Take 1 quarter and exchange it for 2 dimes and 1 nickel. The value stays the same, and the number of coins increases to 6.

=

So, Sonoda has 1 quarter, 3 dimes, and 2 nickels.

Check

Look back at the problem.

	1 quarter	+	3 dimes	+	2 nickels
=	25¢	+	10¢ + 10¢ + 10¢	+	5¢ + 5¢
=	25¢	+	30¢	+	10¢
=			65¢		

So, the answer is correct.

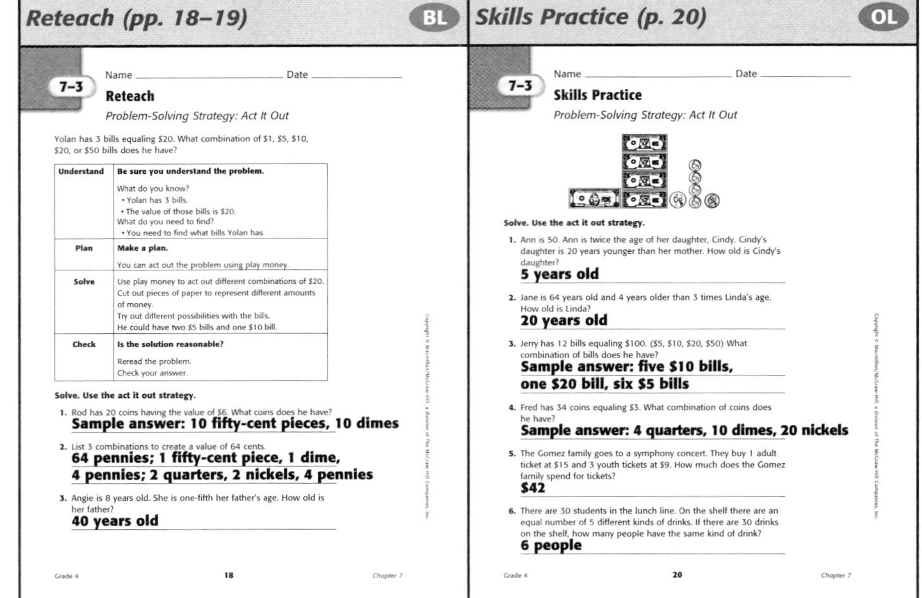

Reteach (pp. 18–19) BL

7-3 Name ______ Date ______

Reteach

Problem-Solving Strategy: Act It Out

Yolan has 3 bills equaling $20. What combination of $1, $5, $10, $20, or $50 bills does he have?

Understand	**Be sure you understand the problem.** What do you know? • Yolan has 3 bills. • The value of those bills is $20. What do you need to find? • You need to find what bills Yolan has.
Plan	**Make a plan.** You can act out the problem using play money.
Solve	Use play money to act out different combinations of $20. Cut out pieces of paper to represent different amounts of money. Try out different possibilities with the bills. He could have two $5 bills and one $10 bill.
Check	**Is the solution reasonable?** Reread the problem. Check your answer.

Solve. Use the act it out strategy.

1. Rod has 20 coins having the value of $6. What coins does he have?
   Sample answer: 10 fifty-cent pieces, 10 dimes
2. List 3 combinations to create a value of 64 cents.
   64 pennies; 1 fifty-cent piece, 1 dime, 4 pennies; 2 quarters, 2 nickels, 4 pennies
3. Angie is 8 years old. She is one-fifth her father's age. How old is her father?
   40 years old

Grade 4 18 Chapter 7

Skills Practice (p. 20) OL

7-3 Name ______ Date ______

Skills Practice

Problem-Solving Strategy: Act It Out

Solve. Use the act it out strategy.

1. Ann is 50. Ann is twice the age of her daughter, Cindy. Cindy's daughter is 20 years younger than her mother. How old is Cindy's daughter?
   5 years old
2. Jane is 64 years old and 4 years older than 3 times Linda's age. How old is Linda?
   20 years old
3. Jerry has 12 bills equaling $100. ($5, $10, $20, $50) What combination of bills does he have?
   Sample answer: five $10 bills, one $20 bill, six $5 bills
4. Fred has 34 coins equaling $3. What combination of coins does he have?
   Sample answer: 4 quarters, 10 dimes, 20 nickels
5. The Gomez family goes to a symphony concert. They buy 1 adult ticket at $15 and 3 youth tickets at $9. How much does the Gomez family spend for tickets?
   $42
6. There are 30 students in the lunch line. On the shelf there are an equal number of 5 different kinds of drinks. If there are 30 drinks on the shelf, how many people have the same kind of drink?
   6 people

Grade 4 20 Chapter 7

ANALYZE the Strategy

Refer to the problem on the previous page.

1. If Sonoda has a few coins that total 55¢, what is the least amount of coins he can have? **2; half-dollar and nickel**
2. Suppose Sonoda had 60¢ in his bank. What 5 coins would he have? **1 quarter, 3 dimes, and 1 nickel**
3. Suppose Sonoda found 3 coins on the sidewalk. The coins total $1. What coins did Sonoda find? Explain. **See Ch. 7 Answer Appendix.**
4. Describe another strategy you could use to solve this problem. **guess and check**

PRACTICE the Strategy

EXTRA PRACTICE See page R18.

Solve. Use the act it out strategy.

5. Angelo's father is 30 years old. This is 10 years older than twice Angelo's age. How old is Angelo? **10 yrs old**
6. Ellen needs to visit 3 Web sites for her homework. In how many different ways can she visit the Web sites? **6**
7. There are five people at a party, and each person has shaken hands with every other person. How many handshakes took place among the five people? **10 handshakes**
8. **Geometry** Can 12 toothpicks be used to form 4 squares that are the same size and same shape? **no**
9. Berta, Maya, and Zach are in different checkout lines at a store. Berta has 3 more people in front of her than are in front of Maya. There are 2 times as many people in front of Zach as there are in front of Maya. The total number of people in front of the girls is 11. How many people are in front of each person? **Berta 7; Maya 4; and Zach 8**
10. **Geometry** How many different rectangles can you make using all of the squares shown below?

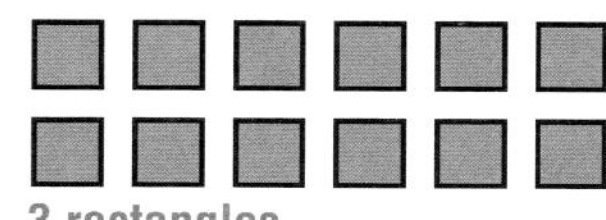

3 rectangles

11. List five different money combinations that equal 34¢. **See Ch. 7 Answer Appendix.**
12. Jamaica has 8 coins with a value of $1. What coins does she have? **2 quarters, 4 dimes, and 2 nickels or 3 quarters, 5 nickels**
13. Dane needs to set up tables for his nine family members and himself to eat dinner. The square tables will seat one person on each side. Explain how Dane can arrange six square tables in a rectangle so that there is one seat for each person with no extra seats. **13, 14. See Ch. 7 Answer Appendix.**
14. **WRITING IN MATH** When should the act it out strategy be used to solve a problem? Explain.

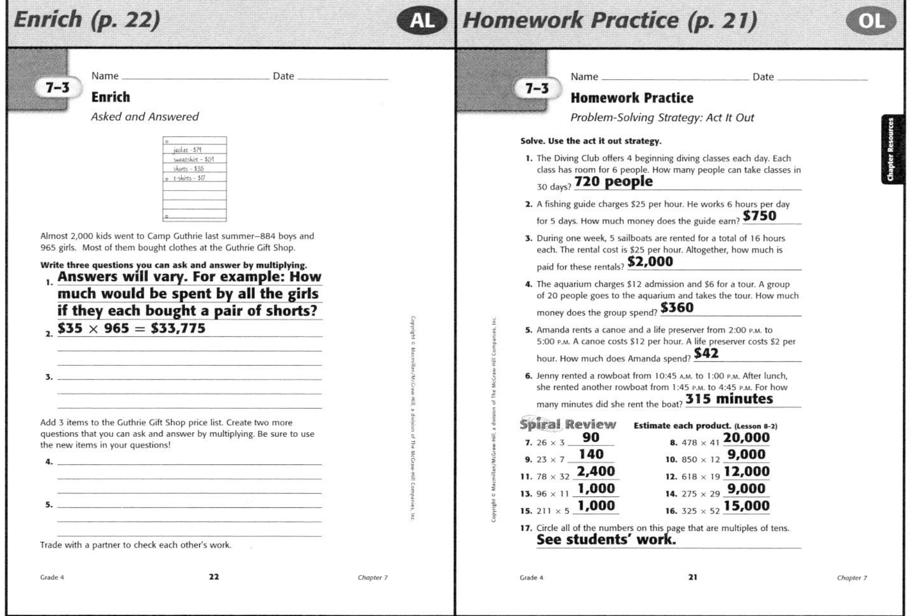

Enrich (p. 22) AL

7-3 Name ______ Date ______

Enrich

Asked and Answered

jacket - $79
sweatshirt - $59
shorts - $35
t-shirts - $17

Almost 2,000 kids went to Camp Guthrie last summer–884 boys and 965 girls. Most of them bought clothes at the Guthrie Gift Shop.

Write three questions you can ask and answer by multiplying.

1. **Answers will vary. For example: How much would be spent by all the girls if they each bought a pair of shorts?**
2. **$35 × 965 = $33,775**
3. ______

Add 3 items to the Guthrie Gift Shop price list. Create two more questions that you can ask and answer by multiplying. Be sure to use the new items in your questions!

4. ______
5. ______

Trade with a partner to check each other's work.

Grade 4 22 Chapter 7

Homework Practice (p. 21) OL

7-3 Name ______ Date ______

Homework Practice

Problem-Solving Strategy: Act It Out

Chapter Resources

Solve. Use the act it out strategy.

1. The Diving Club offers 4 beginning diving classes each day. Each class has room for 6 people. How many people can take classes in 30 days? **720 people**
2. A fishing guide charges $25 per hour. He works 6 hours per day for 5 days. How much money does the guide earn? **$750**
3. During one week, 5 sailboats are rented for a total of 16 hours each. The rental cost is $25 per hour. Altogether, how much is paid for these rentals? **$2,000**
4. The aquarium charges $12 admission and $6 for a tour. A group of 20 people goes to the aquarium and takes the tour. How much money does the group spend? **$360**
5. Amanda rents a canoe and a life preserver from 2:00 P.M. to 5:00 P.M. A canoe costs $12 per hour. A life preserver costs $2 per hour. How much does Amanda spend? **$42**
6. Jenny rented a rowboat from 10:45 A.M. to 1:00 P.M. After lunch, she rented another rowboat from 1:45 P.M. to 4:45 P.M. For how many minutes did she rent the boat? **315 minutes**

Spiral Review **Estimate each product.** (Lesson 8-2)

7. 26 × 3 **90**
8. 478 × 41 **20,000**
9. 23 × 7 **140**
10. 850 × 12 **9,000**
11. 78 × 32 **2,400**
12. 618 × 19 **12,000**
13. 96 × 11 **1,000**
14. 275 × 29 **9,000**
15. 211 × 5 **1,000**
16. 325 × 52 **15,000**
17. Circle all of the numbers on this page that are multiples of tens. **See students' work.**

Grade 4 21 Chapter 7

Analyze the Strategy Use Exercises 1–4 to analyze and discuss the problem-solving strategy.

BL Alternate Teaching Strategy

If students have trouble using play money to find the combined value of coins…

Then use one of these reteach options:

1. CRM **Daily Reteach Worksheet** (pp. 18–19)
2. Have students work with a partner. Have pairs first tape each type of coin to a separate index card and label the card with the coin's name and value in cents. Pairs may use the cards to help them as they act out and solve the problem.

3 Practice

Using the Exercises

Exercise 8 Have groups of five students work together to act out and solve this problem.

Exercise 10 Students may use square pattern blocks to act out this exercise.

4 Assess

Formative Assessment

- **When might you use the act it out strategy to solve a problem?** Sample answer: when I can do things or use materials to show what happens in a problem
- **Why is it useful to use the act it out strategy to solve some money problems?** I can use play money to help me find the answer.

Quick Check **Are students continuing to struggle with using the act it out strategy?**

If Yes → Small Group Options (p. 306B)

If No → Independent Work Options (p. 306B)
CRM Skills Practice Worksheet (p. 20)
CRM Enrich Worksheet (p. 22)

Explore Math Activity for 7-4

Lesson Planner

Objective

Explore multiplying by two-digit numbers.

Vocabulary

Distributive Property of Multiplication

Resources

Materials: grid paper, red, blue, orange, and green colored pencils

Manipulatives: two-colored counters

Introduce

Introduce the Concept

- Write 14 × 12 on the board. Have students combine their counters and model 14 groups of 12 yellow counters.
- Tell students to separate 4 of the 14 groups from the other 10. Have them turn the counters in those 4 groups over to show the red side up.
- Point out to students that the total number of counters is the same whether we show 14 groups of 12 or separate the groups into 10 groups of 12 and 4 groups of 12.
- **How can we use the yellow and red groups to find the product of 14 × 12?** Sample answer: Multiply 10 × 12 and 4 × 12 and add the products.

Explore Math Activity for 7-4

Multiply Two-Digit Numbers

MAIN IDEA

I will explore multiplying by two-digit numbers.

You Will Need

colored pencils
graph paper

In Lesson 4-6, you learned that the **Distributive Property of Multiplication** allows you to break apart factors to find a product. You can use the Distributive Property to multiply two-digit numbers.

Distributive Property — Key Concept

To multiply a sum by a number, multiply each addend by the number and add the products.

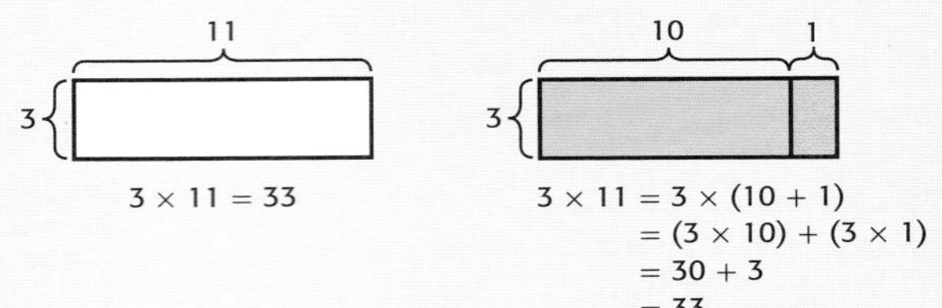

$3 \times 11 = 33$

$$3 \times 11 = 3 \times (10 + 1) = (3 \times 10) + (3 \times 1) = 30 + 3 = 33$$

ACTIVITY Find 12 × 15.

Step 1 Draw a rectangle.

Draw a rectangle on graph paper. Use 12 and 15 as the dimensions.

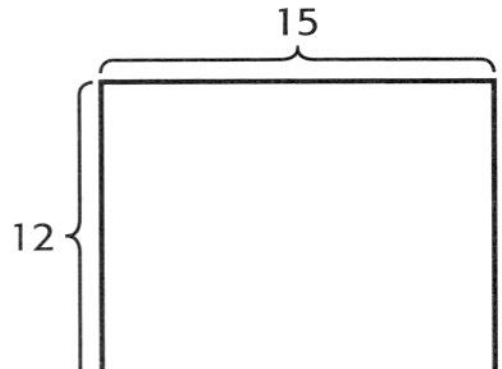

Step 2 Separate the tens and ones.

First, break up the 15 as 10 and 5. Next, break up the 12 as 10 and 2.

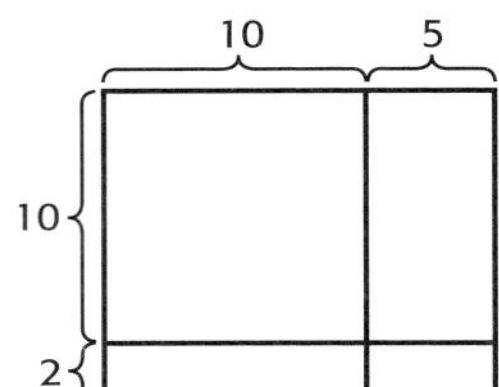

Additional Answers

4.

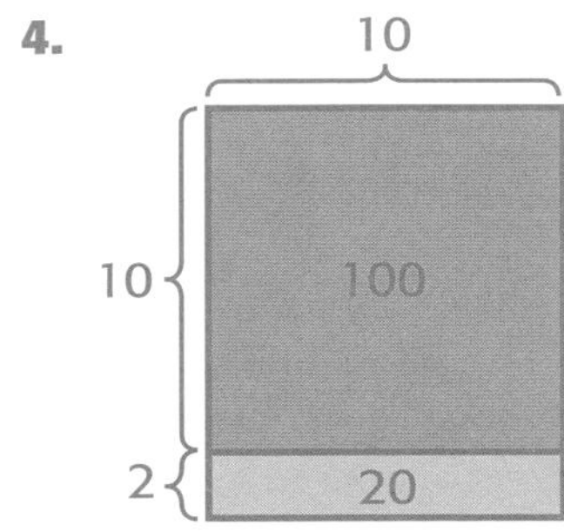

5.

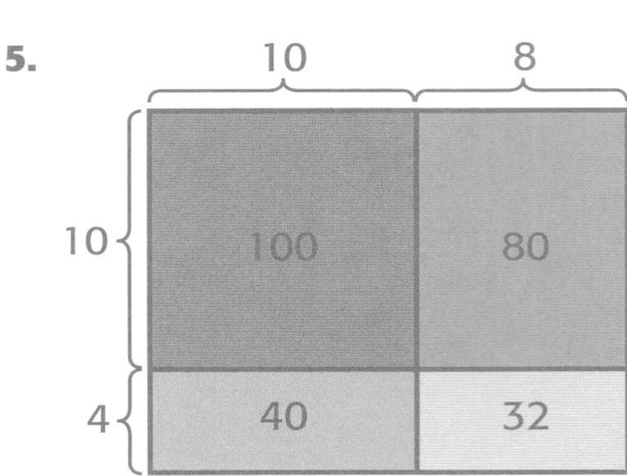

Step 3 **Find each product. Then add.**

10 × 10	=	100
10 × 5	=	50
2 × 10	=	20
2 × 5	=	+ 10
		180

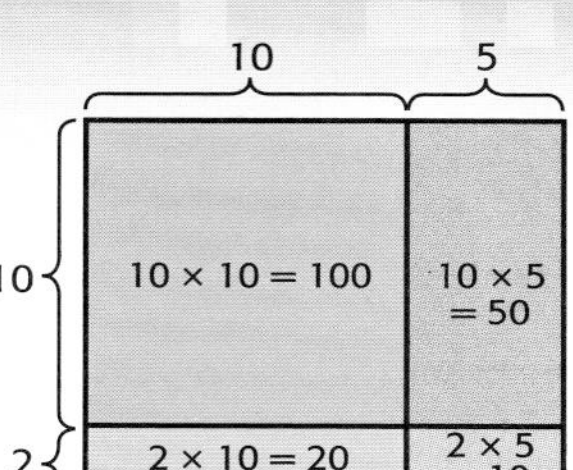

Step 4 **Make the connection.**

Distributive Property

$12 \times 15 = (10 \times 15) + (2 \times 15)$
$= (10 \times 10) + (10 \times 5) + (2 \times 10) + (2 \times 5)$
$= 100 + 50 + 20 + 10$
$= 180$

Partial Products

15	
× 12	
10	2 × 5
20	2 × 10
50	10 × 5
+ 100	10 × 10
180	Add partial products.

Think About It

1. How would you use the Distributive Property to find 12 × 18? Break up 12 into 10 + 2. Break up 18 into 10 + 8.

CHECK What You Know

Write the multiplication sentence for each area model. Multiply.

2.

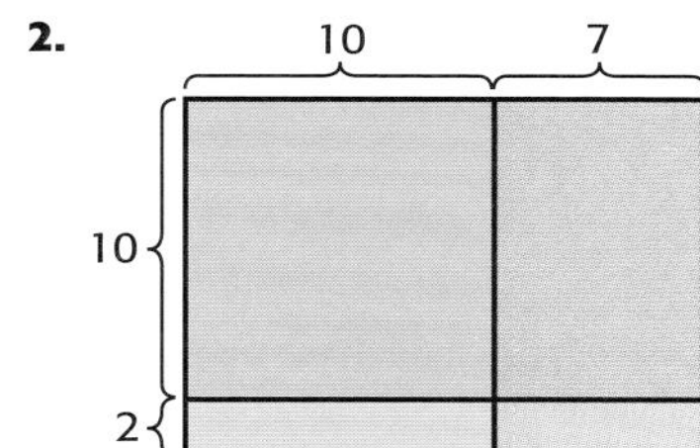

12 × 17 = 204

3.

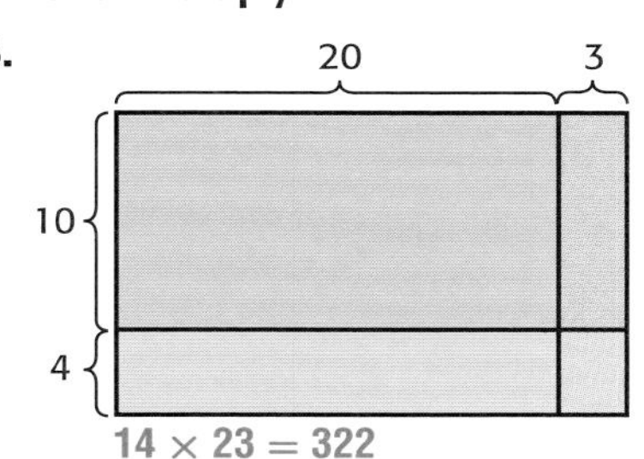

14 × 23 = 322

Multiply. Use an area model and the Distributive Property.

4. 12 × 10 120 **5.** 14 × 18 252 **6.** 25 × 28 700

4–6. See margin for models.

7. WRITING IN MATH Explain how to find 16 × 19. See margin.

6.

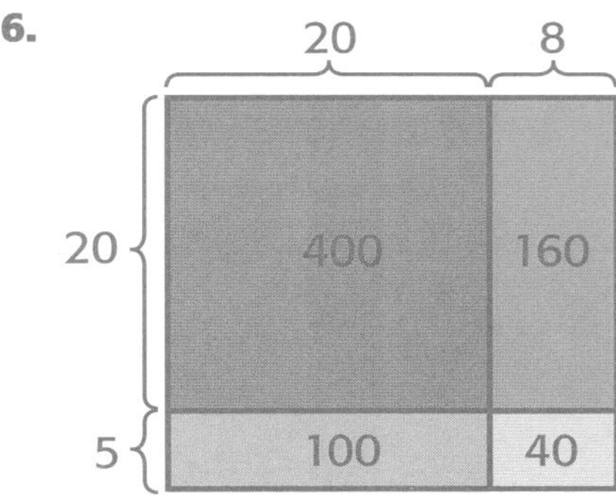

7. Sample answer: Separate each 2-digit factor into tens and ones. Then multiply every number together. Then add all the products.

2 Teach

Activity Before beginning, define the Distributive Property of Multiplication and relate the Introduce the Concept activity to this property. Go over the example at the top of p. 282 carefully. Tell students that they will use the Distributive Property of Multiplication to explore multiplying two-digit numbers in the activity.

Provide students with grid paper and colored pencils. Have them follow Steps 1–2 to draw and label an array showing 12 × 15. Point out that each factor is separated into tens and ones.

Have students complete Steps 3 and 4 and record their work. Ask students to match each rectangle from their grid to a multiplication fact in parentheses.

Think About It

Assign **Think About It** Exercise 1 to assess student comprehension of the concept presented in the Activity.

3 Assess

Formative Assessment

Use **Check What You Know** Exercises 2–10 to assess whether students understand multiplying by two-digit numbers.

From Concrete to Abstract Use Exercises 3 and 5 to bridge the gap between drawing rectangles on grid paper and multiplying a two-digit number by a two-digit number.

LESSON 7-4

Multiply Two-Digit Numbers

Lesson Planner

Objective

Multiply two-digit numbers.

Review Vocabulary

Distributive Property of Multiplication

Resources

Materials: grid paper

Manipulatives: base-ten blocks

Literature Connection: *Sea Squares* by Joy Hulme

Teacher Technology
Interactive Classroom • TeacherWorks

Alternate Lesson: Use *IMPACT Mathematics: Unit A* to provide practice with multiplication.

Daily Routine

Use these suggestions before beginning the lesson on p. 284.

5-Minute Check

(Reviews Lesson 7-3)

Solve. Use the act it out strategy.

Carlos has 8 coins in his pocket. The total value of the coins is 73¢. What coins does Carlos have? 2 quarters, 1 dime, 2 nickels, 3 pennies

Problem of the Day

The product of two numbers is 1,500. The difference between the two numbers is 20. What are the numbers? 50 and 30

Focus on Math Background

Students have some background with using area models to represent multiplication of single-digit numbers. In this lesson, students use area models to represent multiplication of larger numbers. These models depend on the Distributive Property of Multiplication. For example, to model 4×18, you can decompose 18 into $10 + 8$. Then the Distributive Property allows you to multiply:

$$\begin{aligned} 4 \times (10 + 8) &= 4 \times 10 + 4 \times 8 \\ &= 40 + 32 \\ &= 72 \end{aligned}$$

The visual model presented in this lesson encourages students to use their basic facts and what they know about multiplying by powers of ten to determine the partial products. The power of the model is that it helps students make the connections between the partial products shown in the diagram and the partial products shown in the standard algorithm.

Review Math Vocabulary

Write the review vocabulary word and its definition on the board.

Write $3 \times 9 = 27$ on the board. Have students rewrite the multiplication sentence to illustrate the Distributive Property of Multiplication. If necessary, suggest that they start by writing the second factor as the sum of two numbers. Have students share their examples with the class.

Differentiated Instruction

Small Group Options

LOGICAL, SOCIAL

Option 1 Gifted and Talented AL

Materials: spinner numbered from 0–9

- Have students take turns spinning four numbers on a spinner.
- Each student uses these numbers to write algorithms for multiplying a two-digit number by a two-digit number.
- Students try to write two-digit numbers that will yield the greatest product.
- Tell students to add the products from each turn.

$$\begin{array}{r} 72 \\ \times\ 21 \\ \hline 1{,}512 \end{array} \qquad \begin{array}{r} 43 \\ \times\ 52 \\ \hline 2{,}236 \end{array}$$

$$\begin{array}{r} 1{,}512 \\ +\ 2{,}236 \\ \hline 3{,}748 \end{array}$$

- The first student to get a 10,000 total wins the game.

LINGUISTIC, INTRAPERSONAL

Option 2 English Language Learners ELL

Materials: times tables
Core Vocabulary: right, wrong, both must solve
Common Use Verb: challenge

Talk Math This strategy allows students to practice integrating verbal response with sight understanding of multiplication.

- Pair off students. Give one a times table and have him or her call a multiplication problem with either a right or wrong answer.
- The partner says "**right**" or "**wrong**."
- The caller says "check" if he or she agrees with the right or wrong call, or "challenge" if he or she disagrees with the right or wrong call.
- If challenged, both students must solve the problem.
- Repeat as time permits.

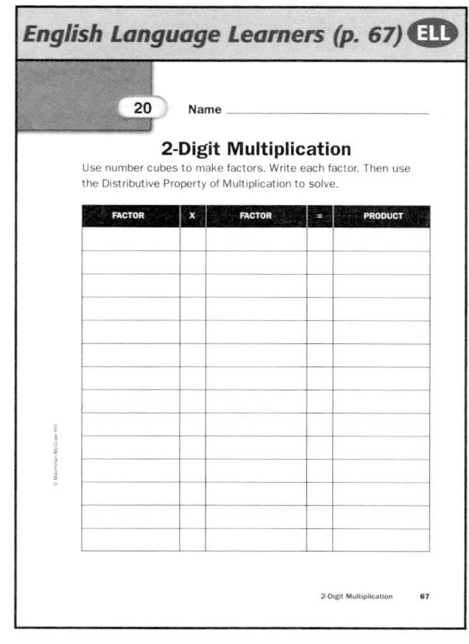

English Language Learners (p. 67) ELL

20 Name ______________

2-Digit Multiplication

Use number cubes to make factors. Write each factor. Then use the Distributive Property of Multiplication to solve.

FACTOR	X	FACTOR	=	PRODUCT

2-Digit Multiplication 67

Use this worksheet to provide additional support for English Language Learners.

Independent Work Options

LOGICAL, INTRAPERSONAL

Option 1 Early Finishers OL AL

Materials: paper and pencil

- Have students calculate the greatest and least possible products of 2 two-digit numbers. 9,801 and 100
- To extend the activity, challenge students to find the least possible product of a two-digit and a three-digit number and of 2 three-digit numbers. Have students describe any patterns that they see.

Option 2 Student Technology

Math Online macmillanmh.com

Personal Tutor • Extra Examples

 Math Adventures

Option 3 Learning Station: Science (p. 270H)

Direct students to the Science Learning Station for opportunities to explore and extend the lesson concept.

Option 4 Problem-Solving Practice

Reinforce problem-solving skills and strategies with the Problem-Solving Practice worksheet.

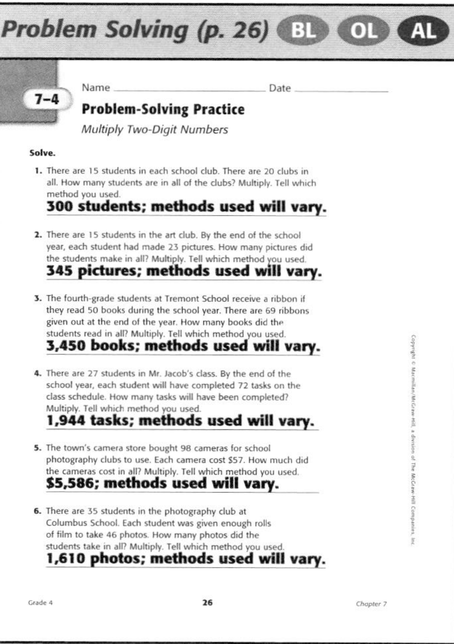

Problem Solving (p. 26) BL OL AL

Name ______________ Date ______________

7–4 **Problem-Solving Practice**

Multiply Two-Digit Numbers

Solve.

1. There are 15 students in each school club. There are 20 clubs in all. How many students are in all of the clubs? Multiply. Tell which method you used.
300 students; methods used will vary.

2. There are 15 students in the art club. By the end of the school year, each student had made 23 pictures. How many pictures did the students make in all? Multiply. Tell which method you used.
345 pictures; methods used will vary.

3. The fourth-grade students at Tremont School receive a ribbon if they read 50 books during the school year. There are 69 ribbons given out at the end of the year. How many books did the students read in all? Multiply. Tell which method you used.
3,450 books; methods used will vary.

4. There are 27 students in Mr. Jacob's class. By the end of the school year, each student will have completed 72 tasks on the class schedule. How many tasks will have been completed? Multiply. Tell which method you used.
1,944 tasks; methods used will vary.

5. The town's camera store bought 98 cameras for school photography clubs to use. Each camera cost $57. How much did the cameras cost in all? Multiply. Tell which method you used.
$5,586; methods used will vary.

6. There are 35 students in the photography club at Columbus School. Each student was given enough rolls of film to take 46 photos. How many photos did the students take in all? Multiply. Tell which method you used.
1,610 photos; methods used will vary.

Grade 4 26 Chapter 7

7-4 Multiply Two-Digit Numbers

1 Introduce

Activity Choice 1 • Hands-On 

- Have students practice saying and writing several two-digit numbers in expanded form.
- Remind students how the Distributive Property of Multiplication allows us to multiply numbers in expanded form. Write 8×22 on the board.
- **What is the expanded form of 22?** 20 + 2
- Then write $8 \times (20 + 2) = (8 \times 20) + (8 \times 2)$.
- Have students multiply and add to solve.

Activity Choice 2 • Literature

Introduce the lesson with *Sea Squares* by Joy Hulme. For a related math activity, see p. TR53.

2 Teach

Scaffolding Questions

Write 23×11 on the board. Have students make an array on grid paper to model and solve.

- **What is the expanded form of 23?** 20 + 3 **of 11?** 10 + 1
- **How many products did you add?** 4
- **Explain how you made the array and solved the problem.** Show 11 rows and 23 columns. Draw lines to model 10 + 1 and 20 + 3. Multiply to find the product for each of the four rectangles, and then add.

GET READY to Learn

Have students open their books and read the information in **Get Ready to Learn**. Review **Distributive Property of Multiplication**. As a class, work through **Examples 1 and 2**.

7-4 Multiply Two-Digit Numbers

MAIN IDEA

I will multiply two-digit numbers.

Math Online

macmillanmh.com

- Extra Examples
- Personal Tutor
- Self-Check Quiz

GET READY to Learn

A coyote travels 27 miles per hour. How far would a coyote travel in 12 hours?

There is more than one way to multiply two-digit numbers.

Real-World EXAMPLE

1 MEASUREMENT A coyote travels 27 miles each hour. Multiply 27×12 to find how far a coyote can travel in 12 hours.

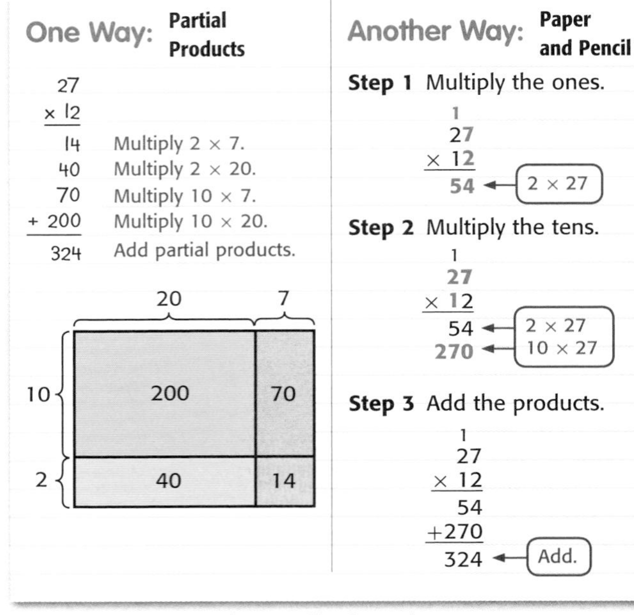

One Way: Partial Products

27	
× 12	
14	Multiply 2×7.
40	Multiply 2×20.
70	Multiply 10×7.
+ 200	Multiply 10×20.
324	Add partial products.

Another Way: Paper and Pencil

Step 1 Multiply the ones.

$$\begin{array}{r} {}^{1}\\ 27 \\ \times\ 12 \\ \hline 54 \end{array} \leftarrow 2 \times 27$$

Step 2 Multiply the tens.

$$\begin{array}{r} {}^{1}\\ 27 \\ \times\ 12 \\ \hline 54 \\ 270 \end{array} \begin{array}{l} \\ \\ \\ \leftarrow 2 \times 27 \\ \leftarrow 10 \times 27 \end{array}$$

Step 3 Add the products.

$$\begin{array}{r} {}^{1}\\ 27 \\ \times\ 12 \\ \hline 54 \\ +270 \\ \hline 324 \end{array} \leftarrow \text{Add.}$$

So, a coyote can travel 324 miles in 12 hours.

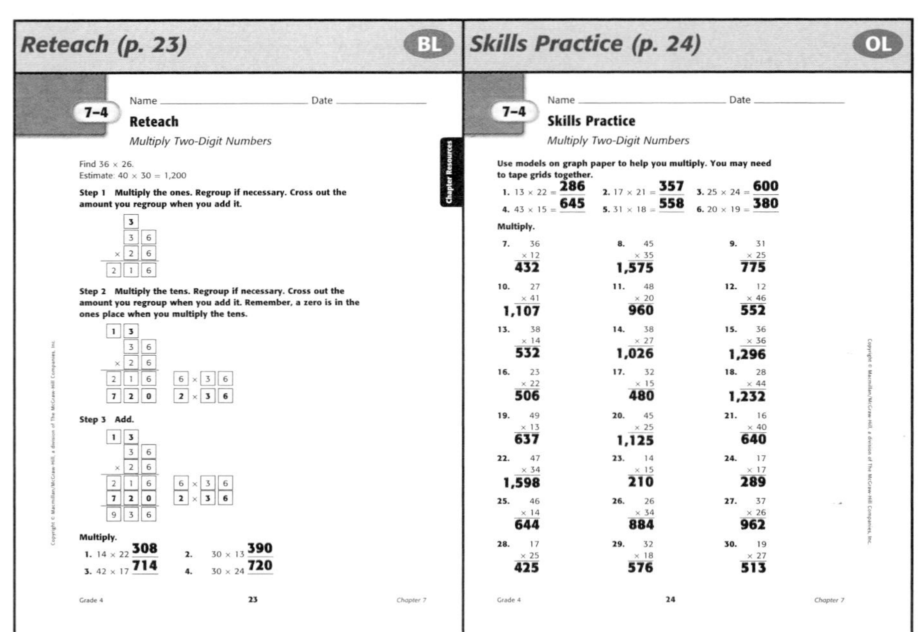

Reteach (p. 23) BL

7-4 Name ________ Date ________

Reteach

Multiply Two-Digit Numbers

Find 36×26.
Estimate: $40 \times 30 = 1,200$

Step 1 Multiply the ones. Regroup if necessary. Cross out the amount you regroup when you add it.

$$\begin{array}{r} {}^{3}\ \ \\ 36 \\ \times\ 26 \\ \hline 216 \end{array}$$

Step 2 Multiply the tens. Regroup if necessary. Cross out the amount you regroup when you add it. Remember, a zero is in the ones place when you multiply the tens.

$$\begin{array}{r} {}^{1\,3}\ \ \\ 36 \\ \times\ 26 \\ \hline 216 \\ 720 \end{array} \quad \begin{array}{l} \\ \\ \\ 6 \times 36 \\ 2 \times 36 \end{array}$$

Step 3 Add.

$$\begin{array}{r} {}^{1\,3}\ \ \\ 36 \\ \times\ 26 \\ \hline 216 \\ 720 \\ \hline 936 \end{array} \quad \begin{array}{l} \\ \\ \\ 6 \times 36 \\ 2 \times 36 \\ \\ \end{array}$$

Multiply.

1. 14×22 **308**
2. 30×13 **390**
3. 42×17 **714**
4. 30×24 **720**

Grade 4 23 Chapter 7

Chapter Resources

Skills Practice (p. 24) OL

7-4 Name ________ Date ________

Skills Practice

Multiply Two-Digit Numbers

Use models on graph paper to help you multiply. You may need to tape grids together.

1. $13 \times 22 =$ **286**
2. $17 \times 21 =$ **357**
3. $25 \times 24 =$ **600**
4. $43 \times 15 =$ **645**
5. $31 \times 18 =$ **558**
6. $20 \times 19 =$ **380**

Multiply.

7. 36×12 = **432**
8. 45×35 = **1,575**
9. 31×25 = **775**
10. 27×41 = **1,107**
11. 48×20 = **960**
12. 12×46 = **552**
13. 38×14 = **532**
14. 38×27 = **1,026**
15. 36×36 = **1,296**
16. 23×22 = **506**
17. 32×15 = **480**
18. 28×44 = **1,232**
19. 49×13 = **637**
20. 45×25 = **1,125**
21. 16×40 = **640**
22. 47×34 = **1,598**
23. 14×15 = **210**
24. 17×17 = **289**
25. 46×14 = **644**
26. 26×34 = **884**
27. 37×26 = **962**
28. 17×25 = **425**
29. 32×18 = **576**
30. 19×27 = **513**

Grade 4 24 Chapter 7

Real-World EXAMPLE — Multiply Money

2 **EXPENSES** **Heidi's monthly bills are shown. How much does she spend on her cell phone service in 2 years?**

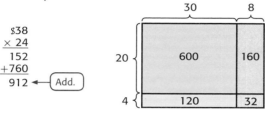

Monthly Bills	
Cable	$55
Cell phone	$38
Movie club	$21
Water	$93

Heidi's cell phone bill is $38. There are 24 months in 2 years. So multiply $38 by 24 to find how much she spends in 2 years.

Estimate $40 \times 20 = 800$

Remember

Make an estimate to check the reasonableness of the answer.

Step 1 Multiply the ones.

$$\begin{array}{r} \$38 \\ \times\ 24 \\ \hline 152 \end{array} \leftarrow 4 \times 38$$

Step 2 Multiply the tens.

$$\begin{array}{r} \$38 \\ \times\ 24 \\ \hline 152 \\ +\ 760 \end{array} \leftarrow 20 \times 38$$

Step 3 Add the products.

$$\begin{array}{r} \$38 \\ \times\ 24 \\ \hline 152 \\ +760 \\ \hline 912 \end{array} \leftarrow \text{Add.}$$

	30	8
20	600	160
4	120	32

So, the cost of cell phone service for 2 years is $912.

Check for Reasonableness

912 is close to the estimate of 800. The answer is reasonable. ✓

CHECK What You Know

Multiply. See Examples 1 and 2 (pp. 284–285)

1. 35×24 840
2. $\$57 \times 42$ $2,394
3. 92×81 7,452
4. A farmer plants 35 rows of tomatoes. There are 25 plants in each row. How many plants are there altogether? 875 plants
5. 

Explain the steps needed to find the product of 23 and 56.

5. Sample answer: Multiply 3 ones times 56, regrouping where necessary, then multiply 2 tens times 56, regrouping when necessary. Finally, add the partial products.

Enrich (p. 27) AL

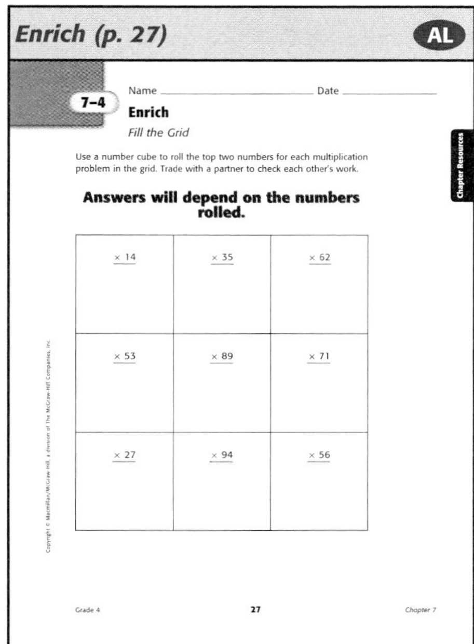

Name ______ Date ______

7-4 **Enrich**

Fill the Grid

Use a number cube to roll the top two numbers for each multiplication problem in the grid. Trade with a partner to check each other's work.

Answers will depend on the numbers rolled.

× 14	× 35	× 62
× 53	× 89	× 71
× 27	× 94	× 56

Grade 4 — 27 — Chapter 7

Real-World Example

Example 1 Make sure students understand the connection between the pencil and paper algorithm and the array model. Define the term *partial products* for students. Point out that that the pencil and paper method allows us to add two partial products instead of four.

ADDITIONAL EXAMPLES

1 How far can a truck travel in 14 hours if it is traveling an average of 57 miles per hour? 798 miles

2 The Jones family spends an average of $48 a month going to the movies. How much does the family spend in 3 years? $1,728

CHECK What You Know

As a class, have students complete Exercises 1–5 in **Check What You Know** as you observe their work.

Exercise 5 Assess student comprehension before assigning practice exercises.

BL Alternate Teaching Strategy

If students have trouble using the pencil and paper method to multiply two-digit numbers or relating this method to grid paper arrays…

Then use one of these reteach options:

1. CRM **Daily Reteach Worksheet** (p. 23)
2. Guide groups of students to make an array showing 32×23 with base-ten blocks instead of grid paper. Have them break each factor into expanded form and use hundreds, tens, and ones blocks to show 30×20, 2×20, 30×3, and 2×3. Help students connect this model to the pencil and paper algorithm.

COMMON ERROR!

Students may forget to write the zero in the second partial product when multiplying the tens. Have students write the factors next to each partial product, as shown in Examples 1 and 2. Encourage them to look for zeros or estimate to check their partial products.

3 Practice

Differentiate practice using these leveled assignments for Exercises 6–27.

Level	Assignment
BL Below/Approaching Level	6–9, 14, 15, 19, 20, 23, 24
OL On Level	7–13, 15–17, 19–21, 22–24, 26
AL Above/Beyond Level	6–24 even, 25–27

Have students discuss and complete the Higher Order Thinking problems. For Exercise 29, encourage students to begin by using pencil and paper to find the products.

WRITING IN MATH Have students complete Exercise 30 in their Math Journals. You may choose to use this exercise as an optional formative assessment.

4 Assess

Formative Assessment

Write 13 × 24 on the board.

- **How does multiplying 2 two-digit numbers with an array model relate to multiplying with paper and pencil? Use 13 × 24 in your example.** Sample answer: The model shows 10 × 24 on the top part of the array and 3 × 24 on the bottom part. This corresponds to the two partial products when you use paper pencil.

Quick Check **Are students continuing to struggle with multiplying two-digit numbers?**

If Yes → CRM Reteach Worksheet (p. 23)

If No → Independent Work Options (p. 310B)
CRM Skills Practice Worksheet (p. 24)
CRM Enrich Worksheet (p. 27)

Name the Math Have students use pencil and paper to multiply 88 × 47. They should show all their work and explain how they used regrouping when they multiplied the ones and the tens.

Practice and Problem Solving

EXTRA PRACTICE See page R18.

Multiply. See Examples 1 and 2 (pp. 284–285)

6. 19 × 15 285
7. 36 × 24 864
8. 42 × 38 1,596
9. 52 × 47 2,444

10. \$54 × 51 \$2,754
11. \$68 × 46 \$3,128
12. \$74 × 63 \$4,662
13. \$82 × 49 \$4,018

14. 47 × 24 1,128
15. 64 × 46 2,944
16. 83 × 67 5,561
17. 91 × 78 7,098

18. Bamboo plants can grow up to 36 inches in a day. How many inches could they grow in 3 weeks? 756 in.

19. Josie earns about 28 points on each quiz she takes. How many points will Josie earn on 12 quizzes? 336 points

20. **Measurement** A greyhound dog can jump a distance of 27 feet. How many feet will a greyhound travel if it jumps 12 times? 324 ft

21. **Measurement** Each day, enough paper is recycled in the U.S. to fill 15 miles of train boxcars. How many miles of boxcars could be filled over 25 days? 375 miles

Real-World PROBLEM SOLVING

Food The table shows the average amount of hot dogs and pizza slices each person eats per year.

Amount of Food Eaten Each Year

Food	Number
Hot dog	60
Slice of pizza	46

Source: National Association of Pizza Operators

22. How many hot dogs will a person eat in 11 years? 660

23. How many slices of pizza will a person eat in 12 years? 552

24. How many more hot dogs than pizza slices will a person eat in 15 years? 210

H.O.T. Problems

25. **OPEN ENDED** Copy and complete the multiplication problem to make a true sentence. Sample answer: 10; 2

20
× ■■
■00

26. **WHICH ONE DOESN'T BELONG?** Identify the multiplication problem that does not belong with the other three. Explain.

22 × 15 | \$45 × 28 | 37 × 18 | \$66 × 25

26, 27. See Ch. 7 Answer Appendix.

27. **WRITING IN MATH** Explain why the product of two 2-digit numbers can never be two digits.

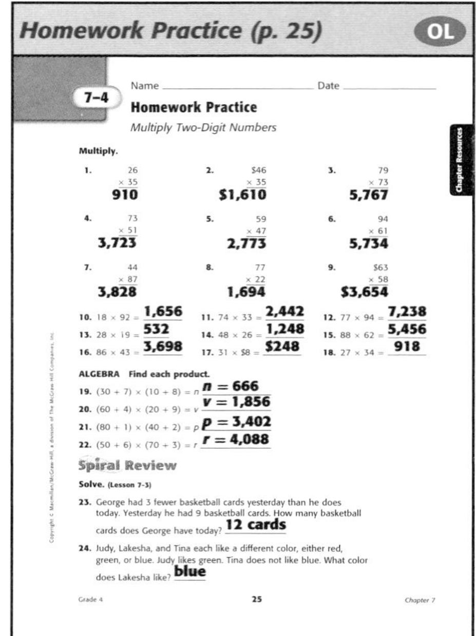

Homework Practice (p. 25) OL

Name ______ Date ______

7–4 **Homework Practice**
Multiply Two-Digit Numbers

Multiply.

1. 26 × 35 = **910**
2. \$46 × 35 = **\$1,610**
3. 79 × 73 = **5,767**
4. 73 × 51 = **3,723**
5. 59 × 47 = **2,773**
6. 94 × 61 = **5,734**
7. 44 × 87 = **3,828**
8. 77 × 22 = **1,694**
9. \$63 × 58 = **\$3,654**

10. 18 × 92 = **1,656**
11. 74 × 33 = **2,442**
12. 77 × 94 = **7,238**
13. 28 × 19 = **532**
14. 48 × 26 = **1,248**
15. 88 × 62 = **5,456**
16. 86 × 43 = **3,698**
17. 31 × \$8 = **\$248**
18. 27 × 34 = **918**

ALGEBRA Find each product.

19. $(30 + 7) \times (10 + 8) = n$ **$n = 666$**
20. $(60 + 4) \times (20 + 9) = v$ **$v = 1,856$**
21. $(80 + 1) \times (40 + 2) = p$ **$p = 3,402$**
22. $(50 + 6) \times (70 + 3) = r$ **$r = 4,088$**

Spiral Review

Solve. (Lesson 7-3)

23. George had 3 fewer basketball cards yesterday than he does today. Yesterday he had 9 basketball cards. How many basketball cards does George have today? **12 cards**

24. Judy, Lakesha, and Tina each like a different color, either red, green, or blue. Judy likes green. Tina does not like blue. What color does Lakesha like? **blue**

Chapter Resources

Grade 4 25 Chapter 7

Mid-Chapter Check

Lessons 7-1 through 7-4

Multiply. (Lesson 7-1)

1. 38 × 30 **1,140**

2. 52 × 20 **1,040**

3. **Measurement** John jogs 30 miles every week. There are 52 weeks in a year. How many miles does John jog in a year? (Lesson 7-1) **1,560 miles**

4. **MULTIPLE CHOICE** What is the total length of 30 newborn Florida alligators? (Lesson 7-1) **B**

10 in.

A 200 inches **C** 400 inches

B 300 inches **D** 500 inches

Estimate. Tell whether the estimate is *greater than* or *less than* the actual product. (Lesson 7-2)

5. 24 × 14 **200; less**

6. $37 × 21 **$800; greater**

7. **MULTIPLE CHOICE** There are 365 days in a year. Which is the best estimate of the number of days in 23 years? (Lesson 7-2) **J**

F 4,000 days **H** 7,000 days

G 5,000 days **J** 8,000 days

8. The average person sends about 25 E-mails a month. About how many E-mails is this each year? (Lesson 7-2) **300 E-mails**

For Exercises 9 and 10, use the act it out strategy. (Lesson 7-3)

9. Talia's mother is 40 years old. This is 13 years older than three times Talia's age. How old is Talia? **9**

10. Emil has 4 coins in his pocket equaling 41¢. What combination of coins does he have in his pocket? **1 quarter, 1 dime, 1 nickel, 1 penny**

Multiply. (Lesson 7-4)

11. 27 × 13 **351**

12. 45 × 14 **630**

13. $67 × 42 **$2,814**

14. 77 × 53 **4,081**

15. **Measurement** A person breathes 95 gallons of air every hour. How many gallons of air does a person breathe in one day? (Lesson 7-4) **2,280 gal**

16. **WRITING IN MATH** Mae is finding the product to the multiplication problem shown below. How many zeros will the product have? Explain. (Lesson 7-1)

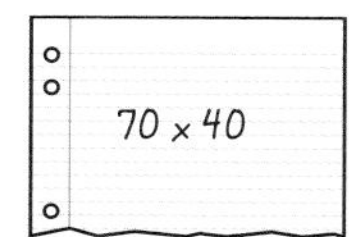

See Ch. 7 Answer Appendix.

Mid-Chapter Check

Lessons 7-1 through 7-4

Formative Assessment

Use the Mid-Chapter Check to assess students' progress in the first half of the chapter.

ExamView Assessment Suite Customize and create multiple versions of your Mid-Chapter Check and the test answer keys.

FOLDABLES Dinah Zike's Foldables

Use these lesson suggestions for incorporating the Foldables during the chapter.

Lesson 7-2 On the first tab of the Foldables, students provide examples of rounding to estimate products.

Lesson 7-3 Students use the second layer of the Foldables to demonstrate their ability to multiply two-digit numbers.

Lesson 7-4 Students use the third layer of the Foldables to show their ability to multiply a three-digit number by a two-digit number.

Data-Driven Decision Making

Based on the results of the Mid-Chapter Check, use the following resources to review concepts that continue to give students problems.

Exercises	State/Local Standards	What's the Math?	Error Analysis	Resources for Review
1–4 Lesson 7-1		Multiply a whole number by a multiple of 10.	Multiplies incorrectly. Does not put zero on the end of the answer.	Strategic Intervention Guide (pp. 72, 76, 78) CRM Chapter 7 Resource Masters (Reteach Worksheets) Math Adventures My Math Zone Chapter 7 Math Online Extra Examples • Concepts in Motion
5–8 Lesson 7-2		Use rounding to estimate products.	Does not know how to estimate. Does not know multiplication facts. Does not consider/use place value when multiplying by a two-digit number.	
11–15 Lesson 7-4		Multiply two-digit numbers using various methods.	Does not know multiplication facts. Does not consider/use place value when multiplying by a two-digit number.	

LESSON 7-5

Multiply Three-Digit Numbers by Two-Digit Numbers

Lesson Planner

Objective

Multiply a three-digit number by a two-digit number.

Review Vocabulary

regroup

Resources

Literature Connection: *Snakes: Long Longer Longest* by Jerry Pallotta

Teacher Technology

TeacherWorks Interactive Classroom • Math Tool Chest

Focus on Math Background

Multiplying a three-digit number by a two-digit number is just an extension of multiplying two-digit numbers together. However, the lack of essential difference does not guarantee that students will not have trouble. If they have understood their work so far, then multiplication with three-digit numbers can be built on that foundation.

Daily Routine

Use these suggestions before beginning the lesson on p. 288.

5-Minute Check

(Reviews Lesson 7-4)

Multiply.

1. 17×11 = 187
2. 35×24 = 840
3. 59×46 = 2,714
4. \$64 × 37 = \$2,368
5. \$77 × 66 = \$5,082
6. 92×84 = 7,728

Problem of the Day

Karen left her house to go to the park at 20 minutes to 1 o'clock in the afternoon. She returned home from the park 2 hours and 25 minutes later. At what time did Karen return home? 3:05 P.M.

Review Math Vocabulary

Write the review vocabulary word and its definition on the board.

Give groups of students the following base-ten blocks: 1 hundred, 11 tens, and 23 ones. Provide them with extra hundreds and tens blocks in a separate pile. Ask students to regroup to help them name the number shown by their blocks. Tell them to use the extra blocks to trade ones for tens and tens for hundreds. 233

Differentiated Instruction

Small Group Options

LOGICAL

Option 1 Below Level BL

Materials: paper, pencils, chart paper

- Write the following problem on chart paper:
- Ask students to write this problem on their paper.

$$\begin{array}{r} 509 \\ \times\ 15 \\ \hline 2545 \\ 509 \\ \hline 3054 \end{array}$$

- Tell them that there is a mistake in this problem. They need to find the mistake and rewrite the problem with the correct answer. The student forgot to place a zero before multiplying the second digit.
- Upon completion of this task, ask them to solve the following problem on their own:

$$\begin{array}{r} 603 \\ \times\ 18 \\ \hline \end{array}$$

SOCIAL

Option 2 English Language Learners ELL

Materials: chart paper, base-ten blocks
Core Vocabulary: more than one way, another, explain
Common Use Verb: solve

Do Math This strategy allows students to write about the process of multiplication.

- Show manipulatives that lend themselves to multiplication problems.
- Have students write a multiplication problem that corresponds to the manipulatives displayed.
- Allow students to form cooperative groups to solve it and write out the explanation of how they got their answer.
- Have each group present its solution, with each subsequent group solving in a different way.
- Post solutions and discuss as time permits.

Independent Work Options

VISUAL, SPATIAL

Option 1 Early Finishers OL AL

Materials: 10 index cards

- Have students write five exercises on index cards showing multiplication of a three-digit number by a two-digit number. Students write the answer on the back of each card.
- Have students take turns choosing one of their partner's cards and multiplying to find the product. Have them turn over each card to check their answer.
- Students score one point for each correct answer. The partner with the highest score after all cards have been chosen wins.

Option 2 Student Technology

Math Online macmillanmh.com

Math Tool Chest Place Value Level 2

Personal Tutor • Extra Examples

Math Adventures

Option 3 Learning Station: Writing (p. 270G)

Direct students to the Writing Learning Station for opportunities to explore and extend the lesson concept.

Option 4 Problem-Solving Practice

Reinforce problem-solving skills and strategies with the Problem-Solving Practice worksheet.

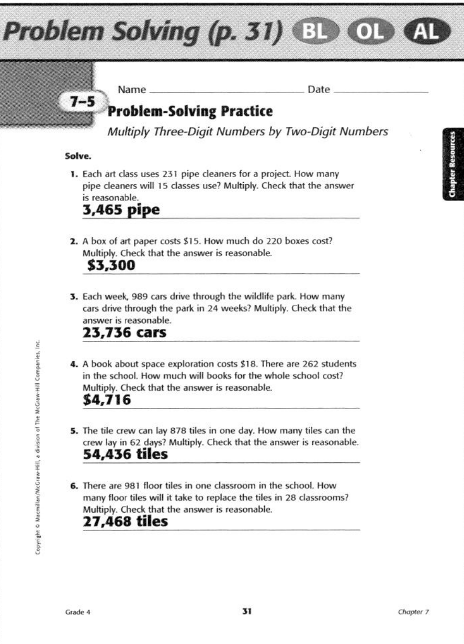

Problem Solving (p. 31) BL OL AL

Name ______________ Date ______________

7–5 Problem-Solving Practice

Multiply Three-Digit Numbers by Two-Digit Numbers

Chapter Resources

Solve.

1. Each art class uses 231 pipe cleaners for a project. How many pipe cleaners will 15 classes use? Multiply. Check that the answer is reasonable.
   3,465 pipe
2. A box of art paper costs $15. How much do 220 boxes cost? Multiply. Check that the answer is reasonable.
   $3,300
3. Each week, 989 cars drive through the wildlife park. How many cars drive through the park in 24 weeks? Multiply. Check that the answer is reasonable.
   23,736 cars
4. A book about space exploration costs $18. There are 262 students in the school. How much will books for the whole school cost? Multiply. Check that the answer is reasonable.
   $4,716
5. The tile crew can lay 878 tiles in one day. How many tiles can the crew lay in 62 days? Multiply. Check that the answer is reasonable.
   54,436 tiles
6. There are 981 floor tiles in one classroom in the school. How many floor tiles will it take to replace the tiles in 28 classrooms? Multiply. Check that the answer is reasonable.
   27,468 tiles

Grade 4 31 Chapter 7

Multiply Three-Digit Numbers by Two-Digit Numbers

1 Introduce

Activity Choice 1 • Hands-On

- Have students practice saying and writing several three-digit numbers in expanded form.
- Write 3×145 on the board. Remind students how they can use the Distributive Property of Multiplication to help them multiply. Then write $3 \times (100 + 40 + 5) = (3 \times 100) + (3 \times 40) + (3 \times 5)$.
- Have students multiply and add to solve.
- Ask students if they can predict a shorter way to multiply these numbers.

Activity Choice 2 • Literature

Introduce the lesson with *Snakes: Long Longer Longest* by Jerry Pallotta. For a related math activity, see p. TR53.

2 Teach

Scaffolding Questions

Write 123×35 on the board in vertical form.

- **How would you estimate 123×35?** Round 123 to 100 and 35 to 40, $100 \times 40 = 4{,}000$.
- **If you multiply 123×35 using pencil and paper, what do you think your first step would be?** Multiply 123 by 5.
- **How do you think multiplying a three-digit number by a two-digit number will be like multiplying 2 two-digit numbers?** The steps used will be the same, but there will be one extra digit in the number being multiplied.

GET READY to Learn

Have students open their books and read the information in **Get Ready to Learn**. Review **regroup**. As a class, work through **Examples 1 and 2**.

7-5 Multiply Three-Digit Numbers by Two-Digit Numbers

MAIN IDEA

I will multiply a three-digit number by a two-digit number.

Math Online

macmillanmh.com
- Extra Examples
- Personal Tutor
- Self-Check Quiz

GET READY to Learn

Rose uses about 275 minutes on her cell phone each month. How many minutes does she use in a year?

You can multiply 3-digit numbers by 2-digit numbers.

Real-World EXAMPLE

1 PHONES How many minutes does Rose use in a year?

There are 12 months in 1 year. So, multiply the number of minutes each month by 12. Find 275×12.

Estimate $300 \times 10 = 3{,}000$

Step 1 Multiply 275 by 2.

$$\begin{array}{r} {}^{1\,1} \\ 275 \\ \times\ 12 \\ \hline 550 \end{array} \leftarrow 2 \times 275$$

Step 2 Multiply 275 by 1 ten.

$$\begin{array}{r} {}^{1\,1} \\ 275 \\ \times\ 12 \\ \hline 550 \\ 2{,}750 \end{array} \leftarrow 10 \times 275$$

Step 3 Add the products.

$$\begin{array}{r} {}^{1\,1} \\ 275 \\ \times\ 12 \\ \hline 550 \\ +2{,}750 \\ \hline 3{,}300 \end{array} \leftarrow \text{Add.}$$

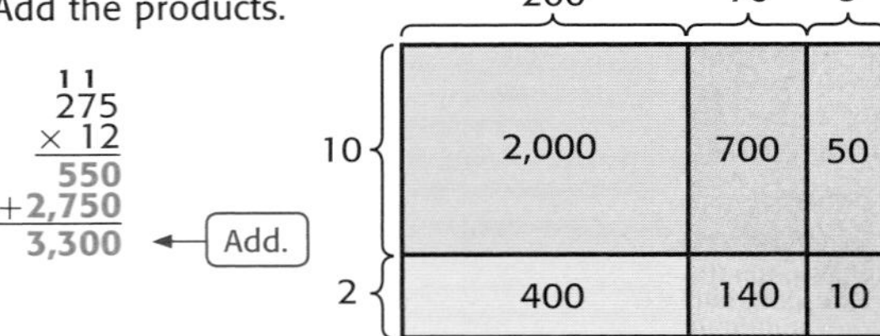

So, Rose uses 3,300 minutes in a year.

Check for Reasonableness

Since 3,300 is close to the estimate, the answer is reasonable. ✓

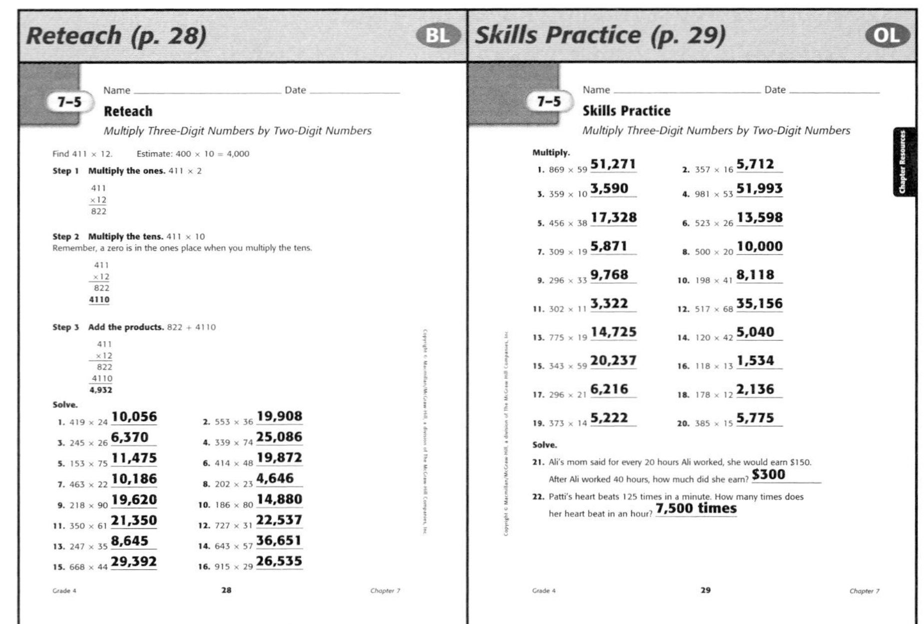

Reteach (p. 28) BL

7-5 Name ______ Date ______

Reteach

Multiply Three-Digit Numbers by Two-Digit Numbers

Find 411×12. Estimate: $400 \times 10 = 4{,}000$

Step 1 Multiply the ones. 411×2

$$\begin{array}{r} 411 \\ \times 12 \\ \hline 822 \end{array}$$

Step 2 Multiply the tens. 411×10

Remember, a zero is in the ones place when you multiply the tens.

$$\begin{array}{r} 411 \\ \times 12 \\ \hline 822 \\ \mathbf{4110} \end{array}$$

Step 3 Add the products. $822 + 4110$

$$\begin{array}{r} 411 \\ \times 12 \\ \hline 822 \\ 4110 \\ \hline \mathbf{4{,}932} \end{array}$$

Solve.

1. 419×24 **10,056**
2. 553×36 **19,908**
3. 245×26 **6,370**
4. 339×74 **25,086**
5. 153×75 **11,475**
6. 414×48 **19,872**
7. 463×22 **10,186**
8. 202×23 **4,646**
9. 218×90 **19,620**
10. 186×80 **14,880**
11. 350×61 **21,350**
12. 727×31 **22,537**
13. 247×35 **8,645**
14. 643×57 **36,651**
15. 668×44 **29,392**
16. 915×29 **26,535**

Grade 4 28 Chapter 7

Skills Practice (p. 29) OL

7-5 Name ______ Date ______

Skills Practice

Multiply Three-Digit Numbers by Two-Digit Numbers

Chapter Resources

Multiply.

1. 869×59 **51,271**
2. 357×16 **5,712**
3. 359×10 **3,590**
4. 981×53 **51,993**
5. 456×38 **17,328**
6. 523×26 **13,598**
7. 309×19 **5,871**
8. 500×20 **10,000**
9. 296×33 **9,768**
10. 198×41 **8,118**
11. 302×11 **3,322**
12. 517×68 **35,156**
13. 775×19 **14,725**
14. 120×42 **5,040**
15. 343×59 **20,237**
16. 118×13 **1,534**
17. 296×21 **6,216**
18. 178×12 **2,136**
19. 373×14 **5,222**
20. 385×15 **5,775**

Solve.

21. Ali's mom said for every 20 hours Ali worked, she would earn \$150. After Ali worked 40 hours, how much did she earn? **\$300**
22. Patti's heart beats 125 times in a minute. How many times does her heart beat in an hour? **7,500 times**

Grade 4 29 Chapter 7

Real-World EXAMPLE

2 MONEY A school bought 25 of the computers shown. What was the total cost?

Computers: $749 each

You need to multiply $749 by 25.

Estimate $700 × 30 = $21,000

Step 1 Multiply $749 by 5.

$$\begin{array}{r} {}^{4} \\ \$749 \\ \times\ 25 \\ \hline \$3{,}745 \end{array} \leftarrow \boxed{\$749 \times 5}$$

Remember

You may need to regroup when multiplying the ones, tens, and hundreds.

Step 2 Multiply $749 by 20.

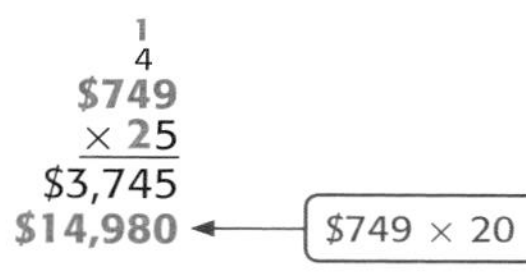

$$\begin{array}{r} {}^{1} \\ {}^{4} \\ \$749 \\ \times\ 25 \\ \hline \$3{,}745 \\ \$14{,}980 \end{array} \leftarrow \boxed{\$749 \times 20}$$

Step 3 Add the partial products.

$$\begin{array}{r} {}^{1} \\ {}^{4} \\ \$749 \\ \times\ 25 \\ \hline \$3{,}745 \\ +\$14{,}980 \\ \hline \$18{,}725 \end{array} \leftarrow \boxed{\text{Add.}}$$

So, the product of $749 and 25 is $18,725.

Check for Reasonableness

Since $18,725 is close to the estimate, the answer is reasonable. ✓

★ indicates multi-step problem

CHECK What You Know

Multiply. See Examples 1 and 2 (pp. 288–289)

1. 135 × 18 2,430
2. 340 × 32 10,880
3. $703 × 89 $62,567
4. A herd of elephants can travel 50 miles a day. At this rate, how far could a herd travel in a year? 18,250 miles
5. Talk About It Explain how to find the product of 56 and 945. See Ch. 7 Answer Appendix.

Enrich (p. 32) AL

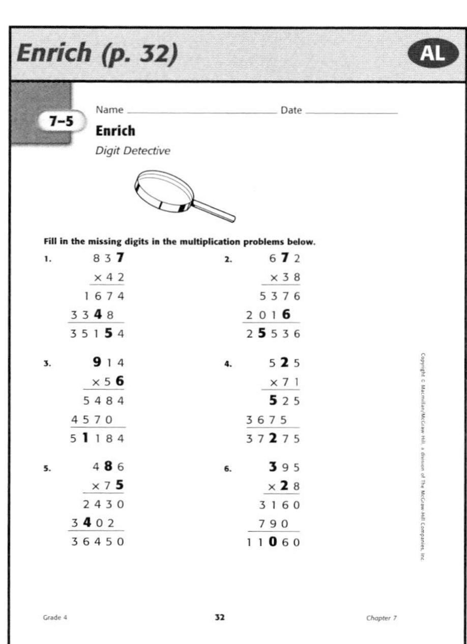

7-5 Name ______ Date ______

Enrich

Digit Detective

Fill in the missing digits in the multiplication problems below.

1. 837 × 42 = 1674 + 3348 = 35154
2. 672 × 38 = 5376 + 2016 = 25536
3. 914 × 56 = 5484 + 4570 = 51184
4. 525 × 71 = 525 + 3675 = 37275
5. 486 × 75 = 2430 + 3402 = 36450
6. 395 × 28 = 3160 + 790 = 11060

Grade 4 32 Chapter 7

Real World Example

Example 2 Students may become confused when looking at examples that have "stacked" regrouping numbers. Point out that when regrouping numbers are stacked, this means that they belong to different partial products. In this example, the "4" belongs to the first partial product ($3,745) and the "1" belongs to the second partial product ($14,980).

ADDITIONAL EXAMPLES

1. Antonio spends 194 minutes taking piano lessons each month. How many minutes does he spend taking piano lessons in a year? 2,328 minutes
2. Rai is paid $308 a week for her part-time job at the city library. What is Rai's annual salary? $16,016

CHECK What You Know

As a class, have students complete Exercises 1–5 in **Check What You Know** as you observe their work.

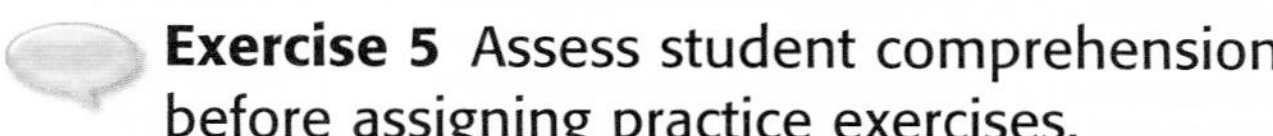

Exercise 5 Assess student comprehension before assigning practice exercises.

BL Alternate Teaching Strategy

If students have trouble multiplying three-digit numbers by two-digit numbers…

Then use one of these reteach options:

1. CRM **Daily Reteach Worksheet** (p. 28)
2. Have students break apart each factor to multiply. Provide the following example as a guide: 356 × 27.

$$\begin{array}{rcr} 300 \times 7 &=& 2{,}100 \\ 50 \times 7 &=& 350 \\ 6 \times 7 &=& 42 \\ 300 \times 20 &=& 6{,}000 \\ 50 \times 20 &=& 1{,}000 \\ +\ 6 \times 20 &=& 120 \\ \hline && 9{,}612 \end{array}$$

3. Have students use Math Tool Chest to help complete the problem-solving exercises. Use the Place-Value Tool and the Calculator.

3 Practice

Differentiate practice using these leveled assignments for Exercises 6–26.

Level	Assignment
BL Below/Approaching Level	6–9, 14–17, 22–23
OL On Level	6–15, 18–21, 23–24
AL Above/Beyond Level	6–24 even, 25–26

Have students discuss and complete the Higher Order Thinking problems. For Exercise 25, suggest that students use the pencil and paper method to work through the steps of the problem to help them identify the error.

WRITING IN MATH Have students complete Exercise 26 in their Math Journals. You may choose to use this exercise as an optional formative assessment.

Additional Answers

25. Sample answer: Michelle; Alberto did not regroup the 1 from the ones place to the tens place.

26. Sample answer: Nancy bought 12 books that had about 225 pages each. How many pages will Nancy read altogether if she reads every book?

Practice and Problem Solving

See page R19.

Multiply. See Examples 1 and 2 (pp. 288–289)

6. 106 × 12 **1,272**
7. 248 × 24 **5,952**
8. 283 × 33 **9,339**
9. 362 × 35 **12,670**
10. 467 × 41 **19,147**
11. 489 × 53 **25,917**
12. $508 × 59 **$29,972**
13. $632 × 66 **$41,712**
14. $770 × 71 **$54,670**
15. $862 × 87 **$74,994**
16. $901 × 96 **$86,496**
17. $934 × 97 **$90,598**

18. Every second, 630 steel cans are recycled. How many cans are recycled in 1 minute? **37,800 cans**

19. **Measurement** If a city receives 451 inches of rainfall each year, how much rainfall will the city receive in 35 years? **15,785 in.**

20. **Measurement** Aiden's pet cat is 13 years old. How many days old is Aiden's cat? **4,745 days**

21. Suppose a city has 206 days of fog each year. How many days of fog will occur in 12 years? **2,472 days**

Real-World PROBLEM SOLVING

Sports The table shows facts about balls used in sports.

Sports Ball Facts

Ball	Fact
Golf ball	450 dimples
Baseball	108 stitches
Soccer ball	32 panels

22. How many dimples are on a dozen golf balls? **5,400 dimples**

23. How many stitches do 75 baseballs have? **8,100 stitches**

24. ★ Find the difference in the number of dimples on 25 golf balls and the number of stitches on 25 baseballs. **8,550**

H.O.T. Problems

25. **FIND THE ERROR** Michelle and Alberto are finding 351 × 26. Who is correct? Explain. **25, 26. See margin.**

Michelle
351
× 26
9,126

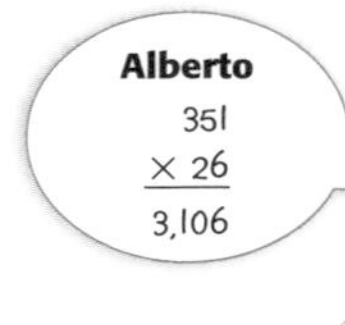

Alberto
351
× 26
3,106

26. WRITING IN MATH Write a real-world problem that involves multiplying a 3-digit number by a 2-digit number.

COMMON ERROR!

Students may add regrouped numbers more than once when regrouping twice in the same place. To avoid confusion, have students put an X through a regrouped number once they have finished adding it to the partial product.

Practice

27. While riding in a car, Denzel counted 17 blue cars on a highway in 1 minute. At this rate, how many blue cars will Denzel see in 45 minutes? (Lesson 7-4) C

A 360

B 400

C 765

D 775

28. There are 24 hours in a day and 365 days in a year. How many hours are in a year? (Lesson 7-5) J

F 2,190

G 7,440

H 8,000

J 8,760

Spiral Review

Multiply. (Lesson 7-4)

29. 34 × 10 340

30. 55 × 49 2,695

31. $72 × 66 $4,752

32. The tables shown need to be joined together so that 20 students can sit down for a student council meeting. Two people can sit on each side of a table. Draw a picture to show how the tables should be arranged. (Lesson 7-3)
See students' work.

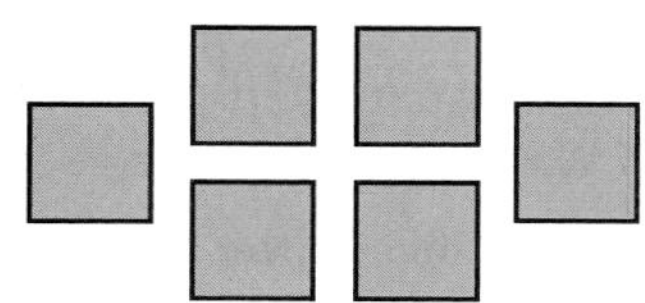

Estimate. Tell whether the estimate is *greater than* or *less than* the actual product. (Lesson 7-2)

33. 26 × 17 600; greater

34. 61 × 33 1,800; less

35. $87 × 75 $72,000; greater

Find the value of each expression if $a = 2$ and $b = 5$. (Lesson 5-6)

36. $24 \div (a \times 4)$ 3

37. $6 \times (11 - b)$ 36

38. $b \times (23 - 15)$ 40

Find all of the factors of each number. (Lesson 4-9) 42. 1, 2, 3, 4, 6, 9, 12, 18, 36

39. 8 1, 2, 4, 8

40. 11 1, 11

41. 24 1, 2, 3, 4, 6, 8, 12, 24

42. 36

43. For every 4 magazines Avery sells, his school receives $2. Use the table to find how much money he will raise if he sells 20 magazines. (Lesson 3-3) $10

Magazines Sold	4	8	12	16	20
Money	$2	$4	$6		

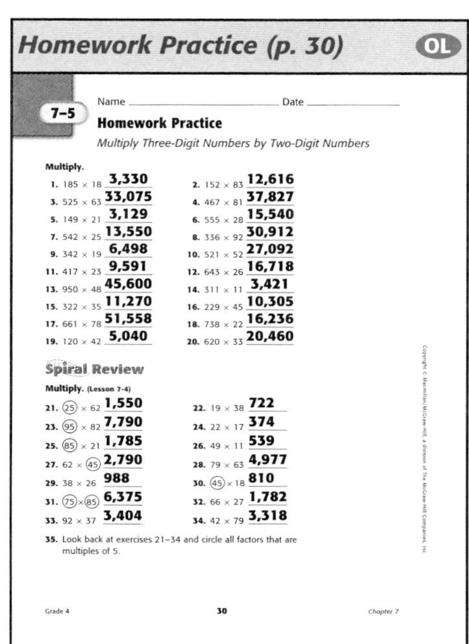

Homework Practice (p. 30) OL

7-5

Name ______________ Date ______________

Homework Practice

Multiply Three-Digit Numbers by Two-Digit Numbers

Multiply.

1. 185 × 18 **3,330**
2. 152 × 83 **12,616**
3. 525 × 63 **33,075**
4. 467 × 81 **37,827**
5. 149 × 21 **3,129**
6. 555 × 28 **15,540**
7. 542 × 25 **13,550**
8. 336 × 92 **30,912**
9. 342 × 19 **6,498**
10. 521 × 52 **27,092**
11. 417 × 23 **9,591**
12. 643 × 26 **16,718**
13. 950 × 48 **45,600**
14. 311 × 11 **3,421**
15. 322 × 35 **11,270**
16. 229 × 45 **10,305**
17. 661 × 78 **51,558**
18. 738 × 22 **16,236**
19. 120 × 42 **5,040**
20. 620 × 33 **20,460**

Spiral Review

Multiply. (Lesson 7-4)

21. (25) × 62 **1,550**
22. 19 × 38 **722**
23. (95) × 82 **7,790**
24. 22 × 17 **374**
25. (85) × 21 **1,785**
26. 49 × 11 **539**
27. 62 × (45) **2,790**
28. 79 × 63 **4,977**
29. 38 × 26 **988**
30. (45) × 18 **810**
31. (75)×(85) **6,375**
32. 66 × 27 **1,782**
33. 92 × 37 **3,404**
34. 42 × 79 **3,318**
35. Look back at exercises 21–34 and circle all factors that are multiples of 5.

4 Assess

Formative Assessment

- **What steps would you follow to find the product of 613 × 54?** Multiply 613 first by 4, then by 50, and add the partial products.

Quick Check **Are students continuing to struggle with multiplying a three-digit number by a two-digit number?**

If Yes → Small Group Options (p. 314B)

If No → Independent Work Options (p. 314B)
CRM Skills Practice Worksheet (p. 29)
CRM Enrich Worksheet (p. 32)

Ticket Out the Door Write 426 × 72 on the board. Ask students to find the product. Have them show their calculations and write the product on a piece of paper to give you as they leave the classroom at the end of the day.

Practice

Reviews Lessons 7-4 and 7-5

Assign the Test Practice problems to provide daily reinforcement of test-taking skills.

Spiral Review

Reviews Lessons 3-3, 4-9, 5-1, 7-2, 7-3, and 7-4

Review and assess mastery of skills and concepts from previous chapters.

Lesson Planner

Objective

Interpret information and data from social studies to solve problems.

National Standard 

Understands the history of the local community and how communities in North America varied long ago.

Activate Prior Knowledge

Before you turn students' attention to the pages, ask them to discuss forts.

- **Why do people build forts?** for shelter and protection
- **What famous forts have you heard of?** Sample answer: Fort Knox

Using the Student Page

Ask students to read the information on p. 292 and answer these questions:

- **What is the total distance around Fort Clatsop?** 200 feet
- **What is the area (*length multiplied by width) of Fort Clatsop?** 2,500 square feet

*Remind students that measuring area was taught in third grade. Call attention to the hint after Exercise 1.

WALLS WITH HISTORY

Humans have built forts all over the world for thousands of years. There are more than 136 forts in the United States. Some forts can hold hundreds to thousands of people, while others hold less than 100. Fort Sumter, a fort in South Carolina, could house 650 soldiers. This fort is where the shots starting the Civil War were fired.

Some forts like Sutter's Fort are now museums or state parks. However, other forts like Fort Knox in Kentucky are still used by the military today.

Famous Forts

Fort	Size of Main Building
Fort McIntosh (Georgia)	33 yd by 33 yd
The Alamo (Texas)	148 ft by 159 ft
Stone Fort at Harper's Ferry (West Virginia)	40 ft by 100 ft
Sutter's Fort (California)	64 ft by 35 ft
Fort Clatsop (Oregon)	50 ft by 50 ft

Did You Know?
Cannons at Fort Sumter could shoot one and a quarter miles.

Real-World Math

Use the information on pages 292 and 293 to solve each problem.

1. What is the area, or amount of space, that Stone Fort at Harper's Ferry covers? (*Hint:* Multiply the length and width to find its area.) **4,000 square ft**
2. The Alamo's main building is divided into 2 rooms. One room is 148 feet × 74 feet. What is the area of this room? **10,952 square ft**
3. How much larger is the area of the Stone Fort at Harper's Ferry than the area of Fort Clatsop? **1,500 square ft**
4. Fort Sumter has 5 walls. Each wall is between 170 and 190 feet long. What is the total estimated distance around Fort Sumter? **about 1,000 ft**
5. What is the area of Sutter's Fort? **2,240 square ft**
6. What is the distance around The Alamo? **614 ft**
7. Which fort is larger, the Stone Fort at Harper's Ferry or Fort McIntosh? Explain. **See margin.**

Real-World Math

Assign the exercises on p. 293. Encourage students to choose a problem-solving strategy before beginning each exercise. If necessary, review the strategies suggested in Lesson 7-6, p. 294.

Exercise 1 Point out the hint in this exercise regarding the formula for finding the area of a rectangle.

Exercise 4 Tell students that they will need to multiply to get the areas first before they subtract.

Exercise 5 Remind students that they will need to round in order to estimate the distance.

WRITING IN MATH Have students create a word problem that uses the information found in the text and in the chart on p. 292.

Extend the Activity

Have students create a fourth column for the chart on p. 292 and label it *area*. Have them fill in the areas of all of the main fort buildings in this chart column.

Additional Answer

7. Sample answer: Fort McIntosh; Its dimensions are measured in yards, whereas Stone Fort at Harper's Ferry's dimensions are measured in feet.

7-6 Problem-Solving Investigation
Choose a Strategy

Lesson Planner

Objective

Students choose the best strategy to solve a problem.

Resources

Manipulatives: money, clock

Teacher Technology

TeacherWorks • Interactive Classroom

Real-World Problem Solving Library
Math and Social Studies: *What is Recycling?*
Use these leveled books to reinforce and extend problem-solving skills and strategies.

Leveled for:

- OL On Level
- ELL Sheltered English
- SP Spanish

For additional support, see the Real-World Problem Solving Teacher Guide.

Daily Routine

Use these suggestions before beginning the lesson on p. 294.

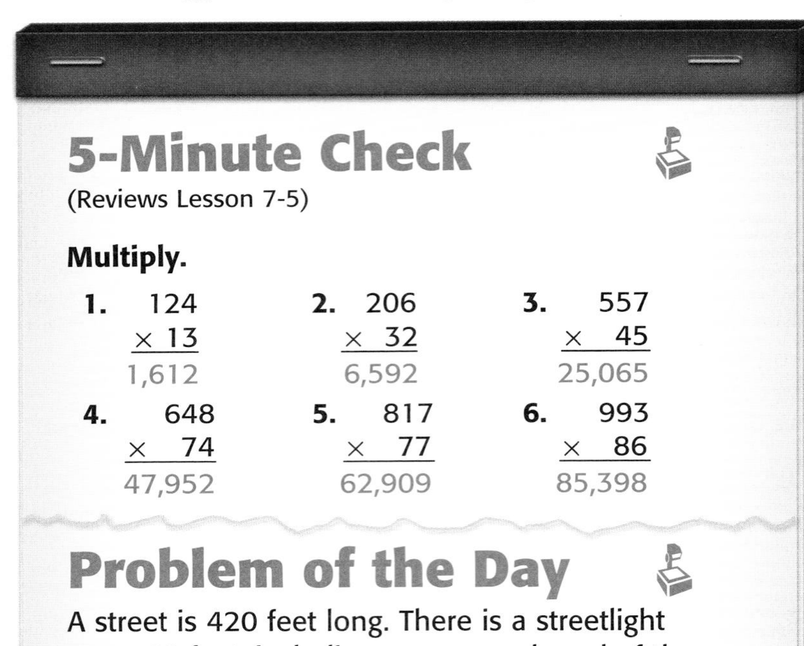

5-Minute Check

(Reviews Lesson 7-5)

Multiply.

1. 124 × 13 = 1,612
2. 206 × 32 = 6,592
3. 557 × 45 = 25,065
4. 648 × 74 = 47,952
5. 817 × 77 = 62,909
6. 993 × 86 = 85,398

Problem of the Day

A street is 420 feet long. There is a streetlight every 60 feet, including one on each end of the street. How many streetlights are there in all?
8 streetlights

Differentiated Instruction

Small Group Options

VISUAL, LOGICAL

Option 1 Gifted and Talented AL

Materials: quarters, dimes, nickels, chart paper, markers

- Copy the following problem on the chart paper:

  Mia has 3 quarters. Paul has the same amount of money in dimes and nickels. Paul has 9 coins. How many dimes and nickels does Paul have?

- Encourage students to try different combinations by acting out the answer with the coins. When they think they have the correct answer, ask them to discuss their answers with another student who has solved the problem. Paul has 6 dimes and 3 nickels.

INTRAPERSONAL

Option 2 English Language Learners ELL

Materials: posted solutions from 8-5
Core Vocabulary: step, following a plan, used
Common Use Verb: tried
Talk Math This strategy provides practice using "selecting and explaining" language.

- Choose a solution (repeated addition if possible) from the previous day and have the group review the plan they used to solve it.
- As they explain, rewrite the solution in a standard form. For each step that required choosing a computational method, ask the group to justify the choice. Solicit other ways to solve the problem, and allow students to discuss which is the better method.
- Allow students to use native language or incomplete forms of English. Be sure you restate their ideas in complete sentences.

Independent Work Options

LOGICAL, AUDITORY

Option 1 Early Finishers OL

Materials: paper and pencil

- Have pairs of students compare the strategies they used to solve the Mixed Problem Solving Exercises on p. 294.
- For exercises where their strategies differed, have students explain to their partners how they used the strategy to solve the problem.

Option 2 Student Technology

Math Online macmillanmh.com

Personal Tutor • Extra Examples

Option 3 Learning Station: Reading (p. 270G)

Direct students to the Reading Learning Station for opportunities to explore and extend the lesson concept.

1 Introduce

Activity • Review

- Present students with the following problem:
  Jen has 7 coins with a total value of 75¢. What coins does she have?
- **What problem-solving strategy could you use to solve the problem?** act it out
- Provide students with play money to use to act out and solve the problem. 2 quarters, 5 nickels

2 Teach

Have students read the problem on how Gregory spent his time at the carnival. Guide them through the problem-solving steps.

Understand Using the questions, review what students know and need to find.

Plan Have them discuss their strategy.

Solve Guide students to use reasonable answers to solve the problem.

- **How do you convert 4 hours to minutes?** Multiply 60 minutes by 4.
- **How will you find out if Gregory was correct?** Multiply to find out how many minutes he spent on rides, then add that to the time he spent eating and playing games.

Check Have students look back at the problem to make sure that the answer fits the facts given.

- **How could you check your answer?** Work backward to subtract the numbers from 240.
- **What mistake might Gregory have made when describing his time?** He may have spent less time on one of the activities than he thought.

COMMON ERROR!

Students may round incorrectly. Have students name the two multiples of ten a number is between and then draw a number line to find which multiple is closer.

7-6 Problem-Solving Investigation

MAIN IDEA I will choose the best strategy to solve a problem.

P.S.I. TEAM +

GREGORY: I spent 4 hours at a carnival. I spent 45 minutes eating and 55 minutes playing games. I also rode 12 rides, which took about 15 minutes each.

YOUR MISSION: Determine if Gregory is correct in saying that he spent 4 hours at the carnival.

Understand You know the amount of time Gregory spent at the carnival and on each activity. Find if he is correct.

Plan Solve a multi-step problem. Find the total number of minutes spent on activities and compare to 4 hours.

Solve First, change hours to minutes. Then compare.

60 minutes	15	
60 minutes	× 12	45 minutes
60 minutes	30	55 minutes
+ 60 minutes	+ 150	+ 180 minutes
240 minutes	180	280 minutes
time Gregory said he spent at carnival	time spent riding rides	time spent on carnival activities

Since 240 minutes does not equal 280 minutes, Gregory is not correct.

Check Look back at the problem. Use subtraction to check amount of time spent on carnival activities.
280 − 180 − 55 − 45 = 0. So, Gregory was not correct.

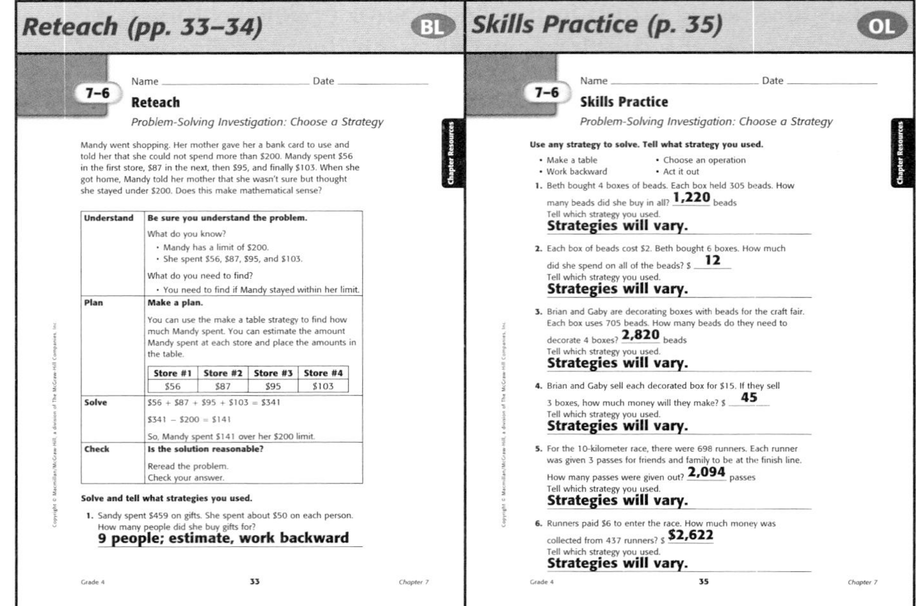

Reteach (pp. 33–34) BL

7-6 Name ______ Date ______

Reteach

Problem-Solving Investigation: Choose a Strategy

Mandy went shopping. Her mother gave her a bank card to use and told her that she could not spend more than $200. Mandy spent $56 in the first store, $87 in the next, then $95, and finally $103. When she got home, Mandy told her mother that she wasn't sure but thought she stayed under $200. Does this make mathematical sense?

Understand	**Be sure you understand the problem.** What do you know? • Mandy has a limit of $200. • She spent $56, $87, $95, and $103. What do you need to find? • You need to find if Mandy stayed within her limit.
Plan	**Make a plan.** You can use the make a table strategy to find how much Mandy spent. You can estimate the amount Mandy spent at each store and place the amounts in the table. Store #1: $56; Store #2: $87; Store #3: $95; Store #4: $103
Solve	$56 + $87 + $95 + $103 = $341 $341 − $200 = $141 So, Mandy spent $141 over her $200 limit.
Check	**Is the solution reasonable?** Reread the problem. Check your answer.

Solve and tell what strategies you used.

1. Sandy spent $459 on gifts. She spent about $50 on each person. How many people did she buy gifts for?
   9 people; estimate, work backward

Grade 4 33 Chapter 7

Chapter Resources

Skills Practice (p. 35) OL

7-6 Name ______ Date ______

Skills Practice

Problem-Solving Investigation: Choose a Strategy

Use any strategy to solve. Tell what strategy you used.

- Make a table
- Work backward
- Choose an operation
- Act it out

1. Beth bought 4 boxes of beads. Each box held 305 beads. How many beads did she buy in all? **1,220** beads
   Tell which strategy you used. **Strategies will vary.**
2. Each box of beads cost $2. Beth bought 6 boxes. How much did she spend on all of the beads? $ **12**
   Tell which strategy you used. **Strategies will vary.**
3. Brian and Gaby are decorating boxes with beads for the craft fair. Each box uses 705 beads. How many beads do they need to decorate 4 boxes? **2,820** beads
   Tell which strategy you used. **Strategies will vary.**
4. Brian and Gaby sell each decorated box for $15. If they sell 3 boxes, how much money will they make? $ **45**
   Tell which strategy you used. **Strategies will vary.**
5. For the 10-kilometer race, there were 698 runners. Each runner was given 3 passes for friends and family to be at the finish line. How many passes were given out? **2,094** passes
   Tell which strategy you used. **Strategies will vary.**
6. Runners paid $6 to enter the race. How much money was collected from 437 runners? $ **$2,622**
   Tell which strategy you used. **Strategies will vary.**

Grade 4 35 Chapter 7

Chapter Resources

★ indicates multi-step problem

Mixed Problem Solving

See page R19.

Use any strategy shown below to solve. Tell what strategy you used.

★**1.** A coach bought 5 pizzas. Each pizza has 12 slices. There are 18 players on the team. Is it reasonable to say that each player can eat 3 slices? Explain. See Ch. 7 Answer Appendix.

★**2.** Betty has 12 vases to make gifts for her family. Each vase will need ribbon that costs 30¢ and beads that cost $1. She estimates she will spend $15. Is her estimate reasonable? Explain. See Ch. 7 Answer Appendix.

3. Measurement Javon hikes the trail shown below 3 times a week. Is it reasonable to say that he hikes more than 20 miles in one month? Explain. Yes; he hikes 24 mi each month.

4. Two numbers have a sum of 16 and a product of 48. What are the numbers? 12 and 4

5. Carson has 57¢. He has 3 kinds of coins and 9 coins in all. What coins does Carson have? 4 dimes, 3 nickels, 2 pennies

6. Ashanti has 13 trophies. Three of the trophies are for swimming. She has two times as many soccer trophies as swimming trophies. The rest of the trophies are for tennis. How many tennis trophies does she have? 4

7. Edmundo has $36 saved and needs to buy the items below. Does he have enough money? Explain. See Ch. 7 Answer Appendix.

8. Measurement At 6:00 A.M. the temperature was 45°F. At 12:00 P.M. the temperature was 55°F. At 8:00 P.M. the temperature was 49°F. Create a number sentence to show the changes in temperatures. $45 + 10 - 6 = 49$

9. Every teacher at Elmwood Elementary is provided with 3,000 sheets of paper. How many sheets of paper do the 40 teachers have altogether? 120,000

10. WRITING IN MATH Isaac is baking four batches of bran muffins. There are 12 muffins in each batch. The answer is 144 muffins. What is the question? See Ch. 7 Answer Appendix.

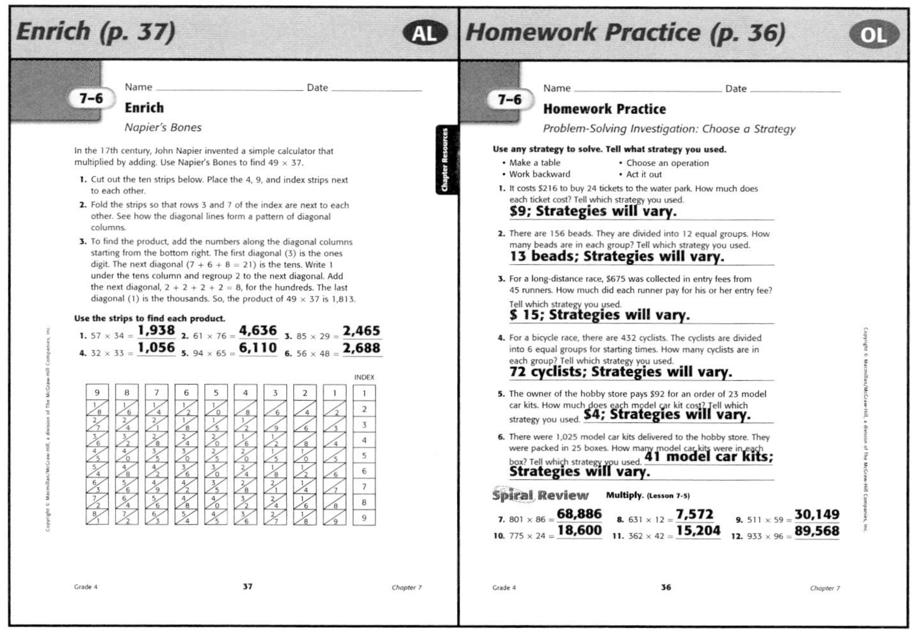

Enrich (p. 37) AL

7–6 Name ______ Date ______

Enrich

Napier's Bones

In the 17th century, John Napier invented a simple calculator that multiplied by adding. Use Napier's Bones to find 49 × 37.

1. Cut out the ten strips below. Place the 4, 9, and index strips next to each other.
2. Fold the strips so that rows 3 and 7 of the index are next to each other. See how the diagonal lines form a pattern of diagonal columns.
3. To find the product, add the numbers along the diagonal columns starting from the bottom right. The first diagonal (3) is the ones digit. The next diagonal (7 + 6 + 8 = 21) is the tens. Write 1 under the tens column and regroup 2 to the next diagonal. Add the next diagonal, 2 + 2 + 2 + 2 = 8, for the hundreds. The last diagonal (1) is the thousands. So, the product of 49 × 37 is 1,813.

Use the strips to find each product.

1. 57 × 34 = **1,938** 2. 61 × 76 = **4,636** 3. 85 × 29 = **2,465**
4. 32 × 33 = **1,056** 5. 94 × 65 = **6,110** 6. 56 × 48 = **2,688**

INDEX

Grade 4 37 Chapter 7

Homework Practice (p. 36) OL

7–6 Name ______ Date ______

Homework Practice

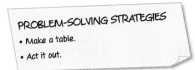

Problem-Solving Investigation: Choose a Strategy

Use any strategy to solve. Tell what strategy you used.

- Make a table
- Work backward
- Choose an operation
- Act it out

1. It costs $216 to buy 24 tickets to the water park. How much does each ticket cost? Tell which strategy you used. **$9; Strategies will vary.**
2. There are 156 beads. They are divided into 12 equal groups. How many beads are in each group? Tell which strategy you used. **13 beads; Strategies will vary.**
3. For a long-distance race, $675 was collected in entry fees from 45 runners. How much did each runner pay for his or her entry fee? Tell which strategy you used. **$ 15; Strategies will vary.**
4. For a bicycle race, there are 432 cyclists. The cyclists are divided into 6 equal groups for starting times. How many cyclists are in each group? Tell which strategy you used. **72 cyclists; Strategies will vary.**
5. The owner of the hobby store pays $92 for an order of 23 model car kits. How much does each model car kit cost? Tell which strategy you used. **$4; Strategies will vary.**
6. There were 1,025 model car kits delivered to the hobby store. They were packed in 25 boxes. How many model car kits were in each box? Tell which strategy you used. **41 model car kits; Strategies will vary.**

Spiral Review **Multiply.** (Lesson 7-5)

7. 801 × 86 = **68,886** 8. 631 × 12 = **7,572** 9. 511 × 59 = **30,149**
10. 775 × 24 = **18,600** 11. 362 × 42 = **15,204** 12. 933 × 96 = **89,568**

Grade 4 36 Chapter 7

BL Alternate Teaching Strategy

If students have trouble deciding if the situation makes mathematical sense…

Then use one of these reteach options:

1 CRM **Daily Reteach Worksheet** (pp. 33–34)

2 Have students work in pairs or small groups and use a clock to act out and solve the problem. Tell them to suppose that Gregory arrived at the carnival at 2:00 P.M.

- **If Gregory spent 4 hours at the carnival, at what time did he leave?** 6:00 P.M.

Have students move the clock hands as they work through the problem and determine if it makes sense.

3 Practice

Using the Exercises

Exercise 4 Students may also use the guess and check strategy for this exercise.

Exercise 5 Students may use the act it out strategy to solve this problem.

4 Assess

Formative Assessment

- **When might you use estimation to solve a word problem?** Sample answers: when an exact answer is not necessary to solve the problem; when I need to find if a mathematical situation is reasonable

Quick Check **Are students continuing to struggle with choosing the best strategy to solve a problem?**

If Yes → CRM Reteach Worksheet (pp. 33–34)

If No → Independent Work Options (p. 294B)
CRM Skills Practice Worksheet (p. 35)
CRM Enrich Worksheet (p. 37)

LESSON 7-7

Multiply Greater Numbers

Lesson Planner

Objective

Multiply four- and five-digit numbers by a two-digit number.

Review Vocabulary

factor, **product**

Resources

Materials: colored pencils

Literature Connection: *882 $\frac{1}{2}$ Amazing Answers to Your Questions About the Titanic* by Hugh Brewster and Laurie Coulter

Teacher Technology

TeacherWorks • Interactive Classroom

Daily Routine

Use these suggestions before beginning the lesson on p. 296.

5-Minute Check

(Reviews Lesson 7-6)

Use any strategy to solve. Tell what strategy you used.

Nitin spent 55 minutes mowing the lawn, 48 minutes cleaning his room, 23 minutes vacuuming, and 32 minutes doing laundry. Is it reasonable to say that Nitin spent 3 hours on completing his chores? Strategy: reasonable answers; no, it does not make sense because he spent less than 3 hours doing the chores.

Problem of the Day

On a pictograph, one symbol represents 14 people. How many people are shown by a row with $4\frac{1}{2}$ symbols? 63 people

Focus on Math Background

This lesson builds on previous multiplication of numbers with lesser number of digits. However, the greater number of digits may confuse students and they may forget a certain step when multiplying. Remind students to review the process for one-digit and two-digit numbers.

This lesson ties together everything students have been taught about multiplication. At this point students should

- understand place value,
- know what multiplication means,
- understand and be able to use the properties of multiplication,
- know the basic facts,
- understand the concept of regrouping when multiplying larger numbers, and
- be able to multiply larger numbers by two-digit numbers.

Review Math Vocabulary

Write the review vocabulary words and their definitions on the board.

Write several different multiplication sentences on the board in horizontal and vertical form (include basic facts; one-, two-, and three-digit numbers multiplied by one- and two-digit numbers; three factors). Have students take turns choosing a multiplication sentence and underlining the factors and circling the product.

Visual Vocabulary Cards

Use Visual Vocabulary Card 18 to reinforce the vocabulary reviewed in this lesson. (The Define/Example/Ask routine is printed on the back of each card.)

factor

Differentiated Instruction

Small Group Options

LOGICAL

Option 1 Gifted and Talented AL

Materials: paper, pencils, chart paper

- Review the long multiplication method with a two-digit number on the bottom and a three- or four-digit number on the top.
- Write the following problem on the chart paper:

  5,378
  × 432

- Go through this problem step by step and remind the students that when multiplying by 400 in this case, it is necessary to use 2 placeholder zeros.
- Complete this problem and try one or two more.

5378
× 432
10756
161340
2151200
2323296

SOCIAL, LINGUISTIC

Option 2 English Language Learners ELL

Materials: colored dry erase marker and overhead
Core Vocabulary: comma, decimal point, usually
Common Use Verb: signals

Talk Math This strategy clarifies how large numbers are written and read.

- Put a number in the ones place. Say it and allow students to practice speaking.
- Repeat for all the values. At the thousands and millions places, insert commas. Say: "**Commas *signal*** a pause when saying a number. They happen after every third number."
- Add the decimal point. Say, "In a number, this is a **decimal point** and **usually *signals*** money (add $ sign). When speaking a **decimal point,** you say 'and.'"
- Erase and repeat with new numbers as time permits.

Independent Work Options

LINGUISTIC, LOGICAL

Option 1 Early Finishers OL AL

Materials: paper and pencil

- Challenge students to write a word problem that can be solved by multiplying a four- or five-digit number by a two-digit number.
- Have students exchange problems with a partner and solve.

Option 2 Student Technology

Math Online macmillanmh.com

Personal Tutor • Extra Examples

 Math Adventures

Option 3 Learning Station: Art (p. 270G)

Direct students to the Art Learning Station for opportunities to explore and extend the lesson concept.

Option 4 Problem-Solving Practice

Reinforce problem-solving skills and strategies with the Problem-Solving Practice worksheet.

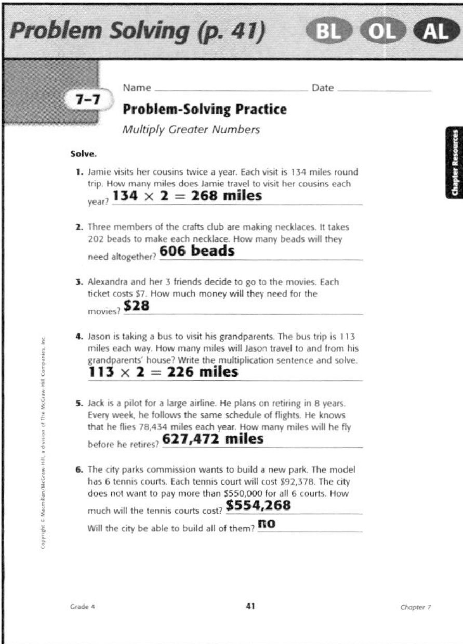

Problem Solving (p. 41) BL OL AL

7–7

Name ____________ Date ____________

Problem-Solving Practice

Multiply Greater Numbers

Chapter Resources

Solve.

1. Jamie visits her cousins twice a year. Each visit is 134 miles round trip. How many miles does Jamie travel to visit her cousins each year? **134 × 2 = 268 miles**
2. Three members of the crafts club are making necklaces. It takes 202 beads to make each necklace. How many beads will they need altogether? **606 beads**
3. Alexandra and her 3 friends decide to go to the movies. Each ticket costs $7. How much money will they need for the movies? **$28**
4. Jason is taking a bus to visit his grandparents. The bus trip is 113 miles each way. How many miles will Jason travel to and from his grandparents' house? Write the multiplication sentence and solve. **113 × 2 = 226 miles**
5. Jack is a pilot for a large airline. He plans on retiring in 8 years. Every week, he follows the same schedule of flights. He knows that he flies 78,434 miles each year. How many miles will he fly before he retires? **627,472 miles**
6. The city parks commission wants to build a new park. The model has 6 tennis courts. Each tennis court will cost $92,378. The city does not want to pay more than $550,000 for all 6 courts. How much will the tennis courts cost? **$554,268**
   Will the city be able to build all of them? **no**

Grade 4 41 Chapter 7

Multiply Greater Numbers

1 Introduce

Activity Choice 1 • Hands-On

- Divide students into groups of three. Give each group three number cubes.
- Have each student roll a number cube to generate a three-digit number. Students write that number on a sheet of paper.
- Then have two of the students roll their number cubes again to generate a two-digit number. Students write that number on a sheet of paper.
- Have students work together to multiply the numbers they have generated. Invite groups to share their problems and solutions with the class.

Activity Choice 2 • Literature

Introduce the lesson with *$882\frac{1}{2}$ Amazing Answers to Your Questions About the Titanic* by Hugh Brewster and Laurie Coulter. For a related math activity, see p. TR53.

2 Teach

Scaffolding Questions

Write the following on the board: 2,835 × 37.

- **Estimate the answer.** 3,000 × 40 = 120,000
- **What is the first step to take when solving this problem?** Multiply 2,835 by 7.
- **How do you think multiplying four-digit or greater numbers by a two-digit number will be like multiplying a three-digit number by a two-digit number?** There will be an extra step in the multiplication because of the additional digit.

GET READY to Learn

Have students open their books and read the information in **Get Ready to Learn**. Review **factor** and **product**. As a class, work through **Examples 1 and 2**.

7-7 Multiply Greater Numbers

MAIN IDEA

I will multiply four- and five-digit numbers by a two-digit number.

Math Online

macmillanmh.com
- Extra Examples
- Personal Tutor
- Self-Check Quiz

GET READY to Learn

Suppose 7,275 visitors go to a certain zoo every week. How many visitors go to the zoo in a year?

You can multiply multi-digit numbers by two-digit numbers.

Real-World EXAMPLE

1 ZOOS If 7,275 visitors go to a zoo every week, how many visitors go to the zoo in a year? Find 7,275 × 52.

Estimate 7,000 × 50 = 350,000

Step 1 Multiply the ones. Regroup if necessary.

```
   1 1
 7,275
×   52
14,550  ← 7,275 × 2
```

Step 2 Multiply the tens.

```
  1 3 2
    1 1
  7,275
×    52
 14,550
363,750  ← 7,275 × 50
```

Step 3 Add the partial products. Check for reasonableness.

```
   1 3 2
     1 1
   7,275
 ×    52
  14,550
+363,750
 378,300  ← Add.
```

So, the zoo gets 378,300 visitors in a year.

Check for Reasonableness

Since 378,300 is close to the estimate, the answer is reasonable. ✓

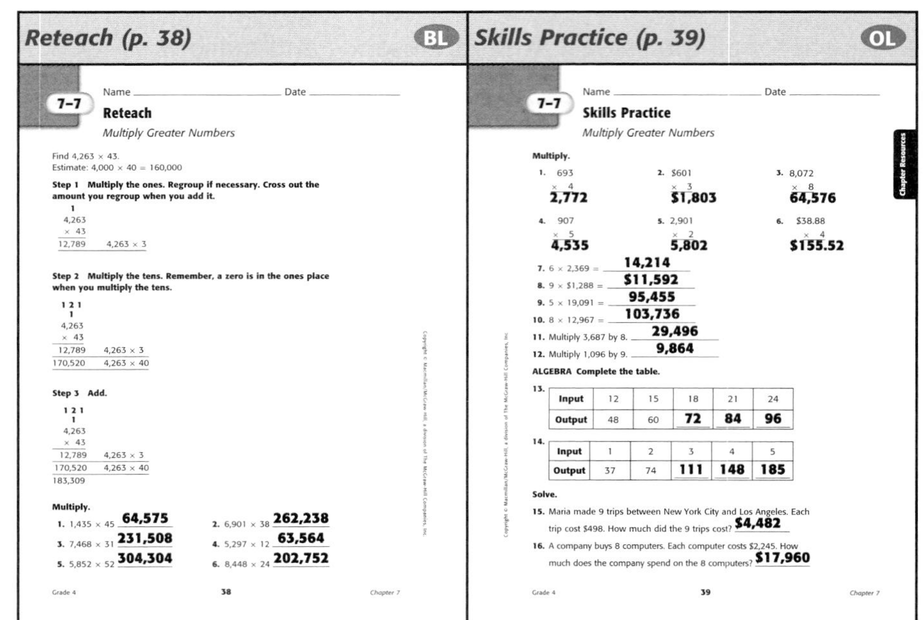

Reteach (p. 38) BL

7-7 Name ______ Date ______

Reteach

Multiply Greater Numbers

Find 4,263 × 43.
Estimate: 4,000 × 40 = 160,000

Step 1 Multiply the ones. Regroup if necessary. Cross out the amount you regroup when you add it.

```
    1
 4,263
 ×  43
12,789   4,263 × 3
```

Step 2 Multiply the tens. Remember, a zero is in the ones place when you multiply the tens.

```
  1 2 1
    1
  4,263
  ×  43
 12,789   4,263 × 3
170,520   4,263 × 40
```

Step 3 Add.

```
  1 2 1
    1
  4,263
  ×  43
 12,789   4,263 × 3
170,520   4,263 × 40
183,309
```

Multiply.

1. 1,435 × 45 **64,575**
2. 6,901 × 38 **262,238**
3. 7,468 × 31 **231,508**
4. 5,297 × 12 **63,564**
5. 5,852 × 52 **304,304**
6. 8,448 × 24 **202,752**

Skills Practice (p. 39) OL

7-7 Name ______ Date ______

Skills Practice

Multiply Greater Numbers

Multiply.

1. 693 × 4 = **2,772**
2. $601 × 3 = **$1,803**
3. 8,072 × 8 = **64,576**
4. 907 × 5 = **4,535**
5. 2,901 × 2 = **5,802**
6. $38.88 × 4 = **$155.52**
7. 6 × 2,369 = **14,214**
8. 9 × $1,288 = **$11,592**
9. 5 × 19,091 = **95,455**
10. 8 × 12,967 = **103,736**
11. Multiply 3,687 by 8. **29,496**
12. Multiply 1,096 by 9. **9,864**

ALGEBRA Complete the table.

13.

Input	12	15	18	21	24
Output	48	60	**72**	**84**	**96**

14.

Input	1	2	3	4	5
Output	37	74	**111**	**148**	**185**

Solve.

15. Maria made 9 trips between New York City and Los Angeles. Each trip cost $498. How much did the 9 trips cost? **$4,482**
16. A company buys 8 computers. Each computer costs $2,245. How much does the company spend on the 8 computers? **$17,960**

Chapter Resources

Real-World EXAMPLE

2 SPORTS **Suppose a stadium can seat 45,050 fans. There are 81 home games in a season. What is the greatest number of fans that can attend the home games in one season?**

You need to find 45,050 × 81.

Estimate 50,000 × 80 = 4,000,000

Remember

Write a zero in the ones place when you multiply the tens.

Step 1 Multiply the ones.

```
  45,050
×     81
  45,050   ← 45,050 × 1
```

Step 2 Multiply the tens.

```
    4 4
   45,050
×      81
   45,050
3,604,000   ← 45,050 × 80
```

Step 3 Add the partial products.

```
     4 4
    45,050
×       81
    45,050
+ 3,604,000
  3,649,050   ← Add.
```

So, 3,649,050 fans can attend all of the home games.

Check for Reasonableness

3,649,050 is close to the estimate. The answer is reasonable. ✓

5. Sample answer: The same steps are used in both cases; multiply by the ones, then by the tens.

★ indicates multi-step problem

CHECK What You Know

Multiply. See Examples 1 and 2 (pp. 296–297)

1. 1,360 × 29 39,440
2. 7,251 × 58 420,558
3. $23,973 × 41 $982,893
4. An average professional baseball player earns $15,750 per game. How much money does a player earn in a month in which 23 games are played? $362,250
5. **Talk About It** How is multiplying a 3-digit number by a 2-digit number like multiplying a 5-digit number by a 2-digit number?

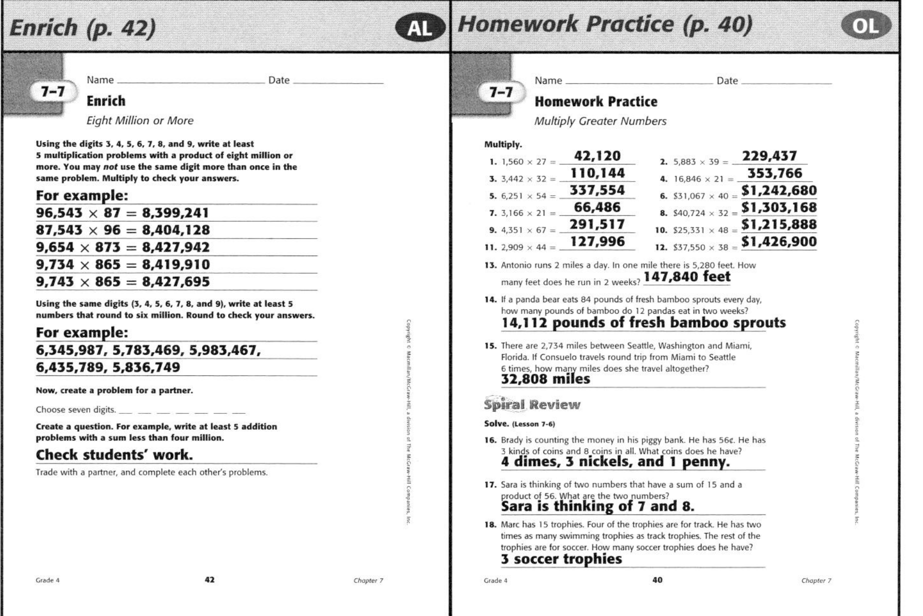

Enrich (p. 42) AL

7–7 Name ______ Date ______

Enrich

Eight Million or More

Using the digits 3, 4, 5, 6, 7, 8, and 9, write at least 5 multiplication problems with a product of eight million or more. You may *not* use the same digit more than once in the same problem. Multiply to check your answers.

For example:
96,543 × 87 = 8,399,241
87,543 × 96 = 8,404,128
9,654 × 873 = 8,427,942
9,734 × 865 = 8,419,910
9,743 × 865 = 8,427,695

Using the same digits (3, 4, 5, 6, 7, 8, and 9), write at least 5 numbers that round to six million. Round to check your answers.

For example:
6,345,987, 5,783,469, 5,983,467, 6,435,789, 5,836,749

Now, create a problem for a partner.

Choose seven digits. ___ ___ ___ ___ ___ ___ ___

Create a question. For example, write at least 5 addition problems with a sum less than four million.

Check students' work.

Trade with a partner, and complete each other's problems.

Grade 4 42 Chapter 7

Homework Practice (p. 40) OL

7–7 Name ______ Date ______

Homework Practice

Multiply Greater Numbers

Multiply.

1. 1,560 × 27 = **42,120**
2. 5,883 × 39 = **229,437**
3. 3,442 × 32 = **110,144**
4. 16,846 × 21 = **353,766**
5. 6,251 × 54 = **337,554**
6. $31,067 × 40 = **$1,242,680**
7. 3,166 × 21 = **66,486**
8. $40,724 × 32 = **$1,303,168**
9. 4,351 × 67 = **291,517**
10. $25,331 × 48 = **$1,215,888**
11. 2,909 × 44 = **127,996**
12. $37,550 × 38 = **$1,426,900**
13. Antonio runs 2 miles a day. In one mile there is 5,280 feet. How many feet does he run in 2 weeks? **147,840 feet**
14. If a panda bear eats 84 pounds of fresh bamboo sprouts every day, how many pounds of bamboo do 12 pandas eat in two weeks? **14,112 pounds of fresh bamboo sprouts**
15. There are 2,734 miles between Seattle, Washington and Miami, Florida. If Consuelo travels round trip from Miami to Seattle 6 times, how many miles does she travel altogether? **32,808 miles**

Spiral Review

Solve. (Lesson 7-6)

16. Brady is counting the money in his piggy bank. He has 56¢. He has 3 kinds of coins and 8 coins in all. What coins does he have? **4 dimes, 3 nickels, and 1 penny.**
17. Sara is thinking of two numbers that have a sum of 15 and a product of 56. What are the two numbers? **Sara is thinking of 7 and 8.**
18. Marc has 15 trophies. Four of the trophies are for track. He has two times as many swimming trophies as track trophies. The rest of the trophies are for soccer. How many soccer trophies does he have? **3 soccer trophies**

Grade 4 40 Chapter 7

Real World Example

Example 1 Point out that to find the total number of zoo visitors in one year, you need to multiply the number of visitors in one week by the number of weeks in one year. If necessary, remind students that there are 52 weeks in one year.

ADDITIONAL EXAMPLES

1. A science museum gets an average of 4,562 visitors every week. How many visitors does it get in a year? 237,224 visitors
2. A Web site gets an average of 23,149 hits each month. How many hits does it get in 15 months? 347,235 hits

CHECK What You Know

As a class, have students complete Exercises 1–5 in **Check What Your Know** as you observe their work.

Exercise 5 Assess student comprehension before assigning practice exercises.

BL Alternate Teaching Strategy

If students have trouble multiplying greater numbers by two-digit numbers…

Then use one of these reteach options:

1. CRM **Daily Reteach Worksheet** (p. 38)
2. Have students break apart the two-digit factor to make two easier multiplication problems: a greater number multiplied by a multiple of ten and by a one-digit number. Have students add the products to solve. Provide the following example for 39,824 × 23 as a guide:

```
  39,824      39,824      796,480
×     20    ×      3    + 119,472
 796,480     119,472      915,952
```

39,824 × 23 = 915,952

COMMON ERROR!

Students may become confused over which regrouped numbers to use when finding each partial product. Have students use two different colored pencils: one color to write regrouped numbers and the partial product when multiplying the ones and another color to write regrouped numbers and the partial product when multiplying the tens.

3 Practice

Differentiate practice using these leveled assignments for Exercises 6–24.

Level	Assignment
BL Below/Approaching Level	6–9, 14–17, 20
OL On Level	6–15, 18–20, 22–23
AL Above/Beyond Level	7–21 odd, 22–24

Have students discuss and complete the Higher Order Thinking problems. For Exercise 23, suggest that students first use mental math to find the product of 11 and 1,000. They can then use number sense to solve the problem.

WRITING IN MATH Have students complete Exercise 24 in their Math Journals. You may choose to use this exercise as an optional formative assessment.

4 Assess

Formative Assessment

- **How is multiplying a four-digit number by a two-digit number like multiplying a three-digit number by a two-digit number? How is it different?** Sample answer: The same method is used to find each product. Each partial product is greater and the final product is greater when multiplying a four-digit number.

Quick Check **Are students continuing to struggle with multiplying a four- or five-digit number by a two-digit number?**

If Yes → Strategic Intervention Guide (p. 80)

If No → Independent Work Options (p. 322B)
CRM Skills Practice Worksheet (p. 39)
CRM Enrich Worksheet (p. 42)

Into the Future Ask students to decide if they think the following statement is true or false:

If you know how to multiply a five-digit number by a two-digit number, you can multiply a six-, seven-, or eight-digit number by a two-digit number.

Have students discuss their answers and reasoning.

Practice and Problem Solving

EXTRA PRACTICE See page R19.

Multiply. See Examples 1 and 2 (pp. 296–297)

6. $1,418 \times 12$ **17,016**
7. $2,983 \times 24$ **71,592**
8. $4,166 \times 35$ **145,810**
9. $6,873 \times 39$ **268,047**
10. $8,316 \times 14$ **116,424**
11. $9,809 \times 67$ **657,203**
12. $\$13,820 \times 21$ **$290,220**
13. $\$17,846 \times 26$ **$463,996**
14. $25,067 × 30 **$752,010**
15. $29,452 × 38 **$1,119,176**
16. $30,824 × 43 **$1,325,432**
17. $37,525 × 48 **$1,801,200**
18. **Measurement** Gabrielle rides her bike 2 miles a day. In one mile there are 5,280 feet. How many feet does she ride her bike in 2 weeks? **147,840 ft**
19. **Measurement** If a cow produces 2,305 gallons of milk each year, how many gallons of milk do 75 cows produce in a year? **172,875 gal**

Real-World PROBLEM SOLVING

Measurement The map shows distances between some cities in the United States.

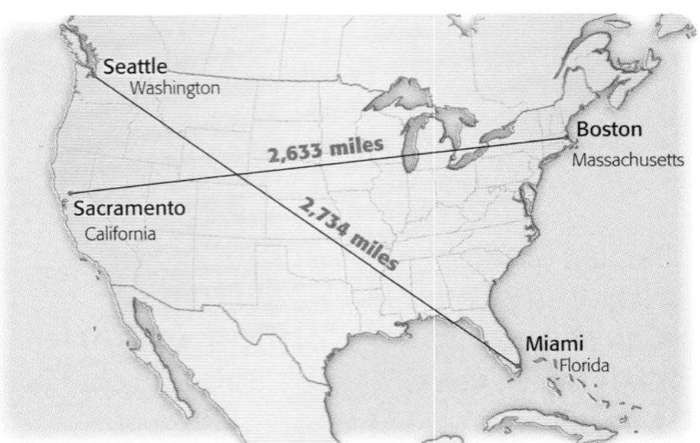

20. ★ Meliah traveled round trip from Sacramento to Boston 6 times during the summer months. How many miles did she travel altogether? **31,596 miles**
21. ★ Marcos traveled round trip from Miami to Seattle 8 times. How many miles did he travel altogether? **43,744 miles**

H.O.T. Problems

22. **OPEN ENDED** Create a multiplication exercise that has a product greater than 1,000,000. **Sample answer: 54,049 × 56**
23. **NUMBER SENSE** Is the product of 11 and 1,000 greater or less than 10,000? How can you tell without multiplying? **Sample answer: greater than; 10 × 1,000 = 10,000, so 11 × 1,000 is greater.**
24. **WRITING IN MATH** What is the greatest number of digits a product could have if a 2-digit factor is multiplied by a 5-digit number? Explain. **See margin.**

Additional Answer

24. Sample answer: 7 digits; The greatest factors you could multiply are 99 and 99,999, which give a 7-digit product.

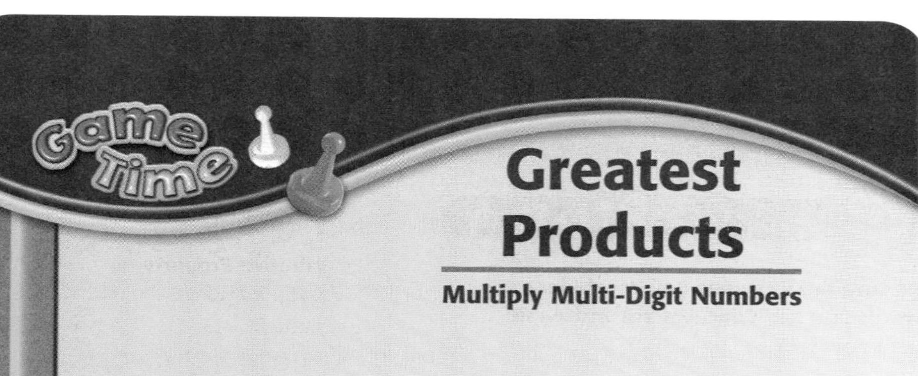

Greatest Products

Multiply Multi-Digit Numbers

Get Ready!

Players: 2

Get Set!

Each player should have a sheet of notebook paper.

Go!

- Player 1 rolls all 6 number cubes.
- Player 1 uses the number cubes to create a problem that involves multiplying a 4-digit number by a 2-digit number.
- Player 1 can arrange the digits in any place value and then find the product of the 2 factors.
- Player 2 takes a turn.
- The player who creates the greatest product earns 1 point.
- The player to earn 5 points first wins.

You will need: 6 number cubes labeled 0–5, paper and pencil

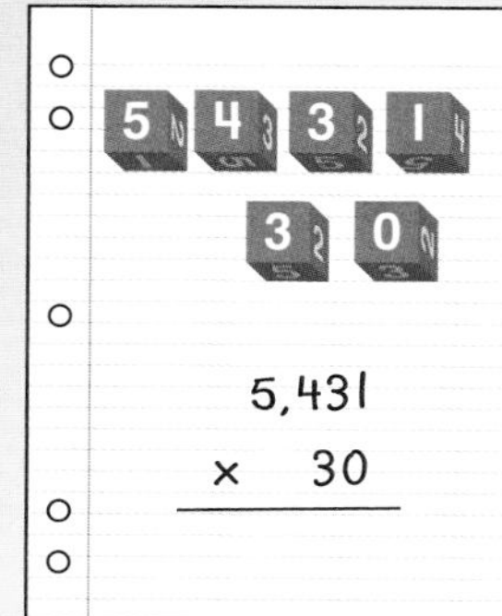

Differentiated Practice

Use these leveled suggestions to differentiate the game for all learners.

Level	Assignment
BL Below/Approaching Level	Students estimate the product of the two numbers.
OL On Level	Have students play the game with the rules as written.
AL Above/Beyond Level	Player 2 solves the problem that Player 1 creates, and vice versa.

Greatest Products

Math Concept:
Multiply Multi-Digit Numbers

Materials: 7 number cubes, paper, pencil

Introduce the game on p. 299 to your students to play as a class, in small groups, or at a learning workstation to review concepts introduced in this chapter.

Instructions

- Students create multiplication problems multiplying a 5-digit number by a 2-digit number, as shown on p. 299.
- Player 1 rolls 7 number cubes and creates a multiplication problem, arranging the digits in any place value, using five of the numbers rolled to create a 5-digit number and the other two numbers rolled to create a 2-digit number. Player 1 finds the product of the two numbers.
- Player 2 does the same. The player whose problem creates the greatest product earns 1 point.
- Play continues until one player gets 5 points. The player to do so first wins.

Extend the Game

Have students try to get the lowest product using the same rolling procedure.

CHAPTER 7 Study Guide and Review

FOLDABLES Dinah Zike's Foldables

Use these lesson suggestions for incorporating the Foldables during the chapter. Students can then use their Foldables to review for the test.

Lesson 7-6 On the fourth tab of the Foldable, students provide examples of multiplying a four- and five-digit number by a two-digit number.

Vocabulary: Students use the last tab of the Foldable to define key terms and chapter vocabulary.

Key Vocabulary

The page references after each word denote where that term was first introduced. If students have difficulty answering Exercises 1–5, remind them that they can use the page references to review the vocabulary terms.

Vocabulary Review

Review chapter vocabulary using one of the following options.

- **Visual Vocabulary Cards** (15, 18, 42)
- **eGlossary** at macmillanmh.com

CHAPTER 7 Study Guide and Review

Math Online macmillanmh.com
- STUDY TO GO
- Vocabulary Review

FOLDABLES Study Organizer GET READY to Study

Be sure the following Key Vocabulary words and Key Concepts are written in your Foldable.

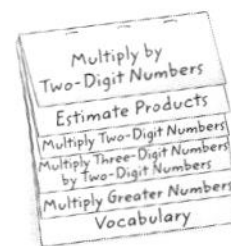

Key Concepts

Estimate Products (p. 276)
Round each factor, then multiply.

$$\begin{array}{r} 36 \\ \times\ 28 \end{array} \longrightarrow \begin{array}{r} 40 \\ \times\ 30 \\ \hline 1{,}200 \end{array}$$

36 rounds to 40.
28 rounds to 30.

Multiply by Two-Digit Numbers (p. 284)

$$\begin{array}{r} 178 \\ \times\ \ 34 \\ \hline 712 \\ +5{,}340 \\ \hline 6{,}052 \end{array}$$

Multiply the ones, tens, and hundreds. Regroup as needed.

Add the partial products.

	100	70	8
30	3,000	2,100	240
4	400	280	32

3,000 + 2,100 + 240 + 400 + 280 + 32 = 6,052

Key Vocabulary

Distributive Property of Multiplication (p. 282)
estimate (p. 276)
factor (p. 276)
multiple (p. 273)
product (p. 276)

Vocabulary Check

1. A number that is close to an exact value is a(n) ____?____. estimate
2. The numbers 1, 2, 3, and 6 are ____?____ of the number 6. factors
3. A(n) ____?____ of a number is the product of that number and any whole number. multiple
4. The ____?____ allows you to multiply a sum by a number by multiplying each addend by the number and adding the products. Distributive Property of Multiplication
5. A(n) ____?____ is a number that divides into a whole number evenly. factor
6. A number is a(n) ____?____ of its factors. product

Chapter 7 Project

Name That Digit

Alone, in pairs, or in small groups, have students discuss the results of their completed chapter project with the class. Assess their work using the Chapter Project rubric found in Chapter 7 Resource Masters, p. 53.

Lesson-by-Lesson Review

7-1 Multiply by Tens (pp. 273–275)

Example 1
A football coach is ordering 30 jerseys for his football team. The jerseys cost $29 each. What will the total cost of the jerseys be?

Step 1 Multiply the ones.

$$\begin{array}{r} 29 \\ \times\ 30 \\ \hline 0 \end{array}$$ ← 0 ones × 29 = 0

Step 2 Multiply the tens.

$$\begin{array}{r} 29 \\ \times\ 30 \\ \hline 870 \end{array}$$ ← 3 tens × 29 = 87 tens

So, the total cost will be $870.

Multiply.

7. $\begin{array}{r} 90 \\ \times\ 90 \\ \hline \end{array}$ 8,100 **8.** $\begin{array}{r} 34 \\ \times\ 80 \\ \hline \end{array}$ 2,720

9. $28 × 40 $1,120 **10.** $45 × 30 $1,350

11. Jeremy reads the number of books shown in a month. How many books will he read in 2 years? 240 books

12. There are 30 students in each class. There are 27 classrooms. How many students are there? 810 students

7-2 Estimate Products (pp. 276–279)

Example 2
Estimate 33 × 18.

Step 1 Round each factor to the nearest ten.

33 → 30 ← Round 33 to 30.
×18 → ×20 ← Round 18 to 20.

Step 2 Multiply.

$$\begin{array}{r} 30 \\ \times\ 20 \\ \hline 600 \end{array}$$ ← 0 ones × 30 = 0; 2 tens × 30 = 60 tens

So, 33 × 18 is about 600.

Estimate. Tell whether the estimate is *greater than* or *less than* the actual product. 13–18. See margin.

13. $\begin{array}{r} 82 \\ \times 38 \\ \hline \end{array}$ **14.** $\begin{array}{r} \$76 \\ \times 24 \\ \hline \end{array}$

15. $244 × 31 **16.** 482 × 49

17. 371 × 66 **18.** 527 × 84

19. Tamara makes $12 an hour. She worked 28 hours this week. About how much money will she make? $10 × 30 = $300; less than

Lesson-by-Lesson Review

Have students complete the Lesson-by-Lesson Review on pp. 300–304. Then you can use ExamView® Assessment Suite to customize another review worksheet that practices all the objectives of this chapter or only the objectives on which your students need more help.

Intervention If the given examples are not sufficient to review the topics covered by the questions, use the page references next to the exercises to review that topic in the Student Edition.

Additional Answers

13. 80 × 40 = 3,200; greater than
14. $80 × 20 = $1,600; less than
15. $200 × 30 = $6,000; less than
16. 500 × 50 = 25,000; greater than
17. 400 × 70 = 28,000; greater than
18. 500 × 80 = 40,000; less than

CHAPTER 7

Study Guide and Review

7-3 Problem-Solving Strategy: Act It Out (pp. 280–281)

Example 3

Elvio has 6 coins in his pocket equaling 72¢. What combination of coins does he have in his pocket?

Understand

What facts do you know?

- Elvio has 6 coins in his pocket.
- The value of the coins is 72¢.

What do you need to find?

- The coins Elvio has.

Plan Act out the problem.

Solve One way to make 72¢ is with 1 fifty-cent piece, 2 dimes, and 2 pennies. You need one more coin.

Take the fifty-cent piece and exchange it for 2 quarters.

The value of the coins stays the same, and the number of coins increases to six.

So, Elvio has 2 quarters, 2 dimes, and 2 pennies.

Check The answer makes sense for the facts given in the problem. You have 6 coins that have a total value of 72¢.

20. There are cartons of milk in 10 rows of 8. You remove 4 cartons from each of 5 rows. How many cartons are left? 60 cartons

21. Jewel is painting a pattern on a bowl in art class. She is using the shapes below to form the pattern. How many ways can Jewel arrange the shapes to form a repeating pattern if she uses each shape once? 6 ways

 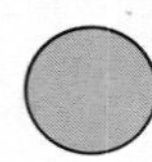 

22. Joan saved $8 the first week, three times that the second week, and $15 the third week. How much did she save in three weeks? $47

23. **Geometry** Look at the pattern below. How many squares are needed to make the 6th figure in the pattern shown? 20 squares

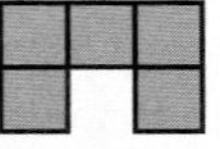

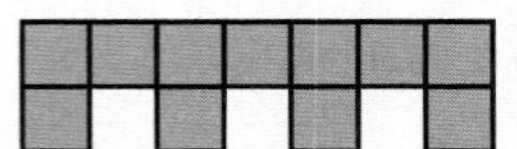

24. Can nine toothpicks be used to make four triangles that are the same size and same shape? yes

302 Chapter 7 Multiply by Two-Digit Numbers

7-4 Multiply Two-Digit Numbers (pp. 284–286)

Example 4
Julio scores 18 points in each basketball game. If there are 14 games in a season, how many points will Julio score?

Multiply the number of games by the number of points scored in each game.

```
    3
   18
  ×14
   72  ← Multiply the ones.
+ 180  ← Multiply the tens.
  252  ← Add.
```

So, Julio will score 252 points.

Multiply.

25. 63×46 2,898

26. 26×34 884

27. \$72 × 49 \$3,528

28. \$55 × 41 \$2,255

29. 37×68 2,516

30. 89×53 4,717

31. \$19 × 72 \$1,368

32. 95×84 7,980

33. **Measurement** Kittens can run up to 31 miles per hour. At this rate, how much distance would a kitten cover in a day? 744 miles

7-5 Multiply Three-Digit Numbers by Two-Digit Numbers (pp. 288–291)

Example 5
Find 803 × 42.

Estimate \$800 × 40 = \$32,000

```
       1
    $803
   ×  42
   1,606  ← Multiply the ones.
 +32,120  ← Multiply the tens.
 $33,726  ← Add.
```

Check for Reasonableness
Since \$33,726 is close to the estimate, the answer is reasonable. ✓

Multiply.

34. 712×87 61,944

35. 841×96 80,736

36. 367×71 26,057

37. 670×87 58,290

38. \$705 × 88 \$62,040

39. \$234 × 45 \$10,530

40. 103×33 3,399

41. 632×35 22,120

42. A school bought 35 microscopes at \$125 each for the science lab. What was the total cost? \$4,375

43. If a person makes \$625 each week, how much will that person have made after one year? \$32,500

Chapter 7 Study Guide and Review **303**

Study Guide and Review

Additional Answers

46. no; In 3 months Toni will earn \$60. Since $\$60 < \$75$, it is not reasonable to say that Toni will have enough money to buy the tennis racquet.

53. 184,800 ft

7-6 Problem-Solving Investigation: Choose a Strategy (pp. 294–295)

Example 6
A theater can seat 785 people. There are 23 performances in a month. Is it reasonable to say that more than 20,000 people can attend the performances in a month?

Multiply 785 by 23. Then compare.

```
   11
   21
   785
 × 23
 2,355  ← Multiply the ones.
+15,700 ← Multiply the tens.
 18,055 ← Add the products.
```

Since $18{,}055 < 20{,}000$, it is not reasonable to say that more than 20,000 people can attend the performances in a month.

Use any strategy to solve.

44. By the end of the school year, Lolita wants to read 50 books. If she reads 3 books each month for the 9 months she is in school, will she reach her goal? no

45. Elan has a \$20 bill. He wants to buy a ball cap that costs \$16. What will his change be? \$4

46. Toni wants to save enough money to buy a tennis racquet for \$75. She earns \$5 a week for doing chores. Is it reasonable to say that Toni will have enough money to buy the tennis racquet in 3 months? Explain. See margin.

7-7 Multiply Greater Numbers (pp. 296–298)

Example 7
One of the fastest planes in the world can fly up to 5,329 miles per hour. At this rate, how far would this plane fly in 24 hours?

```
      1
    11 3
    5,329
  ×    24
   21,316
 +106,580
  127,896 ← Add.
```

So, this plane would fly 127,896 miles in 24 hours.

Multiply.

47. 1,418 × 14 = 19,852

48. 2,983 × 21 = 62,643

49. 13,720 × 31 = 425,320

50. 17,946 × 25 = 448,650

51. \$24,017 × 30 \$720,510

52. \$39,402 × 48 \$1,891,296

53. **Measurement** Jena's grandparents live 35 miles away. There are 5,280 feet in one mile. How many feet away do Jena's grandparents live? See margin.

Chapter Test

Multiply.

1. 26 ×10 260
2. 43 ×30 1,290
3. 89 × 33 2,937
4. 82 × 91 7,462
5. **Measurement** Elio jogs for 30 minutes each time he exercises. If he exercises 18 times in a month, how many minutes will he jog? 540 min

Estimate.

6. 152 × 47 10,000
7. 439 × 81 32,000
8. Shannon is reading a book that has about 18 pages in each chapter. The book has 12 chapters. About how many pages does the book have? 200 pages
9. Lina buys groceries for $14 at the store. She gives the cashier a $20 bill. List two combinations of bills she could receive as change. See. Ch. 7 Answer Appendix.
10. **MULTIPLE CHOICE** A school needs to buy 475 math books for its fourth grade students. Each book costs $85. What will the total cost be? B
    - **A** $40,000
    - **B** $40,375
    - **C** $45,000
    - **D** $53,150
11. Roxana brought 6 dozen snacks for her birthday party at school. Each person got 3 snacks. How many people are in her class? Explain your answer. See Ch. 7 Answer Appendix.

Multiply.

12. 107 × 12 1,284
13. 258 × 24 6,192
14. 1,324 × 12 15,888
15. 2,831 × 24 67,944
16. **Measurement** The table shows how many miles Ari biked each week of a month. If Ari bikes the same number of miles each month, how many miles will Ari bike in a year? 528 miles

Distance Biked	
Week	**Miles**
1	12
2	14
3	8
4	10

17. A store has 275 boxes of oranges. Each box costs $12. Find the total cost. $3,300
18. **MULTIPLE CHOICE** There are 24 hours in a day. There are 365 days in a year. How many hours are there in a year? G
    - **F** 9,560
    - **G** 8,760
    - **H** 8,670
    - **J** 8,000

19. See. Ch. 7 Answer Appendix.

19. **WRITING IN MATH** What is the greatest number of digits a product could have if a 4-digit number is multiplied by a 3-digit number? Explain.

Chapter 7 Chapter Test

Summative Assessment

Use these alternate leveled chapter tests to differentiate assessment for the specific needs of your students.

Leveled Chapter 7 Tests			
Form	**Type**	**Level**	**CRM Pages**
1	Multiple Choice	BL	55–56
2A	Multiple Choice	OL	57–58
2B	Multiple Choice	OL	59–60
2C	Free Response	OL	61–62
2D	Free Response	OL	63–64
3	Free Response	AL	65–66

BL = below/approaching grade level
OL = on grade level
AL = above/beyond grade level

Vocabulary Test

CRM **Chapter 7 Resource Masters** (p. 50)

ExamView Assessment Suite Customize and create multiple versions of your Chapter Test and the test answer keys.

Data-Driven Decision Making

Based on the results of the Chapter Test, use the following to review concepts that continue to present students with problems.

Exercises	State/Local Standards	What's the Math?	Error Analysis	Resources for Review
1–5		Multiply whole numbers by a multiple of 10.	Does not put zero on the end of the answer when multiplying by tens.	Strategic Intervention Guide (pp. 72, 76, 78) CRM Chapter 7 Resource Masters (Reteach Worksheets) Math Adventures My Math Zone Chapter 7 Math Online Extra Examples • Concepts in Motion
6–8		Use rounding to estimate products.	Does not know how to estimate. Gives exact answer.	
10, 12–13, 16, 18		Multiply three-digit numbers by two-digit numbers.	Does not know multiplication facts. Does not know what to do with place value in multiplying two digits.	

Test Practice

Formative Assessment

- Use Student Edition pp. 306–307 as practice and cumulative review. These questions are written in the same style as many state tests.
- You can also use these two pages to benchmark student progress, or as an alternate homework assignment.

Additional practice pages can be found in the Chapter 7 Resource Masters.

CRM **Chapter 7 Resource Masters**
Cumulative Test Practice

- Multiple Choice format (pp. 55–60)
- Free Response format (pp. 61–66)

Create practice worksheets or tests that align to your state standards.

Math Online Have students visit macmillanmh.com for additional practice to reinforce your state standards.

Test Practice

Cumulative, Chapters 1–7

PART 1 Multiple Choice

Read each question. Then fill in the correct answer on the answer sheet provided by your teacher or on a sheet of paper.

1. Blake planted 12 rows of corn. Each row had 15 corn plants. How many corn plants will he have in all? B

A 170 **C** 225
B 180 **D** 240

2. What number should come next in the pattern? H

4, 7, 10, 13, 16, 19, ■

F 20 **H** 22
G 21 **J** 23

3. If Sean buys all the items, about how much will he spend? C

Baseball Equipment

Item	Cost
mitt	$39
bat	$34
ball	$19
T-shirt	$12

A $80 **C** $100
B $90 **D** $120

4. Leslie surveyed 30 students about their favorite kind of books.

Favorite Kind of Books	
Kind	**Tally**
Adventure	卌 卌
Science fiction	卌 |||
Mystery	卌 ||||
Poetry	|||

Which 2 kinds of books do 19 students enjoy reading most? H

F Adventure and science fiction
G Science fiction and mystery
H Mystery and adventure
J Poetry and science fiction

5. Miguela mowed 54 lawns over the summer. She charged $23 a lawn. How much money did she earn over the summer? A

A $1,242 **C** $1,132
B $1,232 **D** $124

6. While playing a board game, Vera scored 10 points on her first turn. At the end of the game, she had a total of 38 points. Which equation describes her points? G

F $p - 10 = 38$ **H** $10 + 38 = p$
G $10 + p = 38$ **J** $10 - p = 38$

Test-Taking Tip

Remind students that as they examine a multiple-choice test item, they should eliminate answer choices they know to be incorrect.

Preparing for Standardized Tests
For test-taking strategies and practice, see pages R42–R55.

7. Which number is 100,000 more than 873,496? D

A 773,496 **C** 883,496
B 874,496 **D** 973,496

8. Emanuel has 72 photos. His photo album holds 6 pictures on a page. How many pages will he use? F

F 12 **H** 9
G 10 **J** 8

9. Which number is represented by c in the equation $12 \times c = 108$? D

A 5 **C** 8
B 6 **D** 9

10. Which statement best describes the relationship between a and b? G

Input (a)	1	2	3	4	5
Output (b)	3	6	9	12	15

F b is 3 more than a
G b is 3 times a
H b is 3 less than a
J b is 2 times a

PART 2 Short Response

Record your answers on the answer sheet provided by your teacher or on a sheet of paper.

11. Kamilah read 38 pages in a book each day for 11 days. About how many pages did she read in all? 418

12. How many total visitors came to Wyatt Park in May and July? 14,587

Wyatt Park	
Month	**Visitors**
May	6,453
June	7,782
July	8,134
August	7,996

PART 3 Extended Response

Record your answers on the answer sheet provided by your teacher or on a sheet of paper.

13. Mr. Cook has 32 students in his homeroom. He makes groups with 8 students in each group. How many groups are there? Explain.

14. Fran baked 15 trays of muffins for a bake sale. Each tray has 6 muffins. How many muffins did Fran bake in all? Explain. 13, 14. See margin.

NEED EXTRA HELP?														
If You Missed Question...	1	2	3	4	5	6	7	8	9	10	11	12	13	14
Go to Lesson...	7-4	5-4	2-2	3-1	7-4	5-2	2-4	4-6	5-8	5-8	7-3	2-4	4-5	7-4

Summative Assessment 307

Answer Sheet Practice

Have students simulate taking a state test by recording their answers on a practice recording sheet.

CRM Chapter 7 Resource Masters
Student Recording Sheet (p. 71)

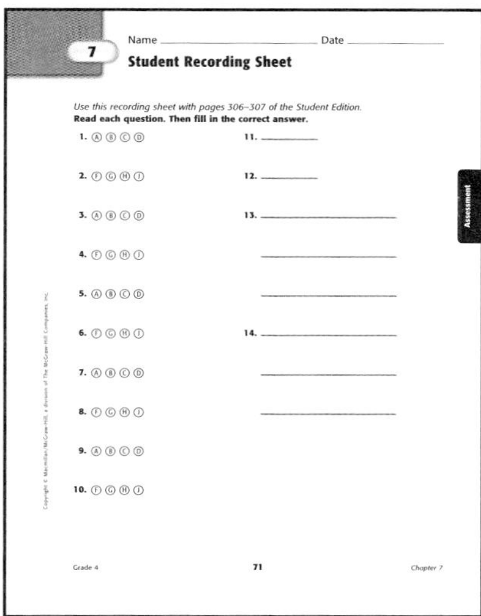
7 Name Date
Student Recording Sheet
Use this recording sheet with pages 306–307 of the Student Edition.
Read each question. Then fill in the correct answer.

Additional Answers

13. Sample answer: 4; Since $32 \div 8 = 4$, there are 4 groups of students.

14. Sample answer: 90; Multiply the number of trays by the number of muffins per tray, $15 \times 6 = 90$.

Page 275, Lesson 7-1

30. Sample answer: 41×21; 21 is not a multiple of 10.

31. There are 3 zeros because both factors have a zero in the ones place and $5 \times 6 = 30$.

Page 279, Lesson 7-2

40. rule: multiply by 4; $w \times 4 = v$; 28, 36, and 44

41. Sample answer: The extra information is he has been mowing for 3 months; $480

Page 281, Lesson 7-3

3. half-dollar and 2 quarters; Since three quarters equals only 75¢ we know that 1 coin has to be greater than a quarter and the only coin that is greater than a quarter and less than a dollar is a half-dollar. Once the half-dollar is discovered it's easy to determine that the other coins are 2 quarters.

11. Sample answer: 34 pennies; 6 nickels and 4 pennies; 2 dimes, 2 nickels, and 4 pennies; 1 dime, 4 nickels, and 4 pennies; 1 quarter, 1 nickel, and 4 pennies

13. Sample answer: To seat 10 people exactly, Dane can arrange the tables in a 2×3 rectangle.

14. Sample answer: The act it out strategy works well in guess and check situations where manipulations can be used to model the problem.

Page 286, Lesson 7-4

26. Sample answer: 37×18 does not belong with the other three problems because it is the only problem whose product has a zero in the ones place.

27. Sample answer: The lowest product of two 2-digit factors is 100, which is a result of multiplying 10×10; the lowest 2-digit factors.

Page 287, Mid-Chapter Check

16. Sample answer: 2 zeros; Each factor has one zero and the other digits do not result in a product containing a zero.

Page 289, Lesson 7-5

5. Sample answer: Multiply 6 ones times 945, regrouping when necessary. Next, multiply 5 tens times 945, regrouping when necessary. Last, add the partial products, and the product is 52,920.

Page 295, Lesson 7-6

1. Sample answer: yes; There are 60 slices of pizza for 18 players. Each player can eat 3 slices and there will be 6 slices left over.

2. Sample answer: yes; The total cost for the supplies is $15.60. So, $15 is reasonable.

7. Sample answer: no; Edmundo has $36, which is not enough to buy the items that have a total cost of $38.

10. Sample answer: How many muffins did Isaac make?

Page 305, Chapter Test

9. Sample answer: 1 five-dollar bill and 1 one-dollar bill, or 6 one-dollar bills.

11. Sample answer: 24; $6 \times 12 = 72$ snacks, then divide 72 by 3. So, there are 24 students in Roxana's class.

19. Sample answer: 7; the greatest 4- and 3-digit numbers that can be multiplied together are 9,999 and 999. These two factors result in a 7-digit product.

NOTES

Chapter Overview

Chapter-at-a-Glance

In Chapter 8, the emphasis is on finding and estimating quotients by dividing multi-digit numbers by one-digit numbers.

Lesson		Math Objective	Standards
EXPLORE 8-1	**Model Division** (pp. 311–312)	Explore dividing by one-digit numbers.	
8-1	**Division with Remainders** (pp. 313–315)	Carry out division with and without remainders.	
8-2	**Divide Multiples of 10, 100, and 1,000** (pp. 316–319)	Use basic facts and patterns to divide mentally.	
8-3	**Problem-Solving Strategy: Guess and Check** (pp. 320–321)	Solve problems by using the guess and check strategy.	
8-4	**Estimate Quotients** (pp. 322–324)	Estimate quotients.	
8-5	**Two-Digit Quotients** (pp. 326–329)	Solve division problems that result in two-digit quotients.	
8-6	**Problem-Solving Investigation: Choose a Strategy** (pp. 330–331)	Choose the best strategy to solve a problem.	
8-7	**Three-Digit Quotients** (pp. 332–334)	Solve division problems that result in three-digit quotients.	
EXTEND 8-7	**Division** (p. 335)	Use technology to divide three-digit dividends.	
8-8	**Quotients with Zeros** (pp. 326–339)	Solve division problems that result in quotients that have zeros.	
8-9	**Divide Greater Numbers** (pp. 342–345)	Divide four-digit dividends by a one-digit number.	

Divide by One-Digit Numbers

BIG Idea Division skills are used in a variety of contexts in mathematics instruction. Students will use division to determine unit cost, and to compare and order fractions, decimals, and percents. Knowledge of division will be essential when working with integers and rational numbers.

Students must learn to use the division algorithm. Using this algorithm requires a mastery of basic division facts and strong estimation skills. To develop these concepts, provide opportunities for discovering patterns in division with multiples of 10, 100, and 1,000.

Algebra Students use patterns to divide numbers by multiples of 10, 100, and 1,000. Finding and using patterns will help them prepare for algebra concepts, such as functions. (Lesson 8-2)

G4-FP8C *Number and Operations:* Building on their work in grade 3, students extend their understanding of place value and ways of representing numbers to 100,000 in various contexts. They use estimation in determining the relative sizes of amounts or distances. Students develop understandings of strategies for multidigit division by using models that represent division as the inverse of multiplication, as partitioning, or as successive subtraction. By working with decimals, students extend their ability to recognize equivalent fractions. Students' earlier work in grade 3 with models of fractions and multiplication and division facts supports their understanding of techniques for generating equivalent fractions and simplifying fractions.

Skills Trace

Vertical Alignment

Third Grade

In third grade, students learned to:

- Use models to divide by 1, 2, 3, 4, 5, 6, 7, 8, 9, 10, 11, and 12.
- Identify patterns in related division sentences.

Fourth Grade

During this chapter, students learn to:

- Carry out division with and without remainders.
- Use basic facts and patterns to divide mentally.
- Divide multi-digit dividends by a one-digit number and estimate results for reasonableness.

After this chapter, students learn to:

- Understand the meaning of and perform operations with fractions and decimals.

Fifth Grade

In fifth grade, students learn to:

- Use basic facts and patterns to divide multiples of 10, 100, and 1,000 mentally.
- Estimate quotients using compatible numbers.

Backmapping and Vertical Alignment **McGraw-Hill's *Math Connects*** program was conceived and developed with the final results in mind: student success in Algebra 1 and beyond. The authors, using the **NCTM Focal Points and Focal Connections** as their guide, developed this brand-new series by backmapping from Algebra 1 concepts, and vertically aligning the topics so that they build upon prior skills and concepts and serve as a foundation for future topics.

Math Vocabulary

The following math vocabulary words for Chapter 8 are listed in the glossary of the ***Student Edition***. You can find interactive definitions in 13 languages in the ***eGlossary*** at macmillanmh.com.

compatible numbers Numbers in a problem or related numbers that are easy to work with mentally. (p. 322A)

Example: 720 and 90 are compatible numbers for division because $72 \div 9 = 8$.

dividend A number that is being divided. (p. 313A)

Example: $3\overline{)12}$ (12 is the dividend)

divisor The number by which the dividend is being divided. (p. 313A)

Example: $3\overline{)12}$ (3 is the divisor)

quotient The result of a division problem. (p. 313A)

Example: $36 \div 4 = 9$ (9 is the quotient)

remainder The number that is left after one whole number is divided by another. (p. 313A)

Example: $27 \div 5 = 5$ R2 (2 is the remainder)

Visual Vocabulary Cards
Use Visual Vocabulary Card 5 to reinforce the vocabulary in this lesson. (The Define/Example/Ask routine is printed on the back of each card.)

compatible numbers

Chapter Planner

Suggested Pacing		
Instruction	Review & Assessment	TOTAL
11 days	1 day	**12 days**

Diagnostic Assessment
Quick Check (p. 310)

	Explore 8-1 (Pacing: 1 day)	Lesson 8-1 (Pacing: 1 day)	Lesson 8-2 (Pacing: 1 day)
Lesson/ Objective	**Model Division** (pp. 311–312) **Objective:** Explore dividing by one-digit numbers.	**Division with Remainders** (pp. 313–315) **Objective:** Carry out division with and without remainders.	**Divide Multiples of 10, 100, and 1,000** (pp. 316–319) **Objective:** Use basic facts and patterns to divide mentally.
State/Local Standards			
Math Vocabulary	**dividend**, **divisor**, **quotient remainder**		
Lesson Resources	**Manipulatives** base-ten blocks	**Materials** index cards **Other Resources** CRM Leveled Worksheets (pp. 8–12) Daily Reteach • 5-Minute Check • Problem of the Day	**Manipulatives** base-ten blocks **Other Resources** CRM Leveled Worksheets (pp. 13–17) Daily Reteach • 5-Minute Check • Problem of the Day
Technology Math Online		Math Adventures Personal Tutor	Math Tool Chest Math Adventures Personal Tutor
Reaching All Learners		English Learners, p. 313B ELL Gifted and Talented, p. 313B AL Early Finishers, p. 313B AL	English Learners, p. 316B ELL Below Level, p. 316B BL Early Finishers, p. 316B AL
Alternate Lesson		*IMPACT Mathematics:* Unit A	

KEY

BL Below/Approaching Level | OL On Level | AL Above/Beyond Level | ELL English Learners
SE Student Edition | TE Teacher Edition | CRM Chapter 8 Resource Masters | CD-Rom
Transparency | Real-World Problem Solving Library

	Lesson 8-3 (Pacing: 1 day)	Lesson 8-4 (Pacing: 1 day)	Lesson 8-5 (Pacing: 1 day)
Lesson/ Objective	**Problem-Solving Strategy Guess and Check** (pp. 320–321) **Objective:** Solve problems by using the guess and check strategy.	**Estimate Quotients** (pp. 322–324) **Objective:** Estimate quotients.	**Two-Digit Quotients** (pp. 326–329) **Objective:** Solve division problems that result in two-digit quotients.
State/Local Standards			
Math Vocabulary		**compatible numbers**	
Lesson Resources	**Manipulatives** money **Other Resources** CRM Leveled Worksheets (pp. 18–22) Daily Reteach • 5-Minute Check • Problem of the Day *Riding the Mail Trail*	**Other Resources** CRM Leveled Worksheets (pp. 23–27) Daily Reteach • 5-Minute Check • Problem of the Day	**Materials** grid paper **Manipulatives** two-colored counters, base-ten blocks **Other Resources** CRM Leveled Worksheets (pp. 28–32) Daily Reteach • 5-Minute Check • Problem of the Day
Technology		Math Adventures	
Math Online		Personal Tutor	Personal Tutor
Reaching All Learners	English Learners, p. 320B ELL Gifted and Talented, p. 320B AL Early Finishers, p. 320B OL AL	English Learners, p. 322B ELL Below Level, p. 322B BL Early Finishers, p. 322B AL	English Learners, p. 326B ELL Below Level, p. 326B BL Early Finishers, p. 326B AL
Alternate Lesson		*IMPACT Mathematics:* Unit C	

Formative Assessment
Mid-Chapter Check (p. 325)

Chapter Planner

	Lesson 8-6 (Pacing: 1 day)	Lesson 8-7 (Pacing: 1 day)	Extend 8-7 (Pacing: 1 day)
Lesson/ Objective	**Problem-Solving Investigation** **Choose a Strategy** (pp. 330–331) **Objective:** Choose the best strategy to solve a problem.	**Three-Digit Quotients** (pp. 332–334) **Objective:** Solve division problems that result in three-digit quotients.	**Division** (p. 335) **Objective:** Use technology to divide three-digit dividends.
State/Local Standards			
Math Vocabulary			
Lesson Resources	**Other Resources** CRM Leveled Worksheets (pp. 33–37) Daily Reteach • 5-Minute Check • Problem of the Day *Riding the Mail Trail*	**Manipulatives** base-ten blocks **Other Resources** CRM Leveled Worksheets (pp. 38–42) Daily Reteach • 5-Minute Check • Problem of the Day	
Technology		Math Adventures	Math Tool Chest Student Work Plus Interactive Classroom
Math Online		Personal Tutor	
Reaching All Learners	English Learners, p. 330B ELL Gifted and Talented, p. 330B AL Early Finishers, p. 330B OL AL	English Learners, p. 332B ELL Gifted and Talented, p. 332B AL Early Finishers, p. 332B AL	
Alternate Lesson			

Lesson 8-8

Pacing: 1 day

Quotients with Zeros
(pp. 336–339)

Objective: Solve division problems that result in quotients that have zeros.

Manipulatives
base-ten blocks

Other Resources
CRM Leveled Worksheets (pp. 43–47)
Daily Reteach • 5-Minute Check • Problem of the Day

Math Adventures

Personal Tutor

English Learners, p. 336B ELL
Below Level, p. 336B BL
Early Finishers, p. 336B AL

Game Time
Division Shuffle (p. 339)

Problem Solving in Science
A Desert Safari (p. 340)

Lesson 8-9

Pacing: 1 day

Divide Greater Numbers
(pp. 342–345)

Objective: Divide four-digit dividends by a one-digit number.

Other Resources
CRM Leveled Worksheets (pp. 48–52)
Daily Reteach • 5-Minute Check • Problem of the Day

Math Adventures

Personal Tutor

English Learners, p. 342B ELL
Gifted and Talented, p. 342B AL
Early Finishers, p. 342B AL

Summative Assessment
- Study Guide/Review (p. 346)
- Chapter Test (p. 353)
- Test Practice (p. 354)

Assessment Options

Diagnostic Assessment

SE *Option 1:* Quick Check (p. 310)
Option 2: Online Quiz macmillanmh.com
CRM *Option 3:* Diagnostic Test (p. 54)
CRM *Option 4:* Chapter Pretest (p. 55)

Formative Assessment

TE Alternate Teaching Strategies (in every lesson)
SE Talk About It (in every lesson)
SE Writing in Math (in every lesson)
SE Check What You Know (in every lesson)
TE Into the Future (pp. 315, 324, 338)
TE Yesterday's News (p. 345)
TE Name the Math (p. 319)
SE Mid-Chapter Check (p. 325)
CRM Lesson Quizzes (pp. 56–58)
CRM Mid-Chapter Test (p. 59)

Summative Assessment

SE Chapter Test (p. 353)
SE Test Practice (p. 354)
CRM Vocabulary Test (p. 60)
CRM Leveled Chapter Tests (pp. 65–76)
CRM Cumulative Test Practice (pp. 79–81)
CRM Oral Assessment (p. 61)
ExamView® Assessment Suite
Advance Tracker

McGraw-Hill Professional Development

Targeted professional development has been articulated throughout **McGraw-Hill's *Math Connects*** program. The **McGraw-Hill Professional Development Video Library** provides short videos that support the **NCTM Focal Points and Focal Connections.** For more information visit macmillanmh.com.

Model Lessons

Instructional Strategies

Learning Stations

Cross-Curricular Links

Writing

group | LOGICAL

What is the Difference?

- Divide into groups of three. Each group should have a set of three index cards. Label one "dividend," one "divisor," and one "quotient." Shuffle the cards and spread them facedown on the table.
- Each group member picks one of the cards and then writes a definition for the word he or she picked. Students share the definitions among the group.
- Draw a large long division symbol on a piece of paper. Then, using your definitions to guide you, place each word in its proper place with respect to the long division symbol.

Materials:

- index cards
- paper
- pencils

Art

pair | SPATIAL

Studio Sharing

- Choose 24 artists from art books and make artist cards, one for each artist. Each partner can make 12 cards. Label each card with the artist's name under his or her picture.
- Imagine your artists are at a retreat together and they will have to share studio space. Take turns rolling the number cube to see how many artists you need to fit into each studio.
- Using the number you rolled, how many studios will you need? Model each studio by dividing up the cards into groups. Is there a remainder? If so, place those cards in the remainder studio.

Materials:

- art books
- index cards
- colored markers
- number cube
- pencils

Social Studies

individual | LOGICAL

Equal Representation

In the United States, each state gets two representatives in the Senate. Voters are divided up evenly into groups for representation in the House of Representatives.

- Use base-ten blocks to model the number of people in your grade. How would you divide your grade evenly into groups for representation? Would you have two representatives and therefore two groups? three representatives and three groups? more than three? Use the blocks to model your groups.
- If the number of people in your grade is not evenly divisible, you may round the number to make an estimate that is divisible.

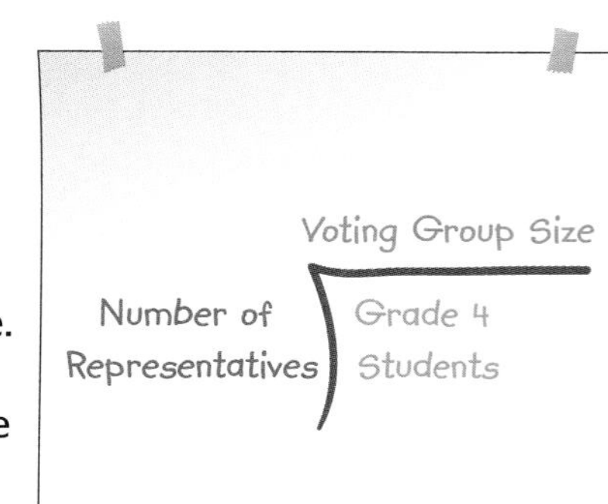

Materials:

- card displaying number of students in the grade
- base-ten blocks
- paper
- pencil

Science

pair | LOGICAL

Lab Division

Design a science lab for your class to do a magnetism experiment.

- If each student has one lab partner, how many lab tables will you need? What about for teams of three? Model each division using counters.
- Choose the lab team size you want, and draw the number of tables you will need for your lab on a piece of paper.
- Divide supplies for each team: magnets, pennies, and paper clips. Write a lab list for each table, one of each item. If you expressed the total amount of each item as a dividend, what would be your equation?

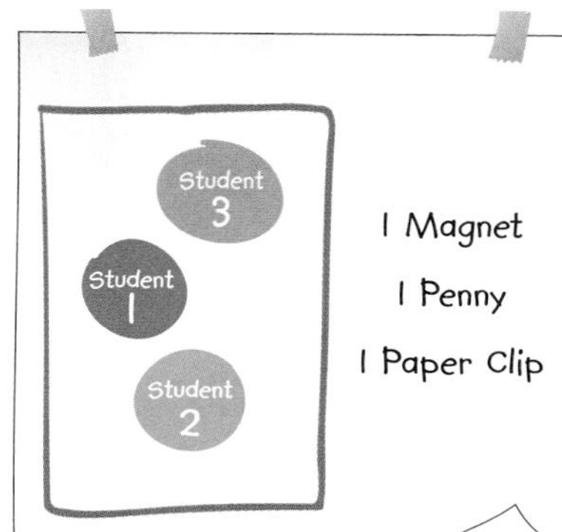

Materials:
- counters
- magnets
- pennies
- paper clips
- paper
- pencils

Health

group | SPATIAL

On Your Mark

Mark out a relay race with four stations and test it out.

- Measure your school gymnasium, in feet, going from one end to the other side of the gym. Then mark off four relay runner stations with masking tape.
- Make a chart on a posterboard, with space to record each team's time for running the relay race. At the bottom of the posterboard, write an expression to show how you figured out the distance between stations.

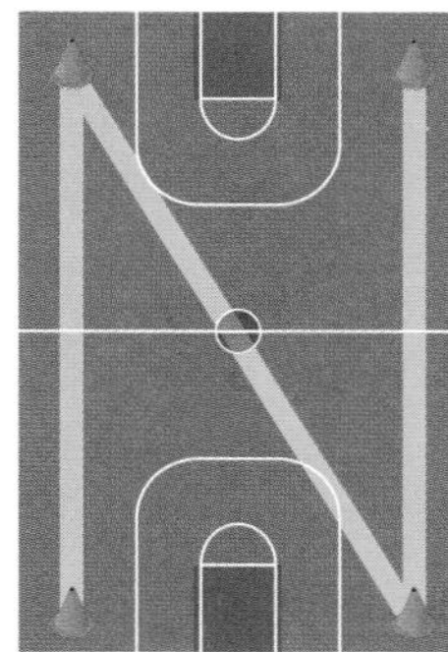

Total course measurement: 224 feet

Materials:
- yardstick or measuring tape
- posterboard
- markers
- masking tape
- stopwatch

Music

pair | LOGICAL

Long Song Contest

Music is divided up into measures. In some songs, there can be four beats in each measure. If you know the number of beats, you can figure out the number of measures in a song.

- Each of you rolls the number cube three times and makes a three-digit number with the numbers you rolled. Give your number to your partner.
- The number your partner gave you is the number of beats in your song. Find out how many measures are in your song using counters to model the beats in each measure. You may end up with a remainder, or a partial measure. The one with the longest song wins.

4 beats = 1 measure
654 beats = $163\frac{1}{2}$ measures

Materials:
- number cube
- counters
- paper
- pencils

CHAPTER 8

Introduce the Chapter

 Real World: Sports Tournament

Share with students that they are going to learn about division by a one-digit number in this chapter. Explain that this means that they will be dividing numbers by 1–9.

Give students the following scenario:

- The physical education teacher would like to organize a badminton tournament that requires teams of two. The teacher needs to know how many teams the class will form.
- Have students divide themselves into groups of two.
- **How many groups of two are there?** Answers will vary.
- **Is there anyone left over?** Answers will vary.
- Model the division problem on the board. For example:

$$2\overline{)26}^{\,13} \quad \text{or} \quad 2\overline{)25}^{\,12\text{ R}1}$$

- Repeat this activity, only this time, form teams of 4 or 5.

Direct students to Student Edition p. 308. Have students read the paragraph at the top of the page.

- **Give an example of when you needed to use division to solve a problem.** Sample answers: dividing game money among players, dividing pieces of pizza among people in the family

WRITING IN MATH

Starting the Chapter
Have students write about when they might need to divide a number by 5. If students need a hint, suggest that they think about when they might need to divide a number of items into five equal groups.

Key Vocabulary Introduce the key vocabulary in the chapter using the routine below.

Define: A remainder is the number that is left over after one whole number is divided by another.
Example: 20 divided by 6 is 3, with a remainder of 2.
Ask: Why do you sometimes get a remainder when you divide?

Read-Aloud Anthology For an optional reading activity to introduce this chapter's math concepts, see the Read-Aloud Anthology on p. TR32.

CHAPTER 8

Divide by One-Digit Numbers

BIG Idea **How do you divide by a one-digit number?**

Divide each digit of the dividend by the divisor.

Example A toll worker on the Mackinac Bridge in Michigan collected \$75 in tolls. How many cars passed through the toll booth if the toll cost is \$3 per car?

```
  25
3)75
 -6↓
  15
 -15
   0
```

For each place, divide, multiply, subtract, and compare. Then bring down the next digit in the dividend.

So, 25 cars passed through the toll booth.

What will I learn in this chapter?

- Divide two-, three-, or multi-digit numbers by a one-digit number.
- Estimate quotients.
- Solve problems by using the guess and check strategy.

Key Vocabulary

dividend **remainder**
divisor **compatible numbers**
quotient

Math Online **Student Study Tools at macmillanmh.com**

 Chapter 8 Project

Division Game Day

Students set up game stations and play division games together.

- In Musical Quotients, students walk around a line of 5 hula hoops on the floor as music plays. When the music stops, the group rushes to divide itself evenly among the hula hoops. There may or may not be a remainder player! Take away a hula hoop each time until there is only one left.
- In Division Hangman, teams take turns writing division problems, leaving out one digit from the divisor, the dividend, or the quotient for the other team to guess. A wrong guess gets a part of the hangman drawn. Keep playing until one team completes the hangman and loses.

CRM *Refer to Chapter 8 Resource Masters, p. 63, for a rubric to assess students' progress on this project.*

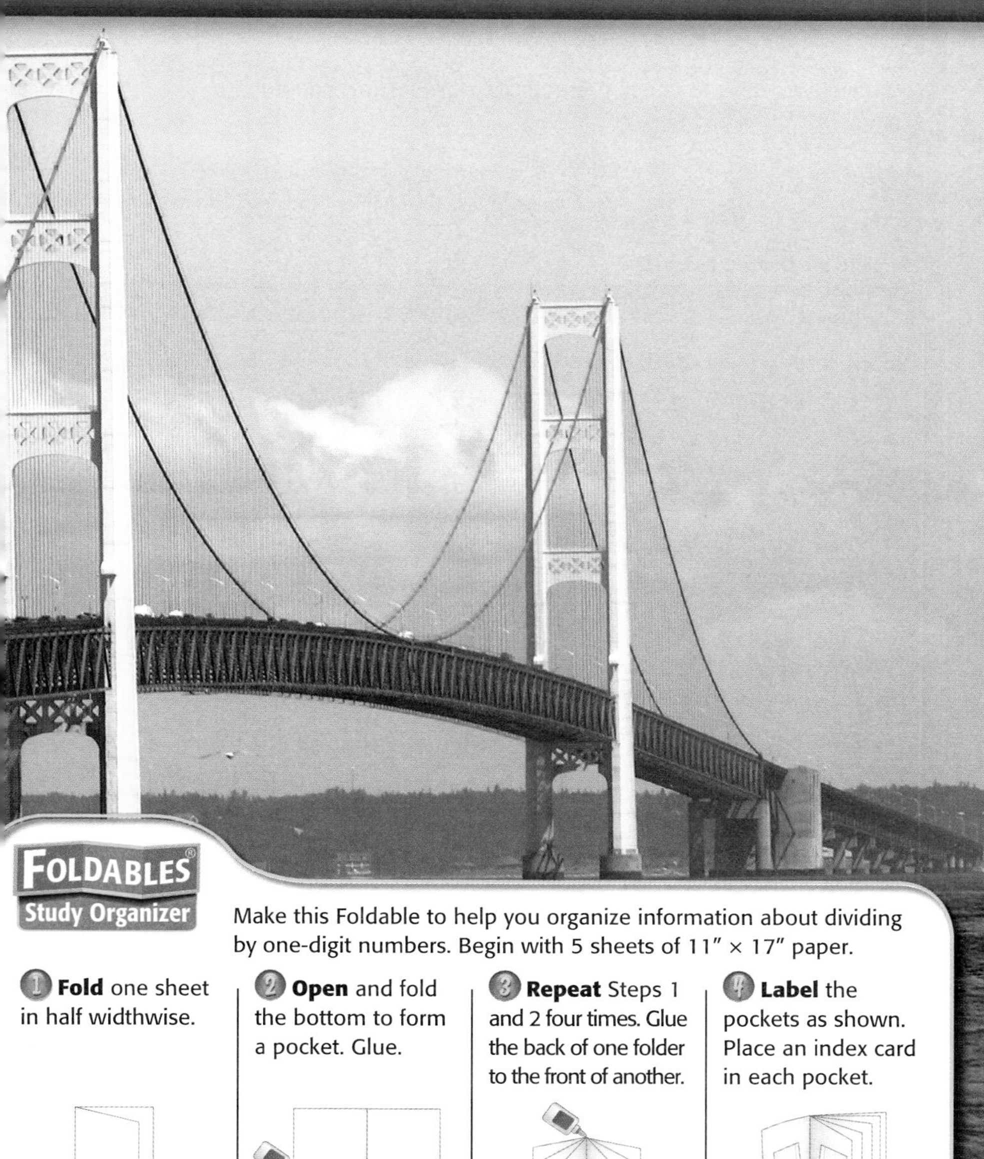

FOLDABLES Study Organizer

Make this Foldable to help you organize information about dividing by one-digit numbers. Begin with 5 sheets of 11″ × 17″ paper.

1. **Fold** one sheet in half widthwise.
2. **Open** and fold the bottom to form a pocket. Glue.
3. **Repeat** Steps 1 and 2 four times. Glue the back of one folder to the front of another.
4. **Label** the pockets as shown. Place an index card in each pocket.

ELL National ESL Standards Alignment for Chapter 8			
Lesson, Page	ESL Standard	Modality	Level
8-1, p. 313B	Goal 2, Standard 2, i	Auditory	Intermediate
8-2, p. 316B	Goal 2, Standard 2, c	Kinesthetic	Intermediate
8-3, p. 320B	Goal 2, Standard 2, j	Visual, Logical	Advanced
8-4, p. 322B	Goal 2, Standard 3, b	Logical	Intermediate
8-5, p. 326B	Goal 1, Standard 3, c	Auditory	Intermediate
8-6, p. 330B	Goal 1, Standard 3, c	Interpersonal, Auditory	Intermediate
8-7, p. 332B	Goal 2, Standard 2, a	Linguistic	Advanced
8-8, p. 336B	Goal 3, Standard 3, a	Linguistic, Social	Intermediate
8-9, p. 342B	Goal 2, Standard 3, g	Social, Kinesthetic	Intermediate

The National ESL Standards can be found in the Teacher Reference Handbook.

FOLDABLES Dinah Zike's Foldables

Guide students through the directions on p. 309 to create their own Foldable graphic organizers for dividing by one-digit numbers. Students may also use their Foldables to study and review for chapter assessments.

When to Use It Lessons 8-1, 8-4, 8-6, 8-7, and 8-8. (Additional instructions for using the Foldables with these lessons are found on pp. 325 and 346.)

Chapter 8 Literature List

Lesson	Book Title
8-1	**A Remainder of One** Elinor J. Pinczes
8-2	**The Doorbell Rang** Pat Hutchins
8-3	**The Doorbell Rang** Pat Hutchins
8-4	**The Great Divide** Dayle Ann Dodds
8-5	**Chewing Gum** Elaine Landau
8-7	**The Doorbell Rang** Pat Hutchins
8-8	**Olympics** Dorling Kindersley Eyewitness Books
8-9	**Stellaluna** Janell Cannon

- Read the Math at Home letter found in the Chapter 8 Resource Masters, p. 4, with the class and have each student sign it. (A Spanish version is found on p. 5.)
- Send home copies of the Math at Home letter with each student.

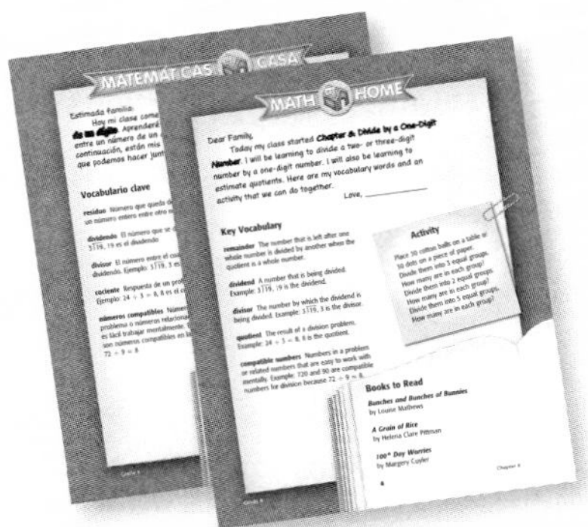

Diagnostic Assessment

Check for students' prerequisite skills before beginning the chapter.

- **Option 1:** ***Quick Check***

  SE Student Edition, p. 310

- **Option 2:** ***Online Assessment***

  Math Online macmillanmh.com

- **Option 3:** ***Diagnostic Tests***

  CRM Chapter 8 Resource Masters, p. 54–55

RTI (Response to Intervention)

Apply the Results Based on the results of the diagnostic assessment on Student Edition p. 310, use the chart below to address individual needs before beginning the chapter.

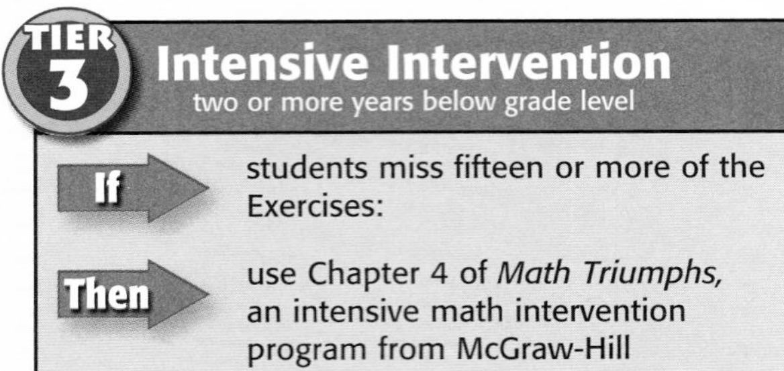

TIER 3 Intensive Intervention
two or more years below grade level

If students miss fifteen or more of the Exercises:

Then use Chapter 4 of *Math Triumphs,* an intensive math intervention program from McGraw-Hill

ARE YOU READY for Chapter 8?

You have two ways to check prerequisite skills for this chapter.

Option 2

Math Online Take the Chapter Readiness Quiz at macmillanmh.com.

Option 1

Complete the Quick Check below.

QUICK Check

Subtract. (Prior Grade) (Used in Lesson 8-1)

1. 25 − 6 19 **2.** 42 − 8 34 **3.** 67 − 29 38 **4.** 93 − 54 39

5. 24 − 15 9 **6.** 31 − 17 14 **7.** 50 − 23 27 **8.** 86 − 49 37

9. There are 81 pages in Gerardo's book. He has read 38 pages. How many pages are left to read? 43

Divide. (Lesson 4-5) (Used in Lesson 8-1)

10. 2)3 1R1 **11.** 4)5 1R1 **12.** 6)7 1R1 **13.** 8)9 1R1

14. 4 ÷ 3 1R1 **15.** 7 ÷ 5 1R2 **16.** 9 ÷ 6 1R3 **17.** 9 ÷ 7 1R2

18. Sharon has $32. She wants to buy CDs that cost $8 each. How many can she buy? 4

Round each number to its greatest place value. (Lesson 1-6) (Used in Lesson 8-4)

19. 269 300 **20.** $2,513 $3,000 **21.** 14,895 10,000 **22.** 56,071 60,000

23. A zoo has 2,515 mammals and 3,496 animals that are not mammals. About how many animals are at the zoo? 6,000

310 **Chapter 8** Divide by One-Digit Numbers

TIER 2 Strategic Intervention below/approaching grade level	TIER 1 On-Level	Above/Beyond Level
If students miss seven to fourteen in: **Exercises 1–23**	**If** students miss three to six in: **Exercises 1–23**	**If** students miss two or less in: **Exercises 1–23**
Then choose a resource:	**Then** choose a resource:	**Then** choose a resource:
Strategic Intervention Guide (pp. 78, 88) TE Start Smart 2: Numbers and Operations (p. 4) **Math Online** Extra Examples • Personal Tutor • Concepts in Motion	TE Learning Stations (pp. 308G–308H) TE Chapter Project (p. 308) CRM Game: Division Moves Math Adventures My Math Zone Chapter 7 **Math Online** Fact Dash	TE Learning Stations (pp. 308G–308H) TE Chapter Project (p. 308) Real-World Problem-Solving: *Riding the Mail Trail* My Math Zone Chapters 7 and 8 **Math Online** Games

Math Activity for 8-1

Model Division

MAIN IDEA

I will explore dividing by one-digit numbers.

You Will Need
base-ten blocks

New Vocabulary
dividend
divisor
quotient
remainder

In division, the **dividend** is the number that is being divided. The **divisor** is the number that divides the dividend. The **quotient** is the result.

$$\text{divisor}\overline{)\text{dividend}}\ \text{quotient}$$

ACTIVITY

1 **Find 39 ÷ 3.**

Step 1 **Model the dividend, 39.**

Use 3 tens and 9 ones to show 39.

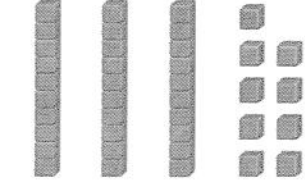

Step 2 **Divide the tens.**

The divisor is 3. So, divide the tens into 3 equal groups. There is a ten in each group.

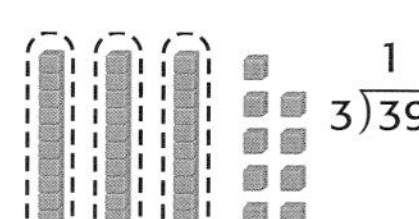

$$\begin{array}{r} 1 \\ 3\overline{)39} \end{array}$$

Step 3 **Divide the ones.**

Divide the ones into 3 equal groups. There are 1 ten and 3 ones in each group.
So, 39 ÷ 3 = 13.

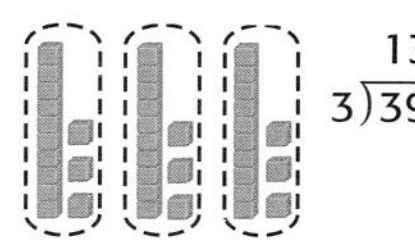

$$\begin{array}{r} 13 \\ 3\overline{)39} \end{array}$$

Math Activity for 8-1

Lesson Planner

Objective

Explore dividing by one-digit numbers.

Vocabulary

dividend, **divisor**, **quotient**, **remainder**

Resources

Manipulatives: base-ten blocks

1 Introduce

Give each student 12 counters and tell them to separate the counters into groups of 4.

- **How many groups of counters do you have?** 3 groups
- **How many counters are there in each group?** 4 counters
- Point out that they are modeling 12 ÷ 4 = 3.
- **What happens if you separate your 12 counters into groups of 5?** Sample answer: You get only 2 groups with 2 counters left over. Explain that the 2 leftover counters are called *remainders*.

2 Teach

Activity 1 **Step 1:** Make sure students have modeled the dividend correctly. **Steps 2 and 3:** Check students' work to be sure that they have divided their tens and ones into equal groups. Then point out that the quotient represents the amount in each equal group. Have students check their work by using base ten blocks to model the inverse operation and repeated subtraction.

Activity 2 Continue this activity in the same manner. Some students may need help in Step 2 regrouping the leftover ten as 10 ones. Have students check their division using multiplication or subtraction. Model.

Think About It

Assign Exercises 1 and 2 to assess student comprehension of the concept presented in the Activity.

3 Assess

Formative Assessment

Use **Check What You Know** Exercises 5–9 to assess whether students can model dividing by one-digit numbers.

From Concrete to Abstract Use Exercise 9 to bridge students' understanding of division from manipulatives to concepts.

Extending the Concept

- **When might you have a remainder of 5?** when the divisor is greater than 5

ACTIVITY

2 **Find 68 ÷ 5.**

Step 1 **Model the dividend, 68.**
Use 6 tens and 8 ones to show 68.

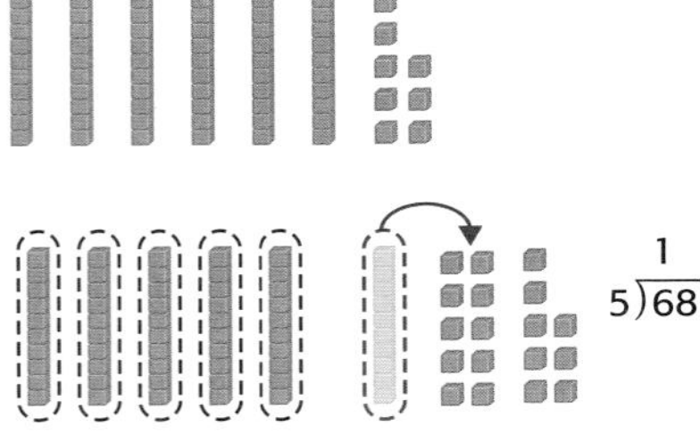

Step 2 **Divide the tens.**
The divisor is 5. So, divide the tens into 5 equal groups. There is a ten in each group.

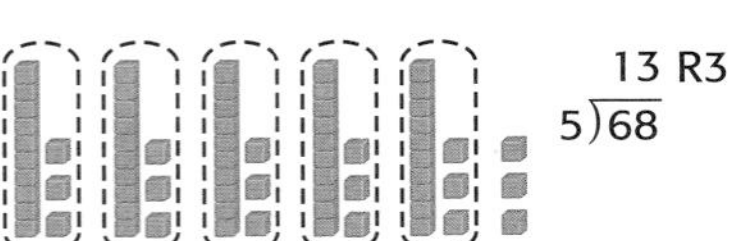

Regroup one ten as ten ones.

Step 3 **Divide the ones.**
Divide the ones into 5 equal groups. There is 1 ten and 3 ones in each group. There are 3 ones left over. The 3 is the **remainder**.
So, 68 ÷ 5 = 13 R3.

Think About It

1. How would you use base-ten blocks to find 58 ÷ 4? 1, 2. See margin.
2. Explain what it means to have a remainder when dividing.

CHECK What You Know

Write the division expression shown by each model. Then divide.

3. 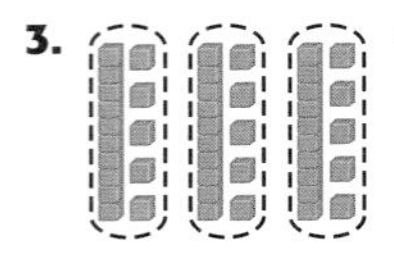 45 ÷ 3; 15

4. 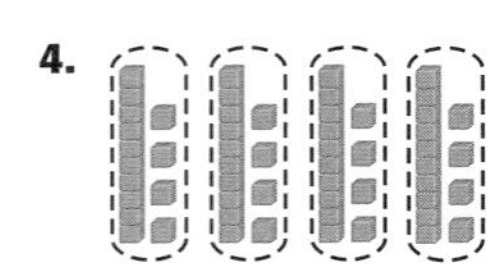 57 ÷ 4; 14 R1

Use models to find each quotient. 5–8. See Ch. 8 Answer Appendix for models.

5. 36 ÷ 2 18
6. 48 ÷ 3 16
7. 57 ÷ 4 14 R1
8. 77 ÷ 5 15 R2
9. **WRITING IN MATH** Explain how to use models to find 79 ÷ 6. See margin.

312 **Chapter 8** Divide by One-Digit Numbers

Additional Answers

1. 5 tens and 8 ones to model 58, then 1 ten needs to be broken into 10 ones, so 10 more ones are needed, then continue dividing
2. Sample answer: In division, a remainder occurs when there are left over ones after the division has taken place.
9. Sample answer: Use 7 tens and 9 ones base-ten blocks to model 79. Divide the tens into 6 equal groups. Divide the ones into 6 equal groups. There is 1 one left over. So, 79 ÷ 6 = 13 R1.

LESSON 8-1

Division with Remainders

Lesson Planner

Objective

Divide with and without remainders.

Review Vocabulary

dividend, divisor, quotient

Resources

Materials: index cards

Literature Connection: *A Remainder of One* by Elinor J. Pinczes

Alternate Lesson: Use *IMPACT Mathematics:* Unit A to provide practice with division.

Teacher Technology
TeacherWorks • Interactive Classroom

Focus on Math Background

In Chapter 4, students learned the basic division facts through 10 and were also introduced to the following properties of division:

- Zero divided by any number, except 0, is 0 ($a \div 0 = 0$).
- It is not possible to divide by 0.
- Any number, except 0, divided by itself is 1 ($a \div a = 1$).

In this chapter, students will use these properties and facts to explore simple division problems, some of which have remainders. It is important for students to understand that the amount left over when a number cannot be divided into equal groups (the remainder) can be handled in different ways, depending on the context of the problem:

- Sometimes the amount left over is dropped.
- Sometimes the quotient is raised to the next number.
- Sometimes the remainder is part of the answer.

Daily Routine

Use these suggestions before beginning the lesson on p. 339.

5-Minute Check

(Reviews Lesson 7-7)

Multiply.

1. 3,270 × 25 81,750 **2.** 5,741 × 53 304,273
3. 98,304 × 24 2,359,296 **4.** $34,811 × 45 $1,566,495

Problem of the Day

How many whole numbers round to 60? What are the numbers? 10 numbers including 60; 55–64

Review Math Vocabulary

Write the review vocabulary words and their definitions on the board.

- Write the following sentence on the board: *When a dividend is divided by a divisor, the answer is called a quotient.*
- Then write this problem on the board: *When a dividend of 24 is divided by a divisor of 3, the quotient is 8.* Have students rewrite the sentence as the number sentence $24 \div 3 = 8$.

Differentiated Instruction

Small Group Options

LOGICAL

Option 1 Gifted and Talented AL

Materials: paper and pencil

- Tell students that in mathematics, divisibility rules exist. One of these rules is divisibility by 5, which states: Any division problem with a divisor of 5 whose dividend ends in 0 or 5 will always have 0 for a remainder.
- Give the following examples: 95 ÷ 5 = 19 with no remainder. 70 ÷ 5 = 14. **Can you explain why this is true?** The multiplication tables by 5 gives the answer.
- **Is this rule true for 3-digit dividends? 4-digit dividends?** yes **Is this rule true for all dividends no matter how large?** yes
- Check out the divisibility rule for 2 and see what you discover. Any number that ends in 0, 2, 4, 6, or 8 is divisible by 2.

AUDITORY

Option 2 English Language Learners ELL

Materials: overhead counters, transparency of tree and baskets, picture of harvesting
Learning Style: Visual
Core Vocabulary: picked clean, remains/remainders, basket
Common Use Verb: put

See Math: This strategy uses background knowledge to help students visualize division and remainders.

- Show harvesting picture and act out picking "fruit" and putting into baskets.
- Discuss how all the fruit is put into equal amounts in each basket.
- Allow students to sort the fruit on the transparency
- If the student leaves counters in the tree, prompt: "Is the tree picked clean?"
- Discuss what to do with remains/remainders.

Use this worksheet to provide additional support for English Language Learners.

English Language Learners (p. 49) ELL

15 Name ______________________

Division with Remainders

Divide the number of students in your class by the number of players it takes to play each sport. How many teams could your class make. Record that number and the remainder.

SPORTS	NUMBER OF PLAYERS	NUMBER OF STUDENTS IN THE CLASS	NUMBER OF TEAMS FORMED	NUMBER OF EXTRA PLAYERS (remainder)
Basketball	5			
Baseball	9			
Crew	8			
Ice Hockey	6			
Polo	4			
Water Polo	7			
Lacrosse	10			
Cricket (Challenge)	2			
*Soccer (Challenge)	11			
*Football (Challenge)	11			

Dividing with Remainders 49

Independent Work Options

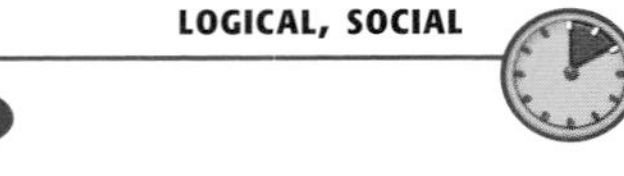

LOGICAL, SOCIAL

Option 1 Early Finishers OL AL

Materials: paper and pencil

- Have students write two division problems, one in which the dividend has two digits and a second in which quotient has two digits. Have them explain how they chose the dividends and divisors for each problem.

Option 2 Student Technology

Math Online macmillanmh.com

Personal Tutor • Extra Examples

 Math Adventures

Option 3 Learning Station: Writing (p. 308G)

Direct students to the Writing Learning Station for opportunities to explore and extend the lesson concept.

Option 4 Problem-Solving Practice

Reinforce problem-solving skills and strategies with the Problem-Solving Practice worksheet.

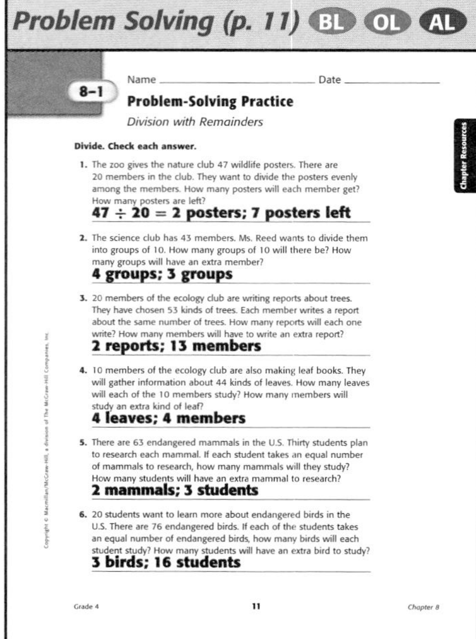

Problem Solving (p. 11) BL OL AL

8–1 Name ______________________ Date ____________

Problem-Solving Practice

Division with Remainders

Divide. Check each answer.

1. The zoo gives the nature club 47 wildlife posters. There are 20 members in the club. They want to divide the posters evenly among the members. How many posters will each member get? How many posters are left?
   47 ÷ 20 = 2 posters; 7 posters left
2. The science club has 43 members. Ms. Reed wants to divide them into groups of 10. How many groups of 10 will there be? How many groups will have an extra member?
   4 groups; 3 groups
3. 20 members of the ecology club are writing reports about trees. They have chosen 53 kinds of trees. Each member writes a report about the same number of trees. How many reports will each one write? How many members will have to write an extra report?
   2 reports; 13 members
4. 10 members of the ecology club are also making leaf books. They will gather information about 44 kinds of leaves. How many leaves will each of the 10 members study? How many members will study an extra kind of leaf?
   4 leaves; 4 members
5. There are 63 endangered mammals in the U.S. Thirty students plan to research each mammal. If each student takes an equal number of mammals to research, how many mammals will they study? How many students will have an extra mammal to research?
   2 mammals; 3 students
6. 20 students want to learn more about endangered birds in the U.S. There are 76 endangered birds. If each of the students takes an equal number of endangered birds, how many birds will each student study? How many students will have an extra bird to study?
   3 birds; 16 students

Chapter Resources

Grade 4 11 Chapter 8

8-1 Division with Remainders

MAIN IDEA

I will carry out division with and without remainders.

Math Online

macmillanmh.com
- Extra Examples
- Personal Tutor
- Self-Check Quiz

GET READY to Learn

Mr. Hein's class is going to a natural history museum. Each seat on the bus can hold 2 people. There are 28 students and 8 adults. How many seats are needed?

You have used models to divide. You can also use paper and pencil.

Real-World EXAMPLE

1 **SCHOOL How many bus seats are needed for the field trip?**

There are 36 people. Each seat holds 2 people. Find $36 \div 2$.

Step 1 Divide the tens.

$2\overline{)36}$ Can 3 tens be divided equally into groups of 2?

$\begin{array}{r}1\\2\overline{)36}\end{array}$ There is one ten in each group. Put 1 in the quotient over the tens place.

Step 2 Multiply, subtract, and compare.

$\begin{array}{r}1\\2\overline{)36}\\-2\\\hline1\end{array}$ Multiply. $2 \times 1 = 2$ Subtract. $3 - 2 = 1$ Compare. $1 < 2$

Step 3 Bring down the ones.

$\begin{array}{r}1\\2\overline{)36}\\-2\downarrow\\\hline16\end{array}$ Bring down 6 ones. 16 ones in all.

Step 4 Divide the ones.

$\begin{array}{r}18\\2\overline{)36}\\-2\downarrow\\\hline16\\-16\\\hline0\end{array}$ Divide. $16 \div 2 = 8$ Put 8 in the quotient over the ones place. Multiply. $2 \times 8 = 16$ Subtract. $16 - 16 = 0$ Compare. $0 < 2$

So, 18 seats are needed.

8-1 Division with Remainders

1 Introduce

Activity Choice 1 • Hands-On 

Materials: 23 index cards

- Choose 5 students to come to the front of the room.
- Tell students that you have 23 cards and that you are going to deal the cards to the students.
- Explain that after you give out the cards, each student in the group will have the same number of cards and any leftover cards will be placed in a leftover pile.
- Deal the cards.
- Write $23 \div 5 = 4$ R3 on the board. Tell students that this number sentence can be used to represent the dealing of the cards.
- Divide students into groups and repeat this activity. Give each group a different number of cards. Have them write a division sentence to represent their results and have groups share their results with the class.

Activity Choice 2 • Literature

Introduce the lesson with *A Remainder of One* by Elinor J. Pinczes. For a related math activity, see p. TR53.

2 Teach

Scaffolding Questions

Have students think about dealing a set of 17 cards to a group of 3 students.

- **How many cards are being given out?** 17 cards
- **How many equal groups will there be?** 3 groups
- **After the cards are given out, how many cards will each student have?** 5 cards
- **How many cards will be left over?** 2 cards
- **Write a number sentence to represent this division.** $17 \div 3 = 5$ R2

GET READY to Learn

Have students open their books and read the information in **Get Ready to Learn**. Review **dividend, divisor,** and **quotient**. As a class, work through **Examples 1 and 2**.

Division with Remainders

Example 2 Point out to students that Step 1 and Step 2 from Example 1 have been combined to form Example 2 Step 1. Steps 3 and 4 have been combined to form Step 2. Have students model multiplication or repeated subtraction to check.

ADDITIONAL EXAMPLES

1. Jose wants to change the buttons on his school uniform shirts. Each shirt has 7 buttons. He bought a package of 84 buttons. On how many shirts will he be able to change the buttons? 12 shirts
2. Markus wants to go to the go-cart park with his friends. The group rate is $63 for 5 guests. How much will each person need to pay for his or her share of the group price? 12 R3, or a little more than $12

CHECK What You Know

As a class, have students complete Exercises 1–10 in **Check What You Know** as you observe their work.

Exercise 10 Assess student comprehension before assigning practice exercises.

BL Alternate Teaching Strategy

If students incorrectly align digits when completing the subtraction portion of a division problem...

Then use one of these reteach options:

1. CRM **Daily Reteach Worksheet** (p. 8)
2. Tell students to line up digits according to place value in each step. If students need help with this alignment, suggest that they use grid paper when they divide.

When a remainder occurs, there is an amount left over that cannot be divided equally into the number of groups set by the divisor. You can interpret the remainder in division problems.

Real-World EXAMPLE — Division with Remainders

2 MONEY Manuel wants to buy 4 comic books that each cost the same amount. If the total cost is $74, how much does each book cost?

Manuel has $74. Each comic book costs the same amount. So, divide $74 by 4 to find how much each book will cost.

Step 1 Divide the tens.

```
   1
4)$74
  -4
   3
```

Divide. 7 ÷ 4 = 1
So, put 1 in the quotient over the tens place.
Multiply. 4 × 1 = 4
Subtract. 7 − 4 = 3
Compare. 3 < 4

Step 2 Divide the ones.

```
  18 R2
4)$74
  -4↓
   34
  -32
    2
```

Bring down the ones.
Divide. 34 ÷ 4 = 8
Put 8 over the ones place.
Multiply. 4 × 8 = 32
Subtract. 34 − 32 = 2
Compare. 2 < 4
Remainder = 2

Remember

To check a division answer, multiply the quotient by the divisor.

```
  18
×  4
  72
+  2  ← Add the remainder.
  74
```

So, each comic book will cost a little more than $18.

Check The model shows that $74 ÷ 4 is a little more than $18.

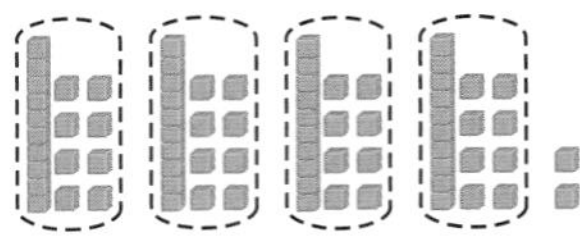

9. no; 21 animals will be fed by 4 zookeepers. One animal will be fed by somene else.

CHECK What You Know

Divide. Check each answer. See Examples 1 and 2 (pp. 313–314)

1. 2)26 — 13
2. 3)36 — 12
3. 5)59 — 11 R4
4. 8)84 — 10 R4
5. 93 ÷ 3 — 31
6. 84 ÷ 4 — 21
7. 61 ÷ 2 — 30 R1
8. 86 ÷ 3 — 28 R2
9. There are 4 zookeepers to feed 85 animals. If each zookeeper feeds the same number of animals, will all of the animals be fed by the 4 zookeepers? Explain.
10. Talk About It Why is the remainder always less than the divisor? Sample answer: If the remainder is greater than or equal to the divisor, then the quotient should be greater.

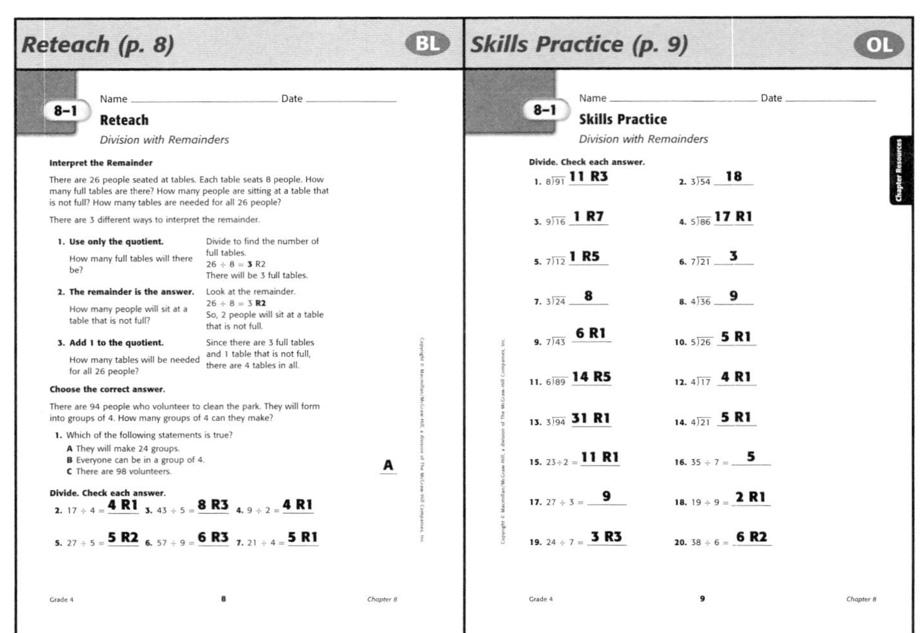

Reteach (p. 8) BL

8-1 Name ________ Date ________

Reteach

Division with Remainders

Interpret the Remainder

There are 26 people seated at tables. Each table seats 8 people. How many full tables are there? How many people are sitting at a table that is not full? How many tables are needed for all 26 people?

There are 3 different ways to interpret the remainder.

1. **Use only the quotient.** How many full tables will there be? — Divide to find the number of full tables. 26 ÷ 8 = **3** R2 There will be 3 full tables.
2. **The remainder is the answer.** How many people will sit at a table that is not full? — Look at the remainder. 26 ÷ 8 = 3 **R2** So, 2 people will sit at a table that is not full.
3. **Add 1 to the quotient.** How many tables will be needed for all 26 people? — Since there are 3 full tables and 1 table that is not full, there are 4 tables in all.

Choose the correct answer.

There are 94 people who volunteer to clean the park. They will form into groups of 4. How many groups of 4 can they make?

1. Which of the following statements is true? **A**
   - A They will make 24 groups.
   - B Everyone can be in a group of 4.
   - C There are 98 volunteers.

Divide. Check each answer.

2. 17 ÷ 4 = **4 R1**
3. 43 ÷ 5 = **8 R3**
4. 9 ÷ 2 = **4 R1**
5. 27 ÷ 5 = **5 R2**
6. 57 ÷ 9 = **6 R3**
7. 21 ÷ 4 = **5 R1**

Grade 4 8 Chapter 8

Skills Practice (p. 9) OL

8-1 Name ________ Date ________

Skills Practice

Division with Remainders

Chapter Resources

Divide. Check each answer.

1. 8)91 **11 R3**
2. 3)54 **18**
3. 9)16 **1 R7**
4. 5)86 **17 R1**
5. 7)12 **1 R5**
6. 7)21 **3**
7. 3)24 **8**
8. 4)36 **9**
9. 7)43 **6 R1**
10. 5)26 **5 R1**
11. 6)89 **14 R5**
12. 4)17 **4 R1**
13. 3)94 **31 R1**
14. 4)21 **5 R1**
15. 23 ÷ 2 = **11 R1**
16. 35 ÷ 7 = **5**
17. 27 ÷ 3 = **9**
18. 19 ÷ 9 = **2 R1**
19. 24 ÷ 7 = **3 R3**
20. 38 ÷ 6 = **6 R2**

Grade 4 9 Chapter 8

Practice and Problem Solving

EXTRA PRACTICE See page R20.

Divide. Check each answer. See Examples 1 and 2 (pp. 313–314)

11. 2)28 14	**12.** 4)48 12	**13.** 3)33 11	**14.** 2)26 13
15. 5)53 10 R3	**16.** 6)67 11 R1	**17.** 7)73 10 R3	**18.** 9)96 10 R6
19. 93 ÷ 3 31	**20.** 84 ÷ 4 21	**21.** 64 ÷ 2 32	**22.** 69 ÷ 3 23
23. 79 ÷ 2 39 R1	**24.** 91 ÷ 4 22 R3	**25.** 77 ÷ 3 25 R2	**26.** 99 ÷ 4 24 R3

27. Marlene makes $4 an hour babysitting. If she earned $48, how many hours did she babysit? 12

28. Seven scouts need to sell 75 boxes of cookies. Each scout gets the same number of boxes. How many boxes will be left to sell? 10 R5; So, if each scout sells 10 boxes, there will still be 5 boxes to sell.

Real-World PROBLEM SOLVING

Science There are many different insects on Earth.

29. Measurement The lifespan of a firefly is 7 days. How many fireflies have a total lifespan of 77 days? 11

30. Measurement A cockroach can travel 3 miles per hour. How long would it take the cockroach to travel 32 miles?

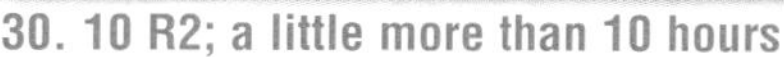
30. 10 R2; a little more than 10 hours

H.O.T. Problems

31. OPEN ENDED Identify a two-digit dividend that will result in a quotient with a remainder of 1 when the divisor is 4. Sample answer: 49

32. FIND THE ERROR Kate and Yutaka found 46 ÷ 4. Who is correct? Explain.

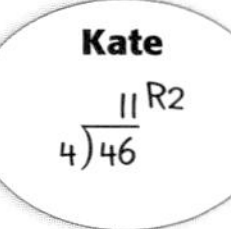

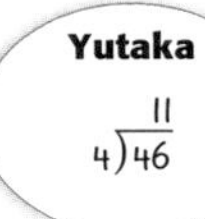

Sample answer: Kate; she wrote the remainder, and Yutaka did not.

33. WRITING IN ▶MATH When you divide a number by 6, can the remainder be 6? Explain. Sample answer: no; The remainder is always less than the divisor.

Enrich (p. 12) AL

8–1 Name ______ Date ______
Enrich
Division Rules

Work across each row of problems to discover a division rule.

36 ÷ 2 = **18** ÷ 3 = **6** → 36 ÷ 6 = **6**
42 ÷ 2 = **21** ÷ 3 = **7** → 42 ÷ 6 = **7**
12 ÷ 2 = **6** ÷ 3 = **2** → 12 ÷ 6 = **2**
54 ÷ 3 = **18** ÷ 2 = **9** → 54 ÷ 6 = **9**
48 ÷ 3 = **16** ÷ 2 = **8** → 48 ÷ 6 = **8**
30 ÷ 3 = **10** ÷ 2 = **5** → 30 ÷ 6 = **5**

Complete this statement:
If a number can be divided evenly by 2 and by 3, then it is also divisible by **6**.

Keep in mind
1. All even numbers are divisible by 2.
2. If the sum of the digits in a number is divisible by 3, then the number is divisible by 3.

Circle the numbers that are divisible by 6.
(432) 746 (330) 895 (546)

Grade 4 12 Chapter 8

Homework Practice (p. 10) OL

8–1 Name ______ Date ______
Homework Practice
Division with Remainders

Divide. Check each answer.

1. 6)56 **9 R2**	2. 5)42 **8 R2**	3. 6)25 **4 R1**
4. 2)32 **16**	5. 5)41 **8 R1**	6. 9)53 **5 R8**
7. 6)54 **9**	8. 6)34 **5 R4**	9. 8)21 **2 R5**
10. 7)35 **5**	11. 72 ÷ 8 **9**	12. 15 ÷ 7 **2 R1**
13. 64 ÷ 7 **9 R1**	14. 49 ÷ 3 **16 R1**	15. 28 ÷ 3 **9 R1**

16. Andy's mom would not tell her age, but she did give these clues: Divide my age by 4, and it is 10. I am between 50 and 30. **40**

Spiral Review (Lesson 7-7)

Multiply.
17. 63 × 99 **6,237**
18. 144 × 33 **4,752**
19. 706 × 67 **47,302**
20. 4,371 × 42 **183,582**

21. Through his telescope, Jose identified 12 stars each night for 64 nights. How many different stars has Jose seen? **768 stars**

22. Look back over this page. Circle all of the numbers on the page that can be divided by 2 without a remainder. **See students' work.**

Grade 4 10 Chapter 8

3 Practice

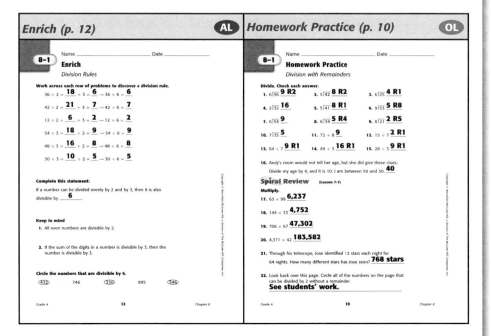

Differentiate practice using these leveled assignments for Exercises 11–33.

Level	Assignment
BL Below/Approaching Level	11–14, 19–23, 27–29
OL On Level	11–27, 29–30, 32
AL Above/Beyond Level	11–29 odd, 31–33

Have students discuss and complete the Higher Order Thinking problems. Remind students to use problem-solving strategies.

WRITING IN ▶MATH Have students complete Exercise 33 in their Math Journals. You may choose to use this exercise as an optional formative assessment.

4 Assess

Formative Assessment

- **Explain why the quotient of 29 ÷ 2 has a remainder.** Sample answer: 29 is an odd number and cannot be divided evenly by 2.

Quick Check **Are students continuing to struggle dividing with and without remainders?**

If Yes → Strategic Intervention Guide (p. 78)

If No → Independent Work Options (p. 313B)
CRM Skills Practice Worksheet (p. 9)
CRM Enrich Worksheet (p. 12)

Into the Future Have students write how what they learned in today's lesson will help them divide greater numbers.

COMMON ERROR!

Exercises 4, 7, 15, 17, and 18 Students often forget to write the zero in the quotient. Remind students to check their answers by multiplication.

LESSON 8-2

Divide Multiples of 10, 100, and 1,000

Lesson Planner

Objective

Use basic facts and patterns to divide mentally.

Review Vocabulary

product, multiple

Resources

Manipulatives: base-ten blocks

Literature Connection: *The Doorbell Rang* by Pat Hutchins

Teacher Technology

TeacherWorks • Interactive Classroom • Math Tool Chest

Daily Routine

Use these suggestions before beginning the lesson on p. 316.

5-Minute Check

(Reviews Lesson 8-1)

Divide.

1. 68 ÷ 2 34 **2.** 78 ÷ 3 26

3. 59 ÷ 5 11 R4 **4.** 97 ÷ 8 12 R1

Problem of the Day

A case of blueberries costs $10. There are 12 containers in each case. Sold separately, one container of blueberries costs $1. How much will you save by buying one case blueberries instead of 12 individual containers? $2

Focus on Math Background

In Chapter 5, students learned the basic facts for division, and in Chapter 7 they explored multiplying by multiples of 10, 100, and 1,000. In the same way that basic facts and patterns of zeros can help you multiply powers of ten and their multiples, they can help you divide. Once again, it is important that students relate multiplication and division through the use of fact families and inverse operations. For example, if $4 \times 60 = 240$, then $240 \div 4 = 60$.

Review Math Vocabulary

Write the review vocabulary words and their definitions on the board.

Have students name the multiples of 10 from 10 through 100. Have them write the basic facts that result in these products, for example, $2 \times 10 = 20$, $3 \times 10 = 30$, and so on.

Ask student what these number sentences have in common. They all have 10 as a factor.

Visual Vocabulary Cards

Use Visual Vocabulary Card 27 to reinforce the vocabulary reviewed in this lesson. (The Define/Example/Ask routine is printed on the back of each card.)

Differentiated Instruction

Small Group Options

Option 1 Below Level BL

LOGICAL

Materials: paper and pencil

Have students use the table for Exercises 42–44 and answer these questions:

- **How many times longer does the Galapagos turtle live than a boa constrictor?** 5 times
- **How many times longer does the box turtle live than a komodo dragon?** 6 times
- **How many years will 5 generations of komodo dragons live?** 100 years

Option 2 English Language Learners ELL

TACTILE

Materials: construction paper

Core Vocabulary: think, lift, stays the same

Common Use Verb: keep

See Math This strategy uses a visual aid to simplify dividing with multiple zeros.

- Assign students partners. Write a division problem that has a multiple of 10, 100, or 1,000 in the divisor on the board.
- Tape construction paper over the zeros inside the problem and write zeros on the construction paper.
- Ask students to solve the problem by thinking, not writing.
- Model keeping the same number of zeros that are in the dividend in the answer.
- Lift the construction paper zeros up to show the answer.
- Repeat several times.

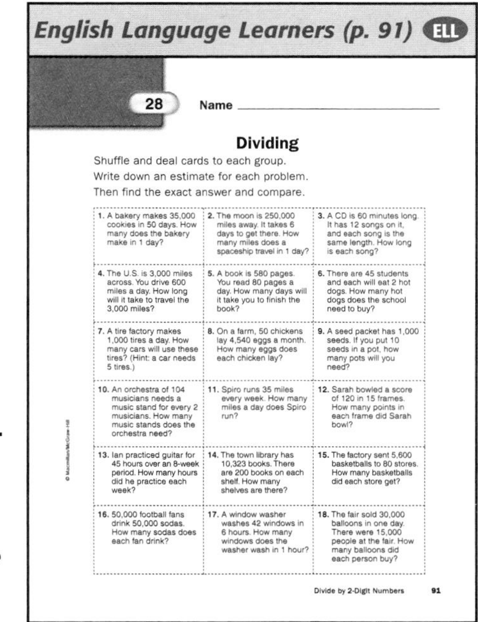

English Language Learners (p. 91) ELL

28 Name ____________

Dividing

Shuffle and deal cards to each group.
Write down an estimate for each problem.
Then find the exact answer and compare.

1. A bakery makes 35,000 cookies in 50 days. How many does the bakery make in 1 day?	2. The moon is 250,000 miles away. It takes 6 days to get there. How many miles does a spaceship travel in 1 day?	3. A CD is 60 minutes long. It has 12 songs on it, and each song is the same length. How long is each song?
4. The U.S. is 3,000 miles across. You drive 600 miles a day. How long will it take to travel the 3,000 miles?	5. A book is 580 pages. You read 80 pages a day. How many days will it take you to finish the book?	6. There are 45 students and each will eat 2 hot dogs. How many hot dogs does the school need to buy?
7. A tire factory makes 1,000 tires a day. How many cars will use these tires? (Hint: a car needs 5 tires.)	8. On a farm, 50 chickens lay 4,540 eggs a month. How many eggs does each chicken lay?	9. A seed packet has 1,000 seeds. If you put 10 seeds in a pot, how many pots will you need?
10. An orchestra of 104 musicians needs a music stand for every 2 musicians. How many music stands does the orchestra need?	11. Spiro runs 35 miles every week. How many miles a day does Spiro run?	12. Sarah bowled a score of 120 in 15 frames. How many points in each frame did Sarah bowl?
13. Ian practiced guitar for 45 hours over an 8-week period. How many hours did he practice each week?	14. The town library has 10,323 books. There are 200 books on each shelf. How many shelves are there?	15. The factory sent 5,600 basketballs to 80 stores. How many basketballs did each store get?
16. 50,000 football fans drink 50,000 sodas. How many sodas does each fan drink?	17. A window washer washes 42 windows in 6 hours. How many windows does the washer wash in 1 hour?	18. The fair sold 30,000 balloons in one day. There were 15,000 people at the fair. How many balloons did each person buy?

Divide by 2-Digit Numbers 91

Use this worksheet to provide additional support for English Language Learners.

Independent Work Options

Option 1 Early Finishers OL AL

LOGICAL

Materials: paper and pencil

- Have students write multiplication word problems to go with Exercises 16, 20, and 25. Answers will vary.

Option 2 Student Technology

Math Online macmillanmh.com

Math Tool Chest Counters Level 2

Personal Tutor • Extra Examples

Math Adventures

Option 3 Learning Station: Music (p. 308H)

Direct students to the Music Learning Station for opportunities to explore and extend the lesson concept.

Option 4 Problem-Solving Practice

Reinforce problem-solving skills and strategies with the Problem-Solving Practice worksheet.

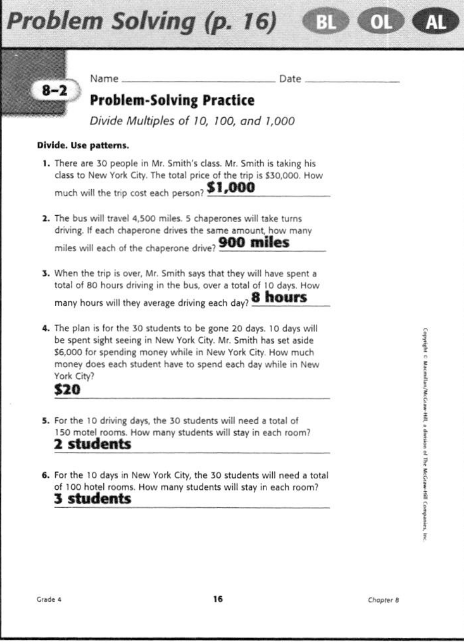

Problem Solving (p. 16) BL OL AL

8–2 Name ____________ Date ____________

Problem-Solving Practice

Divide Multiples of 10, 100, and 1,000

Divide. Use patterns.

1. There are 30 people in Mr. Smith's class. Mr. Smith is taking his class to New York City. The total price of the trip is $30,000. How much will the trip cost each person? **$1,000**
2. The bus will travel 4,500 miles. 5 chaperones will take turns driving. If each chaperone drives the same amount, how many miles will each of the chaperone drive? **900 miles**
3. When the trip is over, Mr. Smith says that they will have spent a total of 80 hours driving in the bus, over a total of 10 days. How many hours will they average driving each day? **8 hours**
4. The plan is for the 30 students to be gone 20 days. 10 days will be spent sight seeing in New York City. Mr. Smith has set aside $6,000 for spending money while in New York City. How much money does each student have to spend each day while in New York City? **$20**
5. For the 10 driving days, the 30 students will need a total of 150 motel rooms. How many students will stay in each room? **2 students**
6. For the 10 days in New York City, the 30 students will need a total of 100 hotel rooms. How many students will stay in each room? **3 students**

Grade 4 16 Chapter 8

Divide Multiples of 10, 100, and 1,000

1 Introduce

Activity Choice 1 • Hands-On 

Materials: base-ten blocks to use as needed

Remind students that they learned to multiply by multiples of 10, 100, and 1,000 in Chapter 6. Put the following on the board to help review:

$5 \times 1 = 5$	$7 \times 1 = 7$
$5 \times 10 = ?$	$7 \times 10 = ?$
$5 \times 100 = ?$	$7 \times 100 = ?$
$5 \times 1{,}000 = ?$	$7 \times 1{,}000 = ?$

- **Find each of the products.**
  50, 500, 5,000; 70, 700, 7,000
- **What pattern do you see?**
  Sample answer: When a zero is added to a factor, a zero is also added to the product.
- Now write the following on the board:

  $7 \times 5 = 35$
  $7 \times 50 = ?$
  $7 \times 500 = ?$
- Have students find the products and tell what pattern they see. 350, 3,500; Sample answer: When you multiply by a multiple of 10 (or 100), the product has one zero (or two zeros) after the product of the basic fact.

Activity Choice 2 • Literature

Introduce the lesson with *The Doorbell Rang* by Pat Hutchins. For a related math activity, see p. TR54.

2 Teach

Scaffolding Questions

- Write the following multiplication sentences vertically on the board:

  $3 \times 7 = 21$; $3 \times 70 = 210$; $3 \times 700 = 2{,}100$
- **Write the related division sentences for each.**
  $21 \div 3 = 7$; $210 \div 3 = 70$; $2{,}100 \div 3 = 700$
- **What pattern do you see in the number of zeros in the dividend and the quotient?**
  The number of zeros is the same.

GET READY to Learn

Have students open their books and read the information in **Get Ready to Learn**. Review **product** and **multiple**. As a class, work through **Examples 1 and 2**.

8-2 Divide Multiples of 10, 100, and 1,000

MAIN IDEA

I will use basic facts and patterns to divide mentally.

Math Online

macmillanmh.com

- Extra Examples
- Personal Tutor
- Self-Check Quiz

GET READY to Learn

A certain amusement park has 5 entrances. If 1,500 people entered the amusement park and separated into equal lines, how many people are in each line?

You can find and use patterns to divide multiples of 10, 100, and 1,000. Using patterns makes it easy to divide.

Real-World EXAMPLE Divide Multiples of 10, 100, and 1,000

1. **AMUSEMENT PARKS How many people are in each line at the amusement park?**

You need to divide 1,500 people into 5 equal groups. Find $1{,}500 \div 5$.

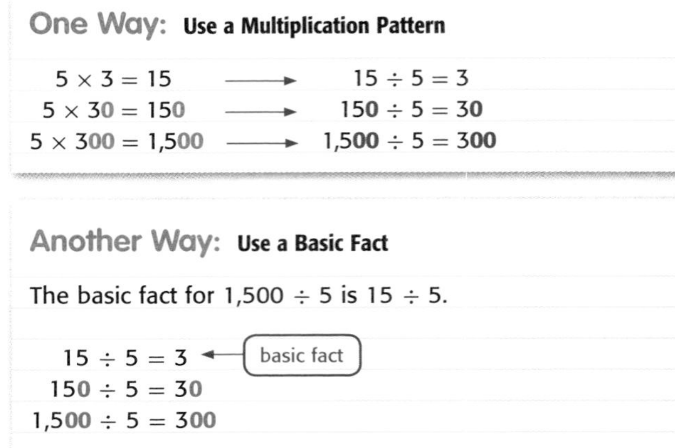

One Way: Use a Multiplication Pattern

$5 \times 3 = 15 \longrightarrow 15 \div 5 = 3$
$5 \times 30 = 150 \longrightarrow 150 \div 5 = 30$
$5 \times 300 = 1{,}500 \longrightarrow 1{,}500 \div 5 = 300$

Another Way: Use a Basic Fact

The basic fact for $1{,}500 \div 5$ is $15 \div 5$.

$15 \div 5 = 3$ ← basic fact
$150 \div 5 = 30$
$1{,}500 \div 5 = 300$

So, there are 300 people in each line.

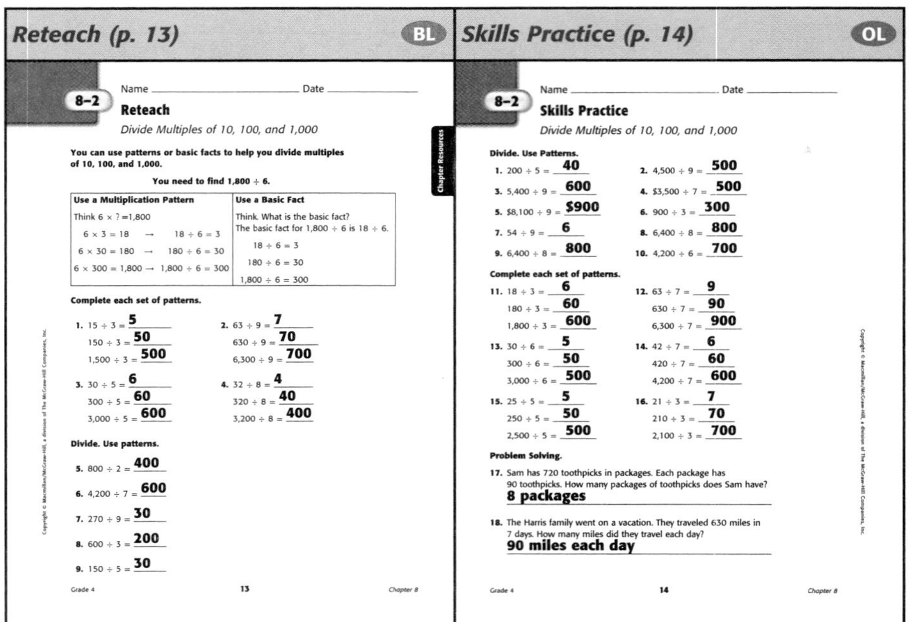

Reteach (p. 13) BL

8-2 Name ______ Date ______

Reteach

Divide Multiples of 10, 100, and 1,000

You can use patterns or basic facts to help you divide multiples of 10, 100, and 1,000.

You need to find 1,800 ÷ 6.

Use a Multiplication Pattern	Use a Basic Fact
Think 6 × ? = 1,800	Think. What is the basic fact? The basic fact for 1,800 ÷ 6 is 18 ÷ 6.
6 × 3 = 18 → 18 ÷ 6 = 3	18 ÷ 6 = 3
6 × 30 = 180 → 180 ÷ 6 = 30	180 ÷ 6 = 30
6 × 300 = 1,800 → 1,800 ÷ 6 = 300	1,800 ÷ 6 = 300

Complete each set of patterns.

1. 15 ÷ 3 = **5**; 150 ÷ 3 = **50**; 1,500 ÷ 3 = **500**
2. 63 ÷ 9 = **7**; 630 ÷ 9 = **70**; 6,300 ÷ 9 = **700**
3. 30 ÷ 5 = **6**; 300 ÷ 5 = **60**; 3,000 ÷ 5 = **600**
4. 32 ÷ 8 = **4**; 320 ÷ 8 = **40**; 3,200 ÷ 8 = **400**

Divide. Use patterns.

5. 800 ÷ 2 = **400**
6. 4,200 ÷ 7 = **600**
7. 270 ÷ 9 = **30**
8. 600 ÷ 3 = **200**
9. 150 ÷ 5 = **30**

Grade 4 13 Chapter 8

Chapter Resources

Skills Practice (p. 14) OL

8-2 Name ______ Date ______

Skills Practice

Divide Multiples of 10, 100, and 1,000

Divide. Use Patterns.

1. 200 ÷ 5 = **40**
2. 4,500 ÷ 9 = **500**
3. 5,400 ÷ 9 = **600**
4. $3,500 ÷ 7 = **500**
5. $8,100 ÷ 9 = **$900**
6. 900 ÷ 3 = **300**
7. 54 ÷ 9 = **6**
8. 6,400 ÷ 8 = **800**
9. 6,400 ÷ 8 = **800**
10. 4,200 ÷ 6 = **700**

Complete each set of patterns.

11. 18 ÷ 3 = **6**; 180 ÷ 3 = **60**; 1,800 ÷ 3 = **600**
12. 63 ÷ 7 = **9**; 630 ÷ 7 = **90**; 6,300 ÷ 7 = **900**
13. 30 ÷ 6 = **5**; 300 ÷ 6 = **50**; 3,000 ÷ 6 = **500**
14. 42 ÷ 7 = **6**; 420 ÷ 7 = **60**; 4,200 ÷ 7 = **600**
15. 25 ÷ 5 = **5**; 250 ÷ 5 = **50**; 2,500 ÷ 5 = **500**
16. 21 ÷ 3 = **7**; 210 ÷ 3 = **70**; 2,100 ÷ 3 = **700**

Problem Solving.

17. Sam has 720 toothpicks in packages. Each package has 90 toothpicks. How many packages of toothpicks does Sam have? **8 packages**
18. The Harris family went on a vacation. They traveled 630 miles in 7 days. How many miles did they travel each day? **90 miles each day**

Grade 4 14 Chapter 8

Remember

Multiplication can be used to check division.

EXAMPLE Divide Multiples of 10, 100, and 1,000

2 Find the quotient of 2,400 and 4.

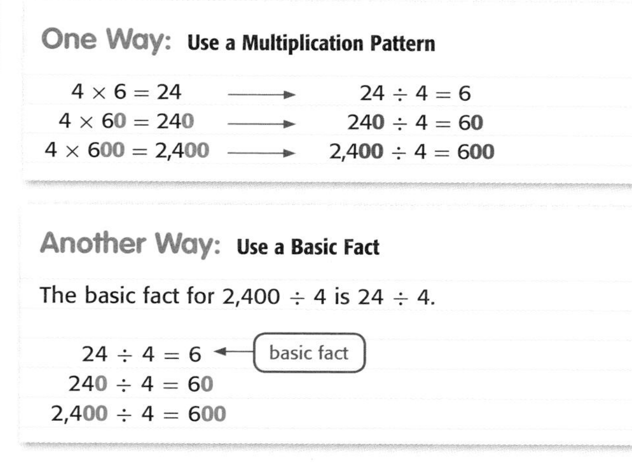

One Way: **Use a Multiplication Pattern**

$4 \times 6 = 24$	→	$24 \div 4 = 6$
$4 \times 60 = 240$	→	$240 \div 4 = 60$
$4 \times 600 = 2{,}400$	→	$2{,}400 \div 4 = 600$

Another Way: **Use a Basic Fact**

The basic fact for $2{,}400 \div 4$ is $24 \div 4$.

$24 \div 4 = 6$ ← basic fact
$240 \div 4 = 60$
$2{,}400 \div 4 = 600$

So, $2{,}400 \div 4$ is 600.

Check

You know that $2{,}400 \div 4 = 600$ because $4 \times 600 = 2{,}400$. ✓

★ indicates multi-step problem

CHECK What You Know

Copy and complete each set of patterns. See Examples 1 and 2 (pp. 316–317)

1. $12 \div 4 =$ ■ 3
$120 \div 4 =$ ■ 30
$1{,}200 \div 4 =$ ■ 300

2. $36 ÷ 6 = ■ $6
$360 ÷ 6 = ■ $60
$3,600 ÷ 6 = ■ $600

3. $45 \div 9 =$ ■ 5
$450 \div 9 =$ ■ 50
$4{,}500 \div 9 =$ ■ 500

Divide. Use patterns. See Examples 1 and 2 (pp. 316–317)

4. $400 ÷ 2 $200

5. $1{,}600 \div 4$ 400

6. $3,200 ÷ 8 $400

For Exercise 7, use the information at the right.

★**7.** There are 4 members of a family planning a weekend camping trip. How much will the trip cost for each person? $50

8. Talk About It What basic fact will help you find the quotient of 4,200 and 7? $42 \div 7$

Family Vacation

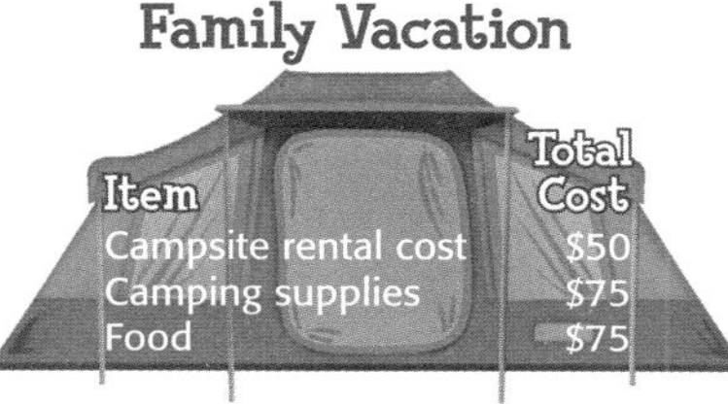

Item	Total Cost
Campsite rental cost	$50
Camping supplies	$75
Food	$75

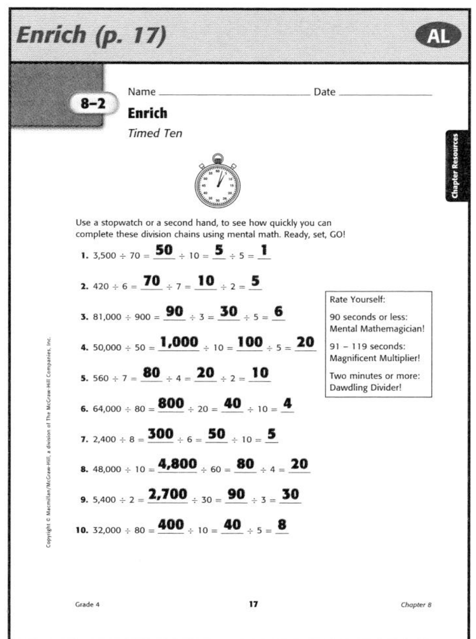

Enrich (p. 17) AL

8–2 Name ______ Date ______

Enrich

Timed Ten

Use a stopwatch or a second hand, to see how quickly you can complete these division chains using mental math. Ready, set, GO!

1. $3{,}500 \div 70 =$ **50** $\div 10 =$ **5** $\div 5 =$ **1**
2. $420 \div 6 =$ **70** $\div 7 =$ **10** $\div 2 =$ **5**
3. $81{,}000 \div 900 =$ **90** $\div 3 =$ **30** $\div 5 =$ **6**
4. $50{,}000 \div 50 =$ **1,000** $\div 10 =$ **100** $\div 5 =$ **20**
5. $560 \div 7 =$ **80** $\div 4 =$ **20** $\div 2 =$ **10**
6. $64{,}000 \div 80 =$ **800** $\div 20 =$ **40** $\div 10 =$ **4**
7. $2{,}400 \div 8 =$ **300** $\div 6 =$ **50** $\div 10 =$ **5**
8. $48{,}000 \div 10 =$ **4,800** $\div 60 =$ **80** $\div 4 =$ **20**
9. $5{,}400 \div 2 =$ **2,700** $\div 30 =$ **90** $\div 3 =$ **30**
10. $32{,}000 \div 80 =$ **400** $\div 10 =$ **40** $\div 5 =$ **8**

Rate Yourself:
90 seconds or less: Mental Mathemagician!
91 – 119 seconds: Magnificent Multiplier!
Two minutes or more: Dawdling Divider!

Chapter Resources

Grade 4 17 Chapter 8

Divide Multiples of 10

Example 2 Point out that the difference between this example and Example 1 is that in this example, both the dividend and the divisor are multiples of 10 or 100.

ADDITIONAL EXAMPLES

1 The factory just completed 600 wheels for their tricycles. How many tricycles can they make with the 600 wheels? 200 tricycles

2 Find the quotient of $3{,}200 \div 80$. 40

CHECK What You Know

As a class, have students complete Exercises 1–8 in **Check What You Know** as you observe their work.

Exercise 8 Assess student comprehension before assigning practice exercises.

BL Alternate Teaching Strategy

If students place too many zeros in the quotient…

Then use one of these reteach options:

1 CRM **Daily Reteach Worksheet** (p. 13)

2 Have them underline the basic fact in the quotient. Suggest also that they count the number of zeros that come after the basic fact quotient. For example,

$\underline{5}{,}\underline{6}00 \div \underline{8}0 = \underline{7}0$

3 Tech Link Have students use Math Tool Chest to help complete the problem-solving exercises.

3 Practice

Differentiate practice using these leveled assignments for Exercises 9–33.

Level	Assignment
BL Below/Approaching Level	9–12, 17–21, 27, 29–30
OL On Level	9–15, 19–26, 29–32
AL Above/Beyond Level	10–30 even, 32–33

Have students discuss and complete the Higher Order Thinking problems. Suggest that students pay close attention to the basic facts.

WRITING IN MATH Have students complete Exercise 33 in their Math Journals. You may choose to use this exercise as an optional formative assessment.

COMMON ERROR!

Exercise 30 Students may assume that the locusts are traveling 24 hours for the day. Suggest that they check for the important facts within the problem using Step 1 of the four-step plan.

Practice and Problem Solving

See page R20.

Copy and complete each set of patterns. See Examples 1 and 2 (pp. 316–317)

9. 12 ÷ 2 = ■ 6
120 ÷ 2 = ■ 60
1,200 ÷ 2 = ■ 600

10. \$28 ÷ 7 = ■ \$4
\$280 ÷ 7 = ■ \$40
\$2,800 ÷ 7 = ■ \$400

11. 54 ÷ 9 = ■ 6
540 ÷ 9 = ■ 60
5,400 ÷ 9 = ■ 600

12. \$36 ÷ 4 = ■ \$9
\$360 ÷ 4 = ■ \$90
\$3,600 ÷ 4 = ■ \$900

13. 42 ÷ 6 = ■ 7
420 ÷ 6 = ■ 70
4,200 ÷ 6 = ■ 700

14. \$72 ÷ 8 = ■ \$9
\$720 ÷ 8 = ■ \$90
\$7,200 ÷ 8 = ■ \$900

Divide. Use patterns. See Examples 1 and 2 (pp. 316–317)

15. 200 ÷ 5 40
16. \$600 ÷ 3 \$200
17. 800 ÷ 2 400
18. 900 ÷ 3 300
19. \$1,400 ÷ 7 \$200
20. 4,500 ÷ 5 900
21. 6,300 ÷ 9 700
22. \$6,400 ÷ 8 \$800
23. \$3,500 ÷ 5 \$700
24. 1,600 ÷ 8 200
25. 5,400 ÷ 6 900
26. \$8,100 ÷ 9 \$900

27. The cost of a used car is \$3,200. If the payments are spread over 8 months, what is the payment each month? \$400

★**28.** The Nair family collected 2,400 pennies. The pennies will be divided evenly among the 4 children. How many dollars will each child get? \$6

Measurement Animals migrate due to factors such as climate and food availability. The table shows a few migration distances.

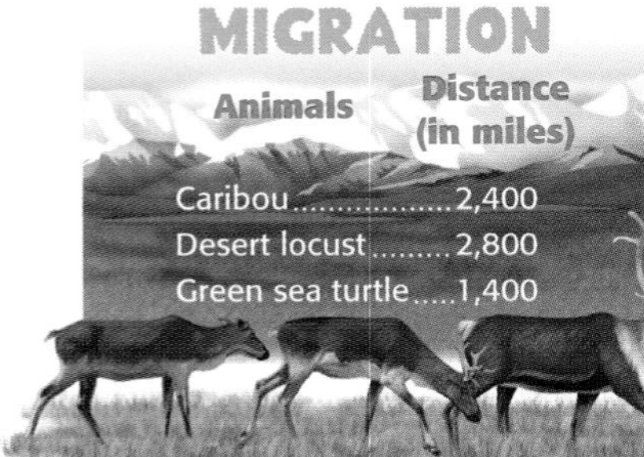

MIGRATION

Animals	Distance (in miles)
Caribou	2,400
Desert locust	2,800
Green sea turtle	1,400

Source: U.S. Fish and Wildlife Service

29. Suppose a group of green sea turtles travels 7 miles a day. How many days will the migration take? 200 days

30. ★ Suppose a swarm of desert locusts travels 7 miles per hour. They travel 10 hours per day. How many days will the migration take? 40 days

31. A herd of caribou migrated the distance shown in 8 months. If they traveled the same distance each month, how many miles did the herd travel each month? 300 miles

H.O.T. Problems

32. **NUMBER SENSE** Without actually dividing, tell which has the greater quotient, 1,500 ÷ 3 or 2,400 ÷ 6? Explain. See margin.

33. **WRITING IN MATH** Explain how you would know that the quotient of 600 ÷ 2 is a 3-digit number. Sample answer: 2 is less than 6. Since 6 is in the hundreds place, the quotient will be a 3-digit number.

TEST Practice

34. Rosita read a 75-page book in 5 days. She read the same number of pages each day. How many pages did she read each day? (Lesson 8-1) C

A 5

B 10

C 15

D 150

35. Antoine went to his sister's college graduation. There were 1,200 students graduating. They were separated equally into 4 sections of the auditorium. How many students were seated in each section? (Lesson 8-2) H

F 3　　**H** 300

G 30　　**J** 3,000

Spiral Review

Divide. Check each answer. (Lesson 8-1)

36. $2\overline{)37}$ 18 R1

37. $5\overline{)49}$ 9 R4

38. $7\overline{)81}$ 11 R4

Multiply. (Lesson 7-7)

39. 1,672 × 18 　30,096

40. 4,061 × 39 　158,379

41. 9,544 × 65 　620,360

Measurement **For Exercises 42–44, use the table. It shows the life spans of reptiles. Choose the best operation. Then solve.** (Lesson 4-4)

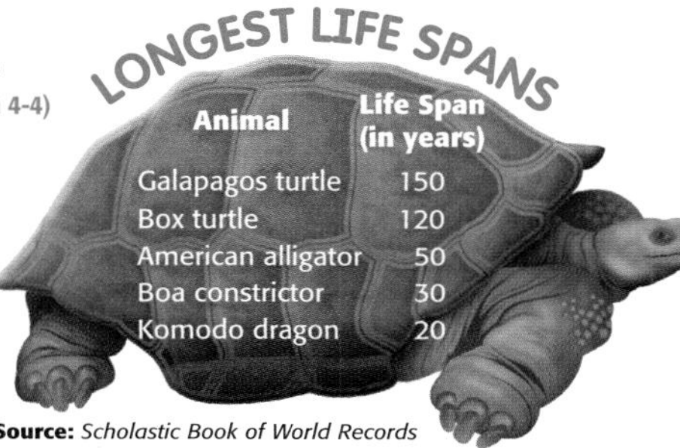

LONGEST LIFE SPANS

Animal	Life Span (in years)
Galapagos turtle	150
Box turtle	120
American alligator	50
Boa constrictor	30
Komodo dragon	20

Source: *Scholastic Book of World Records*

42. How many years will three generations of Galapagos turtles live? multiply; 450

43. How much longer can an American alligator live than a komodo dragon? subtraction; 30 yrs

44. Which animal lives 90 years longer than the boa constrictor? addition; box turtle

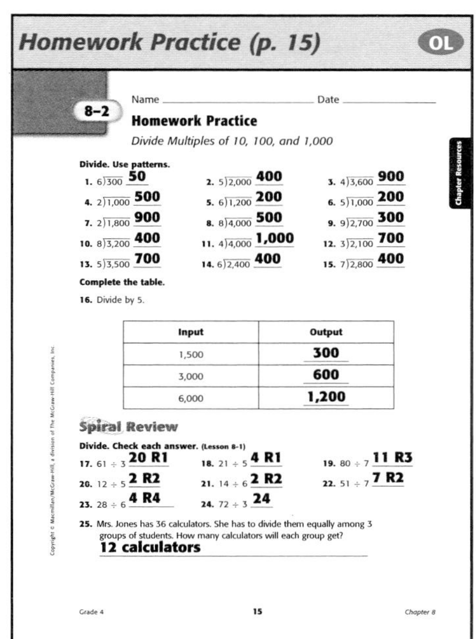

Homework Practice (p. 15) OL

8-2

Name ______________ Date ______________

Homework Practice

Divide Multiples of 10, 100, and 1,000

Divide. Use patterns.

1. $6\overline{)300}$ **50**　**2.** $5\overline{)2,000}$ **400**　**3.** $4\overline{)3,600}$ **900**

4. $2\overline{)1,000}$ **500**　**5.** $6\overline{)1,200}$ **200**　**6.** $5\overline{)1,000}$ **200**

7. $2\overline{)1,800}$ **900**　**8.** $8\overline{)4,000}$ **500**　**9.** $9\overline{)2,700}$ **300**

10. $8\overline{)3,200}$ **400**　**11.** $4\overline{)4,000}$ **1,000**　**12.** $3\overline{)2,100}$ **700**

13. $5\overline{)3,500}$ **700**　**14.** $6\overline{)2,400}$ **400**　**15.** $7\overline{)2,800}$ **400**

Complete the table.

16. Divide by 5.

Input	Output
1,500	**300**
3,000	**600**
6,000	**1,200**

Spiral Review

Divide. Check each answer. (Lesson 8-1)

17. 61 ÷ 3 **20 R1**　**18.** 21 ÷ 5 **4 R1**　**19.** 80 ÷ 7 **11 R3**

20. 12 ÷ 5 **2 R2**　**21.** 14 ÷ 6 **2 R2**　**22.** 51 ÷ 7 **7 R2**

23. 28 ÷ 6 **4 R4**　**24.** 72 ÷ 3 **24**

25. Mrs. Jones has 36 calculators. She has to divide them equally among 3 groups of students. How many calculators will each group get? **12 calculators**

Chapter Resources

Grade 4　15　Chapter 8

4 Assess

Formative Assessment

- **How can you use basic facts to find 4,200 ÷ 7?** Sample answer: 42 ÷ 7 = 6; 4,200 ÷ 7 = 600.

Quick Check **Are students continuing to struggle with dividing multiples of 10, 100, and 1,000?**

If Yes → Strategic Intervention Guide (p. 80)

If No → Independent Work Options (p. 342B)
CRM Skills Practice Worksheet (p. 14)
CRM Enrich Worksheet (p. 17)

Name the Math Have students show how basic facts and patterns can be used to solve the problem 6,300 ÷ 70.

Reviews Lessons 8-1 and 8-2

Assign the Test Practice problems to provide daily reinforcement of test-taking skills.

Spiral Review

Reviews Lessons 4-4, 7-7, and 8-1

Review and assess mastery of skills and concepts from previous chapters.

Additional Answer

32. Sample answer: Look at the basic multiplication facts. 15 ÷ 3 = 5 and 24 ÷ 6 = 4, so 1,500 ÷ 3 has the greater quotient.

8-3 Problem-Solving Strategy Guess and Check

Lesson Planner

Objective

Solve problems by using the guess and check strategy.

Resources

Manipulatives: money

Literature Connection: *The Doorbell Rang* by Pat Hutchins

Teacher Technology
TeacherWorks • Interactive Classroom

Real-World Problem Solving Library
Math and Social Studies: *Riding the Mail Trail*
Use these leveled books to reinforce and extend problem-solving skills and strategies.

Leveled for:

- OL On Level
- ELL Sheltered English
- SP Spanish

For additional support, see the Real-World Problem Solving Teacher Guide.

Daily Routine

Use these suggestions before beginning the lesson on p. 320.

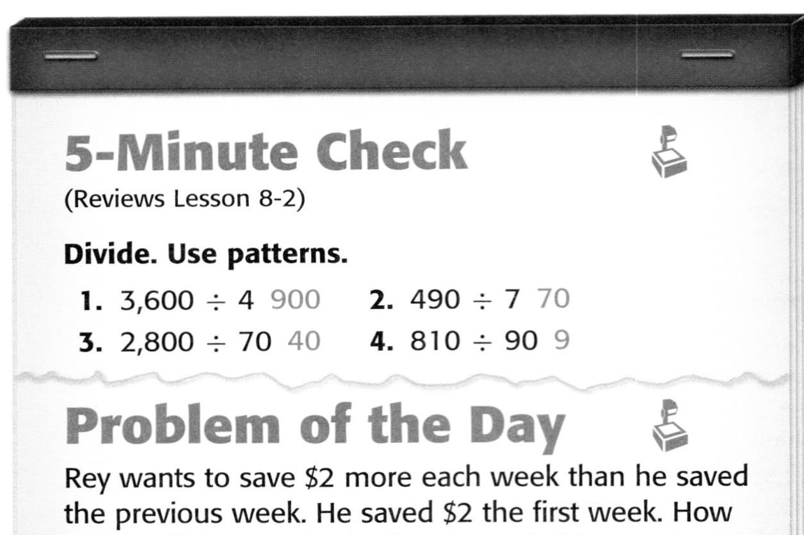

5-Minute Check

(Reviews Lesson 8-2)

Divide. Use patterns.

1. 3,600 ÷ 4 900 **2.** 490 ÷ 7 70
3. 2,800 ÷ 70 40 **4.** 810 ÷ 90 9

Problem of the Day

Rey wants to save $2 more each week than he saved the previous week. He saved $2 the first week. How much will he save in the fourth week if he continues his plan? How much will he have saved altogether after the fourth week? $8; $20

Differentiated Instruction

Small Group Options

LOGICAL 

Option 1 Gifted and Talented AL

Materials: paper and pencil

Ask students to revisit Exercise 5 and answer the following question:

- **What are some other combinations you could make and still have 64 legs all together?** 12 dogs, 8 owners; 13 dogs, 6 owners; 14 dogs, 4 owners; 11 dogs, 10 owners

VISUAL, LOGICAL 

Option 2 English Language Learners ELL

Materials: classroom items with note cards
Core Vocabulary: price, match, item
Common Use Verb: guess

See Math This strategy uses a game to help students practice the guess and check strategy.

- Set up your classroom for a game show.
- Stack or bundle various items on a desk, with the prices written on both sides of folded index cards.
- Have students guess the amount for each group of items.
- After the student makes his or her guess, have someone from the opposing team count the number of items and multiply by the price.
- The group with the closest estimate wins a point. Continue with remaining stacks and bundles as time permits. High score wins.

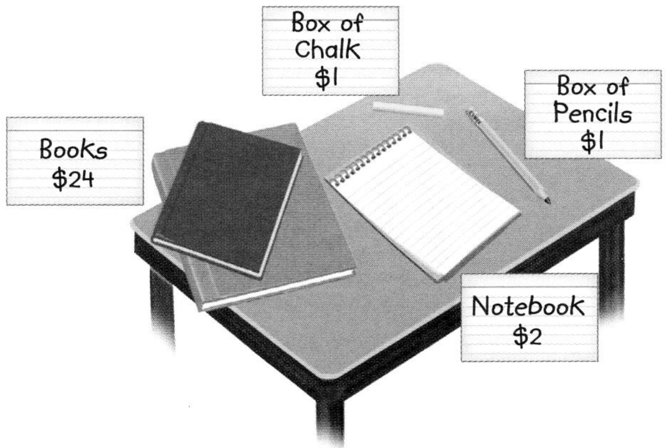

Independent Work Options

VISUAL, SPATIAL, LOGICAL 

Option 1 Early Finishers OL AL

Materials: number cubes

Have students work in pairs, taking turns rolling the number cubes and giving the clue "the sum of the numbers is …" Their partner attempts to guess the two numbers. If there seems to be two different possibilities for values, let the student give another clue. Example: "And the difference of the numbers is …"

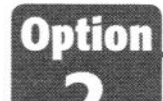

Option 2 Student Technology

Math Online macmillanmh.com

Personal Tutor • Extra Examples

Option 3 Learning Station: Art (p. 308G)

Direct students to the Art Learning Station for opportunities to explore and extend the lesson concept.

8-3 Problem-Solving Strategy

1 Introduce

Activity Choice 1 • Review

Materials: play coins

- Put students in groups of 3 or 4. Give each group a set of play coins and ask them to solve the following problem:

  What is the least amount of coins a person can have to equal a value of 43¢?

- **What strategy could you use to solve this problem?** Answers may vary; sample answer: the act it out strategy.
- Have groups use the coins to act out different combinations and solve the problem. Ask a volunteer group to come to the front of the room and demonstrate his or her solution. 6 coins: 1 quarter, 1 dime, 1 nickel, 3 pennies

Activity Choice 2 • Literature

Introduce the lesson with *The Doorbell Rang* by Pat Hutchins. For a related math activity, see p. TR54.

2 Teach

Have students read the problem on buying gifts. Guide them through the problem-solving steps.

Understand Using the questions, review what students know and need to find.

Plan Have them discuss their strategy.

Solve Guide students to use guess and check to solve the problem.

- **What is the total cost of the 3 gifts?** \$27
- **What is the greatest amount any one gift can be if the same amount is spent on each? Explain.** \$9, because $3 \times \$9 = \$27$
- **When you check 9, what do you get for the total cost?** \$30
- **How should you change your next guess? Explain.** Sample answer: Decrease the guess and try \$8 because \$9 was too large.

Check Have students look back at the problem to make sure that the answer fits the facts given.

- **How else could you check this problem?** Sample answer: Add the three numbers in a different order.

8-3 Problem-Solving Strategy

MAIN IDEA I will solve problems by using the guess and check strategy.

Ruben bought 3 gifts for his sisters. Two of the gifts cost the same. The other gift costs \$3 more than the other two. If the total amount of money spent was \$27, how much did each gift cost?

Understand	**What facts do you know?** • There are 3 gifts, and two gifts cost the same. • One gift is \$3 more than the other two. • Ruben spent \$27 on all 3 gifts. **What do you need to find?** • The cost of each gift.
Plan	You can guess and check to solve the problem.
Solve	Use gift + gift + (gift + \$3) = \$27 and make logical guesses. Start with numbers smaller than \$10 because $\$10 \times 3 = \$30$ and the total is less than \$30. Try \$9. \$9 + \$9 + (\$9 + \$3) = \$30 No, too large. Try \$8. \$8 + \$8 + (\$8 + \$3) = \$27 Yes So, two gifts cost \$8 each and the third gift costs \$8 + \$3, or \$11.
Check	Subtract the cost of each gift from the total cost. First gift: \$27 − \$8 = \$19 Second gift: \$19 − \$8 = \$11 Third gift: \$11 − \$11 = \$0 So, the answer is correct.

320 **Chapter 8** Divide by One-Digit Numbers

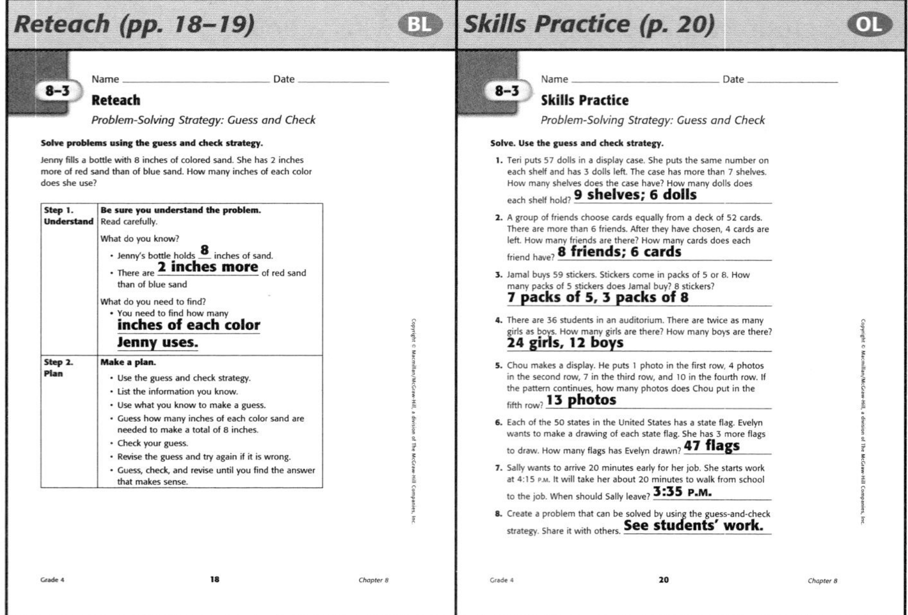

Reteach (pp. 18–19) BL

8-3 Name ________ Date ________

Reteach

Problem-Solving Strategy: Guess and Check

Solve problems using the guess and check strategy.

Jenny fills a bottle with 8 inches of colored sand. She has 2 inches more of red sand than of blue sand. How many inches of each color does she use?

Step 1. Understand	**Be sure you understand the problem.** Read carefully. What do you know? • Jenny's bottle holds **8** inches of sand. • There are **2 inches more** of red sand than of blue sand What do you need to find? • You need to find how many **inches of each color Jenny uses.**
Step 2. Plan	**Make a plan.** • Use the guess and check strategy. • List the information you know. • Use what you know to make a guess. • Guess how many inches of each color sand are needed to make a total of 8 inches. • Check your guess. • Revise the guess and try again if it is wrong. • Guess, check, and revise until you find the answer that makes sense.

Grade 4 18 *Chapter 8*

Skills Practice (p. 20) OL

8-3 Name ________ Date ________

Skills Practice

Problem-Solving Strategy: Guess and Check

Solve. Use the guess and check strategy.

1. Teri puts 57 dolls in a display case. She puts the same number on each shelf and has 3 dolls left. The case has more than 7 shelves. How many shelves does the case have? How many dolls does each shelf hold? **9 shelves; 6 dolls**
2. A group of friends choose cards equally from a deck of 52 cards. There are more than 6 friends. After they have chosen, 4 cards are left. How many friends are there? How many cards does each friend have? **8 friends; 6 cards**
3. Jamal buys 59 stickers. Stickers come in packs of 5 or 8. How many packs of 5 stickers does Jamal buy? 8 stickers? **7 packs of 5, 3 packs of 8**
4. There are 36 students in an auditorium. There are twice as many girls as boys. How many girls are there? How many boys are there? **24 girls, 12 boys**
5. Chou makes a display. He puts 1 photo in the first row, 4 photos in the second row, 7 in the third row, and 10 in the fourth row. If the pattern continues, how many photos does Chou put in the fifth row? **13 photos**
6. Each of the 50 states in the United States has a state flag. Evelyn wants to make a drawing of each state flag. She has 3 more flags to draw. How many flags has Evelyn drawn? **47 flags**
7. Sally wants to arrive 20 minutes early for her job. She starts work at 4:15 P.M. It will take her about 20 minutes to walk from school to the job. When should Sally leave? **3:35 P.M.**
8. Create a problem that can be solved by using the guess-and-check strategy. Share it with others. **See students' work.**

Grade 4 20 *Chapter 8*

ANALYZE the Strategy

Refer to the problem on the previous page. 1, 2, 4. See Ch. 8 Answer Appendix.

1. Explain why gift + gift + (gift + $3) is used to solve the equation.
2. Explain why the first guess was $9 instead of a smaller number.
3. Suppose Ruben spent $39 on the gifts. How much does each gift cost? $12, $12, and $15
4. Explain how you found the answer to Exercise 3.

★ indicates multi-step problem

PRACTICE the Strategy

EXTRA PRACTICE See page R20.

Solve. Use the guess and check strategy.

5. Kendra took photographs at the park. She photographed 20 dogs and owners in all. If there was a total of 64 legs, how many dogs and owners were there?
12 dogs and 8 people

6. **Measurement** Corrine is making twice as much fruit punch as lemonade. She is making 12 gallons total. How many gallons will be fruit punch and how many will be lemonade?
fruit punch: 8 gal; lemonade: 4 gal

7. **Measurement** Theo lives twice as far from Cassidy as Jarvis. How far do Theo and Jarvis live from Cassidy?

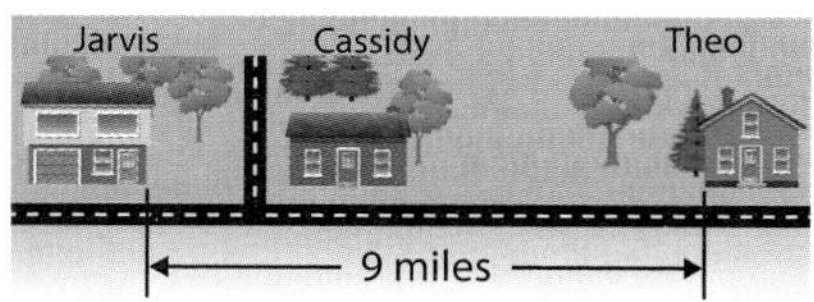

Theo: 6 miles; Jarvis: 3 miles

★8. The total number of tickets sold for a play was 450. On Friday, 150 tickets were sold. Fifty more tickets sold on Saturday than on Sunday. How many tickets sold on Saturday and Sunday?
See Ch. 8 Answer Appendix.

★9. At a zoo gift shop, Jeffrey bought two of the items shown. He gave the cashier $20, and received $4 in change. Which two items did he buy?

hat and mug

10. **Algebra** Denzell and Marco collect miniature cars. Marco has 37 fewer cars than Denzell. They have 249 cars altogether. How many cars does each boy have?
Denzell: 143; Marco: 106

★11. Mirna's basketball team has played 14 games. They have lost and tied an equal number of times. They have won 5 times as many games as they have lost. How many games have they won, lost, and tied?
10 wins, 2 losses, 2 ties

12. **WRITING IN MATH** Explain what it means to solve a problem by guess and check.
See Ch. 8 Answer Appendix.

Analyze the Strategy Use Exercises 1–4 to analyze and discuss the problem-solving strategy.

BL Alternate Teaching Strategy

If students struggle with organizing their guesses…

Then use one of these reteach options:

1. CRM **Daily Reteach Worksheet** (pp. 18–19)
2. Have students make a table or make a list of the guesses they have made. Also suggest that they tell whether their guesses were too large or too small.

3 Practice

Using the Exercises

Exercises 5–11 provide students with practice using the guess and check strategy.

Exercise 8 Watch for students who add 50 tickets to Friday's number rather than using the 50 tickets to show the increase for Saturday and Sunday.

4 Assess

Formative Assessment

- **Explain what to do when you use the guess and check strategy and your first guess does not solve the problem.** Change your next guess by raising or lowering the values depending on whether the first try was too high or too low.

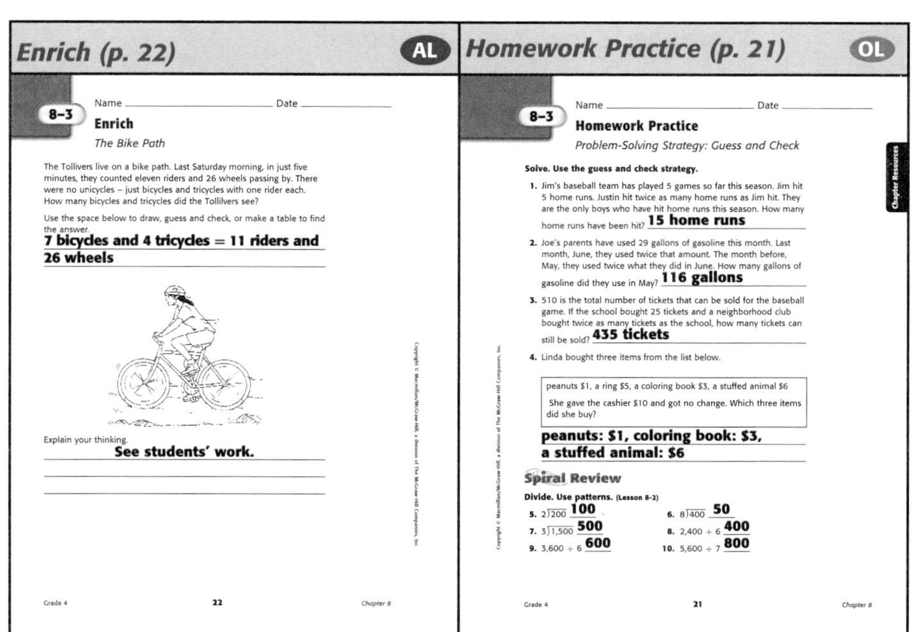

Enrich (p. 22) AL

8-3 Name ________ Date ________

Enrich

The Bike Path

The Tollivers live on a bike path. Last Saturday morning, in just five minutes, they counted eleven riders and 26 wheels passing by. There were no unicycles – just bicycles and tricycles with one rider each. How many bicycles and tricycles did the Tollilvers see?

Use the space below to draw, guess and check, or make a table to find the answer.

7 bicycles and 4 tricycles = 11 riders and 26 wheels

Explain your thinking.
See students' work.

Homework Practice (p. 21) OL

8-3 Name ________ Date ________

Homework Practice

Problem-Solving Strategy: Guess and Check

Chapter Resources

Solve. Use the guess and check strategy.

1. Jim's baseball team has played 5 games so far this season. Jim hit 5 home runs. Justin hit twice as many home runs as Jim hit. They are the only boys who have hit home runs this season. How many home runs have been hit? **15 home runs**
2. Joe's parents have used 29 gallons of gasoline this month. Last month, June, they used twice that amount. The month before, May, they used twice what they did in June. How many gallons of gasoline did they use in May? **116 gallons**
3. 510 is the total number of tickets that can be sold for the baseball game. If the school bought 25 tickets and a neighborhood club bought twice as many tickets as the school, how many tickets can still be sold? **435 tickets**
4. Linda bought three items from the list below.

peanuts $1, a ring $5, a coloring book $3, a stuffed animal $6

She gave the cashier $10 and got no change. Which three items did she buy?

peanuts: $1, coloring book: $3, a stuffed animal: $6

Spiral Review

Divide. Use patterns. (Lesson 8-2)

5. 2)200 **100**
6. 8)400 **50**
7. 3)1,500 **500**
8. 2,400 ÷ 6 **400**
9. 3,600 ÷ 6 **600**
10. 5,600 ÷ 7 **800**

Quick Check

Are students continuing to struggle using the guess and check strategy?

If Yes → CRM Reteach Worksheets (pp. 18–19)

If No → Independent Work Options (p. 320B)
CRM Skills Practice Worksheet (p. 20)
CRM Enrich Worksheet (p. 22)

! COMMON ERROR!

Exercise 5 Students are often overwhelmed by the information and cannot give a first, logical guess. Encourage them to focus on the understand part of the four-step problem-solving plan.

LESSON 8-4

Estimate Quotients

Lesson Planner

Objective

Estimate quotients.

Vocabulary

compatible numbers

Resources

Literature Connection: *The Great Divide* by Dayle Ann Dodds

Alternate Lesson: Use *IMPACT Mathematics:* Unit C to provide practice with estimation.

Teacher Technology

Interactive Classroom: TeacherWorks

Daily Routine

Use these suggestions before beginning the lesson on p. 322.

5-Minute Check

(Reviews Lesson 8-3)

Solve. Use the guess and check strategy.

A unicycle has one wheel and a bicycle has two. Steve walks into Hanson's Cycling Shop and counts 19 unicycles and bicycles, and 27 wheels. How many unicycles are there? 11 unicycles

Problem of the Day

Mrs. Washer wrote checks for $421 and $375. Her bank account now has $1,873 in it. How much money was in her bank account before she wrote the checks? $2,669

Focus on Math Background

In the real world, people probably estimate quotients more often than they find an exact quotient. As with estimating products, estimating quotients depends on a student's recall of the basic facts. There are two main reasons why students should be able to estimate quotients: (1) when using the division algorithm, students need to estimate each time they place a digit in the quotient and (2) estimation can be used to check to see than an exact quotient is reasonable.

Building Math Vocabulary

Write the lesson vocabulary term and its definition on the board.

Write the following on the board:

$13 \div 3$ $12 \div 3$ $17 \div 5$
$15 \div 5$ $30 \div 6$ $32 \div 6$

Have volunteers circle the expressions that show compatible numbers and have them explain why they are compatible. $12 \div 3$, $15 \div 5$, $30 \div 6$; Sample answer: These numbers are easy to divide mentally.

Visual Vocabulary Cards

Use Visual Vocabulary Card 5 to reinforce the vocabulary introduced in this lesson. (The Define/Example/Ask routine is printed on the back of each card.)

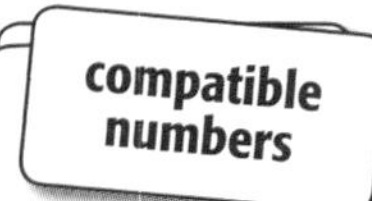

Differentiated Instruction

Small Group Options

LINGUISTIC

Option 1 Gifted and Talented AL

Materials: paper and pencil

- Tell the students: Use the information in the Data File again. The Valdez family asks a cousin to go along on another hut hike because the total cost is the same. About how much will it cost per person now that there are 6 members in the group? about $400
- A football field is 100 yards long from goal line to goal line. Is Harold's climb longer or shorter? longer
- About how much difference is there between Harold's climb and a football field? about 20 yards

LOGICAL

Option 2 English Language Learners ELL

Materials: chalkboard

Core Vocabulary: use your finger, about/actual, everything but

Common Use Verb: scan

Do Math This strategy gives students choices of matching to increase comprehensibility.

324 divided by 8

$8 \times 1 = 8, 8 \times 2 = 16, 8 \times 3 = 24, 8 \times 4 = 32, 8 \times 5 = 40, 8 \times 6 = 48, 8 \times 7 = 56, 8 \times 8 = 64, 8 \times 9 = 72, 8 \times 10 = 80$

- Write the division problem $324 \div 8$ on the board.
- Model using your fingers to cover up the 24 and say: "Scan the 8 times table for the number 3."
- Repeat, covering 4 and scanning for 32.
- When students find the 32, say: "You can use your 8 × facts to get a close answer."
- Have students work the problem and decide if the estimate is close to the actual answer. Ask students how $32 \div 8$ relates to $324 \div 8$.

Use this worksheet to provide additional support for English Language Learners.

English Language Learners (p. 93) ELL

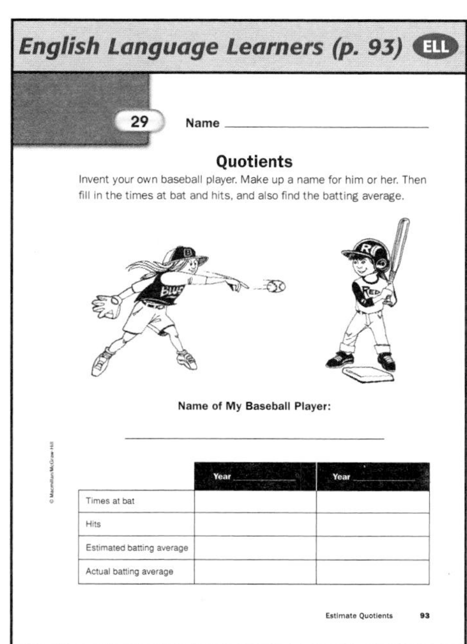

29 Name ____________

Quotients

Invent your own baseball player. Make up a name for him or her. Then fill in the times at bat and hits, and also find the batting average.

Name of My Baseball Player: ____________

	Year ____	Year ____
Times at bat		
Hits		
Estimated batting average		
Actual batting average		

Estimate Quotients 93

Independent Work Options

LOGICAL, SOCIAL

Option 1 Early Finishers OL AL

Materials: paper and pencil

- For Exercises 9–16, have students decide if their estimates are greater than or less than the exact quotient. Have them explain how they know.

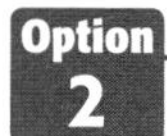

Option 2 Student Technology

Math Online macmillanmh.com

Personal Tutor • Extra Examples

Math Adventures

Option 3 Learning Station: Social Studies (p. 308G)

Direct students to the Social Studies Learning Station for opportunities to explore and extend the lesson concept.

Option 4 Problem-Solving Practice

Reinforce problem-solving skills and strategies with the Problem-Solving Practice worksheet.

Problem Solving (p. 26) BL OL AL

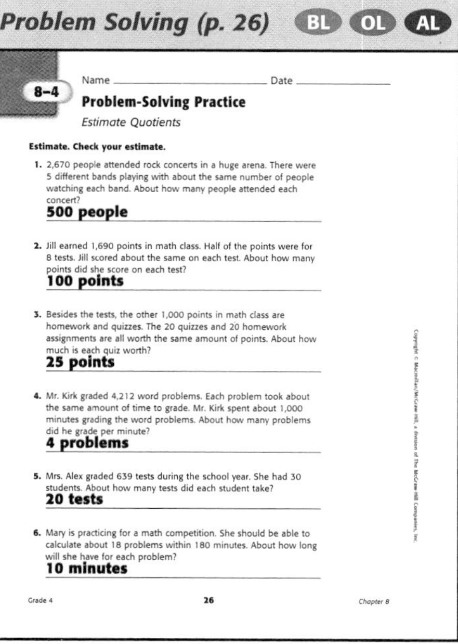

Name ____________ Date ____________

8–4 **Problem-Solving Practice**

Estimate Quotients

Estimate. Check your estimate.

1. 2,670 people attended rock concerts in a huge arena. There were 5 different bands playing with about the same number of people watching each band. About how many people attended each concert? **500 people**
2. Jill earned 1,690 points in math class. Half of the points were for 8 tests. Jill scored about the same on each test. About how many points did she score on each test? **100 points**
3. Besides the tests, the other 1,000 points in math class are homework and quizzes. The 20 quizzes and 20 homework assignments are all worth the same amount of points. About how much is each quiz worth? **25 points**
4. Mr. Kirk graded 4,212 word problems. Each problem took about the same amount of time to grade. Mr. Kirk spent about 1,000 minutes grading the word problems. About how many problems did he grade per minute? **4 problems**
5. Mrs. Alex graded 639 tests during the school year. She had 30 students. About how many tests did each student take? **20 tests**
6. Mary is practicing for a math competition. She should be able to calculate about 18 problems within 180 minutes. About how long will she have for each problem? **10 minutes**

Grade 4 26 Chapter 8

8-4 Estimate Quotients

1 Introduce

Activity Choice 1 • Hands-On 

- Review basic facts with students by having volunteers write various multiplication and division basic facts on the board.
- Remind students that compatible numbers are numbers that are easy to divide. Tell them that 35 and 7 are compatible numbers because they know that 35 ÷ 7 = 5. Point out that 350 and 7 are also compatible because they know that 350 ÷ 7 = 50.
- Have students write on the board several examples of compatible numbers. Sample answers: 42 and 6; 4,200 and 6; 72 and 8

Activity Choice 2 • Literature

Introduce the lesson with *The Great Divide* by Dayle Ann Dodds. For a related math activity, see p. TR54.

2 Teach

Scaffolding Questions

Write the following on the board: 64 ÷ 7.

- **How can you change the dividend so the numbers are compatible and the quotient can be estimated mentally?** change it to 63 or 70
- **Explain which multiple of 7 is the better choice.** 63 is the better choice because it is closer to 64.

Repeat these questions using the problem 533 ÷ 6. The dividend could be changed to 480, 540, or 600. 540 is the best choice.

GET READY to Learn

Have students open their books and read the information in **Get Ready to Learn**. Introduce **compatible numbers**. As a class, work through **Examples 1 and 2**.

8-4 Estimate Quotients

MAIN IDEA

I will estimate quotients.

New Vocabulary

compatible numbers

Math Online

macmillanmh.com

- Extra Examples
- Personal Tutor
- Self-Check Quiz

GET READY to Learn

Circuses have been around for more than 200 years. They sometimes travel by train. Suppose a circus travels 642 miles in 8 hours. *About* how many miles per hour did the train travel?

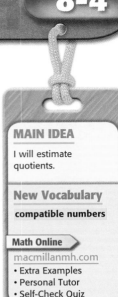

There are different ways to estimate quotients. One way is to use compatible numbers. **Compatible numbers** are numbers that are easy to divide mentally.

Real-World EXAMPLE Estimate Quotients

1 MEASUREMENT **Estimate the quotient of 642 and 8 to find how fast the train is traveling.**

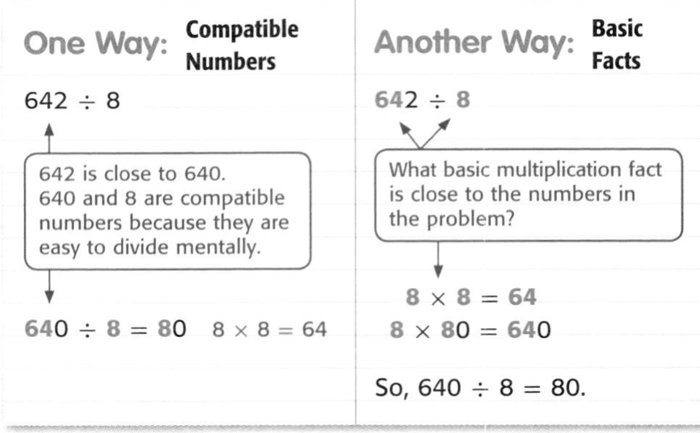

One Way: Compatible Numbers	Another Way: Basic Facts
642 ÷ 8	642 ÷ 8
642 is close to 640. 640 and 8 are compatible numbers because they are easy to divide mentally.	What basic multiplication fact is close to the numbers in the problem?
	8 × 8 = 64
640 ÷ 8 = 80 8 × 8 = 64	8 × 80 = 640
	So, 640 ÷ 8 = 80.

So, the circus train is traveling about 80 miles per hour.

Check

You know that 640 ÷ 8 = 80 because 8 × 80 = 640. ✓

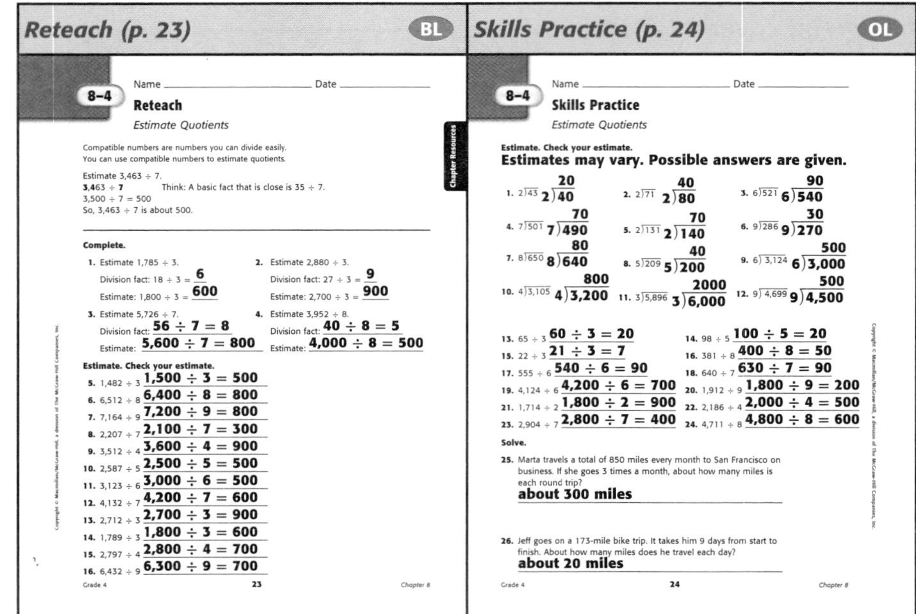

Reteach (p. 23) BL

8-4 Name ______ Date ______

Reteach

Estimate Quotients

Compatible numbers are numbers you can divide easily.
You can use compatible numbers to estimate quotients.

Estimate 3,463 ÷ 7.
3,463 ÷ **7**   Think: A basic fact that is close is 35 ÷ 7.
3,500 ÷ 7 = 500
So, 3,463 ÷ 7 is about 500.

Complete.

1. Estimate 1,785 ÷ 3.
   Division fact: 18 ÷ 3 = **6**
   Estimate: 1,800 ÷ 3 = **600**
2. Estimate 2,880 ÷ 3.
   Division fact: 27 ÷ 3 = **9**
   Estimate: 2,700 ÷ 3 = **900**
3. Estimate 5,726 ÷ 7.
   Division fact: **56 ÷ 7 = 8**
   Estimate: **5,600 ÷ 7 = 800**
4. Estimate 3,952 ÷ 8.
   Division fact: **40 ÷ 8 = 5**
   Estimate: **4,000 ÷ 8 = 500**

Estimate. Check your estimate.

5. 1,482 ÷ 3 **1,500 ÷ 3 = 500**
6. 6,512 ÷ 8 **6,400 ÷ 8 = 800**
7. 7,164 ÷ 9 **7,200 ÷ 9 = 800**
8. 2,207 ÷ 7 **2,100 ÷ 7 = 300**
9. 3,512 ÷ 4 **3,600 ÷ 4 = 900**
10. 2,587 ÷ 5 **2,500 ÷ 5 = 500**
11. 3,123 ÷ 6 **3,000 ÷ 6 = 500**
12. 4,132 ÷ 7 **4,200 ÷ 7 = 600**
13. 2,712 ÷ 3 **2,700 ÷ 3 = 900**
14. 1,789 ÷ 3 **1,800 ÷ 3 = 600**
15. 2,797 ÷ 4 **2,800 ÷ 4 = 700**
16. 6,432 ÷ 9 **6,300 ÷ 9 = 700**

Grade 4   23   Chapter 8

Chapter Resources

Skills Practice (p. 24) OL

8-4 Name ______ Date ______

Skills Practice

Estimate Quotients

Estimate. Check your estimate.

Estimates may vary. Possible answers are given.

1. $2\overline{)43}$ **$2\overline{)40}$ = 20**
2. $2\overline{)71}$ **$2\overline{)80}$ = 40**
3. $6\overline{)521}$ **$6\overline{)540}$ = 90**
4. $7\overline{)501}$ **$7\overline{)490}$ = 70**
5. $2\overline{)131}$ **$2\overline{)140}$ = 70**
6. $9\overline{)286}$ **$9\overline{)270}$ = 30**
7. $8\overline{)650}$ **$8\overline{)640}$ = 80**
8. $5\overline{)209}$ **$5\overline{)200}$ = 40**
9. $6\overline{)3,124}$ **$6\overline{)3,000}$ = 500**
10. $4\overline{)3,105}$ **$4\overline{)3,200}$ = 800**
11. $3\overline{)5,896}$ **$3\overline{)6,000}$ = 2000**
12. $9\overline{)4,699}$ **$9\overline{)4,500}$ = 500**
13. 65 ÷ 3 **60 ÷ 3 = 20**
14. 98 ÷ 5 **100 ÷ 5 = 20**
15. 22 ÷ 3 **21 ÷ 3 = 7**
16. 381 ÷ 8 **400 ÷ 8 = 50**
17. 555 ÷ 6 **540 ÷ 6 = 90**
18. 640 ÷ 7 **630 ÷ 7 = 90**
19. 4,124 ÷ 6 **4,200 ÷ 6 = 700**
20. 1,912 ÷ 9 **1,800 ÷ 9 = 200**
21. 1,714 ÷ 2 **1,800 ÷ 2 = 900**
22. 2,186 ÷ 4 **2,000 ÷ 4 = 500**
23. 2,904 ÷ 7 **2,800 ÷ 7 = 400**
24. 4,711 ÷ 8 **4,800 ÷ 8 = 600**

Solve.

25. Marta travels a total of 850 miles every month to San Francisco on business. If she goes 3 times a month, about how many miles is each round trip?
    about 300 miles
26. Jeff goes on a 173-mile bike trip. It takes him 9 days from start to finish. About how many miles does he travel each day?
    about 20 miles

Grade 4   24   Chapter 8

Real-World EXAMPLE Estimate Quotients

2 DOLLS **Isabella has 6 dolls in her doll collection. The collection is worth $1,168. Each doll is worth the same amount of money. About how much is each doll worth?**

You need to estimate $1,168 ÷ 6.

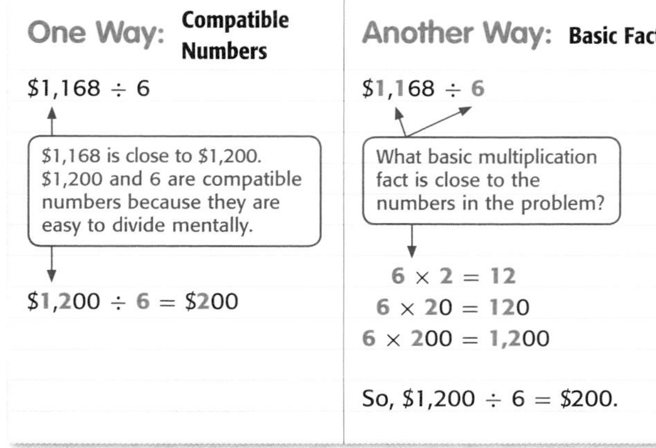

One Way: Compatible Numbers

$1,168 ÷ 6

$1,168 is close to $1,200. $1,200 and 6 are compatible numbers because they are easy to divide mentally.

$1,200 ÷ 6 = $200

Another Way: Basic Facts

$1,168 ÷ 6

What basic multiplication fact is close to the numbers in the problem?

6 × 2 = 12
6 × 20 = 120
6 × 200 = 1,200

So, $1,200 ÷ 6 = $200.

So, each doll is worth about $200.

Check

You know that $1,200 ÷ 6 = $200 because 6 × $200 = $1,200. ✓

8. Sample answer: $4,782 ÷ 6 ⟶ $4,800 ÷ 6 because 6 × 8 = 48.

CHECK What You Know

Estimate. Check your estimate. See Examples 1 and 2 (pp. 322–323)

1. 161 ÷ 4 160 ÷ 4 = 40
2. $424 ÷ 6 $420 ÷ 6 = $70
3. 715 ÷ 8 720 ÷ 8 = 90
4. 2,660 ÷ 9 2,700 ÷ 9 = 300
5. $5,643 ÷ 8 $5,600 ÷ 8 = $700
6. 8,099 ÷ 9 8,100 ÷ 9 = 900

7. On Saturday, 1,164 people saw a movie at Upcity Theater. There were a total of 4 movie screens with the same number of people in each audience. About how many people watched each screen? 1,200 ÷ 4 = 300

8. Talk About It Explain how to estimate $4,782 ÷ 6.

Enrich (p. 27) AL

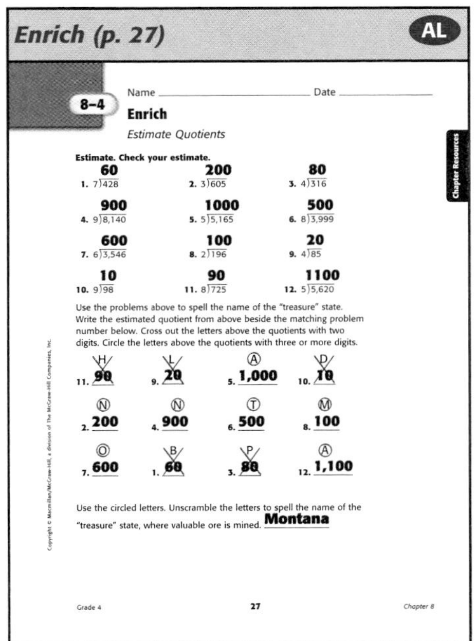

8-4 Name ______ Date ______
Enrich
Estimate Quotients

Estimate. Check your estimate.

1. 7)428 **60**
2. 3)605 **200**
3. 4)316 **80**
4. 9)8,140 **900**
5. 5)5,165 **1000**
6. 8)3,999 **500**
7. 6)3,546 **600**
8. 2)196 **100**
9. 4)85 **20**
10. 9)98 **10**
11. 8)725 **90**
12. 5)5,620 **1100**

Use the problems above to spell the name of the "treasure" state. Write the estimated quotient from above beside the matching problem number below. Cross out the letters above the quotients with two digits. Circle the letters above the quotients with three or more digits.

H	L	A	D
11. 90	9. 20	5. 1,000	10. 10

N	N	T	M
2. 200	4. 900	6. 500	8. 100

O	B	P	A
7. 600	1. 60	3. 80	12. 1,100

Use the circled letters. Unscramble the letters to spell the name of the "treasure" state, where valuable ore is mined. **Montana**

Grade 4 27 Chapter 8

Estimate Quotients

Example 1 Tell students that rounding numbers when you estimate quotients does not necessarily make division easier. Point out that rounding 642 to 600 in this example does not help you with the division, but if you use a compatible number such as 640, the division is easier.

ADDITIONAL EXAMPLES

1 A small wading pool holds 225 gallons of water and it takes 3 hours to fill. About how many gallons are put into the pool in one hour? Estimate the quotient of 225 and 3. 210 ÷ 3 = 70 gallons

2 The hotdog stand at the school carnival earned $1,215 today and sold only $4 combination meals. About how many meals did they sell? $1,200 ÷ $4 = 300 meals

CHECK What You Know

As a class, have students complete Exercises 1–8 in **Check What You Know** as you observe their work.

Exercise 8 Assess student comprehension before assigning practice exercises.

BL Alternate Teaching Strategy

If students have trouble finding compatible numbers…

Then use one of these reteach options:

1 CRM **Daily Reteach Worksheet** (p. 23)

2 Review dividing multiples of 10, 100, and 1,000. Also, for some students a multiplication table might be helpful. Point out that students who need a table should focus on the divisor when searching for a compatible number.

3 Practice

Differentiate practice using these leveled assignments for Exercises 9–26.

Level	Assignment
BL Below/Approaching Level	9–16, 21, 23
OL On Level	10–20, 22–24, 25
AL Above/Beyond Level	9–23 odd, 25–26

Have students discuss and complete the Higher Order Thinking problems. Have students write the basic division facts for Exercises 25 and 26.

WRITING IN MATH Have students complete Exercise 26 in their Math Journals. You may choose to use this exercise as an optional formative assessment.

4 Assess

Formative Assessment

Have students estimate 412 ÷ 6. Ask them to explain how they made their estimates.
70; Sample answer: I changed 412 to 420 because 42 is compatible with 6. I know that 42 ÷ 6 is 7, so 420 ÷ 6 = 70.

Quick Check **Are students continuing to struggle with estimating quotients?**

If Yes → Small Group Options (p. 322B)

If No → Independent Work Options (p. 322B)
CRM Skills Practice Worksheet (p. 24)
CRM Enrich Worksheet (p. 27)

Into the Future Tell students that in the next lesson they will solve problems like 327 ÷ 5. Ask students to write how they think today's lesson on estimating quotients will help with this new lesson.

COMMON ERROR!

Exercises 21 and 22 Some students may give an exact answer to these problems. Remind them that the word *about* indicates that an estimate is wanted.

Practice and Problem Solving

Estimate. Check your estimate. See Examples 1 and 2 (pp. 322–323)

9. 123 ÷ 3 — 120 ÷ 3 = 40
10. \$244 ÷ 6 — \$240 ÷ 6 = \$40
11. 162 ÷ 2 — 160 ÷ 2 = 80
12. 345 ÷ 7 — 350 ÷ 7 = 50
13. \$538 ÷ 6 — \$540 ÷ 6 = \$90
14. 415 ÷ 6 — 420 ÷ 6 = 70
15. \$1,406 ÷ 7 — \$1,400 ÷ 7 = \$200
16. 2,431 ÷ 8 — 2,400 ÷ 8 = 300
17. \$2,719 ÷ 9 — \$2,700 ÷ 9 = \$300
18. 4,187 ÷ 7 — 4,200 ÷ 7 = 600
19. \$7,160 ÷ 9 — \$7,200 ÷ 9 = \$800
20. 8,052 ÷ 9 — 8,100 ÷ 9 = 900

21. Terrence earned 806 points on 9 tests. If he earned about the same number of points on each test, about how many points did he earn on each test? 810 ÷ 9 = 90

22. **Measurement** Gloria ran 1,575 miles in 8 months. If she runs the same number of miles each month, about how many miles does she run each month? 1,600 ÷ 8 = 200

Data File

Hut hiking involves hiking and spending the night in huts instead of tents. You can go hut hiking on the Appalachian Trail. This trail starts in Maine, runs through New Jersey, and ends in Georgia.

23. The total cost for the 5 members in the Valdez family to hut hike for 6 days is \$2,475. About how much does it cost for each family member? \$2,500 ÷ 5 = \$500

24. **Measurement** Harold needs to climb a 361-foot hill to get to the next hut. About how many yards away is he from the next hut? (*Remember:* 3 feet = 1 yard) 360 ÷ 3 = 120 yards

26. Sample answer: The estimated dividend is less than the actual dividend, so the estimated quotient will be less than the actual quotient.

H.O.T. Problems

25. **OPEN ENDED** The estimated quotient of a division sentence is 200. What could the division sentence be? Sample answer: 1,755 ÷ 9 → 1,800 ÷ 9 = 200

26. **WRITING IN MATH** Estimate 5,425 ÷ 6 using 5,400 ÷ 6. Is the estimate greater than or less than the actual quotient? Explain.

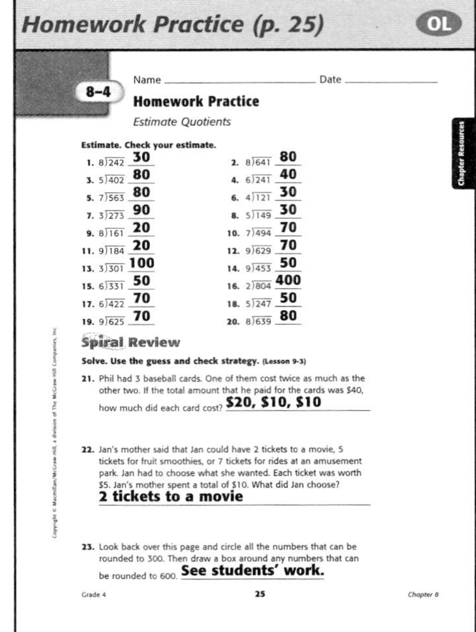

Homework Practice (p. 25) OL

8–4 Name ______ Date ______

Homework Practice

Estimate Quotients

Estimate. Check your estimate.

1. 8)242 **30**
2. 8)641 **80**
3. 5)402 **80**
4. 6)241 **40**
5. 7)563 **80**
6. 4)121 **30**
7. 3)273 **90**
8. 5)149 **30**
9. 8)161 **20**
10. 7)494 **70**
11. 9)184 **20**
12. 9)629 **70**
13. 3)301 **100**
14. 9)453 **50**
15. 6)331 **50**
16. 2)804 **400**
17. 6)422 **70**
18. 5)247 **50**
19. 9)625 **70**
20. 8)639 **80**

Spiral Review

Solve. Use the guess and check strategy. (Lesson 9-3)

21. Phil had 3 baseball cards. One of them cost twice as much as the other two. If the total amount that he paid for the cards was \$40, how much did each card cost? **\$20, \$10, \$10**

22. Jan's mother said that Jan could have 2 tickets to a movie, 5 tickets for fruit smoothies, or 7 tickets for rides at an amusement park. Jan had to choose what she wanted. Each ticket was worth \$5. Jan's mother spent a total of \$10. What did Jan choose? **2 tickets to a movie**

23. Look back over this page and circle all the numbers that can be rounded to 300. Then draw a box around any numbers that can be rounded to 600. **See students' work.**

Chapter Resources

Grade 4 25 Chapter 8

CHAPTER 8

Mid-Chapter Check

Lessons 8-1 through 8-4

Divide. Check each answer. (Lesson 8-1)

1. $92 \div 3$ 30 R2 **2.** $37 \div 2$ 18 R1

3. Gwen earns $5 an hour delivering newspapers. If she earned $35 this week, how many hours did she spend delivering newspapers? (Lesson 8-1) 7

4. MULTIPLE CHOICE Gabriel solved the problem below. Which expression could be used to check his answer? (Lesson 8-1) B

$136 \div 5 = 27$ R1

A $(27 \times 1) + 5$ **C** $(27 + 5) \times 1$

B $(27 \times 5) + 1$ **D** $(27 + 1) \times 5$

Copy and complete each set of patterns. (Lesson 8-2)

5. $42 \div 7 =$ ▒
$420 \div 7 =$ ▒
$4{,}200 \div 7 =$ ▒
6; 60; 600

6. $25 \div 5 =$ ▒
$250 \div 5 =$ ▒
$2{,}500 \div 5 =$ ▒
5; 50; 500

Divide. Use patterns. (Lesson 8-2)

7. $150 \div 5$ 30 **8.** $600 \div 2$ 300

9. Measurement Cheri has 200 minutes left on her cell phone plan for the last five days of the month. If Cheri uses the same number of minutes each day, how many minutes can Cheri use her cell phone each day? (Lesson 8-2) 40

Solve. Use the guess and check strategy. (Lesson 8-3)

10. Patricia and Ashley collect stamps. Patricia has 13 more stamps than Ashley. Together they have 229 stamps. How many stamps do Patricia and Ashley each have? Patricia: 121; Ashley: 108

11. Dion bought three of the items shown below. He gave the cashier $10 and received $1 in change. Which three items did he buy?

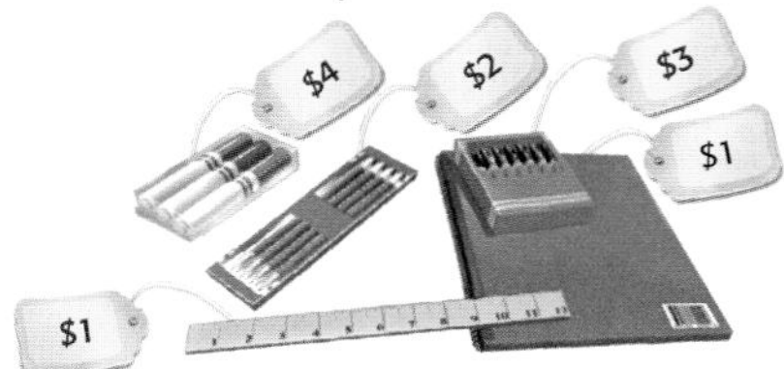

crayons, pencils, and markers

Estimate. Check your estimate. (Lesson 8-4)

12. $156 \div 3$ **13.** $182 \div 9$

12. $150 \div 3 = 50$; $3 \times 50 = 150$
13. $180 \div 9 = 20$; $9 \times 20 = 180$

14. MULTIPLE CHOICE Vikas drove 325 miles in five hours. Approximately how many miles did Vikas drive each hour? (Lesson 8-4) F

F 60 **H** 68

G 64 **J** 70

15. See Ch. 8 Answer Appendix.

15. WRITING IN MATH If you estimate $4{,}225 \div 6$ using $4{,}200 \div 6$, is the estimate greater than or less than the actual quotient? Explain. (Lesson 8-4)

CHAPTER 8

Mid-Chapter Check

Lessons 8-1 through 8-4

Formative Assessment

Use the Mid-Chapter Check to assess students' progress in the first half of the chapter.

Customize and create multiple versions of your Mid-Chapter Check and the test answer keys.

FOLDABLES Dinah Zike's Foldables

Use these lesson suggestions to incorporate the Foldables during the chapter.

Lesson 8-1 Students record notes, define terms, and solve problems dividing two-digit numbers on quarter sheets of paper or index cards and store in the first pocket of the first pocket book Foldable.

Lesson 8-4 Students demonstrate their ability to estimate quotients on quarter sheets of paper or index cards and store in the second pocket of the pocket book Foldable.

Data-Driven Decision Making

Based on the results of the Mid-Chapter Check, use the following resources to review concepts that continue to give students problems.

Exercises	State/Local Standard	What's the Math?	Error Analysis	Resources for Review
1–4 Lesson 8-1		Divide by one-digit numbers with and without remainders.	Does not know multiplication facts.	Strategic Intervention Guide (pp. 78, 86) CRM Chapter 8 Resource Masters (Reteach Worksheets) Math Adventures My Math Zone Chapter 8 Math Online Extra Examples • Concepts in Motion
5–9 Lesson 8-2		Use basic multiples of 10, 100, and 1,000 and their patterns to divide.	Does not know multiplication facts. Does not recognize patterns of multiples of 10.	
12–15 Lesson 8-4		Estimate quotients. Use "less than" or "greater than" to compare number sentences.	Uses wrong place value of number to estimate. Reverses signs for comparing number sentences.	

LESSON 8-5 Two-Digit Quotients

Lesson Planner

Objective

Solve division problems that result in two-digit quotients.

Review Vocabulary

remainder

Resources

Materials: grid paper

Manipulatives: two-colored counters; base-ten blocks

Literature Connection: *Chewing Gum* by Elaine Landau

Teacher Technology
TeacherWorks • Interactive Classroom

Daily Routine

Use these suggestions before beginning the lesson on p. 326.

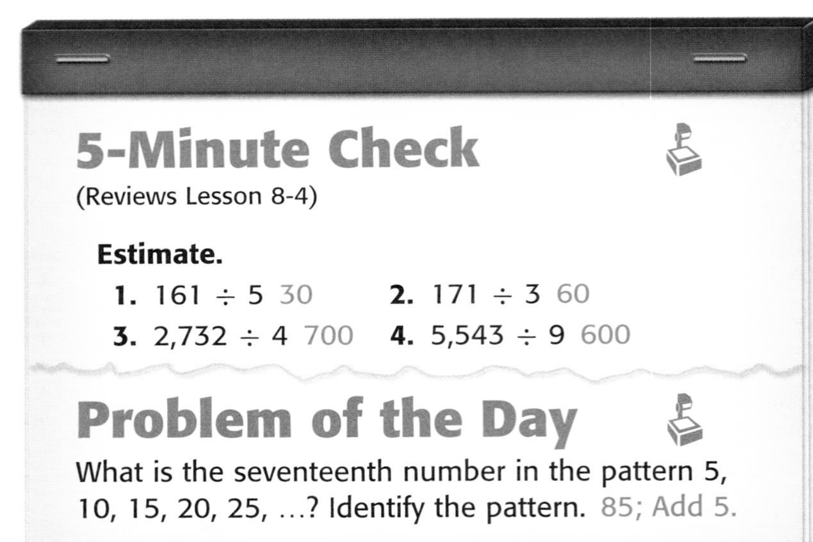

5-Minute Check

(Reviews Lesson 8-4)

Estimate.

1. 161 ÷ 5 30 **2.** 171 ÷ 3 60

3. 2,732 ÷ 4 700 **4.** 5,543 ÷ 9 600

Problem of the Day

What is the seventeenth number in the pattern 5, 10, 15, 20, 25, ...? Identify the pattern. 85; Add 5.

Focus on Math Background

This lesson focuses on dividing two- and three-digit numbers by one-digit numbers to get two-digit quotients. It is important for students to see that the standard algorithm is not meaningless. As students move from the concrete model that uses base-ten blocks to the standard algorithm, sometimes an intermediate approach, often referred to as the pyramid algorithm, is useful. For example,

$$\begin{array}{r} \underline{37} \\ 7 \\ 30 \\ 4\overline{)148} \\ \underline{-120} \\ 28 \\ \underline{-28} \\ 0 \end{array}$$

Review Math Vocabulary

Write the review vocabulary word and its definition on the board.

Have students use 20 two-colored counters and model the quotient 20 ÷ 3. Have students draw a picture to explain the remainder of the quotient.

Differentiated Instruction

Small Group Options

SPATIAL, KINESTHETIC

Option 1 Below Level BL

Materials: place-value models, construction paper

Use this activity to help students make the connections from concrete to pictorial to abstract representations for division. Provide support and prompting as needed. Have students:

- Model 56 ÷ 4 using manipulatives.
- Draw a picture of their model.
- Record the division. 56 ÷ 4 = 14
- Show the algorithm.
- Reinforce by reminding students to check their answers using multiplication or subtraction.

AUDITORY

Option 2 English Language Learners ELL

Materials: picture of divers at a swimming pool
Core Vocabulary: into, sounds like, pool
Common Use Verb: dive into

Hear Math This strategy clarifies how to use the preposition *into* when reading division problems.

- Post 16 ÷ 4 and say: "4 divided into 16 is one way to read 16 ÷ 4."
- Show a picture of 4 people diving into a swimming pool. Pantomime diving.
- Say, "4 **dive** into the pool sounds like 4 **divided** into 16."
- Write 42 ÷ 7 and have students pantomime 7 people diving into a pool.
- Allow students to practice. Say, "7 divided into 42 is ___."
- Repeat for other problems as time permits.

Independent Work Options

LINGUISTIC, AUDITORY

Option 1 Early Finishers OL AL

Materials: index cards

- Have students contribute to a word problem file for the class. Have students write word problems that use division. On one side of an index card, they write problem. On the other side of the card, they write the answer to the problem.
- Students can exchange cards and solve the problems. They can check their answers by turning the cards over.

Option 2 Student Technology

Math Online macmillanmh.com

Personal Tutor • Extra Examples

Option 3 Learning Station: Music (p. 308H)

Direct students to the Music Learning Station for opportunities to explore and extend the lesson concept.

Option 4 Problem-Solving Practice

Reinforce problem-solving skills and strategies with the Problem-Solving Practice worksheet.

Problem-Solving (p. 31) BL OL AL

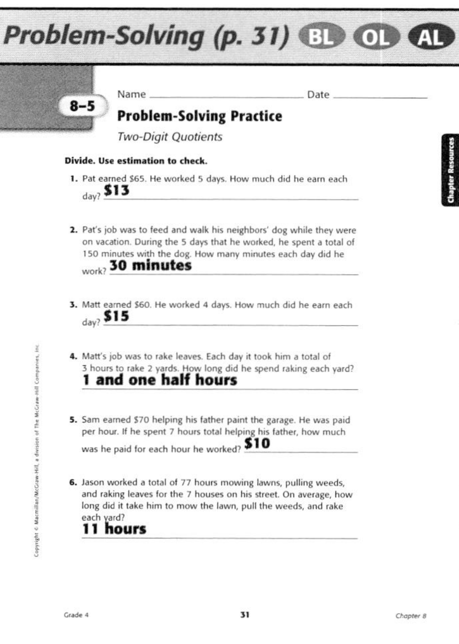

Name ______ Date ______

8–5 **Problem-Solving Practice**

Two-Digit Quotients

Divide. Use estimation to check.

1. Pat earned $65. He worked 5 days. How much did he earn each day? **$13**
2. Pat's job was to feed and walk his neighbors' dog while they were on vacation. During the 5 days that he worked, he spent a total of 150 minutes with the dog. How many minutes each day did he work? **30 minutes**
3. Matt earned $60. He worked 4 days. How much did he earn each day? **$15**
4. Matt's job was to rake leaves. Each day it took him a total of 3 hours to rake 2 yards. How long did he spend raking each yard? **1 and one half hours**
5. Sam earned $70 helping his father paint the garage. He was paid per hour. If he spent 7 hours total helping his father, how much was he paid for each hour he worked? **$10**
6. Jason worked a total of 77 hours mowing lawns, pulling weeds, and raking leaves for the 7 houses on his street. On average, how long did it take him to mow the lawn, pull the weeds, and rake each yard? **11 hours**

Chapter Resources

Grade 4 31 Chapter 8

8-5 Two-Digit Quotients

1 Introduce

Activity Choice 1 • Hands-On 

- Assign partners. One student uses base-ten blocks to model the number 79. The partner identifies the place value of each digit.
- Together, partners divide the blocks equally. This task requires trading blocks.
- Then, together, partners write a division sentence that shows the sharing they did. $79 \div 2 = 39$ R1

Activity Choice 2 • Literature

Introduce the lesson with *Chewing Gum* by Elaine Landau. For a related math activity, see p. TR54.

2 Teach

Scaffolding Questions

Use $99 \div 4$ to review the division algorithm. Show the division on the board:

```
   24
 4)99
  -8↓
   19
  -16
    3
```

- **What do you divide first?** the tens
- **How do you know where to place the first digit in the quotient?** Sample answer: There are 2 groups of 4 tens in 9 tens, so a 2 goes in the tens place.
- **Then what do you do?** multiply, subtract, and compare
- **What gets done next? Explain.** Sample answer: You bring down the ones, divide the ones, multiply, and subtract.
- **How do you know when you are finished dividing?** Sample answer: when there are no more numbers to bring down
- **What is the remainder in this problem?** 3

GET READY to Learn

Have students open their books and read the information in **Get Ready to Learn**. Review **remainder**. As a class, work through **Examples 1 and 2**.

8-5 Two-Digit Quotients

MAIN IDEA

I will solve division problems that result in two-digit quotients.

Math Online

macmillanmh.com

- Extra Examples
- Personal Tutor
- Self-Check Quiz

GET READY to Learn

More than 75% of the world's geysers are found in Yellowstone National Park. Suppose one of Yellowstone's geysers erupts every 7 minutes, how many times does it erupt in 95 minutes?

Recall that to divide a two-digit number by a one-digit number, you need to divide the tens, then divide the ones.

Real-World EXAMPLE Two-Digit Quotients

1 How many times does the geyser erupt in 95 minutes?

The geyser erupts every 7 minutes. You need to find the number of times it erupts in 95 minutes. So, find $95 \div 7$.

Estimate $95 \div 7 \longrightarrow 100 \div 10 = 10$

Step 1 Divide the tens.

```
   1      Divide. 9 ÷ 7 = 1
 7)95     Put 1 in the quotient over the tens place.
  -7      Multiply. 7 × 1 = 7
   2      Subtract. 9 − 7 = 2
          Compare. 2 < 7
```

Step 2 Divide the ones.

```
   13 R4   Bring down the ones.
 7)95      Divide. 25 ÷ 7 = 3
  -7↓      Put 3 in the quotient over the ones place.
   25      Multiply. 7 × 3 = 21
  -21      Subtract. 25 − 21 = 4
    4      Compare. 4 < 7
           Remainder = 4
```

So, the geyser will erupt about 13 times in 95 minutes.

Check for Reasonableness

13 is close to the estimate. The answer is reasonable. ✓

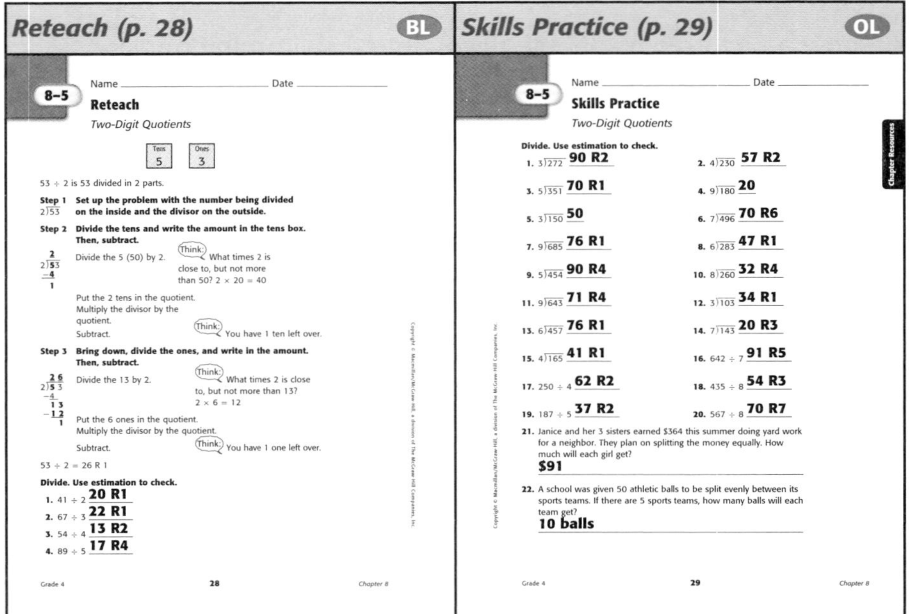

Reteach (p. 28) BL

8–5 Name ______ Date ______

Reteach

Two-Digit Quotients

Tens	Ones
5	3

$53 \div 2$ is 53 divided in 2 parts.

Step 1 $2\overline{)53}$ **Set up the problem with the number being divided on the inside and the divisor on the outside.**

Step 2 **Divide the tens and write the amount in the tens box. Then, subtract.**

Divide the 5 (50) by 2. Think: What times 2 is close to, but not more than 50? $2 \times 20 = 40$

Put the 2 tens in the quotient.
Multiply the divisor by the quotient.
Subtract. Think: You have 1 ten left over.

Step 3 **Bring down, divide the ones, and write in the amount. Then, subtract.**

Divide the 13 by 2. Think: What times 2 is close to, but not more than 13? $2 \times 6 = 12$

Put the 6 ones in the quotient.
Multiply the divisor by the quotient.
Subtract. Think: You have 1 one left over.

$53 \div 2 = 26$ R 1

Divide. Use estimation to check.

1. $41 \div 2$ **20 R1**
2. $67 \div 3$ **22 R1**
3. $54 \div 4$ **13 R2**
4. $89 \div 5$ **17 R4**

Grade 4 28 Chapter 8

Skills Practice (p. 29) OL

8–5 Name ______ Date ______

Skills Practice

Two-Digit Quotients

Divide. Use estimation to check.

1. $3\overline{)272}$ **90 R2**
2. $4\overline{)230}$ **57 R2**
3. $5\overline{)351}$ **70 R1**
4. $9\overline{)180}$ **20**
5. $3\overline{)150}$ **50**
6. $7\overline{)496}$ **70 R6**
7. $9\overline{)685}$ **76 R1**
8. $6\overline{)283}$ **47 R1**
9. $5\overline{)454}$ **90 R4**
10. $8\overline{)260}$ **32 R4**
11. $9\overline{)643}$ **71 R4**
12. $3\overline{)103}$ **34 R1**
13. $6\overline{)457}$ **76 R1**
14. $7\overline{)143}$ **20 R3**
15. $4\overline{)165}$ **41 R1**
16. $642 \div 7$ **91 R5**
17. $250 \div 4$ **62 R2**
18. $435 \div 8$ **54 R3**
19. $187 \div 5$ **37 R2**
20. $567 \div 8$ **70 R7**
21. Janice and her 3 sisters earned $364 this summer doing yard work for a neighbor. They plan on splitting the money equally. How much will each girl get? **$91**
22. A school was given 50 athletic balls to be split evenly between its sports teams. If there are 5 sports teams, how many balls will each team get? **10 balls**

Chapter Resources

Grade 4 29 Chapter 8

Sometimes it is not possible to divide the first digit of the dividend by the divisor.

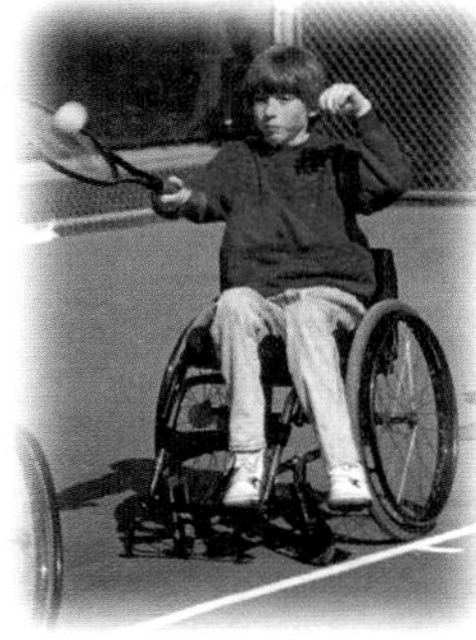

Real-World EXAMPLE Divide with Remainders

2 SPORTS **A tennis coach has 125 tennis balls. There are 4 members on the team. How many balls does each player get for practice if each player gets the same number of balls?**

There are 125 tennis balls and 4 team members. Divide 125 by 4 to find how many balls each player gets.

Estimate $125 \div 4 \longrightarrow 120 \div 4 = 30$, so about 30 balls per person

Step 1 Estimate to place the first digit.

$4\overline{)125}$

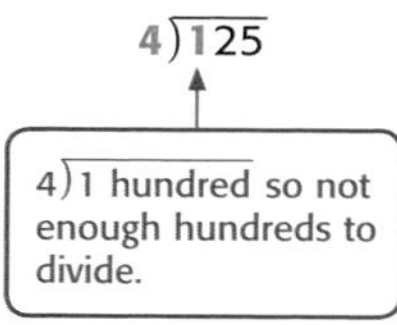

$4\overline{)1}$ hundred so not enough hundreds to divide.

x
$4\overline{)125}$

$4\overline{)12}$ tens so enough tens to divide. So, the first digit goes over the tens place.

Step 2 Divide the tens.

$$\begin{array}{r} 3 \\ 4\overline{)125} \\ -12 \\ \hline 0 \end{array}$$

Divide. $12 \div 4 = 3$
Put 3 in the quotient over the tens place.
Multiply. $4 \times 3 = 12$
Subtract. $12 - 12 = 0$
Compare. $0 < 4$

Step 3 Divide the ones.

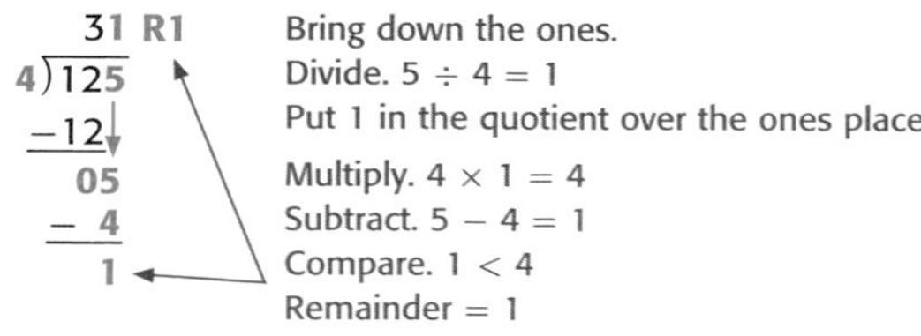

$$\begin{array}{r} 31 \text{ R1} \\ 4\overline{)125}\phantom{\text{ R1}} \\ -12\downarrow\phantom{\text{ R1}} \\ \hline 05\phantom{\text{ R1}} \\ -\ \ 4\phantom{\text{ R1}} \\ \hline 1\phantom{\text{ R1}} \end{array}$$

Bring down the ones.
Divide. $5 \div 4 = 1$
Put 1 in the quotient over the ones place.
Multiply. $4 \times 1 = 4$
Subtract. $5 - 4 = 1$
Compare. $1 < 4$
Remainder = 1

So, each team member gets 31 balls.

Check for Reasonableness
The answer is close to the estimate. So, it is reasonable. ✓

Remember
When a real-world problem has a remainder, you have to interpret the remainder.

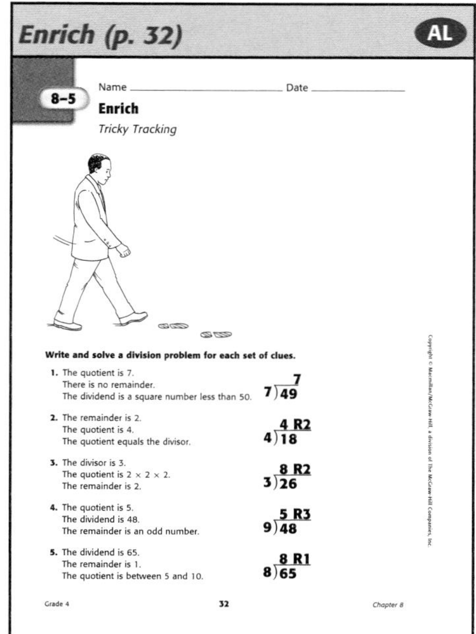

Enrich (p. 32) AL

8–5 Name ________________ Date ________

Enrich

Tricky Tracking

Write and solve a division problem for each set of clues.

1. The quotient is 7.
   There is no remainder.
   The dividend is a square number less than 50. $7\overline{)49}$ **7**
2. The remainder is 2.
   The quotient is 4.
   The quotient equals the divisor. $4\overline{)18}$ **4 R2**
3. The divisor is 3.
   The quotient is $2 \times 2 \times 2$.
   The remainder is 2. $3\overline{)26}$ **8 R2**
4. The quotient is 5.
   The dividend is 48.
   The remainder is an odd number. $9\overline{)48}$ **5 R3**
5. The dividend is 65.
   The remainder is 1.
   The quotient is between 5 and 10. $8\overline{)65}$ **8 R1**

Grade 4 32 Chapter 8

Two-Digit Quotients

Example 1 Explain to students that the first digit of the quotient, which is a 1, goes in the tens place of the quotient (above the 9) because there is 1 group of 7 tens in 9 tens.

ADDITIONAL EXAMPLES

1. There are 96 cans of tennis balls in 4 boxes. How many cans are in each box? 24 cans
2. Shelley and her 6 friends are using beads to make necklaces. She has 338 beads to share. How many beads will each of them get? 48 R2

CHECK What You Know

As a class, have students complete Exercises 1–8 in **Check What You Know** as you observe their work.

Exercise 8 Assess student comprehension before assigning practice exercises.

BL Alternate Teaching Strategy

If students have trouble using the division algorithm…

Then use one of these reteach options:

1 CRM **Daily Reteach Worksheet** (p. 28)

2 Try one of the following strategies:

- Have students work with a partner.
- Provide pairs of students with base-ten blocks. Allow them to model the problem before using the algorithm to find the quotient.
- Allow students to use grid paper to align digits.

3 Practice

Differentiate practice using these leveled assignments for Exercises 9–31.

Level	Assignment
BL Below/Approaching Level	9–15, 25–28
OL On Level	10–23, 26–28
AL Above/Beyond Level	10–28 even, 29–31

Have students discuss and complete the Higher Order Thinking problems. For Exercise 30, suggest that students find the quotient themselves before analyzing the students' sample work.

WRITING IN MATH Have students complete Exercise 31 in their Math Journals. You may choose to use this exercise as an optional formative assessment.

Additional Answers

9. 18 R1; 40 ÷ 2 = 20
10. 21 R1; 60 ÷ 3 = 20
11. 19 R3; 80 ÷ 4 = 20
12. 16 R2; 80 ÷ 5 = 16
13. 10 R4; 70 ÷ 7 = 10
14. 15 R1; 90 ÷ 6 = 15
15. 75 R1; 150 ÷ 2 = 75
16. 95 R1; 300 ÷ 3 = 100
17. 77 R2; 390 ÷ 5 = 78
18. 98 R3; 500 ÷ 5 = 100
19. 94 R3; 600 ÷ 6 = 100
20. 97 R3; 700 ÷ 7 = 100
21. 99 R1; 700 ÷ 7 = 100
22. 97 R7; 800 ÷ 8 = 100
23. 99 R3; 800 ÷ 8 = 100
24. 98 R1; 900 ÷ 9 = 100

COMMON ERROR!

Students may get a remainder that is larger than the divisor. When this occurs, remind students that after they subtract, they must always compare their difference to the divisor. The difference must always be less than the divisor; otherwise the quotient is wrong.

CHECK What You Know

Divide. Use estimation to check. See Examples 1 and 2 (pp. 326–327)

1. 2)33 16 R1; 30 ÷ 2 = 15
2. 4)56 14; 60 ÷ 4 = 15
3. 5)71 14 R1; 70 ÷ 5 = 14
4. 179 ÷ 3 59 R2; 180 ÷ 3 = 60
5. 387 ÷ 4 96 R3; 400 ÷ 4 = 100
6. 697 ÷ 7 99 R4; 700 ÷ 7 = 100
7. Holden and Alma earned $32 by doing yard work in their neighborhood. They will share their money equally. How much money will each person get? $16
8. **Talk About It** Estimation is one method that can be used to check division answers. Identify another method. Sample answer: multiplication

Practice and Problem Solving

EXTRA PRACTICE See page R21.

Divide. Use estimation to check. See Examples 1 and 2 (pp. 326–327) 9–24. See margin.

9. 2)37
10. 3)64
11. 4)79
12. 5)82
13. 7)74
14. 6)91
15. 2)151
16. 3)286
17. 387 ÷ 5
18. 493 ÷ 5
19. 567 ÷ 6
20. 682 ÷ 7
21. 694 ÷ 7
22. 783 ÷ 8
23. 795 ÷ 8
24. 883 ÷ 9

25. There are 78 campers at a summer camp. There are 6 campers per cabin. How many cabins are there? 13 cabins
26. Carlo has $46 to spend on trading cards. If each pack of cards costs $3, how many packages can he buy? 15 packages

Real-World PROBLEM SOLVING

Recycling Every month, Americans throw out enough bottles and jars to fill up a giant skyscraper. All of these jars are recyclable.

27. When one aluminum can is recycled, enough energy is saved to run a television for 3 hours. How many cans need to be recycled to run a television for 75 hours? 25 cans
28. Most Americans use 7 trees a year in products that are made from trees. How old is a person who has used 85 trees? 12 R1; so just over 12

H.O.T. Problems

29. OPEN-ENDED When Kira's father's age is divided by Kira's age, you get a quotient of 13 R1. Identify one possibility for their ages. Sample answer: Kira = 2 and father = 27

30. FIND THE ERROR Amber and Paul are finding 53 ÷ 3. Who is correct? Explain. 30, 31. See margin.

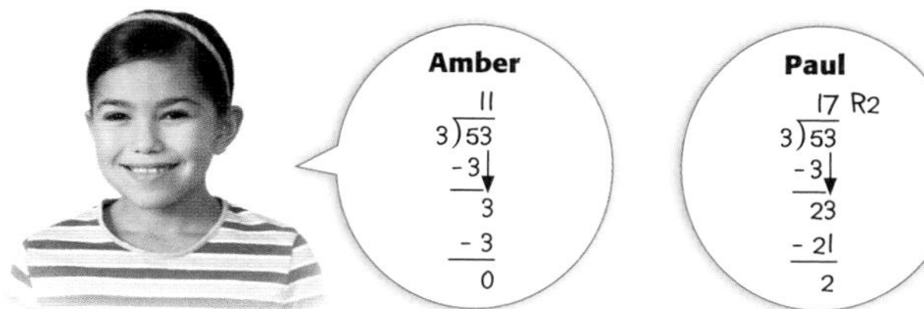

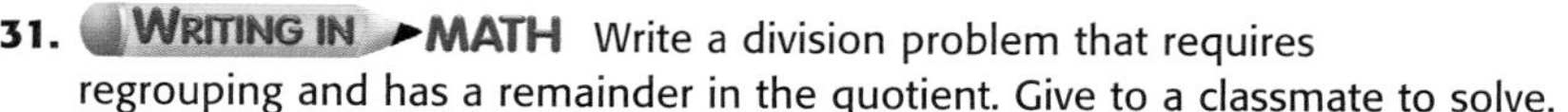

31. WRITING IN MATH Write a division problem that requires regrouping and has a remainder in the quotient. Give to a classmate to solve.

TEST Practice

32. Cailin biked 78 miles in 5 days. About how many miles did she bike each day? (Lesson 8-4) B

A 14 **C** 18

B 16 **D** 20

33. Tyrone ran 54 feet during a football game. If there are 3 feet in one yard, how many yards did he run? (Lesson 8-5) G

F 17 **H** 19

G 18 **J** 20

Spiral Review

Estimate. Check your estimate. (Lesson 8-4) 37. $90; 9 × $90 = $810

34. 139 ÷ 2 70; 2 × 70 = 140

35. $449 ÷ 5 $90; 5 × $90 = $450

36. 562 ÷ 7 80; 7 × 80 = 560

37. $805 ÷ 9

38. Pablo works at an animal hospital. Last week he took care of 49 birds and snakes. He took care of four birds for every three snakes. How many of each animal did he take care of? (Lesson 8-3) 21 snakes and 28 birds

Divide. Use patterns. (Lesson 8-2)

39. $600 ÷ 3 $200 **40.** 2,400 ÷ 4 600 **41.** 4,900 ÷ 7 700 **42.** 4,800 ÷ 8 600

43. Jerry was given 3 CDs from his friends, 4 from his parents, and 1 from his sister. He now has 38. How many did he have originally? (Lesson 4-4) 30

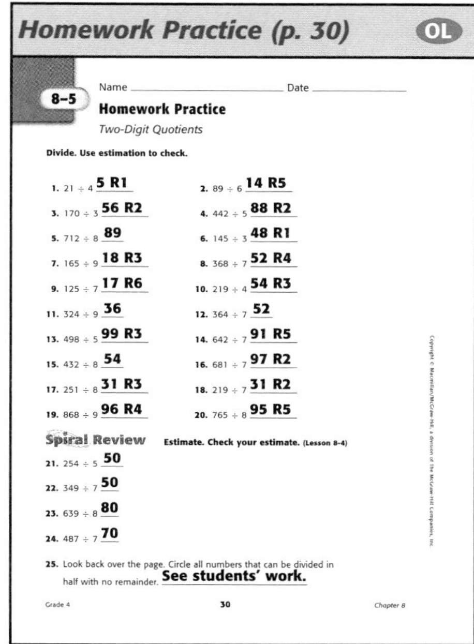

Homework Practice (p. 30) OL

8–5

Name ______ Date ______

Homework Practice

Two-Digit Quotients

Divide. Use estimation to check.

1. 21 ÷ 4 **5 R1**
2. 89 ÷ 6 **14 R5**
3. 170 ÷ 3 **56 R2**
4. 442 ÷ 5 **88 R2**
5. 712 ÷ 8 **89**
6. 145 ÷ 3 **48 R1**
7. 165 ÷ 9 **18 R3**
8. 368 ÷ 7 **52 R4**
9. 125 ÷ 7 **17 R6**
10. 219 ÷ 4 **54 R3**
11. 324 ÷ 9 **36**
12. 364 ÷ 7 **52**
13. 498 ÷ 5 **99 R3**
14. 642 ÷ 7 **91 R5**
15. 432 ÷ 8 **54**
16. 681 ÷ 7 **97 R2**
17. 251 ÷ 8 **31 R3**
18. 219 ÷ 7 **31 R2**
19. 868 ÷ 9 **96 R4**
20. 765 ÷ 8 **95 R5**

Spiral Review **Estimate. Check your estimate.** (Lesson 8-4)

21. 254 ÷ 5 **50**
22. 349 ÷ 7 **50**
23. 639 ÷ 8 **80**
24. 487 ÷ 7 **70**

25. Look back over the page. Circle all numbers that can be divided in half with no remainder. **See students' work.**

Grade 4 30 Chapter 8

Assess

Formative Assessment

- **What steps would you follow to find 435 ÷ 6? Find the quotient.** Sample answer: Since there are not enough hundreds to divide, divide 43 by 6. Place the first digit of the quotient in the tens place. After placing the digit, multiply, subtract, and compare. Then bring down the 5 ones and divide the ones. Multiply, subtract, and compare to find the remainder. 72 R3

Quick Check **Are students continuing to struggle with two-digit quotients?**

If Yes → Small Group Options (p. 326B)

If No → Independent Work Options (p. 326B)
CRM Skills Practice Worksheet (p. 29)
CRM Enrich Worksheet (p. 32)

Name the Math Have students explain why you compare each difference to the divisor when you use the division algorithm.

TEST Practice

Reviews Lessons 8-4 and 8-5

Assign the Test Practice problems to provide daily reinforcement of test-taking skills.

Spiral Review

Reviews Lessons 4-4, 8-2, 8-3, and 8-4

Review and assess mastery of skills and concepts from previous chapters.

Additional Answers

30. Sample answer: Paul; Amber forgot to subtract 3 from 5 when she worked on dividing the tens place of the dividend. Also, since 11 × 3 is 33, you know Amber's answer is wrong.

31. Sample answer: Ron is arranging his stuffed animals on shelves. He can fit 5 on each shelf. If he has 23 stuffed animals, how many shelves does he need? Answer: 5 shelves

8-6 Problem-Solving Investigation
Choose a Strategy

Lesson Planner

Objective

Choose the best strategy to solve a problem.

Resources

Teacher Technology

TeacherWorks • Interactive Classroom

Real-World Problem Solving Library
Math and Social Studies: *Riding the Mail Trail*
Use these leveled books to reinforce and extend problem-solving skills and strategies.

Leveled for:

- OL On Level
- ELL Sheltered English
- SP Spanish

For additional support, see the Real-World Problem Solving Teacher Guide.

Daily Routine

Use these suggestions before beginning the lesson on p. 330.

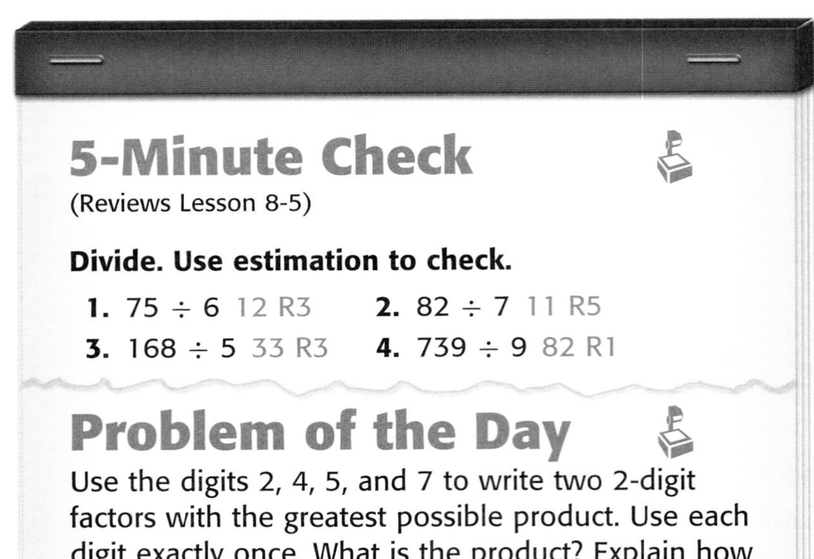

5-Minute Check

(Reviews Lesson 8-5)

Divide. Use estimation to check.

1. 75 ÷ 6 12 R3
2. 82 ÷ 7 11 R5
3. 168 ÷ 5 33 R3
4. 739 ÷ 9 82 R1

Problem of the Day

Use the digits 2, 4, 5, and 7 to write two 2-digit factors with the greatest possible product. Use each digit exactly once. What is the product? Explain how you found the factors. 72 × 54 = 3,888; Sample answer: Form the two greatest possible factors, multiply, and adjust.

Differentiated Instruction

Small Group Options

Option 1 LOGICAL

Gifted and Talented AL

Materials: paper and pencil

- Give students the following problem:

  Carlos works for his neighbors. His goal is to earn $23 per week from his job. Some weeks he is able to earn more and some weeks he earns less. The last 3 weeks he has earned $36, $17, and $21.
- **How much does he need to earn the fourth week to make his goal?** $18
- Now write and solve another problem like this one.

Option 2 INTERPERSONAL, AUDITORY

English Language Learners ELL

Materials: paper, pencil
Core Vocabulary: by, dividend, divisor
Common Use Verb: comes first

See Math This strategy further clarifies the use of prepositions relative to divisors and dividends.

- Say: "15 ÷ 5 is read '5 divided into 15.' The divisor comes first, then the dividend."
- "There is another way to read 15 ÷ 5. You can start with the dividend 15 and then say 'divided by 5.'"
- Write problems on the overhead. Go around the group, prompting them to respond with "divided by" or "divided into" according to where the greater number is placed as you wrote it.
- Repeat as time permits.

English Language Learners (p. 77) ELL

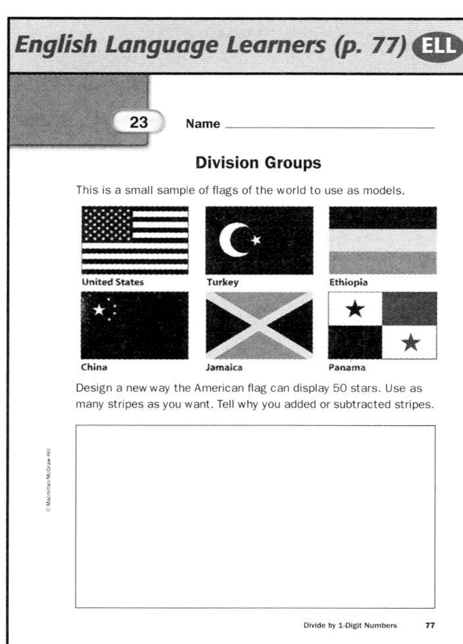

23 Name ____________

Division Groups

This is a small sample of flags of the world to use as models.

United States, Turkey, Ethiopia, China, Jamaica, Panama

Design a new way the American flag can display 50 stars. Use as many stripes as you want. Tell why you added or subtracted stripes.

Divide by 1-Digit Numbers 77

Use this worksheet to provide additional support for English Language Learners.

Independent Work Options

Option 1 KINESTHETIC, SOCIAL

Early Finishers OL AL

Materials: 3 number cubes, each marked 0–5

- Each student rolls the 3 number cubes and tells the partner the sum of the three numbers showing.
- Each students makes a table of the possible numbers that were rolled by the partner.
- Partners discuss their strategies and answers.

Option 2

Student Technology

Math Online macmillanmh.com

Personal Tutor • Extra Examples

Option 3

Learning Station: Science (p. 308H)

Direct students to the Science Learning Station for opportunities to explore and extend the lesson concept.

8-6 Problem-Solving Investigation

1 Introduce

Activity • Review

Present the following problem:

There are 40 people riding 12 vehicles at the carnival. Motorcycles hold 2 people and cars hold 4. How many motorcycles and cars are there?

- **What strategy could be used to solve this exercise?** guess and check, make a table, act it out
- **Which strategy would work best to begin?** guess and check
- **Solve the problem.** 4 motorcycles and 8 cars

2 Teach

Have students read the problem on stamps. Guide them through the problem-solving steps.

Understand Using the questions, review what students know and need to find.

Plan Have them discuss their strategy.

Solve Guide students to use the work backward strategy to solve the problem.

- **How many stamps does Cindy have now?** 32
- **If she has 32 stamps now, how many stamps did she have before she received 8 from a friend?** 24
- **How did you find your answer?** Subtract; 32 − 8.
- **How many did she have before she traded 4 stamps?** 28
- **How did you find your answer?** Add; 24 + 4.
- **How many did she have before she bought 6 stamps?** 22
- **How did you find your answer?** Subtract; 28 − 6.

Check Have students look back at the problem to make sure that the answer fits the facts given.

COMMON ERROR!

Exercise 2 Some students may only look at the first two numbers in a sequence to find the rule for the pattern. Encourage students to think in terms of multiples to find the rule.

8-6 Problem-Solving Investigation

MAIN IDEA I will choose the best strategy to solve a problem.

P.S.I. TEAM +

CINDY: I had some stamps. I bought 6 more stamps. I traded 4 of my stamps for 8 of my friend's stamps. I now have 32 stamps.

YOUR MISSION: Find how many stamps Cindy started with.

Understand	You know that Cindy bought 6 stamps. She traded 4 stamps for 8 stamps. She now has 32 stamps. You need to find the number of stamps Cindy started with.
Plan	You need to find how many stamps Cindy started with. So, the work backward strategy is a good choice.
Solve	Start with the end result, then work backward. End result ⟶ 32 stamps Cindy has now − 8 stamps Cindy received from a friend 24 24 + 4 stamps Cindy gave to a friend 28 28 − 6 stamps Cindy bought 22
Check	Look back. Cindy gained 14 stamps and lost 4. This means she has 10 more stamps then she started with. If she now has 32 stamps, then she started with 22 stamps. The answer is correct.

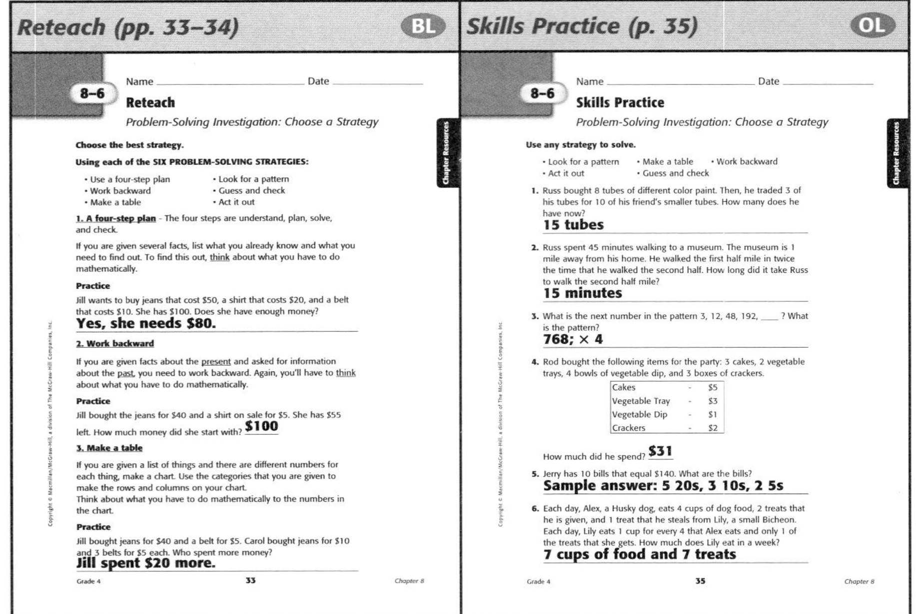

Reteach (pp. 33–34) BL

8-6 Name ______ Date ______

Reteach

Problem-Solving Investigation: Choose a Strategy

Choose the best strategy.

Using each of the SIX PROBLEM-SOLVING STRATEGIES:

- Use a four-step plan
- Work backward
- Make a table
- Look for a pattern
- Guess and check
- Act it out

1. A four-step plan - The four steps are understand, plan, solve, and check.

If you are given several facts, list what you already know and what you need to find out. To find this out, think about what you have to do mathematically.

Practice

Jill wants to buy jeans that cost $50, a shirt that costs $20, and a belt that costs $10. She has $100. Does she have enough money?

Yes, she needs $80.

2. Work backward

If you are given facts about the present and asked for information about the past, you need to work backward. Again, you'll have to think about what you have to do mathematically.

Practice

Jill bought the jeans for $40 and a shirt on sale for $5. She has $55 left. How much money did she start with? **$100**

3. Make a table

If you are given a list of things and there are different numbers for each thing, make a chart. Use the categories that you are given to make the rows and columns on your chart.
Think about what you have to do mathematically to the numbers in the chart.

Practice

Jill bought jeans for $40 and a belt for $5. Carol bought jeans for $10 and 3 belts for $5 each. Who spent more money?

Jill spent $20 more.

Chapter Resources

Skills Practice (p. 35) OL

8-6 Name ______ Date ______

Skills Practice

Problem-Solving Investigation: Choose a Strategy

Use any strategy to solve.

- Look for a pattern
- Act it out
- Make a table
- Guess and check
- Work backward

1. Russ bought 8 tubes of different color paint. Then, he traded 3 of his tubes for 10 of his friend's smaller tubes. How many does he have now?
   15 tubes
2. Russ spent 45 minutes walking to a museum. The museum is 1 mile away from his home. He walked the first half mile in twice the time that he walked the second half. How long did it take Russ to walk the second half mile?
   15 minutes
3. What is the next number in the pattern 3, 12, 48, 192, ____ ? What is the pattern?
   768; × 4
4. Rod bought the following items for the party: 3 cakes, 2 vegetable trays, 4 bowls of vegetable dip, and 3 boxes of crackers.

Cakes	-	$5
Vegetable Tray	-	$3
Vegetable Dip	-	$1
Crackers	-	$2

   How much did he spend? **$31**

5. Jerry has 10 bills that equal $140. What are the bills?
   Sample answer: 5 20s, 3 10s, 2 5s
6. Each day, Alex, a Husky dog, eats 4 cups of dog food, 2 treats that he is given, and 1 treat that he steals from Lily, a small Bicheon. Each day, Lily eats 1 cup for every 4 that Alex eats and only 1 of the treats that she gets. How much does Lily eat in a week?
   7 cups of food and 7 treats

Chapter Resources

Mixed Problem Solving

See page R21.

Use any strategy shown below to solve. Tell what strategy you used.

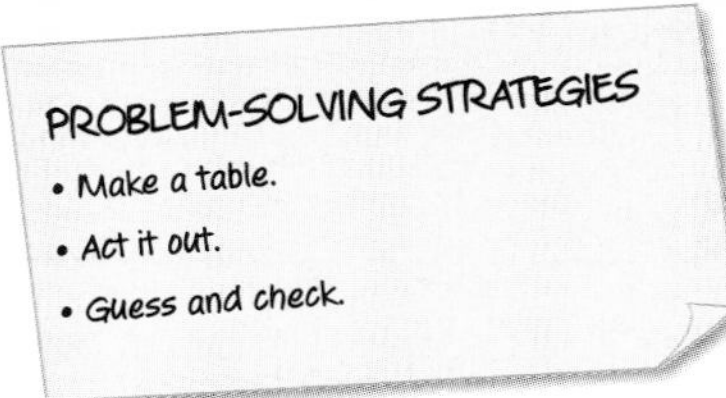

1. Ellis rode his bike to and from his cousin's home over the weekend. His cousin lives 5 miles away. If Ellis rode a total of 20 miles, how many times did he visit his cousin? **2 times**

2. **Algebra** What is the next number in the pattern 2, 5, 11, 23, ■? **47**

3. Judie and her dad caught 63 fish over the summer. The license allowed them to keep fish longer than 8 inches. Only 2 out of every 5 fish were long enough to keep. About how many did they keep? **about 24 fish**

4. Alvin buys 2 pairs of jeans, 2 pairs of shoes, 3 T-shirts, and 2 dress shirts for school. How much did he spend? **$132**

5. There are 24 cars in a parking lot. There are twice as many 4-door cars as 2-door. How many of each are there? **4-door: 16; 2-door: 8**

6. **Measurement** Lucy the Great Dane eats the amount of dog food shown each day. Roscoe the Pug eats 1 cup for every 2 that Lucy eats each day. How much food does Roscoe eat in a week? **14 cups**

7. A worker at an arcade is handing out 30 tokens for a party. There are more than 6 people at the party. The tokens are shared equally among the people. After the tokens are handed out, 6 are left. How many people are at the party? How many tokens does each person get? **8; 3**

8. Darin has 5 coins that total 62¢. What are the coins? **2 quarters, 1 dime, 2 pennies**

9. **Measurement** Selena is going to a birthday party at 12 P.M. She needs to complete the activities shown before the party starts. What time should Selena start to get ready? **8:30 A.M.**

Activity	Time
Shower/get ready	30 minutes
Eat breakfast	30 minutes
Chores	2 hours
Pick up Felix and go	30 minutes

10. **WRITING IN ►MATH** Identify the problem-solving strategy you used to solve Exercise 9. Explain how you used the strategy to solve the problem. **See margin.**

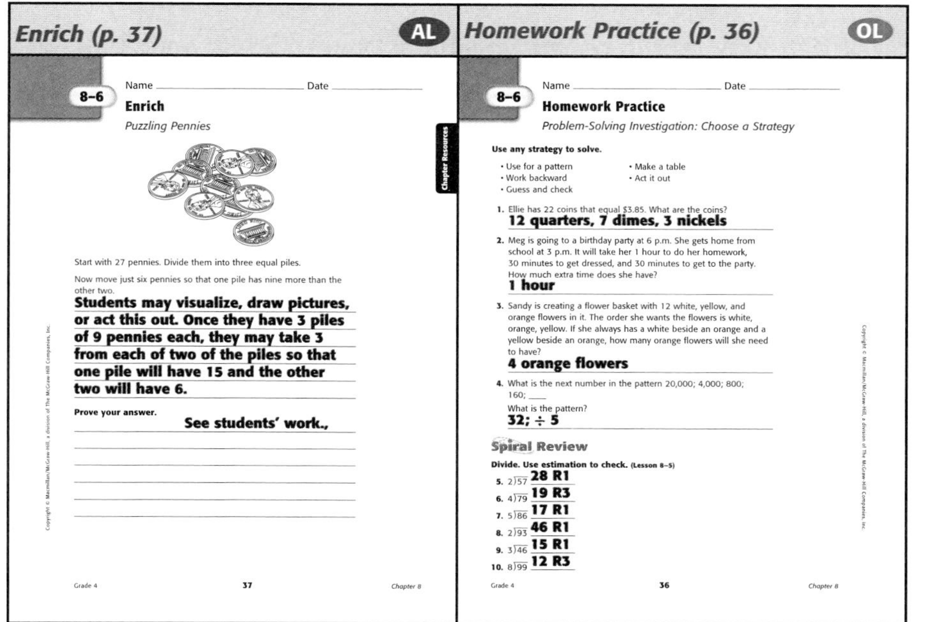

Enrich (p. 37) AL

8-6 Name ______ Date ______

Enrich

Puzzling Pennies

Start with 27 pennies. Divide them into three equal piles.

Now move just six pennies so that one pile has nine more than the other two.

Students may visualize, draw pictures, or act this out. Once they have 3 piles of 9 pennies each, they may take 3 from each of two of the piles so that one pile will have 15 and the other two will have 6.

Prove your answer. **See students' work.,**

Chapter Resources

Copyright © Macmillan/McGraw-Hill, a division of The McGraw-Hill Companies, Inc.

Grade 4 37 Chapter 8

Homework Practice (p. 36) OL

8-6 Name ______ Date ______

Homework Practice

Problem-Solving Investigation: Choose a Strategy

Use any strategy to solve.

- Use for a pattern
- Work backward
- Guess and check
- Make a table
- Act it out

1. Ellie has 22 coins that equal $3.85. What are the coins? **12 quarters, 7 dimes, 3 nickels**
2. Meg is going to a birthday party at 6 p.m. She gets home from school at 3 p.m. It will take her 1 hour to do her homework, 30 minutes to get dressed, and 30 minutes to get to the party. How much extra time does she have? **1 hour**
3. Sandy is creating a flower basket with 12 white, yellow, and orange flowers in it. The order she wants the flowers is white, orange, yellow. If she always has a white beside an orange and a yellow beside an orange, how many orange flowers will she need to have? **4 orange flowers**
4. What is the next number in the pattern 20,000; 4,000; 800; 160; ____
What is the pattern? **32; ÷ 5**

Spiral Review

Divide. Use estimation to check. (Lesson 8–5)

5. 2)57 **28 R1**
6. 4)79 **19 R3**
7. 5)86 **17 R1**
8. 2)93 **46 R1**
9. 3)46 **15 R1**
10. 8)99 **12 R3**

Copyright © Macmillan/McGraw-Hill, a division of The McGraw-Hill Companies, Inc.

Grade 4 36 Chapter 8

BL Alternate Teaching Strategy

If students have trouble deciding on a strategy…

Then use one of these reteach options:

1. CRM **Daily Reteach Worksheet** (pp. 33–34)
2. Allow students to use the strategy list as a guide. Refer them back to it often.
   - **Which strategies might work?**
   - **What is the best strategy?**

   Consider posting the list of strategies on a bulletin board.

3 Practice

Using the Exercises

Exercise 3 asks students to estimate the answers.

Exercises 4 and 9 provide additional practice using the work backward strategy.

Exercise 10 requires students to write an explanation of a strategy they used.

4 Assess

Formative Assessment

Have students answer the following question.

- How did you determine the best strategy to use for each exercise? Explain that there is often more than one way to solve a problem.

Additional Answer

10. Sample answer: work backward; start with the end result and work backward one step at a time. 12 P.M. − 30 min = 11:30 A.M. − 2 hours = 9:30 A.M. − 30 min = 9 A.M. − 30 min = 8:30 A.M.

Quick Check **Are students continuing to struggle with choosing a strategy?**

If Yes → CRM Reteach Worksheets (pp. 33–34)

If No → Independent Work Options (p. 330B)
CRM Skills Practice Worksheet (p. 35)
CRM Enrich Worksheet (p. 37)

LESSON 8-7

Three-Digit Quotients

Lesson Planner

Objective

Solve divison problems that result in three-digit quotients.

Review Vocabulary

compatible numbers

Resources

Manipulatives: base-ten blocks

Literature Connection: *The Doorbell Rang* by Pat Hutchins

Teacher Technology

TeacherWorks • Interactive Classroom

Focus on Math Background

The focus of this lesson is on three-digit quotients that are obtained by dividing three- and four-digit numbers by one-digit divisors. The algorithm presented in the previous lesson does not get more difficult with the increase in the number of digits in the dividend. It is just that finding a three-digit quotient requires a bit more endurance. The steps of *divide, multiply, subtract, and compare* are the same. They are just repeated more times.

Daily Routine

Use these suggestions before beginning the lesson on p. 332.

5-Minute Check

(Reviews Lesson 8-6)

Choose the best strategy. Then solve the problem.

What is the fifteenth number in the pattern: 8, 16, 24, 32, 40, ...? Identify the pattern. 120; Add 8.

Problem of the Day

Which word does not belong with the others? Explain your reasoning.

three, eleven, eight, and twenty-seven 8; It is the only even number.

mode, equation, median, tally equation; You use tallies to represent data. Mode and median are measures of data.

sum, multiply, product, factor sum; The other words relate to multiplication.

Review Math Vocabulary

Write the review vocabulary term and its definition on the board.

Have students show examples on the board of how compatible numbers can be used to estimate quotients. Explain that you can use the compatible numbers 24 and 6 to estimate 26 ÷ 4. Have them circle compatible numbers in the examples they wrote on the board.

Visual Vocabulary Cards

Use Visual Vocabulary Card 5 to reinforce the vocabulary reviewed in this lesson. (The Define/Example/Ask routine is printed on the back of each card.)

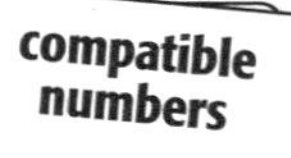

Differentiated Instruction

Small Group Options

Option 1 Gifted and Talented AL

LOGICAL, SOCIAL

Materials: index cards labeled 0–9, paper, pencil

- Have students play this game in pairs or small groups.
- Students mix the cards and place them facedown in a pile. On his or her paper, each student draws a symbol, three blanks for the dividend, and one blank for the divisor.

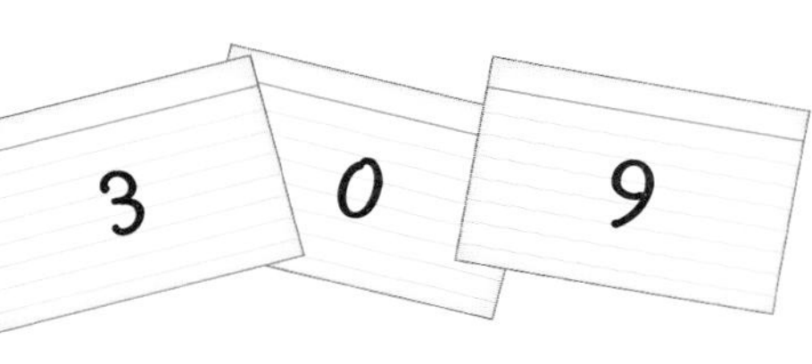

- Students take turns drawing a card and writing the number in any of the blanks. The student with the lowest quotient wins.

Option 2 English Language Learners ELL

LINGUISTIC

Materials: paper, pencil
Core Vocabulary: native, language, country
Common Use Verb: explain

Write Math This strategy allows students to use their native language to comprehend the steps of dividing a three-digit number.

- Ask students to fold two pieces of paper in half.
- Ask students to draw their native country on the top half of one of the pages. On the other page, draw the United States on the top half.
- Post the division problem 298 ÷ 3 on the board.
- On the bottom half of the page with their native country, ask students to demonstrate how a division problem looks in their native language.
- Repeat for the United States, explaining the same problem in English.
- Discuss the similarities and differences in forms.

Independent Work Options

Option 1 Early Finishers OL AL

KINESTHETIC, SOCIAL

Materials: spinner, marked 1–4 and number cube, marked 1–6

- Have students roll the number cube 3 times and record the numbers showing. Have them use the numbers from the rolls to form a 3-digit dividend. Next, have students spin for a divisor number.
- Together, students analyze the numbers and determine if the quotient will have 2 or 3 digits.
- Together, students complete the division.

Option 2 Student Technology

Personal Tutor • Extra Examples

Math Adventures

Option 3 Learning Station: Health (p. 308H)

Direct students to the Health Learning Station for opportunities to explore and extend the lesson concept.

Option 4 Problem-Solving Practice

Reinforce problem-solving skills and strategies with the Problem-Solving Practice worksheet.

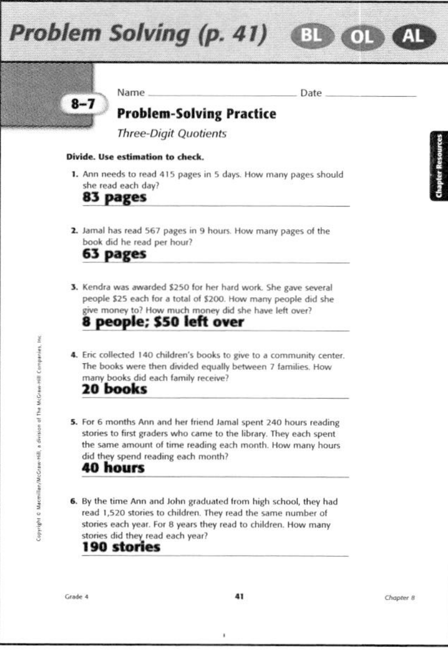

Problem Solving (p. 41) BL OL AL

8–7 Name ______ Date ______

Problem-Solving Practice

Three-Digit Quotients

Divide. Use estimation to check.

1. Ann needs to read 415 pages in 5 days. How many pages should she read each day?
   83 pages
2. Jamal has read 567 pages in 9 hours. How many pages of the book did he read per hour?
   63 pages
3. Kendra was awarded $250 for her hard work. She gave several people $25 each for a total of $200. How many people did she give money to? How much money did she have left over?
   8 people; $50 left over
4. Eric collected 140 children's books to give to a community center. The books were then divided equally between 7 families. How many books did each family receive?
   20 books
5. For 6 months Ann and her friend Jamal spent 240 hours reading stories to first graders who came to the library. They each spent the same amount of time reading each month. How many hours did they spend reading each month?
   40 hours
6. By the time Ann and John graduated from high school, they had read 1,520 stories to children. They read the same number of stories each year. For 8 years they read to children. How many stories did they read each year?
   190 stories

Chapter Resources

Grade 4 41 Chapter 8

Three-Digit Quotients

1 Introduce

Activity Choice 1 • Hands-On 

Materials: base-ten blocks

- Have students use base-ten blocks to model the number 349. Have them divide the blocks into three equal groups.
- **How many are in each group?** 116 blocks
- **Did you have to trade? Explain.** Yes, 1 ten block had to be traded for 10 ones.
- **How many are left over?** 1
- Then have them draw a diagram of base-ten blocks to model the number. Student drawings should include 3 large squares, 4 thin rectangles, and 9 small squares.
- Have them make a diagram that shows how to divide 349 into 3 groups. Check students' diagrams.

Activity Choice 2 • Literature

Introduce the lesson with *The Doorbell Rang* by Pat Hutchins. For a related math activity, see p. TR55.

2 Teach

Scaffolding Questions

Write the following problems on the board:

$456 \div 8 \qquad 456 \div 4$

- **What compatible numbers can be used to estimate the first quotient?** $480 \div 8 = 60$
- **What basic facts can be used to estimate the second quotient?** $4 \times 100 = 400$ or $400 \div 4 = 100$
- **Why will the estimate for the first quotient be 2 digits and the second quotient be 3 digits?** Sample answer: There are 4 hundreds in 456. Four hundreds can be divided by 4 without regrouping, but not 8.

GET READY to Learn

Have students open their books and read the information in **Get Ready to Learn**. Review **compatible numbers**. As a class, work through **Examples 1 and 2**.

8-7 Three-Digit Quotients

MAIN IDEA

I will solve division problems that result in three-digit quotients.

Math Online

macmillanmh.com

- Extra Examples
- Personal Tutor
- Self-Check Quiz

GET READY to Learn

There are 678 people in line to ride a roller coaster. Each coaster car holds 6 people. How many coaster cars are needed so that everyone in line rides the coaster once?

Finding a quotient like $678 \div 6$ is similar to dividing a two-digit number by a one-digit number.

Real-World EXAMPLE Three-Digit Quotients

1 ROLLER COASTERS **How many coaster cars are needed?**

Divide 678 by 6 to find the number of coaster cars needed.

Estimate $678 \div 6 \longrightarrow 700 \div 7 = 100$

Step 1 Divide the hundreds.

```
   1
6)678
 -6
  0
```

Divide. $6 \div 6 = 1$
Put 1 in hundreds place.
Multiply. $6 \times 1 = 6$
Subtract. $6 - 6 = 0$
Compare. $0 < 6$

Step 2 Divide the tens.

```
   11
6)678
 -6↓
  07
  -6
   1
```

Bring down the tens.
Divide. $7 \div 6 = 1$
Put 1 in the tens place.
Multiply. $6 \times 1 = 6$
Subtract. $7 - 6 = 1$
Compare. $1 < 6$

Step 3 Divide the ones.

```
  113
6)678
 -6↓
  07
  -6↓
   18
  -18
    0
```

Bring down the ones.
Divide.
Divide. $18 \div 6 = 3$
Put 3 in ones place.
Multiply. $6 \times 3 = 18$
Subtract. $18 - 18 = 0$
Compare. $0 < 6$

Check

Since $113 \times 6 = 678$, the answer is correct. ✓

So, 113 coaster cars are needed.

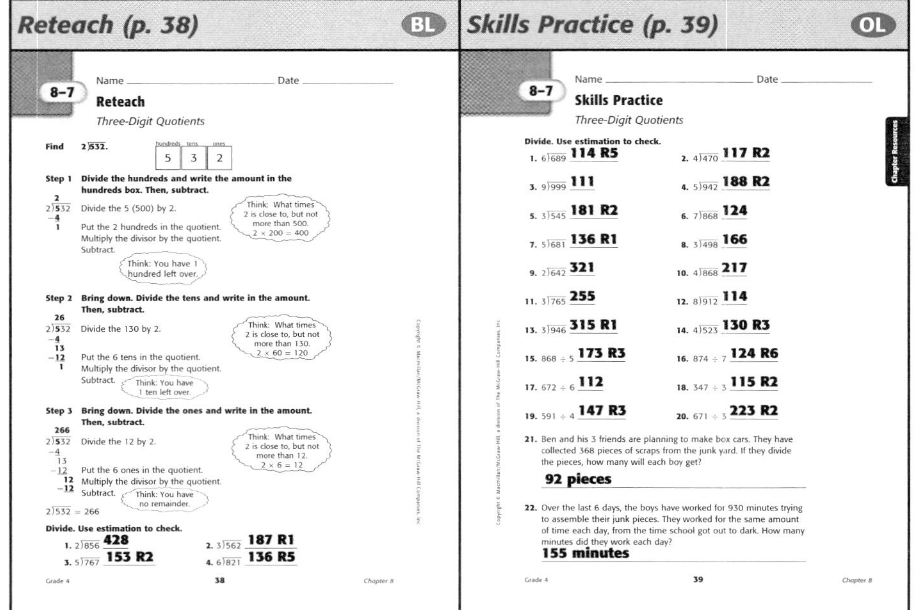

Reteach (p. 38) BL

8–7 Name ______ Date ______

Reteach

Three-Digit Quotients

Find 2)532.

hundreds	tens	ones
5	3	2

Step 1 **Divide the hundreds and write the amount in the hundreds box. Then, subtract.**

```
   2
2)532
 -4
  1
```

Divide the 5 (500) by 2.
Put the 2 hundreds in the quotient.
Multiply the divisor by the quotient.
Subtract.

Think: What times 2 is close to, but not more than 500. $2 \times 200 = 400$

Think: You have 1 hundred left over.

Step 2 **Bring down. Divide the tens and write in the amount. Then, subtract.**

```
  26
2)532
 -4
  13
 -12
   1
```

Divide the 130 by 2.
Put the 6 tens in the quotient.
Multiply the divisor by the quotient.
Subtract.

Think: What times 2 is close to, but not more than 130. $2 \times 60 = 120$

Think: You have 1 ten left over.

Step 3 **Bring down. Divide the ones and write in the amount. Then, subtract.**

```
  266
2)532
 -4
  13
 -12
   12
  -12
```

Divide the 12 by 2.
Put the 6 ones in the quotient.
Multiply the divisor by the quotient.
Subtract.

Think: What times 2 is close to, but not more than 12. $2 \times 6 = 12$

Think: You have no remainder.

2)532 = 266

Divide. Use estimation to check.

1. 2)856 **428**
2. 3)562 **187 R1**
3. 5)767 **153 R2**
4. 6)821 **136 R5**

Grade 4 38 Chapter 8

Skills Practice (p. 39) OL

8–7 Name ______ Date ______

Skills Practice

Three-Digit Quotients

Chapter Resources

Divide. Use estimation to check.

1. 6)689 **114 R5**
2. 4)470 **117 R2**
3. 9)999 **111**
4. 5)942 **188 R2**
5. 3)545 **181 R2**
6. 7)868 **124**
7. 5)681 **136 R1**
8. 3)498 **166**
9. 2)642 **321**
10. 4)868 **217**
11. 3)765 **255**
12. 8)912 **114**
13. 3)946 **315 R1**
14. 4)523 **130 R3**
15. $868 \div 5$ **173 R3**
16. $874 \div 7$ **124 R6**
17. $672 \div 6$ **112**
18. $347 \div 3$ **115 R2**
19. $591 \div 4$ **147 R3**
20. $671 \div 3$ **223 R2**
21. Ben and his 3 friends are planning to make box cars. They have collected 368 pieces of scraps from the junk yard. If they divide the pieces, how many will each boy get?
92 pieces
22. Over the last 6 days, the boys have worked for 930 minutes trying to assemble their junk pieces. They worked for the same amount of time each day, from the time school got out to dark. How many minutes did they work each day?
155 minutes

Grade 4 39 Chapter 8

When dividing three-digit numbers, you can have a remainder like you sometimes have when dividing two-digit numbers.

Remember

Always start a division problem by dividing the greatest place value.

Real-World EXAMPLE Three-Digit Quotients with Remainders

2 MEASUREMENT **A roller coaster takes about 2 minutes to travel its 985-foot track. How many feet does the coaster travel in one minute?**

The coaster travels 985 feet in 2 minutes. To find how far it travels in 1 minute, divide 985 by 2.

Estimate $985 \div 2 \longrightarrow 1{,}000 \div 2 = 500$

```
   492 R1
 2)985
  -8
   18
  -18
    05
    -4
     1
```

THINK A remainder of 1 tells you that the quotient is just over 492.

So, the roller coaster travels a little more than 492 feet each minute.

Check for Reasonableness

The answer, a little more than 492, is close to the estimate. So, it is reasonable. ✓

8. Sample answer: Three digits because the divisor is less than the digit in the hundreds place.

CHECK What You Know

Divide. Use estimation to check. See Examples 1 and 2 (pp. 332–333)

1. 2)286 143
2. 3)345 115
3. 4)492 123
4. 745 ÷ 2 372 R1
5. 679 ÷ 3 226 R1
6. 917 ÷ 4 229 R1
7. **Measurement** A tug-of-war team weighs a total of 774 pounds. The 6 members on the team weigh the same amount. How much does each person weigh? 129 lbs
8. **Talk About It** How would you mentally figure out how many digits the quotient of 795 ÷ 5 will have? Explain your reasoning.

Enrich (p. 42) AL

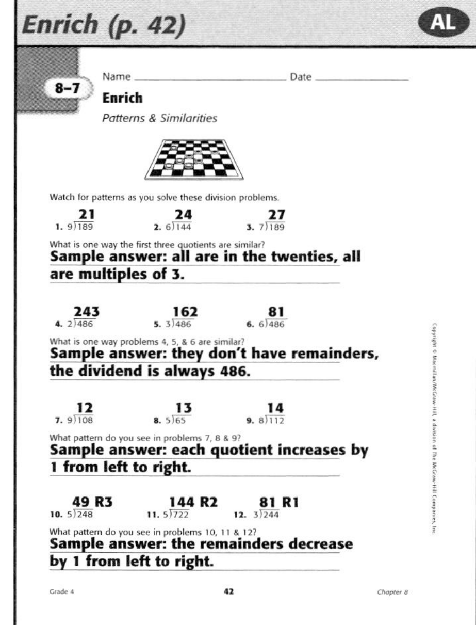

8-7 Name ________ Date ________

Enrich

Patterns & Similarities

Watch for patterns as you solve these division problems.

1. 9)189 **21** 2. 6)144 **24** 3. 7)189 **27**

What is one way the first three quotients are similar?
Sample answer: all are in the twenties, all are multiples of 3.

4. 2)486 **243** 5. 3)486 **162** 6. 6)486 **81**

What is one way problems 4, 5, & 6 are similar?
Sample answer: they don't have remainders, the dividend is always 486.

7. 9)108 **12** 8. 5)65 **13** 9. 8)112 **14**

What pattern do you see in problems 7, 8 & 9?
Sample answer: each quotient increases by 1 from left to right.

10. 5)248 **49 R3** 11. 5)722 **144 R2** 12. 3)244 **81 R1**

What pattern do you see in problems 10, 11 & 12?
Sample answer: the remainders decrease by 1 from left to right.

Grade 4 42 Chapter 8

Three-Digit Quotients with Remainders

Example 2 Emphasize that you always begin the division algorithm by dividing with the greatest place value first.

ADDITIONAL EXAMPLES

1. A teacher orders pencils in large plastic jars. Each jar holds of 276 pencils. To how many students can he give 2 pencils? 138 students
2. The principal wants to form reading groups of 4 for 567 students. How many groups will be formed? 141 R3, or at least 142 groups

CHECK What You Know

As a class, have students complete Exercises 1–8 in **Check What You Know** as you observe their work.

Exercise 8 Assess student comprehension before assigning practice exercises.

BL Alternate Teaching Strategy

If students have trouble with the standard division algorithm…

Then use one of these reteach options:

1. CRM **Daily Reteach Worksheet** (p. 38)
2. Allow students to use base-ten blocks to model a problem. Then ask questions similar to the following as they use the division algorithm to find the quotient:
   - Are there enough hundreds to divide? How do you record the number in the quotient?
   - Are there enough tens to divide? How do you record the number in the quotient?
   - Are there enough ones to divide? How do you record the number in the quotient? Is there a remainder?

COMMON ERROR!

Exercises 19 and 20 Students may be tempted to write the first digit of the quotient above the thousands place of the dividend. Remind them to start at the leftmost digit in the dividend to see if there are enough thousands to divide. If not, then the first digit in the quotient goes above the hundreds place.

3 Practice

Differentiate practice using these leveled assignments for Exercises 9–30.

Level	Assignment
BL Below/Approaching Level	9–16, 21–22, 25
OL On Level	10–20, 23–26
AL Above/Beyond Level	9–25 odd, 27–30

Have students discuss and complete the Higher Order Thinking problems. If students have difficulty with Exercise 27, remind them that the quotient times the divisor is equal to the dividend.

WRITING IN ▸MATH Have students complete Exercise 30 in their Math Journals. You may choose to use this exercise as an optional formative assessment.

4 Assess

Formative Assessment

- **How can you tell that the quotient of 732 ÷ 4 is a 3-digit number?**
  Sample answer: It is possible to divide 7 hundreds into four equal groups of 1, so the quotient will have a 1 in the hundreds place.

Quick Check **Are students continuing to struggle with three-digit quotients?**

If Yes → Strategic Intervention Guide (p. 88)

If No → Independent Work Options (p. 332B)
CRM Skills Practice Worksheet (p. 39)
CRM Enrich Worksheet (p. 42)

Ticket Out the Door On a small piece of paper, students write a division problem in which the dividend has four digits, the divisor has one digit, and the quotient has three digits. Have them hand their papers to you as they leave the room.

Practice and Problem Solving

EXTRA PRACTICE See page R22.

Divide. Use estimation to check. See Examples 1 and 2 (pp. 332–333)

9. 2)324 162
10. 3)585 195
11. 5)775 155
12. 6)696 116
13. 7)847 121
14. 7)973 139
15. 2)573 286 R1
16. 3)787 262 R1
17. 849 ÷ 2 424 R1
18. 994 ÷ 4 248 R2
19. 1,863 ÷ 3 621
20. 3,974 ÷ 4 993 R2

21. A coach ordered 6 soccer goals for $678. How much did each goal cost? $113

22. Britney needs to finish reading a book in 3 days. If the book is 348 pages long, how many pages does she need to read each day? 116

Real-World PROBLEM SOLVING

Architecture The White House is the official home and workplace of the President of the United States. President Theodore Roosevelt gave the White House its name, based on its color.

23. **Measurement** It takes 570 gallons of paint to paint the outside of the White House. If the number of gallons used to paint each of its 4 sides is equal, how many gallons of paint are used on each side? 142 R2, so just over 142 cans for each side

24. There are 132 rooms and 6 floors in the White House. If each floor had the same number of rooms, how many rooms would each floor have? 22 rooms

H.O.T. Problems

25. **OPEN ENDED** Write a division problem that results in a quotient that is greater than 200 and less than 250. Sample answer: 2)454

26. **WRITING IN ▸MATH** Write a real-world division problem that involves dividing a 3-digit number by a 1-digit number that results in a 2-digit quotient with a remainder. See Ch. 8 Answer Appendix.

Homework Practice (p. 40) OL

8–7 Name ______ Date ______

Homework Practice

Three-Digit Quotients

Divide. Use estimation to check.

1. 5)569 **113 R4**
2. 2)873 **436 R1**
3. 5)675 **135**
4. 4)845 **211 R1**
5. 3)334 **111 R1**
6. 6)727 **121 R1**
7. 8)895 **111 R7**
8. 5)567 **113 R2**
9. 9)999 **111**
10. 4)850 **212 R2**
11. 3)673 **224 R1**
12. 7)849 **121 R2**
13. 5)997 **199 R2**
14. 8)978 **122 R2**
15. 7)987 **141**
16. 3)673 **224 R1**
17. 6)674 **112 R2**
18. 5)584 **116 R4**
19. 3)534 **178**
20. 5)563 **112 R3**

Spiral Review **Use any strategy to solve.** (Lesson 8-6)

21. What is the next number in the pattern 16, 32, 64, 128, ___ ? What is the pattern?
256; × 2

22. Janice has 8 coins that total 80 cents. What are the coins?
1 quarter, 4 dimes, 3 nickels; or 8 dimes

Grade 4 40 Chapter 8

Extend Technology Activity for 8-7 Division

MAIN IDEA

I will use technology to divide three-digit dividends.

Elizabeth downloads many CDs throughout the year. The total cost of downloaded CDs for last year was $324. If she paid this in 6 payments, how much would each payment be?

You can use the *Math Tool Chest* to show $324 divided by 6.

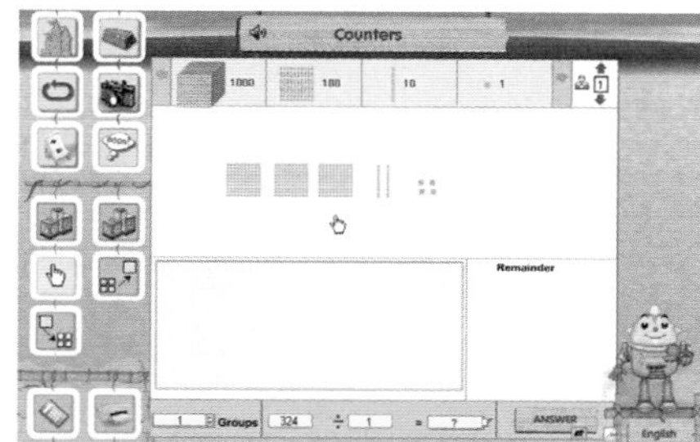

- Click on the counters tool box.
- Click on level 2. Then click on mat type.
- Choose base ten. Then click on OK.
- Stamp out 3 hundreds, 2 tens, and 4 ones.
- Choose to divide this number into 6 groups.
- Click on answer to find the amount each payment will be.

CHECK What You Know

Model each division problem. Then solve.

1. 155 ÷ 7 22 R1 **2.** 225 ÷ 8 28 R1 **3.** 352 ÷ 4 88

Use technology to solve.

4. A group of 9 friends bought tickets to a baseball game. The total cost of the tickets was $153. What was the cost of each ticket? $17

5. A case of trading cards has 5 boxes. The total cost of the case is $130. What is the cost of each box of trading cards? $26

6. **Analyze** How can modeling help you find the solution to a division problem? Sample answer: It shows the answer in concrete form so it can be seen and proven.

Math Tool Chest: Counters Tool Box Level 2

Mat Type Students click Mat Type on the Button Bar to open the Mat Type window and select a mat to use. Choose Base ten.

Select Students use  to choose a place-value model on which to perform an action.

Erase Students use [eraser] to remove place-value models from the mat.

Stamp When the Stamp button appears highlighted, students can click a place-value model and stamp it on the mat.

Explore Technology Activity for 8-7

Lesson Planner

Objective

Use technology to divide three-digit dividends.

Resources

Math Tool Chest *(accessible in three ways)*

- Math Online macmillanmh.com
- StudentWorks Plus
- Interactive Classroom

Getting Started

- Share with students that this activity requires them to use Math Tool Chest, a computer program that allows them to explore mathematical concepts and develop math skills.
- Have students read each example on p. 335.
- As a class, work through each activity in each example following the instructions on the page.

Using Math Tool Chest

The [icon] in Math Tool Chest provides opportunities for students to make base 10 models quickly and easily.

- The Division mat is made up of two parts: the top part for the dividend and the bottom for the answer, with a separate box for the remainder.
- By clicking the Answer button, Math Tool Chest solves the problem. Math Tool Chest automatically moves the base-ten models to the bottom part of the mat, regroups the models and solves the problem.
- When solving a problem, students can click the number box switch to hide the answer.

LESSON 8-8

Quotients with Zeros

Lesson Planner

Objective

Solve division problems that result in quotients that have zeros.

Review Vocabulary

estimate

Resources

Manipulatives: base-ten blocks

Literature Connection: *Olympics* by DK Eyewitness Books (Dorling Kindersley)

Teacher Technology

TeacherWorks • Interactive Classroom

Daily Routine

Use these suggestions before beginning the lesson on p. 336.

5-Minute Check

(Reviews Lesson 8-7)

Divide. Check your answers.

1. 678 ÷ 6 113 **2.** 457 ÷ 4 114 R1

3. 889 ÷ 5 177 R4 **4.** 956 ÷ 7 136 R4

Problem of the Day

Jasmeen practices the piano 5 days a week. If she practices for 45 minutes a day, what is her total practice time for one week? 3h 45min

Focus on Math Background

An area that is often troublesome for students is problems with a zero or zeros in the quotient. For example, students sometimes incorrectly determine that 416 ÷ 4 is 14 rather than 104. Using concrete models such as base-ten blocks or money to act out the problem can minimize difficulties of this type. Also, having students estimate the quotient is critical to this lesson. In the case of 416 ÷ 4, most students will estimate the quotient as 100 and then realize that an exact quotient of 14 is probably incorrect.

Review Math Vocabulary

Write the review vocabulary word and its definition on the board.

Have each student estimate the width of his or her desk or table by using a hand width, including the thumb. Discuss why students may have very different estimates.

Visual Vocabulary Cards

Use Visual Vocabulary Card 15 to reinforce the vocabulary reviewed in this lesson. (The Define/Example/Ask routine is printed on the back of each card.)

Differentiated Instruction

Small Group Options

Option 1 Below Level BL

LINGUISTIC

Materials: pencil and paper to solve and plain paper to illustrate the problems

Provide students with a copy of the following problems:

- *The Kincaids are really having fun on their vacation. The family members had such a good time swimming with the dolphins that they want to visit a museum, which is 5 miles away with lots more information about them. What is the new total mileage for the trip? Use Example 2 on p. 363 to help you.* 425 miles
- *Tickets to the museum cost $10 each for adults and $5 each for children. There are 4 adults and 3 children in the family. What is the total cost of the tickets?* $55
- Draw a picture to show all your work and explain it to a classmate.

Option 2 English Language Learners ELL

LINGUISTIC, SOCIAL

Materials: construction paper, string

Core Vocabulary: yell, too small, I've got enough

Common Use Verb: don't have enough

Hear Math This strategy teaches vocabulary to vocalize when quantities are divisible.

- Tell students that to *not have enough* means that a number is too small to be divided by another.
- Say, "I don't have enough!"
- Write a problem on the board to work together that will have a zero quotient.
- Model and prompt by saying "I don't have enough!"
- Repeat with a division problem, saying "I've got enough."
- Repeat as time permits.

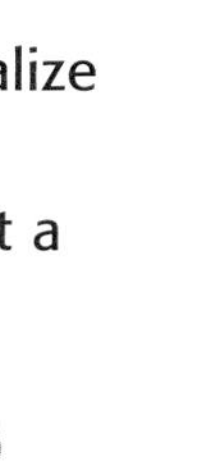

Independent Work Options

Option 1 Early Finishers OL AL

SOCIAL, LINGUISTIC

Materials: paper and pencil

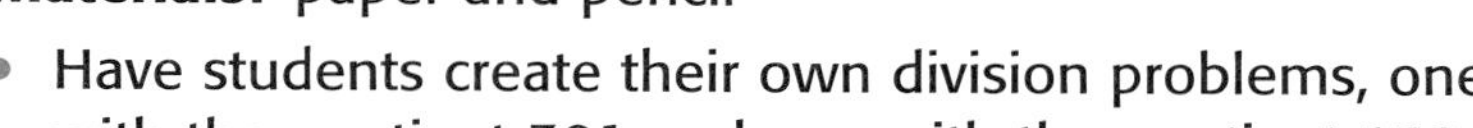

- Have students create their own division problems, one with the quotient 301 and one with the quotient 150.
- Have partners trade problems and check answers. If they do not get the given quotients, partners should work together to determine the errors.

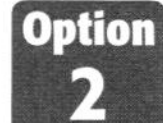

Option 2 Student Technology

Math Online macmillanmh.com

Personal Tutor • Extra Examples

Math Adventures

Option 3 Learning Station: Writing (p. 308G)

Direct students to the Writing Learning Station for opportunities to explore and extend the lesson concept.

Option 4 Problem-Solving Practice

Reinforce problem-solving skills and strategies with the Problem-Solving Practice worksheet.

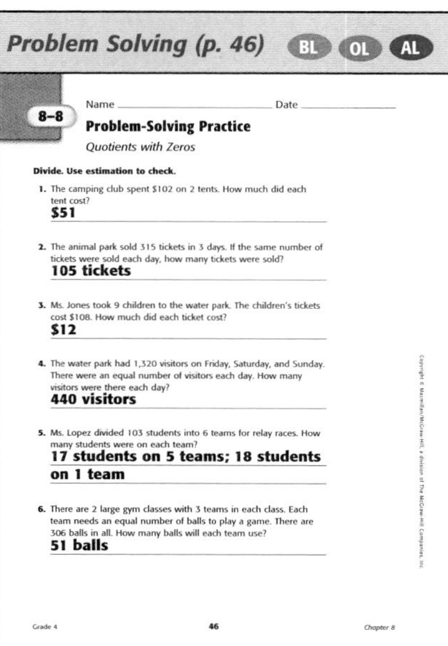

Problem Solving (p. 46) BL OL AL

Name ________ Date ________

8–8 **Problem-Solving Practice**

Quotients with Zeros

Divide. Use estimation to check.

1. The camping club spent $102 on 2 tents. How much did each tent cost? **$51**
2. The animal park sold 315 tickets in 3 days. If the same number of tickets were sold each day, how many tickets were sold? **105 tickets**
3. Ms. Jones took 9 children to the water park. The children's tickets cost $108. How much did each ticket cost? **$12**
4. The water park had 1,320 visitors on Friday, Saturday, and Sunday. There were an equal number of visitors each day. How many visitors were there each day? **440 visitors**
5. Ms. Lopez divided 103 students into 6 teams for relay races. How many students were on each team? **17 students on 5 teams; 18 students on 1 team**
6. There are 2 large gym classes with 3 teams in each class. Each team needs an equal number of balls to play a game. There are 306 balls in all. How many balls will each team use? **51 balls**

Grade 4 46 Chapter 8

8-8 Quotients with Zeros

1 Introduce

Activity Choice 1 • Hands-On

Materials: base-ten blocks

- Have students use base-ten blocks to model 448. Review place values.
- Then have them model how they would divide their blocks into 4 equal groups.
- **How many hundreds are in each group?** 1
- **How many tens?** 1
- **How many ones?** 2
- **What is 448 ÷ 4?** 112

Activity Choice 2 • Literature

Introduce the lesson with *Olympics* by DK Eyewitness Books. For a related math activity, see p. TR55.

2 Teach

Scaffolding Questions

Materials: base-ten blocks

- Have students use base-ten blocks to model the division of 428 into 4 equal groups.
- **How many hundreds are in each group?** 1
- **How many tens?** 0
- **How many ones?** 7
- **What is 428 ÷ 4?** 107
- Now have students use the division algorithm to divide 428 by 4.
- **How do you know where to place the first digit in the quotient?** Sample answer: The 4 divides the first digit of the dividend.
- **Why do you need to write a zero in the quotient?** Sample answer: You need to show that there are not enough tens to divide by 4.

GET READY to Learn

Have students open their books and read the information in **Get Ready to Learn**. Review **estimate**. As a class, work through **Examples 1 and 2**.

8-8 Quotients with Zeros

MAIN IDEA

I will solve division problems that result in quotients that have zeros.

Math Online

macmillanmh.com

- Extra Examples
- Personal Tutor
- Self-Check Quiz

GET READY to Learn

The Ramos family is going on a behind-the-scenes tour of a wildlife reserve in a park. How much will it cost for each person?

Cost of Tour	
Number of People	Cost ($)
3	$327

In division, a quotient will sometimes contain zeros.

Real-World EXAMPLE — Divide Greater Numbers

1 ANIMALS **How much it will cost for each family member to go on the tour?**

You need to find $327 ÷ 3.

Step 1 Divide the hundreds.

$\$1$ over $3\overline{)\$327}$, -3, 0

Divide. $3 \div 3 = 1$
Put 1 in hundreds place.
Multiply. $3 \times 1 = 3$
Subtract. $3 - 3 = 0$
Compare. $0 < 3$

Step 2 Divide the tens.

$\$10$ over $3\overline{)\$327}$, -3, 02, -0, 2

Bring down the tens.
Divide. Since $2 < 3$, there is not enough to divide. So, put 0 in the tens place.
Multiply. $3 \times 0 = 0$
Subtract. $2 - 0 = 0$
Compare. $2 < 3$

Step 3 Divide the ones.

$\$109$ over $3\overline{)\$327}$, -3, 02, -0, 27, -27, 0

Bring down the ones.
Divide. $27 \div 3 = 9$
Put 9 in the ones place.
Multiply. $3 \times 9 = 27$
Subtract. $27 - 27 = 0$
Compare. $0 < 3$

So, it will cost each family member $109.

336 **Chapter 8** Divide by One-Digit Numbers

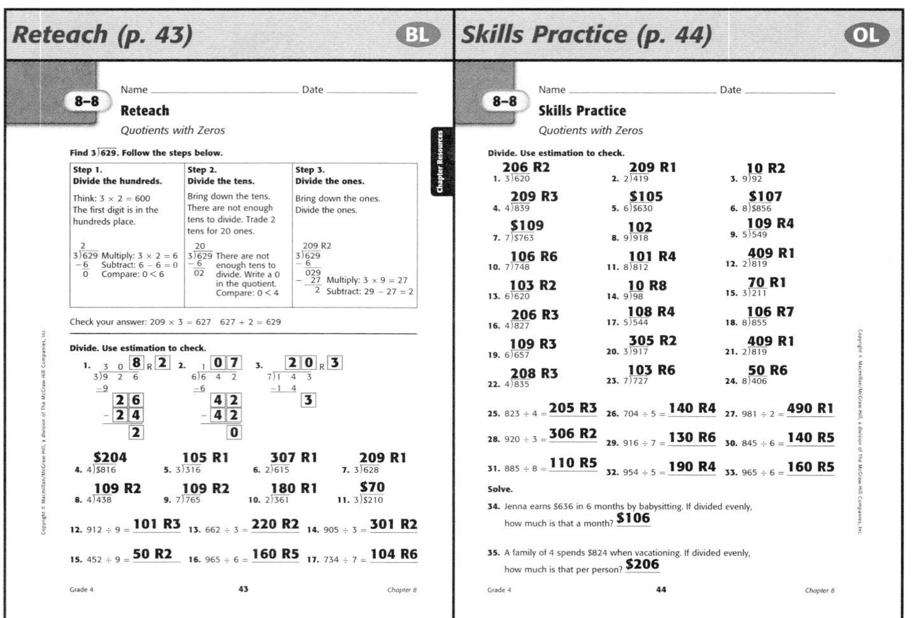

Reteach (p. 43) BL

8-8 Name ______ Date ______

Reteach

Quotients with Zeros

Find $3\overline{)629}$. Follow the steps below.

Step 1. Divide the hundreds.	Step 2. Divide the tens.	Step 3. Divide the ones.
Think: 3 × 2 = 600 The first digit is in the hundreds place.	Bring down the tens. There are not enough tens to divide. Trade 2 tens for 20 ones.	Bring down the ones. Divide the ones.
2 over 3)629, −6, 0. Multiply: 3 × 2 = 6 Subtract: 6 − 6 = 0 Compare: 0 < 6	20 over 3)629, −6, 02. There are not enough tens to divide. Write a 0 in the quotient. Compare: 0 < 4	209 R2 over 3)629, −6, 029, −27, 2. Multiply: 3 × 9 = 27 Subtract: 29 − 27 = 2

Check your answer: 209 × 3 = 627   627 + 2 = 629

Divide. Use estimation to check.

1. 3)926 = 308 R2 (−9, 26, −24, 2)
2. 6)642 = 107 (−6, 42, −42, 0)
3. 7)143 = 20 R3 (−14, 3)
4. 4)$816 **$204**
5. 3)316 **105 R1**
6. 2)615 **307 R1**
7. 3)628 **209 R1**
8. 4)438 **109 R2**
9. 7)765 **109 R2**
10. 2)361 **180 R1**
11. 3)$210 **$70**
12. 912 ÷ 9 = **101 R3**
13. 662 ÷ 3 = **220 R2**
14. 905 ÷ 3 = **301 R2**
15. 452 ÷ 9 = **50 R2**
16. 965 ÷ 6 = **160 R5**
17. 734 ÷ 7 = **104 R6**

Grade 4 43 Chapter 8

Skills Practice (p. 44) OL

8-8 Name ______ Date ______

Skills Practice

Quotients with Zeros

Divide. Use estimation to check.

1. 3)620 **206 R2**
2. 2)419 **209 R1**
3. 9)92 **10 R2**
4. 4)839 **209 R3**
5. 6)$630 **$105**
6. 8)$856 **$107**
7. 7)$763 **$109**
8. 9)918 **102**
9. 5)549 **109 R4**
10. 7)748 **106 R6**
11. 8)812 **101 R4**
12. 2)819 **409 R1**
13. 6)620 **103 R2**
14. 9)98 **10 R8**
15. 3)211 **70 R1**
16. 4)827 **206 R3**
17. 5)544 **108 R4**
18. 8)855 **106 R7**
19. 6)657 **109 R3**
20. 3)917 **305 R2**
21. 2)819 **409 R1**
22. 4)835 **208 R3**
23. 7)727 **103 R6**
24. 8)406 **50 R6**
25. 823 ÷ 4 = **205 R3**
26. 704 ÷ 5 = **140 R4**
27. 981 ÷ 2 = **490 R1**
28. 920 ÷ 3 = **306 R2**
29. 916 ÷ 7 = **130 R6**
30. 845 ÷ 6 = **140 R5**
31. 885 ÷ 8 = **110 R5**
32. 954 ÷ 5 = **190 R4**
33. 965 ÷ 6 = **160 R5**

Solve.

34. Jenna earns $636 in 6 months by babysitting. If divided evenly, how much is that a month? **$106**
35. A family of 4 spends $824 when vacationing. If divided evenly, how much is that per person? **$206**

Grade 4 44 Chapter 8

Real-World EXAMPLE — Divide with Remainders

2 VACATIONS The Kincaid family is going on vacation. They have to drive 415 miles to get to and from Dolphin Cove. How far is it to Dolphin Cove?

The total distance the Kincaids will travel is 415 miles. To find the distance to Dolphin Cove, divide 415 by 2.

Estimate 415 ÷ 2 ⟶ 400 ÷ 2 = 200

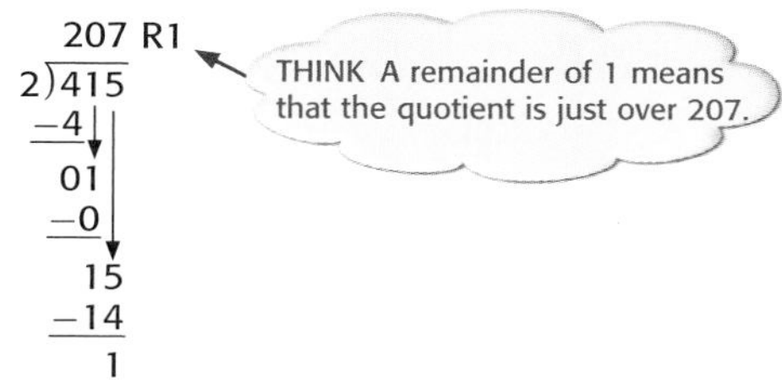

207 R1
2)415
−4
01
−0
15
−14
1
THINK A remainder of 1 means that the quotient is just over 207.

Remember

Remember to divide, multiply, subtract, and compare. Then bring down the next number in the dividend.

So, the distance to Dolphin Cove is a little more than 207 miles.

Check for Reasonableness

The quotient, 207 R1, is close to the estimate. So, the answer is reasonable. ✓

CHECK What You Know

Divide. Use estimation to check. See Examples 1 and 2 (pp. 336–337)

1. 2)212 106
2. 3)$627 $209
3. 4)416 104
4. 617 ÷ 2 308 R1
5. $913 ÷ 3 $304 R$1
6. 825 ÷ 4 206 R1
7. Clara's total score for 3 games of bowling is 312. If Clara earned the same score for each game, what was her score for each game? 104
8.  Explain how to find the quotient of 624 ÷ 3. Sample answer: Divide each place by 3, starting with the hundreds place.

Enrich (p. 47) AL

8-8

Name ________________ Date ________

Enrich

Strategic Division

Use one-digit divisors to create 20 division problems. Choose divisors carefully to earn points as follows:

Zeros in the quotient's hundreds place are not worth any points.
Zeros in the quotient's tens place are worth 2 points.
Zeros in the quotient's ones place are worth 1 point.

1.)604	2.)781	3.)852	4.)509	5.)619
6.)775	7.)423	8.)170	9.)875	10.)181
11.)363	12.)725	13.)211	14.)321	15.)354
16.)104	17.)545	18.)323	19.)906	20.)806

Answers will vary, but students should gain the understanding that they can earn more points by thinking ahead, and choosing the divisor carefully. For example, if they choose 6 to be the divisor in the first problem, there will be zeros in the tens and ones place (100 R4)

Zeros in the 10's Place = ____ × 2 = ____

Zeros in the 1's Place = ____ × 1 = ____

Total Points Earned = ____

Chapter Resources

Grade 4 47 Chapter 8

Divide with Remainders

Example 2 Explain to students that interpreting the remainder in a real-world exercise demonstrates strong mathematical reasoning of division.

ADDITIONAL EXAMPLES

1. Rita is using 315 beads to make beaded necklaces for 3 of her friends. If each necklace has the same number of beads, how many beads will each necklace have? 105
2. The camping club spent $217 on 2 large tents. How much did each tent cost? 108 R1, or a little more than $108 each

CHECK What You Know

As a class, have students complete Exercises 1–8 in **Check What You Know** as you observe their work.

Exercise 8 Assess student comprehension before assigning practice exercises.

BL Alternate Teaching Strategy

If students have trouble using zeros in the correct place value…

Then use one of these reteach options:

1. CRM **Daily Reteach Worksheet** (p. 43)
2. Allow students to use base-ten blocks to model their division algorithms.
   - **Are there enough hundreds to divide?**
   - **Are there enough tens to divide?**
   - **Are there enough ones to divide?**
   - **How do you record the number when there is not enough to divide in a place value?** Write a zero.

COMMON ERROR!

Exercises 1–6 Students may forget to write the zeros in quotients or place additional zeros in quotients when they are not necessary. To help them avoid these errors, suggest that they always use estimation and check their answers by multiplication.

3 Practice

Differentiate practice using these leveled assignments for Exercises 9–26.

Level	Assignment
BL Below/Approaching Level	9-12, 19-22, 24
OL On Level	9–18, 21–24
AL Above/Beyond Level	9–23 odd, 25–26

Have students discuss and complete the Higher Order Thinking problems. Encourage students to use compatible numbers and to check their answers by multiplication.

WRITING IN ▸MATH Have students complete Exercise 26 in their Math Journals. You may choose to use this exercise as an optional formative assessment.

4 Assess

Formative Assessment

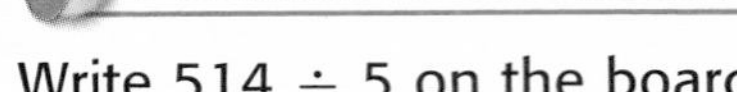

Write 514 ÷ 5 on the board.

- **Have students explain the steps used in finding the quotient.** Sample answer: Divide the hundreds digit; multiply, subtract, compare; bring down the tens. Since there is not enough to divide, place a zero in the tens place in the quotient; multiply, subtract, and compare. Bring down the ones; divide, multiply, subtract and compare. Label the remainder.

Quick Check **Are students continuing to struggle with quotients with zeros?**

If Yes → Strategic Intervention Guide (p. 78)

If No → Independent Work Options (p. 336B)
CRM Skills Practice Worksheet (p. 44)
CRM Enrich Worksheet (p. 47)

Into the Future Tell students the next lesson is about dividing greater numbers. Have them write how they think today's lesson on quotients with zeros will help them divide greater numbers.

Practice and Problem Solving

Divide. Use estimation to check. See Examples 1 and 2 (pp. 336–337)

9. 2)214 107
10. 3)327 109
11. 5)$545 $109
12. 6)648 108
13. 7)742 106
14. 8)$824 $103
15. 2)417 208 R1
16. 3)622 207 R1
17. $613 ÷ 3 $204 R1
18. 837 ÷ 4 209 R1
19. 1,819 ÷ 2 909 R1
20. $2,429 ÷ 3 809 R2

21. There are 412 toys to be put on 4 shelves at a toy store. If the same number of toys fit on each shelf, how many toys fit on each shelf? 103

22. There are 408 students at a school. There are 4 lunch periods. If there are the same number of students in each lunch period, how many students are in each period? 102

Real-World PROBLEM SOLVING

Treasure Geocaching is an outdoor treasure hunting game in which participants use a Global Positioning System to hide and seek "treasures" all over the world. The "treasures" are usually toys or trinkets.

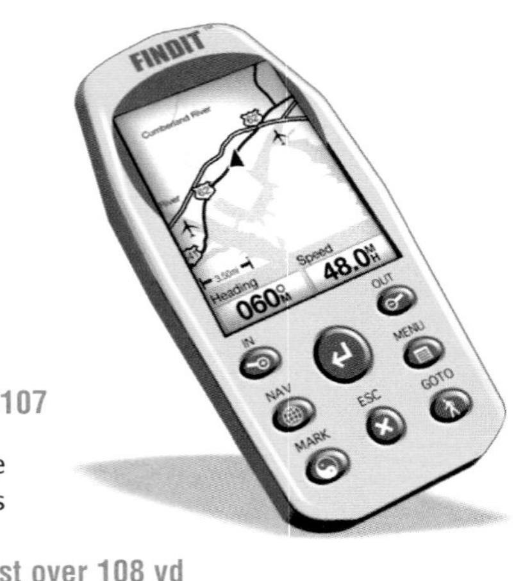

23. Chad is saving his money to buy a Global Positioning System receiver so that he can go geocaching. He has 2 months to save $215. How much money does he need to save each month? $107 R$1, so just over $107

24. Measurement Some of the treasures have been hidden on mountains. If the treasure is 325 feet away, how many yards away is it? (*Remember:* 3 feet = 1 yard) 108 R1, so just over 108 yd

H.O.T. Problems

25. OPEN ENDED Identify a 3-digit dividend that will result in a 3-digit quotient that has a zero in the tens place when the divisor is 6. Sample answer: 646

26. WRITING IN ▸MATH Explain how an estimate could help you remember to write a zero in a quotient that results in a 2-digit quotient with a remainder. Sample answer: If the estimate is 3 digits, then the quotient will most likely be 3 digits.

338 Chapter 8 Divide by One-Digit Numbers

Homework Practice (p. 45) OL

8–8 Name ______ Date ______

Homework Practice

Quotients with Zeros

Divide. Use estimation to check.

1. 5)512 **102 R2**
2. 3)624 **208**
3. 4)837 **209 R1**
4. 7)764 **109 R1**
5. 3)926 **308 R2**
6. 9)943 **104 R7**
7. 2)642 **321**
8. 4)813 **203 R1**
9. 4)436 **109**
10. 2)218 **109**
11. 5)543 **108 R3**
12. 6)643 **107 R1**
13. 3)629 **209 R2**
14. 4)839 **209 R3**
15. 6)658 **109 R4**
16. 6)643 **107 R1**
17. 4)822 **205 R2**
18. 3)319 **106 R1**
19. 2)611 **305 R1**
20. 9)984 **109 R3**

Spiral Review

Divide. Use estimation to check. (Lesson 8-7)

21. 7)878 **125 R3**
22. 3)561 **187**
23. 6)684 **114**
24. 8)937 **117 R1**

Solve.

25. 4 plums fit in a box. How many boxes can be filled with 968 plums? **242 boxes**

Grade 4 45 Chapter 8

Chapter Resources

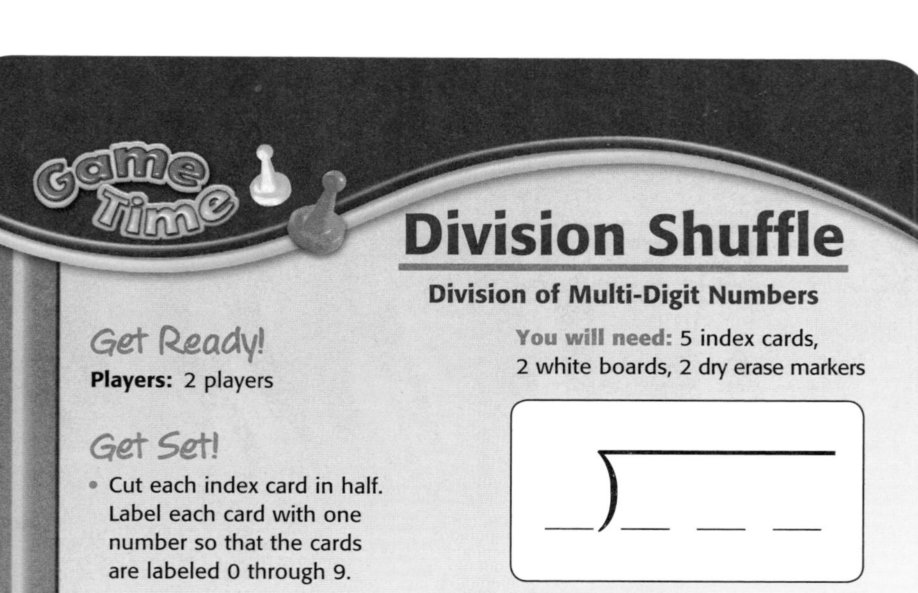

Division Shuffle

Division of Multi-Digit Numbers

Get Ready!

Players: 2 players

You will need: 5 index cards, 2 white boards, 2 dry erase markers

Get Set!

- Cut each index card in half. Label each card with one number so that the cards are labeled 0 through 9.

Go!

- Shuffle and then place the cards facedown on the table.
- Both players draw a division symbol on their white boards.
- Player 1 draws four cards, and then turns them over one at a time. After each card is turned over, Players 1 and 2 write each number in any blank on their white boards.
- After all of the numbers are recorded, Players 1 and 2 find and check the quotients.
- The player that has the greatest quotient gets 1 point.
- Continue playing until a player earns 5 points. Reshuffle the cards if needed.

Differentiated Practice

Use these leveled suggestions to differentiate the game for all learners.

Level	Assignment
BL Below/Approaching Level	Students use unit blocks to model their answers.
OL On Level	Have students play the game with the rules as written.
AL Above/Beyond Level	Students make more cards and the judge chooses five numbers, to make a four-digit dividend.

Division Shuffle

Math Concept: Division of Multi-Digit Numbers

Materials: 5 index cards, 2 white boards, 2 dry erase markers

Introduce the game on p. 339 to your students to play as a class, in small groups, or at a learning workstation to review concepts introduced in this chapter.

Instructions

- Students form teams of two. Each team makes a set of number cards, cutting the index cards in half and numbering them with one number for each card, so that they are labeled 0–9 (two cards for each number).
- Students shuffle the cards and lay them facedown. Both players draw a division house as shown.
- Player 1 selects 4 cards and turns them over one at a time. After each card is turned over, both players write the number in one of the blanks in their division house. Note that if a zero is one of the numbers, students should not use zero as the divisor.
- After all numbers have been placed, players find the quotient of the division problem they have created. The player with the greatest quotient gets 1 point. If the quotients are equal, each player gets 1 point.
- Play continues until one player reaches 5 points. That person is the winner. Reshuffle as necessary.

Extend the Game

Have students make the game using a larger game board, such as the standard 5 × 5 Bingo size, and more cards.

Lesson Planner

Objective

Interpret information and data from science to solve problems.

National Standard 

Students should develop understanding of organisms and environments.

Activate Prior Knowledge

Before you turn students' attention to the pages, ask them to discuss deserts.

- **What do all deserts have in common?** They are hot and dry.
- **What are some desert animals who are endangered species?** elephants

Using the Student Page

Ask students to read the information on p. 340 and answer these questions:

- **If it took you 5 days to travel the width of the Sahara desert and you traveled the same amount each day, how many miles would you travel each day?** 200 miles
- **If each hippopotamus eats the same amount of food each day, how much does one hippopotamus eat in one day?** 150 pounds of food

The Sahara desert in Africa is 800 to 1,200 miles wide and 3,000 miles long. Animals like elephants, giraffes, lions, and chimpanzees live in or near this desert. Many African desert animals can also be found in zoos, where they are protected and fed.

Some animals, such as the elephant, are very large. An average elephant weighs 12,250 pounds, and its trunk weighs 400 pounds!

Food Eaten by Zoo Animals

Animal	Number of Animals	Daily Food (lb)
Hippopotamus	6	900
Elephant	10	1,600
Giraffe	6	360
Lion	7	218
Camel	5	94
Hyena	8	144
Chimpanzee	9	117
Flamingo	8	1

Real-World Math

Use the information on page 340 to solve each problem.

1. Suppose each camel eats the same amount of food. About how much food would one camel eat in one week? **about 140 lb**
2. A visitor travels the length of the Sahara desert in 10 days and travels the same amount each day. How many miles does the visitor travel each day? **300 miles**
3. Suppose each elephant eats the same amount of food. How much food do four elephants eat in a day? **640 lb**
4. How many ounces of food does each flamingo eat per day? (*Hint*: 1 pound = 16 ounces) **2 ounces**
5. Does a hyena or a chimpanzee eat more each day? Explain. **hyena; 18 lb > 13 lb**
6. How much more do three elephants eat than three hippopotamus? **30 lb**
7. How much food is eaten each day by one giraffe, one hyena, and one lion? Order these animals in order from greatest to least with respect to the amount of food each eats. **See margin.**

Did You Know?
The African elephant is the largest land mammal.

 Real-World Math

Assign the exercises on p. 341. Encourage students to choose a problem-solving strategy before beginning each exercise. If necessary, review the strategies suggested in Lesson 8-6, p. 330.

Exercise 1 Remind students that the daily amount of food listed in the chart is for the whole group of animals in the exhibit.

Exercise 3 Tell students that they need to find how much one elephant eats first before they can solve this problem.

Exercise 5 Remind students that there are more chimpanzees in the exhibit than hyenas, so it is important to figure out how much one of each eats before answering the question.

WRITING IN MATH Have students create a word problem that uses the information found in the text and in the chart on p. 340.

Extend the Activity

Have students make a chart showing how much one of each animal would eat per day, and per week.

Additional Answer

7. giraffe: 60 lb,
   lion: 31 R1 lb
   hyena: 18 lb
   giraffe, lion, hyena

LESSON 8-9

Divide Greater Numbers

Lesson Planner

Objective

Divide four-digit dividends by a one-digit number.

Review Vocabulary

place value

Resources

Literature Connection: *Stellaluna* by Janell Cannon

Teacher Technology

TeacherWorks • Interactive Classroom

Daily Routine

Use these suggestions before beginning the lesson on p. 342.

5-Minute Check

(Reviews Lesson 8-8)

Divide.

1. 525 ÷ 5 105 **2.** 621 ÷ 3 207

3. 967 ÷ 9 107 R4 **4.** 635 ÷ 6 105 R5

Problem of the Day

Kelton earned $63 for babysitting last weekend. He charges $4 for each hour, and he also received $15 in tips. How many hours did he babysit last weekend? 12 hours

Focus on Math Background

The focus of this lesson is on dividing four-digit numbers by one-digit divisors. Again, the algorithm does not change, but students must be more persistent as they work with the larger dividends. Continue to stress the importance of basic facts and place value. Also note that estimating quotients may become more difficult as the dividends get greater. This happens because the number that connects the divisor and dividend is sometimes more difficult for students to find.

Review Math Vocabulary

Write the review vocabulary term and its definition on the board.

Have students identify the place value of each number in the Real-World Examples 1 and 2. Have volunteers read the numbers aloud to the class and then identify the place value of each digit.

Differentiated Instruction

Small Group Options

LOGICAL, LINGUISTIC

Option 1 Gifted and Talented AL

Materials: paper and pencil

- Have students write a word problem that requires division of four- or five-digit dividends to solve. Challenge students to use numbers that can be divided using any of the three ways presented in the lesson.

SOCIAL, LINGUISTIC, KINESTHETIC

Option 2 English Language Learners ELL

Materials: chalkboard
Core Vocabulary: stars, know the step, help
Common Use Verb: hit

Talk Math This strategy demonstrates the separate steps in dividing greater numbers.

- Draw two stars on the board and a problem between them. Have students form 2 groups and line up.
- If the first student in line knows the first step in solving the problem, they will hit the star with their hand.
- The first student to hit the star will tell you the first step in completing the problem and go to the end of the time.
- Continue until the problem is solved.
- Repeat for other problems as time permits.
- For struggling students, allow their teammates to help them solve the step.

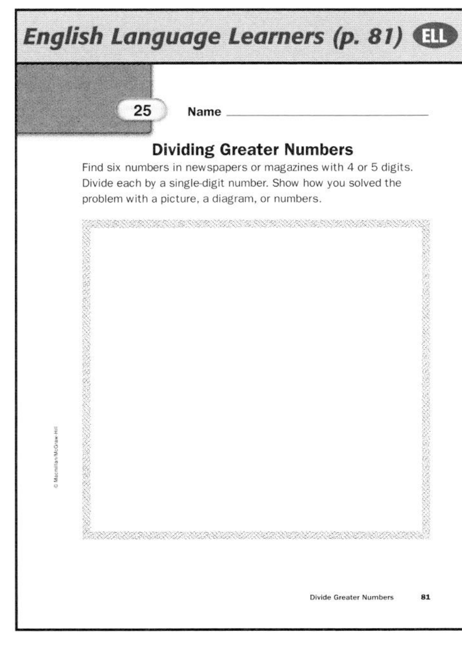

English Language Learners (p. 81) ELL

25 Name ______

Dividing Greater Numbers

Find six numbers in newspapers or magazines with 4 or 5 digits. Divide each by a single-digit number. Show how you solved the problem with a picture, a diagram, or numbers.

Divide Greater Numbers 81

Use this worksheet to provide additional support for English Language Learners.

Independent Work Options

LOGICAL, SOCIAL

Option 1 Early Finishers OL AL

- Have students write a division problem using a large three-digit number as a dividend and a one-digit number as a divisor.
- Students exchange problems with a classmate and solve the problems they receive.
- Students compare answers and discuss any errors they find.
- Remind students to use estimation or multiplication to check their work.

Option 2 Student Technology

Math Online macmillanmh.com

Personal Tutor • Extra Examples

 Math Adventures

Option 3 Learning Station: Art (p. 308G)

Direct students to the Art Learning Station for opportunities to explore and extend the lesson concept.

Option 4 Problem-Solving Practice

Reinforce problem-solving skills and strategies with the Problem-Solving Practice worksheet.

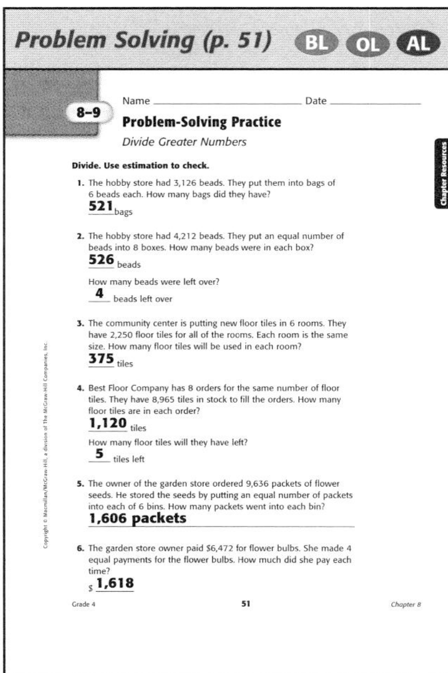

Problem Solving (p. 51) BL OL AL

8–9 Name ______ Date ______

Problem-Solving Practice

Divide Greater Numbers

Chapter Resources

Divide. Use estimation to check.

1. The hobby store had 3,126 beads. They put them into bags of 6 beads each. How many bags did they have?
   521 bags
2. The hobby store had 4,212 beads. They put an equal number of beads into 8 boxes. How many beads were in each box?
   526 beads
   How many beads were left over?
   4 beads left over
3. The community center is putting new floor tiles in 6 rooms. They have 2,250 floor tiles for all of the rooms. Each room is the same size. How many floor tiles will be used in each room?
   375 tiles
4. Best Floor Company has 8 orders for the same number of floor tiles. They have 8,965 tiles in stock to fill the orders. How many floor tiles are in each order?
   1,120 tiles
   How many floor tiles will they have left?
   5 tiles left
5. The owner of the garden store ordered 9,636 packets of flower seeds. He stored the seeds by putting an equal number of packets into each of 6 bins. How many packets went into each bin?
   1,606 packets
6. The garden store owner paid $6,472 for flower bulbs. She made 4 equal payments for the flower bulbs. How much did she pay each time?
   $ **1,618**

Grade 4 51 Chapter 8

Divide Greater Numbers

1 Introduce

Activity Choice 1 • Hands-On 

- Write 449 ÷ 4 on the board. Review basic division and patterns such as 4 ÷ 4 = 1, 40 ÷ 4 = 10, 400 ÷ 4 = 100.
- Have students use the division algorithm to find 449 ÷ 4. As you review the algorithm with them, stress place value and the position of the digits in the quotient.
- Now write 4,495 ÷ 4 on the board. Ask students to use compatible numbers and patterns to estimate the quotient.
  4 ÷ 4 = 1, 40 ÷ 4 = 10, 400 ÷ 4 = 100, so 4,000 ÷ 4 = 1,000

Activity Choice 2 • Literature

Introduce the lesson with *Stellaluna* by Janell Cannon. For a related math activity, see p. TR55.

2 Teach

Scaffolding Questions

Write 6,938 ÷ 3 on the board. Have students use the division algorithm to find the quotient.

- **Why is 2 written above the 6 in the thousands place of the dividend?** Sample answer: There are 2 groups of 3 thousands in 6 thousands.
- **After dividing the thousands, what do you do?** Multiply, subtract, compare, and bring down the hundreds. Continue in that pattern until the division is complete. Write the remainder in the quotient.
- **What is 6,938 ÷ 3?** 2,312 R2
- **How many digits will be in the quotient for 6,321 ÷ 3. Explain.** 4; The first digit of the quotient is placed above the thousands place of the dividend.

GET READY to Learn

Have students open their books and read the information in **Get Ready to Learn**. Review **place value**. As a class, work through **Examples 1 and 2**.

Divide Greater Numbers

MAIN IDEA

I will divide four-digit dividends by a one-digit number.

Math Online

macmillanmh.com
- Extra Examples
- Personal Tutor
- Self-Check Quiz

GET READY to Learn

One of the largest holes in the world is a copper mine in Utah. It is 5,808 feet wide. How many yards wide is the hole?

You can use the same process to divide greater numbers that you use with smaller numbers.

Real-World EXAMPLE Divide Greater Numbers

1 MEASUREMENT How many yards wide is the copper mine?

The mine is 5,808 feet wide. There are 3 feet in 1 yard. So, to find the width in yards, divide 5,808 by 3.

Step 1 Divide the thousands.

$$\begin{array}{r} 1 \\ 3\overline{)5,808} \\ -3 \\ 2 \end{array}$$

Divide. 5 ÷ 3 = 1
Put 1 in thousands place.
Multiply. 3 × 1 = 3
Subtract. 5 − 3 = 2
Compare. 2 < 3

Step 2 Divide the hundreds.

$$\begin{array}{r} 19 \\ 3\overline{)5,808} \\ -3 \\ 28 \\ -27 \\ 1 \end{array}$$

Bring down the hundreds.
Divide. 28 ÷ 3 = 9
Multiply. 3 × 9 = 27
Put 9 in hundreds place.
Subtract. 28 − 27 = 1
Compare. 1 < 3

Step 3 Divide each place.

$$\begin{array}{r} 1,936 \\ 3\overline{)5,808} \\ -3 \\ 28 \\ -27 \\ 10 \\ -9 \\ 18 \\ -18 \\ 0 \end{array}$$

For each place, divide, multiply, subtract, compare, and bring down the next digit to form a new number to be divided.

So, the copper mine is 1,936 yards wide.

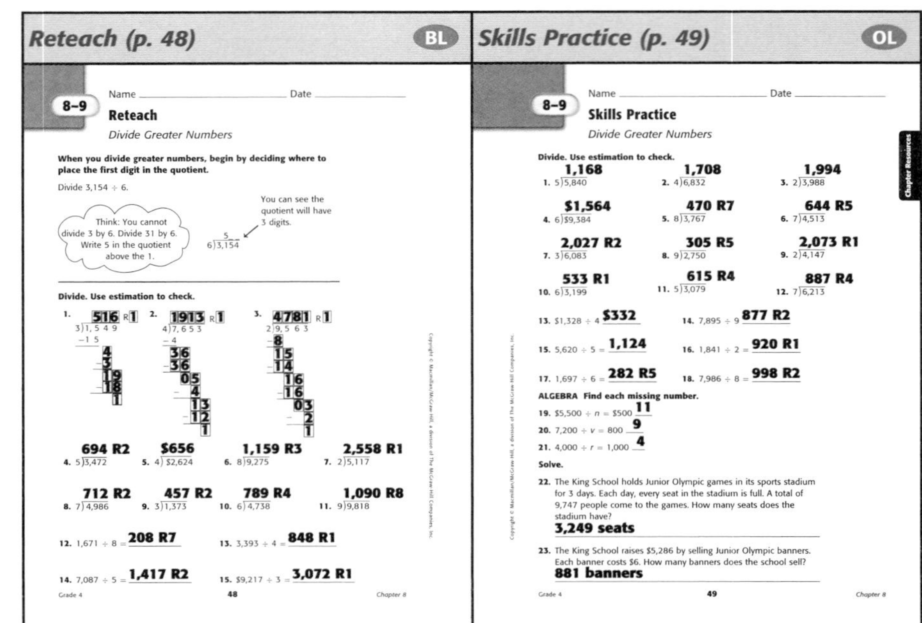

Reteach (p. 48) BL

8–9 Name ______ Date ______
Reteach
Divide Greater Numbers

When you divide greater numbers, begin by deciding where to place the first digit in the quotient.

Divide 3,154 ÷ 6.

Think: You cannot divide 3 by 6. Divide 31 by 6. Write 5 in the quotient above the 1.

$6\overline{)3,154}$ with 5 above the 1 — You can see the quotient will have 3 digits.

Divide. Use estimation to check.

1. $3\overline{)1,549}$ = **516** R**1** (−15, 4, −3, 19, −18, 1)
2. $4\overline{)7,653}$ = **1913** R**1** (−4, 36, −36, 05, −4, 13, −12, 1)
3. $2\overline{)9,563}$ = **4781** R**1** (−8, 15, −14, 16, −16, 03, −2, 1)
4. $5\overline{)3,472}$ **694 R2**
5. $4\overline{)\$2,624}$ **$656**
6. $8\overline{)9,275}$ **1,159 R3**
7. $2\overline{)5,117}$ **2,558 R1**
8. $7\overline{)4,986}$ **712 R2**
9. $3\overline{)1,373}$ **457 R2**
10. $6\overline{)4,738}$ **789 R4**
11. $9\overline{)9,818}$ **1,090 R8**
12. 1,671 ÷ 8 = **208 R7**
13. 3,393 ÷ 4 = **848 R1**
14. 7,087 ÷ 5 = **1,417 R2**
15. $9,217 ÷ 3 = **3,072 R1**

Grade 4 48 Chapter 8

Skills Practice (p. 49) OL

8–9 Name ______ Date ______
Skills Practice
Divide Greater Numbers

Divide. Use estimation to check.

1. $5\overline{)5,840}$ **1,168**
2. $4\overline{)6,832}$ **1,708**
3. $2\overline{)3,988}$ **1,994**
4. $6\overline{)\$9,384}$ **$1,564**
5. $8\overline{)3,767}$ **470 R7**
6. $7\overline{)4,513}$ **644 R5**
7. $3\overline{)6,083}$ **2,027 R2**
8. $9\overline{)2,750}$ **305 R5**
9. $2\overline{)4,147}$ **2,073 R1**
10. $6\overline{)3,199}$ **533 R1**
11. $5\overline{)3,079}$ **615 R4**
12. $7\overline{)6,213}$ **887 R4**
13. $1,328 ÷ 4 **$332**
14. 7,895 ÷ 9 **877 R2**
15. 5,620 ÷ 5 = **1,124**
16. 1,841 ÷ 2 = **920 R1**
17. 1,697 ÷ 6 = **282 R5**
18. 7,986 ÷ 8 = **998 R2**

ALGEBRA Find each missing number.

19. $5,500 ÷ *n* = $500 **11**
20. 7,200 ÷ *v* = 800 **9**
21. 4,000 ÷ *r* = 1,000 **4**

Solve.

22. The King School holds Junior Olympic games in its sports stadium for 3 days. Each day, every seat in the stadium is full. A total of 9,747 people come to the games. How many seats does the stadium have? **3,249 seats**
23. The King School raises $5,286 by selling Junior Olympic banners. Each banner costs $6. How many banners does the school sell? **881 banners**

Grade 4 49 Chapter 8

Chapter Resources

Real-World EXAMPLE — Divide Greater Numbers

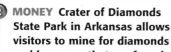

2 MONEY Crater of Diamonds State Park in Arkansas allows visitors to mine for diamonds and keep any that are found. If a person finds a 2-carat diamond that is worth $7,585, how much is each carat worth?

Divide $7,585 by 2 to find how much each carat is worth.

Estimate $7,585 ÷ 2 ⟶ $8,000 ÷ 2 = $4,000

Step 1 Divide the thousands.

```
    $3
 2)$7,585
   −6
    1
```

Divide. 7 ÷ 2 = 3
Put 3 in the quotient over the thousands place.

Multiply. 2 × 3 = 6
Subtract. 7 − 6 = 1
Compare. 1 < 2

Step 2 Divide the hundreds.

```
    $37
 2)$7,585
   −6↓
    15
   −14
     1
```

Bring down the hundreds.
Divide. 15 ÷ 2 = 7
Put 7 in the quotient over the hundreds place.

Multiply. 2 × 7 = 14
Subtract. 15 − 14 = 1
Compare. 1 < 2

Step 3 Divide each place.

```
    $3,792 R1
 2)$7,585
   −6↓
    15
   −14↓
     18
    −18↓
      05
     −04
       1
```

For each place, divide, multiply, subtract, and compare. Then bring down the next digit in the dividend.

So, each carat is worth a little more than $3,792.

Check for Reasonableness
The answer is close to the estimate. So, it is reasonable. ✓

Remember

For each place, divide, multiply, subtract, compare, and bring the next digit in the dividend directly down to form a new number to be divided.

Divide Greater Numbers

Example 2 Point out the remainder. Take time to review what the remainder means.

ADDITIONAL EXAMPLES

1. Mrs. Chi wants to bundle 4 muffins in a package for a fundraiser at school. Parents donated 4,576 muffins. How many bundles will be ready to sell? 1,144 bundles
2. The school play earned $6,530 for the day. If admission costs $5 a ticket, how many tickets were sold? 1,306

CHECK What You Know

As a class, have students complete Exercises 1–8 in **Check What You Know** as you observe their work.

Exercise 8 Assess student comprehension before assigning practice exercises.

BL Alternate Teaching Strategy

If students struggle using the division algorithm to divide greater numbers...

Then use one of these reteach options:

1. CRM **Daily Reteach Worksheet** (p. 48)
2. Have students design posters showing the division algorithm. Make sure the poster has the steps of the algorithm (divide, multiply, subtract, compare, bring down) labeled and shows an example, such as 3,687 ÷ 3.

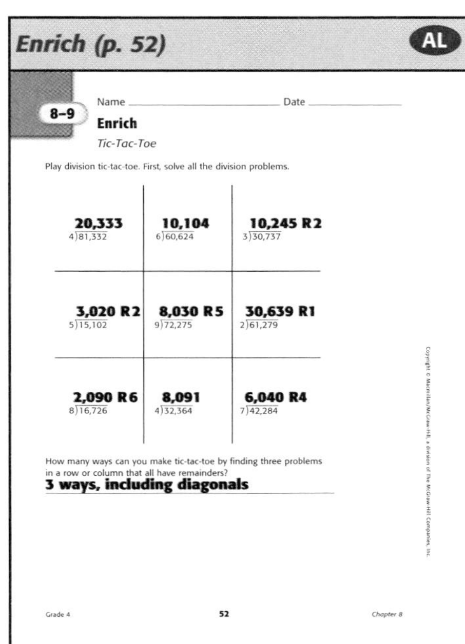

Enrich (p. 52) AL

8–9 Name ______ Date ______

Enrich

Tic-Tac-Toe

Play division tic-tac-toe. First, solve all the division problems.

20,333 4)81,332	**10,104** 6)60,624	**10,245 R2** 3)30,737
3,020 R2 5)15,102	**8,030 R5** 9)72,275	**30,639 R1** 2)61,279
2,090 R6 8)16,726	**8,091** 4)32,364	**6,040 R4** 7)42,284

How many ways can you make tic-tac-toe by finding three problems in a row or column that all have remainders?
3 ways, including diagonals

Grade 4 52 Chapter 8

3 Practice

Differentiate practice using these leveled assignments for Exercises 9–27.

Level	Assignment
BL Below/Approaching Level	9–16, 21, 23
OL On Level	9–18, 21–24, 27
AL Above/Beyond Level	9–23 odd, 25–27

Have students discuss and complete the Higher Order Thinking problems. Encourage students to use mental estimation before beginning a division problem and mental multiplication to check the answer.

WRITING IN MATH Have students complete Exercise 27 in their Math Journals. You may choose to use this exercise as an optional formative assessment.

Additional Answers

1. 1,382; 2,800 ÷ 2 = 1,400
2. $2,054 R1; $6,000 ÷ 3 = $2,000
3. 1,609; 8,000 ÷ 5 = 1,600
4. 2,109; 8,000 ÷ 4 = 2,000
5. $1,032 R5; $6,000 ÷ 6 = $1,000
6. 986 R5; 8,000 ÷ 8 = 1,000
8. Sample answer: They are very similar processes. You start dividing the greatest digit of the dividend by the divisor, then follow the same steps as you would when dividing a 3-digit divisor; the quotient will be larger.

COMMON ERROR!

Exercises 3, 4, 7, 11, 15–17 Students may forget to place the zero in the quotient. If students' quotients are missing zeros, ask if they checked their answers with their estimates. If not, ask them to do so to see if they can find their errors. Encourage the practice of checking quotients with estimates. Tell students that they can catch many of their mistakes by doing so.

CHECK What You Know

Divide. Use estimation to check. See Examples 1 and 2 (pp. 342–343)

1. $2\overline{)2,764}$
2. $3\overline{)\$6,163}$
3. $5\overline{)8,045}$
4. 8,436 ÷ 4
5. $6,197 ÷ 6
6. 7,893 ÷ 8

1–6. See margin.

7. An art museum hosted an exhibit. One day, 6,414 people attended the exhibit during the 6 hours it was open. If the same number of people attended each hour, how many people attended each hour? 1,069
8. Talk About It Explain how dividing a 4-digit dividend by a 1-digit divisor is similar to dividing a 3-digit dividend by a 1-digit divisor. How is it different? See margin.

Practice and Problem Solving

EXTRA PRACTICE See page R22.

9–20. See margin.

Divide. Use estimation to check. See Examples 1 and 2 (pp. 342–343)

9. $2\overline{)2,418}$
10. $3\overline{)3,428}$
11. $4\overline{)\$4,228}$
12. $5\overline{)7,465}$
13. $6\overline{)8,802}$
14. $8\overline{)\$9,597}$
15. $7\overline{)7,248}$
16. $8\overline{)8,072}$
17. $7,621 ÷ 4
18. 6,417 ÷ 6
19. 84,932 ÷ 2
20. $91,387 ÷ 3
21. Kirby bought a used car for $3,626. He plans on paying for it in two years. How much will he pay each year? $1,813
22. **Measurement** The farthest distance a pumpkin has ever been thrown is 4,434 feet. How many yards is this? 1,478 yds

Real-World PROBLEM SOLVING

Measurement The map shows distances between cities in the United States.

Distance Between U.S. Cities

From	To	Distance (miles)
Boston, MA	San Francisco, CA	3,102
Anchorage, AL	Miami, FL	4,999

VACATION

23. The Regan family is driving cross country for a vacation. They are driving from San Francisco to Boston. If they drive an equal distance each day, how many miles will they travel each day if they make the trip in 6 days? 517 mi
24. The Collins family is moving to Miami from Anchorage. If they drive an equal distance each day, about how many miles would they travel each day if they make the trip in 8 days? 625 mi

Additional Answers

9. 1,209; 2,000 ÷ 2 = 1,000
10. 1,142 R2; 3,000 ÷ 3 = 1,000
11. $1,057; $4,000 ÷ 4 = $1,000
12. 1,493; 7,000 ÷ 5 = 1,400
13. 1,467; 9,000 ÷ 6 = 1,500
14. $1,199 R5; $10,000 ÷ 8 = $1,250
15. 1,035 R3; 7,000 ÷ 7 = 1,000
16. 1,009; 8,000 ÷ 8 = 1,000
17. $1,905 R1; $8,000 ÷ 4 = $2,000
18. 1,069 R3; 6,000 ÷ 6 = 1,000
19. 42,466; 80,000 ÷ 2 = 40,000
20. $30,462 R1; $90,000 ÷ 3 = $30,000

H.O.T. Problems

25. OPEN ENDED Write a division problem that involves dividing a 4-digit number by a 1-digit number. The quotient must be between 1,000 and 1,200. Sample answer: 8,510 ÷ 8

26. CHALLENGE Divide 218,376 by 2. 109,188

27. WRITING IN MATH How many digits would be in the quotient of 12,495 ÷ 5? Explain how you know. See margin.

TEST Practice

28. The map shows the distance in feet to the treasure.

Find 318 ÷ 3 to find how many yards it is from X to the treasure. (Lesson 8-8) C

A 104 **C** 106

B 105 **D** 107

29. Derrick's horse ate 3,150 pounds of food in 3 months. How many pounds of food did it eat each month if it ate the same amount each month? (Lesson 8-9) G

F 1,025 pounds

G 1,050 pounds

H 1,500 pounds

J 1,550 pounds

Spiral Review

Divide. Use estimation to check. (Lesson 8-8)

30. $3\overline{)624}$ 208 **31.** $4\overline{)\$824}$ \$206 **32.** $5\overline{)537}$ 107 R2

Divide. Use estimation to check. (Lesson 8-7)

33. $2\overline{)468}$ 234 **34.** $3\overline{)\$645}$ \$215 **35.** $4\overline{)872}$ 218

36. Janise bought the items shown to the right. If the shirts are equal in price and the total cost was \$80, how much did each item cost? (Lesson 8-6) shirts: \$25, pants: \$30

37. Algebra Find the value of $n \times 317$ if $n = 4$. (Lesson 5-6) 1,268

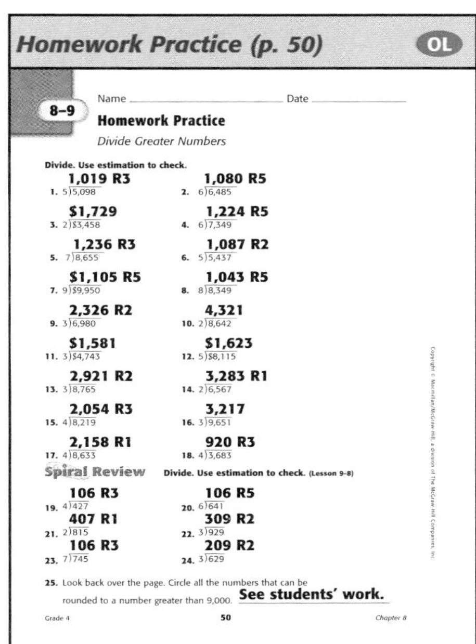

Homework Practice (p. 50) OL

8–9

Name ______________ Date ______________

Homework Practice

Divide Greater Numbers

Divide. Use estimation to check.

1. $5\overline{)5,098}$ **1,019 R3**
2. $6\overline{)6,485}$ **1,080 R5**
3. $2\overline{)\$3,458}$ **\$1,729**
4. $6\overline{)7,349}$ **1,224 R5**
5. $7\overline{)8,655}$ **1,236 R3**
6. $5\overline{)5,437}$ **1,087 R2**
7. $9\overline{)\$9,950}$ **\$1,105 R5**
8. $8\overline{)8,349}$ **1,043 R5**
9. $3\overline{)6,980}$ **2,326 R2**
10. $2\overline{)8,642}$ **4,321**
11. $3\overline{)\$4,743}$ **\$1,581**
12. $5\overline{)\$8,115}$ **\$1,623**
13. $3\overline{)8,765}$ **2,921 R2**
14. $2\overline{)6,567}$ **3,283 R1**
15. $4\overline{)8,219}$ **2,054 R3**
16. $3\overline{)9,651}$ **3,217**
17. $4\overline{)8,633}$ **2,158 R1**
18. $4\overline{)3,683}$ **920 R3**

Spiral Review **Divide. Use estimation to check.** (Lesson 9-8)

19. $4\overline{)427}$ **106 R3**
20. $6\overline{)641}$ **106 R5**
21. $2\overline{)815}$ **407 R1**
22. $3\overline{)929}$ **309 R2**
23. $7\overline{)745}$ **106 R3**
24. $3\overline{)629}$ **209 R2**

25. Look back over the page. Circle all the numbers that can be rounded to a number greater than 9,000. **See students' work.**

Grade 4 50 Chapter 8

4 Assess

Formative Assessment

- **Find 5,478 ÷ 6. Explain how you knew where to place the first digit of the quotient.** 913; Sample answer: I could not divide 5 thousands into 6 equal groups so I looked at the hundreds place and divided 54 hundreds by 6. So the 9 went in the hundreds place.

Quick Check **Are students continuing to struggle with dividing greater numbers?**

If Yes → Strategic Intervention Guide (p. 80)

If No → Independent Work Options (p. 342B)
CRM Skills Practice Worksheet (p. 49)
CRM Enrich Worksheet (p. 52)

Yesterday's News Have students explain how yesterday's lesson on zeros in a quotient helped them with today's lesson on dividing greater numbers.

TEST Practice

Reviews Lessons 8-8 and 8-9

Assign the Test Practice problems to provide daily reinforcement of test-taking skills.

Spiral Review

Reviews Lessons 5-6, 8-6, 8-7, and 8-8

Review and assess mastery of skills and concepts from previous lessons.

Additional Answer

27. Sample answer: 4; The divisor does not divide into the digit in the ten-thousands place, but it does divide into 12 thousands.

CHAPTER 8 Study Guide and Review

FOLDABLES Dinah Zike's Foldables

Use these lesson suggestions to incorporate the Foldables during the chapter. Students can then use their Foldables to review for the test.

Lesson 8-5 Students solve problems involving division of two-digit numbers by a one-digit number and store their work in the third pocket of the multi-pocketed booklet.

Lesson 8-7 Students solve problems involving division of three-digit numbers by a one-digit number and store their work in the fourth pocket of the multi-pocketed booklet.

Lesson 8-8 Students demonstrate their ability to divide with zeros in the quotients and store their work in the fifth pocket of the multi-pocketed booklet.

Lesson 8-9 Students solve problems involving division of four-digit numbers by a one-digit number and store their work in the sixth pocket of the multi-pocketed booklet.

Key Vocabulary

The page references after each word denote where that term was first introduced. If students have difficulty answering Exercises 1–6, remind them they can use the page references to review the vocabulary terms.

Vocabulary Review

Review chapter vocabulary using one of the following options.

- **Visual Vocabulary Cards** (5, 15, 27)
- **eGlossary** at macmillanmh.com

CHAPTER 8 Study Guide and Review

Math Online macmillanmh.com
- STUDY TO GO
- Vocabulary Review

FOLDABLES Study Organizer GET READY to Study

Be sure the following Key Vocabulary words and Key Concepts are written in your Foldable.

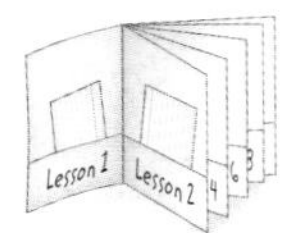

Key Concepts

Estimate Quotients (p. 322)

- You can use **compatible numbers** to estimate quotients.

722 ÷ 9

THINK 722 is close to 720. 720 and 9 are compatible numbers because they are easy to divide mentally.

720 ÷ 9 = 80   9 × 8 = 72

Division of Multi-Digit Numbers (p. 332)

- Divide a multi-digit number by a one-digit number.

```
   $234
2)$468
  -4
   06
  - 6
   08
  - 8
    0
```

For each place, divide, multiply, subtract, and compare. Then bring down the next digit in the dividend.

Key Vocabulary

compatible numbers (p. 322)
dividend (p. 311)
divisor (p. 311)
quotient (p. 311)
remainder (p. 312)

Vocabulary Check

Complete each sentence with the correct vocabulary word.

1. The number that is left over in a division problem is the ___?___. remainder
2. The number that divides the dividend is the ___?___. divisor
3. The number you are dividing is the ___?___. dividend
4. ___?___ are numbers that are easy to divide mentally. compatible numbers
5. The result of a division problem is the ___?___. quotient
6. In the division problem 4)136, the number 136 is the ___?___. dividend

Chapter 8 Project

Division Game Day

Alone, in pairs, or in small groups, have students discuss the results of their completed chapter project with the class. Assess their work using the Chapter Project rubric found in Chapter 8 Resource Masters, p. 63.

Lesson-by-Lesson Review

8-1 Division with Remainders (pp. 313–315)

Example 1
Find 59 ÷ 3.

```
  19 R2
3)59
 -3↓
  29
 -27
   2
```

For each place, divide, multiply, subtract, and compare.

Then bring down the next digit in the dividend.

Check

```
 19
× 3
 57
+ 2
 59
```

So, the answer is correct. ✓

Divide.

7. $5\overline{)53}$ 10 R3 **8.** $6\overline{)67}$ 11 R1

9. 91 ÷ 4 22 R3 **10.** 77 ÷ 3 25 R2

11. Christy has 37 books. She wants to put them evenly on her 4 shelves. How many books will she not be able to fit? 1 book

12. Rafael wants to earn $40 for a new pair of skates. If he earns $6 an hour for yard work, how many hours will he have to work to have the money for the skates? 7 hrs

8-2 Divide Multiples of 10, 100, and 1,000 (pp. 316–319)

Example 2
Find 1,600 ÷ 4.

Use patterns to divide.

16 ÷ 4 = 4
160 ÷ 4 = 40
1,600 ÷ 4 = 400

So, 1,600 ÷ 4 = 400.

Check
Use addition to check.

```
  400
  400
  400
+ 400
1,600
```

So, the answer is correct. ✓

Divide. Use patterns.

13. 27 ÷ 9 = ■
270 ÷ 9 = ■
2,700 ÷ 9 = ■
3; 30; 300

14. 49 ÷ 7 = ■
490 ÷ 7 = ■
4,900 ÷ 7 = ■
7; 70; 700

15. 900 ÷ 3 300 **16.** 1,800 ÷ 9 200

17. 3,600 ÷ 4 900 **18.** 4,900 ÷ 7 700

19. 6,400 ÷ 8 800 **20.** 7,200 ÷ 9 800

21. Chuck collected 150 shells during his five days of vacation. If Chuck collected the same number of shells each day, how many shells did he collect each day? 30 shells

Lesson-by-Lesson Review

Have students complete the Lesson-by-Lesson Review on pp. 347–352. Then you can use ExamView® Assessment Suite to customize another review worksheet that practices all the objectives of this chapter or only the objectives on which your students need more help.

Intervention If the given examples are not sufficient to review the topics covered by the questions, use the page references next to the exercises to review that topic in the Student Edition.

CHAPTER 8 Study Guide and Review

8-3 Problem-Solving Strategy: Guess and Check (pp. 320–321)

Example 3
Opal and Steve collect coins. Opal has 32 more coins than Steve. They have 146 coins altogether. How many coins does each person have?

Understand

What facts do you know?

- Opal has 32 more coins than Steve.
- They have 146 coins altogether.

What do you need to find?

- The number of coins each person has.

Plan You can guess and check to solve the problem.

Solve Make logical guesses.

Think of two addends that have a difference of about 30, and a sum of about 150.

Try 90 + 60. 90 + 60 = 150

The sum is too high. Try smaller numbers until you find the correct answer.

The correct answers are 89 and 57 because 89 + 57 = 146.

Check The answers are correct because 89 − 57 = 32 and 89 + 57 = 146.

Solve. Use the guess and check strategy.

22. Juanita made a vegetable tray. There are 2 times more cucumber slices than tomato slices and 4 times more carrot slices than cucumber slices. If there are 5 tomato slices, how many slices of carrots and cucumbers are there on the tray? **40 carrot slices; 10 cucumber slices**

23. Toru bought a CD and a DVD. The CD cost $5 less than the DVD, and the total was $29. How much was each item? **CD $12 and DVD $17**

24. There are rabbits, ponies, and goats at a petting zoo. There are eight times as many goats as ponies. There are six more rabbits than ponies. The number of ponies is shown. Find how many rabbits and goats there are. **goats: 16; rabbits: 8**

25. Etta is buying a sweater and a pair of pants. The sweater cost $12 more than the pants. The total cost will be $84. What is the cost of each clothing item? **sweater: $48; pants: $36**

348 Chapter 8 Divide by One-Digit Numbers

8-4 Estimate Quotients (pp. 322–324)

Example 4
Find 273 ÷ 9.

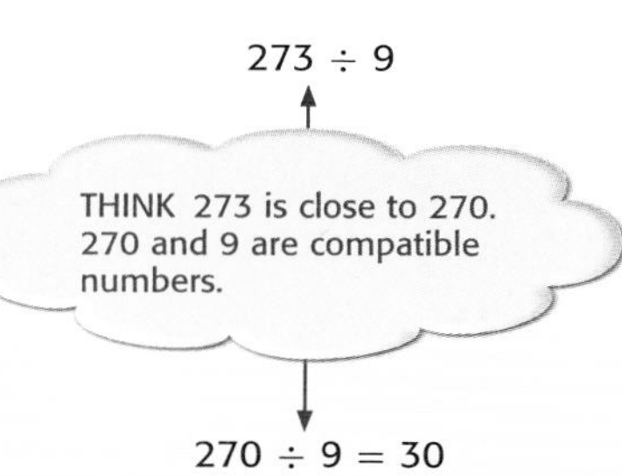

273 ÷ 9
THINK 273 is close to 270. 270 and 9 are compatible numbers.
270 ÷ 9 = 30

So, 273 ÷ 9 is about 30.

Estimate. 26–31. See margin.

26. $254 ÷ 5 **27.** 634 ÷ 7

28. 5,571 ÷ 8 **29.** 7,218 ÷ 9

30. **Measurement** A roller coaster car made it to the bottom of a 318-foot hill in 5 seconds. About how many feet did the car travel each second?

31. A skate park has $3,225 to spend on 8 new ramps. About how much can be spent on each ramp?

8-5 Two-Digit Quotients (pp. 326–329)

Example 5
Find 95 ÷ 4.

Step 1 Divide the tens.

```
  2
4)95
 -8
  1
```

Divide. 9 ÷ 4 = 2
Put 2 in the quotient.
Multiply. 4 × 2 = 8
Subtract. 9 − 8 = 1
Compare. 1 < 4

Step 2 Divide the ones.

```
  23 R3
4)95
 -8↓
  15
 -12
   3
```

Bring down the ones.
Divide. 15 ÷ 4 = 3
Put 3 in the quotient.
Multiply. 4 × 3 = 12
Subtract. 15 − 12 = 3
Compare. 3 < 4
Remainder = 3

So, 95 ÷ 4 = 23 R3.

Divide.

32. 3)86 28 R2 **33.** 6)96 16

34. 87 ÷ 4 21 R3 **35.** 95 ÷ 3 31 R2

36. Miranda has 85 crayons. She wants to share them equally with two of her friends. How many crayons will Miranda and her friends each get? How many will be left? 28 R1

37. Garcia placed his baseball cards into 3 envelopes. He ended up with 17 cards in each envelope and 2 left over. How many cards did Garcia have to begin with? 53 cards

Additional Answers

26. $250 ÷ 5 = $50
27. 630 ÷ 7 = 90
28. 5,600 ÷ 8 = 700
29. 7,200 ÷ 9 = 800
30. 300 ft ÷ 5 = 60 ft
31. $3,200 ÷ 8 = $400

CHAPTER 8

Study Guide and Review

8-6 Problem-Solving Investigation: Choose a Strategy (pp. 330–331)

Example 6
There are 1,323 students trying out for basketball teams. Is it reasonable to say that more than 150 teams will be formed if there are nine players on each team?

Understand

There are 1,323 students trying out for basketball teams. Nine players will be on each team.

Will there be more than 150 teams formed?

Plan Divide the number of students trying out by the number of players per team.

Solve Divide 1,323 by 9.

$$\begin{array}{r} 147 \\ 9\overline{)1,323} \\ -9 \\ 42 \\ -36 \\ 63 \\ -63 \\ 0 \end{array}$$

There will be 147 teams. So, it is not reasonable to say there will be more than 150 teams.

Check Use multiplication to check.

$90 \times 147 = 1,323$

So, the answer is correct. ✓

Use any strategy to solve.

38. Frida had 3 pencils. Then her teacher gave her some of the packs of pencils shown. Now Frida has 11 pencils. How many packs of pencils did the teacher give Frida? 2 packs

39. Each hand in the human body has 27 bones. There are 6 more bones in the fingers than in the wrist. There are 3 fewer bones in the palm than in the wrist. How many bones are in the fingers and wrist? fingers: 14; wrist: 8; palm: 5

40. One banner is made using three sheets of paper. How many different banners can be made using red, yellow, and black paper one time each if the paper is placed in a row? 6 banners

41. **Algebra** What number is missing from the pattern 2, 7, 12, 17, ■? 22

42. A number is divided by 5. Next, 4 is subtracted from the quotient. Then, 6 is added to the difference. The result is 10. What is the number? 40

350 Chapter 8 Divide by One-Digit Numbers

8-7 Three-Digit Quotients (pp. 332–334)

Example 7
Find 426 ÷ 4.

Estimate 426 ÷ 4 ⟶ 400 ÷ 4 = 100

```
  106 R2
4)426
 -4↓
  02
 - 0↓
  26
 -24
   2
```

For each place, divide, multiply, subtract, and compare.

Then bring down the next digit in the dividend.

So, 426 ÷ 4 = 106 R2.

Check for Reasonableness

The quotient, 106 R2, is close to the estimate. So, the answer is reasonable. ✓

Divide.

43. $3\overline{)787}$ 262 R1 **44.** 994 ÷ 4 248 R2

45. There are 7 teachers and 147 students in the 4th grade. If the same number of students are in each class, how many students will be in each class? 21 students

46. There are 1,035 cars in the airport parking lot. The lot has 9 rows of parked cars. How many cars are in each row if the same number of cars are in each row? 115 cars

47. Explain how to check Exercise 46 to be sure your answer is correct.

47. Use multiplication to check the answer. 115 × 9 = 1,035

8-8 Quotients with Zeros (pp. 336–338)

Example 8
Find $416 ÷ 2.

```
  $208
2)$416
 -4↓
  01
 -0↓
  16
 -16
   0
```

For each place, divide, multiply, subtract, and compare.

Then bring down the next digit in the dividend.

So, $416 ÷ 2 = $208.

Divide.

48. $2\overline{)217}$ 108 R1 **49.** $3\overline{)621}$ 207

50. 817 ÷ 4 204 R1 **51.** 925 ÷ 3 308 R1

52. The number of students who ride the bus home each day is 432. The students are divided evenly into 8 buses. How many students fit on each bus? 54 students

53. Tamera wants to fit all of her 749 marbles into 7 jars. How many should she put in each jar? 107 marbles

Chapter 8 Study Guide and Review **351**

CHAPTER 8 Study Guide and Review

8-9 Divide Greater Numbers (pp. 342–345)

Example 9
Find 6,213 ÷ 3.

Estimate 6,213 ÷ 3 → 6,000 ÷ 3 = 2,000

Step 1 Divide the thousands.

$$\begin{array}{r} 2 \\ 3\overline{)6,213} \\ -6 \\ \hline 0 \end{array}$$

Step 2 Divide the hundreds.

$$\begin{array}{r} 20 \\ 3\overline{)6,213} \\ -6 \\ \hline 02 \\ -\ 0 \\ \hline 2 \end{array}$$

Step 3 Divide each place.

$$\begin{array}{r} 2,071 \\ 3\overline{)6,213} \\ -6 \\ \hline 02 \\ -\ 0 \\ \hline 21 \\ -21 \\ \hline 03 \\ -\ 3 \\ \hline 0 \end{array}$$

For each place, divide, multiply, subtract, and compare.

Then bring down the next digit in the dividend.

So, 6,213 ÷ 3 = 2,071.

Check for Reasonableness
The quotient, 2,071, is close to the estimate. So the answer is correct ✓

Divide.

54. $3\overline{)\$6,597}$ **$2,199**

55. $5\overline{)8,802}$ **1,760 R2**

56. 7,561 ÷ 6 **1,260 R1**

57. $9,387 ÷ 8 **$1,173 R3**

58. **Measurement** Candice is making bows. She uses a 8-inch piece of ribbon for each bow. How many bows can she make with 1,827 inches of ribbon? **228 bows**

59. A total of 3,915 people attended three orchestra concerts. How many people attended each concert if the same number of people attended each concert? **1,305 people**

60. There are 1,440 students who attend a school. There are four lunch periods. If the same number of students eat during each lunch period, how many students eat during each lunch period? **360 students**

61. **Measurement** A 3-kilometer race is about 9,842 feet long. How many yards long is the race? (*Remember*: 3 feet = 1 yard) **3,280 R2 yd**

Chapter Test

For Exercises 1 and 2, decide whether each statement is *true* or *false*.

1. A quotient is the number being divided. false
2. In the problem 62 ÷ 2, the number 2 is the divisor. true

3. 22 R1; 2 × 22 = 44; 44 + 1 = 45

Divide. Check each answer.

3. 2)45 **4.** 73 ÷ 4

4. 18 R1; 4 × 18 = 72; 72 + 1 = 73

5. **MULTIPLE CHOICE** There are 5,280 feet in a mile. Since 1 yard equals 3 feet, how many yards are in one mile? A

A 1,760 yd **C** 1,780 yd

B 1,770 yd **D** 1,790 yd

Copy and complete each set of patterns.

6. 24 ÷ 4 = ■ **7.** 18 ÷ 2 = ■

240 ÷ 4 = ■ 180 ÷ 2 = ■

2,400 ÷ 4 = ■ 1,800 ÷ 2 = ■

6; 60; 600 9; 90; 900

Divide. Use patterns.

8. \$3,200 ÷ 4 \$800 **9.** 5,400 ÷ 6 900

10. Three members of the Cotter family are flying to Washington, D.C., for vacation. The total cost of the tickets is \$1,250. About how much was each person's ticket? \$400

Divide. Use estimation to check.

11. 5)410 **12.** 863 ÷ 3

11. 82; 400 ÷ 5 = 80

12. 287 R2; 900 ÷ 3 = 300

13. Sara earned the same score on her last 2 tests. Her total score was 184. What was her score on each of the 2 tests? 92

Divide. Use estimation to check.

14. 2)417 **15.** \$929 ÷ 3

14. 208 R1; 400 ÷ 2 = 200

15. \$309 R\$2; \$900 ÷ 3 = \$300

16. **Measurement** The Toshiro family is moving across the country. They will drive a total of 2,835 miles over 7 days. If they drive the same distance each day, how far will they drive each day? 405 mi

Divide. Use estimation to check.

17. 2)4,302 **18.** 6,932 ÷ 7

17. 2,151; 2,000 ÷ 2 = 1,000

18. 990 R2; 7,000 ÷ 7 = 1,000

19. A family is buying a boat. They hope to have it paid off in 3 years. How much do they have to pay each year to reach their goal? \$2,043

20. **MULTIPLE CHOICE** Jed hiked a trail that is 7,920 feet long. Since there are 3 feet in a yard, how many yards did Jed hike? J

F 2,540 **H** 2,630

G 2,580 **J** 2,640

21. WRITING IN MATH How many digits would be in the quotient of 2,795 ÷ 5? Explain how you know.

21. See Ch. 8 Answer Appendix.

Summative Assessment 353

Chapter 8 Chapter Test

Summative Assessment

Use these alternate leveled chapter tests to differentiate assessment for the specific needs of your students.

Leveled Chapter 8 Tests			
Form	Type	Level	CRM Pages
1	Multiple Choice	BL	65–66
2A	Multiple Choice	OL	67–68
2B	Multiple Choice	OL	69–70
2C	Free Response	OL	71–72
2D	Free Response	OL	73–74
3	Free Response	AL	75–76

BL = below/approaching grade level
OL = on grade level
AL = above/beyond grade level

Vocabulary Test

CRM **Chapter 8 Resource Masters** (p. 60)

ExamView Assessment Suite Customize and create multiple versions of your Chapter Test and the test answer keys.

Data-Driven Decision Making

Based on the results of the Chapter Test, use the following to review concepts that continue to present students with problems.

Exercises	State/Local Standard	What's the Math?	Error Analysis	Resources for Review
1–3		Use a variety of methods to explain mathematical reasoning in division.	Does not know "dividend," "divisor," or "quotient." Mixes up divisor and dividend.	Strategic Intervention Guide (pp. 78, 86) CRM Chapter 8 Resource Masters (Reteach) Math Adventures My Math Zone Chapter 8 Math Online Extra Examples • Concepts in Motion
6–10		Use basic multiples of 10, 100, and 1,000 and their patterns to divide.	Does not understand how to estimate.	
11–18		Estimate quotients.	Does not know basic multiplication facts. Does not recognize patterns of multiples of 10s.	

Chapter 8 Test Practice

Formative Assessment

- Use Student Edition pp. 354–355 as practice and cumulative review. The questions are written in the same style as many state tests.
- You can also use these two pages to benchmark student progress, or as an alternate homework assignment.

Additional practice pages can be found in the Chapter 8 Resource Masters.

CRM **Chapter 8 Resource Masters**
Cumulative Test Practice
- Multiple Choice format (pp. 65–70)
- Free Response format (pp. 71–76)

Create practice worksheets or tests that align to your state standards.

Math Online Have students visit macmillanmh.com for additional practice to reinforce your state standards.

Chapter 8 Test Practice

Cumulative, Chapters 1–8

PART 1 Multiple Choice

Read each question. Then fill in the correct answer on the answer sheet provided by your teacher or on a sheet of paper.

1. What is the mode of {2, 3, 3, 3, 5, 5}? B

   A 2 C 5
   B 3 D 7

2. Which number is represented by n in the equation $n + 938 = 1{,}456$? F

   F 518 H 528
   G 522 J 594

3. Which of the following has the least value? A

   A 45,034,653 C 45,689,236
   B 45,073,542 D 45,856,494

4. How many students live 8 or more miles from school? H

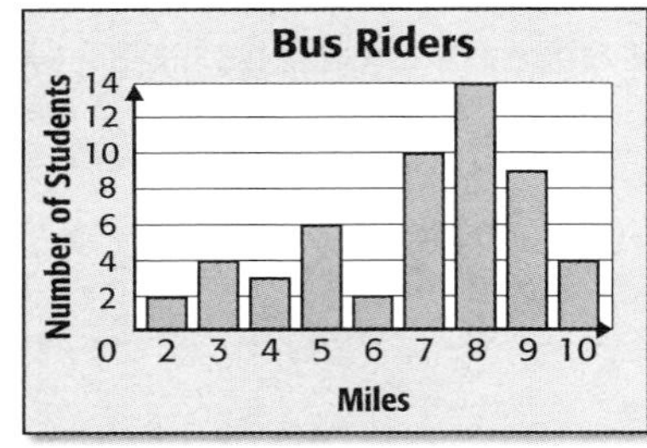

   F 25 H 27
   G 26 J 28

5. Which number makes each equation true? B

   54 ÷ 6 = ■
   540 ÷ 60 = ■
   5,400 ÷ 600 = ■

   A 6 C 60
   B 9 D 90

6. What multiplication expression does this model represent? H

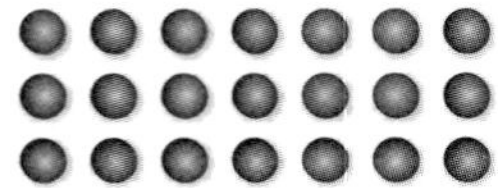

   F 3 × 6 H 3 × 7
   G 4 × 6 J 4 × 7

7. Josh has 84 toy cars to share equally among himself and 3 friends. How many toy cars will each person receive? B

   A 18 C 28
   B 21 D 30

8. There are 8,000 fans at a sold out baseball game. Each section of the stadium holds 100 people. How many sections are there in the stadium? H

   F 8 H 80
   G 40 J 800

Test-Taking Tip

Remind students to read through each statement or question carefully, and pay attention to qualifiers and keywords.

Preparing for Standardized Tests
For test-taking strategies and practice, see pages R42–R55.

9. The soccer team has 144 water bottles in 6 boxes. How many water bottles are in each box? C

A 20 **C** 24
B 22 **D** 25

10. Which number is 100,000 more than 7,186,335? H

F 7,086,335 **H** 7,286,335
G 7,196,335 **J** 8,186,335

11. Use the graph. Which two students collected a sum of cans fewer than 750? D

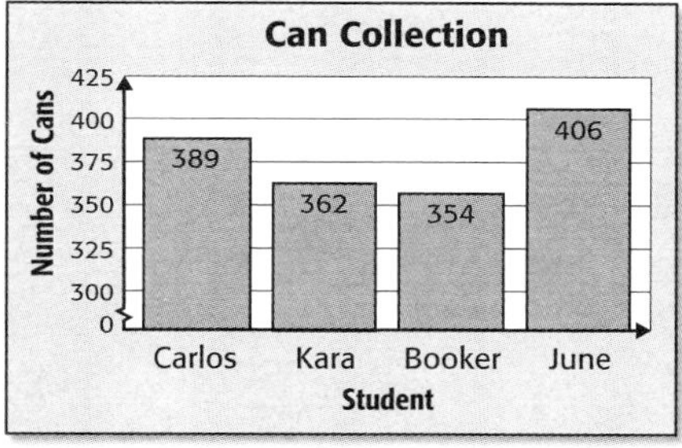

A Carlos and Kara
B Kara and June
C June and Booker
D Booker and Carlos

PART 2 Short Response

Record your answers on the answer sheet provided by your teacher or on a sheet of paper.

12. Write a rule to describe the pattern below. Multiply by 3.

Input (x)	Output (y)
3	9
5	15
7	21
9	27
11	33

13. Which number makes this equation true? 8

$88 \div \blacksquare = 11$

PART 3 Extended Response

Record your answers on the answer sheet provided by your teacher or on a sheet of paper.

14. Rosa has 150 goldfish. She wants to put about the same number of fish into each of 8 ponds. About how many fish will be in each pond? Explain.

15. What is a good estimate for $351 \div 5$? Explain your reasoning.

NEED EXTRA HELP?															
If You Missed Question...	1	2	3	4	5	6	7	8	9	10	11	12	13	14	15
Go to Lesson...	3-2	5-2	1-4	3-5	8-2	4-3	8-5	8-2	8-5	2-4	3-5	5-8	4-6	8-4	8-4

Answer Sheet Practice

Have students simulate taking a state test by recording their answers on a practice recording sheet.

CRM **Chapter 8 Resource Masters**
Student Recording Sheet (p. 81)

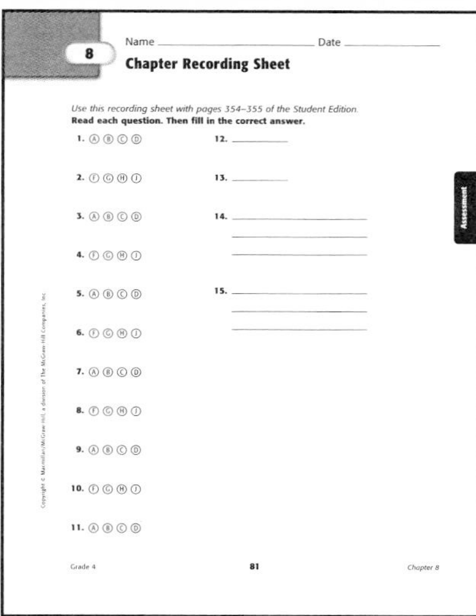
8 Chapter Recording Sheet
Name ______ Date ______

Use this recording sheet with pages 354–355 of the Student Edition.
Read each question. Then fill in the correct answer.

1. Ⓐ Ⓑ Ⓒ Ⓓ
2. Ⓕ Ⓖ Ⓗ Ⓙ
3. Ⓐ Ⓑ Ⓒ Ⓓ
4. Ⓕ Ⓖ Ⓗ Ⓙ
5. Ⓐ Ⓑ Ⓒ Ⓓ
6. Ⓕ Ⓖ Ⓗ Ⓙ
7. Ⓐ Ⓑ Ⓒ Ⓓ
8. Ⓕ Ⓖ Ⓗ Ⓙ
9. Ⓐ Ⓑ Ⓒ Ⓓ
10. Ⓕ Ⓖ Ⓗ Ⓙ
11. Ⓐ Ⓑ Ⓒ Ⓓ
12. ______
13. ______
14. ______
15. ______

Assessment

Grade 4 81 Chapter 8

Additional Answers

14. Sample answer: 20; The word *about* tells you to estimate $150 \div 8 \rightarrow 160 \div 8 = 20$.

15. Sample answer: 70; Look for compatible numbers that are closest to 351 and 5. $350 \div 5 = 70$

Page 312, Explore 8-1

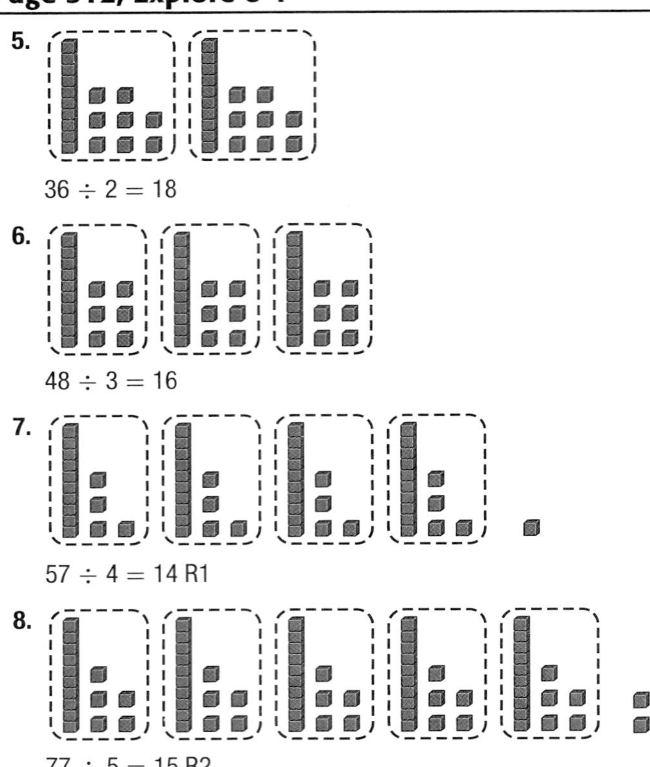

5. $36 \div 2 = 18$
6. $48 \div 3 = 16$
7. $57 \div 4 = 14$ R1
8. $77 \div 5 = 15$ R2

Page 321, Lesson 8-3

1. Sample answer: Two of the gifts were equal in price, the third gift cost $3 more than the other two, and the total cost was $27. So, gift + gift + (gift + 3) = $27 fits this situation.
2. Sample answer: The cost of the gifts is close to $30, so a first guess should be close to $10 for each gift.
4. Sample answer: The total cost was more than $30 for three gifts, so start guessing numbers greater than $10. $11 was the first guess, and $12 was the second guess, which worked.
8. Saturday show = 175 tickets, Sunday show = 125 tickets
12. Sample answer: The first step is to make a logical guess for the solution of a problem. Then you work out the problem using your guess to see if it was correct.

Page 325, Mid-Chapter Check

15. Sample answer: less than because the dividend was rounded down

Page 334, Lesson 8-7

26. Sample answer: Roberta baked 235 muffins for the bake sale and put 4 muffins in each bag. How many bags are there? Answer: 58 bags

Page 353, Chapter Test

21. Sample answer: 3 digits; The divisor is greater than the digit in the thousands place.

NOTES

Student Handbook

Built-In Workbooks

Reference

How to Use the Student Handbook

The Student Handbook is the additional skill and reference material found at the end of books. The Student Handbook can help answer these questions.

What If I Need More Practice?

You, or your teacher, may decide that working through some additional problems would be helpful. The **Extra Practice** section provides these problems for each lesson so you have ample opportunity to practice new skills.

What If I Need to Prepare for a Standardized Test?

The **Preparing for Standardized Tests** section provides worked-out examples and practice problems for multiple-choice, short-response, and extended response questions.

What if I Want to Learn Additional Concepts and Skills?

Use the Concepts and Skills Bank section to either refresh your memory about topics you have learned in other math classes or learn new math concepts and skills.

What If I Forget a Vocabulary Word?

The **English-Spanish Glossary** provides a list of important, or difficult, words used throughout the textbook. It provides a definition in English and Spanish as well as the page number(s) where the word can be found.

What If I Need to Find Something Quickly?

The **Index** alphabetically lists the subjects covered throughout the entire textbook and the pages on which each subject can be found.

What If I Forget Measurement Conversions, Multiplication Facts, or Formulas?

Inside the back cover of your math book is a list of measurement conversions and formulas that are used in the book. You will also find a multiplication table inside the back cover.

Extra Practice

Lesson 1-1

Pages 17–19

Write the value of the underlined digit.

1. 1,<u>6</u>37 600
2. <u>3</u>7,904 30,000
3. 56,5<u>7</u>2 70
4. <u>2</u>09,631 200,000

Write each number in word form and expanded form.

5. 2,493
6. 6,319
7. 7,085
8. 9,160
9. 28,482
10. 71,045
11. 523,608
12. 347,281

5–12. See Student Handbook Answer Appendix.

Write each number in standard form and expanded form.

13. fifty-six thousand, seven hundred twenty 56,720; 50,000 + 6,000 + 700 + 20
14. two hundred thirty-four thousand, eight hundred three 234,803; 200,000 + 30,000 + 4,000 + 800 + 3

Lesson 1-2 1–11. See Extra Practice Answer Appendix.

Pages 22–25

Write each number in word form and expanded form.

1. 9,005
2. 19,860
3. 26,010
4. 360,508
5. 408,040
6. 26,053,107
7. 730,000,520
8. 800,530,700

Write each number in standard form and expanded form.

9. nine million, twenty-four thousand, ten
10. six hundred thirty-five million, eight hundred fifty-seven thousand, five
11. Write in word form and standard form.
    300,000 + 20,000 + 1,000 + 50 + 8

Lesson 1-3

Pages 26–27

Solve. Use the four-step plan.

1. Mrs. Beal's students earned a class party. An extra large pizza cost $28. If she bought 3 pizzas, how much did she spend? $84
2. Carisa can draw 3 pictures in the morning and 3 pictures in the afternoon. If she draws for 5 days, how many pictures can she make? 30 pictures
3. Tom watched 45 movies this year. Each movie was two hours long. How many hours did he spend watching movies this year? 90 hours
4. A basketball game has 4 quarters. If 5 players each score 2 points during each quarter, how many total points are scored? 40 points

Lesson 1-4

Pages 28–30

Compare. Use >, <, or =.

1. 9,719 ● 9,791 <
2. 3,780 ● 3,080 >
3. 34,925 ● 34,952 <
4. 89,629 ● 89,635 <
5. 47,283 ● 42,283 >
6. 72,036 ● 72,300 <
7. 325,614 ● 235,614 >
8. 758,438 ● 758,438 =
9. 7,863,403 ● 7,863,304 >
10. 9,604,138 ● 9,064,946 >

Copy and complete to make the number sentence true.

11. 4,■58 < 4,859 8 or less
12. 34,199 = 3■,199 4
13. 214,166 > 2■4,166 0
14. 5,877,820 > 5,877,8■0 0 or 1

Lesson 1-5

Pages 32–34

Order the numbers from greatest to least.

1. 1,443; 1,434; 1,444; 1,344
   1,444; 1,443; 1,434; 1,344
2. 6,519; 6,600; 3,941; 4,872
   6,600; 6,519; 4,872; 3,941
3. 19,400; 9,400; 19,004; 10,440
   19,400; 19,004; 10,440; 9,400
4. 52,951; 49,384; 51,954; 52,865
   52,951; 52,865; 51,954; 49,384
5. 85,610; 85,185; 85,611; 85,625
   85,625; 85,611; 85,610; 85,185
6. 94,846; 49,846; 84,694; 46,948
   94,846; 84,694; 49,846; 46,948
7. 275,391; 2,086,344; 258,983
   2,086,344; 275,391; 258,983
8. 361,259; 361,084; 61,999; 846,465
   846,465; 361,259; 361,084; 61,999
9. 568,208; 559,876; 59,986; 58,869
   568,208; 559,876; 59,986, 58,869
10. 768,635; 792,456; 741,056; 78,318
    792,456; 768,635; 741,056; 78,318
11. 3,849,257; 38,492,570; 38,492,057
    38,492,570; 38,492,057; 3,849,257
12. 4,608,056; 4,608,942; 4,608,924
    4,608,942; 4,608,924; 4,608,056

Lesson 1-6

Pages 36–39

Round each number to the given place-value position.

1. 451; hundred 500
2. 949; hundred 900
3. 4,965; thousand 5,000
4. 20,368; thousand 20,000
5. 36,801; hundred 36,800
6. 42,204; ten thousand 40,000
7. 70,988; thousand 71,000
8. 83,756; ten 83,760
9. 437,947; ten thousand 440,000
10. 455,877; ten 455,880
11. 849, 604; thousand 850,000
12. 934,567; hundred thousand 900,000

Lesson 1-7

Pages 40–41

Use the four-step plan to solve.

1. Lisa lives 7 miles from school. She bikes to school and back every day. How many miles does she bike in 1 school week? 70 miles
2. A chicken runs 5 miles an hour. An ostrich runs 40 miles an hour. How many hours would it take a chicken to run the same distance it took an ostrich to run in two hours? 16 hrs
3. Aaron bought a shirt that cost $27 and a hat that cost $3. How much change will he receive if he pays with two $20 bills? $10
4. A bag of 15 oranges costs $20. Oranges that are sold individually cost $2. Is it cheaper to buy 15 oranges in a bag or 15 oranges sold individually? Explain. bag; 15 individual oranges cost $30, which is more than $20.

Lesson 2-1

Pages 55–57

Copy and complete each number sentence. Identify the property or rule used.

1. 20 − ■ = 0
   20; Subtraction Rule
2. 14 + 37 = ■ + 14
   37; Commutative Property (+)
3. 7 + (4 + 8) = (7 + 4) + ■
   8; Associative Property (+)
4. 197 + 0 = ■
   197; Identity Property
5. 233 − ■ = 233
   0; Subtraction Rule
6. 72 + 9 = ■ + 72
   9; Commutative Property (+)
7. (14 + 3) + 8 = 14 + (3 + ■)
   8; Associative Property (+)
8. 863 + 44 = ■ + 863
   44; Commutative Property (+)
9. 21 + (■ + 9) = (21 + 17) + 9
   17; Associative Property (+)
10. 541 − ■ = 0
    541; Subtraction Rule

Lesson 2-2

Pages 58–61

Estimate. Round to the indicated place value.

1. 43 + 29; tens 40 + 30 = 70
2. 664 + 49; tens 660 + 50 = 710
3. 1,329 + 755; hundreds
   1,300 + 800 = 2,100
4. 9,488 + 2,061; thousands
   9,000 + 2,000 = 11,000
5. $34,163 + $29,982; hundreds
   $34,200 + $30,000 = $64,200
6. 59 − 34; tens
   60 − 30 = 30
7. 859 − 42; tens
   860 − 40 = 820
8. 2,495 − 468; hundreds
   2,500 − 500 = 2,000
9. $6,295 − $1,402; thousands
   $6,000 − $1,000 = $5,000
10. 37,423 − 18,196; ten thousands
    40,000 − 20,000 = 20,000

Lesson 2-3

Pages 62–63

Tell whether an estimate or exact answer is needed. Then solve.

1. Nina bought a CD that cost $11. She gave the cashier a $20 bill. About how much change should she get back? estimate; about $10
2. Carlos wants to buy a new football that costs $32. He earns $6 every week delivering newspapers. How many weeks will it take to save enough money for the ball? exact; 6 weeks
3. The 29 students in Jin's science class are riding in vans on a field trip. Each van can hold 8 students. How many vans will be needed? exact; 4 vans
4. Mika spends about $1\frac{1}{2}$ hours practicing the piano each day, Monday through Friday. About how many hours does she practice each month? estimate; about 40 h

Lesson 2-4

Pages 64–67

Find each sum. Check your work by estimating.

1. 456 + 233 = 689
2. $3,879 + $ 348 = $4,227
3. 5,678 + 2,431 = 8,109
4. $38,406 + $ 6,744 = $45,150
5. 60,483 + 98,218 = 158,701
6. $32,819 + $67,375 = $100,194
7. 357,816 + 93,402 = 451,218
8. $572,938 + $118,476 = $691,414
9. $983,107 + $645,815 = $1,628,922

Lesson 2-5

Pages 72–74

Subtract. Use addition or estimation to check.

1. 721 − 563 = 158
2. $807 − $328 = $479
3. 926 − 644 = 282
4. $1,766 − $ 819 = 947
5. 9,663 − 5,201 = 4,462
6. $6,741 − $3,983 = $2,758
7. $24,509 − $ 7,625 = $16,884
8. 55,788 − 34,223 = 21,565
9. 71,864 − 49,667 = 22,197

Lesson 2-6

Pages 76–77

Use any strategy to solve. Tell what strategy you used.

1. Mr. Lee spent about $23 on paintbrushes, $50 dollars on paint, and $15 on colored chalk. How much did he spend on art supplies? $88
2. Tia is hanging lights around her window. The window is a square with sides that are 28 inches. How many inches of lights will Tia need? 112 in.
3. The cats in the animal shelter eat 18 pounds of food each day. How many pounds of food do the cats eat each week? 126 lbs
4. Casey has $6. He buys a sandwich for $2, a salad for $2, and milk for $1. How much money will he have left? $1

Lesson 2-7

Pages 80–83

Subtract. Use addition to check.

1. $400 − $298 = $102
2. 800 − 567 = 233
3. 1,000 − 703 = 297
4. 3,600 − 1,695 = 1,905
5. 5,000 − 2,367 = 2,633
6. $9,000 − $4,890 = $4,110
7. 7,000 − 5,804 = 1,196
8. 6,400 − 3,166 = 3,234
9. 9,600 − 1,879 = 7,721
10. $2,200 − $883 $1,317
11. $4,700 − $2,864 $1,836
12. 8,600 − 7,621 979
13. 7,000 − 4,386 2,614

Lesson 3-1 1, 2. See Extra Practice Answer Appendix.

Pages 95–97

Organize each set of data in a tally chart and a frequency table.

1. George recorded the types of pets that his classmates have. His recordings are shown at the right.

Pets		
cat	cat	dog
cat	dog	lizard
dog	fish	bird
bird	dog	fish

2. Tina conducted a survey to find out the favorite sports of the children in the park. Her recordings are shown at the right.

Favorite Sports		
soccer	baseball	football
soccer	basketball	football
football	football	basketball
basketball	soccer	tennis

Lesson 3-2

Pages 98–101

Find the mode and median of the set of data. Identify any outliers. 1. 22; 24; no outliers 2. no mode; 39; outlier: 17

1.

Students in Each Grade					
Grade	1	2	3	4	5
Number of Students	26	22	27	24	22

2.

Roller Coaster Riders at an Amusement Park							
Roller Coaster	1	2	3	4	5	6	7
Number of Riders	46	38	41	17	45	39	36

Lesson 3-3

Pages 102–103

Solve. Use the make a table strategy.

1. Akira mailed invitations to his birthday party. The postage to mail each invitation was 42¢. Akira paid 252¢ in all for postage. How many invitations did he send? 6 invitations
2. During the soccer season, for every 3 penalty kicks he took, Jamil scored on 2 of them. If he scored on 12 penalty kicks, how many penalty kicks did he take? 18 kicks
3. Nick earns $7 an hour walking dogs. He works the same number of hours each week. Nick earns $252 in 1 month. How many hours does he work each week if there are 4 weeks in a month? 9 h
4. Maria bought some six-packs of soda. She bought 48 cans of soda in all. How many six-packs of soda did she buy? 8 six-packs

Lesson 3-4 1, 2. See Extra Practice Answer Appendix.

Pages 104–107

Organize each set of data in a line plot.

1. Number of seeds that sprouted

Seeds That Sprouted	
Week	Seeds
Week 1	6
Week 2	9
Week 3	11
Week 4	10
Week 5	9
Week 6	6
Week 7	9

2. Miles hiked by campers

Miles Hiked per Day	
Day	Miles Hiked
Monday	5
Tuesday	7
Wednesday	6
Thursday	4
Friday	5
Saturday	4
Sunday	3

Extra Practice

Lesson 3-5
Pages 108–110

For Exercises 1–4, use the graph shown.

Average Life Spans of Mammals

Animal	Life Span (years)
African Elephant	70
Blue Whale	80
Gorilla	35
Human	75
Killer Whale	90

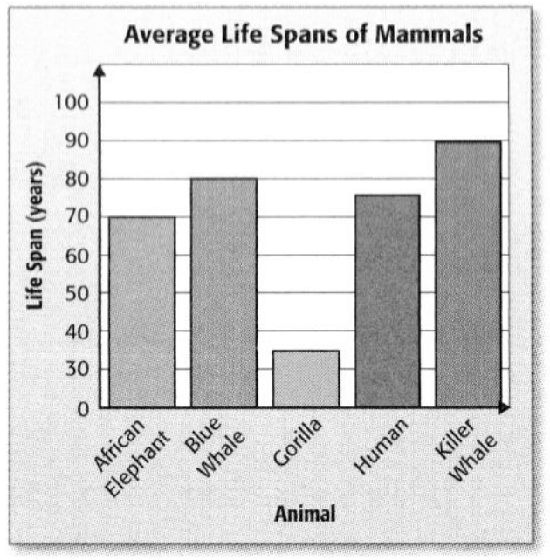

1. Which animal has the longest life span? killer whale
2. Which animal has a life span of 70 years? African elephant
3. Which animal has a life span that is 45 years longer than a gorilla's life span? blue whale
4. How many years would three generations of humans last? 225 years

Lesson 3-6
Pages 112–114

For Exercises 1–4, use the graph shown.

Fruits Produced on a Farm

Type of Fruit	Pounds Produced
Peaches	150
Apples	400
Plums	100
Strawberries	250

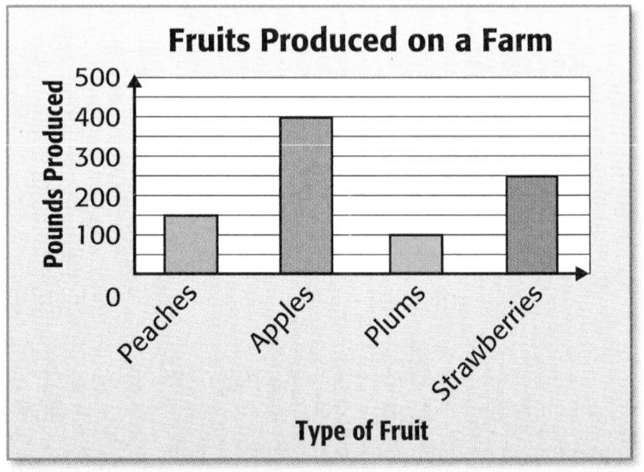

1. Which fruit did the farm produce the most of? apples
2. Which fruit did the farm produce the least of? plums
3. How many more pounds of strawberries were produced than pounds of plums? 150 lb
4. Which two fruits added together equal the amount of the fruit that the farm produced the most of? strawberries and peaches

Lesson 3-7
Pages 118–119

Use any strategy to solve. Tell what strategy you used.

1. Luis has an aquarium with 47 fish. There are 12 orange fish, 13 blue fish, 9 white fish, and 8 yellow fish. The rest of the fish are red. How many are red? 5 fish
2. There were 45 action, 60 comedy, 25 drama, and 50 mystery movies rented from a video store in one day. How many more comedies than dramas were rented? 35

Lesson 3-8 1–4. See Extra Practice Answer Appendix.
Pages 124–127

1. Draw a grid to find the number of possible outcomes if two counters are tossed once. Each counter is red on one side and yellow on the other.
2. Draw a grid to find the number of possible outcomes if a coin is tossed and a 0–5 number cube is rolled.
3. Draw a tree diagram to find the number of possible outcomes if a coin is tossed and a spinner with four equal sections labeled 1, 2, 3, and 4, is spun.
4. Draw a tree diagram to find the number of possible outcomes if a spinner with three equal sections labeled 1, 2, and 3, is spun twice.

Lesson 3-9
Pages 128–130

Describe the probability of each outcome. Write *certain, likely, equally likely, unlikely,* or *impossible.*

1. What is the probability of rolling a number? certain
2. What is the probability of rolling a number that is less than 5? likely
3. What is the probability of rolling an even number? equally likely
4. What is the probability of rolling a number that is greater than 6? impossible

Lesson 4-1
Pages 147–149

Algebra Copy and complete each fact family.

1. $3 \times 8 = \blacksquare$ 24 $8 \times \blacksquare = 24$ 3 $24 \div \blacksquare = 3$ 8 $24 \div 3 = \blacksquare$ 8
2. $9 \times \blacksquare = 72$ 8 $8 \times \blacksquare = 72$ 9 $72 \div 9 = \blacksquare$ 8 $72 \div 8 = \blacksquare$ 9

Algebra Divide. Use a related multiplication fact.

3. $27 \div 3 = \blacksquare$ 9; $3 \times 9 = 27$
4. $54 \div 9 = \blacksquare$ 6; $9 \times 6 = 54$
5. $36 \div 6 = \blacksquare$ 6; $6 \times 6 = 36$
6. $88 \div 11 = \blacksquare$ 8; $11 \times 8 = 88$
7. $32 \div 8 = \blacksquare$ 4; $8 \times 4 = 32$
8. $50 \div 5 = \blacksquare$ 10; $5 \times 10 = 50$

Lesson 4-2
Pages 150–153

Identify the property or rule shown by each number sentence.

1. $7 \times 4 = 4 \times 7$ Comm. Prop. (×)
2. $0 \div 15 = 0$ Zeros in Division
3. $3 \times (4 \times 5) = (3 \times 4) \times 5$ Assoc. Prop. (×)
4. $24 \div 1 = 24$ Divide by 1
5. $36 \div 36 = 1$ Ones in Division
6. $(5 \times 8) \times 6 = 5 \times (8 \times 6)$ Assoc. Prop. (×)

Algebra **Copy and complete each number sentence. Identify the property or rule used.**

7. $6 \div ■ = 1$ 6; Ones in Division
8. $16 \times ■ = 0$ 0; Zero Prop. of Multiplication
9. $14 \div ■ = 1$ 14; Divide by the same number
10. $■ \times 8 = 8 \times 5$ 5; Commutative Property (×)

Lesson 4-3
Pages 154–157

Multiply or divide. Use arrays or area models if needed.

1. 3×8 24
2. 5×5 25
3. 4×7 28
4. 2×9 18
5. 9×4 36
6. 2×7 14
7. 3×6 18
8. 12×3 36
9. $27 \div 3$ 9
10. $32 \div 4$ 8
11. $30 \div 5$ 6
12. $15 \div 3$ 5
13. $45 \div 5$ 9
14. $28 \div 4$ 7
15. $24 \div 4$ 6
16. $45 \div 3$ 15

Lesson 4-4
Pages 158–159

Tell which operation you would use to solve each problem. Then solve.

1. Sanjay and 3 of his teammates together scored 52 points in a basketball game. They each scored the same number of points. How many points did each boy score? division; 13 points
2. Sherri jogged 9 miles last week, which is 3 times as many miles as her sister and half as much as her brother. How many miles did her sister and brother jog? division, multiplication; 3 miles, 18 miles
3. There are 6 rows of desks in a classroom. There are 7 desks in each row. How many desks are in the classroom? multiplication; 42 desks
4. Roger earns $3,600 a year delivering papers. How much does he earn in one month? division; $300

Lesson 4-5
Pages 160–162

Multiply or divide. Use arrays or area models if needed.

1. 9×6 54
2. 6×8 48
3. 7×7 49
4. 8×10 80
5. 5×8 40
6. 9×5 45
7. 6×10 60
8. 7×9 63
9. $42 \div 6$ 7
10. $48 \div 6$ 8
11. $90 \div 10$ 9
12. $56 \div 7$ 8
13. $35 \div 5$ 7
14. $81 \div 9$ 9
15. $36 \div 6$ 6
16. $72 \div 8$ 9

Lesson 4-6
Pages 166–169

Multiply or divide. Use arrays or area models if needed.

1. 3×11 33
2. 4×12 48
3. 11×6 66
4. 8×12 96
5. 7×11 77
6. 4×12 48
7. $11\overline{)88}$ 8
8. $11\overline{)110}$ 10
9. $12\overline{)48}$ 4
10. $120 \div 12$ 10
11. $99 \div 11$ 9
12. $96 \div 12$ 8

Lesson 4-7
Pages 170–171

Use any strategy to solve. Tell what strategy you used.

1. Manuel earns $4 for every 3 dozen cookies he sells. How much will Manuel earn if he sells 9 dozen cookies? 12 dozen cookies? $12; $16
2. Laura has 24 jazz CDs and 7 country CDs. She has 2 times as many pop CDs as country CDs. How many CDs does she have in all? 45 CDs
3. Kim wants to buy a snowboard that costs $160. She has $88 in the bank. If she earns $6 an hour babysitting, how many hours will Kim have to work to earn enough money to buy the snowboard? 12 hrs
4. An art gallery has paintings on display in 7 rooms. There are 12 paintings in each room. How many paintings are on display in the art gallery? 84 paintings

Extra Practice

Lesson 4-8
Pages 172–174

Multiply.

1. $6 \times 3 \times 4$ 72 **2.** $5 \times 7 \times 3$ 105 **3.** $8 \times 2 \times 5$ 80

4. $9 \times 3 \times 2$ 54 **5.** $6 \times 4 \times 5$ 120 **6.** $9 \times 1 \times 4$ 36

7. $8 \times 4 \times 3$ 96 **8.** $3 \times 3 \times 12$ 108 **9.** $10 \times 3 \times 5$ 150

10. $6 \times 11 \times 1$ 66 **11.** $9 \times 4 \times 2$ 72 **12.** $12 \times 2 \times 4$ 96

Lesson 4-9
Pages 176–179

Find all of the factors of each number.

1. 36 1, 2, 3, 4, 6, 9, 12, 18, and 36 **2.** 18 1, 2, 3, 6, 9, and 18 **3.** 16 1, 2, 4, 8, and 16

4. 35 1, 5, 7, and 35 **5.** 11 1 and 11 **6.** 24 1, 2, 3, 4, 6, 8, 12, and 24

7. 48 1, 2, 3, 4, 6, 8, 12, 16, 24, and 48 **8.** 40 1, 2, 4, 5, 8, 10, 20, and 40 **9.** 23 1 and 23

Identify the first six multiples for each number.

10. 4 0, 4, 8, 12, 16, and 20 **11.** 7 0, 7, 14, 21, 28, and 35 **12.** 6 0, 6, 12, 18, 24, and 30

13. 12 0, 12, 24, 36, 48, and 60 **14.** 8 0, 8, 16, 24, 32, and 40 **15.** 9 0, 9, 18, 27, 36, and 45

16. 10 0, 10, 20, 30, 40, and 50 **17.** 11 0, 11, 22, 33, 44, and 55 **18.** 3 0, 3, 6, 9, and 12

Lesson 5-1
Pages 193–195

Find the value of each expression if $x = 6$ and $c = 7$.

1. $c + 5$ 12 **2.** $x - 3$ 3 **3.** $c + 9$ 16

4. $7 + x$ 13 **5.** $c - 2$ 5 **6.** $14 - x$ 8

7. $(x - 2) + 9$ 13 **8.** $16 - (c + 5)$ 4 **9.** $5 + (6 + x)$ 17

Write an expression for each situation.

10. five less than *y* $y - 5$ **11.** the sum of *b* and seventeen $b + 17$

12. *d* minus twenty-four $d - 24$ **13.** fifty-one subtracted from *f* $f - 51$

Lesson 5-2
Pages 198–201

Solve each equation.

1. $4 + b = 12$ 8 **2.** $7 + m = 18$ 11 **3.** $p - 8 = 6$ 14 **4.** $18 - 13 = y$ 5

5. $9 - x = 2$ 7 **6.** $q + 14 = 22$ 8 **7.** $8 + d = 18$ 10 **8.** $7 + 6 = f$ 13

Write and solve an equation for each situation.

9. Twelve less than a number is sixteen. What is the number? $y - 12 = 16$; 28

10. Eight subtracted from a number equals thirteen. What is the number? $n - 8 = 13$; 21

11. The sum of nine and a number is twenty-eight. Find the number. $9 + b = 28$; 19

12. A number plus eleven equals twenty-five. What is the number? $q + 11 = 25$; 14

Lesson 5-3
Pages 202–203

Identify any missing or extra information. Then solve if possible. 2. extra: There are 3 tennis balls in each can; 5

1. Monkeys at the zoo eat 9 bananas and 4 apples each day. How many pieces of fruit do the monkeys eat in one week? missing: the number of monkeys at the zoo

2. Sandra has $21. She wants to buy cans of tennis balls for $4 each. There are 3 tennis balls in each can. How many cans can she buy?

3. Marco has soccer practice 3 days a week. He has 17 teammates. Practice lasts for 2 hours each day. How many hours does Marco practice soccer each week? extra: He has 17 teammates; 6

4. Kayla earns $5 per hour. She is saving to buy a new game that costs $36 dollars. How many weeks will Kayla have to work to earn enough money for the game? missing: how many hours Kayla works each week

Lesson 5-4
Pages 204–206

Identify, describe, and extend each pattern.

1. 3, 7, 11, 15, 19, ■ + 4; 23

2. 27, 22, 17, 12, 7, ■ − 5; 2

3. 2, 5, 3, 6, 4, ■ + 3 then − 2; 7

4. 5, 1, 7, 3, 9, ■ − 4 then + 6; 5

5. Sara jogs on a track five days a week. What is the rule for the pattern shown in the table? × 8

Distance Jogged					
Day	1	2	3	4	5
Laps	8	16	24	32	40

6. Trevor practices the guitar every day. What is the rule for the pattern shown in the table? × 45

Time Spent Practicing					
Day	1	2	3	4	5
Minutes	45	90	135	180	225

Lesson 5-5

Pages 208–211

Write an equation that describes each pattern. Then use the equation to find the next three numbers.

1.

Rule: ■						
Input (b)	4	6	10	14	20	24
Output (x)	13	15	19	■	■	■

$b + 9 = x$; 23, 29, 33

2.

Rule: ■						
Input (y)	11	15	19	23	27	31
Output (c)	4	8	12	■	■	■

$y - 7 = c$; 16, 20, 24

3.

Rule: ■						
Input (f)	\$24	\$32	\$40	\$48	\$56	\$64
Output (q)	\$16	\$24	\$32	■	■	■

$f - 8 = q$; \$40, \$48, \$56

4.

Rule: ■						
Input (m)	\$16	\$19	\$22	\$25	\$28	\$31
Output (p)	\$27	\$30	\$33	■	■	■

$m + 11 = p$; \$36, \$39, \$42

Lesson 5-6

Pages 214–216

Find the value of each expression if $v = 4$ and $x = 8$.

1. $x \div 4$ 2
2. $6 \times v$ 24
3. $x \div v$ 2
4. $v \div v$ 1
5. $x \times 7 =$ 56
6. $5 \times v$ 20
7. $(v \times 4) \div x$ 2
8. $32 \div (x \div v)$ 16
9. $(x \div 2) \times 9$ 36

Write an expression for each situation.

10. a number divided by 5 $n \div 5$
11. The product of 3 and a number $3 \times n$
12. a number divided by 10 $n \div 10$
13. 9 times a number $9 \times n$

Lesson 5-7

Pages 218–219

Use any strategy to solve. Tell what strategy you used.

1. Ty wants to buy posters that cost \$7 each. He has \$50. How many posters can he buy? 7 posters
2. Ian is eating pizza with 5 friends. They ordered 3 pizzas. If each pizza is cut into 6 slices, how many slices can each person have? 3 slices
3. A vine in the park grows 2 inches every week. The vine is 13 inches tall now. How many inches tall will the vine be in 2 weeks? 4 weeks? 8 weeks? 17 in.; 21 in.; 29 in.
4. Amy is putting photos in an album. Each page in the album can hold 4 photos. There are 32 pages in the album. How many photos can Amy put in the album? 128 photos

Lesson 5-8

Pages 220–223

Write an equation that describes each pattern. Then use the equation to find the next three numbers.

1.

Input (a)	Output (q)
2	12
4	24
6	36
8	■
10	■
12	■

Multiply by 6; $a \times 6 = q$; 48, 60, 72

2.

Input (g)	Output (v)
21	3
28	4
35	5
42	■
49	■
56	■

Divide by 7; $g \div 7 = v$; 6, 7, 8

Lesson 6-1

Pages 237–239

Multiply. Use basic facts and patterns.

1. 4×5 20
4×50 200
4×500 2,000
$4 \times 5{,}000$ 20,000

2. 3×7 21
3×70 210
3×700 2,100
$3 \times 7{,}000$ 21,000

3. 8×6 48
8×60 480
8×600 4,800
$8 \times 6{,}000$ 48,000

4. 3×9 27
3×90 270
3×900 2,700
$3 \times 9{,}000$ 27,000

5. 5×6 30
5×60 300
5×600 3,000
$5 \times 6{,}000$ 30,000

6. 7×4 28
7×40 280
7×400 2,800
$7 \times 4{,}000$ 28,000

Multiply. Use mental math.

7. 7×80 560
8. 60×6 360
9. 90×3 270
10. 500×7 3,500
11. 9×400 3,600
12. $8{,}000 \times 5$ 40,000

Lesson 6-2

Pages 240–241

Decide whether each answer is reasonable. Explain your reasoning.

1. Ebony practices the guitar 30 minutes every day. Is it reasonable to say that she practices the guitar 3,000 minutes each month?
2. The soccer fields in a park are each 130 yards long. Is it reasonable to say that 4 soccer fields are a total of 1,560 feet long? yes; $(4 \times 130) \times 3 = 1{,}560$
3. The chickens on a farm produce about 4,200 eggs per week. Is it reasonable to say that the chickens produce 600 eggs each day? yes; $600 \times 7 = 4{,}200$
4. An album can hold 24 stamps on each page. There are 200 pages. Is it reasonable to say that the album can hold 48,000 stamps? no; $24 \times 200 = 4{,}800$

1. no; Ebony practices for 210 minutes each week, so 3,000 is not a good estimate.

Extra Practice

Lesson 6-3

Pages 242–244

Estimate each product. Then tell if the estimate is *greater than* or *less than* the actual product.

1. 584×3 600 × 3 = 1,800; greater
2. 484×5 500 × 5 = 2,500; greater
3. 723×8 700 × 8 = 5,600, less
4. 3 × 692 3 × 700 = 2,100; greater
5. 6 × $472 $6 × 500 = $3,000; greater
6. 9 × $460 9 × $500 = $4,500; greater
7. 7 × 1,986 7 × 2,000 = 14,000; greater
8. 8 × $5,420 8 × $5,000 = $40,000; less
9. 5 × 6,752 5 × 7,000 = 35,000; greater
10. 3 × $478 3 × $500 = $1,500; greater
11. 6 × $9,810 6 × $10,000 = $60,000; greater
12. 8 × 3,755 8 × 4,000 = 32,000; greater

Lesson 6-4

Pages 246–248

Multiply. Check for reasonableness.

1. 18×6 108
2. 28×5 140
3. $17 × 9 $153
4. 2 × 99 198
5. 6 × 25 150
6. 7 × $43 $301
7. 5 × 73 365
8. 4 × $86 $344
9. 9 × 39 351
10. 3 × $92 $276
11. 8 × 78 624
12. 7 × $56 $392

Lesson 6-5

Pages 250–251

Use any strategy to solve. Tell what strategy you used.

1. Jesse bikes 224 miles each month. He bikes the same number of miles each week. How many miles does Jesse bike each week? Assume that there are four weeks in each month. 56 miles
2. Movie tickets are $7 for adults and $4 for children. What is the total cost if three adults and five children go to the theater? $41
3. Rita is making muffins. There are 36 muffins in each batch. How many muffins will be in 3 batches? How many muffins will be in 7 batches? 108 muffins; 252 muffins
4. At the zoo, the big cats are in a row. The lions are last. The jaguars are to the left of the tigers. The cheetahs are to the left of the jaguars. In what order are the big cats? cheetahs, jaguars, tigers, lions

Lesson 6-6

Pages 252–255

Multiply. Check for reasonableness.

1. 538×3 1,614
2. 392×6 2,352
3. $256 × 8 $2,048
4. 734×7 5,138
5. $493 × 6 $2,958
6. $724 × 4 $2,896
7. 6 × 5,630 33,780
8. 6 × $8,562 $51,372
9. 5 × 2,845 14,225
10. 4 × 3,488 13,952
11. 8 × 2,376 19,008
12. 9 × 5,670 51,030

Lesson 6-7

Pages 258–261

Multiply. Check for reasonableness.

1. 408×4 1,632
2. 507×8 4,056
3. 906×7 6,342
4. 2 × 6,009 12,018
5. 7 × $3,408 $23,856
6. 5 × 9,206 46,030
7. 3 × $8,702 $26,106
8. 6 × 4,090 24,540
9. 9 × $6,205 $55,845
10. 4 × 7,084 28,336
11. 8 × 9,502 76,016
12. 5 × 5,047 25,235

Lesson 7-1

Pages 273–275

Multiply.

1. 18×30 540
2. 24×50 1,200
3. 48×90 4,320
4. 47×60 2,820
5. 75×40 3,000
6. 56×90 5,040
7. 64×30 1,920
8. $49 × 60 $2,940
9. 85×70 5,950
10. $28 × 30 $840
11. 92×70 6,440
12. 63×90 5,670

Lesson 7-2
Pages 276–279

Estimate. Tell whether the estimate is *greater than* or *less than* the actual product.

1. 38×26 — $40 \times 30 = 1{,}200$; greater
2. 63×44 — $60 \times 40 = 2{,}400$; less
3. 59×37 — $60 \times 40 = 2{,}400$; greater
4. $98 × 57 — $\$100 \times 60 = \$6{,}000$; greater
5. 43×82 — $40 \times 80 = 3{,}200$; less
6. $67 × 38 — $\$70 \times 40 = \$2{,}800$; greater
7. 322×64 — $300 \times 60 = 18{,}000$; less
8. 668×27 — 700×30; 21,000 greater
9. 982×34 — $1{,}000 \times 30 = 30{,}000$; less
10. 441×33 — $400 \times 30 = 12{,}000$; less
11. 877×59 — $900 \times 60 = 54{,}000$; greater
12. 799×87 — $800 \times 90 = 72{,}000$; greater

Lesson 7-3
Pages 280–281

Solve. Use the act it out strategy.

1. There are 4 tennis players at the court. Each one played one set of tennis against every other player. How many sets of tennis were played? 6 sets
2. Keisha has 450¢ in her piggy bank. She has the same number of dimes and quarters. She has half as many nickels as dimes. What coins does she have?
   6 nickels, 12 dimes, 12 quarters
3. Linda is 12 years old. Her mother is 2 years less than 3 times her age. How old is Linda's mother?
   34 years old
4. Jaime has 17 coins in his pocket. The coins have a value of 120¢. What coins does he have?
   5 pennies, 7 nickels, 3 dimes, and 2 quarters

Lesson 7-4
Pages 284–286

Multiply.

1. 17×25 — 425
2. 56×33 — 1,848
3. $84 × 42 — $3,528
4. 62×55 — 3,410
5. 74×93 — 6,882
6. $65 × 48 — $3,120
7. 36×56 — 2,016
8. 49×77 — 3,773
9. $44 × 83 — $3,652
10. 64×95 — 6,080
11. $58 × 17 — $986
12. 75×73 — 5,475

Lesson 7-5
Pages 288–291

Multiply.

1. 104×18 — 1,872
2. 186×32 — 5,952
3. 207×49 — 10,143
4. 275×64 — 17,600
5. 377×53 — 19,981
6. 309×81 — 25,029
7. 452×37 — 16,724
8. 438×27 — 11,826
9. 588×39 — 22,932
10. 542×64 — 34,688
11. 663×46 — 30,498
12. 738×56 — 41,328

Lesson 7-6
Pages 294–295

Use any strategy to solve. Tell what strategy you used.

1. Natalie is thinking of two numbers with a sum of 13 and a product of 36. What are the two numbers?
   9 and 4
2. The fish at the pet store eat 28 jars of food every week. How many jars of food will the fish eat in 4 weeks? in 6 weeks? in 8 weeks?
   112; 168; 224
3. Ramón saves $15 every week to buy a skateboard. The skateboard costs $105. How many weeks will it take him to save half as much as he needs to buy the skateboard?
   $3\frac{1}{2}$ weeks
4. Every fourth grader washed 4 cars at the car wash. The fourth graders washed 284 cars in all. How many fourth grade students are there?
   71

Lesson 7-7
Pages 296–298

Multiply.

1. $1{,}877 \times 24$ — 45,048
2. $2{,}345 \times 62$ — 145,390
3. $3{,}906 \times 59$ — 230,454
4. $5{,}792 \times 48$ — 278,016
5. $6{,}504 \times 96$ — 624,384
6. $7{,}708 \times 85$ — 655,180
7. $8{,}544 \times 38$ — 324,672
8. $12{,}304 \times 65$ — 799,760
9. $17{,}455 \times 92$ — 1,605,860

Extra Practice

Lesson 8-1

Pages 313–315

Divide. Check each answer.

1. $36 \div 3$ 12; $3 \times 12 = 36$
2. $60 \div 5$ 12; $5 \times 12 = 60$
3. $54 \div 3$ 18; $3 \times 18 = 54$
4. $70 \div 5$ 14; $5 \times 14 = 70$
5. $98 \div 7$ 14; $7 \times 14 = 98$
6. $91 \div 7$ 13; $7 \times 13 = 91$
7. $79 \div 3$ 26 R1; $3 \times 26 + 1 = 79$
8. $66 \div 4$ 16 R2; $4 \times 16 + 2 = 66$
9. $95 \div 7$ 13 R4; $7 \times 13 + 4 = 95$

Lesson 8-2

Pages 316–319

Copy and complete each set of patterns.

1. $48 \div 6 =$ ■ 8; $480 \div 6 =$ ■ 80; $4{,}800 \div 6 =$ ■ 800
2. $63 \div 9 =$ ■ 7; $630 \div 9 =$ ■ 70; $6{,}300 \div 9 =$ ■ 700
3. $\$40 \div 8 =$ ■ \$5; $\$400 \div 8 =$ ■ \$50; $\$4{,}000 \div 8 =$ ■ \$500
4. $72 \div 9 =$ ■ 8; $720 \div 9 =$ ■ 80; $7{,}200 \div 6 =$ ■ 800
5. $\$27 \div 3 =$ ■ \$9; $\$270 \div 3 =$ ■ \$90; $\$2{,}700 \div 3 =$ ■ \$900
6. $35 \div 7 =$ ■ 5; $350 \div 7 =$ ■ 50; $3{,}500 \div 7 =$ ■ 500

Divide. Use patterns.

7. $420 \div 6$ 70
8. $300 \div 5$ 60
9. $\$280 \div 7$ \$40
10. $\$210 \div 3$ \$70
11. $5{,}600 \div 7$ 800
12. $7{,}200 \div 8$ 900
13. $8{,}100 \div 9$ 900
14. $1{,}600 \div 4$ 400
15. $3{,}000 \div 6$ 500
16. $\$2{,}700 \div 3$ \$900
17. $4{,}500 \div 9$ 500
18. $5{,}400 \div 9$ 600

Lesson 8-3

Pages 320–321

Solve. Use the guess and check strategy.

1. Ren bought 5 CDs for \$55. One of the CDs cost \$5 more than the others. How much did each CD cost? 4 of the CDs each cost \$10 and 1 of them cost \$15.
2. Carmen has 49 more mystery novels than adventure novels. She has 223 novels in all. How many mystery novels and adventure novels does Carmen have? 2. 136 mystery novels and 87 adventure novels
3. The chickens on a farm eat 3 times as much grain as the turkeys do per week. The chickens and turkeys eat a total of 52 pounds of grain every week. How much grain do the chickens and turkeys each eat every week? turkeys: 13 pounds, chickens: 39 pounds
4. A toy store has at least 10 wagons and at least 10 tricycles on sale. There are a total of 89 wheels. How many tricycles and how many wagons are on sale? 11 tricycles and 14 wagons

Lesson 8-4

Pages 322–324

Estimate. Check your estimate.

1. $24 \div 4$ $20 \div 4 = 5$
2. $510 \div 7$ $490 \div 7 = 70$
3. $433 \div 5$ $430 \div 5 = 86$
4. $476 \div 8$ $480 \div 8 = 60$
5. $\$537 \div 6$ $\$540 \div 6 = \$90$
6. $298 \div 4$ $280 \div 4 = 70$
7. $337 \div 8$ $320 \div 8 = 40$
8. $\$259 \div 5$ $\$250 \div 5 = \$50$
9. $1{,}244 \div 6$ $1{,}200 \div 6 = 200$
10. $2{,}240 \div 3$ $2{,}400 \div 3 = 800$
11. $\$6{,}580 \div 9$ $\$6{,}300 \div 9 = \$700$
12. $8{,}256 \div 9$ $8{,}100 \div 9 = 900$

Lesson 8-5

Pages 326–329

Divide. Use estimation to check.

1. $7\overline{)47}$ 6 R5; $49 \div 7 = 7$
2. $8\overline{)39}$ 4 R7; $40 \div 8 = 5$
3. $9\overline{)71}$ 7 R8; $72 \div 9 = 8$
4. $6\overline{)33}$ 5 R3; $30 \div 6 = 5$
5. $5\overline{)44}$ 8 R4; $40 \div 5 = 8$
6. $8\overline{)62}$ 7 R6; $64 \div 8 = 8$
7. $9\overline{)25}$ 2 R7; $27 \div 9 = 3$
8. $6\overline{)45}$ 7 R3; $42 \div 6 = 7$
9. $554 \div 8$ 69 R2; $560 \div 8 = 70$
10. $462 \div 9$ 51 R3; $450 \div 9 = 50$
11. $368 \div 6$ 61 R2; $360 \div 6 = 60$
12. $659 \div 8$ 82 R3; $640 \div 8 = 80$

Lesson 8-6

Pages 330–331

Use any strategy to solve. Tell what strategy you used.

1. At the drugstore, pencils are on sale for 10 for \$1. Pens are on sale for 4 for \$2. How much do 20 pencils and 12 pens cost? \$8
2. A plant produces about 45 new flowers every 2 weeks. After 8 weeks, how many flowers will the plant have produced? 180 flowers
3. There are 9 seals at a zoo. Altogether, the seals eat about 750 fish each day. About how many fish does each seal eat every day? 80 fish
4. Mei hiked for 20 minutes every morning from her campsite to the lake. She hiked back to the campsite every afternoon. Mei hiked for a total of 8 hours to and from the lake. How many days was Mei at camp? 12 days

Lesson 8-7
Pages 332–334

Divide. Use estimation to check.

1. $3\overline{)693}$ 231
2. $2\overline{)764}$ 382
3. $7\overline{)875}$ 125
4. $4\overline{)936}$ 234
5. $3\overline{)1,677}$ 559
6. $6\overline{)2,558}$ 426 R2
7. $5\overline{)3,697}$ 739 R2
8. $9\overline{)2,938}$ 326 R4
9. 1,539 ÷ 2 769 R1
10. 7,564 ÷ 8 945 R4
11. 4,255 ÷ 7 607 R6
12. 2,687 ÷ 4 671 R3

Lesson 8-8
Pages 336–338

Divide. Use estimation to check.

1. $3\overline{)315}$ 105
2. $4\overline{)837}$ 209 R1
3. $4\overline{)\$432}$ $108
4. $9\overline{)976}$ 108 R4
5. $3\overline{)625}$ 208 R1
6. $4\overline{)438}$ 109 R2
7. $2\overline{)414}$ 207
8. $7\overline{)756}$ 108
9. $3\overline{)\$317}$ $105 R2
10. $5\overline{)1,039}$ 207 R4
11. $3\overline{)\$2,721}$ $907
12. $9\overline{)9,459}$ 1,051
13. 1,615 ÷ 2 807 R1
14. 4,363 ÷ 4 1,090 R3
15. $611 ÷ 3 $203 R2
16. 1,236 ÷ 4 309

Lesson 8-9
Pages 342–345

Divide. Use estimation to check.

1. $2\overline{)3,664}$ 1,832
2. $3\overline{)4,671}$ 1,557
3. $5\overline{)5,847}$ 1,169 R2
4. $6\overline{)7,248}$ 1,208
5. $4\overline{)6,184}$ 1,546
6. $8\overline{)9,872}$ 1,234
7. $7\overline{)9,256}$ 1,322 R2
8. $6\overline{)57,888}$ 9,648
9. $8\overline{)18,816}$ 2,352
10. $9\overline{)33,786}$ 3,754
11. $7\overline{)25,984}$ 3,712
12. $6\overline{)23,678}$ 3,946 R2
13. 9,634 ÷ 8 1,204 R2
14. 59,510 ÷ 5 11,902
15. 67,651 ÷ 9 7,516 R7
16. 95,785 ÷ 5 19,157

Lesson 9-1
Pages 359–361

Tell the number of faces, edges, and vertices. Then identify each figure.

1. 0 faces, 0 edges, 0 vertices; sphere
2. 2 faces, 0 edges, 0 vertices; cylinder
3. 5 faces, 9 edges, 6 vertices; triangular prism
4. 6 faces, 12 edges, 8 vertices; cube
5. 5 faces, 8 edges, 5 vertices; square pyramid
6. 1 face, 0 edges, 1 vertex; cone

Lesson 9-2
Pages 362–365

Identify each polygon.

1. hexagon
2. quadrilateral
3. octagon

Tell whether each shape is a polygon.

4. yes
5. no
6. no

Lesson 9-3
Pages 366–367

Solve. Use the look for a pattern strategy.

1. A flowering plant produces 15 seeds on the first day of spring. On the second day, it produces 23 seeds. On the third day, it produces 31 seeds. Describe the pattern. How many seeds will the plant produce on the sixth day?
Add 8; 55

2. Copy and complete the table. What is the pattern?

Input	Output
3	21
5	35
7	■ 49
■ 8	56

Multiply by 7.

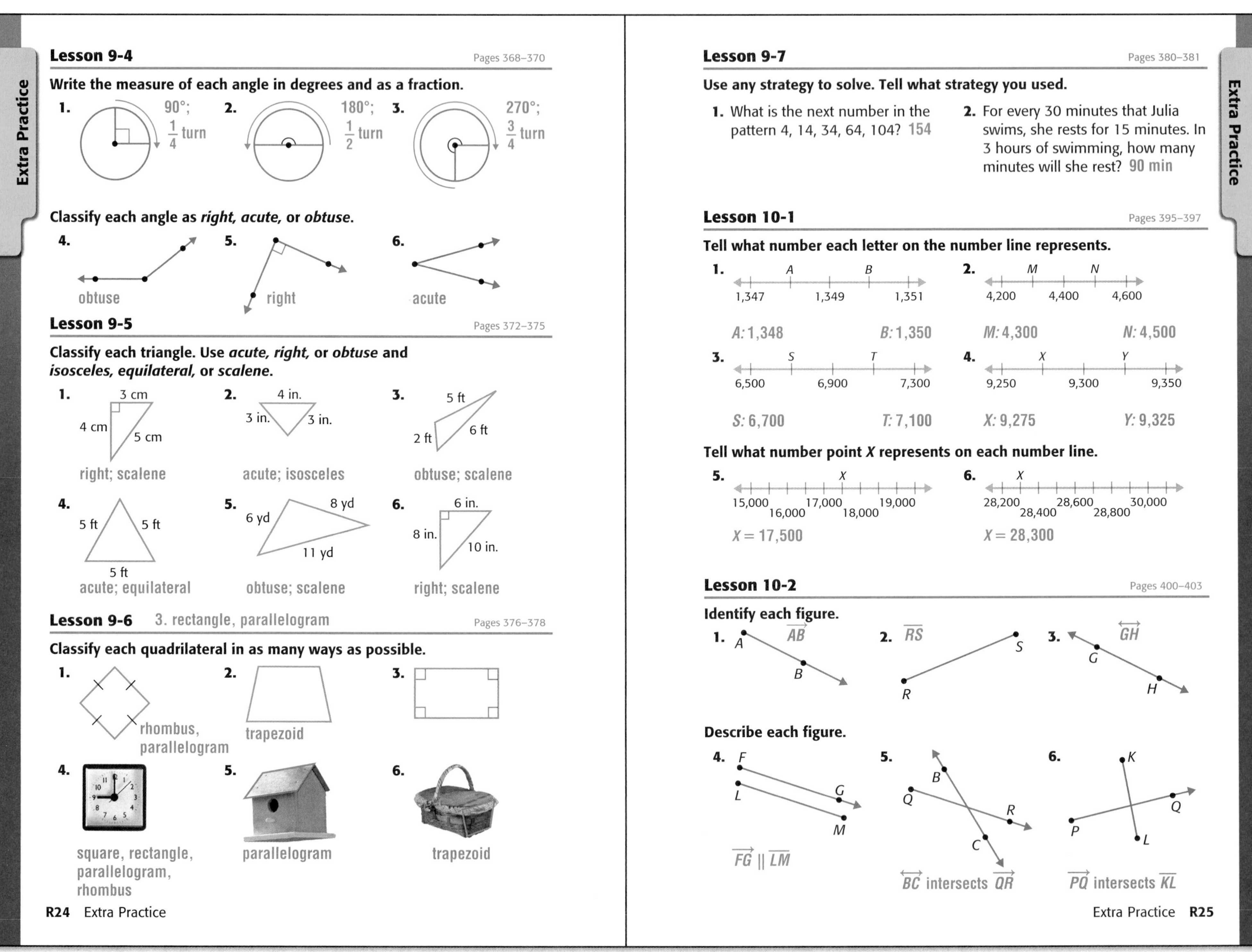

Lesson 9-4
Pages 368–370

Write the measure of each angle in degrees and as a fraction.

1. 90°; $\frac{1}{4}$ turn
2. 180°; $\frac{1}{2}$ turn
3. 270°; $\frac{3}{4}$ turn

Classify each angle as *right, acute,* or *obtuse*.

4. obtuse
5. right
6. acute

Lesson 9-5
Pages 372–375

Classify each triangle. Use *acute, right,* or *obtuse* and *isosceles, equilateral,* or *scalene*.

1. 3 cm, 4 cm, 5 cm — right; scalene
2. 4 in., 3 in., 3 in. — acute; isosceles
3. 5 ft, 2 ft, 6 ft — obtuse; scalene
4. 5 ft, 5 ft, 5 ft — acute; equilateral
5. 6 yd, 8 yd, 11 yd — obtuse; scalene
6. 6 in., 8 in., 10 in. — right; scalene

Lesson 9-6
3. rectangle, parallelogram

Pages 376–378

Classify each quadrilateral in as many ways as possible.

1. rhombus, parallelogram
2. trapezoid
3.
4. square, rectangle, parallelogram, rhombus
5. parallelogram
6. trapezoid

Lesson 9-7
Pages 380–381

Use any strategy to solve. Tell what strategy you used.

1. What is the next number in the pattern 4, 14, 34, 64, 104? 154
2. For every 30 minutes that Julia swims, she rests for 15 minutes. In 3 hours of swimming, how many minutes will she rest? 90 min

Lesson 10-1
Pages 395–397

Tell what number each letter on the number line represents.

1. 1,347 — 1,349 — 1,351; A: 1,348 B: 1,350
2. 4,200 — 4,400 — 4,600; M: 4,300 N: 4,500
3. 6,500 — 6,900 — 7,300; S: 6,700 T: 7,100
4. 9,250 — 9,300 — 9,350; X: 9,275 Y: 9,325

Tell what number point *X* represents on each number line.

5. 15,000, 16,000, 17,000, 18,000, 19,000; $X = 17,500$
6. 28,200, 28,400, 28,600, 28,800, 30,000; $X = 28,300$

Lesson 10-2
Pages 400–403

Identify each figure.

1. $\overrightarrow{AB}$
2. $\overline{RS}$
3. $\overleftrightarrow{GH}$

Describe each figure.

4. $\overrightarrow{FG} \parallel \overline{LM}$
5. $\overleftrightarrow{BC}$ intersects $\overrightarrow{QR}$
6. $\overrightarrow{PQ}$ intersects $\overline{KL}$

Lesson 10-3
Pages 404–405

Solve. Use the make an organized list strategy.

1. Jim has 1 blue jacket, 1 green jacket, and 1 brown jacket. He has 1 tan hat and 1 black hat. How many different combinations of a jacket and hat can he wear? 6
2. Lee, Diego, Tara, and Irena will ride the Ferris wheel. Two people can sit in each car. What pairs are possible for the four friends to ride the Ferris wheel?

2. Lee/Diego and Tara/Irena; Lee/Tara and Diego/Irena; Lee/Irena and Diego/Tara

Lesson 10-4
Pages 406–408

Identify the letter that is located at each ordered pair.

1. (2, −4) *K*
2. (−3, 4) *J*
3. (7, 6) *C*
4. (−4, −2) *M*
5. (−2, 1) *P*
6. (4, 0) *H*
7. (−7, −6) *Q*
8. (7, −6) *X*
9. (0, 0) *A*

Lesson 10-5
Pages 412–415

Identify each transformation. Write *rotation, reflection,* or *translation.*

1. translation
2. rotation
3. reflection
4. translation

Lesson 10-6
Pages 416–417

Use any strategy to solve. Tell what strategy you used.

1. Sam is replacing the wheels on 6 bicycles. He is also replacing the wheels on 4 tricycles and 3 wagons. How many wheels is Sam replacing in all? 36 wheels
2. Suna wants to make 5 bracelets and 3 necklaces. She plans to use 3 shells for every bracelet and 4 shells for every necklace. How many shells does she need? 27 shells
3. Evan has twice as many pairs of mittens as boots. He has 6 times as many pairs of socks as boots. He has 18 pairs of socks. How many pairs of boots and mittens does he have? 3 pairs of boots and 6 pairs of mittens
4. Mike makes $4 an hour babysitting. Omar makes $6 an hour gardening. How many hours will Mike have to work to make the same amount that Omar makes in 8 hours? 12 hrs

Lesson 10-7
Pages 418–420

Tell whether the figures appear to be congruent. Write *yes* or *no*. If they are, describe the movements that show the congruence.

1. no
2. yes; reflection
3. yes; rotation and translation
4. no
5. yes; translation
6. no

Lesson 10-8
Pages 422–424

Tell whether each figure has line symmetry. Write *yes* or *no*. Then tell how many lines of symmetry the figure has.

1. yes; 1
2. no
3. yes; 4

Tell whether each figure has rotational symmetry. Write *yes* or *no*.

4. yes
5. no
6. yes

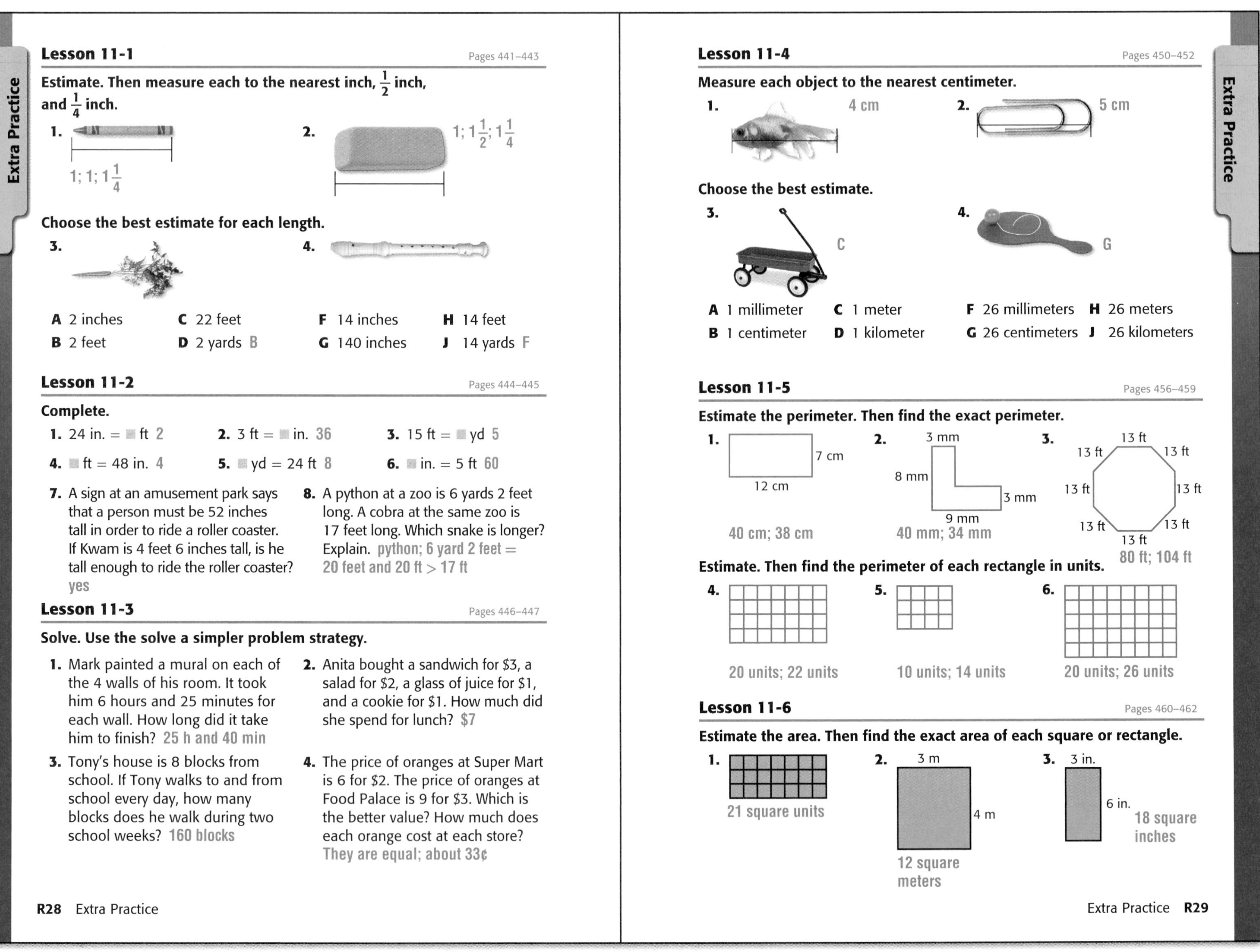

Lesson 11-1
Pages 441–443

Estimate. Then measure each to the nearest inch, $\frac{1}{2}$ inch, and $\frac{1}{4}$ inch.

1. $1; 1; 1\frac{1}{4}$
2. $1; 1\frac{1}{2}; 1\frac{1}{4}$

Choose the best estimate for each length.

3. A 2 inches B 2 feet C 22 feet D 2 yards B
4. F 14 inches G 140 inches H 14 feet J 14 yards F

Lesson 11-2
Pages 444–445

Complete.

1. 24 in. = ■ ft 2
2. 3 ft = ■ in. 36
3. 15 ft = ■ yd 5
4. ■ ft = 48 in. 4
5. ■ yd = 24 ft 8
6. ■ in. = 5 ft 60
7. A sign at an amusement park says that a person must be 52 inches tall in order to ride a roller coaster. If Kwam is 4 feet 6 inches tall, is he tall enough to ride the roller coaster? yes
8. A python at a zoo is 6 yards 2 feet long. A cobra at the same zoo is 17 feet long. Which snake is longer? Explain. python; 6 yard 2 feet = 20 feet and 20 ft > 17 ft

Lesson 11-3
Pages 446–447

Solve. Use the solve a simpler problem strategy.

1. Mark painted a mural on each of the 4 walls of his room. It took him 6 hours and 25 minutes for each wall. How long did it take him to finish? 25 h and 40 min
2. Anita bought a sandwich for \$3, a salad for \$2, a glass of juice for \$1, and a cookie for \$1. How much did she spend for lunch? \$7
3. Tony's house is 8 blocks from school. If Tony walks to and from school every day, how many blocks does he walk during two school weeks? 160 blocks
4. The price of oranges at Super Mart is 6 for \$2. The price of oranges at Food Palace is 9 for \$3. Which is the better value? How much does each orange cost at each store? They are equal; about 33¢

Lesson 11-4
Pages 450–452

Measure each object to the nearest centimeter.

1. 4 cm
2. 5 cm

Choose the best estimate.

3. A 1 millimeter B 1 centimeter C 1 meter D 1 kilometer C
4. F 26 millimeters G 26 centimeters H 26 meters J 26 kilometers G

Lesson 11-5
Pages 456–459

Estimate the perimeter. Then find the exact perimeter.

1. 12 cm, 7 cm — 40 cm; 38 cm
2. 3 mm, 8 mm, 3 mm, 9 mm — 40 mm; 34 mm
3. 13 ft (each side) — 80 ft; 104 ft

Estimate. Then find the perimeter of each rectangle in units.

4. 20 units; 22 units
5. 10 units; 14 units
6. 20 units; 26 units

Lesson 11-6
Pages 460–462

Estimate the area. Then find the exact area of each square or rectangle.

1. 21 square units
2. 3 m, 4 m — 12 square meters
3. 3 in., 6 in. — 18 square inches

Lesson 11-7
Pages 466–467

Use any strategy to solve. Tell what strategy you used.

1. The perimeter of a rectangular yard is 20 meters. What are the possible lengths of the sides? Sample answer: length: 8 units, width: 2 units
2. Stella bought 5 pencils for 25¢. How much would she pay for 15 pencils? 75¢
3. Each bunch of flowers has 12 tulips and 23 daisies. There are 6 bunches of flowers. How many flowers are there in all? 210 flowers
4. There are 324 apples. There are 68 fewer apples than oranges and 127 more apples than limes. How many limes and oranges are there? limes: 197; oranges: 256

Lesson 11-8
Pages 468–471

Write the approximate temperature in degrees Fahrenheit and Celsius.

1. 54°F; 12°C
2. 78°F; 26°C
3. The thermometer reads 2° Celsius. Would Gabrielle go swimming or build a snowman? build a snowman
4. An average person's body temperature is about 99° Fahrenheit. About how many degrees Celsius is this temperature? 37°C

Lesson 12-1
Pages 486–489

Choose the most reasonable estimate for each capacity.

1.
   - A 15 fluid ounces
   - B 15 pints
   - C 15 quarts
   - D 15 gallons A
2.
   - F 2 fluid ounces
   - G 20 fluid ounces
   - H 2 quarts
   - J 2 gallons H
3.
   - A 6 fluid ounces
   - B 6 cups
   - C 6 pints
   - D 6 quarts B
4.
   - F 6 fluid ounces
   - G 60 fluid ounces
   - H 6 cups
   - J 6 pints F
5.
   - A 1 fluid ounce
   - B 1 cup
   - C 1 quart
   - D 1 gallon D
6.
   - F 1 fluid ounce
   - G 1 cup
   - H 1 pint
   - J 1 quart G

Lesson 12-2
Pages 490–491

Complete.

1. 6 c = ▒ pt 3
2. 32 fl oz = ▒ c 4
3. 8 qt = ▒ pt 16
4. 2 gal = ▒ qt 8
5. ▒ fl oz = 5 c 40
6. 10 pt = ▒ c 20

Compare. Use >, <, or =.

7. 3 qt ● 1 gal <
8. 3 c ● 4 fl oz >
9. 3 qt ● 5 pt >

Lesson 12-3
Pages 492–495

Choose the more reasonable estimate for each capacity.

1. 11 mL 11 L 11 L
2. 710 mL 710 L 710 mL
3. 1 mL 1 L 1 L
4. 235 mL 235 L 235 mL

Lesson 12-4
Pages 498–500

Choose the most reasonable estimate for the weight of each object.

1. A
   - A 8 ounces
   - B 80 pounds
   - C 8 pounds
   - D 8 tons
2. J
   - F 70 ounces
   - G 7 pounds
   - H 700 pounds
   - J 7 tons
3. B
   - A 8 ounces
   - B 8 pounds
   - C 80 pounds
   - D 8 tons
4. F
   - F 1 ounce
   - G 10 ounces
   - H 1 pound
   - J 10 pounds

Extra Practice

Lesson 12-5

Pages 502–503

Solve. Use logical reasoning.

1. Mr. Myers is thinking of a number between 20 and 30. The number is not even, not prime, and not divisible by 3. What is the number? 25
2. There are three buildings on a block. The bank is to the left of the school. The museum is not first. What is the order of the buildings? bank, school, museum
3. A group of 3 adults and 7 students rode a ferry. The cost for the entire group was $36. If the cost of a student to ride was $3, what was the cost for an adult? $5
4. The Bears won 18 games. The Lions won one game for every three games the Bears won. The Sharks won 8 more games than the Lions. How many games did the Lions win? 6 games

Lesson 12-6

Pages 504–507

Complete.

1. 2 lb = ■ oz 32
2. 4,000 lb = ■ T 2
3. 64 oz = ■ lb 4
4. 2 T = ■ lb 4,000
5. 1 lb and 2 oz = ■ oz 18
6. 3 T and 400 lb = ■ 6,400
7. **Algebra** Copy and complete the table below.

Pounds	■ 3	5	■ 6	8	■ 10
Ounces	48	■ 80	96	■ 128	160

Lesson 12-7

Pages 508–510

Choose the more reasonable estimate for the mass of each object.

1. 4 g 4 kg 4 kg
2. 350 g 350 kg 350 g
3. 250 g 250 kg 250 kg
3. 300 g 300 kg 300 g

Lesson 12-8

Pages 512–515

Find the volume of each figure.

1. 12 cubic units
2. 18 cubic units

Estimate the volume of each figure.

3. 12 cubic units
4. 15 cubic units

Lesson 12-9

Pages 518–519

Use any strategy to solve. Tell what strategy you used.

1. Leila bought a hat for $5, mittens for $7, and a scarf for $11. The cashier gave her $7 in change. How much did Leila give the cashier? $30
2. Radio station ABC plays songs that are 3 minutes long. How many songs can the station play in 50 minutes? 16 songs
3. Emilio's sister is twice his age. In 6 years, his sister will be 3 times his age right now. How old are Emilio and his sister? Emilio is 6; his sister is 12.
4. A model home has 8 windows on the first floor and 7 windows on the second floor. There are 180 windows all together. How many model homes are there? 12 models

Lesson 12-10

Pages 520–523

The following are times of tennis matches. Find the length of each match.

1. Start Time End Time — 2 hours 15 minutes
2. Start Time End Time — 2 hours 30 minutes

Find each elapsed time.

3. The clock shows when Lydia started ice skating. It is 12:45 when she stops. 1 hour 15 minutes
4. The clock shows when Helki's hockey practice started. It is 6:30 when it stops. 1 hour 45 minutes

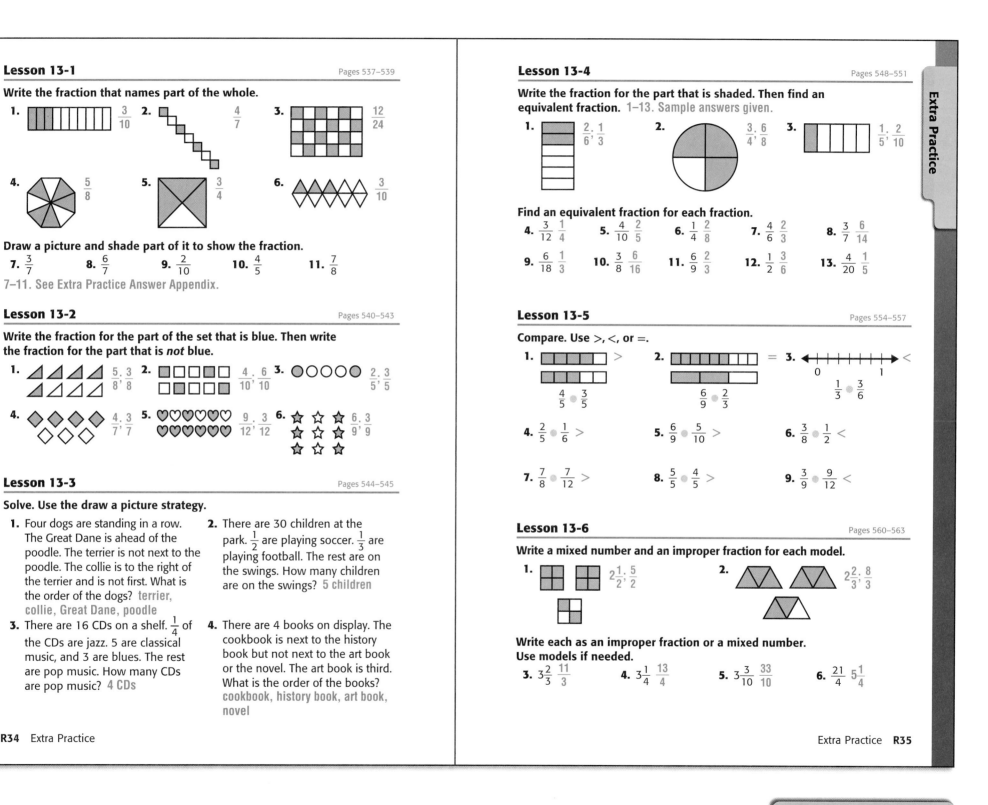

Extra Practice

Lesson 13-1

Pages 537–539

Write the fraction that names part of the whole.

1. $\frac{3}{10}$ 2. $\frac{4}{7}$ 3. $\frac{12}{24}$

4. $\frac{5}{8}$ 5. $\frac{3}{4}$ 6. $\frac{3}{10}$

Draw a picture and shade part of it to show the fraction.

7. $\frac{3}{7}$ 8. $\frac{6}{7}$ 9. $\frac{2}{10}$ 10. $\frac{4}{5}$ 11. $\frac{7}{8}$

7–11. See Extra Practice Answer Appendix.

Lesson 13-2

Pages 540–543

Write the fraction for the part of the set that is blue. Then write the fraction for the part that is *not* blue.

1. $\frac{5}{8}, \frac{3}{8}$ 2. $\frac{4}{10}, \frac{6}{10}$ 3. $\frac{2}{5}, \frac{3}{5}$

4. $\frac{4}{7}, \frac{3}{7}$ 5. $\frac{9}{12}, \frac{3}{12}$ 6. $\frac{6}{9}, \frac{3}{9}$

Lesson 13-3

Pages 544–545

Solve. Use the draw a picture strategy.

1. Four dogs are standing in a row. The Great Dane is ahead of the poodle. The terrier is not next to the poodle. The collie is to the right of the terrier and is not first. What is the order of the dogs? terrier, collie, Great Dane, poodle
2. There are 30 children at the park. $\frac{1}{2}$ are playing soccer. $\frac{1}{3}$ are playing football. The rest are on the swings. How many children are on the swings? 5 children
3. There are 16 CDs on a shelf. $\frac{1}{4}$ of the CDs are jazz. 5 are classical music, and 3 are blues. The rest are pop music. How many CDs are pop music? 4 CDs
4. There are 4 books on display. The cookbook is next to the history book but not next to the art book or the novel. The art book is third. What is the order of the books? cookbook, history book, art book, novel

Lesson 13-4

Pages 548–551

Write the fraction for the part that is shaded. Then find an equivalent fraction. 1–13. Sample answers given.

1. $\frac{2}{6}, \frac{1}{3}$ 2. $\frac{3}{4}, \frac{6}{8}$ 3. $\frac{1}{5}, \frac{2}{10}$

Find an equivalent fraction for each fraction.

4. $\frac{3}{12}$ $\frac{1}{4}$ 5. $\frac{4}{10}$ $\frac{2}{5}$ 6. $\frac{1}{4}$ $\frac{2}{8}$ 7. $\frac{4}{6}$ $\frac{2}{3}$ 8. $\frac{3}{7}$ $\frac{6}{14}$

9. $\frac{6}{18}$ $\frac{1}{3}$ 10. $\frac{3}{8}$ $\frac{6}{16}$ 11. $\frac{6}{9}$ $\frac{2}{3}$ 12. $\frac{1}{2}$ $\frac{3}{6}$ 13. $\frac{4}{20}$ $\frac{1}{5}$

Lesson 13-5

Pages 554–557

Compare. Use >, <, or =.

1. $\frac{4}{5}$ ● $\frac{3}{5}$ > 2. $\frac{6}{9}$ ● $\frac{2}{3}$ = 3. $\frac{1}{3}$ ● $\frac{3}{6}$ <

4. $\frac{2}{5}$ ● $\frac{1}{6}$ > 5. $\frac{6}{9}$ ● $\frac{5}{10}$ > 6. $\frac{3}{8}$ ● $\frac{1}{2}$ <

7. $\frac{7}{8}$ ● $\frac{7}{12}$ > 8. $\frac{5}{5}$ ● $\frac{4}{5}$ > 9. $\frac{3}{9}$ ● $\frac{9}{12}$ <

Lesson 13-6

Pages 560–563

Write a mixed number and an improper fraction for each model.

1. $2\frac{1}{2}, \frac{5}{2}$ 2. $2\frac{2}{3}, \frac{8}{3}$

Write each as an improper fraction or a mixed number. Use models if needed.

3. $3\frac{2}{3}$ $\frac{11}{3}$ 4. $3\frac{1}{4}$ $\frac{13}{4}$ 5. $3\frac{3}{10}$ $\frac{33}{10}$ 6. $\frac{21}{4}$ $5\frac{1}{4}$

Lesson 13-7

Pages 564–565

Use any strategy to solve. Tell what strategy you used.

1. Juan has 9 coins that equal 85¢. None of them are pennies. What are the coins? 4 nickels, 4 dimes, and 1 quarter
2. Ramona started reading at 4:20. She stopped reading at 5:15. For how many minutes did she read? 55 min
3. Ten students are in the library. Three students leave the library as 5 students go in. How many students are in the library now? 12 students
4. There are 20 fish in an aquarium. $\frac{1}{5}$ of the fish are blue. $\frac{1}{4}$ of the fish are red. The rest are yellow. How many yellow fish are there? 11 yellow fish

Lesson 14-1

Pages 579–581

Write a fraction and a decimal for each shaded part.

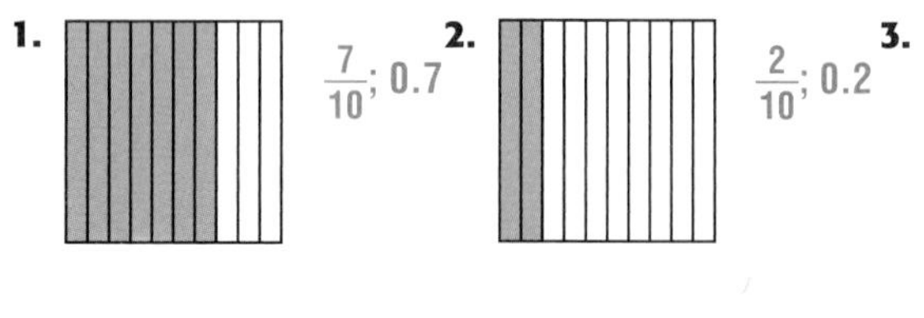

1. $\frac{7}{10}$; 0.7
2. $\frac{2}{10}$; 0.2
3. $\frac{5}{10}$; 0.5

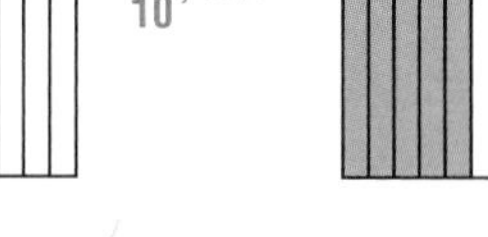

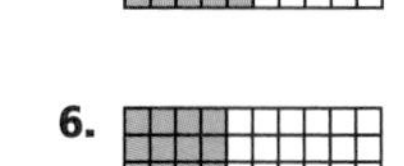

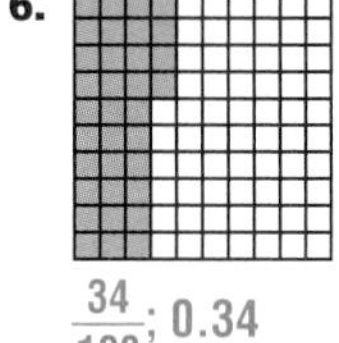

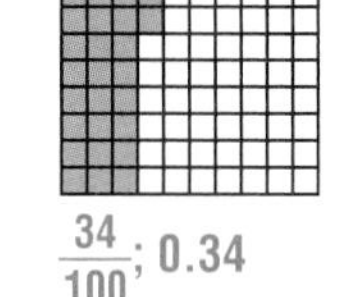

4. $\frac{88}{100}$; 0.88
5. $\frac{7}{100}$; 0.07
6. $\frac{34}{100}$; 0.34

Lesson 14-2

Pages 582–585

Write each as a mixed number and decimal.

1. $1\frac{3}{10}$; 1.3
2. $1\frac{77}{100}$; 1.77

Write each mixed number as a decimal.

3. $4\frac{6}{10}$ 4.6
4. $36\frac{33}{100}$ 36.33
5. $83\frac{45}{100}$ 83.45
6. $99\frac{8}{10}$ 99.8
7. $15\frac{74}{100}$ 15.74
8. $75\frac{3}{10}$ 75.3
9. $62\frac{87}{100}$ 62.87
10. $24\frac{5}{10}$ 24.5

Lesson 14-3

Pages 586–587

Solve. Use the make a model strategy.

1. Marcus has 20 coins. One fourth are dimes. One fifth are nickels. The rest are quarters. How much are Marcus's coins worth? $3.45
2. There are 3 plants in a garden. The first plant is 3 times taller than the second and 2 times taller than the third. The plants are a total of 22 feet tall. How tall is each plant?
3. Simon is hanging wallpaper on 3 walls of his room. Each wall is 10 feet wide and 8 feet tall. Each roll of wallpaper covers 40 square feet. How many rolls of wallpaper does Simon need? 6 rolls
4. Emily walked halfway home from school. She walked back 3 blocks to find a book. Then she walked home. She walked 20 blocks in all. How many blocks is it from Emily's house to school? 14 blocks

2. The first plant is 12 feet tall, the second is 4 feet tall, and the third is 6 feet tall.

Lesson 14-4

Pages 588–589

Tell which letter represents each mixed number on the number line. Write as a decimal.

1. $1\frac{1}{5}$ *A*; 1.2
2. $1\frac{4}{5}$ *C*; 1.8

A B C
1 2

3. Name the point *N* represents on the number line below. $7\frac{3}{4}$

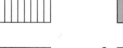

N
7 $7\frac{1}{2}$ 8 $8\frac{1}{2}$ 9

4. Latisha is measuring her height. The top of her head reaches the eighth mark out of 11 marks from 0 feet to 5 feet. How many feet tall is Latisha? $3\frac{1}{2}$ feet
5. A zookeeper measured the length of a newborn kangaroo. The kangaroo ends at the fourth mark out of nine marks between 0 and 1 inch. How many inches long is the kangaroo? 0.4 inches

Lesson 14-5

Pages 590–592

Compare. Use >, <, or =.

1. 6.7 ● 0.67 >
2. 3.96 ● 3.09 >
3. 55.5 ● 55.50 =
4. 0.67 ● 0.76 <
5. 13.80 ● 13.8 =
6. 4.91 ● 4.9 >

Order from greatest to least. 8. 53.33, 53.13, 53.03

7. 2.08, 2.98, 2.88 2.98, 2.88, 2.08
8. 53.03, 53.33, 53.13
9. 65.02, 6.86, 6.5 65.02, 6.86, 6.5
10. 0.78, 0.87, 0.08 0.87, 0.78, 0.08

Lesson 14-6
Pages 594–595

Use any strategy to solve. Tell what strategy you used.

1. A basement is rectangular in shape. One wall is 16 feet long. If the area is 304 square feet, what is the length of the other walls? 16 ft; 19 ft; 19 ft
2. What is the next number in the pattern? What is the rule?
   8, 5, 12, 9, 16, 13, 20, 17
   24; −3, +7
3. Bina began her chores at 3:30 P.M. She stopped at 4:20 to walk her dog. She started her chores again at 5:15 and stopped at 5:45. How long did Bina do her chores? 1 hr and 20 min
4. A pepperoni pizza is cut into 10 slices. A veggie pizza the same size is cut into 6 slices. Which is greater: 4 slices of pepperoni pizza or 3 slices of veggie pizza? 3 slices of veggie pizza

Lesson 14-7
Pages 596–599

Write a fraction and decimal to describe the shaded part of each model.

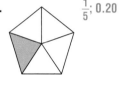

1. $\frac{3}{4}$; 0.75
2. $\frac{3}{5}$; 0.60
3. $\frac{1}{5}$; 0.20
4. $\frac{1}{4}$; 0.25
5. $\frac{3}{10}$; 0.30
6. $\frac{1}{2}$; 0.50

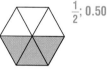

Lesson 14-8
Pages 602–604

Use a number line or model to compare. Use >, <, or =.

1. $\frac{25}{5}$ ● 4 >
2. 12.34 ● 12.3 >
3. $6\frac{1}{2}$ ● 6.89 <
4. $8\frac{1}{10}$ ● 8.75 <
5. 72.07 ● 72.70 <
6. 52 ● 5.02 >

Use a number line to order from greatest to least.

7. $67\frac{2}{100}$, 67.0, 67.70
8. 50.80, $\frac{4}{10}$, $\frac{4}{5}$ 50.80, $\frac{4}{5}$, $\frac{4}{10}$
9. $\frac{25}{100}$, $\frac{2}{3}$, 33.3 33.3, $\frac{2}{3}$, $\frac{25}{100}$
10. $\frac{70}{100}$, 0.75, $\frac{4}{10}$ 0.75, $\frac{70}{100}$, $\frac{4}{10}$

7. 67.70, $67\frac{2}{100}$, 67.0

Lesson 15-1
Pages 617–620

Round to the nearest whole number.

1. 19.8 20
2. 46.21 46
3. 73.81 74
4. 32.41 32
5. 55.79 56
6. 38.11 38
7. 82.7 83
8. 25.5 26

Round to the nearest tenth.

9. 16.72 16.7
10. 93.39 93.4
11. 47.11 47.1
12. 33.76 33.8
13. 29.28 29.3
14. 73.64 73.6
15. 51.82 51.8
16. 85.83 85.8
17. A CD costs the amount shown. What is this amount rounded to the nearest whole number? $12
18. The European mole is 12.7 centimeters long. What is this amount rounded to the nearest whole number? 13

Lesson 15-2
Pages 622–625

Estimate. Round to the nearest whole number.

1. 4.7 + 2.1
   5 + 2 = 7
2. 5.3 + 4.2
   5 + 4 = 9
3. $14.96 + $23.17
   $15 + $23 = $38
4. 17.67 + 23.78
   18 + 24 = 42
5. 9.8 − 3.7
   10 − 4 = 6
6. 13.3 − 7.2
   13 − 7 = 6
7. 26.2 − 14.8
   26 − 15 = 11
8. $25.85 + $16.27
   $26 + $16 = 42
9. 34.95 − 18.50
   35 − 19 = 16
10. 27.8 − 14.7
    28 − 15 = 13
11. $38.91 − $26.78
    $39 − $27 = $12
12. 59.5 − 23.12
    60 − 23 = 37
13. $83.32 − $54.86
    $83 − $55 = $28

Lesson 15-3

Pages 626–627

Solve. Use the work backward strategy.

1. Pedro has $3.75 left from lunch. He bought the items shown in the table below. How much money did he have before lunch? $8.75

Pedro's Lunch	
Item	**Cost**
taco	$1.60
salad	$2.45
milk	$0.95

2. Allison completed the chores shown in the table below. If she finished her chores at 8:30, what time did she start? 7:00

Allison's Chores	
Chore	**Time to Complete (minutes)**
Rake leaves	30
Pull Weeds	15
Mow Grass	45

3. What is the least number of coins worth 25¢ or less that could be used to make $3.49? What are the coins? 19 coins; 13 quarters, 2 dimes, 4 pennies

4. A number is divided by 4. Next, 7 is subtracted from the quotient. Then, the difference is multiplied by 3. The result is 15. What is the number? 48

Lesson 15-4

Pages 630–632

Add. Use estimation to check for reasonableness.

1. 0.5 + 0.7 = 1.2
2. 0.8 + 0.7 = 1.5
3. 2.3 + 0.15 = 2.45
4. 6.4 + 9.34 = 15.74
5. 7.65 + 9.38 = 17.03
6. $7.25 + $6.49 = $13.74
7. 14.79 + 5.55 = 20.34
8. 11.46 + 4.93 = 16.39
9. 22.48 + 18.67 41.15
10. 17.99 + 12.99 30.98
11. 42.52 + 21.84 64.36
12. 6.4 + 3.6 + 2.8 12.8
13. 5.2 + 8.3 + 7.4 20.9
14. 6.6 + 4.7 + 9.9 21.2

Lesson 15-5

Pages 634–635

Use any strategy to solve. Tell what strategy you used.

1. There are two numbers whose product is 48 and difference is 8. What are the numbers? 12 and 4

2. A number is multiplied by 3. The product is subtracted from 50. The result is 11. What is the number? 13

3. A flower shop is selling roses at the price shown at the right. How much would 12 roses cost? $9.60

5 roses for $4

4. Dion surveyed 500 students to find out their favorite color. Blue was the favorite color of 7 out of 10 students. How many students' favorite color is blue? 350

Lesson 15-6

Pages 638–641

Subtract. Use estimation or addition to check.

1. 4.8 − 2.3 = 2.5
2. 6.9 − 3.3 = 3.6
3. 8.3 − 2.7 = 5.6
4. 5.2 − 2.8 = 2.4
5. 3.78 − 1.44 = 2.34
6. 7.56 − 4.43 = 3.13
7. $9.45 − $2.06 = $7.39
8. 8.55 − 4.38 = 4.17
9. 12.61 − 8.75 = 3.86
10. $19.23 − $12.86 = $6.37
11. $26.74 − $16.95 = $9.79
12. 48.03 − 27.12 = 20.91
13. 54.50 − 46.72 7.78
14. 38.04 − 23.60 14.44
15. 41.93 − 15.98 25.95
16. $62.35 − $28.90 $33.45
17. 76.40 − 39.24 37.16
18. 93.19 − 65.38 27.81

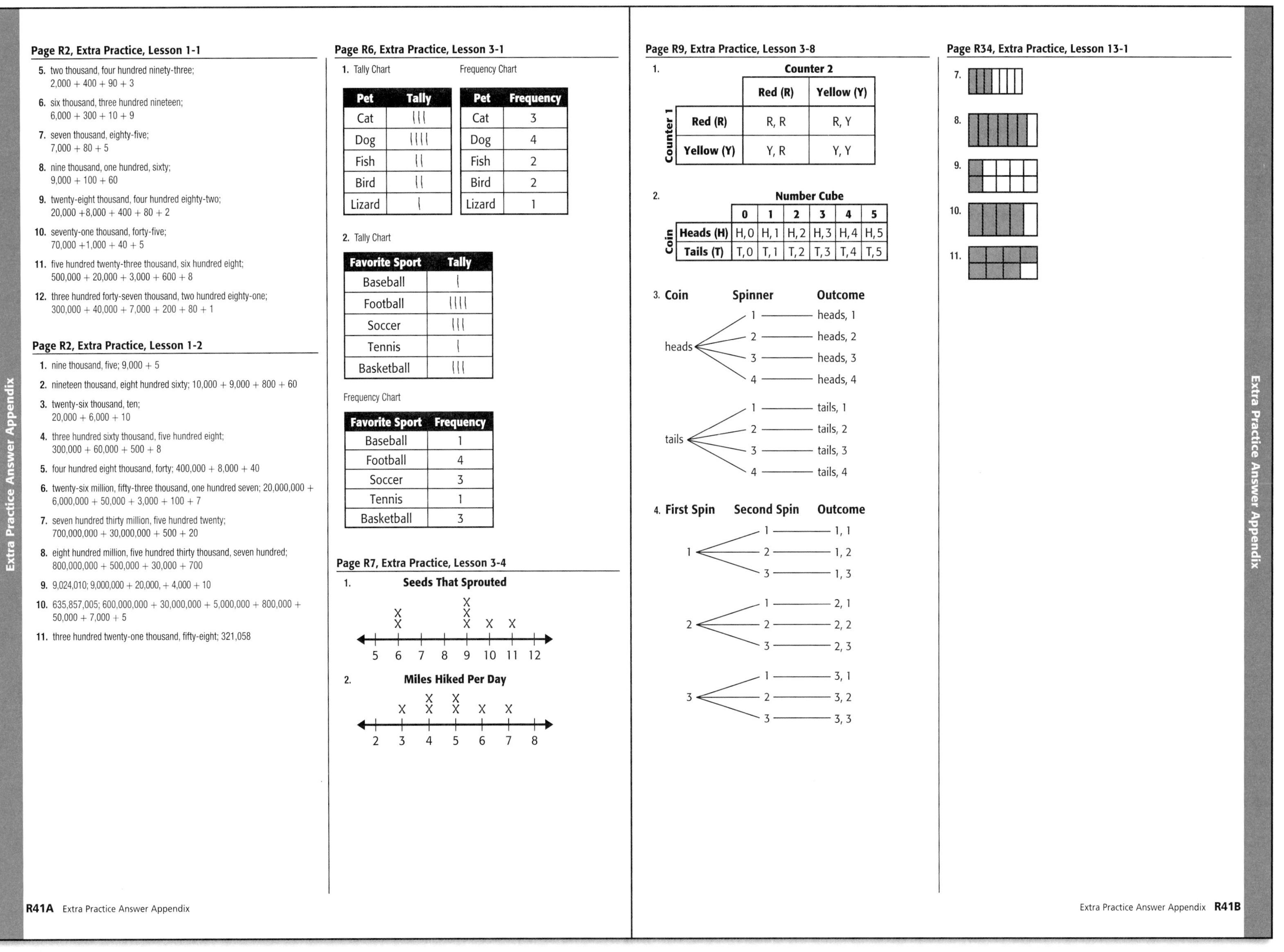

Page R2, Extra Practice, Lesson 1-1

5. two thousand, four hundred ninety-three; 2,000 + 400 + 90 + 3
6. six thousand, three hundred nineteen; 6,000 + 300 + 10 + 9
7. seven thousand, eighty-five; 7,000 + 80 + 5
8. nine thousand, one hundred, sixty; 9,000 + 100 + 60
9. twenty-eight thousand, four hundred eighty-two; 20,000 +8,000 + 400 + 80 + 2
10. seventy-one thousand, forty-five; 70,000 +1,000 + 40 + 5
11. five hundred twenty-three thousand, six hundred eight; 500,000 + 20,000 + 3,000 + 600 + 8
12. three hundred forty-seven thousand, two hundred eighty-one; 300,000 + 40,000 + 7,000 + 200 + 80 + 1

Page R2, Extra Practice, Lesson 1-2

1. nine thousand, five; 9,000 + 5
2. nineteen thousand, eight hundred sixty; 10,000 + 9,000 + 800 + 60
3. twenty-six thousand, ten; 20,000 + 6,000 + 10
4. three hundred sixty thousand, five hundred eight; 300,000 + 60,000 + 500 + 8
5. four hundred eight thousand, forty; 400,000 + 8,000 + 40
6. twenty-six million, fifty-three thousand, one hundred seven; 20,000,000 + 6,000,000 + 50,000 + 3,000 + 100 + 7
7. seven hundred thirty million, five hundred twenty; 700,000,000 + 30,000,000 + 500 + 20
8. eight hundred million, five hundred thirty thousand, seven hundred; 800,000,000 + 500,000 + 30,000 + 700
9. 9,024,010; 9,000,000 + 20,000, + 4,000 + 10
10. 635,857,005; 600,000,000 + 30,000,000 + 5,000,000 + 800,000 + 50,000 + 7,000 + 5
11. three hundred twenty-one thousand, fifty-eight; 321,058

Page R6, Extra Practice, Lesson 3-1

1. Tally Chart

Pet	Tally
Cat	|||
Dog	||||
Fish	||
Bird	||
Lizard	|

Frequency Chart

Pet	Frequency
Cat	3
Dog	4
Fish	2
Bird	2
Lizard	1

2. Tally Chart

Favorite Sport	Tally
Baseball	|
Football	||||
Soccer	|||
Tennis	|
Basketball	|||

Frequency Chart

Favorite Sport	Frequency
Baseball	1
Football	4
Soccer	3
Tennis	1
Basketball	3

Page R7, Extra Practice, Lesson 3-4

1. Seeds That Sprouted

2. Miles Hiked Per Day

Page R9, Extra Practice, Lesson 3-8

1.

Counter 1 \ Counter 2	Red (R)	Yellow (Y)
Red (R)	R, R	R, Y
Yellow (Y)	Y, R	Y, Y

2.

Coin \ Number Cube	0	1	2	3	4	5
Heads (H)	H,0	H,1	H,2	H,3	H,4	H,5
Tails (T)	T,0	T,1	T,2	T,3	T,4	T,5

3.

Coin	Spinner	Outcome
heads	1	heads, 1
	2	heads, 2
	3	heads, 3
	4	heads, 4
tails	1	tails, 1
	2	tails, 2
	3	tails, 3
	4	tails, 4

4.

First Spin	Second Spin	Outcome
1	1	1, 1
	2	1, 2
	3	1, 3
2	1	2, 1
	2	2, 2
	3	2, 3
3	1	3, 1
	2	3, 2
	3	3, 3

Page R34, Extra Practice, Lesson 13-1

7.

8.

9.

10.

11.

Preparing for Standardized Tests

Throughout the school year, you may be required to take several tests, and you may have many questions about them. Here are some answers to help you get ready.

How Should I Study?

The good news is that you've been studying all along—a little bit every day. Here are some of the ways your textbook has been preparing you.

- **Every Day** The lessons had multiple-choice practice questions.
- **Every Week** The Mid-Chapter Check and Chapter Test also had several multiple-choice practice questions.
- **Every Month** The Test Practice pages at the end of each chapter had even more questions, including short-response and extended-response questions.

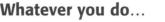

Are There Other Ways to Review?

Absolutely! The following pages contain even more practice for standardized tests.

Tips for SUCCESS

Before the Test

- Go to bed early the night before the test. You will think more clearly after a good night's rest.
- Become familiar with common measurement units and when they should be used.
- Think positively.

During the Test

- Read each problem carefully. Underline key words and think about different ways to solve the problem.
- Watch for key words like *not*. Also look for order words like *least, greatest, first,* and *last*.
- Answer questions you are sure about first. If you do not know the answer to a question, skip it and go back to that question later.
- Check your answer to make sure that it is reasonable.
- Make sure that the number of the question on the answer sheet matches the number of the question on which you are working in your test booklet.

Whatever you do...

- Don't try to do it all in your head. If no figure is provided, draw one.
- Don't rush. Try to work at a steady pace.
- Don't give up. Some problems may seem hard to you, but you may be able to figure out what to do if you read each question carefully or try another strategy.

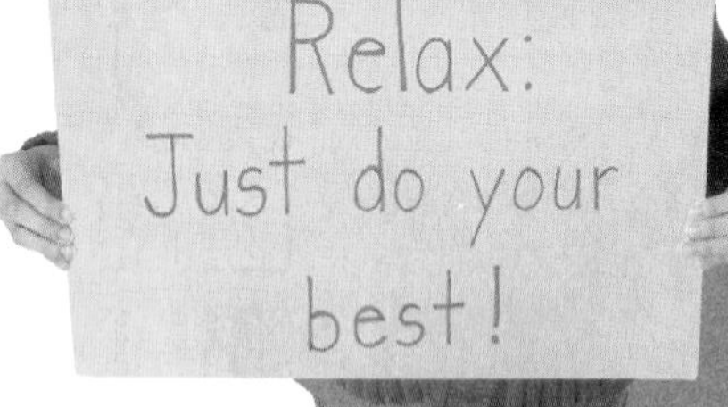

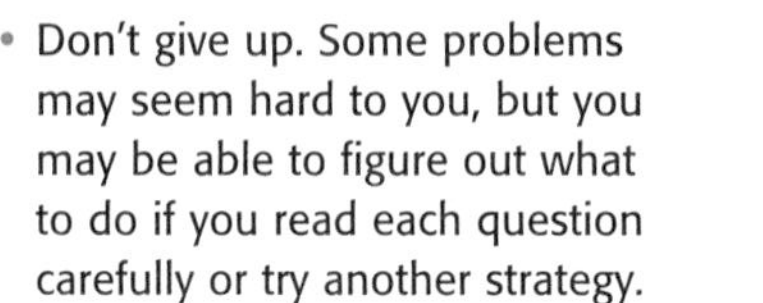

Multiple-Choice Questions

Incomplete shading
Ⓐ Ⓑ Ⓒ Ⓓ
Too light shading
Ⓐ Ⓑ Ⓒ Ⓓ
Correct shading
Ⓐ Ⓑ Ⓒ Ⓓ

Multiple-choice questions are the most common type of questions on standardized tests. You are asked to choose the best answer from four possible answers.

To record a multiple-choice answer, you may be asked to shade in a bubble that is a circle or an oval. Always make sure that your shading is dark enough and completely covers the bubble.

Example

1 The graph shows how many sit-ups a student did each day.

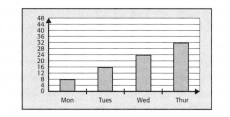

If this pattern continues, how many total sit-ups will be done on Friday and Saturday?

A 88 **B** 48 **C** 40 **D** 8

STRATEGY

Patterns Can you find a pattern to solve the problem?

Read the Problem Carefully You know how many sit-ups were done each day from Monday to Thursday. Find how many total sit-ups will be done on Friday and Saturday.

Solve the Problem Look for a pattern. The student did 8 sit-ups on Monday, 16 on Tuesday, 24 on Wednesday, and 32 on Thursday. Each day, the student did 8 more sit-ups.

Extend the pattern to find how many sit-ups were done on Friday and Saturday. Then add the numbers to find the total.

$32 + 8 = 40$ sit-ups on Friday
$40 + 8 = 48$ sit-ups on Saturday

$$\begin{array}{r} 40 \\ +48 \\ \hline 88 \end{array}$$ total sit-ups

So, 88 sit-ups were done on Friday and Saturday.

The correct choice is A.

Example

2 The shaded part of the figure represents the fraction $\frac{4}{6}$. Which fraction represents the part that is not shaded?

F $\frac{1}{2}$ **G** $\frac{1}{3}$ **H** $\frac{1}{4}$ **J** $\frac{4}{5}$

STRATEGY

Elimination Can you eliminate any of the choices?

Read the Problem Carefully You are asked to find which fraction represents the part of the figure that is not shaded.

Solve the Problem The part that is not shaded is less than half of the figure. Since the answer is less than $\frac{1}{2}$, the choices $\frac{1}{2}$ and $\frac{4}{5}$ can be eliminated. The figure can be divided into 3 equal parts. One of the three, or $\frac{1}{3}$, of the figure is not shaded.

So, the correct choice is G.

Example

3 A family traveled 900 miles. They traveled half of the distance on the first day. How many total days did they travel if they traveled 150 miles each day for the rest of the trip?

A 3 **B** 4 **C** 5 **D** 6

STRATEGY

Work Backward Can you work backward from the total to find the number of days?

Read the Problem Carefully You are asked to find the total number of travel days. You know how many miles were traveled each day and the total number of miles traveled.

Solve the Problem First find the number of miles traveled the first day. Then add 150 miles each day until you reach 900 miles. Count the number of travel days.

Day 1 $900 \div 2 = 450$ miles
Day 2 $450 + 150 = 600$ miles
Day 3 $600 + 150 = 750$ miles
Day 4 $750 + 150 = 900$ miles

The family traveled for 4 days.

So, the family traveled for 4 days.

The correct choice is B.

Preparing for Standardized Tests

Multiple-Choice Practice

DIRECTIONS
Read each question. Choose the best answer.

1. Josh counted 29 desks in each of 3 classrooms in the 4th grade hall. If there are 8 classrooms in the 4th grade hall, about how many desks are there in all? B

A 250
B 240
C 200
D 180

2. Which number sentence best represents the model below? G

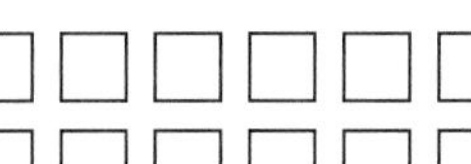

F $7 + 7 = 14$
G $3 \times 7 = 21$
H $3 + 7 = 10$
J $3 + 3 + 3 = 9$

3. What rule best describes the pattern of ordered pairs? C

(1, 10)	(2, 20)	(3, 30)
(4, 40)	(5, 50)	(6, 60)

A Add 10.
B Add 9.
C Multiply by 10.
D Divide by 10.

4. When you multiply a number by 100, you move the decimal point of the number 2 places to the right.

$$630 \times 100 = 63{,}000$$

What is 409×100? G

F 49,000
G 40,900
H 4,900
J 4,090

5. Which of the following objects has a capacity of about 1 gallon? A

A

B

C

D
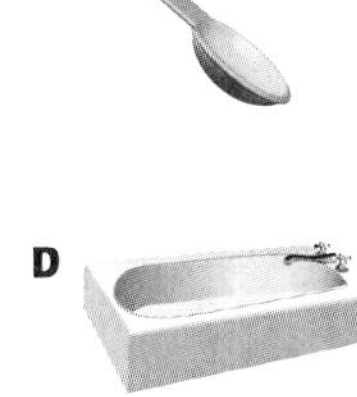

6. Which of the following is the best estimate for the weight of a car? J

F 1,900 tons
G 1,900 ounces
H 1,900 grams
J 1,900 kilograms

7. Look at the three-dimensional figures below. Which figure has exactly two faces? D

A
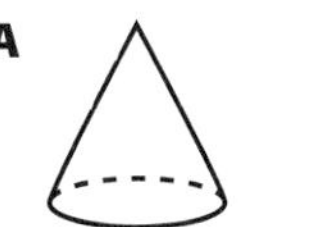

C
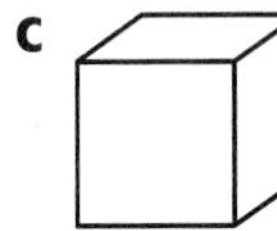

B
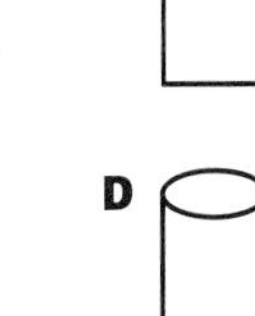

D
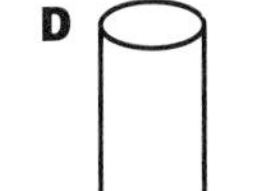

8. Which quadrilateral has 2 pairs of parallel opposite sides and 4 right angles? H

F parallelogram
G pentagon
H square
J trapezoid

9. A piggy bank contains 1 quarter, 3 dimes, 2 nickels, and 2 pennies. If Lindsay picks a coin without looking, what is the probability she will pick a dime? B

A 3 out of 5
B 3 out of 8
C 5 out of 8
D 5 out of 3

10. Refer to the bar graph below. It shows the number of absent students each day last week at Reggie's school. J

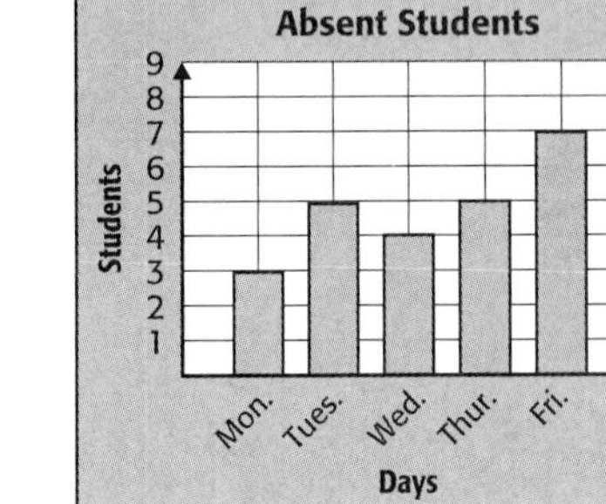

How many students were absent on Thursday and Friday combined last week?

F 5 students
G 7 students
H 11 students
J 12 students

11. Each player in a game spins the spinner below on his or her turn. What is the probability that Carla will spin an odd number on her next turn? A

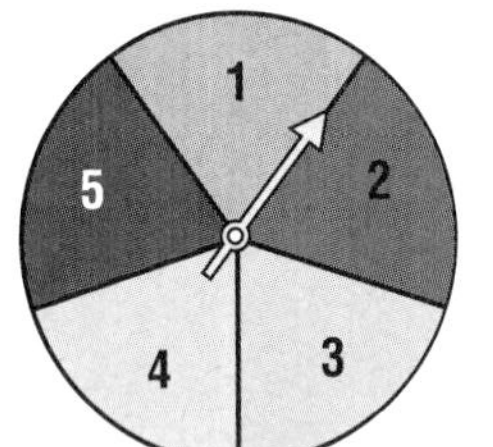

A 3 out of 5
B 3 out of 2
C 2 out of 5
D 2 out of 3

Short-Response Questions

Short-response questions ask you to find the answer to the problem as well as any method, explanation, and/or justification you used to arrive at the solution. You are asked to solve the problem, showing your work.

The following is a sample rubric, or scoring guide, for scoring short-response questions.

Credit	Scores	Criteria
Full	2	Full Credit: The answer is correct and a full explanation is provided that shows each step in arriving at the final answer.
Partial	1	Partial Credit: There are two different ways to receive partial credit. • The answer is correct, but the explanation provided is incomplete or incorrect. • The answer is incorrect, but the explanation and method of solving the problem is correct.
None	0	No credit: Either an answer is not provided or the answer does not make sense.

STRATEGY

Find the Operation Which operation can be used to perform repeated addition?

Example

2 Pencils are on sale at a store. Four pencils cost $1. How many pencils can be bought with $6?

Full Credit Solution

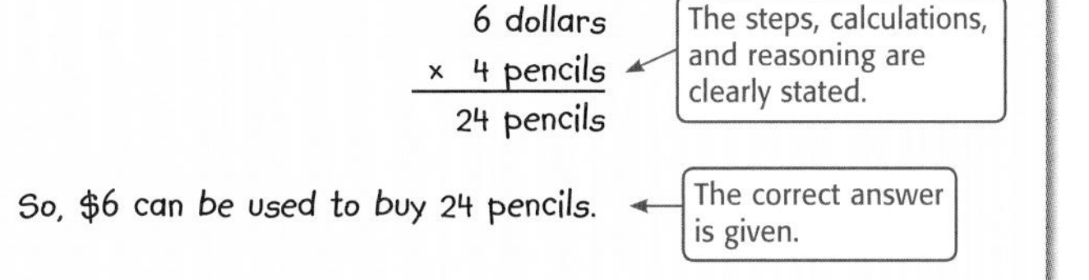

First, I will decide which operation to use. Since each dollar can buy four pencils, I can use repeated addition or multiplication. I will use multiplication to find $6 × 4 pencils.
6 dollars
× 4 pencils
24 pencils
The steps, calculations, and reasoning are clearly stated.
So, $6 can be used to buy 24 pencils.
The correct answer is given.

Partial Credit Solution

In this sample solution, the answer is correct. However, there is no explanation for any of the calculations.

$6,4 pencils

24 pencils

There is no explanation of how the problem was solved.

Partial Credit Solution

In this sample solution, the answer is incorrect. However, the calculations and reasoning are correct.

Each dollar can be used to buy 4 pencils, so I can use repeated addition or multiplication. I will use multiplication to find 6 × 4.

6 dollars
× 4 pencils
12 pencils

The student did not multiply correctly.

12 pencils can be bought with $6.00.

No Credit Solution

In this sample solution, the answer is incorrect, and there is no explanation for any calculations.

6 + 4 = 10

The student does not understand the problem and adds 6 and 4.

There are $10.

Short-Response Practice

DIRECTIONS
Solve each problem.

1. Mrs. Henderson brought 42 boxes of raisins to her daughter's class. She gave 33 of the boxes away to the students. How many boxes of raisins were left? 9 boxes

2. What fraction is represented by the shaded part of the figure below? $\frac{2}{7}$

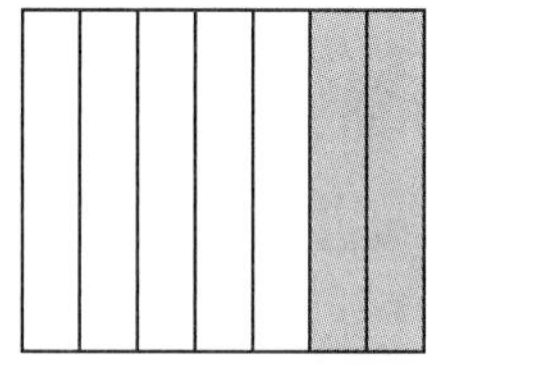

3. There are 14 buses at Millwood Elementary School. Each bus holds up to 56 students. How many students in all can be transported by the buses? 784 buses

4. Juan walks at the park every morning for exercise. The table shows the total number of miles he has walked after different numbers of days.

Morning Walks	
Number of Days	Number of Miles
1	6
2	12
3	18
4	24

If Juan walks the same distance each day, how many miles will he have walked in a week? 42 miles

5. Binta has 11 pages of stickers in a binder with 12 stickers on each page. She calculates that she has $11 \times 12 = 132$ stickers in all. Which number sentence can she use to check her calculation? $132 \div 11 = 12$

6. Molly's patio has the dimensions shown below.

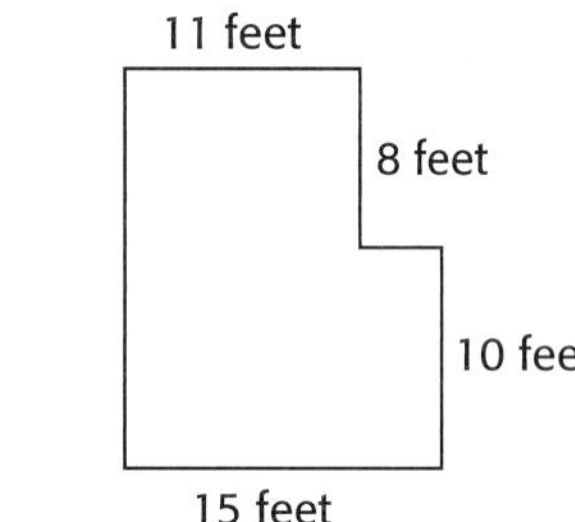

What is the area of the patio? 238 square feet

7. Before leaving for school, Taye checks the outside temperature. What temperature is shown on the thermometer? 62°F

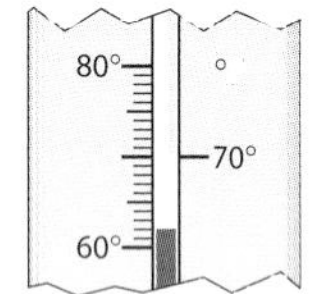

8. How many lines of symmetry does a square have? 4 lines of symmetry

9. What type of angles are formed by two perpendicular lines? right angles

10. Draw a pair of figures that show reflection. See students' work.

11. To play a board game, each player rolls a number cube and chooses a card at random from a deck. There are red and green cards in the deck.

How many possible outcomes are there on each turn? 12 outcomes

12. Refer to the rules for the game in Exercise 11. What is the probability that Eduardo will roll a 3 and select a red card on his next turn? 1 out of 12

13. Look at the bar graph below. It shows the number of points scored by 4 players in a basketball game.

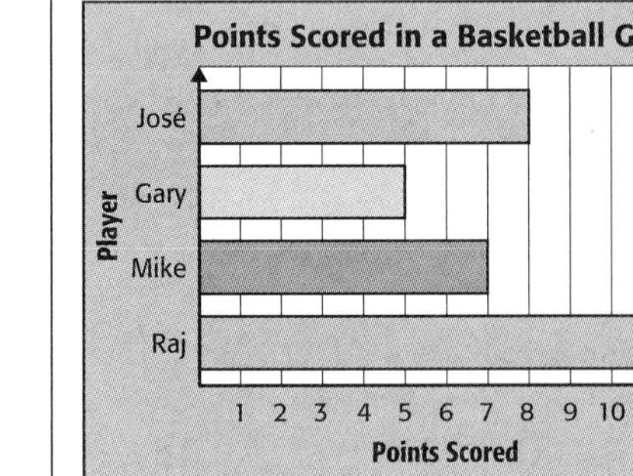

Which players scored a total of 12 points? Gary and Mike

14. Refer to the bar graph in Exercise 13. How many points were scored in all? 31 points

15. Suppose Matt tosses a beanbag onto the game board below. What is the probability that the beanbag will land on a shaded space? 12 out of 32

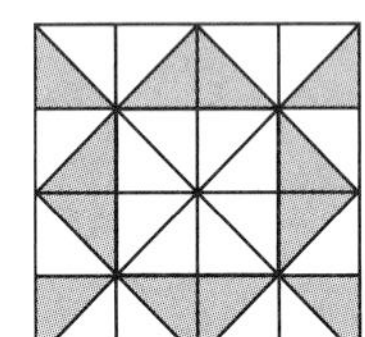

16. Kyle has 70 baseball cards. Write a number sentence that shows how many cards Kyle would have if he gave away half of his cards. $70 \div 2 = 35$

Extended-Response Questions

Most extended-response questions have multiple parts. You must answer all parts to receive full credit.

In extended-response questions, you must show all of your work in solving the problem. A rubric is used to determine if you receive full, partial, or no credit. The following is a sample rubric for scoring extended-response questions.

Credit	Score	Criteria
Full	4	Full Credit: The answer is correct and a full explanation is given that shows each step in finding the answer.
Partial	3, 2, 1	Partial Credit: Most of the solution is correct, but it may have some mistakes in the explanation or solution. The more correct the solution, the greater the score.
None	0	No credit: Either an answer is not provided or the answer does not make sense.

Make sure that when the problem says to *show your work,* you show every part of your solution. This includes figures, graphs, and any explanations for your calculations.

Example

1 Find how much longer it took each student to read *Sounder* than *Charlotte's Web*. Make a bar graph to show the results.

Student	*Charlotte's Web* (hours to read)	*Sounder* (hours to read)
Lisa	9	27
Jason	15	45
Torres	6	18
Monique	12	36

Full Credit Solution

In this sample answer, the student explains what calculations need to be done and finds the correct solution.

First, I will list each student's name and write the expression that will show the difference. Then I will subtract.

Lisa: $27 - 9 = 18$ Jason: $45 - 15 = 30$ Torres: $18 - 6 = 12$ Monique: $36 - 12 = 24$

The steps, calculations, and reasoning are clearly stated.

The difference in hours spent reading the two books for each student is: Lisa: 18, Jason: 30, Torres: 12, and Monique: 24 hours.

The correct answer is given.

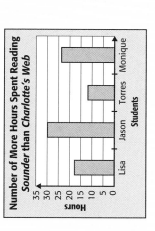

Now I will use the data from the first part to make the bar graph.

Number of More Hours Spent Reading *Sounder* than *Charlotte's Web*

Partial Credit Solution

This sample answer receives partial credit because the student explains how they got each answer, but did not create a bar graph.

First, I will list each student's name and write the expression that will show the difference. Then I will subtract.

Lisa	Jason	Torres	Monique
27	45	18	36
− 9	− 15	− 6	− 12
18	30	12	24

The number of more hours spent on *Sounder* than *Charlotte's Web* for each student is: Lisa: 18, Jason: 30, Torres: 12, and Monique: 24 hours.

No Credit Solution

A solution for this problem that will receive no credit may include incorrect answers and an inaccurate or incomplete bar graph.

Extended-Response Practice

DIRECTIONS 1–16. See students' explanations.
Solve each problem. Show all your work.

1. What is the smallest possible number you can make with the digits below? How did you decide how to arrange the digits? 24,568

5, 2, 8, 6, 4

2. Mark says the model below shows the fraction $2\frac{3}{4}$. Gina says that the model shows $\frac{11}{4}$. Who is correct? Explain.

They are both correct.

3. A pizza is cut into 8 equal slices. How many slices would you have to eat to have eaten $\frac{1}{4}$ of the pizza yourself? Draw a picture and write an equivalent fraction to show how to find the answer. 2 slices

4. Look at the number sentences below.

$532 \times 10 = 5,320$
$75 \times 10 = 750$
$1,248 \times 10 = 12,480$
$49 \times 10 = 490$

How can these number sentences help you find the product of 35 and 10?

5. The table shows input and output numbers.

Input	Output
2	5
4	7
6	9
8	11
10	13

Describe what happened to each input number to result in the output number. add 3

6. Describe two ways to find the perimeter of a soccer field with the dimensions shown below.

75 meters

110 meters

$75 + 75 + 110 + 110$; $2 \times (75 + 110)$

7. Suki returned home at the time shown on the clock, which is 2 hours 15 minutes after school ended. Explain how to find the time that school ended.

8. Artie estimates that the pitcher of lemonade has a capacity of 2 quarts. How can he find whether or not he is correct using a measuring cup that holds 1 cup?

9. Explain why the two figures below are congruent.

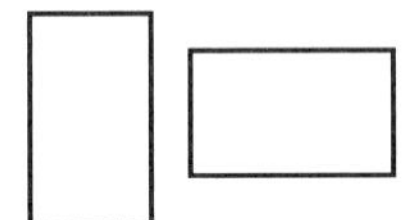

10. Use the figures below to write a definition for *isosceles triangles* and *right triangles.*

Isosceles triangles have at least two equal sides. Right triangles have one right angle.

11. Suppose Kathi tosses a coin and records the result. Then she tosses a second coin and records the result. Let H represent a coin landing on heads, and let T represent a coin landing on tails. List all of the possible outcomes. HH, HT, TH, TT

12. Four coins are placed in a bag. They add up to 41¢. What is the probability that a coin pulled from the bag has a value greater than 10¢? Show how you found the answer. 1 out of 4

13. Two bags of grapes cost $5. Four bags of grapes cost $10. Suppose this pattern continues. Make a bar graph to show the cost of 6, 8, and 10 bags of grapes.

14. The double bar graph shows the number of points scored by two different players during the first 4 games of a basketball season.

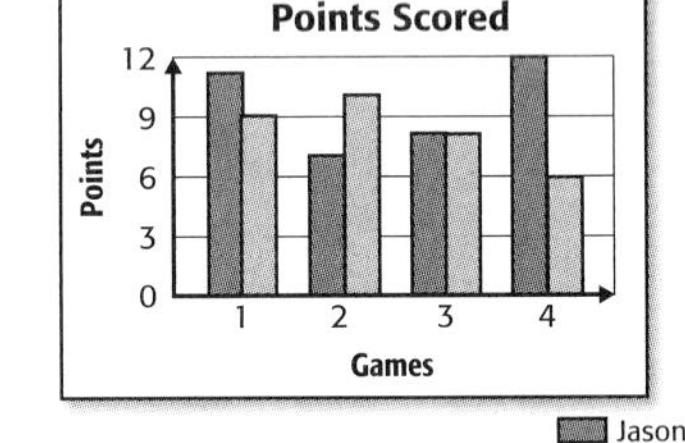

How can you find the overall difference in points scored by both players?

15. Compare and contrast a tally chart and a frequency table. How are they similar? How are they different?

16. There is ham, turkey, mayonnaise, mustard, and two types of bread in a refrigerator. How can a tree diagram be used to find the possible sandwich combinations?

Concepts and Skills Bank

 Order of Operations

Lesson Planner

Objective

I will use order of operations to solve expressions containing two or more operations.

Vocabulary

order of operations

Activate Prior Knowledge

Write a few expressions on the board.

- Ask students to copy expressions, such as 629 + 176, 3 + 8 + 12, and 58 – 40 – 3, from the board. Ask for volunteers to share their solutions.
- Now, write expressions containing more than one operation on the board, such as 16 + 9 × 5, 45 – 5 + 30, and 20 – 8 × 2. Again, ask students to copy and solve. Call on volunteers to share their answers, expecting two different answers to each problem.

Using student page R56.

- Explain to students that when solving an expression with more than one operation, order of operations must be used instead of solving from left to right.
- Tell students that in order to perform order of operations, they can use the saying "**P**lease **E**xcuse **M**y **D**ear **A**unt **S**ally." The first letter of each word in this phrase represents a step in the order of operations. Exponents will be taught in a later grade, and can be skipped for now.

Please	Parentheses
Excuse	Exponents
My	Multiplication
Dear	Division
Aunt	Addition
Sally	Subtraction

Concepts and Skills

Concepts and Skills Bank

Order of Operations

To find the value of an expression with more than one operation, you need to follow the rules for the **order of operations**.

Order of Operations Key Concept

1. Do the operations in the parentheses first.
2. Multiply and divide in order from left to right.
3. Add and subtract in order from left to right.

EXAMPLE Use the Order of Operations

1 **Find 3 + (2 × 4) – 6.**

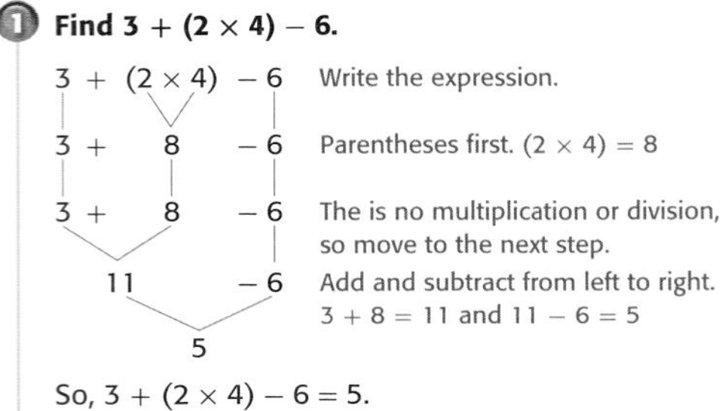

3 + (2 × 4) – 6 Write the expression.
3 + 8 – 6 Parentheses first. (2 × 4) = 8
3 + 8 – 6 The is no multiplication or division, so move to the next step.
11 – 6 Add and subtract from left to right. 3 + 8 = 11 and 11 – 6 = 5
5

So, 3 + (2 × 4) – 6 = 5.

Exercises

Find the value of each expression.

1. (7 + 1) × 3 – 5 19
2. (8 – 5) ÷ 3 + 2 3
3. 13 + 4 – (7 × 2) 3
4. 5 (2 + 3) 25
5. (5 + 4) × 7 – 3 60
6. 8 × (14 – 8) + 7 55
7. 6 × (8 – 5) + 9 27
8. (8 + 6) ÷ (12 – 5) 2

Write and find the value of an expression for the situation.

9. **Measurement** Todd walked 2 miles a day for 4 days and 3 miles on the fifth day. How many miles did he walk? (2 × 4) + 3; 11

R56 Concepts and Skills Bank

- Solve the three expressions again using order of operations.
- Introduce expressions involving parentheses, such as (3 × 7) + 10 and 4(12 – 7). Show students how to find the value of each of these expressions. Then give them a few to solve on their own.

Using the Exercises

Exercises 1–8 Advise students to write each line of the solution on a different line of notebook paper to help them keep their solution organized. Students may need support when finding the value of the expression in Exercise 8 since it contains two sets of parentheses.

Exercise 9 Some students may need guidance with using parentheses when writing the expression for this exercise.

Assess and Close

Made to Order Ask each student to write five multi-operation expressions. Tell students they must use parentheses and each of the operations at least once in their five expressions. Then, have students exchange expressions with someone in the classroom and solve.

Divisibility Rules for 2, 5, and 10

A whole number is **divisible** by another number if the remainder is 0 when the first number is divided by the second. The divisibility rules for 2, 5, and 10 are stated below.

Divisibility Rules for 2, 5, and 10 — Key Concepts	
Words	**Examples**
A whole number is divisible by:	
• 2 if the ones digit is divisible by 2.	2, 4, 6, 8, 10, 12, ...
• 5 if the ones digit is 0 or 5.	5, 10, 15, 20, 25, ...
• 10 if the ones digit is 0.	10, 20, 30, 40, 50, ...

A whole number is **even** if it is divisible by 2. A whole number is **odd** if it is not divisible by 2.

EXAMPLE Use Divisibility Rules

1 **Tell whether the number 340 is divisible by 2, 5, or 10. Then classify the number as even or odd.**

Use the divisibility rules to determine if 340 is divisible by 2, 5, or 10.
2: Yes, the ones digit, 0, is divisible by 2.
5: Yes, the ones digit is 0.
10: Yes, the ones digit is 0.
Since 340 is divisible by 2, it is an even number.
So, 340 is divisible by 2, 5, and 10, and it is an even number.

Exercises

Tell whether each number is divisible by 2, 5, or 10. They classify each number as even or odd.

1. 40 2, 5, 10; even
2. 65 5; odd
3. 78 2; even
4. 91 none; odd
5. 115 5; odd
6. 136 2; even
7. 150 2, 5, 10; even
8. 194 2; even
9. 216 2; even
10. 280 2, 5, 10; even
11. 311 none; odd
12. 345 5; odd
13. Find a number that is divisible by both 2 and 5. 50
14. Find a number that is divisible by 2, 5, and 10. 90

Concepts and Skills Bank

2 Divisibility Rules for 2, 5, and 10

Lesson Planner

Objective

I will draw conclusions about the divisibility of a number by looking at its ones place.

Vocabulary

divisible, even, odd

Materials: hundreds charts (1 per group); crayons, markers, or colored pencils; One Hundred Hungry Ants by Elinor J. Pinczes

Activate Prior Knowledge

Lead a discussion about how to identify the ones place of a number.

- Write various numbers on the board, such as 4,321, 950, and 2,453. Ask students to identify the ones place of each number. 1, 0 and 3
- Tell students that they will be using the ones place of numbers to tell whether the numbers are divisible by 2, 5, and 10.

Using student page R57.

- Discuss with students the divisibility rules displayed in the table on page R57.
- Pass out hundreds charts to small groups of students. On each hundreds chart, have students mark each number that is divisible by 2 with a blue dot. Second, ask students to mark each number that is divisible by 5 with a green dot. Lastly, ask students to mark each number that is divisible by 10 with a red dot.
- Have students search for patterns on the chart. Possible patterns include: all marked numbers are either even or have 5 in their ones place, every other column is marked in blue (divisible by 2), etc. Have students share and discuss the patterns they find.

- Revisit the numbers written on the board (36, 950, and 2,453). Work with students to determine their divisibility by 2, 5, and 10 to conclude whether they are even or odd.

Using the Exercises

Exercises 1–12 Have students copy the number from each exercise and underline the digit in its ones place before determining its divisibility.

Exercises 13–14 Challenge students who finish early to find numbers in the tens, hundreds, and thousands that fit the descriptions given.

Assess and Close

Ant Arrays Read aloud One Hundred Hungry Ants. In the book, 100 marching ants are arranged into various arrays, including a 2-by-50 array and a 5-by-10 array. Therefore, 100 is divisible by 2, 5, and 10. Have students determine another number that is divisible by 2, 5, and 10. Then, have students write their own story using that number of hungry, marching ants who divide into arrays. Students should write about the arrays involving 2, 5, and 10 in their stories and they should tell whether their chosen number is even or odd.

Concepts and Skills Bank

3 Even and Odd Numbers and Products

Lesson Planner

Objective

I will draw conclusions about the products of expressions involving the multiplication of even and/or odd numbers.

Vocabulary

even, odd

Materials: index cards or sticky notes (1 per student)

Even and Odd Numbers and Products

A whole number is **even** if it is divisible by 2. A whole number is **odd** if it is not divisible by 2.

Even Numbers	Odd Numbers
0, 2, 4, 6, 8, 10, 12, 14, 16, 18, 20, ...	1, 3, 5, 7, 9, 11, 13, 15, 17, 19, ...

The factors in a multiplication problem can help you determine if the product will be even or odd.

Odd and Even Products (Key Concepts)

Words	Examples
even number × even number = even number	$2 \times 4 = 8$ or $6 \times 8 = 48$
even number × odd number = even number	$2 \times 3 = 6$ or $4 \times 5 = 20$
odd number × odd number = odd number	$3 \times 5 = 15$ or $7 \times 9 = 63$

EXAMPLE Tell Whether a Product Will Be Even or Odd

1 Tell whether the product of 14 and 23 will be even or odd.

Classify each factor as even or odd. Then use the information in the Key Concept box to determine if the product will be even or odd.

The product of an even and odd number will be even. So, the product of 14 and 23 will be even.

Exercises

Tell whether each product will be even or odd.

1. 13×21 odd **2.** 34×56 even **3.** 41×118 even **4.** 73×129 odd
5. 134×155 even **6.** 143×167 odd **7.** 184×192 even **8.** 212×257 even

R58 Concepts and Skills Bank

Activate Prior Knowledge

Lead a discussion about how to identify even and odd numbers.

- Recall that even numbers have 0, 2, 4, 6, or 8 in the ones place while odd numbers have 1, 3, 5, 7, or 9 in the ones place.
- Write several numbers, such as 439, 3,567, and 93,020, on the board. Then have students determine whether they are even or odd.

Using student page R58.

- Write a two- or three-digit number on each index card or sticky note. Make about half of the numbers even and the other half odd. Then, write a letter on each card so that two cards have As on them, two have Bs, two have Cs, etc. Some of the matching cards should contain two even numbers, one even and one odd number, and two odd numbers.
- Pass out the cards to students. Tell them to find their partner by looking for a card with the same letter on it.
- After students find their partners, refer them to page R58 to determine whether the product of their two numbers will be even or odd.
- Have students share their number cards and whether they believe the product will be even or odd with the class.

Using the Exercises

Exercises 1–8 Encourage students to identify whether each product will be even or odd before using the "Odd and Even Products" table of page R58 to confirm their thinking.

Assess and Close

Product Predictions On a piece of notebook paper, ask students to determine whether the products of three expressions, such as 11×19, 38×192, and 521×410, will be even or odd without access to the table on page R58. Have students explain their thinking in words.

Relate Fractions, Decimals, and Percents

Fractions, decimals, and percents are related. A **percent** compares a number to 100.

100%

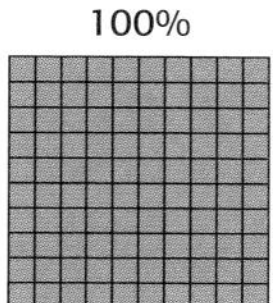

100 out of 100

$\frac{100}{100} = 1 = 1.0$

67%

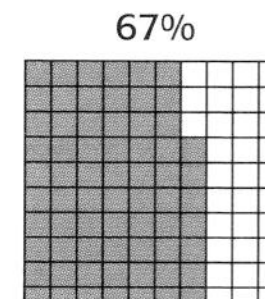

67 out of 100

$\frac{67}{100} = 0.67$

25%

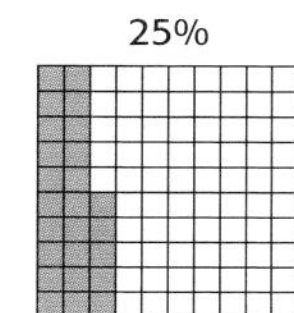

25 out of 100

$\frac{25}{100} = \frac{1}{4} = 0.25$

EXAMPLE Write a Fraction, Decimal, and Percent

1 Write the amount shown by the model as a fraction, decimal, and percent.

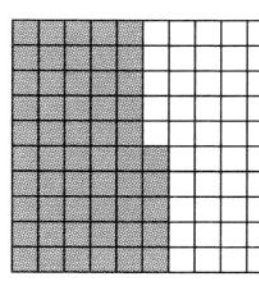

55 out of 100 squares in the model are shaded.

So, the amount shown by the model as a fraction, decimal, and percent is $\frac{55}{100}$, 0.55, and 55%.

Exercises

Write the amount shown by each model as a fraction, decimal, and percent.

1.

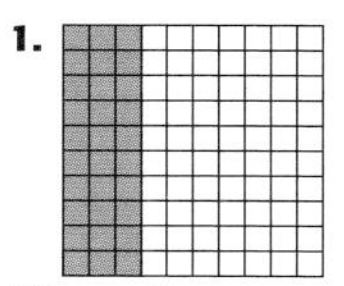

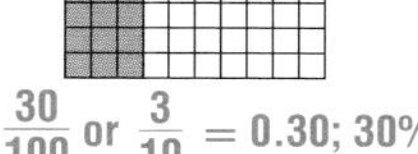

$\frac{30}{100}$ or $\frac{3}{10}$ = 0.30; 30%

2.

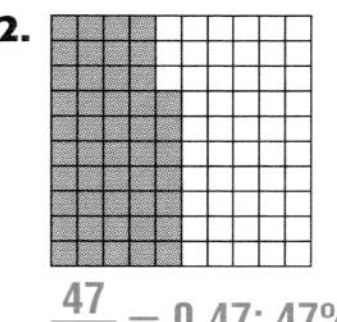

$\frac{47}{100}$ = 0.47; 47%

3.

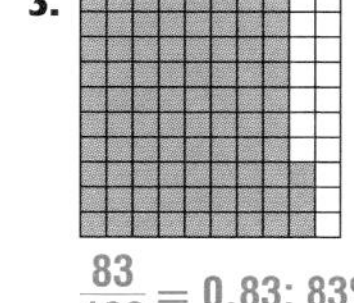

$\frac{83}{100}$ = 0.83; 83%

4. Carisa plays soccer. She makes 0.75 of the goals she shoots. What is the percentage of shots she makes? 75%

5. Miguel read 35 of the 50 pages in his book. What percent of the book has Miguel read? 70%

Concepts and Skills Bank

4 Relate Fractions, Decimals, and Percents

Lesson Planner

Objective

I will explore equivalent fractions, decimals, and percents.

Vocabulary

percent

Materials: transparency of hundredths grid

Manipulatives: base-ten blocks (ones and tens), dice (2 per student)

Activate Prior Knowledge

Initiate discussion about fractions of a hundred.

- Display a transparency of a hundredths grid. Place 3 tens rods and 5 ones units in the hundredths grid to model the fraction $\frac{35}{100}$. Model a few more fractions this way.

Using student page R59.

- Show students how to write a percent. If the denominator of a fraction is 100, then the percent is written as the numerator followed by a percent sign. For example, $\frac{25}{100}$ = 25%.
- When a fraction already has a denominator of 100, it is easy to write the decimal equivalent. Say the fraction aloud to know how to write the decimal. For example, $\frac{35}{100}$ is read as "thirty-five hundredths," so the decimal equivalent is 0.35, or "thirty-five hundredths."

Read	Say	Write
$\frac{35}{100}$	"thirty-five hundredths"	0.35

- The same rule applies when starting with a decimal and writing the fraction equivalent.

Read	Say	Write
0.35	"thirty-five hundredths"	$\frac{35}{100}$

- If time allows, challenge students by giving them a fraction that is less than $\frac{10}{100}$. For example, $\frac{4}{100}$ = 0.04, not 0.4.

Using the Exercises

Exercises 1–3 Advise students to carefully count the shaded squares before writing the fraction, decimal, and percent.

Exercise 5 Students may need help with Exercise 5. The 35 pages will need to be doubled to determine the percent since the book is only 50 pages total.

Assess and Close

I Can Relate Have students roll two dice three times to create three 2-digit numbers. Students are to write each 2-digit number as a numerator over 100 to create three fractions. Then have students write an equivalent decimal and precent for each fraction.

Concepts and Skills Bank

Skip Counting Forward and Backward

Lesson Planner

Objective

I will skip count to find missing numbers in function tables.

Materials: blank paper (1 piece per group); crayons, markers, or colored pencils

Activate Prior Knowledge

Review how to find unknown values in function tables.

- Display a table on the chalkboard with a simple function, such as $y = 2x$. Write the first output value. Invite student volunteers to fill in the rest of the output values.
- Demonstrate how to skip count to find the output values by drawing arrows and showing the addition or subtraction process along the right side of the function table.

Using student page R60.

- As a class, work through examples 1 and 2. Have students brainstorm strategies for determining unknown values. For example, determine whether the output values are increasing or decreasing to decide whether to skip count forward or backward.
- Create a function table using an item in the classroom or a fact from a recent social studies or science unit of study. For example, a function table could be written about the fact that butterflies have six legs. The input values would represent the number of butterflies and the output values would represent the total number of legs the butterflies have.

Skip Counting Forward and Backward

You can skip count forward and backward to find missing numbers in a function table.

EXAMPLES Skip Counting on Function Tables

Use skip counting to find the missing number.

1

$y = 20x$	
Input (x)	Output (y)
1	20
2	40
3	60
4	■

+20, +20, +20

This function table shows $y = 20x$. You can skip count forward by 20 to find the missing number.

$60 + 20 = 80$

So, the missing number is 80.

2

$y = 1{,}000x$	
Input (x)	Output (y)
8	8,000
7	7,000
6	6,000
5	■

−1,000, −1,000, −1,000

The function table shows $y = 1{,}000x$. You can skip count backward by 1,000 to find the missing number.

$6{,}000 - 1{,}000 = 5{,}000$

So, the missing number is 5,000.

Exercises

Use skip counting to find the missing number.

1.

$y = 100x$	
Input (x)	Output (y)
5	500
6	600
7	700
8	■

800

2.

$y = 50x$	
Input (x)	Output (y)
7	350
6	300
5	250
4	■

200

3.

$y = 25x$	
Input (x)	Output (y)
10	250
9	225
8	200
7	■

175

4.

$y = 10{,}000x$				
Input (x)	2	3	4	5
Output (y)	20,000	30,000	40,000	■

50,000

Using the Exercises

Exercises 1–4 Help students in finding the missing values by drawing arrows and recording their skip counting as shown in the examples. Encourage students to work backward to check their work by skip counting in the opposite direction.

Assess and Close

Mascot Mania Divide students into small groups, or teams, and assign them the task of creating team mascots. Each group is to draw and color a mascot on a blank piece of paper. Mascots should have a multiple number of an item, such as a monster with 10 eyes, a ladybug with 6 spots, or a dragon with 2,000 scales. Groups will then create a function table that relates to their mascot. For example, a group using the dragon as a mascot could skip count by 2,000 in the output column to determine how many scales 1, 2, 3, and 4 dragons would have.

Negative Numbers

The numbers +1 and +3 are **positive numbers**. They can be written with or without a + sign. The numbers −1 and −3 are **negative numbers**. A negative number has a − sign.

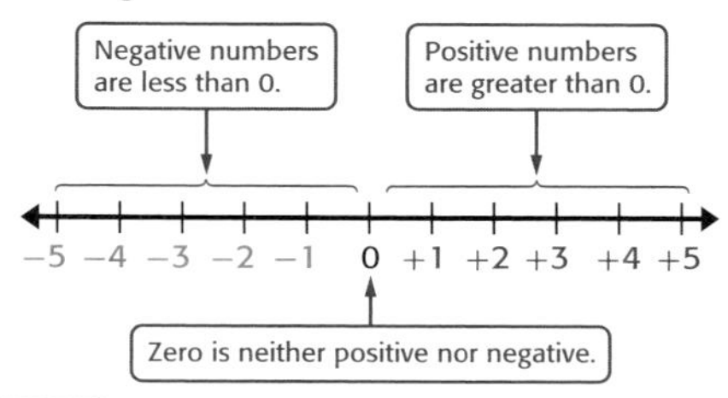

EXAMPLES Write Positive and Negative Numbers

Write the number that represents each situation.

1. **WEATHER 4 degrees below zero**

The temperature is below zero. The number is −4.

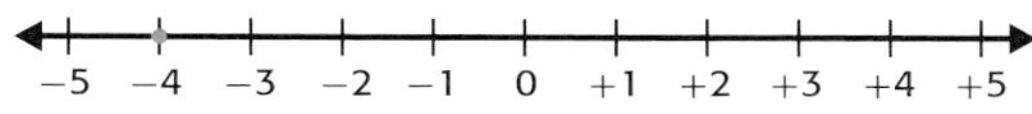

2. **FOOTBALL a gain of 3 yards**

The word *gain* means an increase. The number is +3 or 3.

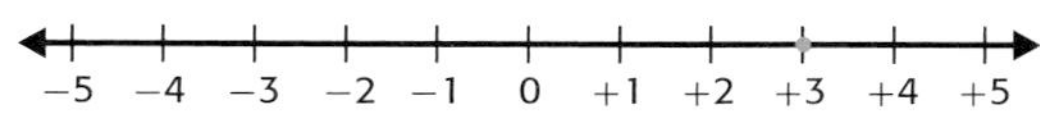

Exercises

Write the number that represents each situation.

1. move back 3 spaces −3
2. move 12 steps forward +12
3. score 10 points +10
4. owe $7 −7
5. 8 degrees below 0 −8
6. distance increases by 5 miles +5
7. earn $15 +15
8. cut 10 seconds off a running time −10

Write the number of each letter on the number line.

9.

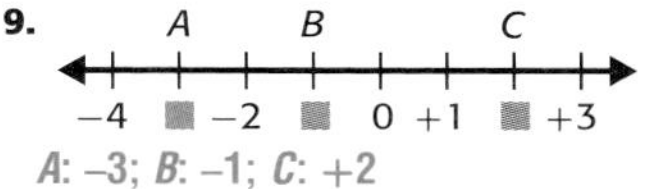

A: −3; B: −1; C: +2

10.

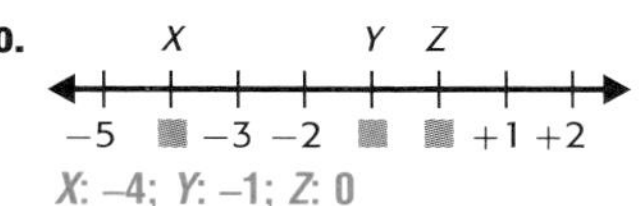

X: −4; Y: −1; Z: 0

Concepts and Skills Bank

6 Negative Numbers

Lesson Planner

Objective

I will explore positive and negative numbers using a number line.

Vocabulary

positive numbers, negative numbers

Materials: sticky notes (1 per student)

Activate Prior Knowledge

Lead a discussion about positive and negative numbers.

- Tell students that up to this point, all the numbers they have worked with have been positive numbers. Positive numbers are located to the right of the number 0 on a number line. As you move to the right on a number line the values of the numbers increase.
- Emphasize that 0 is neither a positive nor a negative number.
- Tell students that negative numbers are located to the left of the number 0 on a number line. They are always preceded by a negative sign. As you move to the left on a number line the values of the numbers decrease.

Using student page R61.

- Write the numbers -10 through +10 on sticky notes, one per note. Pass out the notes to the class.
- Ask students to line up in the correct order to simulate a number line.
- Toss a soft object to a student holding a number that is between -10 and +5. Ask that student to toss it to another student for a gain of 5 (or +5). Then, ask the student who just caught the ball to toss it to another student for a loss of 3 (or -3).
- Continue with the game by using vocabulary seen in the exercises, such as "move back/forward," "increase/decrease," "gain," etc.
- If time allows, play again. This time, have the student who catches the ball decide on and announce the loss or gain.

Using the Exercises

Exercises 1–8 Ask students to think about whether something is being added or taken away when trying to determine if each number should be positive or negative.

Exercises 9–10 Remind students that all numbers to the right of 0 are positive, whereas those to the left of 0 are negative.

Assess and Close

Number Line Know-How Ask students questions like the ones shown below.

Which word, "less" or "greater" would fit correctly in each phrase?

+11 is_____ than -21 -9 is_____ than -4

Concepts and Skills Bank

 Graphing Functions

Lesson Planner

Objective

Given a function, I will create a table. Then I will graph the ordered pairs from the table.

Materials: transparency containing a grid, graph paper (2 pieces per student)

Manipulatives: rulers (1 per student)

Activate Prior Knowledge

Students found unknown values in function tables in a previous lesson. Tell students they will not be able to skip count to determine unknown values in this lesson.

- Solve several simple algebraic expressions on the board such as $y = 4x$ where x equals 2 and $3 + 5x = y$ where x equals 5. $y = 8; 28 = y$

Using student page R62.

- When graphing ordered pairs, always start with the x-coordinate. Since students are used to working in this order, it may be helpful for them to write functions this way too. For example, the function $y = 2x + 1$ can be written as $2x + 1 = y$. It may also benefit students to add a function column to their tables, as seen below.
- Create a function table for $y = 2x + 1$.
- Display a grid using a transparency or large poster paper and invite volunteers to graph the ordered pairs for the function $y = 2x + 1$. Show students how to connect the points using a ruler.

Input (x)	Function $2x + 1 = y$	Output (y)	(x, y)
0	(2 x 0) + 1	1	(0,1)
1	(2 x 1) + 1	3	(1,3)
2	(2 x 2) + 1	5	(2,5)
3	(2 x 3) + 1	7	(3,7)
4	(2 x 4) + 1	9	(4,9)

Graphing Functions

Functions can be placed in a table and then graphed. First, make a table for the function. Then graph the function using the ordered pairs found.

EXAMPLE Graph a Function

Graph ten points on the graph of the function $y = 2x + 1$.

Complete a table to find the ordered pairs. Then graph the ordered pairs. Connect the points with a straight line.

Input (x)	Output (y)	(x, y)
0	1	(0, 1)
1	3	(1, 3)
2	5	(2, 5)
3	7	(3, 7)
4	9	(4, 9)
5	11	(5, 11)
6	13	(6, 13)
7	15	(7, 15)
8	17	(8, 17)
9	19	(9, 19)

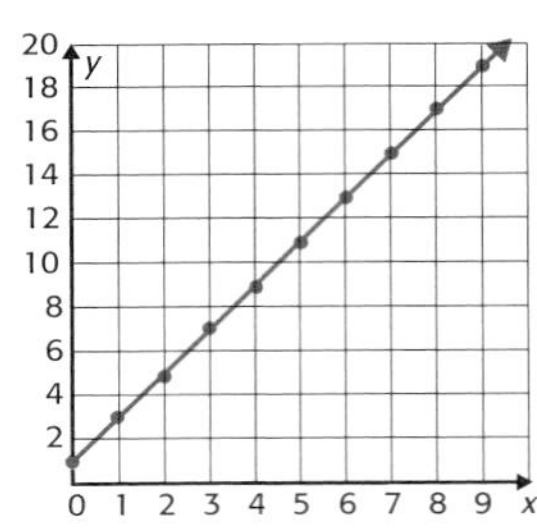

Exercises

Graph ten points on the graph of the function.

1. $y = 1x$ **2.** $y = 6x$ **3.** $y = x + 6$

4. $y = 2x - 1$ **5.** $y = 4x + 2$ **6.** $y = 5x - 3$

7. Laine gives $3 of her weekly allowance to a charity. The rule can be written as $y = 3x$. The function table shows the amount of money Laine has given to a charity after 1, 2, 3, and 4 weeks. Create a graph to show the amount of money given to charity after 10 weeks.

Input (x) Weeks	Output (y) Amount to Charity	(x, y)
1	$3	(1, 3)
2	$6	(2, 6)
3	$9	(3, 9)
4	$12	(4, 12)

1–7 See answer appendix

Using the Exercises

Exercises 1–6 Have students use rulers to connect the ordered pairs.

Exercise 7 Tell students that they will have to extend the table to 10 in the input column before graphing the ordered pairs.

Assess and Close

Figuring Functions Have students complete the function table below and then graph the ordered pairs.

Input (x)	Function $2x + 1 = y$	Output (y)	(x, y)
			(1,2)
2			
3			(3,8)
		11	

Units of Time

Time is a unit of measure. It measures the interval between two or more events. Like other units of measure, units of time can also be converted.

- To convert from larger units to smaller units, multiply.
- To convert from smaller units to larger units, divide.

Units of Time
60 seconds (s) = 1 minute (min)
60 minutes = 1 hour (h)
24 hours = 1 day
7 days = 1 week
12 months = 1 year
52 weeks = 1 year
365 days = 1 year

Concepts and Skills

EXAMPLES Convert Units of Time

MEASUREMENT Complete each conversion.

1 **5 hours = ■ minutes**

$$\begin{array}{r} 60 \\ \times 5 \\ \hline 300 \end{array}$$

Since 1 hour = 60 minutes, multiply by 60.

So, 5 hours = 300 minutes.

2 **42 days = ■ weeks**

$$7\overline{)42}^{\;6}$$

Since 7 days = 1 week, divide by 7.

So, 42 days = 6 weeks

Exercises

MEASUREMENT Complete each conversion.

1. 52 weeks = ■ days 365
2. 7 days = ■ hours 168
3. 24 hours = ■ seconds 86,400
4. 3 years = ■ days 1,095
5. 120 months = ■ years 10
6. 15 minutes = ■ seconds 900
7. 49 days = ■ weeks 7
8. 4 weeks = ■ days 28
9. 1,470 days = ■ weeks 210
10. 216 months = ■ years 18
11. A calendar typically shows one year. Some calendars can show many years. If a calendar shows 5 years, how many months does it show? 60 months
12. James was looking at his calendar and noticed it was a 2-year calendar. How many weeks is that? how many days? 104; 730

Using the Exercises

Exercises 1–10 Remind students to write the related conversion information on their papers and to solve the problem under it. Also, help students recall that they should multiply when converting from larger units to smaller units and divide when converting from smaller units to larger units.

Exercises 11–12 Ask students to think carefully about whether they are converting from larger units to smaller units or vice versa.

Assess and Close

Two-Step Problems Pose two-step word problems involving time conversions. For example: "Lia walked the family dog for 1 hour. The next day, her mom walked the dog for 2 hours. On the third day, Lia's sister walked the dog for $1\frac{1}{2}$ hours. How many minutes was the dog walked during those three days? 270 minutes

Concepts and Skills Bank

8 Units of Time

Lesson Planner

Objective

I will convert units of time.

Vocabulary

time

Activate Prior Knowledge

Discuss units of time as a class.

- Ask students to share facts about time. Record their thoughts in an idea web with the word "time" as the center.
- If students do not offer units of time during the brainstorming session, prompt them by asking how time can be measured.

Using student page R63.

- When making a conversion involving units of time, follow the steps shown below.
- First, read the problem carefully: "James has to practice the piano for 7 hours each week. How many minutes is that?"
- Second, find the conversion information that will help solve the problem. Then write it on a piece of paper. Since the problem deals with hours and minutes, write the conversion information involving hours and minutes.
- Third, under the conversion information, write an equation using information from the problem. Make sure the hours and minutes are lined up. Think, "How do I figure out how many minutes are in 7 hours? I multiplied 1 hour by 7 to get 7 hours. So I will multiply 60 minutes by 7. The answer is 420 minutes because 60 × 7 = 420."

1 hour = 60 minutes
↓x7 ↓x7
7 hours = ____ minutes

Concepts and Skills Bank

9 Parts of a Circle

Lesson Planner

Objective

I will identify the parts of a circle

Vocabulary

circle, center, radius, diameter

Materials: sticky notes (1 per student), blank paper (2 pieces per student)

Manipulatives: compasses (1 per student), rulers (1 per student)

Activate Prior Knowledge

Discuss items with circular shapes.

- Have each student draw a circular object and write its name on a sticky note.
- Have students share their ideas as they post their notes on the board.

Using student page R64.

- Demonstrate for students how to use a compass to draw a circle.
- Then, have students use compasses to draw different-sized circles on a blank piece of paper.
- After allowing a few minutes of experimentation with the compasses, have students construct a circle with a center point.
- Instruct students to use a ruler to draw a line segment through the center of the circle with endpoints located on the circle. Tell students that this line segment is called the diameter of the circle. Label this distance as the diameter.
- Next, tell students to draw a line segment from the circle's center to any point on the circle. Label this distance as the radius.
- Show students how to label the endpoints of the radius and diameter with letters of the alphabet.

Concepts and Skills

Parts of a Circle

A **circle** is a two-dimensional figure in which all points are the same distance from a point called the **center**. The parts of a circle are shown below.

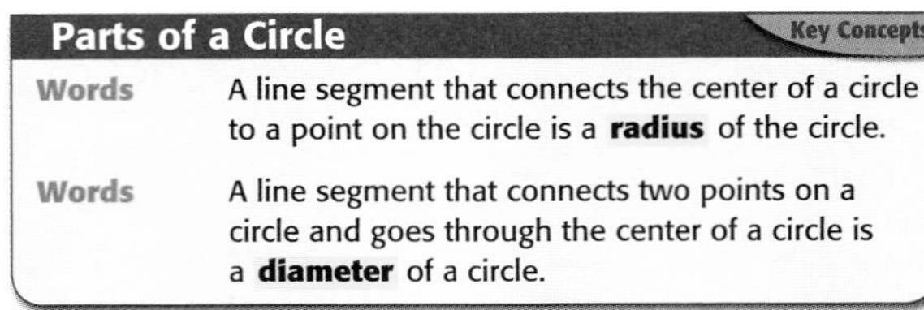

Parts of a Circle — Key Concepts

Words	A line segment that connects the center of a circle to a point on the circle is a **radius** of the circle.
Words	A line segment that connects two points on a circle and goes through the center of a circle is a **diameter** of a circle.

EXAMPLES Parts of a Circle

Identify the part of the circle.

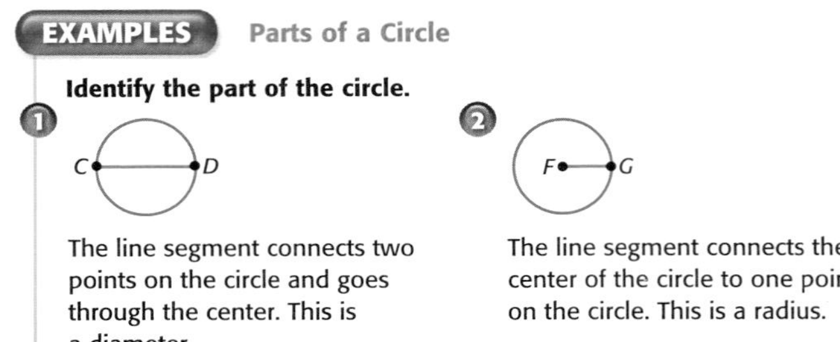

1. The line segment connects two points on the circle and goes through the center. This is a diameter.

2. The line segment connects the center of the circle to one point on the circle. This is a radius.

Exercises

Identify the part of the circle.

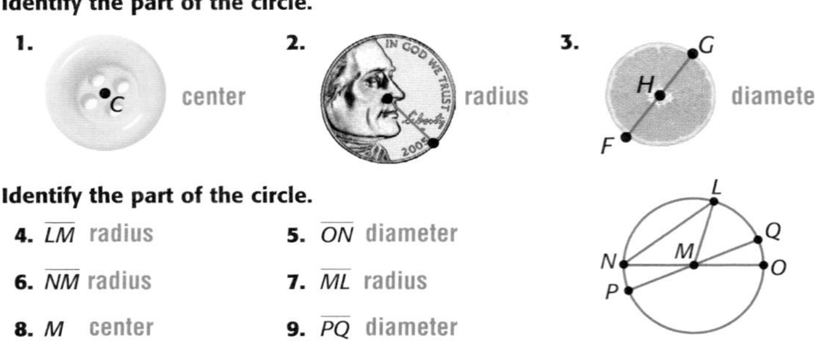

1. center
2. radius
3. diameter

Identify the part of the circle.

4. $\overline{LM}$ radius
5. $\overline{ON}$ diameter
6. $\overline{NM}$ radius
7. $\overline{ML}$ radius
8. M center
9. $\overline{PQ}$ diameter

R64 Concepts and Skills Bank

- If time allows, measure the length of the radius in centimeters or inches. Measure the length of the diameter and then compare the lengths of the two segments. Lead students to draw the conclusion that the length of the diameter is twice the length of the radius.

Using the Exercises

Exercises 1–9 Encourage students to identify each circle part on their own before looking at the information located at the top and middle of page R64 to confirm their thinking.

Assess and Close

Constructing Circles Have students draw a circle according to directions. For example, draw a circle and its center, draw a radius and label it GH, and draw a diameter and label it JK. Have students write the definitions of the parts of a circle under their drawings.

Similarity

In Lesson 10-7, you learned that congruent figures have the same size and shape. Figures that have the same shape but different sizes are **similar figures**.

Similar	Not Similar

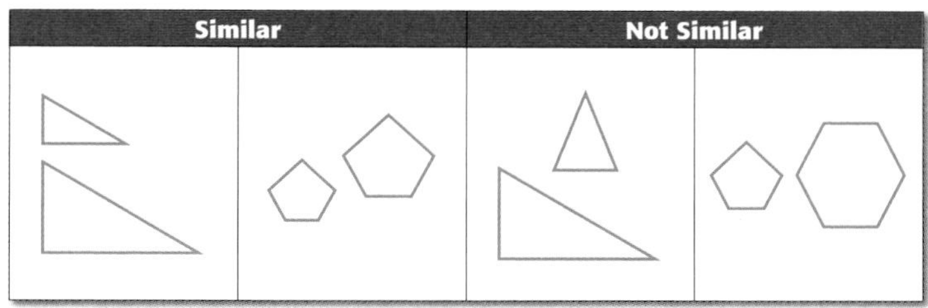

EXAMPLE Identify Similar Figures

Tell whether each pair of figures is similar. Explain.

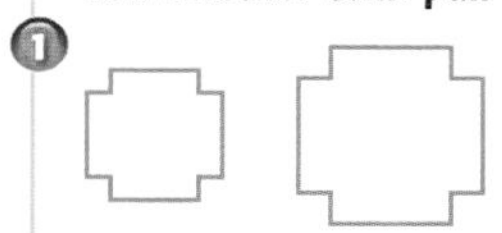

1. The figures have the same shape but different sizes. So, they are similar figures.

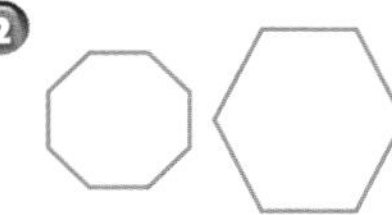

2. The figures do not have the same shape or size. So, they are not similar figures.

Exercises

Tell whether each pair of figures is similar.

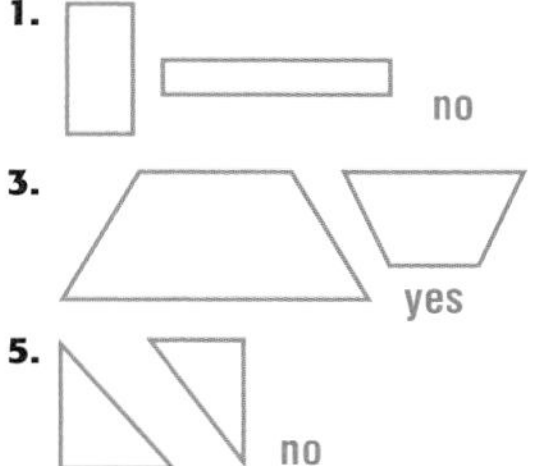

Concepts and Skills Bank **R65**

Concepts and Skills

10 Similarity

Lesson Planner

Objective

I will identify similar figures.

Vocabulary

similar figures

Materials: large piece of blank paper (1 per group), crayons, markers, or colored pencils, page of figures on colored paper (1 per student), blank paper (1 piece per student), scissors, glue

Manipulatives: pattern blocks

Activate Prior Knowledge

Discuss the concept of similarity as a class.

- Write the word "similar" on the chalkboard and ask students what it means.
- Draw two equilateral triangles of varying sizes and one scalene triangle on the chalkboard. Ask students whether they think these figures are similar. Have students discuss their thoughts with a partner and then invite them to share with the class.
- Tell students that the first and second triangles (the equilaterals) are similar because they have the same shape but different sizes. The third triangle is not similar to the first two because it does not have the same shape.
- If students have not determined what similarity means, explain its defintion in mathematical terms.

Using student page R65.

- Pass out piles of pattern blocks to small groups of students. Challenge students to create similar figures using the blocks. For example, create similar squares by using one square pattern block for one of the figures and four square pattern blocks for the other.
- Have groups who finish early trace their similar figures onto pieces of blank paper and color them.

Using the Exercises

Exercises 1–6 Remind students that figures have to have the same shape to be considered similar.

Assess and Close

Similarity Search Create a page of figures, some similar and some not, and make copies on colored paper. Pass out this page and a blank piece of paper to each student. Have them fold the blank paper in half three times and then unfold it to reveal eight boxes. Then, ask students to cut out the similar figures and glue each pair in a different box on the blank piece of paper. Vary the difficulty of the task by either telling students how many pairs of similar figures to find (the easier option) or leaving it to students to determine this fact.

Concepts and Skills Bank

11 Perimeter of Irregular Figures

Lesson Planner

Objective

I will find the perimeter of an irregular figure by adding the lengths of its sides.

Vocabulary

irregular figure

Materials: irregular figures drawn on half pieces of paper (1 figure per paper) with the lengths of their sides labeled (1 per student)

Concepts and Skills

Perimeter of Irregular Figures

An **irregular figure** is made up of two or more figures. You can find the perimeter, or distance around an irregular figure.

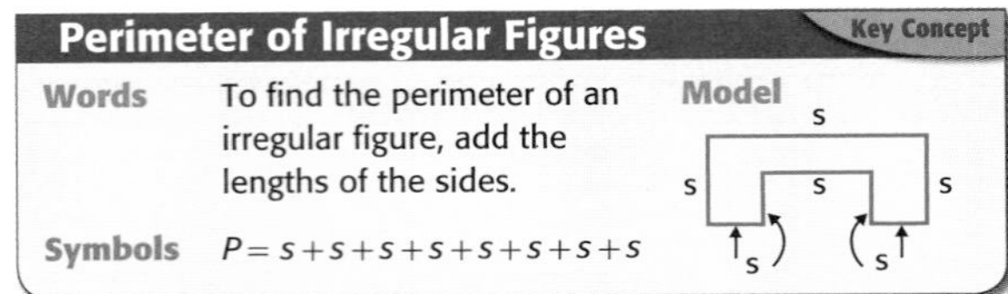

Perimeter of Irregular Figures Key Concept

Words To find the perimeter of an irregular figure, add the lengths of the sides.

Symbols $P = s + s + s + s + s + s + s + s$

Model

EXAMPLE Estimate and Find Perimeter

1. **Estimate then find the perimeter of the figure.**

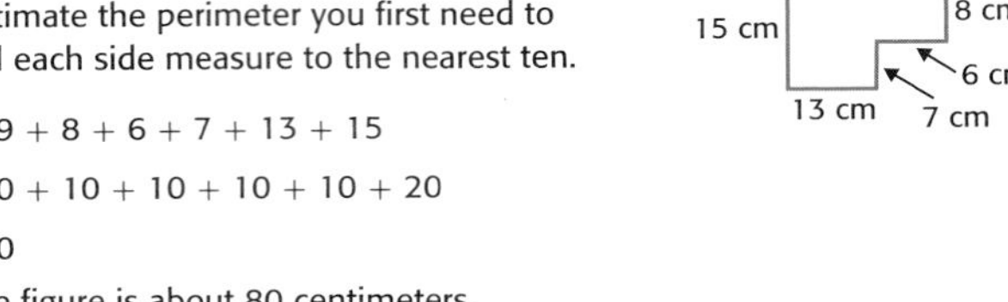

To estimate the perimeter you first need to round each side measure to the nearest ten.

$P = 19 + 8 + 6 + 7 + 13 + 15$

$P = 20 + 10 + 10 + 10 + 10 + 20$

$P = 80$

So the figure is about 80 centimeters.

Next, add the exact measures.

$P = 19 + 8 + 6 + 7 + 13 + 15 = 68$

So, the perimeter of this figure is 68 centimeters.

Check for Reasonableness

The answer, 68, is close to the estimate, 80. ✓

Exercises

Estimate then find the perimeter of each irregular figure.

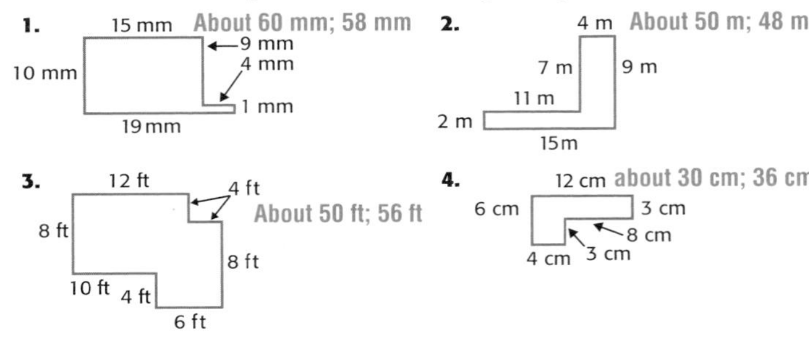

R66 Concepts and Skills Bank

Activate Prior Knowledge

Discuss the meaning of the word "perimeter" as a class.

- Write the word "perimeter" on the board. Ask students to share what they know about its meaning.
- The distance around the outside of an object or shape is its perimeter. You can remember that it is the distance *around* the shape because perimeter has the word "rim" in it, which means edge or border.

Using student page R66.

- Draw an irregular figure on the board and label the lengths of its sides.
- Have students find its perimeter by recording the lengths of each side in a horizontal addition problem on a piece of paper. Tell students to estimate the figure's perimeter first by rounding each side to the nearest ten. After they have finished estimating, have students find the figure's actual perimeter.
- Show students how to make sure each side's length was counted only once by marking off each side of the figure with an *x* after it has been added to the number sentence.
- Next, pass out irregular figures to students (see materials section at top). Give students time to determine the perimeter of the figure. Then, have students switch figures with a classmate and find that figure's perimeter.

Using the Exercises

Exercises 1–4 Remind students to double-check that all sides have been counted only once. They should also estimate before finding the actual perimeter of each figure.

Assess and Close

Perimeter Practice Pose problems that provide students with the perimeter and polygon type and ask them to brainstorm possible side lengths. For example: "A square has a perimeter of 36 centimeters. What are lengths of the four sides?" 9 cm, 9 cm, 9 cm, and 9 cm Another example is: "The perimeter of a rectangle is 28 feet. The length of one of the sides is 8 feet. What are the lengths of the other three sides?" 8 ft, 6 ft, and 6 ft

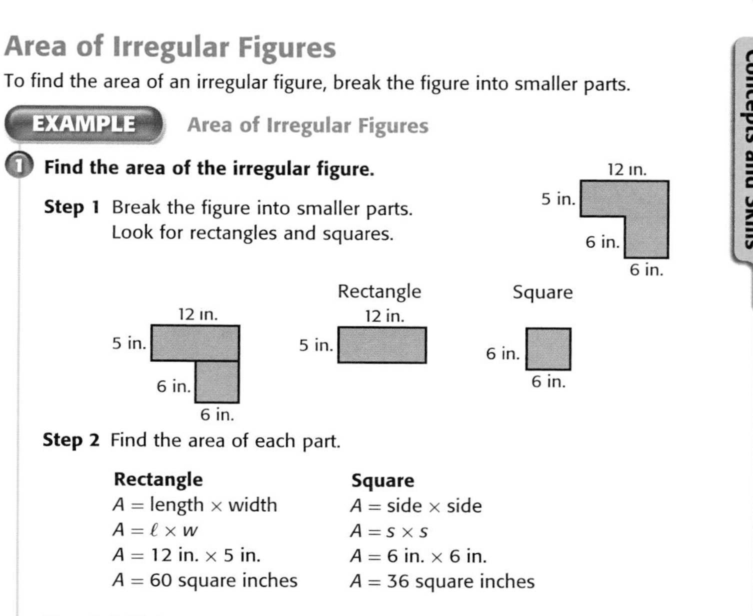

Area of Irregular Figures

To find the area of an irregular figure, break the figure into smaller parts.

EXAMPLE Area of Irregular Figures

1 Find the area of the irregular figure.

Step 1 Break the figure into smaller parts. Look for rectangles and squares.

Step 2 Find the area of each part.

Rectangle	**Square**
A = length × width	A = side × side
$A = \ell \times w$	$A = s \times s$
A = 12 in. × 5 in.	A = 6 in. × 6 in.
A = 60 square inches	A = 36 square inches

Step 3 Add the areas.

The area of the figure is 60 + 36 or 96 square inches.

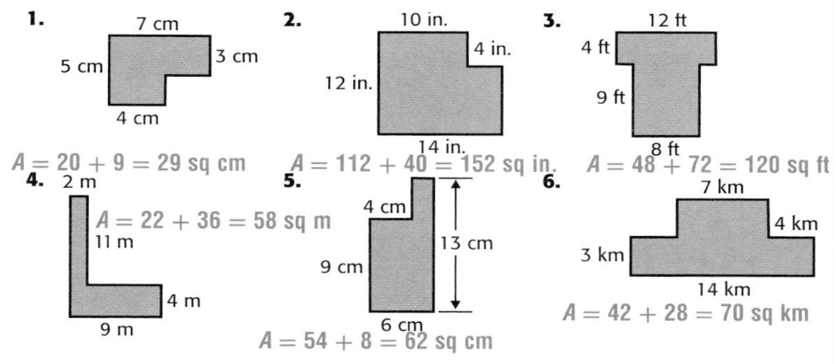

Exercises

Find the area of each figure.

Concepts and Skills Bank **R67**

Concepts and Skills

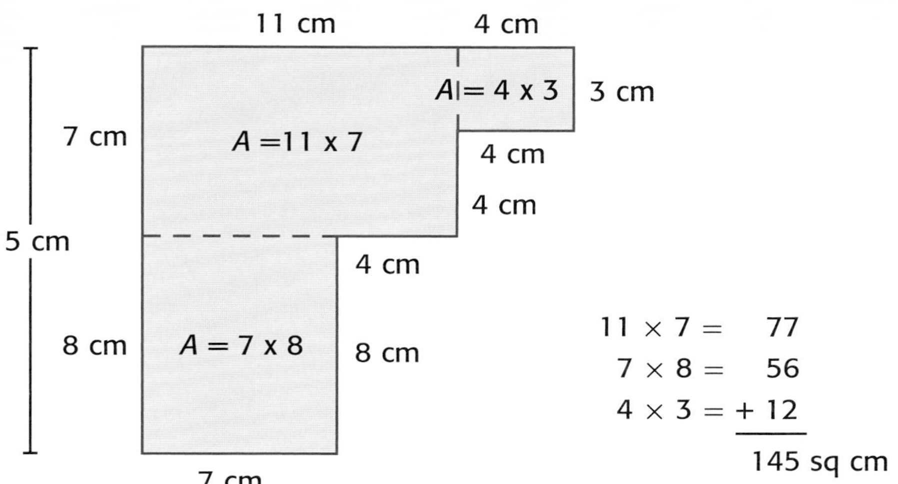

Assess and Close

Area Awareness Provide students with a page containing four large irregular figures. Then have students measure and label each figure's sides to the nearest inch before breaking it into smaller parts and calculating its total area.

Concepts and Skills Bank

12 Area of Irregular Figures

Lesson Planner

Objective

I will calculate the areas of irregular figures by breaking them into smaller parts.

Materials: page containing four large irregular figures

Activate Prior Knowledge

Explore the formulas for finding the areas of rectangles and squares.

- Draw a rectangle on the board and label two of its adjacent sides with their lengths. Then, ask students to work at their desks to calculate its area. Call on student volunteers to show how they found its area. If students did not write the formula for area in their solutions, remind students that the formula for a rectangle's area is A = length x width.
- Repeat the steps above with a square.

Using student page R67.

- Tell students that breaking an irregular figure into smaller parts is an effective strategy for finding its area. It is also helpful to label the lengths of all the sides of the smaller figures it has been broken into (see example to the left).
- Next, tell students to write the area formula in each of the smaller parts.
- Finally, determine each smaller part's area. Then add all of the areas together to determine the area of the entire irregular figure.

Using the Exercises

Exercises 1–6 Students may wish to trace each figure onto another piece of paper so they can draw lines to divide it into smaller parts and write the area formula in each of these parts. Remind students to write their answers in square units.

Concepts and Skills Bank

13 Areas of Parallelograms

Lesson Planner

Objective

I will find areas of parallelograms by using the formula *area = base x height.*

Materials: page of parallelograms (1 per student), scissors, page containing parallelogram areas (1 per student)

Activate Prior Knowledge

Discuss parallelograms as a class.

- Draw a parallelogram on the board. Ask students to identify the figure. If students offer the term "quadrilateral," tell them that they are correct, but that squares, rhombuses, rectangles, etc. are also quadrilaterals. Inform students that you want the specific name of this quadrilateral.
- Discuss why parallelograms are named so. Ask students to name properties of parallelograms. four sides; two pairs of opposite, parallel sides; two pairs of opposite, equal sides and angles, etc.

Using student page R68.

- Pass out a page containing the outlines of five parallelograms to each student. Give students the task of cutting out the parallelograms, and then making one cut to turn them into different shapes (by manipulating the two new shapes created). Give students about five minutes to work, but tell them to save one of the parallelograms on their page.
- Invite volunteers to share their new shapes with the class. If any student shares a rectangle with the class, ask him/her to explain how it was created. If not, then show the class how to do so.
- Have all students cut out their last parallelogram and make one cut along its height to turn it into a rectangle.

Areas of Parallelograms

The areas of a parallelogram and a rectangle are related.

To find the area of a parallelogram, multiply the base and the height.

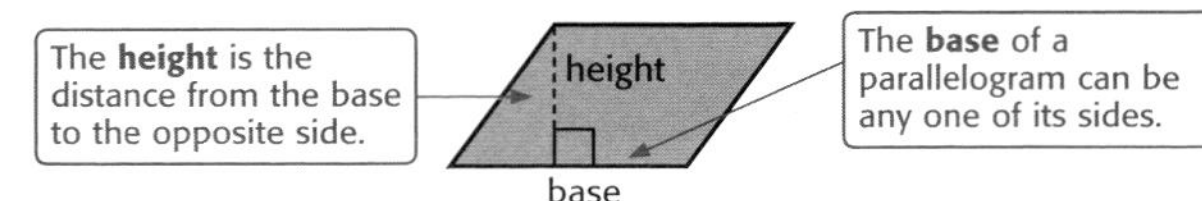

The **height** is the distance from the base to the opposite side.
height
base
The **base** of a parallelogram can be any one of its sides.

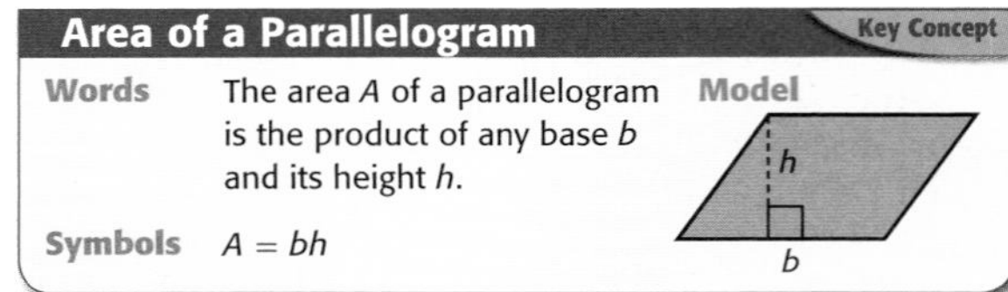

Area of a Parallelogram — Key Concept

Words	The area A of a parallelogram is the product of any base b and its height h.	**Model**
Symbols	$A = bh$	

EXAMPLE Find the Area of a Parallelogram

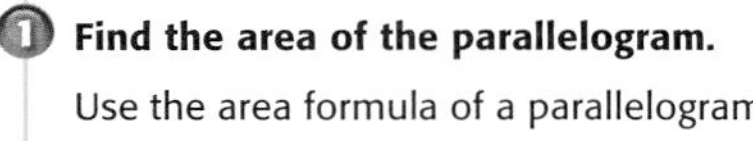

1 **Find the area of the parallelogram.**

Use the area formula of a parallelogram.

$A = bh$ Area formula of a parallelogram.

$A = 6 \times 4$ Replace b with 6 and h with 4.

$A = 24$ Multiply.

The area of the parallelogram is 24 square centimeters.

Exercises

Find the area of each parallelogram.

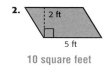

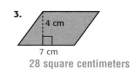

1.
12 square inches

2. 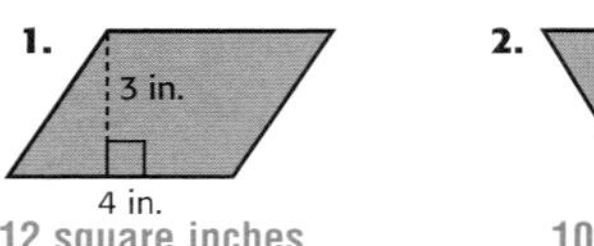

10 square feet

3. 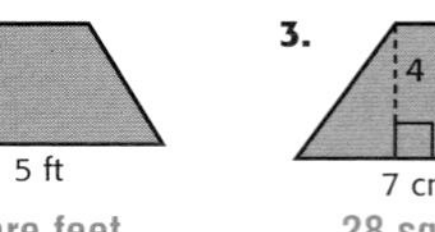

28 square centimeters

- Ask students if, by making the cut and rearranging the two small parts, any part of the parallelogram was lost or taken away. Tell students that since no area was lost, you can use the formula $A = bh$ to determine a parallelogram's area, just like you would a rectangle's area.
- Have students study the information on page R68 in pairs, including the example.
- Draw a few parallelograms on the chalkboard with their bases and heights labeled. Work as a class to find the area of each figure.

Using the Exercises

Exercises 1–3 Remind students that their answers must be in square units. Also, point out that all of the units are not the same.

Assess and Close

Parallelogram Practice Hand out a page containing the areas of six parallelograms. Ask students to write down all the possible lengths of each parallelogram's base and height. At the bottom of the page, ask students to explain how to determine a parallelogram's area.

Areas of Triangles

Notice that a parallelogram is made of two congruent triangles. So, the formula for the area of a triangle can be found by dividing the formula for the area of a parallelogram by two.

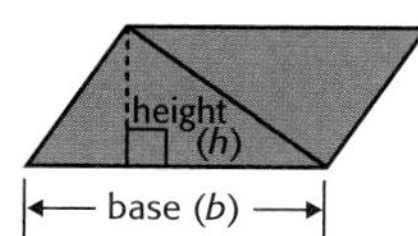

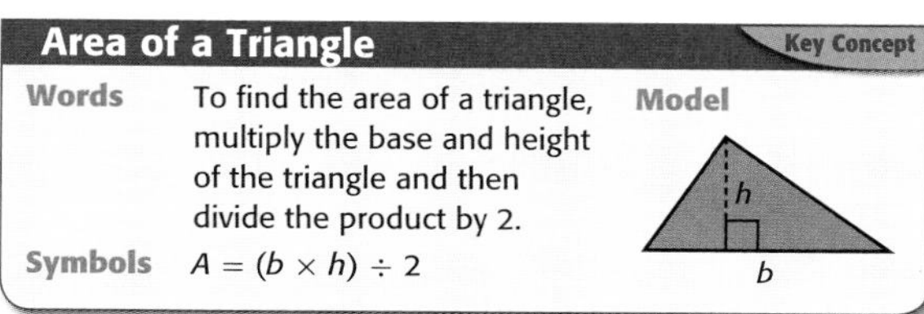

Area of a Triangle *Key Concept*

Words To find the area of a triangle, multiply the base and height of the triangle and then divide the product by 2.

Symbols $A = (b \times h) \div 2$

Model h, b

EXAMPLE Find the Area of a Triangle

1 **Find the area of the triangle.**

Use the area formula of a triangle.

4 cm
8 cm

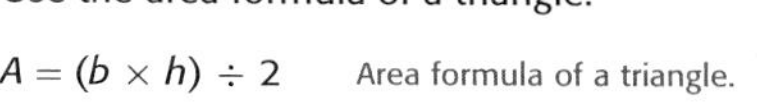

$A = (b \times h) \div 2$ Area formula of a triangle.

$A = (8 \times 4) \div 2$ Replace b with 8 and h with 4.

$A = 32 \div 2$ Multiply.

$A = 16$ Divide. $32 \div 2 = 16$

The area of the triangle is 16 square centimeters.

Exercises

Find the area of each triangle.

1.

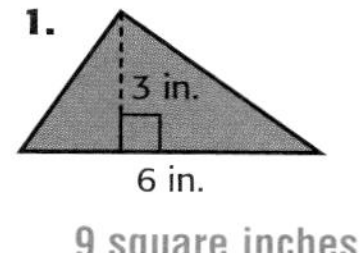

9 square inches

2.

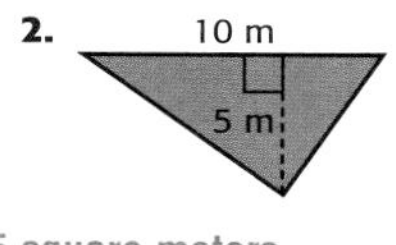

25 square meters

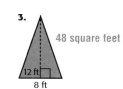

3. 12 ft, 8 ft

48 square feet

Using the Exercises

Exercises 1–3 Remind students to write their answers in square units. Also, help students notice that not all of the answers will be in inches, as in Exercise 1.

Assess and Close

Trying Triangles Provide students with a page of ten triangles where each triangle has the length of every side listed (see below). Ask students to find the area of each triangle and to record the appropriate unit (i.e., sq ft, sq km, etc.) in the answer.

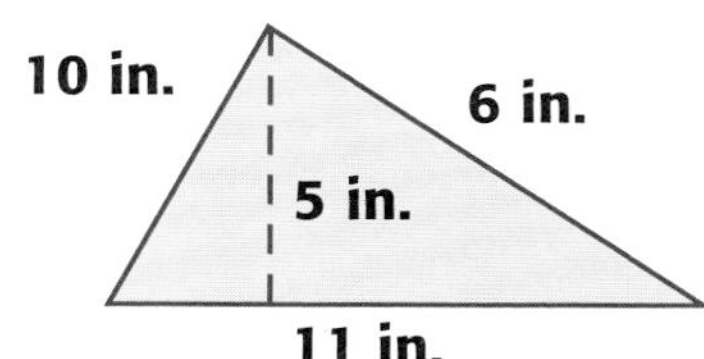

Concepts and Skills Bank

14 Areas of Triangles

Lesson Planner

Objective

I will use the formula *Area = (base × height) ÷ 2* to find the areas of triangles.

Materials: page containing pairs of congruent triangles (1 per group), scissors, cut-out of paper parallelogram, page of ten triangles (1 per student)

Activate Prior Knowledge

Explore making new shapes by manipulating congruent triangles.

- Pass out a page containing pairs of congruent triangles to small groups of students. Ask groups to cut out each pair and rearrange it to create a new shape. Give students five to ten minutes to experiment.
- Have students share their findings with the class. Students' findings should include triangles forming parallelograms.

Using student page R69.

- Display a paper parallelogram with the measure of its base and height labeled. Ask students to find its area. Invite volunteers to the board to share their solutions.
- Now, cut the parallelogram in half to create two equal triangles. Pose the question, "What is the area of each triangle?" Tell students that each triangle's area is exactly half of the parallelogram's area, since the parallelogram was cut in half.
- Write the formula for finding the area of a triangle on the board and have students discuss with a partner why they think it ends with "÷2". Invite volunteers to share their answers with the class.

15 Line Graphs

Lesson Planner

Objective

I will create and interpret line graphs.

Vocabulary

line graph

Materials: Materials: bar graph and line graph examples (1 of each), transparency containing a grid, index cards (1 per student), line graph with corresponding questions (1 per student)

Activate Prior Knowledge

Compare bar graphs and line graphs as a class.

- Draw a Venn diagram on the board. Entitle one region "bar graph" and the other "line graph."
- Ask students if they know the difference between a bar graph and a line graph. Record similarities and differences in the Venn diagram.
- Show students an example of each type of graph to inspire more ideas to record in the diagram.

Using student page R70.

- Tell students that a line graph uses points and lines to show how data changes over time.
- Ask students whether a line graph would be used in the following scenarios: to show how many students like pears (no), to show how the population of a city has grown over ten years (yes, because it would show change over time), to show how much it snowed each month during the winter (yes, because it would show change over time).
- Have small groups of students study the line graph examples on page R70. Then ask them to create a list of the various parts that are needed to make a line graph.

Line Graphs

A **line graph** shows how data changes over time. You can use a line graph to make predictions about future events.

EXAMPLES Interpret a Line Graph

1 Refer to the graph at the right. How tall did the flower grow in three months?

The third month is June.

Move up to find where the point is located on the graph. Then compare the height of the point to the scale on the left.

The point is located between 8 and 10 on the graph's scale. So, the plant grew 9 inches in three months.

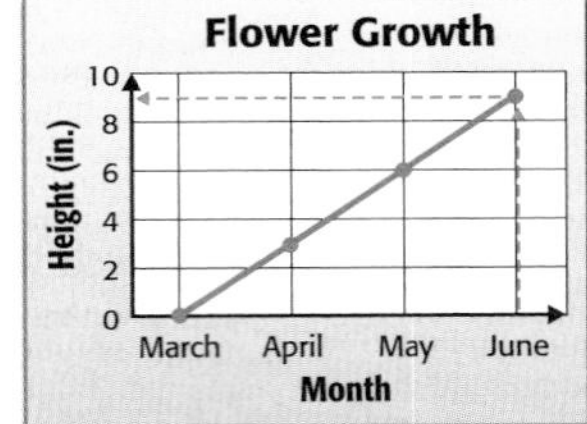

2 The graph shows the growth of a baby panda over four weeks. How much weight did the panda gain between week 1 and week 4?

Subtract the panda's weight at week 1 from its weight at week 4.

Week 1: 11 pounds
Week 4: 14 pounds

14 − 11 = 3

So, the baby panda gained 3 pounds between week 1 and week 4.

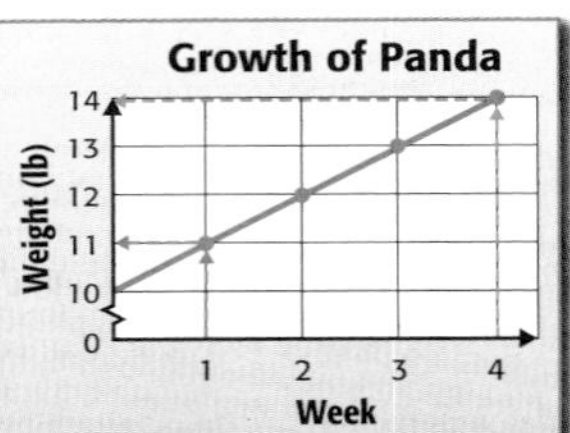

Exercises

For Exercises 1–3, use the line graph.

1. At what time is the least amount of snow on the ground? 6 P.M.
2. How much snow is on the ground at 8:00 P.M.? 3 in.
3. How much snow fell over the 4-hour period shown on the graph? 6 in.

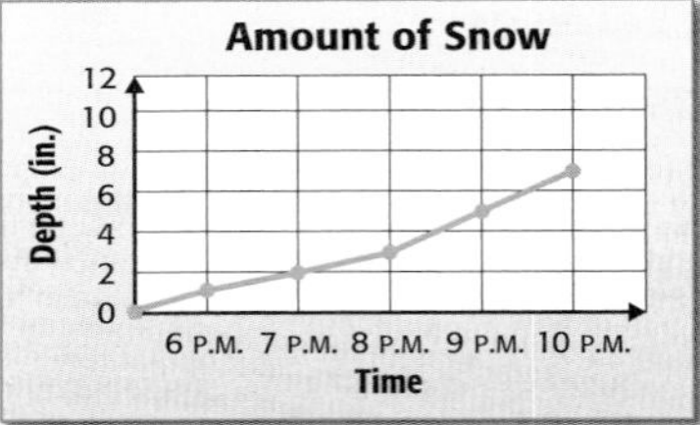

title (tells the main idea of the line graph)
horizontal axis (shows the change over time)
vertical axis (displays what is changing over time, the scale always starts at 0)
labels for both axes (to show what type of data is represented in graph)
points connected by line segments (will show a change over time)

- Now, create a line graph as a class on a grid using a transparency. Possible themes include rainfall over a period of time or amount of money made at a lemonade stand over a week's time. Be sure to include all of the aspects previously listed.
- Pose two questions about the graph for students to answer. Then, pass out index cards to small groups (one per student). Ask students to write their own questions about the line graph. Present the questions to the class.

Using the Exercises

Exercises 1–3 Tell students to study the graph before answering the questions. Advise them to look at the title, the labels for each axis, the shape of the data (is it going up or down over time?), etc.

For Exercises 4–8, use the line graph.

Height of Roberto

Height (in.): 0, 50, 52, 54, 56, 58, 60

Age (years): 8, 9, 10, 11, 12

4. What was Roberto's height when he was 9 years old? 53 inches

5. How many inches did Roberto grow between the ages of 10 and 12? 5 inches

6. How many inches did Roberto grow from age 8 to age 12? 9 inches

7. At this rate, predict how tall Roberto will be when he is 14 years old. See students' work.

8. Can the data shown in the line graph be displayed in a bar graph? Explain. Sample answer: yes; make the height of each bar the same as each point on the line graph.

For Exercises 9–13, use the line graph.

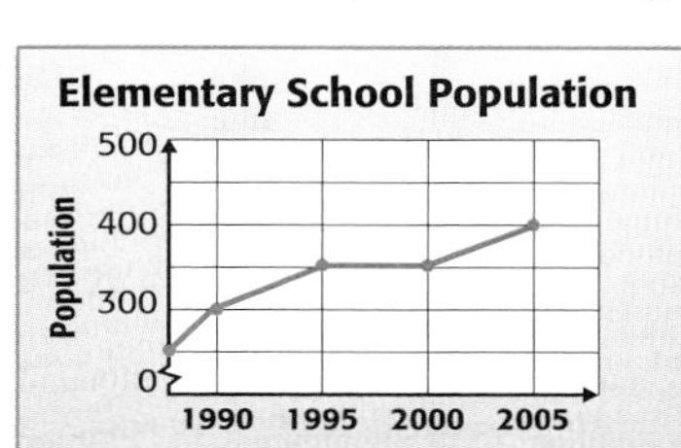

9. Is the school population increasing, decreasing, or varying over time? increasing

10. What was the population in 1995? 350

11. How much did the population grow between 1995 and 2005? 50

12. During which time period did the population stay the same? 1995 and 2000

13. Predict the population in 2020. Explain your reasoning. Sample answer: 600; the population grew by 200 students in the previous 15 years, so if the pattern continues the population in 2020 will be 400 + 200 = 600

Represent each set of data in a line graph.

14.

Plant Growth	
Week	Height (in.)
1	1
2	2
3	3
4	5
5	8

15.

One Day's Temperatures	
Time	Temperature (°F)
12 P.M.	62°
1 P.M.	65°
2 P.M.	72°
3 P.M.	66°
4 P.M.	64°

14-16. See students' work.

16. Collect and organize data about a week's daily high temperatures in your city. Display the data on a line graph.

17. Analyze the graph you made in Exercise 16. Would a bar graph be a more effective way to display the data? Explain. Sample answer: no; A bar graph does not show change over time as effectively as a line graph.

Using the Exercises

Exercises 4–13 Again, have students study each graph before answering the related questions. Also, point out the broken scale and explain that it is used because the data does not start until 51 in the first graph and 100 in the second.

Exercises 14–15 Advise students to begin the scales of their graphs at 0, even though the data begins at 1 in Exercise 14 and 62° in Exercise 15. They should remember all the parts that are necessary to include in a graph.

Exercises 16–17 Direct students to an appropriate source for gathering the weather data needed to complete Exercise 16, such as a local website or newspaper.

Assess and Close

Interpreting Importance Give students an example of a line graph. Then ask them to explain in words why each aspect (such as the title, axes labels, etc.) is important.

Concepts and Skills Bank

16 More Ways to Display Data

Lesson Planner

Objective

I will interpret data displayed in circle graphs, Venn diagrams, and stem-and-leaf plots.

Materials: compasses

Activate Prior Knowledge

Introduce the data used in the examples and ask students to think about how best to display it.

- Write the test scores from page R72 on the board. Ask students which ways they think the data could be organized and displayed well. Make a list of students' ideas on the board.

Using student page R72.

- Work through example 1.
- Take a close look at the circle graph on page R72. Are there any components that students might add to make the graph easier to understand? Sample answers: a title could be added; each region could include a number telling how many scores fall in that range, such as 4 in the A region because 4 students received As
- Have students work in small groups to brainstorm additional questions that can be answered by looking at the circle graph. Have them share their questions with the class.
- Ask students to share what type of information they have seen in Venn diagrams in the past. This method for displaying data is very common and can be used in all subject areas.
- Work through example 2.
- Challenge students to find a different way to list the data in a Venn diagram so that the circles are more balanced. Sample answer: by setting 80 or 85 as the cutoff point

More Ways to Display Data

There are many ways to display sets of data. Three of them are shown.

EXAMPLES Different Displays of Data

Three teachers are reviewing the same test scores. The test scores are: 95, 68, 87, 100, 23, 56, 85, 93, 85, 70, 98, 45, and 85. Each teacher displayed the data in a different way.

1. Teacher 1 displayed the data in a circle graph where it was organized by letter grade. A circle graph shows data as parts of a circle.

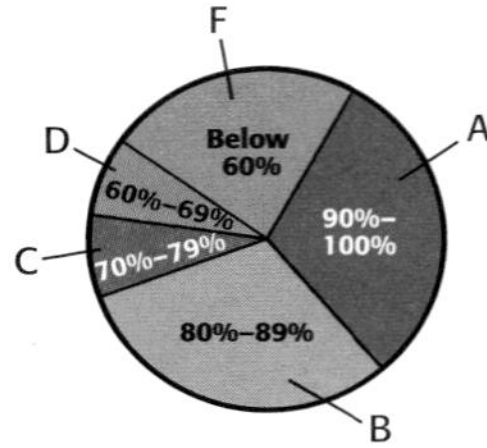

How does the number of students who received an A compare to the number of students who received a B?

The number of students who received an A or B on the test is the same because the sections marked as A and B on the circle graph are the same size.

2. Teacher 2 displayed the data using a Venn diagram showing which students scored 70s or above and 70s or below. A Venn diagram is made of circles and shows the relationships between sets of data.

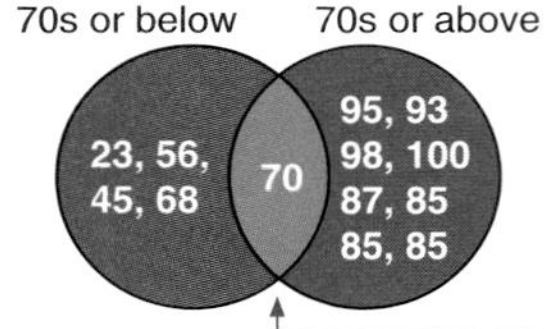

What score did most students receive: 70s or above or 70s or below?

There are 9 scores in 70s or above. There are 5 scores in the 70s or below. So, most students' test scores were 70s or above.

3 Teacher 3 displayed the data using a Stem-and-Leaf plot. A stem-and-leaf plot is a display of data with digits to the left of ones digits as stems and ones digits as leaves.

What are the mode and the median of these test scores?

The median is the middle number in a set of data. In this set of data the middle number is 85.

The mode is the number that is repeated most. In this set of data it is 85.

So, both the median and mode are 85.

Stems	Leaves
2	3
4	5
5	6
6	8
7	0
8	5 5 5 7
9	3 5 8
10	0

Exercises

For Exercises 1–4, use the circle graph.

1. What fraction of students owns 2 dogs? $\frac{1}{4}$
2. What fraction of students owns one dog? $\frac{1}{2}$
3. How many dogs do most students own? One
4. What is the greatest number of dogs a student owns? Three dogs

Number of Dogs per Household

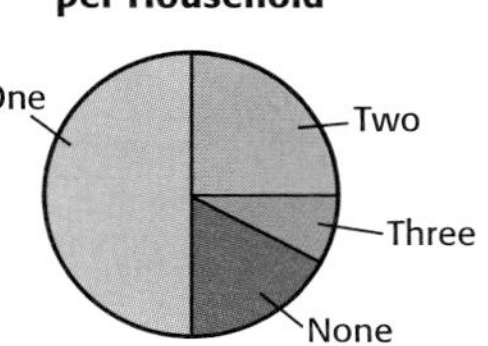

For Exercises 5–7, use the Venn diagram.

5. What may have been the survey question for this Venn diagram? Sample answer: Which type of sport is your favorite, indoor or outdoor?
6. What is the favorite type of sport, indoor or outdoor? Outdoor
7. What does the number 7 mean? 7 students like indoor and outdoor sports the same amount.

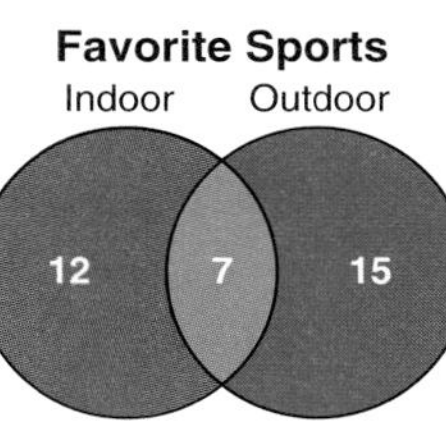

For Exercises 8–10, use the stem-and-leaf plot.

8. What is the greatest number in this set of numbers? 95
9. What is the median for this set of number? 68
10. What is the mode for this set of numbers? 83

Stems	Leaves
1	0 5 6
2	2 4 5 6
6	6 8
7	5 8 9
8	2 3 3 5
9	5

Using student page R73.

- Introduce students to a third way the test scores can be displayed, a stem-and-leaf plot. Some students may not have seen this method of displaying data before, so give them time in small groups to study it. Visit each small group to ensure students understand how a stem-and-leaf plot displays data.
- Ask students to explain why a stem-and-leaf plot might be a better choice than the other two methods when finding the mode and median of a data set.

Using the Exercises

Exercises 1–4 Point out how this circle graph differs from the one shown on page R72. This circle graph has a title and tells how many pieces of data belong in each region of the circle

Exercises 5–7 Before answering this set of questions, ask students to think of types of indoor and outdoor sports. If time allows, create a class list using students' suggestions.

Exercises 8–10 Students may find it helpful to list the pieces of data in numerical order to determine the median and mode.

Assess and Close

Data Decisions Ask students to take another look at the examples of a circle graph, Venn diagram, and stem-and-leaf plot on pages R72 and R73. Have students explain in writing which method helps them to best understand the data and why.

Then, have students take a data set (such as the ages of the first ten presidents when they took office – 57, 61, 57, 57, 58, 57, 61, 54, 68, 51) and display it using one of the three methods. Provide students with compasses if they decide to create a circle graph or Venn diagram.

17 Minimum, Maximum, and Range

Lesson Planner

Objective

I will analyze a data set to determine its minimum, maximum, and range.

Vocabulary

range, **maximum**, **minimum**

Materials: small paper bag (1 per student), reading book (1 per student)

Manipulatives: differently colored links, blocks, or another type of colorful manipulative (between 10 and 30 per student)

Activate Prior Knowledge

Explore the meanings of the terms "minimum" and "maximum."

- On the board create two different word webs using "minimum" and "maximum." Ask students to use thesauruses to find synonyms for the words. Record their findings in the webs.

Using student page R74.

- Pass out a small bag of colorful manipulatives to each student.
- Have students open their bags and record the total of all items. Next, have students' record the total of each color.
- Record students' totals in a list on the board. Rearrange the numbers so they are in numerical order. Show students how to find the data set's minimum, maximum, and range.
- Record the values of each of the colors on the board. Have students work in small groups and assign each group a color that appears in the bag. Assign groups the task of determining their data set's minimum, maximum, and range.

Minimum, Maximum, and Range

The **range** of a set of data describes how much the data varies. It is the difference between the greatest (**maximum**) and least (**minimum**) values of the set.

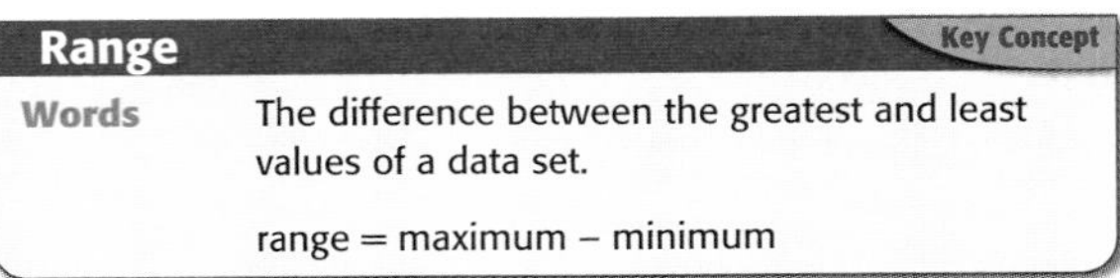
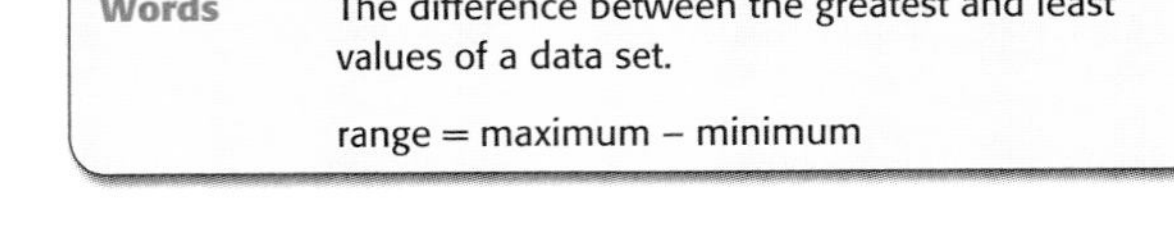

Range — Key Concept

Words	The difference between the greatest and least values of a data set.
	range = maximum − minimum

EXAMPLE Find Range

1 **Find the range of the data set {39, 86, 21, 57, 14, 62}.**

Identify the maximum and minimum of the data set.
Then find the range of the data set.

Step 1 Identify the maximum and minimum.

{39, 86, 21, 57, 14, 62}

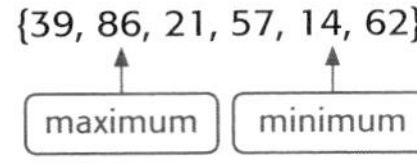

Step 2 Subtract the minimum from the maximum to find the range.

86 − 14 = 72

So, the range of the data set is 72.

Exercises

Identify the maximum, minimum, and range of each data set.

1. Birthdays in May: {4, 22, 18, 2, 29, 15} 29; 2; and 27
2. Ages: {18, 59, 83, 42, 27, 70} 83; 18; and 65
3. Students per grade: {44, 61, 38, 59, 65, 42} 65; 38; and 27
4. Bowling scores: {145, 98, 110, 128, 152, 105} 152; 98; and 54
5. Cailin's test scores were 89, 92, 85, 76, 82, and 98. Find the maximum, minimum, and range of the data set. 98; 76; and 22
6. The daily high temperatures during one week were 45, 53, 58, 62, 64, 55, and 57. Find the maximum, minimum, and range of the data set. 64; 45; and 19

Using the Exercises

Exercises 1–6 Remind students to order numbers from least to greatest to aid in finding the minimum, maximum, and range.

Assess and Close

Page Turner Have each student locate their favorite book or the book they are currently reading. Instruct the class to randomly flip to ten different pages in their books. Record the page number of each page on a piece of notebook paper. Then, identify the minimum and maximum, and calculate the range. Have students repeat the experiment with the same book, or have them swap books with a partner. If time allows, have students give a quick book talk about the book they swapped to their partner.

Mean

You have already learned how to find the median, mode, range, maximum, and minimum of a data set. You will now learn how to find the **mean** or average of a set of data.

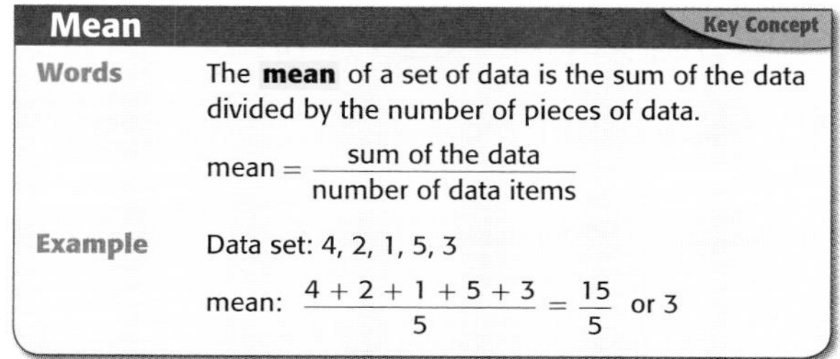

Mean — Key Concept

Words The **mean** of a set of data is the sum of the data divided by the number of pieces of data.

$$\text{mean} = \frac{\text{sum of the data}}{\text{number of data items}}$$

Example Data set: 4, 2, 1, 5, 3

$$\text{mean: } \frac{4+2+1+5+3}{5} = \frac{15}{5} \text{ or } 3$$

EXAMPLE Find the Mean

1 SPORTS **Henry is playing miniature golf. His scores on the first 6 holes are: 5, 2, 6, 3, 7, and 1. What is Henry's mean score?**

Use the definition to find Henry's mean score.

$$\text{mean} = \frac{\text{sum of the data}}{\text{number of data items}}$$

$$= \frac{5+2+6+3+7+1}{6}$$

$$= \frac{24}{6}$$

$$= 4$$

So, Henry's mean score is 4.

Exercises

Find the mean for each set of data.

1. Weekly allowances: \$3, \$5, \$4, \$0, \$2, \$4 \$3
2. Number of siblings: 2, 1, 3, 0, 1, 3, 4 2
3. Number of songs on a CD: 9, 10, 14, 12, 15, 13, 11 12
4. Test scores: 87, 90, 84, 93, 86 88

Concepts and Skills

Concepts and Skills Bank

18 Mean

Lesson Planner

Objective

I will determine the mean of a set of data.

Vocabulary

mean

Activate Prior Knowledge

Build knowledge of the word "mean."

- Tell students that today they will learn the definition of the word "mean." Ask students to share their thoughts about its meaning.
- If students do not know the mathematical definition of mean, explain that it has the same meaning as the word "average." A student's grades in a particular subject are usually averaged to determine his/her final grade.

Using student page R75.

- Have students suggest different types of numerical data, such as ages, test scores, allowance earned, etc. Inform students that a group of numbers is always needed when finding the mean or average.
- Model the formula for finding the mean of a data set. For example: "Here are the life spans of different animals: camel– 50 years, prairie dog– 10 years, bottlenose dolphin– 20 years, hippopotamus– 45 years, and African grey parrot– 50 years. What is the average life span of these animals?" 35 years
- Ask students to study the example about miniature golf on page R75. Change the score of 7 to a score of 1 and ask students to work with a partner to refigure the mean. 3 If time allows, challenge students to use the original scores on page R75, except they are to change the score of 2 to a different score to arrive at a mean of 5. change the score of 2 to 8

Using the Exercises

Exercises 1–4 Inform students that 0 counts as a data point and should be included in the calculations used to determine mean. Advise students to double check their answers to each exercise to ensure they are correct.

Assess and Close

On Average . . . Pose the following problem to students: "Mr. Walsh gave a test, and his students received the following scores: 84, 70, 95, 91, 68, 97, 80, 84, and 96. He gave a homework pass to each student who scored higher than the class's mean score. How many students received a homework pass?" 4 students After students solve the problem on a piece of notebook paper, ask them to explain, in words, the steps they took to solve the problem.

Concepts and Skills Bank

19 Probability and Fractions

Lesson Planner

Objective

I will use a fraction to describe the favorable outcome of an event.

Vocabulary

favorable outcome

Materials: sticky notes (1 per student), index cards (1 per every 2 students), blank paper (1 piece per student), compasses

Activate Prior Knowledge

Expand students' knowledge of probability by relating it to fractions.

- Pass out a sticky note to each student. Tell the class to look around the room to find something that can be expressed in a fraction, like 10 out of 19 students, or $\frac{10}{19}$, are girls.
- Invite volunteers to come to the board, one at a time, to post their fractions. Either have students tell what their fractions represent, or give the class three guesses before they are told the fraction's meaning.

Using student page R76.

- Begin by discussing the probability of a coin landing heads-down after a toss. $\frac{1}{2}$ or 1 out of 2 possible outcomes Next, discuss the probability of rolling either a 1 or 4 when using a 0-5 number cube. $\frac{2}{6}$ or 2 chances out of 6 possible outcomes
- Ask students to work with a partner to study the example on page R76. Have each pair of students develop a probability question about the spinner on an index card. Collect the cards and ask the class as many questions as time allows.

Concepts and Skills

Probability and Fractions

You have already used words to describe probability. You can also use a fraction to describe the probability of a desirable result, called a **favorable outcome**.

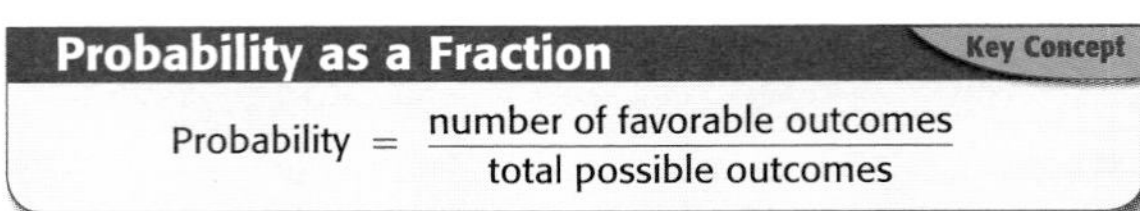

Probability as a Fraction — Key Concept

$$\text{Probability} = \frac{\text{number of favorable outcomes}}{\text{total possible outcomes}}$$

EXAMPLE Find Probability

1 **Use words and a fraction to describe the probability of spinning a star.**

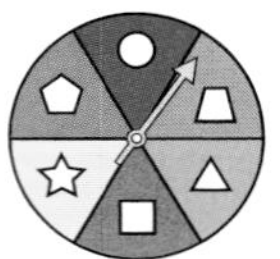

One out of six of the shapes is a star.

$$\text{Probability} = \frac{\text{number of favorable outcomes}}{\text{total possible outcomes}}$$

$$= \frac{\text{number of stars}}{\text{total number of shapes}}$$

$$= \frac{1}{6}$$

So, the probability of spinning a star is 1 out of 6, or $\frac{1}{6}$.

Exercises

The spinner is spun. Use words and a fraction to describe the probability of each outcome.

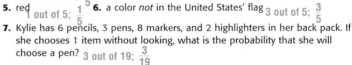

1. yellow 1 out of 5; $\frac{1}{5}$
2. green or blue 2 out of 5; $\frac{2}{5}$
3. white 0 out of 5; $\frac{0}{5}$
4. *not* green 4 out of 5; $\frac{4}{5}$
5. red 1 out of 5; $\frac{1}{5}$
6. a color *not* in the United States' flag 3 out of 5; $\frac{3}{5}$
7. Kylie has 6 pencils, 3 pens, 8 markers, and 2 highlighters in her back pack. If she chooses 1 item without looking, what is the probability that she will choose a pen? 3 out of 19; $\frac{3}{19}$

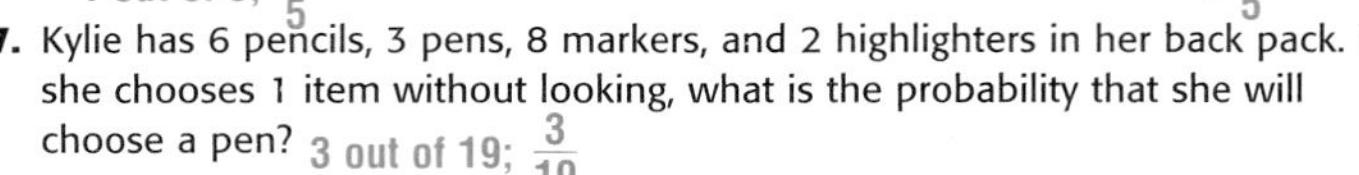

R76 Concepts and Skills Bank

Using the Exercises

Exercises 1–7 Explain to students that using words to describe probability means writing "4 out of 7" for the fraction $\frac{4}{7}$. Also, let students know that when determining the probability of one event or another, as in Exercise 2, the probabilities must be added together. For example, the probability of spinning yellow or green or red is 3 out of 7, or $\frac{3}{7}$.

Assess and Close

Super Spinners Tell students they have to design spinners for board games. They will have to listen carefully to the directions to create two different spinners on their pieces of paper. Have students fold a piece of blank paper in half and then unfold it to reveal two regions. Provide students with compasses to aid them in drawing the spinners. Each spinner will have 8 sections. In the first box, draw a spinner containing numbers upon which the probability of spinning an even number is $\frac{6}{8}$. In the second box, design a spinner containing letters of the alphabet upon which the probability of spinning a vowel is $\frac{2}{8}$.

Photo Credits

Unless otherwise credited, all currency courtesy of the US Mint. **v** Thomas Barwick/Getty Images; **vi** Doug Martin; **vii** (br)courtesy Dinah Zike; (others)Doug Martin; **x–xi** Isidor Stankov/iStockphoto; **xii–xiii** Creatas/SuperStock; **xiv–xv** Kevin Schafer/zefa/CORBIS; **xvi–xvii** Daniel A. Bedell/Animals Animals; **xviii–xix** Brand X/SuperStock; **xx–xxi** CORBIS; **xxii–xxiii** Keren Su/Getty Images; **xxiv–xxv** David Muench/CORBIS; **xxvii** The McGraw-Hill Companies; **xxviii** Tim Fuller; **xxix** Ed-Imaging; **1** Thinkstock/CORBIS; **2** Carl Heilman II/Wild Visions, Inc.; **3** Philip Scalia/Alamy Images; **4** David A. Northcott/CORBIS; **5** (t)Stephen J. Krasemann/Photo Researchers, Inc.; (b)Jeremy Woodhouse/Getty Images; **6** Eduardo Garcia/Getty Images; **7** Siede Preis/Getty Images; **8** David R. Frazier/PhotoEdit; **9** Panoramic Images/Getty Images; **10** Janel Cherry; **11** (l to r, t to b)Colin Young-Wolff; Spencer Grant; Dennis MacDonald; David Frazier/CORBIS; Walter Bibikow/CORBIS; **12** Getty Images; **13** Tom Grill/CORBIS; **14–15** Isidor Stankov/iStockphoto; **19** Elizabeth DeLaney/Index Stock Imagery; **20** Ed-Imaging; **23** Claver Carroll/Jupiterimages; **24** (t)Brand X/SuperStock; (b)Pixtal/SuperStock; **26** Paul Seheult/Eye Ubiquitous/CORBIS; **28** Robert E Daemmrich/Getty Images; **32** (l)Ingram Publishing/Alamy Images; (r)G.K. Vikki Hart/Getty Images; **35** Ed-Imaging; **36** (t)Lon C. Diehl/PhotoEdit; (b)Matthias Kulka/CORBIS; **39** (l)Ed-Imaging; (r)Ryan McVay/Getty Images; **40** Ed-Imaging; **42** (inset) J.Berndes/A.B./Zefa/CORBIS; **42–43** (bkgd)Stuart Westmorland/Getty Images; (inset)J.Berndes/A.B./Zefa/CORBIS; **52–53** The McGraw-Hill Companies; **54** (l)CORBIS; (r)C Squared Studios/Getty Images; **57** Ed-Imaging; **58** (t)Image Source/Jupiterimages; (b)Index Stock Imagery; **60** Ralf-Finn Hestoft/CORBIS; **62** Gary Rhijnsburger/Masterfile; **65** (t)Brand X Pictures/Alamy Images; (b)2006 Photos To Go/Index Open; **66** (l)CORBIS; (2)Ryan McVay/Getty Images; **70** Ed-Imaging; **73** CORBIS; **74** Raymond Forbes/AgeFotostock; **75–76** Ed-Imaging; **77** (t)Photodisc/Getty Images; (b)Getty Images; **78–79** (bkgd)Jeff Rotman/Getty Images; **79** (cr)Paul Springett/Alamy Images; **81** C Squared Studios/Getty Images; **82** (cr)CORBIS; (others)Ed-Imaging; **83** CORBIS; **92–93** Kwame Zikomo/SuperStock; **96** G.K. Vikki Hart/Getty Images; **98** Creatas/SuperStock; **101** Ed-Imaging; **102** Oliver Benn/Royal Philharmonic Orchestra; **103** (l)C Squared Studios/Getty Images; (br)PhotoLink/Getty Images; **104** Darren Bennett/Animals Animals; **115 through 118** Ed-imaging; **119** (br)Ryan McVay/Getty Images; (others)The McGraw-Hill Companies; **120** Stock Disc/Getty Images; **120–121** Tony Craddock/Getty Images; **124** David Young-Wolff/PhotoEdit; **126** Getty Images; **134** CORBIS; **139** (r)Jupiterimages; (others)Stockdisc/PunchStock; **142–143** Denis Scot/CORBIS; **147** The McGraw-Hill Companies; **149** Daniel Dempster Photography/Alamy Images; **151** C Squared Studios/Getty Images; **152** BananaStock/Alamy Images; **154** Lon C. Diehl/PhotoEdit; **160** Getty Images; **162** (cr)Stockdisc/PunchStock; (r)Brian Hagiwara/PictureArts/CORBIS; **164** (l to r)Bettmann/CORBIS; John Van Hasselt/CORBIS Sygma; Webster & Stevens Collection/Museum of History and Industry, Seattle/CORBIS; **164–165** (bkgd)Tracy Hebden/Alamy Images; **165** (l)SuperStock; (r)Rachel Epstein/PhotoEdit; **166** Tetra Images/Alamy Images; **167** D. Hurst/Alamy Images; **168** Kevin Schafer/zefa/CORBIS; **170** David Young-Wolff/PhotoEdit; **172** Ed-Imaging; **174–175** Ed-Imaging; **176** Dennis Macdonald/PhotoEdit; **177** Mark Richards/PhotoEdit; **178** StockTrek/Getty Images; **179** Ed-Imaging; **181** (leaf)Getty Images; (others)The McGraw-Hill Companies; **190–191** Digital Vision/PunchStock; **193** Don Smetzer/PhotoEdit; **198** Stockdisc/Jupiter Images/Getty Images; **200** (l)Ed-Imaging; (r)William Howard/Getty Images; **202** Ed-Imaging; **211** G.K. Vikki Hart/Getty Images; **212–213** (bkgd)Roine Magnusson/Getty Images; **213** Joe McDonald/CORBIS; **214** Jim Cummins/CORBIS; **215** Getty Images; **216** Shaun Cunningham/Alamy; **217 218** Ed-Imaging; **220** Michael Newman/PhotoEdit; **226** Getty Images; **229** (l)C Squared Studios/Getty Images; (r)The McGraw-Hill Companies; **234–235** Denis Scott/CORBIS; **237** Jurgen Freund/JACANA/HOA-QUI/ImageState; **238** George Hall/CORBIS; **239** CORBIS; **240** (tr)C Squared Studios/Getty Images; (tl)G.K. Vikki Hart/Getty Images; **242** Ren Long/AP Images; **245 through 250** Ed-Imaging; **252** Richard Hutchings/PhotoEdit; **254** Age Fotostock/SuperStock; **255** Ed-Imaging; **256** Daniel A. Bedell/Animals Animals; **256–257** (bkgd)David Tipling/Lonely Planet Images; **258** Robin Lynne/Getty Images; **259** AgeFotostock/SuperStock; **261** (l)Jack Hollingsworth/Getty Images; (r)Ed-Imaging; **270–271** David Young-Wolff/PhotoEdit; **273** Cooperphoto/CORBIS; **275** Robert Lubeck/Animals Animals; **276** G.K. & Vikki Hart/Getty Images; **278** Colin Keates/Getty Images; **280** CORBIS; **284** Getty Images; **285** (l)Ryan McVay/Getty Images; (r)Michael Houghton/StudiOhio; **286** C Squared Studios/Getty Images; **288** Getty Images; **290** (l, r)Ed-Imaging; (t)Getty Images; **292–293** JUPITERIMAGES/Thinkstock/Alamy Images; **294** BananaStock/Jupiterimages; **296** Mark Newman/Photo Researchers, Inc.; **297** Christian Petersen/Getty Images; **299** Ed-Imaging; **308–309** Dennis MacDonald; **311** Ed-Imaging; **313** Craig Lovell/CORBIS; **315** (l to r, t to b)GK & Vikki Hart/Getty Images; Patti Murray/Animals Animals; Brand X/Jupiter Images; Ed-Imaging; **321** Ryan McVay/Getty Images; **323** Stockbyte/Getty Images; **324** David Muench/CORBIS; **326** CORBIS; **327** Tony Freeman/PhotoEdit; **328** ThinkStock/Wonderfile; **329 330** Ed-Imaging; **334** Brand X/SuperStock; **336** CORBIS; **339** Ed-Imaging; **340** Mauritius/SuperStock; **342** SuperStock, Inc./SuperStock; **343** Sergio Pitamitz/Robert Harding World Imagery/CORBIS; **348** (l)G.K. Vikki Hart/Getty Images; (r)Getty Images; **352** C Squared Studios/Getty Images; **356–357** Masterfile; **358** Getty Images; **359** (t)GK Hart/Vikki Hart/Getty Images; (b)Thomas Northcut/Getty Images; **360** The McGraw-Hill Companies; **361** (l)C Squared Studios/Getty Images; (tl)Brand X Pictures/Getty Images; (tr)Stockdisc/PunchStock; **362** (t)Getty Images; (c)CORBIS; (b)Comstock Images/Alamy Images; (tr)S. Wanke/PhotoLink/Getty Images; **363** (l)Davies and Starr; (r)Getty Images; **364** (l)C Squared Studios/Getty Images; (r)Ed-Imaging; (t)Ryan McVay/Getty Images; (b)Bridgeman-Giraudon/Art Resource, NY; **365** Ed-Imaging; **370** The McGraw-Hill Companies; **371** Photos.com/Jupiterimages; **372** David Young-Wolff/PhotoEdit; **373** Lawrence Manning/CORBIS; **376** Werner H. Mueller/CORBIS; **377** (l to r, t to b)Alan King/Alamy Images; Stockbyte/Getty Images; Image Source/Alamy Images; Creatas/SuperStock; Purestock/Jupiterimages; Peter Miller/eStock Photo; **378** (l to r, t to b)Jorg Greuel/Getty Images; Burke/Triolo/Brand X Pictures/Jupiterimages; Thomas Northcut/Getty Images; DK Limited/CORBIS; Purestock/Alamy Images; **379 380** Ed-Imaging; **382–383** (bkgd)Visions of America, LLC/Alamy Images; (inset)Mary Ann Sullivan/Bluffton University; (inset)Visions of America, LCC/Alamy Images; **385** Jupiterimages; **392–393** Lawrence Manning/CORBIS; **396** Stockbyte/SuperStock; **399** (l)The McGraw-Hill Companies; (c)David Young-Wolff; (r)Tony Arruza/CORBIS; **400** CORBIS; **402** (tc)Brand X/ImageState; (c)C Squared Studios/Getty Images; (cr)Getty Images; **404** Rob Gage/Getty Images; **407** Getty Images; **409** Photos.com/Jupiterimages; **416 417** Getty Images; **419** Photos.com/Jupiterimages; **420** (cl)Ralph A. Clevenger/CORBIS; (cr, bl)Ryan McVay/Getty Images; (br)Ed-Imaging; **422** Darrell Gulin/CORBIS; **423** Comstock/Alamy Images; **424** Gallo Images/Getty Images; **425** Ed-Imaging; **426–427** (bkgd)The McGraw-Hill Companies; **427** (l to r)SuperStock; The McGraw-Hill Companies; CREATAS; John Pitcher; **430** Getty Images; **436–437** Gary Gerovac/Masterfile; **438** (l)Design Pics Inc./Alamy Images; (r)Creatas Images/Jupiterimages; **439** PhotoLink/Getty Images; **440** 2006 Photos to Go/Index Open; **441** (l to r, t to b)Chris Newbert/Minden Pictures; C Squared Studios/Getty Images; The McGraw-Hill Companies; Jupiterimages; **442** (l to r, t to b)GK Hart/Vikki Hart/Getty Images; Siede Preis/Getty Images; C Squared Studios/Getty Images; The McGraw-Hill Companies; C Squared Studios/Getty Images; **443** (l to r, t to b)Stockdisc/PunchStock; G.K. Vikki Hart/Getty Images; Ken Cavanaugh/The McGraw-Hill Companies; Siede Preis/Getty Images; Image Ideas Inc./Index Stock; **444** STACY GOLD/National Geographic Society Images; **446** C Squared Studios/Getty Images; **447** Getty Images; **449** Jupiterimages; **450** (l to r, t to b)D. Hurst/Alamy Images; Jupiterimages; Michael Grimm; D. Hurst/Alamy Images; **451** (l to r, t to b)Jeffrey Coolidge/CORBIS; Hans Christoph Kappel/npl/Minden Pictures; W.A.N.T. PHOTOGRAPHY/Animals Animals; Comstock Images; The McGraw-Hill Companies; **452** (l to r, t to b)The McGraw-Hill Companies; David Young-Wolff/Photo Edit; Getty Images; Lon C. Diehl/Photo Edit; CORBIS; **453** (tl, b)Getty Images; (tr)Photosindia.com/SuperStock; (c)Jupiterimages; **454** (inset)James Hackett/eStock Photo; **454–455** (bkgd)CORBIS; **455** CORBIS; **458** Michael Freeman/CORBIS; **459** (l)Getty Images; (r)The McGraw-Hill Companies; **463–466** Ed-Imaging; **467** (t)Getty Images; (b)AgeFotostock/SuperStock; **471** Ed-Imaging; **473** (tl)Getty Images; (tr)Stockbyte/PictureQuest; (b)C Squared Studios/Getty Images; **475** (tl)Getty Images; (tr)Creatas/PunchStock; (b)CORBIS; **479** (t)C Squared Studios/Getty Images; (cl)USDA Natural Resources Convservation Service; (b)Joe Polillo/The McGraw-Hill Companies; **484** Getty Images; **483–484** (bkgd)Keren Su; (inset)Getty Images; **485** Ed-Imaging; **486** (polish)Lawrence Manning/CORBIS; (others)Ed-Imaging; (fish)GK Hart/Vikki Hart/The Image Bank/Getty Images; **487** (l to r, t to b)Burke/Triolo Productions/Jupiterimages; Didier Robcis/CORBIS; 2006 Photos to Go; Photos.com/Jupiterimages; CORBIS; David Young-Wolff/

Photo Credits

PhotoEdit; Colin Young-Wolff/PhotoEdit; **488** (l to r, t to b)Jeff Greenberg/PhotoEdit; Jupiterimages; Burke/Triolo/Jupiterimages; The McGraw-Hill Companies; Burke/Triolo Productions/Brand X/CORBIS; Spencer Grant/PhotoEdit; Getty Images; **489** The McGraw-Hill Companies; **490** Ed-Imaging; **492** (t)Amon/PhotoCuisine/CORBIS; (bl)Michael Newman/PhotoEdit; (br)Ed-Imaging; **493** (t)Comstock/Jupiterimages; (c)Getty Images; (bl)Dynamic Graphics Value/SuperStock; (bc)Lawrence Manning CORBIS; (br)Elizabeth Whiting & Associates/CORBIS; **494** (l to r, t to b)Joson/zefa/CORBIS; David Young-Wolff/PhotoEdit; Lawrence Manning CORBIS; The McGraw-Hill Companies; Andy Crawford; DK Limited/CORBIS; **495** (l)Getty Images; (r)Andrea Rugg/Beateworks/CORBIS; **496** (t)Lew Robertson/Jupiterimages; (c, b)Ed-Imaging; **498** (br)Rachel Epstein/Photo Edit; (c, cl)Getty Images; (cr)Paul Gapper/worldphotos.org/Alamy Images; Caren Alpert/Jupiterimages; Rachel Epstein/Photo Edit; **499** (l to r, t to b)Getty Images; C Squared Studios/Getty Images; Thinkstock/Alamy Images; PunchStock; CORBIS/Jupiterimages; **500** (l to r, t to b)Getty Images; CORBIS; Getty Images; David Stares/Alamy Images; G.K. Vikki Hart/Getty Images; Jeffrey Coolidge/CORBIS; AgeFotostock/SuperStock; **501** (l to r, t to b)Michael Matisse/Getty Images; Photodisc/Getty Images; Envision/CORBIS; Russell Illig/Getty Images; G.K. & Vikki Hart/Getty Images; **502** Photodisc/Getty Images; **503** G.K. & Vikki Hart/Getty Images; **504** Envision/CORBIS; **506** Design Pics/FotoSearch; **507** (l to r, t to b) C Squared Studios/Getty Images; G.K. & Vikki Hart/Getty Images; 2006 Photos to Go; **508** Ed-Imaging; **509** (l to r, t to b)Big Cheese Photo/Jupiterimages; Ron Chapple/Jupiterimages; Photodisc/Getty Images; CORBIS; **510** (l to r, t to b)Monotype, LLC; Dave Mager/Index Stock Imagery; C Squared Studios/Getty Images; ThinkStock LLC; Image Farm Inc./Alamy Images; Charlie Roy/Jupiterimages; C Squared Studios/Getty Images; **511** Ed-Imaging; **512** The McGraw-Hill Companies; **515** (l)Stockdisc/PunchStock; (r)Photos.com/Jupiterimages; **516** (l)Mark Cassino/SuperStock; (c)Iconotec/Alamy Images; **516–517** (bkgd)Renee Morris/Alamy Images; (r)Jupiter Images; **518** Ed-Imaging; **519 520** 2006 Photos To Go; **523** (l to r, t to b)Ed-Imaging; G.K. Vikki Hart/Getty Images; G.K. Vikki Hart/Getty Images; G.K. & Vikki Hart/Getty Images; **525** (l)Masterfile; (tr)Hirdes/f1online/Alamy Images; (cr)Mick Broughton/Alamy Images; (br)Jupiterimages; **526** (l to r, t to b)Colin Young-Wolff/Photo Edit; Judith Collins/Alamy Images; Jan Tadeusz/Alamy Images; Purestock/Getty Images; Jeffrey Coolidge/Getty Images; Joe Schmelzer/Beateworks/CORBIS; **527** Rick Gayle Studio/CORBIS; **528** (l to r, t to b)Ed-Imaging; G.K. Vikki Hart/Getty Images; Getty Images; Ann Cutting/Jupiterimages; Siede Preis/Getty Images; **529** (l)Siede Preis/Getty Images; (r)Getty Images; **531** (l to r, t to b)The McGraw-Hill Companies; Brand X Pictures/Alamy Images; Jose Fuste Raga/CORBIS Brand X Pictures/Punchstock; Mitch Diamond/Index Stock Imagery; DARREN BENNETT/Animals Animals; **534–535** (inset)C Squared Studios/Getty Images; (bkgd)Siede Preis/Getty Images; **539** (cr)Photodisc/Getty Images; (r)C Squared Studios/Getty Images; **540** The McGraw-Hill Companies; **541** (l)Don Farrall/Getty Images; (c)Stockdisc/PunchStock; **542** Richard Wear/Design Pics/CORBIS; **543** (l)Ed-Imaging; (r)Getty Images; **544** Stockdisc/PunchStock; **545** (c)Ton Kinsbergen/Beateworks/CORBIS; (r)C Squared Studios/Getty Images; (others)Koopman/CORBIS; **551** (t)Getty Images; (b)Ed-imaging; **552** Ed-Imaging; **557** Getty Images; **558** (inset)Ed Taylor/Getty Images; **558–559** (bkgd)The McGraw-Hill Companies, Inc.; (inset)Ed Taylor/Getty Images; **563** (l)Punchstock; (r)Getty Images; **564** Ed-Imaging; **568** The McGraw-Hill Companies; **570** Photodisc/Getty Images; **574–575** CORBIS; **579** MedioImages/SuperStock; **582** David Muench/CORBIS; **583** Martin Harvey/CORBIS; **584** Scenics of America/PhotoLink/Getty Images; **585** (l)Ed-Imaging; (r)Getty Images; **586 594** Ed-imaging; **595** Michael Houghton/StudiOhio; **596** Greg Probst/CORBIS; **600–601** (bkgd)Digital Vision/Getty Images; (inset)Getty Images; **602** Stockdisc Classic/Alamy Images; **604** (l)Ed-Imaging; (r)Brad Wilson/Getty Images; **605** Ed-Imaging; **614–615** Steve Satushek; **617** Time & Life Pictures/Getty Images; **618** Sam Greenwood/NewSport/CORBIS; **621** Ed-Imaging; **623** Michael Houghton/StudiOhio; **624** Mauritius/SuperStock; **626** CORBIS; **627** G.K. Vikki Hart/Getty Images; **628** Ed-Imaging; **630** BigStockPhoto.com; **631** Deborah Meeks/SuperStock; **634** Getty Images; **635** The McGraw-Hill Companies; **636** Ed-Imaging; **638** Bettmann/CORBIS; **639** John Cancalosi/Peter Arnold, inc.; **641** (l)Image Source/Getty Images; (r)CORBIS; **642–643** (bkgd)Donald Miralle/Getty Images; **643** (l)Empics/SportsChrome; (r)Rob Tringali/SportsChrome; **LA0** Mark Steinmetz/Amanita Pictures; **LA1** Tim Fuller; **LA2** Walter Geiersperger/CORBIS; **LA3** PictureNet/CORBIS; **LA4** Comstock Images/Alamy Images; (r)C Squared Studios/Getty Images; **LA5** (t)The McGraw-Hill Companies; (bl)Ed-Imaging; (br)CORBIS; **LA6** Jeffrey L. Rotman/CORBIS; **LA7** PureStock/AGE fotostock; **LA8** Ryan McVay/Getty Images; **LA9** (t)The McGraw-Hill Companies; (b)Ed-imaging; **LA10** Tom Grill/CORBIS; **LA11** (t)StockTrek/Getty Images; (b)The McGraw-Hill Companies; **LA13** Getty Images; **LA14** Stockbyte; **LA15** (l)Comstock/Alamy Images; (b)D. Hurst/Alamy Images; **LA16** C Squared Studios/Getty Images; **LA18** Chev Wilkinson; **LA25** (l)The McGraw-Hill Companies; (r)2006 Photos To Go/Index Open; (c)Photolibrary; **P0** (t)Getty Images; (c)Punchstock; (b)Bob Daemmrich/PhotoEdit; **P1** (t)Tim Fuller; (b)2006 Photos To Go; **P2** (t)BananaStock/Alamy Images; (b)2006 Photos To Go/Index Open; **P4** (t)Food Image Source/O'Gara/Bissell/StockFood; (b)2006 Photos To Go/Index Open; **P5** Photos.com/Jupiterimages; **P6** Sindre Ellingsen/Alamy Images; **P7** Brand X Pictures/Alamy Images; **P8** (t)Laurie Rubin/Getty Images; (b)Getty Images; **P9** Photos.com/Jupiterimages; **R0** Ed-Imaging; **R9** McGraw-Hill Companies Inc; **R24** (l)gds/zefa/CORBIS; (c)Nancy R. Cohen/Getty Images; (r)Burke/Triolo Productions/Getty Images; **R28** (tl)The McGraw-Hill Companies; (tr)Getty Images; (bl)D. Hurst/Alamy; (br)C Squared Studios/Getty Images; **R29** (tr)C Squared Studios/Getty Images; (bl)C Squared Studios/Getty Images; (br)Photos.com/Jupiterimages; **R30** (l to r, t to b)The McGraw-Hill Companies; Ingram Publishing/Superstock; The McGraw-Hill Companies; CORBIS; Jupiterimages; **R31** (l to r, t to b) Jupiterimages; Photos.com/Jupiterimages; Photos.com/Jupiterimages; Photos.com/Jupiterimages; Stockdisc/PunchStock; Jeremy Woodhouse/Getty Images; Photos.com/Jupiterimages; Image Source/Jupitierimages; **R32** (l to r, t to b)Getty Images; G.K. & Vikki Hart/Getty Images; Jupiterimages; **R39 R41** Getty Images; **R43** Ed-Imaging; **R64** (l)The McGraw-Hill Companies; (r)Masterfile

McGraw-Hill would like to acknowledge the artists and agencies who contributed to illustrating this program: **Cover** Mick McGinty represented by Mendola Artists; Argosy Publishing; Gary Ciccarelli, Keith Batcheller, Jean-pascal Donnot represented by AA Reps. Inc; Dick Gage, Mark Collins, Richard Carbajal represented by Deborah Wolfe Ltd.

Teacher Edition Photo Credits

Unless otherwise credited, all currency courtesy of the US Mint.

T3 LWA-JDC/CORBIS; **T8** Bloom Works Inc./Alamy Images; **T12** CORBIS; **T13** Bananastock/Punchstock; **T14** Blend Images/Alamy Images; **14H** Ed-Imaging; **17 through 36** Eclipse Studios; **52G 52H** Ed-Imaging; **55 through 58** Eclipse Studios; **58B** Ed-Imaging; **62 through 80** Eclipse Studios; **92I** Ed-Imaging; **98 through 128** Eclipse Studios; **142H** Ilene MacDonald/Alamy Images; **147 through 176** Eclipse Studios; **190H** Ed-Imaging; **193 through 220** Eclipse Studios; **234G** Ed-Imaging; **237 through 246** Eclipse Studios; **270G** Ed-Imaging; **270H** (t)Mike Parry/Minden Pictures, (b)Ed-Imaging; **273 through 288** Eclipse Studios; **308G** Ed-Imaging; **316 336** Eclipse Studios; **336B** Ed-Imaging; **342** Eclipse Studios; **342B** Ed-Imaging; **356G** Ed-Imaging; **356H** Daniel Templeton/Alamy Images; **359 362** Eclipse Studios; **363** Ingram Publishing/SuperStock; **366 372** Eclipse Studios; **377** Getty Images; **392H** (t)Ed-Imaging, (b)Steve Kaufman/CORBIS; **395 through 422** Eclipse Studios; **436I** (t)Ed-Imaging, (b)Don S. Montgomery/CORBIS; **436J** Ed-Imaging; **440A** Nick Koudis/Getty Images; **441 444** Eclipse Studios; **444A** The McGraw-Hill Companies; **446A** Eclipse Studios; **450B** Ed-Imaging; **456** Eclipse Studios; **456A** The McGraw-Hill Companies; **460** Eclipse Studios; **482I** 2006 Photos to Go/Index Open; **482J** (t)Peter Arnold/Alamy Images, (c)Getty Images, (b)Tetra Images/Alamy Images; **498A** (l)Christian Darkin/Alamy Images, (r)Jupiterimages; **498B** G.K. Vikki Hart/Getty Images; **502A** (l)Eclipse Studios, (r)G.K. & Vikki Hart/Getty Images; **504** Eclipse Studios; **510** G.K. Vikki Hart/Getty Images; **512** Eclipse Studios; **512A** (t)The McGraw-Hill Companies, (b)CORBIS; **534H** Ed-Imaging; **544 554** Eclipse Studios; **574G** Michael Houghton/StudiOhio; **574H** Ed-Imaging; **579 582** Eclipse Studios; **586B** Ed-Imaging; **588 through 602** Eclipse Studios; **614G 614H** Ed-Imaging; **617 622** Eclipse Studios; **622B** Michael Houghton/StudiOhio; **626** Eclipse Studios.

McGraw-Hill would like to acknowledge the artists and agencies who contributed to illustrating this program: **Cover** Mick McGinty represented by Mendola Artists.

Glossary/Glosario

Math Online A mathematics multilingual glossary is available at www.macmillanmh.com. The glossary includes the following languages.

Arabic	Cantonese	Korean	Tagalog
Bengali	English	Russian	Urdu
Brazilian Portuguese	Haitian Creole	Spanish	Vietnamese
	Hmong		

Cómo usar el glosario en español:

1. Busca el término en inglés que desees encontrar.
2. El término en español, junto con la definición, se encuentran en la columna de la derecha.

A

English

acute angle (p. 369) An *angle* with a measure greater than 0° and less than 90°.

acute triangle (p. 372) A *triangle* with all three *angles* less than 90°.

addend (p. 64) Any numbers being added together.

add (adding, addition) (p. 52) An operation on two or more *addends* that results in a *sum*.

$9 + 3 = 12$

algebra (p. 193) A branch of mathematics that uses symbols, usually letters, to explore relationships between quantities.

angle (p. 368) A figure that is formed by two *rays* with the same *endpoint*.

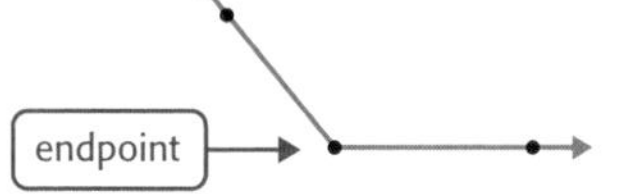

Español

ángulo agudo Un *ángulo* que mide más de 0° y menos de 90°.

triángulo acutángulo Un *triángulo* cuyos tres *ángulos* miden menos de 90°.

sumando Cualquier número que se suma a otro.

suma (sumar, adición) Operación en dos o más *sumandos* que resulta en una *suma*.

$9 + 3 = 12$

álgebra Rama de las matemáticas que usa símbolos, generalmente letras, para explorar relaciones entre cantidades.

ángulo Figura formada por dos *rayos* con el mismo *extremo*.

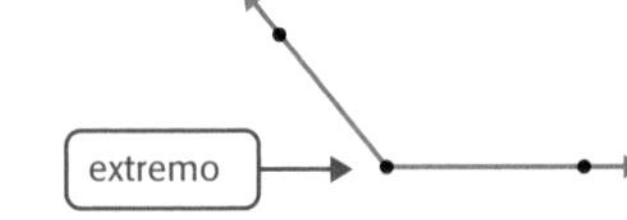

area (p. 460) The number of *square units* needed to cover the inside of a region or plane figure without any overlap.

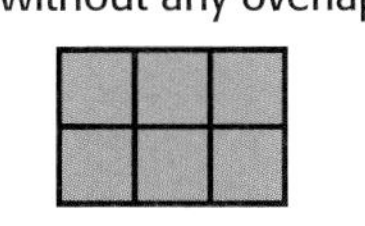

area = 6 square units

área El número de *unidades cuadradas* necesarias para cubrir el interior de una región o figura plana sin traslapes.

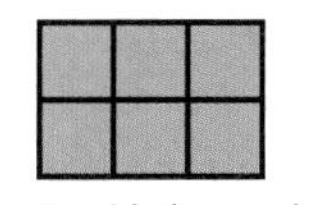

área = 6 unidades cuadradas

Associative Property of Addition (p. 55) The property states that the grouping of the *addends* does not change the *sum*.

$(4 + 5) + 2 = 4 + (5 + 2)$

propiedad asociativa de la suma Propiedad que establece que la agrupación de los *sumandos* no altera la *suma*.

$(4 + 5) + 2 = 4 + (5 + 2)$

Associative Property of Multiplication (p. 150) The property that states that the grouping of the *factors* does not change the *product*.

$3 \times (6 \times 2) = (3 \times 6) \times 2$

propiedad asociativa de la multiplicación Propiedad que establece que la agrupación de los *factores* no altera el *producto*.

$3 \times (6 \times 2) = (3 \times 6) \times 2$

B

bar graph (p. 108) A graph that compares *data* by using bars of different lengths or heights to show the values.

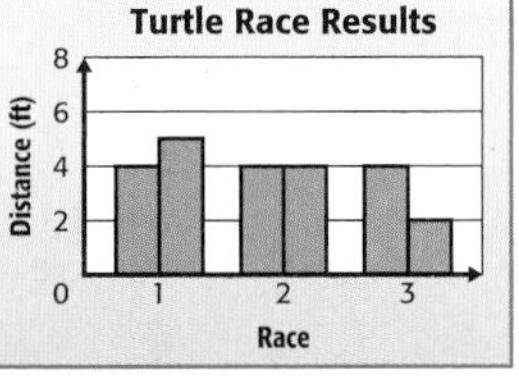

gráfica de barras Gráfica que compara los *datos* usando barras de distintas longitudes o alturas para mostrar los valores.

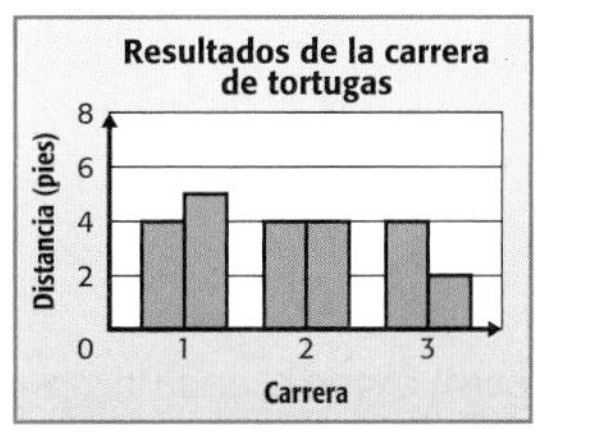

bilateral symmetry (p. 422) The property of a figure that allows it to be folded so the two halves match exactly.

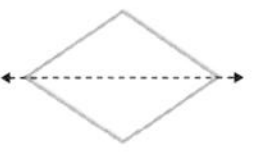

simetría bilateral Propiedad de una figura que le permite ser doblada de manera que las mitades se correspondan exactamente.

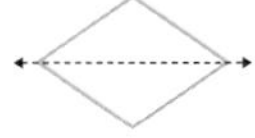

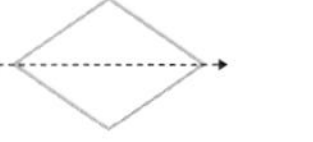

C

capacity (p. 485) The amount of liquid a container can hold.

capacidad Cantidad que puede contener un envase, medida en unidades de volumen.

circle (p. R64) A closed figure in which all points are the same distance from a fixed point, called the center.

círculo Figura cerrada en la cual todos los puntos equidistan de un punto fijo llamado centro.

Commutative Property of Addition (p. 55) The property that states that the order in which two numbers are added does not change the *sum*.

$12 + 15 = 15 + 12$

propiedad conmutativa de la suma Propiedad que establece que el orden en el cual se suman dos o más números no altera la *suma*.

$12 + 15 = 15 + 12$

Commutative Property of Multiplication (p. 150) The property that states that the order in which two numbers are multiplied does not change the *product*.

$7 \times 2 = 2 \times 7$

propiedad conmutativa de la multiplicación Propiedad que establece que el orden en el cual se multiplican dos o más números no altera el *producto*.

$7 \times 2 = 2 \times 7$

compatible numbers (p. 322) Numbers in a problem or related numbers that are easy to work with mentally.

720 and 90 are compatible numbers for division because $72 \div 9 = 8$.

números compatibles Números en un problema o números relacionados con los cuales es fácil trabajar mentalmente.

720 y 90 son números compatibles en la división porque $72 \div 9 = 8$.

cone (p. 359) A 3-dimensional figure with a curved surface, a circular base, and one *vertex*.

cono Figura tridimensional con una superficie curva, una base circular y un *vértice*.

congruent figures (p. 418) Two figures having the same size and the same shape.

figuras congruentes Dos figuras con la misma forma y el mismo tamaño.

coordinate (p. 406) One of two numbers in an *ordered pair*.

In (1, 5), the 1 is the number on the *x*-axis. The 5 is on the *y*-axis.

coordinate plane (p. 406) A graph that displays a set of points and gives the position of a point on a line.

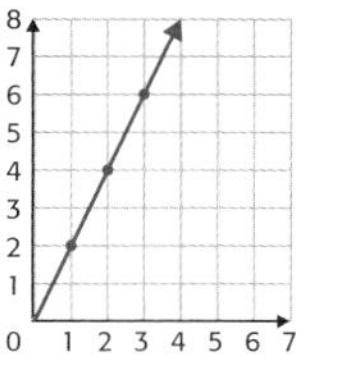

cube (p. 359) A 3-dimensional figure with six *congruent* square *faces*.

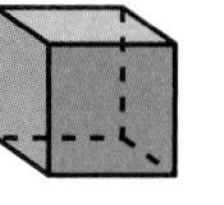

cylinder (p. 359) A 3-dimensional *figure* having two *parallel congruent* circular *bases* and a curved surface connecting the two *bases*.

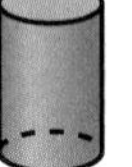

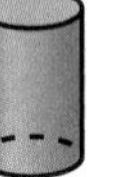

coordenada Uno de los dos números de un *par ordenado*.

(1, 5) El 1 es el número en el eje *x* y el 5 está en el eje *y*.

gráfica de coordenadas o cuadriculado Gráfica que representa un conjunto de puntos y da, en términos numéricos, la posición de un punto sobre una recta.

cubo Figura tridimensional con seis *caras* cuadradas *congruentes*.

cilindro Figura tridimensional que tiene dos bases circulares *paralelas* y *congruentes* y una superficie curva que las une.

D

data (p. 95) Numbers or symbols, sometimes collected from a *survey* or experiment, to show information. Datum is singular; data is plural.

datos Números o símbolos que muestran información, algunas veces reunidos de una *encuesta* o un experimento.

decimal (p. 579) A number that uses *place value*, numbers, and a *decimal point* to show part of a whole.

decimal Número con uno o más dígitos a la derecha del punto *decimal*, tales como 8.37 ó 0.05.

decimal equivalents (p. 596) Decimals that represent the same number.

0.3 and 0.30

decimal point (p. 579) A period separating the ones and the *tenths* in a decimal number.

0.8 OR $3.77

degrees (°) (p. 468) The units of measurement used to describe temperature.

denominator (p. 537) The bottom number in a *fraction*.

In $\frac{5}{6}$, 6 is the denominator.

digit (p. 17) A symbol used to write numbers. The ten digits are 0, 1, 2, 3, 4, 5, 6, 7, 8, and 9.

Distributive Property of Multiplication (p. 166) To multiply a *sum* by a number, multiply each *addend* by the number and add the *products*.

$4 \times (1 + 3) = (4 \times 1) + (4 \times 3)$

division (divide) (p. 142) An operation on two numbers in which the first number is split into the same number of equal groups as the second number.

dividend (p. 311) A number that is being divided.

$3\overline{)19}$ 19 is the dividend

divisor (p. 311) The number by which the *dividend* is being divided.

$3\overline{)19}$ 3 is the divisor

decimales equivalentes Decimales que representan el mismo número.

0.3 y 0.30

punto decimal Punto que separa las unidades de las *décimas* en un número decimal.

0.8 ó $3.77

grado (°) Unidad de temperatura.

denominador El número inferior en una *fracción*.

$\frac{5}{6}$ 6 es el denominador.

dígito Símbolo que se usa para escribir números. Los diez dígitos son 0, 1, 2, 3, 4, 5, 6, 7, 8 y 9.

propiedad distributiva de la multiplicación Para multiplicar una *suma* por un número, puedes multiplica cada *sumando* por el número y suma los *productos*.

$4 \times (1 + 3) = (4 \times 1) + (4 \times 3)$

división (dividir) Operación en dos números en que el primer número se separa en tantos grupos iguales como indica el segundo número.

dividendo El número que se divide.

$3\overline{)19}$ 19 es el dividendo

divisor El número entre el cual se divide el *dividendo*.

$3\overline{)19}$ 3 es el divisor

double bar graph (p. 113) A *bar graph* that compares two related groups of *data*.

E

edge (p. 359) The *line segment* where two *faces* of a *solid figure* meet.

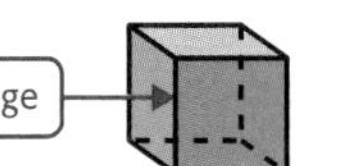

elapsed time (p. 520) The amount of time that has passed from beginning to end.

endpoint (p. 400) The point at either end of a *line segment* or the point at the beginning of a ray.

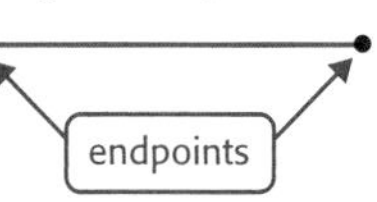

equally likely (p. 128) Having the same chance of occurring.

In a coin toss, you are equally likely to flip a head or a tail.

equation (p. 198) A sentence that contains an equals sign (=), showing that two *expressions* are equal.

gráfica de barras dobles *Gráfica de barras* que compara dos grupos de *datos* relacionados.

arista El *segmento de recta* donde concurren dos *caras* de una *figura sólida.*

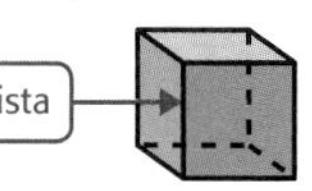

tiempo transcurrido Cantidad de tiempo que ha pasado entre el principio y el fin.

extremo El punto en cualquiera de los dos lados en que termina un *segmento de recta* o el punto al principio de un rayo.

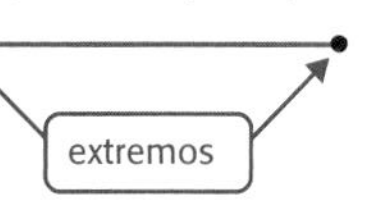

equiprobable Que tiene la misma posibilidad de ocurrir.

Al lanzar una moneda, es equiprobable que caiga cara o cruz.

ecuación Oración matemátia que contiene el signo de igualdad, =, el que indica que las dos *expresiones* son iguales.

equilateral triangle (p. 373) A *triangle* with three *congruent* sides.

equivalent fractions (p. 548) *Fractions* that represent the same number.

$$\frac{3}{4} = \frac{6}{8}$$

estimate (p. 58) A number close to an exact value. An estimate indicates *about* how much.

47 + 22 is about 50 + 20 or 70.

expanded form/expanded notation (p. 18) The representation of a number as a sum that shows the value of each digit.

536 is written as 500 + 30 + 6.

expression (p. 193) A combination of numbers, variables, and at least one operation.

F

face (p. 359) The flat part of a 3-dimensional figure.

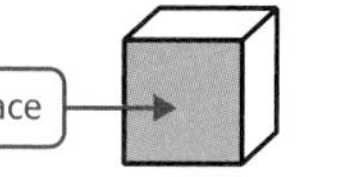

fact family (p. 147) A group of related facts using the same numbers.

$5 + 3 = 8$	$5 \times 3 = 15$
$3 + 5 = 8$	$3 \times 5 = 15$
$8 - 3 = 5$	$15 \div 3 = 5$
$8 - 5 = 3$	$15 \div 5 = 3$

factor (p. 176) A number that divides a whole number evenly. Also a number that is multiplied by another number.

triángulo equilátero *Triángulo* con tres lados *congruentes*.

fracciones equivalentes *Fracciones* que representan el mismo número.

$$\frac{3}{4} = \frac{6}{8}$$

estimación Número cercano a un valor exacto. Una estimación indica *aproximadamente* cuánto.

47 + 22 es aproximadamente 50 + 20; ó 70.

forma desarrollada/notación desarrollada Representación de un número como una suma que muestra el valor de cada dígito.

536 se escribe como 500 + 30 + 6.

expresión Combinación de números, variables y por lo menos una operación.

cara Parte llana de una figura tridimensional.

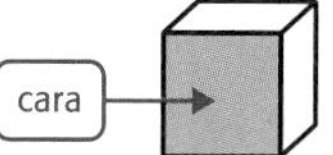

familia de operaciones Grupo de operaciones relacionadas que usan los mismos números.

$5 + 3 = 8$	$5 \times 3 = 15$
$3 + 5 = 8$	$3 \times 5 = 15$
$8 - 3 = 5$	$15 \div 3 = 5$
$8 - 5 = 3$	$15 \div 5 = 3$

factor Número que divide exactamente a otro número entero. También es un número multiplicado por otro número.

fraction (p. 537) A number that represents part of a whole or part of a set.

$\frac{1}{2}, \frac{1}{3}, \frac{1}{4}, \frac{3}{4}$

frequency table (p. 95) A table for organizing a set of *data* that shows the number of times each result has occurred.

function (p. 208) A relationship in which one number depends on another number.

function table (p. 208) A table of ordered pairs that is based on a rule.

H

hexagon (p. 362) A *polygon* with six sides and six *angles*.

hundredth (p. 580) A place value position. One of one hundred equal parts.

In the number 0.05, 5 is in the hundredths place.

I

Identity Property of Addition (p. 55) For any number, zero plus that number is the number.

$3 + 0 = 3$ or $0 + 3 = 3$

Identity Property of Multiplication (p. 150) If you multiply a number by 1, the product is the same as the given number.

$8 \times 1 = 8 = 1 \times 8$

fracción Número que representa parte de un todo o parte de un conjunto.

$\frac{1}{2}, \frac{1}{3}, \frac{1}{4}, \frac{3}{4}$

tabla de frecuencias Tabla para organizar un conjunto de *datos* que muestra el número de veces que ha ocurrido cada resultado.

función Relación en que una cantidad depende de otra cantidad.

tabla de funciones Tabla de pares ordenados que se basa en una regla.

hexágono *Polígono* con seis lados y seis *ángulos*.

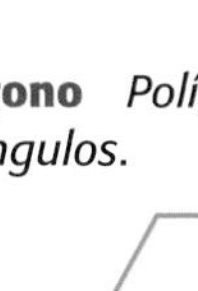

centésima Un valor de posición. Una parte de cien partes iguales.

En el número 4.57, 7 está en el lugar de las centésimas.

propiedad de identidad de la adición Para todo numero, cero más el numero es el número.

$3 + 0 = 3$ ó $0 + 3 = 3$

propiedad de identidad de la multiplicación Si multiplicas un número por 1, el producto es igual al número dado.

$8 \times 1 = 8 = 1 \times 8$

impossible (p. 128) An event that cannot happen. It has a probability of zero.

It is impossible to choose yellow.

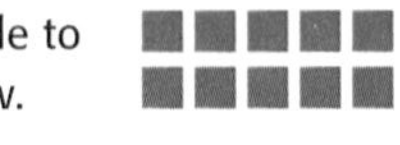

improper fraction (p. 560) A fraction with a *numerator* that is greater than or equal to the *denominator*.

$\frac{17}{3}$ or $\frac{5}{5}$

intersecting lines (p. 401) *Lines* that meet or cross at a point.

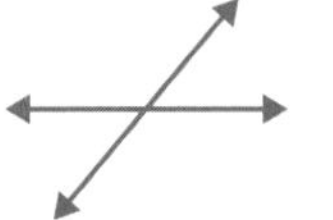

irregular figure (p. R66) A shape that is made up of two or more shapes.

is greater than > (p. 28) An inequality relationship showing that the number on the left of the symbol is greater than the number on the right.

$5 > 3$ 5 is greater than 3

is less than < (p. 28) The number on the left side of the symbol is smaller than the number on the right side.

$4 < 7$ 4 is less than 7

isosceles triangle (p. 373) A *triangle* with at least 2 sides of the same length.

imposible Un evento que no puede suceder, cuya probabilidad es cero.

fracción impropia Fracción con un *numerador* mayor que o igual al *denominador*.

$\frac{17}{3}$ ó $\frac{5}{5}$

rectas secantes *Rectas* que se intersecan o cruzan entre sí.

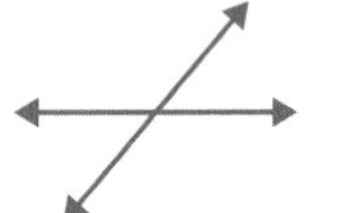

figura compleja Figura compuesta por dos o más formas.

es mayor que > Relación de desigualdad que muestra que el número a la izquierda del símbolo es mayor que el número a la derecha.

$5 > 3$ 5 es mayor que 3

es menor que < El número a la izquierda del símbolo es más pequeño que el número a la derecha.

$4 < 7$ 4 es menor que 7

triángulo isósceles Un *triángulo* que tiene por lo menos 2 lados del mismo largo.

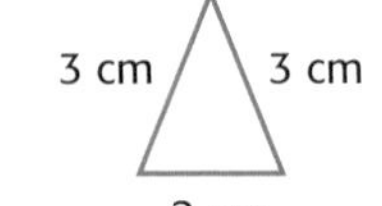

L

length (p. 441) The measurement of a line between two points.

likely (p. 128) An event that will probably happen.
It is likely you will choose a red tile.

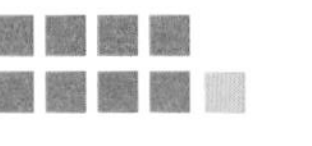

line (p. 400) A straight set of points that extend in opposite directions without ending.

line graph (p. R70) A graph that uses points connected by *line segments* to represent data.

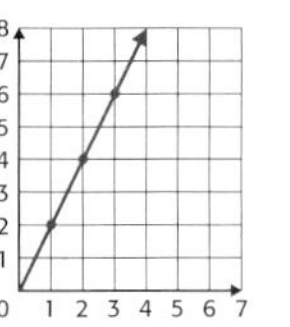

line of symmetry (p. 422) A *line* on which a figure can be folded so that its two halves match exactly.

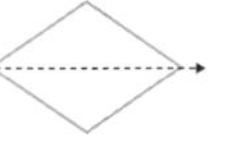

line plot (p. 104) A graph that uses columns of Xs above a *number line* to show frequency of data.

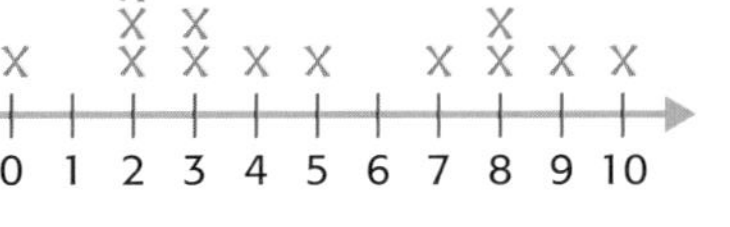

longitud Medida de la distancia entre dos puntos.

posible Un evento que probablemente sucederá
Es posible que elijas una baldosa rojo.

recta Conjunto de puntos dispuestos rectamente que se extienden en direcciones opuestas y sin fin.

gráfica lineal Gráfica que usa puntos unidos por *segmentos de recta* para representar datos.

eje de simetría *Recta* sobre la cual se puede doblar una figura de manera que sus mitades se correspondan exactamente.

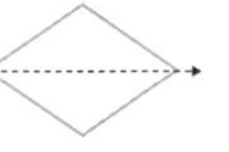

esquema lineal Gráfica que usa columnas de X sobre una *recta numérica* para representar frecuencias de datos.

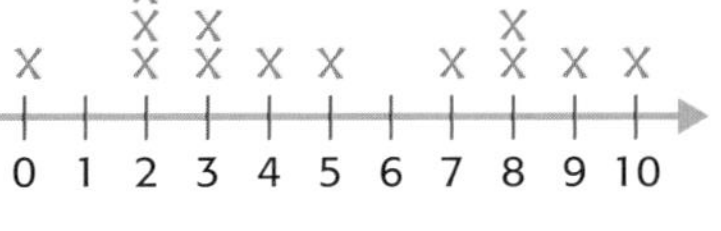

line segment (p. 400) A part of a *line* between two *endpoints*. The length of the line segment can be measured.

line symmetry (p. 422) A figure has *line symmetry* if it can be folded so that the two parts of the figure match, or are *congruent*.

M

median (p. 98) The middle number in a group of numbers arranged in numerical order.
The median of 3, 5, 6, 7, and 8 is 6.

minuend (p. 71) The first number in a subtraction sentence from which a second number is to be subtracted.

$8 - 3 = 5$

minuend, subtrahend, difference

mixed number (p. 560) A number that has a *whole number* part and a *fraction* part.

$6\frac{3}{4}$

mode (p. 98) The number(s) that occurs most often in a set of numbers.

7, 4, 7, 10, 7, and 2
The mode is 7.

multiple (p. 177) A multiple of a number is the *product* of that number and any whole number.
15 is a multiple of 5 because $3 \times 5 = 15$.

multiply (multiplication) (p. 142) An operation on two numbers to find their *product*. It can be thought of as repeated *addition*.

segmento de recta Parte de una *recta* entre dos *extremos*. La longitud de un segmento de recta se puede medir.

simetría lineal Una figura tiene *simetria lineal* si puede doblarse de modo que las dos partes de la figura correspondan o sean *congruentes*.

mediana El número central de un grupo de números ordenados numéricamente.
La mediana de 3, 5, 6, 7 y 8 es 6.

minuendo El primer número en un enunciado de sustracción del cual se restará un segundo número

$8 - 3 = 5$

minuendo, sustraendo, diferencia

número mixto Número compuesto por un *número entero* y una parte *fraccionaria*.

$6\frac{3}{4}$

moda Número o números que ocurre(n) con mayor frecuencia en un conjunto de números.

7, 4, 7, 10, 7 y 2
La moda es 7.

múltiplo Un múltiplo de un número es el *producto* de ese número y cualquier otro número entero.
15 es múltiplo de 5 porque $3 \times 5 = 15$.

multiplicar (multiplicación) Operación en dos números para calcular su *producto*. También se puede interpretar como una *adición* repetida.

N

net (p. 360) A flat pattern that can be folded to make a 3-dimensional figure.

red Patrón llano que se puede doblar para formar una figura tridimensional.

number line (p. 395) A line with numbers on it in order at regular intervals.

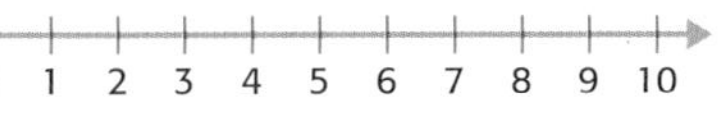

recta numérica Recta con números ordenadosa intervalos regulares.

0 1 2 3 4 5 6 7 8 9 10

numerator (p. 537) The number above the bar in a *fraction*; the part of the fraction that tells how many of the equal parts are being used.

numerador El número que está encima de la barra de *fracción*; la parte de la fracción que te indica cuántas partes iguales están siendo usadas.

O

obtuse angle (p. 369) An *angle* that measures greater than 90° but less than 180°.

ángulo obtuso *Ángulo* que mide más de 90° pero menos de 180°.

obtuse triangle (p. 372) A *triangle* with one *obtuse angle*.

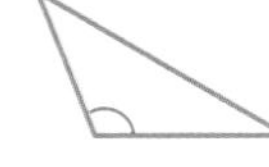
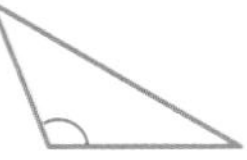

triángulo obtusángulo *Triángulo* con un *ángulo obtuso*.

octagon (p. 362) A *polygon* with 8 sides.

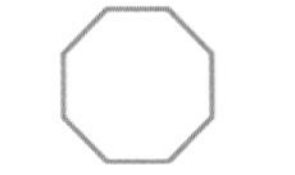
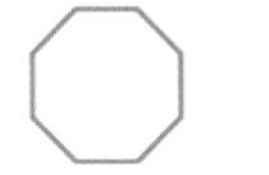

octágono *Polígono* de 8 lados.

operation (p. 52) A mathematical process such as addition, subtraction, multiplication, or division.

operación Proceso matemático como la suma (+), la resta (−), la multiplicación (×) o la división (÷).

order of operations (p. R56) Rules that tell what order to follow use in evaluating an expression:
(1) Do the operations in parentheses first.
(2) Multiply and divide in order from left to right.
(3) Add and subtract in order from left to right.

orden de las operaciones Reglas que te indican qué orden seguir cuando evalúas una expresión:
(1) Evalúa primero las operaciones dentro de los paréntesis ( ).
(2) Multiplica o divide en orden de izquierda a derecha.
(3) Suma o resta en orden de izquierda a derecha.

ordered pair (p. 406) A pair of numbers that are the *coordinates* of a point in a coordinate plane.

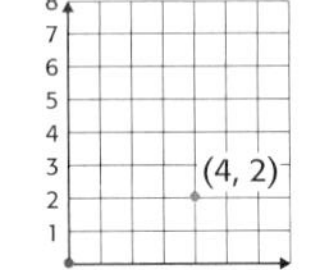

par ordenado Par de números que son las *coordenadas* de un punto en un plano de coordenadas.

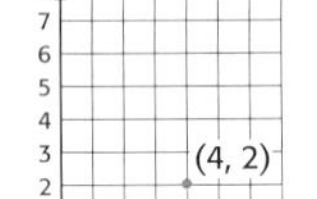

origin (p. 406) The point (0, 0) on a *coordinate plane* where the vertical axis meets the horizontal axis.

origen El punto (0, 0) en una *gráfica de* coordenadas donde el eje vertical interseca el eje horizontal, (0, 0).

outcome (p. 124) A possible result of an experiment.

resultado Resultado posible de un experimento.

outlier (p. 99) A number in a set of data that is much larger or much smaller than most of the other numbers in the set.

valor atípico Número en un conjunto de datos que es mucho mayor o mucho menor que la mayoría de los otros números del conjunto.

P

parallel lines (p. 401) Lines that are the same distance apart. Parallel lines do not meet.

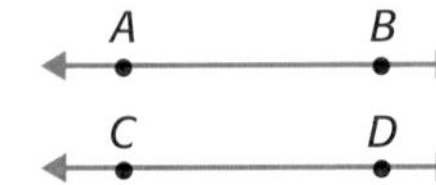

rectas paralelas Rectas separadas por la misma distancia. Las rectas paralelas no se intersecan.

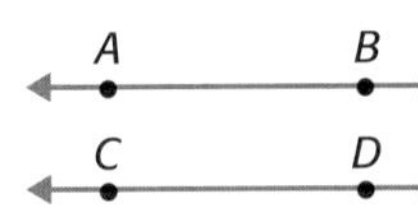

parallelogram (p. 376) A quadrilateral with four sides in which each pair of opposite sides are parallel and equal in length.

6 ft, 2 ft, 2 ft, 6 ft

paralelogramo Cuadrilátero de cuatro lados en el cual cada par de lados opuestos son paralelos y de la misma longitud.

6 pies, 2 pies, 2 pies, 6 pies

pentagon (p. 362) A *polygon* with five sides.

pentágono *Polígono* de cinco lados.

percent (p. R59) A ratio that compares a number to 100.

porcentaje Razón que compara un número con 100.

perimeter (p. 456) The distance around a shape or region.

perímetro Distancia alrededor de una figura o región.

period (p. 17) The name given to each group of three digits on a place-value chart.

período Nombre dado a cada grupo de tres dígitos en una tabla de valores de posición.

perpendicular lines (p. 401) *Lines* that meet or cross each other to form *right angles*.

rectas perpendiculares *Rectas* que se intersecan o cruzan formando *ángulos rectos*.

place value (p. 14) The value given to a *digit* by its position in a number.

valor de posición El valor dado a un *dígito* según su posición en un número.

polygon (p. 362) A closed *plane figure* formed using *line segments* that meet only at their *endpoints*.

polígono *Figura plana* cerrada formada por *segmentos de recta* que sólo se unen en sus *extremos*.

probability (p. 128) A number between 0 and 1 that measures the likelihood of an event happening.

probabilidad Número entre 0 y 1 que mide la posibilidad de que ocurra un evento.

product (p. 145) The answer or result of a multiplication problem. It also refers to expressing a number as the product of its factors.

producto Repuesta o resultado de un problema de multiplicación. También se refiere a la expresión de un número como el producto de sus factores.

pyramid (p. 359) A 3-dimensional figure with a polygon as a base and triangular shaped faces that share a common vertex.

pirámide Figura sólida con un polígono como base y caras triangulares que comparten un vértice común.

Q

quadrilateral (p. 362) A shape that has 4 sides and 4 *angles*.
square, rectangle, and parallelogram

cuadrilátero Figura que tiene 4 lados y 4 *ángulos*.
cuadrado, rectángulo y paralelogramo

quotient (p. 311) The result of a *division* problem.

cociente Respuesta o resultado de un problema de *división*.

R

range (p. R74) The *difference* between the greatest and the least numbers in a set of data.

rango La *diferencia* entre el mayor y el menor de los números en un conjunto de datos.

ray (p. 400) A part of a *line* that has one *endpoint* and extends in one direction without ending.

A B

rayo Parte de una *recta* que tiene un *extremo* y que se extiende en una dirección sin fin.

A B

Glossary/Glosario

rectangle (p. 376) A *quadrilateral* with four *right angles*; opposite sides are equal and *parallel*.

rectangular prism (p. 359) A 3-dimensional figure with six faces that are rectangles.

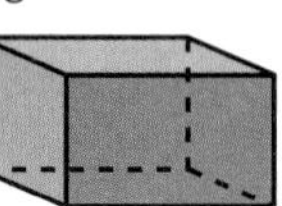

reflection (p. 412) A type of transformation that flips a figure.

remainder (p. 312) The number that is left after one whole number is divided by another.

rhombus (p. 376) A *parallelogram* with four *congruent* sides.

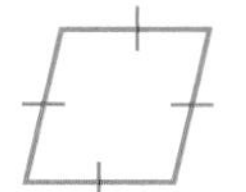

right angle (p. 369) An *angle* with a measure of 90°.

right triangle (p. 372) A *triangle* with one *right angle*.

rotation (p. 412) A type of transformation in which a figure is turned about a central point.

rectángulo *Cuadrilátero* con cuatro *ángulo rectos*; los lados opuestos son iguales y *paralelos*.

prisma rectangular Figura tridimensional de seis caras rectangulares.

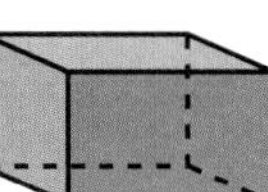

reflexion Tipo de transformación en que seleda vuelta a una figura.

residuo Número que queda después de dividir un número entero entre otro número entero.

rombo *Paralelogramo* con cuatro lados *congruentes*.

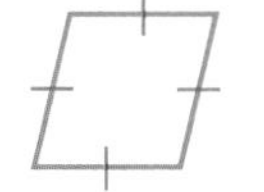

ángulo recto *Ángulo* que mide 90°.

triángulo rectángulo *Triángulo* con un *ángulo recto*.

rotación Tipo de transformación en que se hace girar una figura alrededor de un punto central.

rotational symmetry (p. 423) A figure has rotational symmetry if, after a rotation of the figure about a point, the figure lies in its original position.

round (p. 37) To change the value of a number to one that is easier to work with. To find the nearest value of a number based on a given *place value*.

S

scalene triangle (p. 373) A *triangle* with no *congruent* sides.

2 in. 4 in. 3 in.

similar figures (p. R65) Figures that have the same shape but different sizes.

sphere (p. 359) A solid or 3-dimensional figure that is set of all points that are the same distance from a given point, called the center.

square (p. 376) A rectangle with four *congruent sides*.

square unit (p. 460) A unit for measuring area.

simetría de rotación Una figura posee simetría de rotación si después de rotarla sobre un punto la figura yace en su posición original.

redondear Cambiar el valor de un número a uno con el cual es más fácil trabajar. Calcular el valor más cercano a un número basado en un *valor de posición* dado.

triángulo escaleno *Triángulo* sin lados *congruentes*.

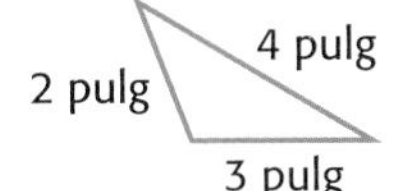

figuras semejantes Figuras que tienen la misma forma, pero diferente tamaño.

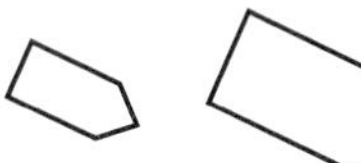

esfera *Figura tridimensional* formada por el conjunto de todos los puntos equidistantes de un punto dado llamado *centro*.

cuadrado Rectángulo de cuatro *lados congruentes*.

unidad cuadrada Unidad para medir el área.

standard form/standard notation (p. 18) The usual way of writing a number that shows only its *digits*, no words.

537   89   1642

subtract (subtraction) (p. 52) An operation on two numbers that tells the *difference*, when some or all are taken away. Subtraction is also used to compare two numbers.

$14 - 8 = 6$

subtrahend (p. 71) A number that is subtracted from another number.

$14 - 5 = 9$ (the 5 is marked "subtrahend")

sum (p. 58) The answer to an addition problem.

surface area (p. LA22) The area of the surface of a three-dimensional figure.

survey (p. 95) A method of collecting data.

T

tally chart (p. 95) A way to keep track of *data* using tally marks to record the number of responses or occurrences.

What is Your Favorite Color?	
Color	Tally
Blue	𝍸 |||
Green	||||

tally mark(s) (p. 95) A mark made to keep track and display *data* recorded from a survey.

forma estándar/notación estandard Manera habitual de escribir un número que sólo muestra sus dígitos, sin palabras.

537   89   1642

restar (resta) Operación en dos números que indica la *diferencia*, cuando algunos o todos son eliminados. La sustracción también se usa para comparar dos números.

$14 - 8 = 6$

sustraendo Un número que se sustrae de otro número.

$14 - 5 = 9$ (the 5 is marked "sustraendo")

suma Respuesta o resultado de un problema de suma.

área de superficie Área de la superficie de una *figura tridimensional.*

encuesta Método para reunir datos.

tabla de conteo Manera de llevar la cuenta de los datos usando marcas de conteo para anotar el número de respuestas o sucesos.

¿Cuál es tu color favorito?	
Color	Conteo
Azul	𝍸 |||
Verde	||||

marcas(s) de conteo Marca que se hace para llevar un registro y representar datos reunidos de una encuesta.

tenth (p. 580) One of ten equal parts or $\frac{1}{10}$.

three-dimensional figure (p. 359) A solid figure has three dimensions: length, width, and height.

transformation (p. 412) A movement of a figure.

translation (p. 412) A type of transformation in which a figure is slid horizontally, vertically, or both.

trapezoid (p. 376) A *quadrilateral* with exactly one pair of *parallel* sides.

tree diagram (p. 125) A diagram of all the possible *outcomes* of an event or series of events or experiments.

triangle (p. 362) A *polygon* with three sides and three angles.

triangular prism (p. 359) A prism whose bases are triangular with *parallelograms* for sides.

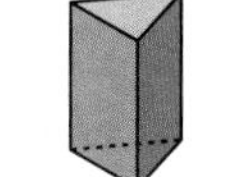

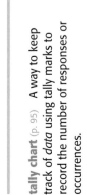

décima Una de diez partes iguales ó $\frac{1}{10}$.

figura sólida Una figura sólida tiene tres dimensiones: largo, ancho y alto.

transformación Movimiento de una figura.

traslación Tipo de transformación en que una figura se desliza en sentido vertical, en sentido horizontal o en ambos sentidos.

trapecio *Cuadrilátero* con exactamente un par de lados *paralelos.*

diagrama de árbol Diagrama de todos los *resultados* posibles de un evento o series de eventos o experimentos.

triángulo *Polígono* con tres lados y tres ángulos.

prisma triangular Prisma cuyas bases son triangulares con *paralelogramos* como lados.

triangular pyramid (p. 359) A pyramid whose base is a *triangle*.

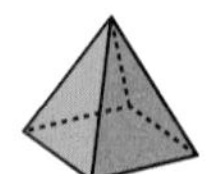

pirámide triangular Pirámide cuya base es un *triángulo*.

two-dimensional figure (p. 362) A figure that lies entirely within one plane.

figura plana Figura que yace completamente en un plano.

U

unlikely (p. 128) An event that is improbable or it will probably *not* happen.

It is unlikely you will choose a yellow tile.

improbable Evento que es improbable o que es probable que *no* suceda.

Es improbable que elijas una baldosa amarilla.

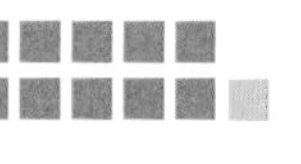

V

variable (p. 193) A letter or symbol used to represent an unknown quantity.

variable Letra o símbolo que se usa para representar una cantidad desconocida.

Venn diagram (p. R72) A diagram that uses circles to display elements of different sets. Overlapping circles show common elements.

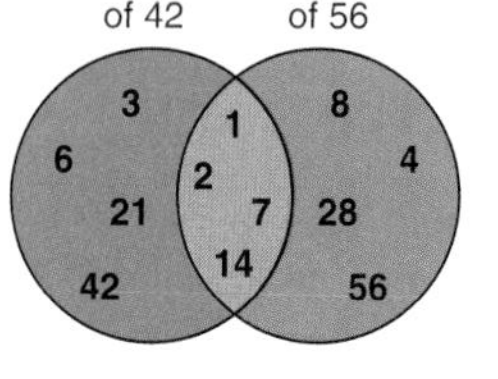

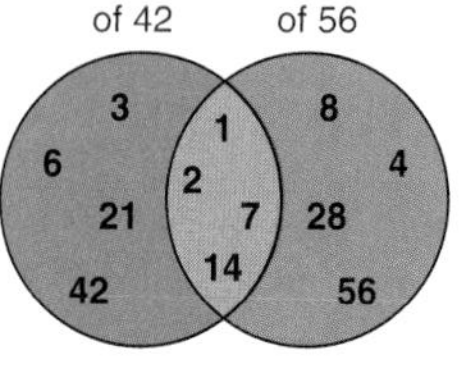

diagrama de Venn Diagrama que usa círculos para mostrar elementos de diferentes conjuntos. Círculos sobrepuestos indican elementos comunes.

Factores de 42 Factores de 56

vertex (p. 359) The point where two rays meet in an *angle*.

vértice Punto donde concurren dos o más rayos.

volume (p. 512) The number of cubic units needed to fill a three-dimensional figure.

volumen Número de unidades cúbicas necesarias para llenar una figura tridimensional o sólida.

W

weight (p. 498) A measurement that tells how heavy an object is.

peso Medida que indica la pesadez un cuerpo.

X

***x*-axis** (p. 406) The horizontal axis (↔) in a coordinate graph.

eje *x* El eje horizontal (↔) en una gráfica de coordenadas.

***x*-coordinate** (p. 406) The first number in an *ordered pair* that indicates how far to the left or the right of the *y*-axis a point is. In (2, 3), 2 is the *x*-coordinate.

coordenada *x* El primer número en un *par ordenado* que indica la distancia a la izquierda o a laderecha del eje *y* a la cual se encuentra un punto. En (2, 3), 3 es la coordenada *x*.

Y

***y*-axis** (p. 406) The vertical axis (↕) in a coordinate graph.

eje *y* El eje vertical (↕) en una gráfica de coordenadas.

***y*-coordinate** (p. 406) The second number in an *ordered pair* that indicates how far above or below the *x*-axis a point is. In (2, 3), 3 is the *y*-coordinate.

coordenada *y* El segundo número en un *par ordenado* que indica la distancia hacia arriba o hacia abajo del eje *x* a la cual se encuentra un punto. En (2, 3), 3 es la coordenada *y*.

Z

Zero Property of Multiplication (p. 150) The property that states any number multiplied by zero is zero.

$0 \times 5 = 0 \qquad 5 \times 0 = 0$

propiedad del producto nulo de la multiplicación Propiedad que establece que cualquier número multiplicado por cero es igual a cero.

$0 \times 5 = 0 \qquad 5 \times 0 = 0$

Index

Index

Index

Index

Index

Index

Index

N

Index

Index

S

Index